TOMORROW'S MATERIALS: TODAY

SOCIETY FOR THE ADVANCEMENT OF
MATERIAL AND PROCESS ENGINEERING

**34TH INTERNATIONAL SAMPE SYMPOSIUM
AND EXHIBITION**

VOLUME 34
Book 1 of 2 Books

TOMORROW'S MATERIALS: TODAY

Edited By
G. A. Zakrzewski
Don Mazenko
Stanley T. Peters
Charles D. Dean

Reno Convention Center
Reno, Nevada

May 8-11, 1989

34th INTERNATIONAL SAMPE SYMPOSIUM AND EXHIBITION

INTERNATIONAL OFFICERS

President	Gayle B. Wadsworth
Executive Vice President	Jerry Bauer
Senior Vice President	Brian A. Wilson
Vice President	Bob J. Hunter
Secretary	Roy E. Henrichsen
Treasurer	W. H. Face, Jr.
Past President	Gary W. Valentine

CHAPTER OFFICERS
(Northern California Chapter)

Chairman	Daniel A. Chafey
First Vice Chairman	Brian D. Boggs
Second Vice Chairman	Lauri C. Crowe
Secretary	James David Holbery
Treasurer	Carroll Ann Bergdahl
Sr. International Director	R. V. Kromrey
Jr. International Director	Kevin S. Marshall

G. A. ZAKRZEWSKI
Lockheed Missiles and Space Co.
General Chairman

DON MAZENKO
Retired
Deputy Chairman

STANLEY T. PETERS
Westinghouse Electric
Program Chairman

CHARLES D. DEAN
Amoco Performance Products
Deputy Program Chairman

MARTY NISHIMURA
Lockheed Missiles and Space Co.
Registration Chairman

DEANE NISHIMURA
Lockheed Missiles and Space Co.
Audio Visual Chairman

BRIAN BOGGS
Lockheed Missiles and Space Co.
Finance Chairman

BOB MILLIGAN
Lockheed Missiles and Space Co.
Publicity Chairman

TONY SEIDE
United Airlines
Security/Transportation Chairman

PAUL YAMAGUCHI
Lockheed Missiles and Space Cc
Secretary/Committee Arrangement

BILL MELLBERG
Fiberite
Arrangements Chairman

SESSIONS AND SESSION CHAIRMEN

COMPOSITE PROCESSING

James C. Seferis, University of Washington

HIGH TEMPERATURE RESINS

T. T. Serafini, TRW, Inc.

CERAMIC COMPOSITES

W. G. Long, Babcock and Wilcox

Helen Moeller, Babcock and Wilcox

THERMOPLASTICS APPLICATIONS

Ted Reinhart, Air Force Wright Aeronautical Laboratory

Ron Kuhbander, University of Dayton Research Institute

FIBER DEVELOPMENT

Roger Bacon, Amoco Performance Products

THERMOSET COMPOSITE MATRICES - REVIEW AND UPDATE

Clayton A. May, Arroyo Research and Consulting Corporation

DAMAGE TOLERANCE

Terry Tsuchiyama, Douglas Aircraft Company

Roy Palmer, Douglas Aircraft Company

MATERIAL AND MANUFACTURING CONCERNS ON EMERGING DOD AIRCRAFT SYSTEMS

Jim Renton, Boeing Airplane Company

MANUFACTURING

George S. Springer, Stanford University

CURE MONITORING

Z. N. Sanjana, Westinghouse Research and Development Center

REPAIR

Thomas Donnellan, Naval Air Development Center

TESTING

L. E. (Roy) Meade, Lockheed-California Company

BISMALEIMIDE TECHNOLOGY I: EVOLVING PREPREG SYSTEMS

Charles L. Segal, OMNIA

H. D. Stenzenberger, Technochemie GmbH

COMPOSITE DESIGN AND ANALYSIS

Stephen W. Tsai, Air Force Materials Laboratory

ADHESIVES TECHNOLOGY

L. J. Hart-Smith, Douglas Aircraft Company

Don Harmston, Naval Air Rework Facility

DESIGN AND ANALYSIS

Les Cohen, McDonnell Douglas

Sam Dastin, Grumman Corporation

SESSIONS AND SESSION CHAIRMEN

COMPOSITE MATERIALS DAMAGE ASSESSMENT

Scott Beckwith, Hercules Aerospace Company

SPACECRAFT APPLICATIONS

Cheng Hsieh, Jet Propulsion Laboratory

METAL MATRIX COMPOSITES

John Tydings, Naval Surface Warfare Center

SANDWICH STRUCTURES

Leonard Marchinski, Consultant

EPOXY RESIN TECHNOLOGY

Paul Hergenrother, NASA Langley Research Center

MANUFACTURING

Tobey Cordell, Air Force Wright Aeronautical Laboratory

REPAIR TECHNOLOGY

Mark Forte, Air Force Wright Aeronautical Laboratory

Bob Urzi, Air Force Wright Aeronautical Laboratory

FILAMENT WINDING

Ralph F. Foral, University of Nebraska

SPACE ENVIRONMENTAL EFFECTS TESTING OF MATERIALS

Ann Whitaker, NASA Marshall Space Flight Center

THERMOPLASTICS – NEW MATERIALS

Ron Kuhbander, University of Dayton Research Institute

Ted Reinhart, Air Force Wright Aeronautical Laboratory

TOOLING FOR COMPOSITES

Steve Rodgers, Heath Tecna

THERMOSET RESIN TECHNOLOGY

Gig Korver, Hexcel Corporation

ENVIRONMENTAL EFFECTS TESTING

Mark Morgan, Hercules, Inc.

TESTING/RESIN CREEP

Donald F. Adams, University of Wyoming

Chad Delano, Accurex

THERMOPLASTIC COMPOSITES

Ted Reinhart, Air Force Wright Aeronautical Laboratory

Ron Kuhbander, University of Dayton Research Institute

HIGH TEMPERATURE COMPOSITES/COMPOSITES DAMAGE

C. L. Sheppard, Boeing Company

Sandra Slivinsky, United Technologies

FILAMENT WINDING

L. Ken Drake, The Aerospace Corporation

SESSIONS AND SESSION CHAIRMEN

DIMENSIONALLY STABLE STRUCTURES/NEW FIBER DEVELOPMENT

Gary Krumweide, Composite Optics, Inc.

A. T. Laskaris, Avco Specialty Materials

GENERAL TECHNOLOGY

Charles Hammermesh, Consultant

THERMOSET RESIN TECHNOLOGY/ADHESIVES

Shaheed Quereshi, Amoco Performance Products

Gig Korver, Hexcel Corporation

IMPACT DYNAMICS OF COMPOSITES

L. B. Greszczuk, McDonnell Douglas Astronautics Company

BISMALEIMIDE TECHNOLOGY II: TOUGHENING AGENTS, PROPERTIES AND APPLICATIONS

Charles Segal, OMNIA

H. D. Stenzenberger, Technochemie GmbH

FILAMENT WINDING

W. D. Humphrey, Brunswick Corporation

COMPOSITE CHARACTERIZATION TESTING

Walter A. Wilson, Merlin Technologies

THERMOPLASTICS -- PROCESSING

Ron Kuhbander, University of Dayton Research Institute

Ted Reinhart, Air Force Wright Aeronautical Laboratory

ADHESIVES

R. B. Kreiger, American Cyanamid Company

PREFACE

The Northern California Chapter of SAMPE is again honored to host an International SAMPE Symposium and Exhibition. We have chosen the theme, "Tomorrow's Materials: Today" because we believe that the new materials, that presently exist will result in dramatic changes in all our lives. SAMPE's task as it has always been, is to permit the exploitation of these new materials by determining and demonstrating how to fabricate them into usable shapes and how to reliably predict their attributes and performance.

Many facets of this program are innovative: the papers are of high quality, since they were generally solicited by the Session Chairmen, who, in turn were solicited as representing the most responsible and technically able candidates in the country. The subject matter represents a blend of the program committee's selections and that which was naturally selected because of present industry-wide interests. A new tutorial has been added and there are extended (1 hour) overview sessions on many matrix resins available during both Monday and Thursday sessions. The program goal was to make a generous amount of high quality technical information available to the attendees. Nowhere else is key technical data presented so cost-effectively to so many.

Our sincere thanks go to all of the speakers, co-authors and session chairmen. Whatever technical success this program enjoys, it is due to the work of paper solicitations by the session chairs and their perseverance in seeing that the papers were submitted on time. We also credit the volunteers from Westinghouse Electric who spent their own time for paper review. Finally, we credit the SAMPE International Business Office for their usual professional, competent effort.

Stan Peters   Dr. Jerry Zakrzewski
Program Chairman   General Chairman

Chuck Dean   Don Mazenko
Deputy Program Chairman   Deputy Chairman

CONTENTS

PAPERS AND AUTHORS

PAPERS AND AUTHORS

PAPERS AND AUTHORS

PAPERS AND AUTHORS

PAPERS AND AUTHORS

PAPERS AND AUTHORS

PAPERS AND AUTHORS

PAPERS AND AUTHORS

PAPERS AND AUTHORS

PAPERS AND AUTHORS

PAPERS AND AUTHORS

PAPERS AND AUTHORS

PAPERS AND AUTHORS

AUTOCLAVE PROCESSING OF CONDENSATION POLYIMIDE
COMPOSITES BASED ON PREPREGS OF AVIMID®K

Alan R. Wedgewood **
E. I. Du Pont de Nemours & Co., Inc.
Wilmington, Delaware 19898
and
David C. Grant
TAD Technical Services
Bala Cynwyd, Pennsylvania 19004

Abstract

High temperature composite materials based on prepregs of Avimid* K possess excellent strength, toughness and environmental resistance, leading to their consideration for applications in the primary structure of fixed-wing aircraft and missiles. Simple molding cycles that yield high quality laminates have been recommended for autoclave processing prepregs of Avimid®K. To further optimize these molding cycles, the effect of key processing parameters on laminate quality and properties are examined. Prepregs of Avimid®K are shown to accommodate the wide range of processing conditions expected under typical autoclave manufacturing operations. The ability to salvage improperly molded or damaged laminates, by simply reprocessing, is demonstrated. This processing versatility combined with the ability to salvage misprocessed parts leads to high production yields with Avimid®K.

1. INTRODUCTION

Processing studies have shown that simple straight ramp molding cycles provide the basis for autoclave processing prepregs based on Avimid®K [1]. The autoclave molding cycle can be divided into stages for detailed analysis. In this work, an in-depth analysis of the condensation reaction and devolatilization management stage and laminate consolidation stage was done to further define the processing window. It is shown that prepregs of Avimid®K accommodate the wide range of processing conditions expected in typical autoclave manufacturing operations. This processibility, coupled with excellent strength, stiffness, toughness, environmental resistance and a water considered glass transition temperature above 204°C (400°F) [2,3], makes prepregs based on Avimid®K prime candidates for structural applications in the aircraft/aerospace industry.

The ability to salvage poor quality laminates that may result during routine autoclave processing has been previously demonstrated [1]. In this paper, the effect of previous process history on the ability to reconsolidate improperly molded laminates is examined. The ability

---

* Du Pont Registered Trademark. Product was previously named Avimid® K-III
** To whom correspondences should be sent.

to achieve expected mechanical performance after reprocessing is demonstrated by repairing and testing open hole compression specimens that were damaged during the hole drilling operation.

2. PRODUCT FORMS

Wet prepregs of Avimid®K are provided as tacky, drapable tapes and fabrics, suitable for processing with currently available tape lay-down and vacuum bag autoclave molding technologies. The wet prepreg is a combination of a monomeric (polyimide precursor) solution and a continuous reinforcing fiber. Tape and fabric prepregs based on a wide variety of reinforcing fibers (graphite, glass, etc.) are available. Tape and fabric prepreg product widths of 24 and 42 inches are routinely produced. Typical prepregs contain 16+/-2 weight percent volatiles and 57+/-2 volume percent fiber on a fully cured basis. The laminates referred to in this work were prepared from 12 inch wide "Magnamite" IM-6 carbon fiber tape prepregs.

3. RECOMMENDED MOLDING CYCLES

Simple straight ramp molding cycles provide the basis for processing wet prepregs of Avimid®K, with the maximum part thickness establishing the maximum recommended heat-up rate. Guideline molding conditions for various thickness parts are given in Figure 1. In general, the use of slower than recommended heat-up rates results in a more conservative cycle. Detailed discussions of the recommended vacuum bag lay-up procedures have been provided elsewhere [1]. Specific details supporting these recommended molding cycles are given below.

4. AUTOCLAVE PROCESSING WINDOW

In this study, the molding cycle is divided into four stages for analysis: binder bleed control, condensation reaction and devolatilization management, laminate consolidation and cool-down.

4.1 Binder Bleed Control

Binder bleed is controlled to an acceptable level by proper selection of the vacuum and temperature profiles in the early stages of the molding cycle [1]. To minimize bleed, a low initial vacuum 50-120 mmHg (2-5"Hg) is applied. Application of full vacuum is delayed until the onset of polymerization increases the solution viscosity to a sufficiently high value to prevent excessive bleed. Thus binder bleed control establishes the minimum vacuum application temperature for a given heat-up rate (see Figure 1).

4.2 Condensation Reaction and Devolatilization Management

The maximum heat-up rate in this stage is chosen to maintain a uniform reaction/temperature profile through the part thickness and to allow for efficient and complete removal of the volatiles before consolidation. Previously recommended heat-up rates [1] have proved too conservative and faster heat-up rates are now recommended for a given part thickness (see Figure 1).

Full vacuum (>710 mmHg (>28"Hg)) is applied to enhance the removal of volatiles and should be applied at the minimum application temperature. However, when processing large area and/or multiple parts with varying thicknesses, sizes and shapes, significant part temperature differences within the autoclave can result. Thus, a maximum limit for full vacuum application temperature must be establish.

Complete removal of volatiles before reaching the final consolidation temperature is readily achieved, for the heat-up rates recommended in Figure 1, even when vacuum application is delayed to 177°C (350°F). Adopting this temperature as the maximum limit for full vacuum application, implies that for typical autoclave heat-up rates vacuum can be applied over a wide range of temperatures. For example, at 2°C/min vacuum can be applied over the 125 to 177°C temperature range, offering a 52°C (94°F) vacuum application process window.

4.3 Laminate Consolidation

4.3.1 Semi-crystalline Precipitate Melt Behavior

A semi-crystalline precipitate forms during the early stages of polymerization. The melting behavior of this precipitate establishes the minimum final consolidation temperature. The effect of vacuum level and vacuum application temperature on the melting behavior was determined by differential scanning calorimetry (DSC) analysis. Samples were prepared using a 1°C/min heat-up rate and the molding cycle was interrupted at 250°C by cooling to room temperature to prevent premature melting before DSC analysis. These DSC melting point determinations and all others reported in this work were made using a 10°C/min ramp rate.

The effect of applied vacuum level on the melting peak temperature is shown in Figure 2a. In all cases, the vacuum was applied at the beginning of the cycle and held constant until after cool-down. No external pressure was applied. Increasing the applied vacuum from 50 to 505 mmHg (2 to 20 "Hg) results in only a slight decrease in the melting temperature from 343 to 341°C. The observed melting peak was sharp and well defined. Above 505 mmHg, a significant decrease in the melt temperature is observed. Applying 730 mmHg (29 "Hg) reduced the melting temperature to 333°C, a full 10°C

lower than the melting temperature found for the 50 mmHg test condition. Processing at these higher vacuum levels caused the melt peak shape to broaden and become skewed towards lower temperatures.

The effect of changing the full vacuum application temperature on the melting behavior is shown in Figure 2b. An initial vacuum of 50 mmHg was applied and then increased to 730 mmHg at the temperature indicated. As is shown, delaying application of full vacuum increased the melt temperature to the value obtained when 50 mmHg of vacuum was used during the entire cycle. The peak shape became sharper as the vacuum application temperature was increased.

Lower vacuum levels and higher full vacuum application temperatures increase the melt temperature of the semi-crystalline precipitate observed for a flat constant thickness and area laminate. This increase in final melt temperature can be significant. For example, varying the full vacuum application temperature from the minimum to maximum temperatures recommended for a 1°C/min heating rate (see Figure 1), increases the melt temperature by approximately 8°C (15°F).

The change in melting behavior described above can be attributed to a transition between a heat and mass transfer controlled precipitation process. At low vacuum levels or delayed vacuum application, the solvent removal rate is slow relative to the heating rate which drives the polymerization. Greater retention of solvent allows higher degrees of polymerization to be reached before the polymer becomes insoluble and precipitates out of solution, resulting in the highest melt temperatures observed. At high vacuum levels or early vacuum application, the rate of solvent removal is increased to the point where mass transfer controls the precipitation process. As the solvent is more quickly removed, the polymer becomes insoluble and precipitates out at lower degrees of polymerization, resulting in the decreased melting temperature and broadened peak. Thus any factor that affects the balance between the heat and mass transfer within the part , such as heat-up rate, part and tool geometry, and vacuum-bag lay-up, can change the semi-crystalline melt behavior.

4.3.2 Final Consolidation
       Temperature Range

To establish the final consolidation temperature range, the effect of varying the consolidation temperature from 343°C (650°F) to 393°C (740°F) was investigated using 0.5 °C/min heat-up rate. Both no hold and a six hour isothermal hold before pressurization were investigated. When no hold was used, pressure application was done based on the lagging part temperature. The difference between the highest and lowest part temperatures was never greater than 5°C (9°F) when pressure was applied. The maximum recommended full vacuum application temperature of 177°C (350°F) was used, since it yields the highest melt temperature expected when operating under recommended conditions and thus represents the most demanding consolidation challenge expected.

The effect of final consolidation temperature on laminate density and open hole compression strength [4] is provided in Figure 3. As is shown, when no hold before pressurization is used, consolidation between 352°C (665°F) and 377°C (710°F) yields the highest densities (1.56 +/- 0.1 g/cc) and open hole compression strengths (294 +/- 14 MPa (42.6 +/- 2.1 Ksi)). Photomicrographs of these samples show no evidence of voids. Microcracking is found in the

343°C laminates (see Figure 4) and 1.3 to 2.6% voids are observed in the 393°C laminates.

The voids in the high temperature laminates are attributed to the onset of side reactions, which increase the melt viscosity and can release by-products that may cause voids. The microcracking in the low temperature laminates may result because the resin viscosity is too high to fully melt fuse as it flows together to fill void space. Unfused weld lines may be opened by thermal stresses that result during cool-down, creating the observed microcracks. The existence of unmelted crystalline material when pressure is applied (see Section 4.3.3) may contribute to this phenomena by behaving as crosslinks, which increase the effective resin viscosity. After consolidation, however, no evidence of this crystallinity is observed by DSC. This suggests that the crystalline structure is disrupted during consolidation flow.

As is shown in Figures 3 and 4, when a six hour isothermal hold before pressurization is used, poor quality laminates were made except when a final consolidation temperature of 360°C (680°F) was used. The poor quality laminates made at 377°C are again attributed to the onset of side reactions. The poor quality laminates made at 343 and 352°C were attributed to annealing during the isothermal hold, that increases the semicrystalline melt temperature above the final consolidation temperature used (see Section 4.3.3). Again, these unmelted crystals may act as crosslinks that significantly increase the melt viscosity. After consolidation, these high melt crystals are still observed by DSC.

Based on these results, no hold before consolidation and a final consolidation temperature range of 360 +/- 8°C is recommended.

Although it is desirable to prevent such conditions, significant part temperature differences (>16°C (>30°F)) within the autoclave can result, making it impossible to keep both the leading and lagging part temperatures within the recommended consolidation temperature range. For temperature differences up to 25°C (45°F), the following two approaches can be taken:
1) Pressurize when the lagging part temperature reaches 352°C. At this point the leading temperature will not exceed 377°C, a temperature where consolidation with no hold yields a high quality laminate (see Figure 3 and 4).
2) Pressurize when the lagging part temperature reaches 343°C, followed by continued heating until the lagging temperature is above 352°C. The second approach is preferred for the following reasons. It has been demonstrated that microcracking expected with 343°C consolidation is eliminated by continued heating under pressure to above 352°C. Also by pressurizing the autoclave early, heat transfer is improved and part temperature difference reduced. If larger temperature differences exist (>25°C), the second approach should still be used because it will result in the lowest leading part temperature.

4.3.3 Preconsolidation State

To further investigate the microcracking and voids observed when a 343°C consolidation temperature was used, unconsolidated laminates were prepared with no hold and a 6 hour hold at both 343°C and 360°C. Vacuum was applied at 177°C and a 0.5°C/min heating rate was used.

Photomicrographs of these unconsolidated laminates are given in Figure 5. This visual examination shows distinct differences between the 343°C and 360°C preconsolidation states. The 343°C unconsolidated laminates contain large voids between and within ply layers and significant microvoiding within the fiber bundles. Estimated volume percent void contents determined from density measurements were 12.0 and 10.5% for the no hold and six hour hold laminates. The 360°C unconsolidated laminates contain only a few large voids and the microvoiding within fiber bundles is reduced. Estimated void contents for these samples were 6.5 and 4.5% for the no hold and six hour hold laminates.

DSC analysis of the unconsolidated laminates prepared at 343°C with no hold revealed the existence of a strong sharp crystalline melting peak at 344-346°C. In the six hour hold sample this peak was significantly reduced and shifted to a higher temperature of 356-358°C. This change in melting behavior is attributed to annealing just below the melting point during the isothermal hold, which results in partial melting of the least perfect crystals and growth of the more stable crystals. As discussed above, these crystals contribute to the microcracks and voids observed in the 343°C consolidated laminates. In comparison, no evidence of crystallinity was observed in either of the 360°C unconsolidated laminates.

4.3.4 Post Consolidation

The effect of post consolidation process conditions on laminate quality and performance is not fully defined. At this time a one hour hold at the final consolidation temperature is recommended.

4.4 Cool-down

A cool-down rate of 0.5°C/min to the dry Tg of 250°C (480°F) is recommended to prevent shrinkage creases due to thermal mismatch between the part and tool. Below the dry Tg, the cool-down rate can be accelerated to 3°C/min. At 60°C

(140°F), the autoclave pressure is released and the part removed.

5.0 REPROCESSIBILITY

5.1 Effect of Previous Process History

Previous processing studies [1] demonstrated the ability to remold poor quality laminates of Avimid®K to produce quality products. To study the effect of previous thermal history on the ability to reprocess Avimid®K, the unconsolidated samples covered in Section 4.3.3 were remolded. The micrographs presented in Figure 5 illustrate the initial laminate conditions prior to being remolded. Two remold cycles were investigated and are presented in Figure 6. Complete consolidation (<0.5% voids, no microcracking) of the 343°C and 360°C no hold laminates was achieved using either cycle.

Cycle A demonstrates remolding with pressurization in the minimum melt viscosity region. Micrographs for the remolded laminates are presented in Figure 6. As is shown, good consolidation (1% voids) of the 343°C (6 hour hold) laminate was attained and can be attributed to using a consolidation temperature just above the crystalline melt temperature (356-358°C; see Section 4.3.3). Poor consolidation (2-3% voids) of the 360°C (6 hour hold) laminate was not expected, since excellent laminates are produced when pressurization is done after a six hour hold at 360°C in a one pass molding cycle (see Figures 3 and 4). The only identified difference between these cases is that the unconsolidated laminate was cooled to room temperature and debagged, before being rebagged and processed a second time.

Cycle B demonstrates pressurization at a high melt viscosity, then heating through the minimum melt viscosity region and holding above the recommended consolidation temperature. Under these conditions consolidation occurs under hydrostatic pressure. Very good consolidation (<1% voids, no microcracking) of the 343°C (6 hour hold) laminate was attained. Again poor consolidation (2-3% voids) of the 360°C (6 hour hold) laminate was unexpected and as discussed above is not fully understood. Excellent results (<0.5% voids, no microcracking) were obtained for a 24 ply control lay-up molded simultaneously, demonstrating the validity of the molding cycle.

5.2 Repair of Damaged Holes

To investigate the ability to repair defects caused by manufacturing, open hole compression samples with good and poor quality holes were prepared from 343°C (no hold) laminates (see Section 4.3.2). The poor quality holes produced a 10% reduction in the compressive strength, which compares well with a similar study reported earlier [5]. The cycles given in Figure 7 were used to remold some of the poor quality hole samples. When the poor hole samples were remolded at 343°C, full recovery of the compression strength was achieved. When remolded at 360°C, compression strength was increased to the higher value expected (see Section 4.3.2).

6.0 SUMMARY

An in-depth investigation of key processing parameters, such as full vacuum application and final consolidation temperature, was performed to further define the optimum processing window for Avimid®K. It was shown that prepregs of Avimid®K can accommodate the wide range of processing conditions expected in typical autoclave operations. The recommended molding cycle was updated to reflect these results. Also presented are demonstrations of the ability to salvage poor quality laminates and repair minor manufacturing defects.

7.0 ACKNOWLEDGEMENTS

Special gratitude is owed to the following Du Pont employees: A. E. Wilkins for her assistance in gathering experimental data and to R. J. Boyce and T. P. Gannett for their helpful discussions of the subject.

8.0 REFERENCES

1. A. R. Wedgewood, "Autoclave Processing of Condensation Polyimide Composites Based on Prepregs of Avimid®K-III, pgs. 420-434, 19th International SAMPE Technical Conference, Crystal City, VA, October 13-15, 1987.

2. R. J. Boyce, T. P. Gannett, H. H. Gibbs and A. R. Wedgewood, "Processing, Properties and Applications of K-Polymer Composite Materials Based on Avimid®K-III Prepregs", pgs. 169-184, 31st Annual SAMPE Symposium and Exhibition, Anaheim, CA, April 6-9, 1987.

3. A. R. Wedgewood, K. B. Su and J. A. Nairn, "Toughness Properties and Service Performance of High Temperature Thermoplastics and Their Composites", pgs. 454-467, 19th International SAMPE Technical Conference, Crystal City, VA, October 13-15, 1987.

4. Boeing Test Method - BSS 7260 "Advanced Composite Compression Test"

5. R. A. Garret, "Effect of Manufacturing Defects and Service-Induced Damage on the Strength of Aircraft Composite Structures", Composite Materials Testing and Design (Seventh Conference), ASTM STP 893, J. M. Whitney, Ed., American society for Testing and Materials, Philadelphia, (1986), pgs. 5-33..

9.0 BIOGRAPHIES

Dr. Alan R. Wedgewood is a Senior Research Scientist with the Fibers Department of the Du Pont Co., where he has been employed since 1982. He received his BSE in Chemical Engineering(1977) from Illinois Institute of Technology, Chicago, and PhD in Chemical Engineering (1982) from the University of Washington, Seattle. During the past seven years he has worked on the development of high temperature polyimides for use in high performance composites.

David C. Grant is a contract Engineer with TAD Technical Services, and has been contracted to the DuPont Co. since 1986. He received his BS (1985) in Chemical Engineering from Widener University, Pa. The past three years he has worked under Dr. Alan Wedgewood in the research and development of polyimides for use in high performance composites.

FIGURE 1: RECOMMENDED AUTOCLAVE MOLDING CYCLE

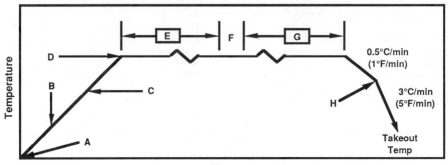

PROCESSING PARAMETERS	RECOMMENDATION
A. Initial Conditions	50-120 mmHg vacuum 0 psig pressure
B. Maximum Heat-up Rate	Determined by maximum part thickness (see below)
C. Full Vacuum Application Temperature	>710 mmHg (>28"Hg) is applied when the lagging part temperature reaches the minimum guideline application temperature, which depends on the maximum part thickness (see below)
D. Consolidation Temperature Range	360+/-8°C (680 +/-15°F)
E. Hold Before Pressurization	None. Pressurize based on lagging part temperature reaching 352°C (665°F)
F. Pressurization Step	Apply 185 psig at (10-20 psi/min)
G. Hold After Pressurization	One hour (not optimized)
H. Cooling Rate Increase	Rate increase at 250°C (480°F), based on highest part temperature

MAXIMUM PART THICKNESS		HEAT-UP RATE		FULL VACUUM APPLICATION TEMPERATURE			
				MINIMUM		MAXIMUM	
mm	(inches)	°C	(°F)	°C	(°F)	°C	(°F)
5.1	(0.20)	2.0	(3.6)	125	(257)	177	(350)
10.2	(0.40)	1.0	(1.8)	115	(239)	177	(350)
14.0	(0.55)	0.5	(0.9)	108	(226)	177	(350)
20.3	(0.80)	0.25	(0.45)	104	(220)	177	(350)

Figure 2A: Effect of Vacuum Level on Melt Temperature

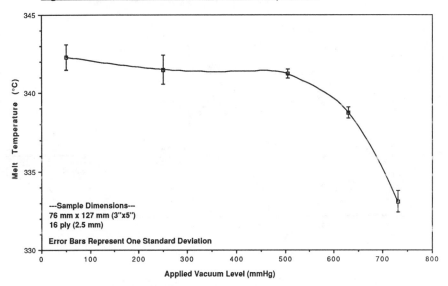

---Sample Dimensions---
76 mm x 127 mm (3"x5")
16 ply (2.5 mm)

Error Bars Represent One Standard Deviation

Figure 2B: Effect of Full Vacuum Application Temperature on Melt Temperature

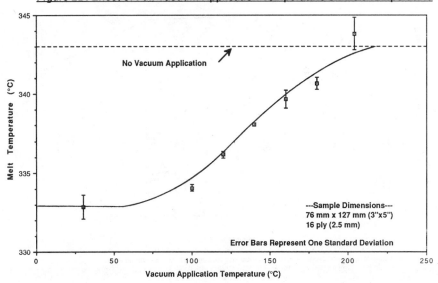

No Vacuum Application

---Sample Dimensions---
76 mm x 127 mm (3"x5")
16 ply (2.5 mm)

Error Bars Represent One Standard Deviation

Figure 3A: Effect of Final Consolidation Temperature on Laminate Density

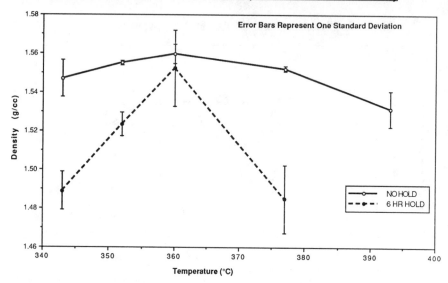

Figure 3B: Effect of Final Consolidation Temperature on Compression Strength

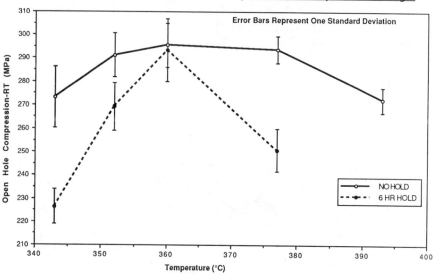

Figure 4: Micrographs
Final Consolidation States
With and Without Isothermal Holds at Final Temperature
Cycle: RT->Final Temp @ 0.5°C/min
(Vacuum @ 177°C--185 Psi Final Pressure)

NO HOLD

| 343°C | 352°C | 360°C | 377°C |

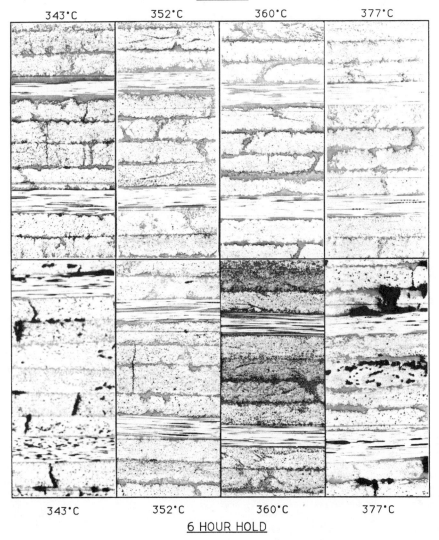

| 343°C | 352°C | 360°C | 377°C |

6 HOUR HOLD

Figure 5: Micrographs

Preconsolidation States

With and Without Isothermal Holds at Final Temperature
Cycle: RT->Final Temp @ 0.5°C/min
(Vacuum @ 177°C--No Pressure)

343°C NO HOLD 360°C

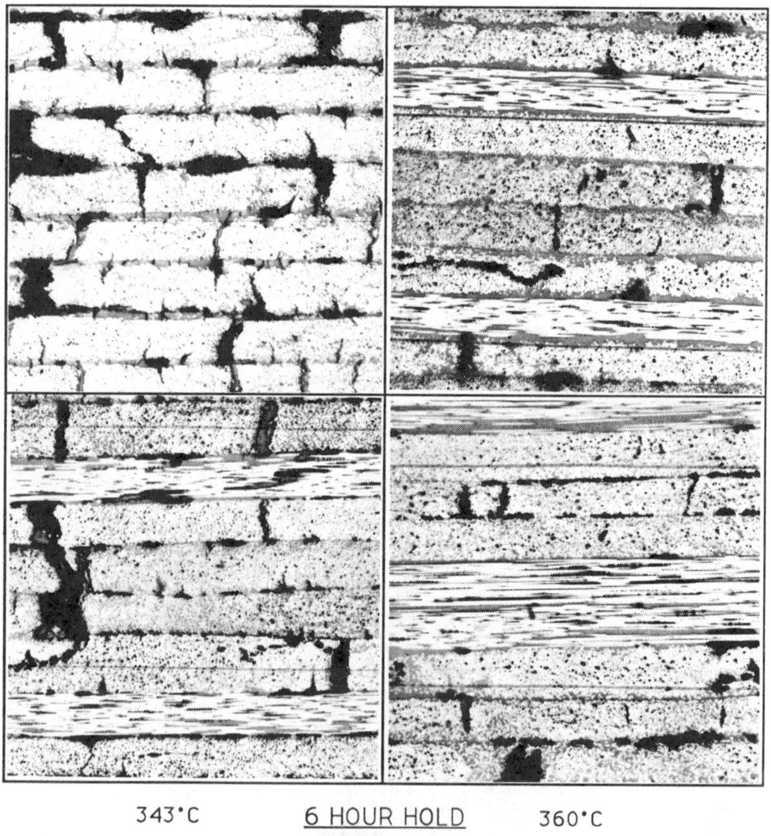

343°C 6 HOUR HOLD 360°C

Figure 6: Micrographs
Remolded "Unconsolidated" Laminates

--- Cycle A ---

RT-->360°C
  @0.5°C/min
--Full Vacuum
  @177°C (710 mmHg)
--Pressure @ 360°C
  (185 Psi)
--Hold 1 hour
--Cool Down

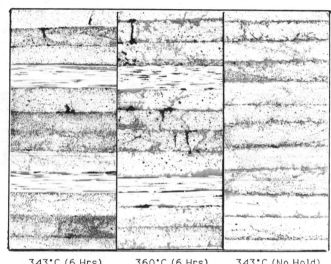

343°C (6 Hrs)   360°C (6 Hrs)   343°C (No Hold)
Previous Thermal History

--- Cycle B ---

RT-->343°C
  @0.5°C/min
--Full Vacuum
  @177°C (710 mmHg)
--Pressure @343°C
  (185 Psi)
343-->377°C
  @0.5°C/min
--Hold 1 hour
--Cool Down

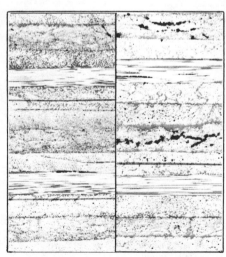

343°C (6 Hrs)   360°C (6 Hrs)
Previous Thermal History

Figure 7: Damaged Hole Repair

Schematic of C-Scans

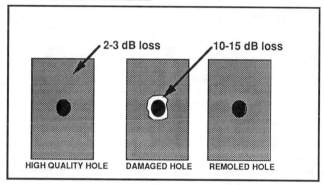

2-3 dB loss   10-15 dB loss

HIGH QUALITY HOLE   DAMAGED HOLE   REMOLED HOLE

Open Hole Compression Strength

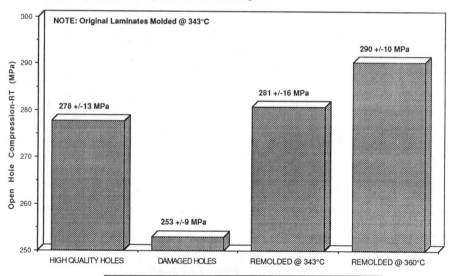

NOTE: Original Laminates Molded @ 343°C

290 +/-10 MPa

281 +/-16 MPa

278 +/-13 MPa

253 +/-9 MPa

Open Hole Compression-RT (MPa)

HIGH QUALITY HOLES   DAMAGED HOLES   REMOLDED @ 343°C   REMOLDED @ 360°C

------Remold Cycle------

RT --> Final Temperature @ 0.5°C/min
--Full Vacuum @ 177°C
--185 Psi Pressure @ Final Temperature
--Hold One Hour @ Temperature
--Cool Down

COMPACTION BEHAVIOR OF THICK COMPOSITE
LAMINATES DURING CURE

T. W. Kim, E. J. Jun
Korea Institute of Machinery & Metals
Changwon, Kyungnam, Korea, 641-010
and
W. I. Lee
Department of Mechanical Engineering
Seoul National University, Seoul, Korea, 151

Abstract

The compaction behavior of the laminate is one of key factors in
determining the optimal cure cycle
of given composite system. A new
method of continuously monitoring
the compaction behavior of thick
laminates during autoclave cure is
investigated by measuring the thickness change as a function of time
with a novel device.

The effects of cure temperature and
pressure on the compaction of thick
laminates were studied in-process.
The cure pressure plays dominant
role to the ultimate compaction
rather than the temperature. The
relative compaction of 96-ply thick
laminates is about 30% less than
that of 16-ply thin laminates.

1. INTRODUCTION

The development of low-cost, efficient production processes for the
manufactures of composite structural
parts is contingent upon the use
of accurate process models which
accurately simulate the complete
production process. In constrast to
the processing of parts such as
automotive applications, composite
parts for aircraft may be very
large, complex, and very expensive.
Therefore, it is important to determine the optimal cure cycle for
composite part since in-process
control is very critical to ensure
high product quality, low processing
cost and zero reject rate of such
large and expensive structures.
The compaction behavior of the
composite thick laminates must be
understood for the determination of
optimal cure cycle of a given
material system. In a large and
thick composite laminates, the
local pressure and temperature are
different through the thickness
direction of prepregs. Accordingly,

determination of the optimal cure cycle required the effects of the applied pressure and temperature on thick composite laminates during autoclave cure. So far, it is inevitable to run many batches of autoclave curing to learn the compaction behavior as a function of time for a given curing condition. The objective of this work, therfore, is to provide an efficient way of measuring the compaction behavior of thick composite laminates continuously as a function of time, and to investigate the effects of cure pressure and temperature on the compaction behavior. The measurement would make it possible to determine the optimal cure cycle of the composite thick laminates.

2. EXPERIMENT

Measuring system and Compaction Tests

The thickness measuring sensor(1) was placed between two unidirectional prepregs to monitor the change of the thickness of laminates of the dimension, 70mm X 80mm. On top of the composite laminates, a perforated steel plate was placed so that the excessive resin could flow in the vertical direction. The thickness and hole size of the perforated steel plate were 4 mm and ϕ 1 mm, respectively. And the number of holes of the plate was 10 per 100 mm^2. Each laminate was surounded by a steel dam jointed by the perforated steel plate. The steel dam was allowed only to move vertically and to prevent the side flow of

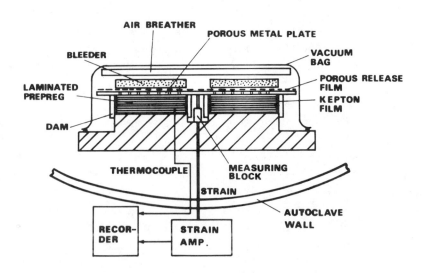

Fig.1. A schematic of the thickness monitoring system

resin. Also, a kepton film was attached to the side surface of the laminates to prevent it more effectively. On top of the perforated steel plate a bleeder was placed. A thermocouple was placed in prepregs to measure the temperature of composites during cure. The lay-up assembly was then vaccum bagged and evaculated to 3.1 kPa. The whole assembly was placed in a autoclave and cured following a prescribed curing parameter. A schematic of the measuring system is shown in Fig. 1.

Experiments were performed to observe the effect of the cure temperature and cure pressure during autoclave cure. The prepreg system used was Graphite/Epoxy unidirectional prepreg product in Korea. The thickness a ply of the prepreg is 0.15 mm. The initial resin content of the prepreg is 50%. The compaction behaviors of the composite laminates were measured for four different cure temperatures of 90, 120, and 150°C under cure pressure of 515 kPa (60 psig), and four different cure pressures of 101, 308, 515 and 722 kPa (0, 30, 60 and 90 psig, respectively) at 120°C. Experiments were also performed to investigate the compaction behavior of laminates with two different thicknesses (64, 96 plies). The heat-up rate was 2°C/min for all the test.

The signal from the sensor indicates the actual compaction of the

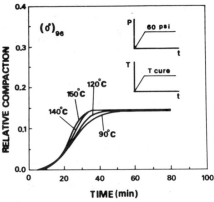

Fig.2. Relative compaction as functions of time for different cure temp.

laminates. Since the initial laminate thicknesses were different, data were reduced using the relative compaction defined as

Relative Compaction =

$$\frac{\text{Actual Compaction}}{\text{Uncompacted Laminate Thickness}}$$

3. RESULTS

Effect of Cure Temperature

Fig. 2. shows the relative compaction as a function of time for the different temperatures (90, 120, 140, 150°C) under cure pressure of 515 kPa. As shown in Fig. 2., the rates of compaction and the times required to reach the ultimate compaction were different for each temperature, but the ultimate compactions were found to be the same. All the specimens reached about the ultimate compaction of 0.15. The compaction time were 50, 45, 37 and 36 minutes for 90, 120, 140 and 150°C, respectively.

It is interesting to note that the rate of compaction and the compaction time are dependent on cure temperature,

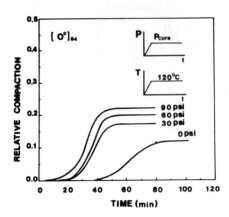

Fig.3. Relative compaction as functions of time for different cure pressure(64-ply laminates)

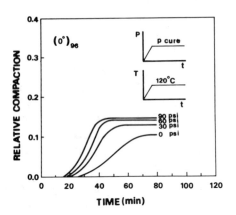

Fig.4. Relative compaction as functions of time for different cure pressures(96-ply laminates)

but the ultimate compaction is independent of cure temperature. These results are similar to those of the thin composite laminates.(1)

Effect of Cure Pressure

Fig. 3., 4. show the relative compactions of 64- and 96-ply laminates as a function of time for different cure pressure of 101, 308, 515 and

and 722 kPa at 120°C, respectively. As shown in Fig. 3., 4., the rate of compaction and the time to reach the ultimate compaction were independent of cure pressure except the case of cure pressure of 101 kPa. The ultimate compaction, however, was very different for each pressure. It is evident that the thicker the composite laminate is, the more the applied pressure is required. It can be found that these results are different from those of thin laminates and compaction behavior of the thick laminates strongly depends on cure pressure.

According to Springer's resin flow model(2), the compaction is in proportion to the root square of the applied pressure. Fig.5. shows the relationship between the relative compaction and cure pressure for 16-, 64- and 96-ply laminates, respectively. The relative compaction decreased as the ply number of

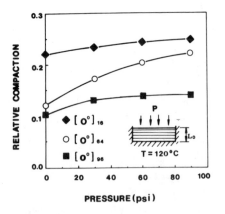

Fig.5. Relative compaction VS. pressure.

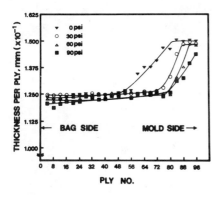

Fig.6. Measured per-ply thickness
after compaction.

laminates increased. For 96-ply
laminate, it reached only the
ultimate relative compaction of 0.12
under 722 kPa, while 16- and 64-ply
laminate reached 0.24 and 0.22,
respectively. It is clear that even
722 kPa is not sufficient enough for
96-ply laminate.

In order to study the compaction
through the thickness in detail,
the absolute compaction of each ply
is measured. Fig.6 shows per-ply
thickness of 96-ply laminate under
cure pressure of 101, 308, 515 and
722 kPa at 120°C.

The compaction at the bag side is
almost completed, even for 0 psi.
Acceptable compaction was shown up
to about 50th-, 72nd-, 82nd-, and
84th- ply for each pressure level
respectively. At the mold side
almost no compaction was measured
for all pressure level.

3. CONCLUSIONS

The measuring system for monitoring
the thickness change of the thick
composite laminate during autoclave
cure was found out to be reliable.
It was shown that the effect of
cure pressure on the compaction of
thick laminate was more dominant
than that of cure temperature.
For the laminate thicker than about
80 plies, no perfect compaction
can be expected at the mold side.
The compaction behavior can be
served as useful data to determine
the optimal process variables of
the thick composite laminate.

REFERENCES

1. KIM, T. W., Jun, E. J. and
   Lee, W. I., "Compaction Behavior
   of Composite Laminates During
   Cure," SAMPE journal, Vol. 24,
   No.5, 1988.

2. Loos, A. C. and Springer, G. S.,
   "Curing of Epoxy Matrix Compo-
   sites," Journal of Composite
   Materials, 1983, 17, 135-169.

CURING THICK LAMINATES USING INTERNAL HEAT SOURCES

Shawn M. Walsh

USAMTL

Watertown, Mass. 02172 - 0001

ABSTRACT

A mathematical model is developed for describing the influence of consolidation on the distribution of the dependent field variables. The model readily accommodates a variety of boundary conditions as well as source terms that might arise from chemical reactions, novel inductive or electrical heating, and microwave curing. The paper deals with certain issues largely unaddressed in composite process modelling, and presents a general solution methodology for treating the simultaneous effects of consolidation and internal heating. Comparisons with conventional "fixed geometry" models reveal the significance of a boundary immobilization technique in the prediction of property and field variable distribution.

1.0 INTRODUCTION

Mathematical models continue to emerge as powerful, versatile tools for assessing both conventional and novel polymer composite processes. A well developed model can bring into play all the significant parameters associated with a typical process scenario, and hence be used to narrow in on an appropriate process window for the system at hand. Of course, experiment is still required to determine the material properties and to validate the models for a wide range of possible processing conditions. The intent of the present paper is to examine certain process model issues that have gone largely unaddressed, and to suggest a modelling philosophy and technique that is capable of supplementing much of the important work currently available in the public literature.

Consolidation has an obviously crucial role in the manufacture of an "acceptable" composite part. Gutowski and his co-workers [1] have recently published a series of papers which conclusively demonstrate that the elastic effects of the fiber bed cannot, in general, be ignored. Their [1] theoretical development draws heavily on porous media treatments, the result of which is a consolidation model that has a number of very attractive features. For example, the model *predicts* the final volume fraction as well as fiber volume fraction distribution at any time during the consolidation phase. The instantaneous laminate thickness and velocity at any time are also calculated. Furthermore, the model can be readily adapted to handle any significant viscosity variations through the laminate thickness.

The prediction of both fiber volume fraction and fiber volume fraction distribution is a critical first step in the continuous updating of the effective composite transport properties. These properties include the thermal conductivity, specific heat, density, and permeability of the laminate.

Figure 1 gives an overview of how the effective thermal conductivity is determined from the constituent properties. Both the resin and fiber may have sufficient dependence on the processing temperatures so as to warrant such a detailed model of the effective thermal conductivity. Furthermore, the degree of cure can have, in some cases, a profound effect on the resin ' properties. Mijovic and Wang [2], for example, showed that the thermal conductivity of an epoxy can change by as much as 127% when one accounts for both temperature and degree of cure dependence during processing.

As stated earlier, two other parameters that play a pivotal role in determining the effective laminate thermal conductivity are fiber volume fraction and fiber volume fraction distribution. Porous media theory dictates that at low fiber volume fractions the <transverse> composite thermal conductivity is dominated by the resin; as the fiber volume fraction increases the composite thermal conductivity approaches that of the fiber. Hence, since there is a considerable change in the fiber volume fraction during consolidation a rigorous process model should update the local transport properties (e.g., thermal conductivity, density, etc.) during the consolidation phase.

The present model consists of three basic components:

1.) a resin flow/laminate consolidation model

2.) a heat transfer/internal heat generation model

3.) a reactive species/conversion model

Of course, other "submodels" such as void and residual stress models could be added but the focus of the present paper is on the influence of consolidation and/or internal heating on the dependent process parameters and properties. Loos and Springer [3], for example, present a very comprehensive epoxy composite model methodology designed to address a variety of relevant process phenomena; as will soon become apparent however, the present methodology differs significantly from certain portions of their [3] work. In the formulation of a typical composite process model one usually identifies the conservation equations that are relevant to the particular process and then proceeds to obtain the necessary transport properties and relations for the materials of interest. For example, resin systems are usually characterized by means of an Arrhenius model [4] or a mechanistic-type model [5]. Additionally, one must consider the nature of the initial and boundary conditions as dicatated by the process method used in the manufacture of a composite.

The objective of the model is to predict the influence of both conventional and novel processing conditions (e.g., new resins, inductive heating, etc.) on the dependent process variables such as temperature, degree of cure, and in the case of consolidation, fiber volume fraction. The present model addresses the effect of consolidation on the distribution of the dependent transport variables in a typical composite laminate. During consolidation hot resin is squeezed out and there is an accompanying decrease in the laminate thickness. Such dimensional changes can have a profound effect on the dependent transport variables as well as the "source" generation terms. It is well known [6], for example, that relatively small changes in thickness result in dramatically different temperature profiles. The present model develops the relevant conservation equations in a manner similar to that presented elsewhere [2,3,7]. However, unlike previous composite process models, the energy and species equations are *not* decoupled from the resin flow model; rather, all three governing equations are solved simulataneously by an iterative technique. Furthermore, at any given instant in the process the transport properties (e.g., thermal conductivity, density, permeability, etc.) are iteratively recalculated so as to account for any temperature, degree of cure, and fiber volume fraction dependence.

As discussed earlier, the dependent variable profiles (e.g., temperature) can have a strong dependence on any dimensional changes. Consolidation can result in rather large dimensional changes, which raises an important (and, to date, ignored) question: how does one mathematically account for the influence of dimensional changes on the governing equations? Consider, for the moment, the formation of ice on a surface as shown in Figure 2. As the surface is cooled *nonuniformly* along its length, the liquid (e.g., water) will begin to solidify. Depending on the imposed conditions, the <ice> layer will continue to grow with time; notice, however, that the nonuniform cooling condition at the surface results in an irregular layer of ice.

Any conventional attempt to model the conduction of heat through the layer would fail to account for the dimensional changes associated with layer growth. Hsu, Sparrow, and Patankar [8] developed a very powerful method for mathematically arresting the moving boundary in the case of ice forming on a coolant pipe. This method was adapted and modified for examining the effect of laminate consolidation on the distribution of dependent variables (e.g, temperature and degree of cure). The method consists of four basic steps: 1) define an appropriate deformable element, 2) "immobilize" the consolidating laminate boundary by instantaneous thickness normalization, 3) cast the governing equations in the newly transformed coordinate system, 4) apply Leibniz rule of integral differentiation and simplify by means of Green's theorem.

2.0 RESULTS AND DISCUSSION

Consider a composite laminate with an initial thickness H_0 and initially at a uniform temperature T_0 everywhere. The surface temperature of the laminate is then ramped at some rate; in this case, a simple linear ramp is applied. Provided that the material does *not* undergo dimensional changes during heating, the transient temperature profiles will form as shown in Figure 3(a). Now consider the exact same initial and applied boundary conditions in the case of a consolidating laminate. That is, as the surface temperature is ramped the laminate is simulataneously consolidated at a prescribed rate; Figure 3(b) illustrates the resulting transient temperature profiles for this latter case. Notice that at each time step the surface has moved inward, appearing to "compress" the temperature distribution.

In order to better appreciate the importance of the results, the temperature profiles for both the stationary and consolidating (moving) cases have been remapped onto the original *fixed* Cartesian coordinate system. Figure 4(a), for example, shows that at small times there is little consolidation, and hence the stationary and moving analyses produce essentially the same results. However, Figure 4(b) shows a very large difference in the results for the two cases, underlining the importance of consolidation effects. Models that do not mathematically account for the influence of consolidation can result in erroneous predictions of temperature (as well as other dependent field variables) in a composite process. The predicitons are erroneous by virtue of the fact that they may not be physically *and* mathematically consistent in resolving the conservation equations during consolidation. The local fiber volume fraction behavior during consolidation was also predicted, and is represented in Figure 5. As could be anticipated, the fiber volume fraction nearest the bleeder rises to a higher value earlier than that of the laminate's center; interestingly, the local permeability near the bleeder drops, adding further resistance to the resin flowing from the center. Figure 6 shows predicitons of fiber volume fraction distribution at an instant during consolidation. In this case η is the independent, normalized parameter resulting from the boundary immobilization technique. The micrographs shown in Figure 6 emphasize that if a laminate is improperly consolidated the fiber volume fractions (and hence, laminate properties) will not necessarily be uniform through the thickness.

3.0 CONCLUSIONS

The philosophy and results of a powerful, readily adaptable solution methodology for modelling consolidation in laminate composite processes has been presented. Although details of the transformation technique have been discussed in an earlier paper [9], the computer code embodying the technique is available free to anyone who may wish to use it. It is the opinion of the author that one cannot, in general, ignore the influence of consolidation on the conservation equations that

24

describe the relevant transport of energy, species, etc. The modelling methodology advanced here is not intended to refute the success of previous composite process models; indeed, the present model was used to reproduce many of the predictions of earlier models. The intent is to supplement the ability of these models such that one might obtain refined accuracy in the predictions, especially when consolidation plays a role in the process.

The original objective of this research was to develop a mathematical model for investigation of "source" or internal heating methods. However, preliminary experiments with such novel curing methods led to appreciable amounts of consolidation, which could not be justifiably ignored in a rigorous process model. Hence, in developing the present model to handle one particular problem (i.e. internally heated laminates) a much more general methodology resulted. There are many instances where the thermal diffusivity or thickness of the laminate is such that one cannot ignore the effect of consolidation. The method described herein was derived to be consistent with both physical and mathematical reasoning, and the results presented clearly show the influence of consolidation on the dependent process variables.

4.0 REFERENCES

1. Gutowski, T.G., T. Morigaki, and Z. Cai. "The Consolidation of Laminate Composites," J. Composite Mat'l., 21 (February 1985).

2. Mijovic, J. and H.T. Wamg. "Modeling of Processing Composites Part II - Temperature Distribution During Cure," SAMPE Journal, 24 (2) (March 1988).

3. Loos, A.C., and G.S. Springer. "Curing of Epoxy Matrix Composites," J. Composite Mat'l., 17 (March 1983).

4. Dusi, M.R., W.I. Lee, P.R. Ciriscioli, and G.S. Springer. "Cure Kinetics and Viscosity of Fiberite 976 Resin," J. Composite Mat'l., 21 (March 1987).

5. Batch, G.L., and C.W. Macosko. "A Computer Analysis of Temperature and Pressure Distributions in a Pultrusion Die," 42nd Ann. Tech. Conf., RP/CI, Soc. Plast. Ind.., 1987.

6. Bird, R.B., W.E. Stewart, and E.N. Lightfoot. Transport Phenomena. Wiley & Sons. 1960.

7. Maffezzoli, A.M., J.M. Kenny, and L. Nicolais. "Welding of PEEK/Carbon Fiber Composite Laminates," SAMPE Journal, 25 (1) (January 1989).

8. Hsu, C.F., E.M. Sparrow, and S.V. Patankar. "Numerical Solution of Moving Boundary Problems by Boundary Immobilization and a Control-Volume-Based Finite Difference Scheme," Int. J. Heat Mass Transfer, 24 (No. 8) (February 1981).

9. Walsh, S.M. "A Model for Source-Term Heating and Property Distribution in Consolidating Laminates," High Temple Workshop IX Proceedings, Jet Propulsion Laboratory, Pasadena, California. (January 1989).

THERMAL CONDUCTIVITY

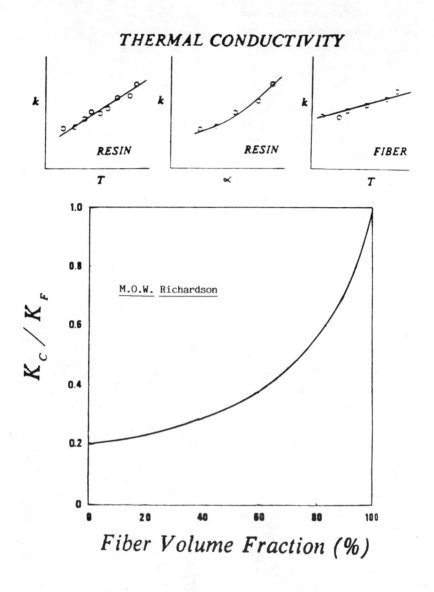

Fiber Volume Fraction (%)

Figure 1. Effective Thermal Conductivity

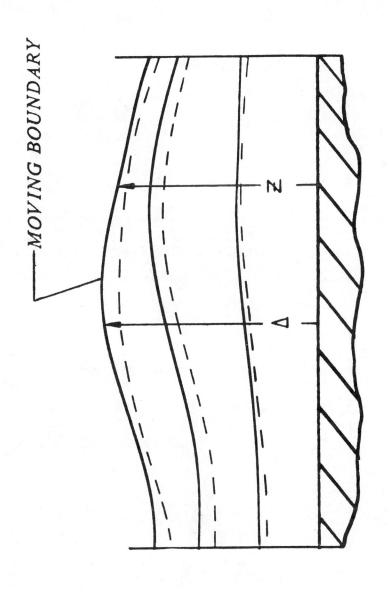

Figure 2. Surface Layer Growth of Ice

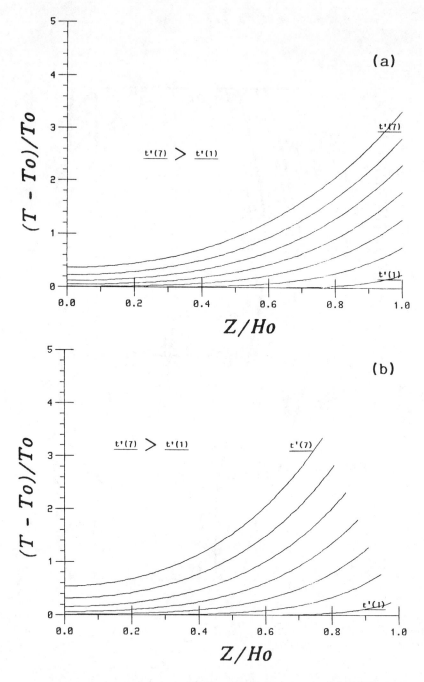

Figure 3.   Comparison of Stationary and Moving Solutions

28

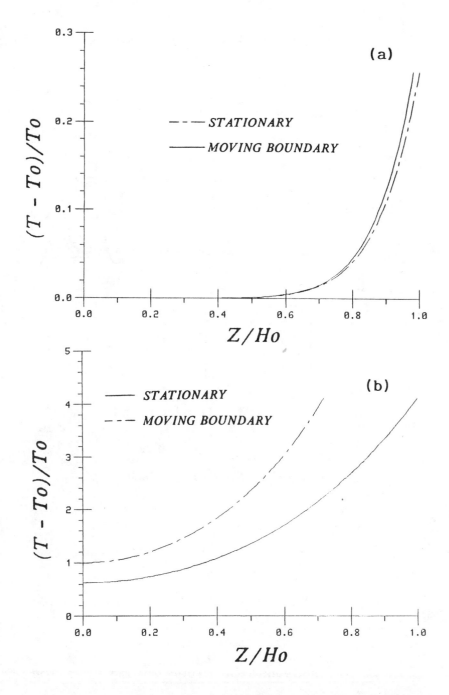

Figure 4. Comparison of Stationary and Moving Solutions

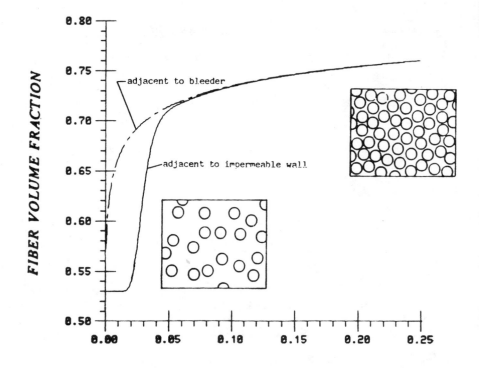

Figure 5. Response of Fiber Volume Fraction

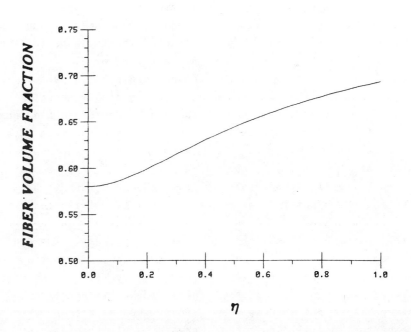

Figure 6. Fiber Volume Fraction Distribution

DIELECTRIC SENSORS FOR LOW-COST CURE CONTROL
W. Michaeli, G. Burkhardt

Institut für Kunststoffverarbeitung (IKV), RWTH Aachen
Pontstr. 49, D-5100 Aachen, Fed. Rep. of Germany

Abstract

The measurement of the complex permittivity of thermoset resins during the cure process in an autoclave or a press is of growing importance. This paper describes low-cost equipment optimized for the use in RP-plastics processing. Simple means for on-line dielectrometry have been developed not only for the sensors, but also for the measurement and signal processing electronics.

Reliable results are achieved by sensor condensors consisting of a twisted pair of very thin enamelled wires. For the tracking of the material properties, a special measurement oscillator was developed which incorporates the capacitive sensor as a part of the oscillator circuit. Changes of sensor capacity and loss resistance cause changes in oscillator frequency and amplitude damping, which can be measured directly by the evaluation computer.

1. INTRODUCTION

Thermoset resins are widely used for consumer goods and technical parts, especially as a matrix material for fiber reinforced plastic parts. The low processing viscosity and the good temperature and media resistance are the main advantages over thermoplastic matrix resins. Problems arise from the fact, that the end product material is generated by crosslinking during the moulding process. Especially the mechanical properties of the final part are therefore affected by the process conditions, such as temperatures or pressures, within all stages of the production. This is the reason for the pursuit of a controlled process, which adapts to the progress of the crosslinking reaction. For industrial processing, the difficult acquisition of the crosslinking condition held back the application of such advanced control systems.

A well-known laboratory method for this acquisition is the measurement of the dielectric material properties /1,2/. The resin normally contains free ions as impurities, which makes it a fairly bad conducting electrolyte /3/. As the mobility of these ions is closely coupled to the viscosity of the liquid resin, the ac-conductivity gives a good measure for the progress of the chemical reaction (Fig. 1). Even after the resin gelation, the dielectric conductivity measurement reveals useable data, as the small ions can penetrate the macromolecular network.

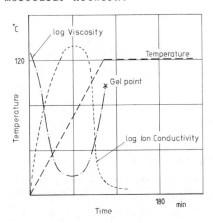

Fig. 1: Viscosity and conductivity of epoxy resin

The measurement equipment and the interpretation of the measured data have been improved significantly within the last years. For applications in industrial process control, however, there are still obstacles, such as inadequate sensor size or shape. Other problems are interference sensitivity of hardware or high equipment cost. They are solved partly by the development of the microdielectrometry measurement, which uses small integrated chip sensors /4/. Due to the costs of the disposable sensors, these measurements are restricted to high value components or random tests, but experimentally a process control for autoclave or compression moulded parts was tested /5/.

2. THE ELECTRONIC OSCILLATOR AS MEASURING SYSTEM

The aim of the research at the Institute of Plastics Processing (IKV) was the development of a cost effective measurement method for the dielectric material properties to be used under process conditions. For the description of the technology which was used a short explanation of the electronic analog circuitry is needed.

Sensors for dielectric measurements are by definition condensors with an insulation,

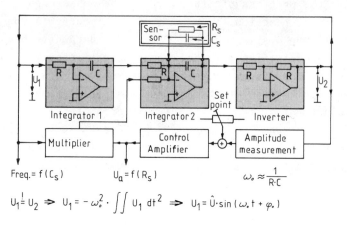

Freq.$= f(C_s)$ $U_a = f(R_s)$ $\omega_o \approx \dfrac{1}{R \cdot C}$

$$U_1 \stackrel{!}{=} U_2 \Rightarrow U_1 = -\omega_o^2 \cdot \iint U_1 \, dt^2 \Rightarrow U_1 = \hat{U} \cdot \sin(\omega_o t + \varphi_o)$$

Fig. 2: Measuring oscillator

consisting of the material to be investigated. The energy of an electrical ac-field, applied to this material is converted partly into heat. Therefore, the sensor is represented not only by the capacity of an ideal condensor, but also by a parallel resistance or a phase shift of the resulting current respectively.

The method used by IKV is based on the well-known technology of influencing an electronic oscillator circuitry by an external condensor. This technology is mostly used for measuring changes in the capacity very precisely by changes of the oscillation frequency, e.g. by a frequency counter /6/. The newly developed electronic system allows furthermore the simultaneous linear measurement of the sensor resistance in the range of 50 kOhms up to 2 GOhms at frequencies from 10 Hz up to 10 kHz.

The oscillator itself consists of an analog computing circuit, set up for the simulation of an oscillation differential equation (Fig. 2). Using ideal electronic components, the circuitry would oscillate with a constant amplitude /7/. The damping of the oscillation by non-ideal components and the sensor losses are compensated by an amplitude regulation circuit. Therefore, the output of the regulation amplifier, which is internally represented by a digital signal, provides for a linear measure of the sensor resistance /8/.

A fiber optic cable up to 20 meters in length links the oscillator and other analog

34

inputs to the host computer, which allows for automatic calibration, error correction and graphic representation. The high tracking speed of 10 measurements per second is well suited for high speed processes, such as SRIM or SMC-moulding. The electronic components expense is fairly small, therefore the complete measurement system costs less than $2000.-

length and one sensor electrode is grounded. This allows the design of very simple and rugged sensors for injection, RTM or SMC moulds.

Fig. 3 displays a sensor configuration, which was successfully tested in an SMC compression tool. It consists mainly of an electrically insulated steel plate, which is mounted within the surface of the tool. The conical back

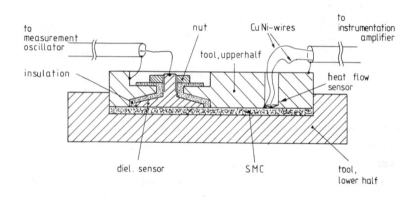

Fig. 3: Dielectric and heat flow sensors for SMC-moulding

3. PROCESS TRACKING FOR SMC COMPRESSION MOULDING

The measurement oscillator is capable of tracking sensor capacities up to 200 picofarads with a resolution of 1/10 picofarad in parallel to the measured loss resistance. The sensor hook-up is a simple coaxial cable up to 2 meters

of the plate gives a good force transmission to the screw bolt, which is also the electrical connection to the coaxial cable. The measured sensor capacity is situated between the steel plate and the opposite tool cavity surface. The parallel capacity and the losses of the plate insulation and the coaxial cable are measured in a single

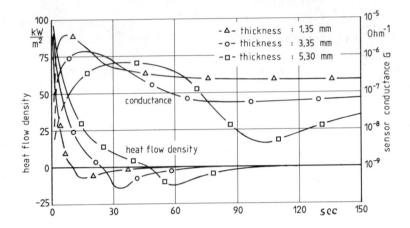

Fig. 4: LP-SMC curing, 150 C
conductance and heat flow

calibration procedure and used
for a correction program during normal measurements.

This sensor geometry has
some advantages against surface-active geometries, e.g.
comb electrodes, as the matrix
conversion is measured through
the entire wall thickness.
While the qualitative tracking
of the loss resistance curve
path allows for crosslinking
supervision or control, the
quantitative evaluation of the
measurement results gives
hints about potentially faulty
material dosage.

Fig. 4 displays conduc-
tance curves (reciprocal of
loss resistance and geometry
dependent measure of conductivity) of SMC parts of varying
wall thickness. First a rise
in conductance (falling visco-

sity) is caused by the rising
material temperature. After
passing a maximum, the proceeding polymerization and crosslinking makes the conductance
drop to a constant end value
at thin walled parts. At thick
walled parts another rise is
to be seen, which might be
caused by exothermal overheating or material degradation
in the middle of the wall.

A membrane heat-flow sen-
sor was installed in the moulding tool to achieve a correlation of the reaction cine-
tics to the measured dielectric data. The results are
also plotted in Fig. 4. The
first sharp peak is caused by
the feeding of the cold SMC
package, which draws an endo-
thermal heat flow from the hot
mould wall. After heating up

to the reaction starting temperature the exponential equalization function is overcome by the exothermal heat flow peak of the crosslinking reaction.

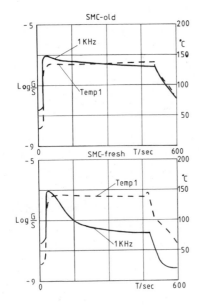

Fig. 5: Conductance of SMC, influence of aging

As a further experiment, thin sheets of standard SMC were pressed. The wall thickness of 1.5 mm prevented from exothermal overheating. Fig. 5 displays the influence of the material pre-aging on the conductance data. The temperature rise is easily visible in the conductance data of both fresh and old material (10 months stored at -10 Celsius). After heating up, the fresh material conductance drops quickly by more than one order of magni-

tude, whereas the crosslinking of the overstored material is hindered by losses of styrene and/or the degradation of the catalysts. Therefore, the conductance of the old material remains nearly constant after heating up.

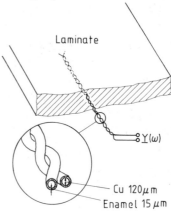

Fig. 6: Twin wire conductivity sensor

4. MEASUREMENTS ON EPOXY RESINS AND PREPREGS

Normally epoxy resins are used in the form of prepregs or wet laminated parts, e.g. made by filament winding. In these cases measurements with plate electrodes in a curing oven or an autoclave are impractical, as there is no defined mould cavity to mount the sensor electrodes. An additional obstacle is the frequent use of conductive carbon fibers for reinforcement, which forbids the integral dielectric measurement through the whole wall thickness.

Therefore it is required to separate the resin from the fibers and measure the pure resin. First successful experiments have been carried out using two thin twisted enamelled copper wires, normally used for the winding of solenoids. The copper cores of the wires are the two electrodes of a condensor, while the enamel layer protects the cores from unwanted contact (Fig 6). The wires are buried into the laminate and the surrounding resin penetrates the electric field at least partly. This sensor is extremely cheap in production, but its electrical performance is not yet satisfying, especially when using carbon fibers.

For this reason the design was slightly changed, according to Fig. 7. As mentioned above, one electrode of the sensor is grounded. This allows a non-symmetrical geometry with only the sensitive electrode wire to be insulated. The wire is formed as a loop, both ends out of the laminate. The grounded counterpart electrode is wound of blank wire around the sensitive electrode. This geometry allows the resin to flow into the spacings of the outer winding, while the fibers are kept away mostly. The winding and the ground connection are made of iron wire with an additional Cu-Ni-wire forming a thermocouple junction for the simultaneous tracking of the process temperature /9/.

The performance of the sensor depends mostly on the quality of the center wire enamel. Best results could be achieved using polyimide covered wires, which are chemically resistant and able to bear processing temperatures up to 250 degrees Celsius.

Fig. 8.a shows a typical plot of the curing of an epoxy-glass-prepreg. A typical effect of a sensor with an isolated electrode is the appearance of two peaks in the conductance plot, which can

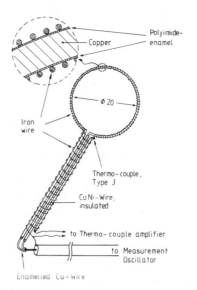

Fig. 7: Enamelled wire sensor

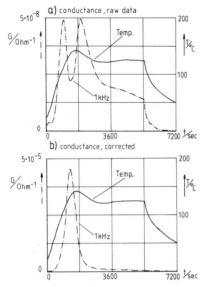

a) conductance, raw data

b) conductance, corrected

Fig. 8: Wire sensor measurement
of epoxy prepreg cure

also be observed at plate
electrodes with an insulating
release film. These peaks are
not associated to "events"
within the resin, as reported
earlier /10/, but solely
effects of the insulating
layer. At the beginning and
the end of the plot the loss
conductance of the sensor is
low, because the resin conductivity is low (cold resin or
crosslinked totally). At the
minimum the resin is hot and
its conductivity is very high.
Therefore, most of the ac voltage applied to the sensor
drops at the insulating enamel
capacity, which has low electrical losses, revealing a low
overall sensor conductance. If
the electrical properties of

the insulating layer are
known, the original conductance plot of the resin, as
measured without enamel layer,
can be regenerated automatically by a correction routine
(Fig. 8.b).

5. FURTHER DEVELOPMENTS

Up to now, the topic of the
research was the development
of cost effective measurement
equipment and sensors. This
measurement technology, however, was not developed for its
own sake, but for applications
in quality improvement by
control of the thermoset material processing.

For the realization of
such control systems knowledge
is needed about the correlation between the mechani-
cal/rheological material properties on the one hand and
the dielectric/thermical data
on the other hand. Literature
in this field of research is
quite rare and mostly concerned with epoxy resins only
/11/. Therefore two measurement devices have been set up
at IKV which are tested for
simultaneous tracking of the
respective properties.

Investigations in the
rheological data of liquid
resins are possible with a
special cone-plate-rheometer
(Fig. 9). A torque sensor with

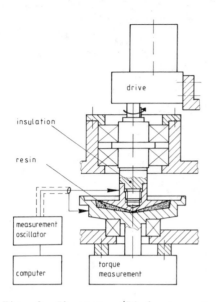

Fig. 9: Rheometer/Dielectrometer

(Fig. 10). A large pneumatic cylinder can press a conical shaft with a rubber sealing ring into this cavity, thus moulding a thimble-type part out of approx. 20 grams resin. The moulding tool is heated with high precision.

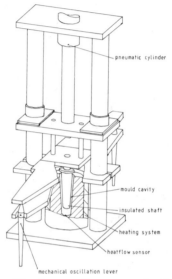

Fig. 10: Press for correlation measurements

extremely progressive characteristics allows viscosity measurements within three orders of magnitude in the same range. At the same time, dielectric measurements are possible, because the electrically insulated rotating cone functions as a condensor electrode against the grounded plate.

At the gel point of the resin viscosity measurements become senseless; for paste-type substances, like SMC, they are doubtful anyway. Only a dynamic-mechanical analysis can give results in these cases, as it works well from the liquid to the solid state. The second correlation measurement set up is a small press with a conical cavity

For dielectric measurements the shaft is also insulated, as condensor electrode against the outer cavity surface. Additionally a heat flow density sensor is integrated into the bottom of the cavity. For measurements of the dynamic mechanical properties, electrically driven levers can force the pressing shaft to rotational oscillations. Amplitude and phase shift of this oscillation in relation to the driving force allow the tracking of the complex shear modulus of the curing resin. Measurements with this new equipment are under way.

The results of the comparison of dielectric, dynamic mechanical and heat flow data will be the base for optimized control strategies to be worked out. As besides the cross-linking reaction there are many influences on the dielectric behavior, e.g. temperature, shear movements or geometry, for each material and each process investigations have to be carried out, which allow the unequivocal connection of causes and effects.

Acknowledgement

This research work was funded by the "Arbeitsgemeinschaft industrieller Forschungsvereinigungen e.V. (AIF)"

References

/1/ Kienle,R.H., Race, H.H.
The electrical, chemical and physical properties of alkyd resins
Trans. Electroch. Soc. 65, 1934, page 87 - 107

/2/ Auckward, J. A. et al.
Change in electrical resistivity of some high polymers during isothermal polymerizat.
Journal of Polym. Sci. 27, 1958, page 199 - 205

/3/ Senturia,S.D.
Sheppard,N.F.
Dielectric analysis of thermoset cure
Advances in polymer science 80
Springer Verlag,
Berlin/Heidelberg 1986

/4/ Sanjana, Z. N.
The use of microdielectrometry in monitoring the cure of resins and composites
Polymer Engin. and Sci. 26, 1986, page 373 - 379

/5/ La Verne, L.
Microdielectrometry: Tiny sensors close the control loop
Reprint Advanced Composites, Jan/Feb 1987

/6/ Hielscher, J.
Digitales Dielektrizitätskon-
stanten-Meßgerät mit direkter
Anzeige
German Democratic Republic
Patent No. 36314, 1965

/7/ Tietze, U., Schenk, Ch.
Halbleiter-Schaltungstechnik
vierte Auflage, page 435-438
Springer Verlag, Berlin,
Heidelberg, New York

/8/ Menges,G., Burkhardt, G.
Verfahren zur Messung von
dielektrischen Materialeigen-
schaften
Federal Republic of Germany
Patent Application P3729031.2
of 31. Aug. 1987

/9/ Berg, M.
Dielektrizitätssensoren für
Vernetzungsmessungen
non-published report
IKV, Aachen 1988

/10/ Lawless, G.
High temperature dielectric
study of epoxy resins
Polymer Egineering and Science
May 1980, page 546 - 550

/11/ Gothro, J. Yandrasits, M.
Cure Monit. using dielectric
and dynamic mech. analysis
SPE, ANTEC '87 Proceedings,
page 1039 - 1042

Biographies

Prof. Dr.-Ing. Walter Michaeli,

born 1946, studied mechanical
engineering with production
technology as the field of
specialization at the Aachen
University of Technology
(Fed. Rep. of Germany). After
diploma degree he was scientific assistant at the Institute
of Plastics Processing (IKV)
in Aachen. Later on he worked
in the scientific management
of Freudenberg Co. Since Jan.
1988 he is head of the IKV and
professor for plastics processing at the Aachen University
of Technology.

Dipl.-Ing. Gert Burkhardt,

born 1954, studied electronics
engineering with telecommuni-
cations as the field of specialization at the Aachen University of technology (Fed.
Rep. of Germany). After three
years of employment as
research engineer for industrial companies, he is scientific assistant at the IKV
since 1985, concerned with
automation and process control
in reinforced plastics processing.

INCREMENTAL FORMING OF LARGE FIBER-REINFORCED
THERMOPLASTIC COMPOSITES
Dr. A. Brent Strong
Paul Hauwiller
Brigham Young University

1.0 Abstract

The incremental forming method for thermoplastic composites has been developed and its viability has been demonstrated. Incremental forming is a method to create large thermoplastic composites utilizing small to medium sized equipment. An incremental forming apparatus was created and then tested to determine if quality parts could be produced from it. The parts produced were subjected to mechanical as well as other quality tests to determine their overall performance. The parts produced by incremental forming were found to have very good mechanical and other quality characteristics.

2.0 Introduction

The composites industry has been rapidly increasing its use of thermoplastic composite materials. Due to the unique combination of properties possessed by thermoplastic composites, applications utilizing these materials will continue to increase. There is, therefore, an increasing need to develop viable, cost effective manufacturing processes. Incremental forming is a viable cost effective manufacturing process for large thermoplastic composites.

In order to present the full range of advantages that incremental forming possesses over the customary thermoplastic composites manufacturing methods, these customary methods will be briefly reviewed and compared to the incremental forming method. 1. Matched Die Molding or Hot Stamping -- The thermoplastic composite laminate is heated outside the mold and then transferred to the mold area and pressed between two non-heated matched rigid molds which are mounted on the platens of a press. Hydroforming is similar to this except that one side of the mold is replaced with an elastomer. Compression molding is a closely related process, extensively used for thermosets, where the material is placed between heated matched dies. Curing occurs in these molds.

DISADVANTAGES: Matched die forming requires a press and an oven the size of the part to be produced. Parts as large as a wing skin for example would not be produced with this method, since the size of such a press and an oven is not economically feasible.

2. Autoclaving -- The laminate layers are layed in a mold which is sealed with a vacuum bagging assembly. The mold is then placed in an autoclave and slowly heated. Pressure is applied to reduce the void content in the material and increase its mechanical properties. After a time at the softening point temperature the mold is slowly cooled.

DISADVANTAGES: The size of the part is restricted by the size of the autoclave. Also an autoclave is an expensive and time consuming piece of equipment to purchase and operate.

3. Continuous Heated Roll Forming -- This method is very similar to the roll forming of metals. In this method a continuous length of thermoplastic composite is passed through a heating section and into a series of forming rollers. This produces long parts with a constant cross-sectional area. Pultrusion is another method to create long, constant cross-section parts. DISADVANTAGES: This process can create large thermoplastic composite parts but only of uniform cross-sectional shape and area (such as C-channels, hat sections, rods etc.).

4. Filament and Tape Winding -- This is a method most often used for thermoset resins. When used for thermoplastics, a tow or tape of fibers that is pre-impregnated with thermoplastic resin is heated and applied to a rotating mandrel. Consolidation of the material is provided by a pressure roller at the point

of contact.

DISADVANTAGES: These processes are usually limited to surfaces of revolution and therefore can not create large laminate parts.

5. Diaphragm Forming -- A thermoplastic layup packet is placed between 2 superplastic alloy sheets. The laminate and the coversheets are placed in an oven. The materials are heated and then formed (using pressure) into a mold.

DISADVANTAGES: This process is at present limited to the size of the heating and pressure vessel. Also the superplastic alloy sheets are costly.

The advantages of incremental forming over the customary methods in the production of large thermoplastic composites will are listed in Table 1.

The incremental forming method has many advantages over traditional manufacturing methods of thermoplastic composites. Incremental forming is similar to matched die forming in that it utilizes a transfer system, an oven, a press, and matched molds. However the incremental forming process can produce large parts on small to medium sized equipment. This is done by forming a large laminate in sections rather than all at once. Since only sections of a large laminate are being formed, the press and oven only need to be the size of the section to be formed instead of the size of the entire part. A section is heated and then transferred to the molding area and formed. The molds are changed, if desired, while the next section is heating up and then the next section is formed. The incremental forming process has been used to mold five non-identical sections in 30 minutes. A diagram of the process is presented in Figure 1.

3.0 EXPERIMENTAL

The incremental forming system consists of 4 basic pieces of equipment. These are the transfer system (which includes the clamping sub-system), the oven, the press, and the modular matching molds (either both rigid molds or a rigid and an elastomeric mold). A detailed presentation of the incremental forming process (focusing on the equipment requirements) follows.

Transfer System

The transfer system consists of transfer rails,

a clamping sub-system, and rollerbars. These three components work together to hold the laminate in the proper position, transfer the section the laminate to be formed from the oven to the forming area (between the platens of a press), and lastly to transfer the formed section out of the forming area.

The transfer rails form the sides of the laminate holding system. This open-ended design allows parts of any length to be molded. The width is dictated by the width of the oven or molds. In the prototype system, two 48 inch long sections of 1.25 inch square steel uni-strut stock were used for the transfer rails.

The first step in molding a part using incremental forming is to clamp the laminate (consisting of oriented plys either in pre-consolidated form or prepreg sheets placed together) into the clamping sub-system which is attached to the transfer rails. (See Figure 2). The clamps were made of .625 inch square aluminum bar stock and machined. Two screws for each clamp were used to hold the material in the jaws of the clamps. Springs connected the

clamps to the transfer rails and were adjusted to exert 950 grams of load when the laminate was being held (the laminate weighed 300 grams). Five clamps, positioned at 4 inch intervals were used to support each of two sides of the laminate.

The clamping system allowed the laminate to move both horizontally and vertically. The laminate moved horizontally during the forming process as the laminate is pulled into the mold to conform to the contours. The springs provided the laminate with horizontal movement capability. The laminate required vertical movement capability so that the laminate could be raised above the surface of the mold (after forming a section). Once the laminate was raised above the mold surface the modular mold could be adjusted to the shape for the next forming section. The vertical movement capability was provided by the method of attaching the springs to the transfer rail. This attachment utilized vertical slots which were milled in the sides of the uni-strut stock to allow the springs from the clamping sub-system and the laminate to move vertically.

The transfer rails were mounted on the roller bars. The roller bars provided a low friction transfer mechanism to move the laminate from the oven to the molding area. The roller bars also retained the transfer rails from moving inward. The roller bars were made of 24 inch long angle iron and had roller bearings press fit into each end.

Oven

Once the laminate was clamped and the transfer rails mounted on the roller bars, the first section to be molded was introduced into the oven. The requirements for the oven are rather simple. It must be able to heat a portion of the material to be formed to the softening temperature. The oven consisted of a heating panel (with controller) and an insulated casing. The heating panel was made from 18 X 21 X 1.25 inch 6061 aluminum plate. Eight 750 Watt, 250 Volt, 16 inch long cartridge heaters were inserted into holes in the side (18 inch side) of the plate at even intervals. A thermocouple was mounted on the side of the plate between two of the cartridge heaters. A three inch thick insulating

casing was built around the heating panel to create an oven (Figure 3). In incremental forming the oven is only required to heat a portion of the material, roughly, the part to be immediately molded and the next section after that.

The specific amount of material that is required to be heated for each section depends on the strain to failure of the fibers and the strain that will be required of the fibers during molding. This molding strain is affected by the degree of contouring of the molds and the size of the forming section. The smaller the ultimate fiber strain and the more complex the mold shape, the greater the size of the section that must be heated. Since the fibers in the forming area are moving (during forming) and the fibers in the cold (solid) material are not some fiber strain occurs. The amount of strain needs to be calculated to determine if it will be below the ultimate. The strain will move through the laminate as the various sections are formed, and will eventually be released out the ends of the fibers.

Forming Press and Modular molds

Once the first section of the laminate has been heated to the softening point, that section was transferred to the forming area. The forming area consisted of a forming press and a pair of matched modular molds mounted on its platens. The requirements for the press are fairly straight forward. First the platens of the press need to be parallel to one another. Second the press must be able to close fast enough so the laminate won't cool down before forming. Third the press must be able to apply approximately 100 psi to its entire work area.

The molding is accomplished by bringing the platens of the press together within 10 seconds and the first section of the laminate was formed between the mold halves (under 100 psi of pressure). The molds were cold and therefore drew heat out of the laminate in five minutes. Once the laminate was sufficiently cooled, the modular molds were separated, the laminate raised above the mold, and the modular molds were adjusted for forming the next section. The entire process was repeated for each succeeding section.

The modular molds have the greatest number of requirements. There are several factors about the molds which need to be controlled in order to produce a good incrementally formed part. Modular molds are designed to have interchangeable sections to allow for the changing contours of the part for each molding section (Figure 4).

First -- The mold needs to be designed so that there is some overlap in forming. In other words, the mold for section 2 should contain a small section which was previously formed in section 1 (approximately 1 inch). This prevents a line of definition between sections being formed, thus helping to create a part indistinguishable from a conventionally formed one. It also facilitates alignment between sections.

Second -- The molds must fit together well. The resin, although highly viscous, will still be forced into any cracks between the mold pieces when under 100 psi of pressure.

Third -- The height of the mold pieces must match

exactly. A deviation of .002 inches is sufficient to create non-uniform consolidation if matching rigid molds are used or deformations if a rigid and an elastomeric mold are used.

Fourth -- The molds may be either both rigid matching modular molds or a rigid modular mold and an elastomeric near matching mold.

The advantages and disadvantages of each type of mold in incremental forming are as follows:

MATCHED ELASTOMERIC -- When a rigid modular mold and an elastomeric (near) matching mold are used, the forming process is a gentler one than occurs when both molds are rigid. Not only that, but the elastomeric mold does not need to be a perfect match of the rigid mold. Under pressure the elastomeric mold will flow to match the shape of the rigid mold. However, the elastomeric mold must be constrained from any horizontal movement. This movement squeezes the surface resin causing the resin to flow and creates resin wrinkles on the part between every section. Therefore a matched elastomeric mold can be used, but care must be exercised.

RIGID MOLDS -- When two rigid molds are used, horizontal flow is not a problem. There must, however, be precision in the mold making since any mismatching of the molds will result in greater or lesser consolidation of the laminate.

The last item to mention about the molds is that the molds should be cooled to prevent thermal expansion when heat is drawn out of the laminate. This expansion can cause the part to be out of tolerance. The expansion problem is greater for metal molds than elastomeric. The cycle time can also be reduced with cooled molds.

4.0 Economic Advantages of Incremental Forming

The incremental forming process has a number of economic advantages over an autoclave processing of a large thermoplastic composites. The areas of interest for comparing incremental forming and autoclaving thermoplastic composites processing are labor, operating expenses, and capital costs. Incremental forming will be compared to autoclaving

49

since autoclaving is the presently predominant method for forming large thermoplastic composites.

1. Labor costs. The labor costs of the traditional thermoplastic molding are very high. These high labor costs result from the following:

a) The layup costs of thermoplastic composites are high and incremental forming doesn't need the same degree of layup time. Thermoplastic composite prepregs are customarily boardy and don't conform well to molds until after the prepregs are processed. (Comingled or cowoven material can be used but the strength values and degree of uniformity are less than that of prepreg). Autoclave processing requires that the material be layed-up in the mold before processing. This lay-up procedure is time consuming and difficult. Also, once the material is layed-up in the mold, a vacuum bagging set-up must be applied. Incremental forming requires no lay-up, but only requires that a flat material packet be put together and clamped in the transfer mechanism. This eliminates the problems of a boardy material.

b) The next labor cost is the amount of operator time during the processing. The autoclave processing requires one person to monitor the processing cycle. However, the incremental method may require more than one person to change the mold between sections. Therefore while the incremental forming method has the advantage during the lay-up of the part, it has a disadvantage during processing. The net result would be a slight labor savings with incremental forming or possibly no net difference.

2. Operating Expenses. The next area for consideration is operating expenses. These are the expenses incurred to produce the part which are not capital expenditures or labor costs.

a) The first area under consideration is the cost of heating the laminate. The heat supplied to the material is a costly operating expense. It is much cheaper to heat a thin oven than a large open autoclave. Therefore the heating cost for incremental forming is less than that of an autoclave. Along with that operating cost is the added cost of the vacuum bagging materials used in autoclave processing which are absent in incremental forming.

b) Another operating expense is the time to process the part. Incremental forming will require less time for a medium size part, but will probably require a slightly longer time for a large part with many section changes. This expense depends on the size of the part, the size of the press and oven and the complexity of the part.

c) The storage costs for the molds used for incremental forming will be less than that for autoclaves. The incremental molds are in pieces so they can be stacked. This is not possible with a large autoclave mold. The incremental mold has less bulk since it isn't designed with a framework to facilitate uniform heating as the autoclave mold is.

3. Capital Expenses. The last area of examination is the capital expenses involved with both manufacturing processes. The initial cost of the equipment is, perhaps, the single largest expense.

a) A large autoclave costs more than a medium sized press, a small oven and a transfer mechanism. Therefore substantial savings can be made for the initial equipment cost.

b) The capital cost of the mold can also be a significant expense. A large mold as used for an autoclave is quite expensive. The incremental mold will usually be cheaper since some sections are reused even though there are two halves. It should be noted that the incremental molds will require the same degree of precision as the autoclave mold.

c) Another cost saving advantage of incremental forming is that an elastomeric mold can be used (if movement is restrained on all four sides). This allows the upper mold to cast to shape instead of machined. If the mold was complex this could be a signifigent cost savings.

5.0 Cost Summary

The incremental forming method has many more cost advantages than disadvantages. It has the potential of bringing down the cost of processing advanced thermoplastic composites. It saves money in all three areas considered which were labor costs, operating costs and capital costs.

6.0 Mechanical and Quality Considerations

The data which we aquired while proving the viability of incremental forming indicate that the incremental forming process using pre-consolidated sheets can produce parts with good surface quality and mechanical strength. The forming process does not signifigently degrade the properties of the composites. Therefore the process can be used to make large parts with medium sized equipment.

The mechanical strength values for the pre-consolidated incrementally formed parts were higher than all others (except the published tensile properties). The surface quality was excellent. These parts were free from surface defects. These parts exhibited good uniformity of properties as indicated by the small standard deviation of the tensile results. The only apparent draw backs were a thickness variance of ± 0.0016 inches which is negligible (Figure 5).

Therefore the incremental forming process can

successfully form large fiber-reinforced thermoplastics using small ovens to heat only part of the laminate and small presses to form parts of the laminate as long as the fiber strain to failure is not exceeded

7.0 Summary and Future

The incremental forming process has a number of advantages and is viable for creating large parts utilizing small to medium sized equipment. The process needs some more research to more fully explore its capabilities in the areas of contouring, increased part thickness and elastomeric molds. Another area of further investigation is the development of proper parameters for using unconsolidated sheets as the raw material instead of pre-consolidated sheets.

We hope that through further research that this process will be able to be used commercially thus lowering the manufacturing costs and increasing the use of thermoplastic composites.

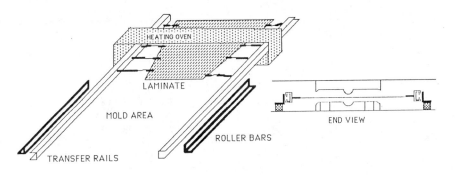

HEATING OVEN

LAMINATE

MOLD AREA

ROLLER BARS

TRANSFER RAILS

END VIEW

FIGURE 1

INCREMENTAL FORMING PROCESSING EQUIPMENT

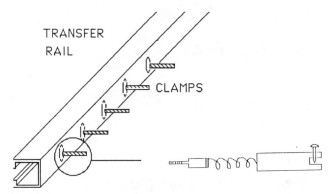

TRANSFER
RAIL

CLAMPS

FIGURE 2

TRANSFER SYSTEM COMPONENTS

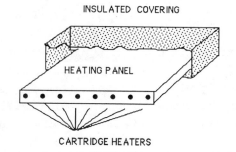

INSULATED COVERING

HEATING PANEL

CARTRIDGE HEATERS

FIGURE 3

HEATING OVEN

53

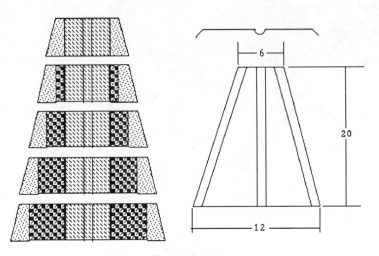

FIGURE 4

MODULAR MOLD AND PART

TENSILE STRENGTH —————————— 87.8 KSI
SURFACE QUALITY ————————— NO DEFECTS
UNIFORMITY OF THICKNESS ——— ± .0016 INCHES

FIGURE 5

INCREMENTAL FORMING PART QUALITY

ADVANTAGES	DISADVANTAGES
Incremental Forming	Customary Forming Methods
No part size restriction.	Size restricted to press or autoclave.
Small equipment required.	Large equipment required.
Lower operating expenses.	High operating expenses.
Lower capital costs.	Higher capital costs.

TABLE 1

RHEOLOGICAL AND THERMAL CURE STUDIES
OF AN EPOXY-AMINE THERMOSET

W. J. Sichina, T. H. Grentzer and C. L. Jaworski
DuPont Instruments Co.
Quillen Building
Concord Plaza
Wilmington, DE 19898

Abstract

The epoxy-amine system EPON 828 and DDS (diamino diphenyl sulfone) was studied using the following techniques: Dielectric Analysis (DEA), Dynamic Mechanical Analysis (DMA) and Differential Scanning Calorimetry (DSC). The viscosity/cure profiles were established using both DMA and DEA. Comparisons were made between the DMA and DEA results for the thermosetting resin. The activation energy of cure was established using the times to gelation from DMA measurements. The cure kinetics of this system were established using DSC. It was found that the cure could be modeled using an autocatalyzed kinetics equation. The activation energy of cure obtained from the DSC results agreed very well with those obtained from the DMA.

tween the degree of cure and the viscoelastic properties using both thermal and rheological techniques.

The rheological properties (e.g., flow characteristics, gelation, vitrification) can be determined using two techniques: Dynamic Mechanical Analysis and Dielectric Analysis. Differential Scanning Calorimetry can be used to investigate the changes in the heat of reaction of various isothermal temperatures and to establish the kinetics of cure associated with a given thermoset. The modeling of the cure kinetics by DSC provides the scientist or engineer with valuable information which can be used to optimize processing conditions or to predict the shelf-life of thermosetting resins.

This presentation will demonstrate the use of DMA, DEA and DSC to fully characterize the rheological and thermal properties of a thermosetting resin.

1. INTRODUCTION

Thermosetting materials, such as epoxies and polyimides, are widely utilized in a variety of applications including composites, coatings and adhesives. The viscoelastic properties exhibited by an uncured thermoset are governed by the competing effects of the temperature profile (decreasing viscosity) and the chemical crosslinking reaction (increasing viscosity).

In order to properly control the processing of high performance thermosetting materials, it is best to establish the relationships be-

2. EXPERIMENTAL

The epoxy-amine system EPON 828 and DDS (diamino diphenyl sulfone) was studied using the three techniques, described above. The thermoset was prepared by heating the EPON 828 resin and adding the DDS until stoichiometric quantities of reactants were present (i.e., B = 1.0). The mixture was stirred until the DDS had visibly dissolved in the EPON.

The DuPont 910 Differential Scanning Calorimeter was used to quantify the cure kinetics of the epoxy-amine system. Approximately 24 mg of the mixture was placed in an open DSC pan and then analyzed with the 910 DSC and 2100 Thermal Analyst. The DSC cell was purged with dry nitrogen at a rate of 40 cc/min.

The cell was preheated to the desired isothermal temperature. Upon complete thermal equilibration the cell was opened and the sample quickly put in place. The run was allowed to proceed after the cell lid and cover were replaced. Isothermal DSC measurements were conducted at temperatures of 145, 150, 160, 170 and 180°C.

The viscoelastic properties of the reacting resin system were monitored using the DuPont 983 Dynamic Mechanical Analyzer and the DuPont 2970 Dielectric Analyzer.

The samples for the DMA testing were prepared by placing the neat resin on two strips of fiberglass cloth. The cloth provides an inert support for the resin. The ends of the cloth were wrapped with a layer of aluminum foil (where the faces of the DMA clamps come in contact with the sample) to prevent the clamps from adhering to the sample after the completion of cure. [This procedure makes it much easier to remove the sample after the analysis is complete]. The resin/cloth were placed in the standard, vertical DMA clamps with a clamping distance (i.e., sample length) of 7.0 mm. The clamping screws were tightened to a torque of 4 inch pounds. This torque was sufficient to prevent the sample from slipping during the analysis. The epoxy/cloth samples were analyzed at a fixed frequency of 1.000 Hz with an oscillation amplitude (i.e., strain) of 1.5 mm.

The viscoelastic properties were measured via the DMA at under isothermal conditions at temperatures of 160, 170 and 180°C and under dynamic conditions by heating the resin specimen at a rate of 3°C/min.

The resin samples were quickly heated to the desired isothermal temperatures at a rate of 40°C/min. The samples were held at the particular isothermal temperature until the epoxy system completely hardened (i.e., the shear modulus G' exceeded 1 GPa).

The dielectric properties were monitored using the DuPont 2970 Dielectric Analyzer. The epoxy-amine resin was analyzed using the ceramic single surface sensor. The measured dielectric properties include e' (permittivity) and e" (loss factor). The permittivity represents the degree of alignment of the molecular dipoles to the applied oscillating electric field while the loss factor measures the amount of energy required to align the dipoles and to move trace ions existing in the resin. Ionic conductivity (σ) can be calculated from e' via Equation 1 and can be used to follow the rheological changes that take place while the thermoset undergoes the curing reaction.

$$\sigma = e'' \, w \, e_o \qquad (1)$$

where: σ = ionic conductivity
w = angular frequency ($2\pi f$)
f = frequency (Hz)
e_o = absolute permittivity of free space.

Ionic conductivity is related to viscosity because the fluidity of a liquid is related to the ease with which the ionic impurities can migrate through the molten resin.

3. RESULTS OF THE DSC ISOTHERMAL ANALYSIS

Shown in Figure 1 are the DSC results obtained from the isothermal analysis and the epoxy-amine system at 150°C. The material exhibits some autocatalyzed behavior as indicated by the fact that the maximum heat flow does not occur at time = 0.

The isothermal data was analyzed to establish the cure kinetics using the DuPont Isothermal Kinetics software. The program operates by taking the isothermal DSC data and generating 25 partial heat areas at various times, t, to determine the degree of conversion, α, and the corresponding heat flow (dH/dt) to determine the rate of cure, $d\alpha/dt$, as a function of cure time at each isothermal temperature.

To determine the kinetic parameters associated with the EPON 828 - DDS system, the autocatalyzed kinetics model, as given in Equation 2, was used:

$$\frac{d\alpha}{dt} = k\,\alpha^m(1 - \alpha)^n \qquad (2)$$

where: $k = Ze^{-E/RT}$

$\begin{array}{l} m \\ n \end{array}$ are reaction orders

$\dfrac{d\alpha}{dt}$ = rate of reaction

α = degree of conversion

E = activation energy

Z = preexponential factor.

The results obtained for the isothermal data at 150°C using the Isothermal Kinetics software are displayed in Figure 2. This plot shows the log reaction rate versus the log of the autocatalyzed rate term, $\alpha(1 - \alpha)$. The proper selection of the autocatalyzed reaction orders, n and m, yield a linear plot. The fact that a linear plot is obtained demonstrates that the autocatalyzed kinetics model successfully accounts for the cure behavior associated with this thermosetting system.

The analysis of the other isothermal DSC runs (at 145, 160, 170 and 180 °C) permits the estimation of the activation energy, E, associated with the cure of the epoxy-amine and the pre-exponential factor, Z. Displayed in Figure 3 are the results of the analyses, where the reduced reaction rates are plotted versus the degree of conversion for each of the isothermal temperatures. The squares represent the data points while the solid lines represent the best-fit autocatalyzed kinetics model based on the calculated values of the activation energy, pre-exponential factor and reaction orders.

Based on the analysis of the EPON

828 - DDS system by the Isothermal Kinetics software, the following autocatalyzed kinetic parameters were obtained:

$$\begin{array}{ll} E = 65.1 \ \pm 0.63 \ \text{kJ/mole} & (3) \\ \log Z = 6.55 \ \pm 0.078 \ \text{1/min} \\ m = 0.277 \pm 0.020 \\ n = 1.29 \ \pm 0.030. \end{array}$$

From these values, and from the integration of the autocatalyzed rate expression, the conversion – time – temperature profiles for the EPON 828 - DDS system can be established. The isothermal conversion curves are displayed in Figure 4.

4. DIELECTRIC AND DYNAMIC MECHANICAL PROPERTIES

The epoxy – amine system was characterized on both the DuPont 983 DMA and the DuPont 2970 DEA by dynamically heating at a rate of 3°C/min from -75 to 250°C. Displayed in Figure 5 are the results obtained from the DMA. This plot shows the log shear storage modulus, G', log shear loss modulus, G", and the log tan delta (where tan delta = G"/G'). Below the glass transition temperature (at approximately 10°C), the resin is in the solid, glassy form and exhibits a relatively high modulus, G'. As the material passes through its Tg, the modulus drops precipitously. The loss modulus yields a peak at the glass transition event, and the value of tan delta shows a significant increase as the resin softens. Between 100 and 150°C, the resin reaches a point of minimum viscosity (where G' reaches its minimum value and where tan delta achieves its maximum value). Above 150°C, the epoxy – amine begins to polymerize as indicated by the slight increase in G' and the decrease in tan delta. At approximately 190°C, the resin undergoes crosslinking as demonstrated by the sudden rise in G' and the rapid drop in tan delta. The temperature of gelation (210°C) is reached when G' = G" or when tan delta = 1.00 (1,2). The material continues to crosslink and stiffen as demonstrated by the continuing increase in G' between 210 and 250°C.

The results obtained on the DEA for the epoxy – amine resin when heated from -75°C at a rate of 3°C/min are displayed in Figure 6. This plot shows the loss factor, e", at frequencies of 100, 300, 1000 and 3000 Hz. These results are consistent with those obtained by DMA. The Tg of the resin occurs at approximately 20°C as indicated by the successive peaks in e". [The shift in the loss factor peaks, with respect to frequency indicates that this is a relaxation transition]. Above Tg, the resin begins to flow which is observed as an increase in e". At approximately 140 °C, the minimum viscosity of the resin is reached as demonstrated by the peak maxima in e". Above 140°C, the loss factor begins to decrease due to the polymerization and crosslinking of the resin system until approximately 225°C, when the reaction is complete. Dielectric analysis is very useful for the study of thermosetting resins as this technique has the advantage of being able to characterize the liquid resin without a supporting medium.

The epoxy – amine system was also studied using isothermal techniques. Displayed in Figure 7 are the DMA results obtained by holding the resin at 170°C for a period of 170 minutes. This plot shows that the minimum viscosity is achieved after 7 minutes as reflected by the minimum in the shear modulus, G'. As the material is held at 170°C, the resin begins to polymerize and then undergoes crosslinking resulting in an increase in G' and a decrease in tan delta. The gel point occurs at 49.2 minutes as tan delta reaches a value of unity at this point. The loss modulus, G", shows a small peak in this vicinity, reflecting the viscoelastic changes that occur due to gelation (3). At times greater than 50 minutes, the modulus of the resin continues to increase reflecting the establishment of additional crosslinks. At about 100 minutes, the resin vitrifies (i.e.,

changes from the rubbery to the glassy phase) as indicated by the peak in tan delta. The slope of the modulus, G', is a sensitive indicator as to the degree of cure achieved by the resin.

The isothermal results obtained from the DEA at 170°C are displayed in Figure 8. This plot shows the log of the loss factor, e", at frequencies of 100, 300, 1000, 3000, 10000 and 30000 Hz. The point of minimum viscosity (or greatest mobility of the trace ions) occurs at approximately 5 minutes based on the peaks observed in e" at the various frequencies. The position of the peak maximum is independent of frequency since this is due to the movement of ions rather than dipolar active groups (4). At times between 5 and 30 minutes, the values of e" drop as the material begins to cure. The resin vitrifies at times beginning at 32 minutes as reflected by the e" peak maxima. Since the vitrification process is relaxational in nature, the transition is time or frequency dependent. This is demonstrated by the increase in time to vitrification with decreasing frequency.

5. ESTABLISHMENT OF THE ACTIVATION ENERGY OF CURE BASED ON DMA GEL TIME MEASUREMENTS.

The activation energy, E, associated with the epoxy – amine cure reaction can be established via the DMA by determining the times to gelation at a number of isothermal temperatures (5). This was done by performing isothermal DMA measurements at temperatures of 160, 170 and 180° C. The DMA results from 160 and 180 °C are displayed in Figures 9 and 10. As the temperature increases, the time to gelation decreases and the activation energy can be established by plotting the log gel time versus the inverse of the isothermal temperature (°K). A straight line is obtained with a slope = $-E/R$ (where $R = 8.314$ J/mole°). For the EPON 828 – DDS system, an activation energy, using the gel point technique, of 59.3 kJ/mole was obtained.

58

This is in good agreement with the activation energy obtained by DSC isothermal measurements.

6. REFERENCES

1. Tung, C.Y.M. and P.J. Dynes, J. Appl. Poly. Sci., 27, 569 (1982).

2. Winter, H.H, Conference Proceedings for the 1987 ANTEC, 1106 (1987).

3. Sichina, W.J., Conference Proceedings for the 1987 ANTEC, 959 (1987).

4. Day, D.R., Conference Proceedings for the 1985 ANTEC, 327 (1985).

5. Prime, R.B., Thermal Characterization of Polymeric Materials, E. Turi, ed., Academic Press, New York (1981).

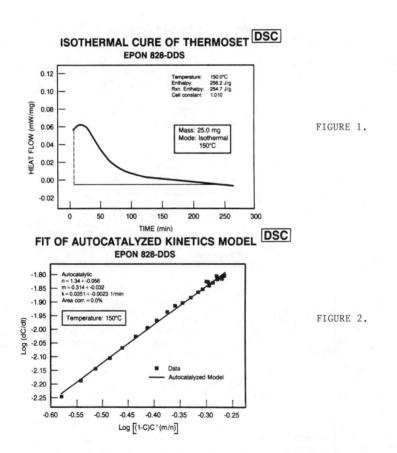

FIGURE 1.

FIGURE 2.

ISOTHERMAL RATE/CONVERSION CURVES DSC
MODEL AND EXPERIMENTAL DATA - EPON 828-DDS

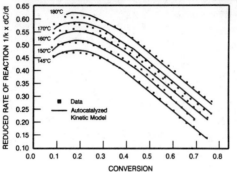

FIGURE 3.

ISOTHERMAL CONVERSION CURVES DSC
AUTOCATALYZED MODEL - EPON 828-DDS

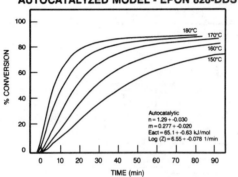

FIGURE 4.

EPON 828–DDS
HEAT AT 3°C/MIN DMA

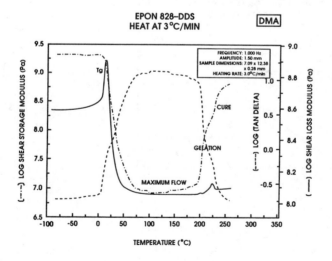

FIGURE 5.

EPON 828–DDS
CURING PROFILE AT 3°C/MIN

DEA

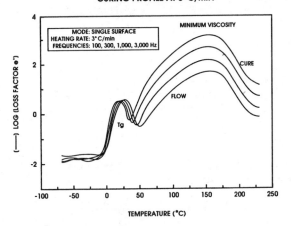

FIGURE 6.

ISOTHERMAL CURE OF
EPON 828–DDS AT 170°C

DMA

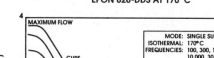

FIGURE 7.

ISOTHERMAL CURE OF
EPON 828-DDS AT 170°C

DEA

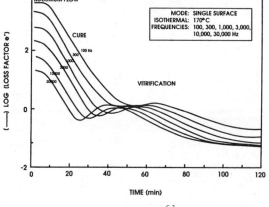

FIGURE 8.

61

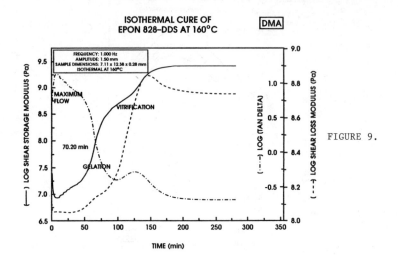

ISOTHERMAL CURE OF
EPON 828–DDS AT 160°C DMA

FIGURE 9.

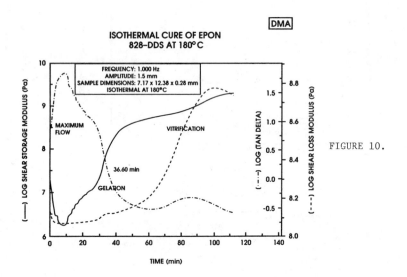

DMA

ISOTHERMAL CURE OF EPON
828–DDS AT 180°C

FIGURE 10.

PREPREG PROCESSING SCIENCE AND ANALYSIS
J. C. Seferis and K. J. Ahn

Polymeric Composites Laboratory
Department of chemical Engineering
University of Washington
Seattle, Washington

Abstract

The hot-melt impregnation of continuous carbon fibers with different resin systems was investigated in this work. Utilizing our uniquely designed scaled-down prepregger, the process was modeled both in terms of constituent material characteristics, as well as product requirements. By defining operational requirements in a nondimensional basis, it was possible to make inferences concerning large-scale prepregging operations as well as compare results previously reported with laboratory equipment.

1. INTRODUCTION

The prepregging process by most viewpoints is the basic starting point in the manufacture of high performance composites. Although it is one of the oldest most established processes, it has been studied very little in comparison to other processes like autoclaving, filament winding, etc. This may be attributed to the fact that the prepregging process is a continuous process leading to an intermediate product form rather than a finished composite part as in the case with a batch autoclaving or press-forming operation. Furthermore, over the years, the prepregging process has been considered more of an art where the unreacted resin adjusted to the right viscosity by trial and error was impregnated in a continuous fiber bundle. As long as the resin matrix considered was confined to relatively few types of thermosetting resins and well-established grades of fibers , the art was serving the industry quite well. However, as more and more end users began demanding increased performance from the matrix polymers, the prepregging process had to be analyzed in more detail (1). Accordingly, several years ago, we constructed a continuous, laboratory scale prepreg apparatus, by scaling down a manufacturing size hot-melt prepregger (2). The apparatus has proven quite versatile in making high quality prepregs with different resin matrices (2,3). In addition, having the capabilities of a commercial type machine in the laboratory, it was possible to undertake a systematic analysis of the process (4). This further allowed us to critically compare traditionally used methods in making prepreg in the laboratory that most often optimize material utilization rather than product quality (5).

As the matrix systems have changed over the years becoming more complex to meet end user demands of increased toughness, durability, and increased temperature performance, we have begun a systematic program for analyzing the prepreg process as well as its product characteristics (6). Accordingly, this work focuses both on our experience in prepregging several thermosetting system ranging from epoxies to bismaleimides and/or our ability to analyze the process on a system independent basis.

2. EXPERIMENTAL

The prepreg apparatus used in this study is schematically illustrated in Figure 1. Its operation has been well described in previous communications (2-5). The different matrix systems examined were amine-cured epoxies, a dicyanate and a bismaleimide systems. All these systems serve as model matrix systems in our studies and have been well characterized both from a processing as well as property viewpoint (7,8,9).

3. RESULTS AND DISCUSSION

The prepreg process in our opinion should be viewed as a non-reacting resin transfer operation to the collimated fibers. For hot-melt prepregging, it was found advantageous to define two important parameters relating the constituent materials to conditions before and after the impregnation zone. The fractional resin uptake, f, was defined as the ratio of weight of resin picked by fibers per linear speed of prepregging to the weight of resin in the impregnation zone per linear speed of prepregging.The fractional area change of the collimated fibers,e, was defined as the ratio of the area occupied by fibers before impregnation to the area occupied by fibers after impregnation. This e may also be expressed as the ratio of fiber width before impregnation times the linear speed of prepregging to the fiber width after impregnation times the linear speed of prepregging. From the above definitions, the efficiency of the prepregging operation may be defined as the product of fractional resin uptake and fractional area width change, viz.

$$E_g = fxe \qquad (1)$$

The efficiency may also be described by more traditional descriptors used in describing prepregs; namely, the areal weight. It is instructive at this point to consider how the parameters f and e are affected by the processing conditions. Figure 2 shows variation of these parameters for carbon fiber-BMI system that has been impregnated at different temperatures. Since at these temperatures there was no reaction in the matrix system, the temperature may be viewed as simply affecting the viscosity of the system. Fiber tension, impregnation pressure, and speed were kept constant throughout the experiments. As can be seen at low temperatures, the viscosity of the resin is quite high to penetrate the tension collimated fibers. As the temperature increases, viscosity decreases and the resin penetrates the fibers causing some spreading to occur (e begins to decrease). Further temperature increases reduce the viscosity further to the point where spreading of the fibers diminishes and e begins to increase. At this point, the resin viscosity is so low that resin is not retained by the fibers as well and thus f begins to decrease. This viscosity-temperature effect on the prepreg efficiency can also be seen on actual prepreg micrographs shown in Figure 3. For the systems shown, impregnation of the fibers was performed from the top side only. As expected, at relatively low temperatures, resin can still be seen on top of the fibers. However, at intermediate temperatures, resin can be seen equally on both top and bottom of the prepreg. However, at higher temperature, the resin has penetrated through the fibers accumulating at the bottom. Based on our practical experience and analysis results, we have come to view the prepregging operation as a combination of viscous/permeable flow of the resin through the collimated fibers. Accordingly, we have been describing the prepreg operation with dimensionless quantities that incorporate the size of the prepreg, its operating conditions and the relative importance of resin viscosity to fiber permeability. One such definition, the prepreg flow number may be defined as

$$PFN = \frac{kP^\star}{\mu VW_o}$$

where

k = fiber permeability (m^2)

μ = resin viscosity (kg/m-sec)

V = Linear speed of prepregging (m/sec)

$P^\star$ = Effective pressure that depends on specific prepregger for roller arrangement ($kg/m-sec^2$)

W_o = final prepreg width (m)

Variations of the different parameters were examined in detail both in relation to operating conditions and prepreg quality. It should be emphasized that the dimensionless number approach allows for direct comparison for prepregs of different size or operating principles. Furthermore, in our opinion, with this non-dimensional approach that has been used in traditional process analyses, a rational description of the prepregging operation may be obtained.

4.   CONCLUSION

Experimental and

analytical studies of the hot-melt prepregging process were undertaken utilizing a variety of thermosetting based matrix systems. Operational and product requirements for the process were defined allowing both comparison of data generated with different systems as well as scaling of the results to different types and sizes of prepreg equipment.

5.   ACKNOWLEDGMENTS

The authors express their appreciation to Dr. Larry Bravenec of Shell Development Company for his invaluable input to this work. Financial support for this work is provided by Shell Development Co. of Houston, Texas, through project support to the Polymeric Composites Laboratory at the University of Washington. Large scale equipment has been provided by California Graphite, Inc., to the Polymeric Composites Laboratory.

6.   REFERENCES

(1)   Seferis, J. C. and L. Nicolais, Eds., "The Role of the Polymeric Matrix on Their Processing and Structural Properties of Composite Materials," Plenum Press (1983).

(2)   Lee, W. J., J. C. Seferis, and D. C. Bonner, "Prepreg Processing Science," SAMPE Qtrly 17 58 (1986).

(3)   Breukers, J. J., E. M. Woo, and J. C. Seferis, "Experimental Evaluation of the Prepregging Process," Am. Soc. for Comp. Proceedings, Third Technical Conf. p. 12 (1988).

(4)   Lee, W. J., "Advanced Composite Prepreg Processing Science," Ph.D. Dissertation, Dept. of Chemical Engineering, University of Washington, Seattle, Washington (1988).

(5)   Lee, W. J., J. C. Seferis, and L. D. Bravenec, "Hot-Melt Prepreg Processing of Advanced Composites: A Comparison of Methods, SPE ANTEC '88 Proceedings, p. 1602 (1988).

(6)   Seferis, J. C. and J. Meissonnier, "Development of A Tack and Drape Test for Prepregs Based on Viscoelastic Principles," SAMPE Qtrly, submitted (1989).

(7)   Chu, H. S. and J. C. Seferis, ""Dynamic Mechanical Experiments for Probing Process-Structure-Property Relations in Amine-Cured Epoxies," Polymer Composites 5 124 (1984).

(8)   Viot, J.-F. and J. C. Seferis, "Process Resolved Morphology of Bismaleimide Matrix Composites," J. of Appl. Poly. Sci., 34 1459 (1987).

(9)   Woo, E. M., B. K. Fukai, and J. C. Seferis, "Dicyanate Blends as Matrices for High Performance Composites," Am. Soc. for Comp. Proceedings, Third Technical Conf. p. 192 (1988).

(10) McCabe, W. L., J. C. Smith, "Unit Operation of Chemical Engineering," 2nd Ed., McGraw Hill (1967).

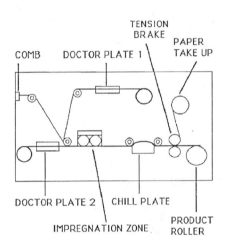

Figure 1. Schematic diagram of laboratory scale prepregger. (Ref.2)

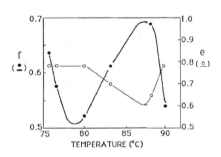

Figure 2. Temperature effect on prepreg fractional resin uptake (f) and fractional width change (e) for a BMI/carbon fiber system.

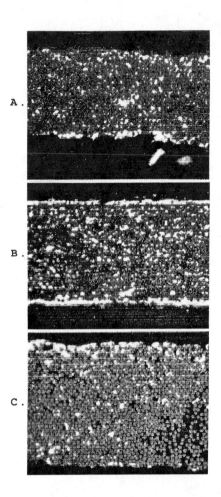

Figure 3. Temperature effect on resin impregnation for a BMI/carbon fiber system. (200x, A: 134°C, B: 110°C, C: 100°C)

DETERMINATION OF SOLVENT INDUCED
CRYSTALLIZATION IN POLYETHERIMIDE MATRIX
COMPOSITES BY WIDE ANGLE X-RAY SCATTERING
K.M. Nelson and J.C. Seferis*
Polymeric Composites Laboratory
Department of Chemical Engineering
University of Washington
Seattle, Washington 98195
and
H.G. Zachmann
University of Hamburg
Institute of Technology and Macromolecular Chemistry
Hamburg, West Germany

Abstract

Solvent induced crystallization represents one of several documented processing induced morphological changes. This investigation reports the first measurement of solvent induced morphologies in a polyetherimide. This amorphous polyetherimide (PEI), used as a matrix in a high performance carbon fiber reinforced prepreg, may crystallize when exposed to certain solvents. PEI prepreg was found to be 16 percent crystalline on a fiber free basis. However, the PEI in the prepreg will not crystallize from the melt and will become completely amorphous once thermally processed. By measuring the degree of crystallinity using WAXS and the heat of melting using DSC, the specific heat of crystallization was calculated to be 82 joules/gram.

1. INTRODUCTION

Under exposure to certain solvents, some normally amorphous polymers crystallize. This is called solvent induced

---

* Author to whom correspondence should be addressed

crystallization. The polymer, regardless of being semicrystalline or amorphous, changes its morphology in the presence of a solvent.

Crystallinity is described as the ordering of the atoms of the polymer chains to achieve a thermodynamically favored lower entropy configuration. Semicrystalline polymers are traditionally modelled as two phase systems made up of crystalline and non-crystalline regions. [1,2]

The degree of crystallinity is usually defined as the fraction of crystalline material. For all semicrystalline polymers, the degree of crystallinity, size of crystals, and orientation of the crystalline and non-crystalline regions form the basis for the micro-structure of the polymer.

In semicrystalline polymers, this micro-structure has been successfully correlated to the polymer bulk properties. [19]

The measurement of crystallinity in a semicrystalline polymer is dependent on the method used to make the measurement. While most commonly used techniques for the determination of crystallization are among themselves reproducible, there may be consistent differences from technique to technique. This may be due to, among other things, the 'level of order' or type of crystallinity the particular technique sees when quantifying crystallinity.

A polymer initially dissolved in solvent may crystallize upon evaporation of the solvent. Alternately, a neat polymer may absorb the solvent, swelling the polymer, increasing the mobility of the chains and thereby increasing the probability of crystal nucleation. [9]

Both methylene chloride and NMP (n-methyl pyrrolidone) induce crystallization in the polyetherimide (PEI). However, NMP was found to be much less effective than methylene chloride.

X-ray diffraction is a preferred method of studying crystallization. An X-ray scattering pattern of a semicrystalline polymer produces crystalline peaks stacked upon an amorphous halo. In a carbon fiber reinforced composite, the X-ray scattering of the carbon fibers is also superimposed onto the scattering of the crystals. [4]

The degree of crystallization is measured by comparing the relative intensity of the crystalline and amorphous scattering curves, once the curves are corrected for carbon fiber scattering.

2. EXPERIMENTAL

A polyetherimide (PEI) thermoplastic polymer was chosen for the analysis. This polymer, made by the General Electric Co., is similar to their Ultem® family of amorphous polymers. This particular PEI is used by American Cyanamid Co. as a matrix in a carbon fiber prepreg manufactured for use in high temperature, high performance composites. [16]

Since the model system crystallizes upon absorption of certain solvents, it represents an ideal basis for the study of solvent induced crystallization in amorphous thermoplastics. The PEI prepreg examined in this study was a woven carbon fiber fabric impregnated with PEI polymer.

X-ray diffraction measurements were performed with a Siemens Diffractometer (D500), using CuKα radiation (1.54 Å) and a Ni filter. All scattering measurements were performed in transmission, as depicted in Figure 1. Scattering was measured at angles of 2θ ranging from 5° to 70°.

Absorption coefficients were calculated from experimental data by measuring the intensity of the incident radiation I_{0} (without a sample) and the intensity of the radiation I with a sample. The absorption coefficient μ was evaluated by the relationship:

$$dI/dx = -\mu I \qquad (1)$$

where x is the thickness of the sample.

To measure the absorption coefficient and the scattering of neat carbon fibers, a method was devised to digest the matrix material from the prepreg using sulfuric acid. Once the polymeric matrix was dissolved, the fibers remain in their original orientation, and their original quantity allowing for direct X-ray measurements.

3. RESULTS AND DISCUSSION

A technique of prepregging high temperature thermoplastic polymers is the solvent process. This allows the carbon fibers to be impregnated close to room temperature, removing the necessity and cost of a high temperature prepregging process.

Solvent processes offer lower viscosities and better wetting than high temperature processes, but the solvent must subsequently be removed. N-methyl pyrrolidone is a common solvent used in the processing of prepreg.

Diffusion of solvent into the bulk polymer increases chain segmental mobility, and in turn induces localized swelling. (17,18) By increasing mobility, the probability of nucleation is increased and thus crystallization occurs. (8)

The role of solvent crystallization of polymers has been extensively studied, in particular for polyethylene terepthalate (PET), polycarbonate (PC), and polyethylene (PE). (6-14)

All data manipulation is done in reciprocal lattice space defined by:

$$s = |\mathbf{s}| = \frac{2\sin\Theta}{\lambda} \quad (2)$$

Where:

λ = Wave length of radiation (Cu Kα = 1.54 Å)
s = Magnitude of the reciprocal lattice vector
Θ = Angle of incident radiation

At any point reciprocal space, if I($\mathbf{s}$) is the intensity of the coherent X-ray scatter, and Ic($\mathbf{s}$) is the intensity of crystalline peaks, then the integral of crystalline peaks over all reciprocal lattice space compared to the integral of the total scattering curve is to a good approximation, the crystallinity fraction. (1,3,4)

$$Xc = \frac{\int_{o}^{\infty} s^2 Ic(s)ds}{\int_{o}^{\infty} s^2 I(s)ds} \quad (3)$$

This approximation calculates a smaller crystalline fraction than other techniques. A portion of the scattered intensity from the crystalline fraction is lost from the peaks due to atomic thermal vibrations and lattice imperfections. (1)

The method of Rulond (3,4) accounts for these factors by including a lattice imperfection factor into the intensity expression. For purposes of measuring crystalline fraction in this work, the method of Rulond was not used because of inaccuracies involved in calculating the lattice imperfection factor.

Before the calculation of crystallinity is assessed, the data is corrected for air scattering, absorption, polarization and incoherent scattering. (1,3,6)

An amorphous halo is a manifestation of the statistical distribution of distances between scattering centers. It is, in a sense, a type of short range order. The result is a broad interference pattern representative of a most probable distance between scattering centers.

Figure 2 shows the amorphous halo of the PEI polymer quenched from a melt. A similar sample slowly cooled from a melt produces an amorphous halo identical to that from the quenched sample, as is expected for amorphous polymers.

The PEI polymer, as with other amorphous polymers, does not crystallize from a melt and is expected to have the same amorphous micro-structure regardless of cooling rate.

The PEI polymer will crystallize from a solution, as is evident in WAXS of PEI prepreg processed with solvent. Figure 3 is a WAXS scan for the PEI virgin prepreg, showing sharp, well defined crystalline peaks, and two broad peaks resulting from carbon fiber scattering.

The orientation of the carbon fibers in the prepreg is the 0/90 of the woven fabric. The carbon fibers in a prepreg (or composite) produce an orientation effect evident when examining scans at different azimuthal angles. The azimuthal angle is the angle of rotation of the sample within the plane defined by the sample.

Figure 4 shows the scattering of the neat carbon fibers in the orientation of figure 3 (0/90: horizontal/ vertical). The sample was prepared by digesting the PEI from the prepreg, as described earlier leaving only the carbon fibers. From this scan, and that of the amorphous resin, the contributions of the fiber and of the amorphous region is evident.

Correcting the prepreg scattering curve for carbon fiber scattering, produces a curve representative of the randomly oriented semi-crystalline structure of the PEI matrix. The amorphous halo shown in figure 2 is fitted using an appropriate scaling factor, and plotted as s^2I verses s as designated by equation 3 in order to calculate the crystalline fraction.

The bounds of integration are chosen to be sufficiently broad to produce consistent results. This is not always practical due to divergence of the data at large scattering angles. However, reasonable bounds of integration are from $s = 1$ to $s = 4$. As the calculation approaches 4, the crystalline fraction levels off and becomes relatively constant.

A similar treatment was applied to data from scattering of neat polymer treated with methylene chloride and NMP. (The effect of carbon fibers does not need to be accounted for.) The PEI surface crystallizes immediately upon contact with methylene chloride, producing a semicrystalline material; the final crystallinity depending on the diffusion rate, the thickness of the film and the rate of crystallization itself.

The scattering for NMP induced crystallization shows very small crystalline peaks. NMP only induces crystallization when a drop of NMP is placed upon the surface of the polymer, allowed to locally swell, dissolve the polymer, and evaporate. Thus, the amount of crystallinity induced by NMP is much less than that induced by methylene chloride.

It is observed that upon processing the material above its crystalline melting point, any history of being crystalline is removed. Upon cooling, the PEI remains non-crystalline, regardless of the cooling rate. Crystallization is exclusively solvent induced for this polymer.

As the PEI prepreg is always processed above the

melting point of the crystals, a finished laminate will always be amorphous and will remain amorphous unless exposed to a solvent which induces crystallization.

The heat of crystalline melting can be conveniently examined by using DSC. Figure 5 is the DSC of the as-received (virgin) prepreg showing a glass transition at 225 $^{\circ}$C and the onset of melting at 280 $^{\circ}$C.

After heat treating the sample above the melt temperature, the DSC shows the expected amorphous trace (shown above the initial trace). The heat of crystallization is the area of the endotherm defined by the DSC.

Examination of the DSC provides a convenient way to quantify the crystallinity once the value of Hxcl is known. The crystallinity is given by:

$$Xcl = \frac{H_{DSCendo}}{(V_f)(H_{xcl})} \qquad (4)$$

All that is needed is a reproducible DSC trace to calculate the degree of crystallinity, provided the fiber volume V_f is known.

4. CONCLUSION

It was found that a previously known amorphous polyetherimide will crystallize in the presence of certain solvents. By wide angle X-ray scattering analysis, the degree of crystallinity was measured and found to be dependent on the severity of exposure to the solvent.

PEI prepreg processed by solvent impregnation is 16 % crystalline on a fiber free basis. Neat PEI resin, exposed to methylene chloride for a period of four hours became 30% crystalline, while the same polymer exposed to NMP would only crystallize when a small amount of solvent was placed on the surface.

From DSC measurements, the heat of crystallization of the neat polyetherimide was calculated based on the fiber volume and the crystalline fraction from X-ray scattering. This value is approximately 85 joules/gram ($\pm$ 15%).

Once the heat of crystallization is known, the crystalline fraction of any PEI sample can be calculated from the intensity of the melting endotherm from DSC, a much simpler and readily utilized technique than WAXS.

Finally, although the as-received prepreg may be 16 % crystalline, all traces of crystallinity are eliminated once the material is thermally processed. Once processed above the melting point of the crystals (300 ^{o}C), the material will not crystallize again, regardless of the cooling rate, producing an amorphous micro-structure.

Solvent induced crystallization represents one of several documented processing induced morphological changes. Perhaps the best known processing induced morphological change is that of cooling rate on the crystallinity in semicrystalline polymers.[20] This investigation reports the first measurement of solvent induced morphologies in a polyetherimide polymer.

5. ACKNOWLEDGEMENTS

The Authors would like to express appreciation to Dr. S. L. Peake of American Cyanamid Co., and to S. Rober, U. Koncke, C. Schipp of the University of Hamburg, and also to B. Coxon of the University of Washington.

Financial assistance for this work was provided for by American Cyanamid Co. in support of the Polymeric Composites Laboratory, University of Washington. The authors are also grateful to the Alexander von Humbolt Foundation for their support to Professor J. C. Seferis.

6. REFERENCES

(1) Alexander, L.E., X-Ray Diffraction Methods in Polymer Science, R. E. Krieger Publ. Co., Malaber FL, 1979

(2) Rodriguez, F., Principles of Polymer Systems, 2nd Ed., Hemisphere Publishing Co, (1982)

(3) Coxon, B.R., Master's Thesis, University of Washington, 1988

(4) Ruland, W., "X-Ray Determination of Crystallinity and Diffuse Disorder Scattering," Auta Cryst., **14** 1180 (1961)

(5) Ruland, W., Polymer, **5** 89 (1964)

(6) Cullity, B.D., Elements of X-Ray Diffraction, 2nd Ed. Addison-Wessley Publ. Co., 1978

(7) Durning, C.J., Russel, W.B., Polymer, **26** 131-140 (1985)

(8) Durning, C.J., Russel, W.B., Polymer, **26** 119 (1985)

(9) Perovic, A., Sundararajan, P.R., Polym. Bull., **6** 277-283 (1982)

(10) Guven, O., Coll. & Polym. Sci. **260** 647-641 (1982)

(11) Makarewiez, P.J., Wilkes, B.L., J. Polym. Sci. Polym., Phys. Edn., **16** 1529 (1978)

(12) Makarewiez, P.J., Wilkes, G.L., J. Polym. Sci. Polym. Phys. Edn., **16** 1559 (1978)

(13) Desai, A.B., Wilkes, G.L., J. Polym. Sci. Symp. **46** 261 (1974)

(14) De Candia, F., Russo, R., Vittoria, V., J. Polym. Sci, **34** 689-701 (1987)

(15) Saldanka, J.M., Kyu, T., Macromolecules, **20** 2840-2847 (1987)

(16) Peake, S.L., Maranci, A., 32nd Intnl SAMPE Symp., 420-430 April (1987)

(17) Stober, E.J., Seferis, J.C., Keenan, J.D., Polymer, **25** 1845-1852, (1984)

(18) Stober, E.J., and Seferis, J.C., Polym. Eng. Sci., **28** 634-639, (1988)

(19) Seferis, J.C., Samuels, R.J., Polym. Eng. Sci., **19** 975-994, (1979)

(20) Velisaris, C.N., Seferis, J.C., Polym. Eng. Sci., **26** 1574-1581, (1986)

Wide Angle X-Ray Scattering

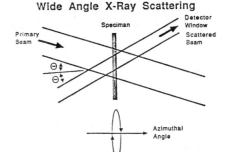

Figure 1. WAXS experimental geometry

PEI Amorphous Halo

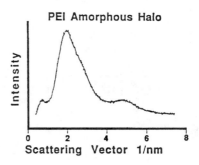

Figure 2. WAXS showing amorphous halo of PEI system quenched from melt

PEI Solvent Induced Crystallization

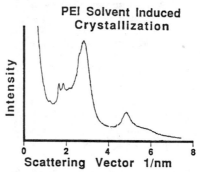

Figure 3. PEI prepreg as received from solvent impregnation process. Azimuthal Angle = 0

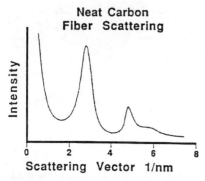

Figure 4. Neat carbon fibers from digested prepreg, azymuthal angle = 45

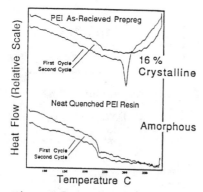

Figure 5. DSC of as-received prepreg, cycled two times in the DSC cell. Top trace is second cycle.

IN-SITU MEASUREMENT AND CONTROL OF HIGH TEMPERATURE
PROCESSING PROPERTIES OF PMR-15

David Kranbuehl, David Eichinger,
David Rice, and Hunter Tully
Department of Chemistry
College of William and Mary
Williamsburg, Virginia 23185

James Koury
Air Force Astronautics Laboratory
Edwards, California 93523-5000

ABSTRACT

An in-situ measuring technique for use in the quality control of PMR-15 resin and in automated PMR-15 composite processing are discussed. Frequency dependent electromagnetic sensors (FDEMS) are used to measure, record and compare the processing properties of PMR-15 resin both prior to processing in a testing environment and during processing in a production tool. FDEMS, which utilizes a small single inert sensor, is one of only a few measurement techniques for monitoring the high temperature fabrication process of high performance composite resins continuously throughout the cure process as the resin goes from a monomeric liquid, through viscosity minima, to a crosslinked insoluble high temperature solid. In this report, the ability of the FDEMS sensor to monitor the processing properties of PMR-15 is demonstrated. The use of the sensor to both predict and monitor the time of occurrence of PMR-15's high temperature point of maximum flow is demonstrated through simultaneous rheological and FDEMS measurements.

1.   INTRODUCTION

PMR-15 is an aromatic polyimide resin of interest to the aerospace industry because of its high temperature stability.

Consistency in achieving good parts using the PMR-15 resin is at best difficult to achieve. Factors influencing these difficulties in processing include variability between vendor batches, resin handling-age, solvent content and moisture.

PMR-15 in its conventional formulation is a mixture of a methyl 5-norbornene-2,3-dicarboxylate (NE), dimethyl 3,3', 4,4'-benzophenone tetracarboxylate (BTDE) and 4,4'-methylenedianiline (MDA). The typical resin mixture consists of monomers in the molar ratio 2(NE): (n+1)(MDA): n(BTDE) stored in 50% weight alcohol solution. Ideally each pair of carboxylate groups consists of an acid and an ester. However, these groups depending on the environment can hydrolyze, esterify, and react with the resin's amines to form amides and imide oligomers, thereby changing the resins processing and final properties. For these reasons a rapid convenient sensing technique is needed for resin quality assurance evaluation prior to processing, for on line automated intelligent feed back control during processing and as a signature verifying the integrity of the final part.

The ability of dielectric sensing to monitor the curing of PMR-15 was first demonstrated by Gluyas(1) and followed by studies in our laboratory (2,3). This report focusus on the ability of the frequency dependence of the complex impedance or dielectric permittivity to monitor the cure process of an ethanol based PMR-15 solution used in filament winding.

The ability of the FDEMS sensor to monitor solvent evaporation, imidization, viscosity-fluidity, reaction onset and reaction completion is discussed. Of particular importance is the ability of the high frequency dipolar relaxation peaks (10^4 to 10^6 Hz) to predict and monitor the time of occurrence of PMR-15's high temperature point of maximum flow.

2. EXPERIMENTAL

The 35% ethanol 65% PMR-15 filament winding solution was used as received from the HITCO materials division of U.S. Polmyeric. Frequency dependent electromagnetic-dynamic dielectric measurements * were made using a Hewlett-Packard 4192A LF Impedance Analyzer and a PC computer. Measurements at frequencies from

50 to 1×10^6 Hz were taken at regular intervals during the cure cycle and converted to the complex permittivity, $\epsilon^* = \epsilon' - i\epsilon''$. (4-8)

Viscosity measurements were made using a Rheometrics RDA dynamic rheometer.

DSC measurements were made using a Perkin-Elmer DSC-7 differential scanning calorimeter.

3. THEORY

Measurements of capacitance, C, and conductance, G, were used to calculate the complex permittivity $\epsilon^* = \epsilon' - \epsilon''$ where:

$$\epsilon' = \frac{C \text{ material}}{C_o}$$

and

$$\epsilon'' = \frac{G \text{ material}}{C_o 2\pi f}$$

at each of 10 frequencies between 50 Hz and 1 MHz.

This calculation is possible when using the DekDyne probe $\neq$ whose geometry independent capacitance, C_o, is invariant over all measurement conditions. Both

the real and the imaginary parts of ϵ^* have an ionic and dipolar component. The dipolar component arises from diffusion of bound charge or molecular dipole moments. The dipolar term is generally the major component of the dielectric signal at high frequencies and in highly viscous media. The ionic component often dominates ϵ^* at low frequencies, low viscosities and/or higher temperatures.

Analysis of the frequency dependence of ϵ^* in the Hz to MHz range is, in general, optimum for determining both the ionic mobility-conductivity, σ, and a mean dipolar relaxation time, τ. These two parameters are directly related on a molecular level to the rate of ionic translational diffusion and dipolar rotational mobility and thereby to changes in the molecular structure of the resin which reflect the reaction rate, changes in viscosity and the degree of cure.

RESULTS AND DISCUSSION

Figure 1 is a plot of the loss factor ϵ'' of the ethanol PRM-15 filament winding solution for a typical cure cycle. The ϵ'' values are multiplied by the frequency and are made over 10 frequencies from 50 Hz to 1×10^6 Hz. As previously discussed ϵ'' times frequency plots are a convenient means of identifying the ionic mobility and the dipolar relaxation time peaks. Overlapping lines indicate the frequencies and time-temperature periods during cure when ϵ'' is dominated by ionic diffusion and

$$e'' = \frac{\sigma(ohm^{-1}cm^{-1})}{8.84 \times 10^{-14}\omega}$$

where σ is the ionic conductivity. Non-overlapping lines, exhibit a series of peaks with frequency and time-temperature (250 to 300 minute interval). They can be used to determine a series of characteristic dipolar relaxation times $\tau = 1/\omega$ at the ϵ'' peaks. Both σ and τ can be used to qualitatively and quantitatively (through coorelation with RDA measurements) monitor the viscosity.

Examining Figure 1, on a log scale, the ionic mobility starts at 9.0. The ϵ'' overlapping lines show the drop in fluidity and increase in viscosity beginning slightly before the onset of the 80° hold and ending at the end

of the hold. In this region ϵ'' is tracking the increase in viscosity as the ethanol vaporizes and some imidization occurs. The slight rise in the ϵ'' overlapping lines near 120 minutes is due to the increase in fluidity during the second temperature ramp.

Comparing these results to Figure 2, a PMR-15 solution left at room temperature for 9 days, shows that the fluidity of the older PMR-15 is different. In this case, the fluidity increases to a greater extent with temperature up to 40 minutes and decreases less in the 80°C hold because most of the free ethanol has already been evaporated. The higher ϵ'' and ionic mobility values in the 80° hold in figure 2 are believed to be due to moisture. These results suggest that the FDEMS signature should be able to detect alcohol and water content, its rate of loss and the point of complete loss as a function of previous handling, time and temperature.

The rapid drop in the ϵ'' overlapping lines in the 130 to 160 minute, (110°C to 160°C) time-temperature interval monitors the onset of BDTE imidization and the rapid build up in viscosity. The gradual decrease in all ϵ'' values

82

during the 200°C hold hour is tracking the continual buildup in modulus as the imidization reaction continues.

The absence of a constant value of ϵ'' during this hold indicates that cure is not complete in one hour. Similarly, the rate of decline during the 300°C hold shows that the FDEMS sensor monitors the rate of the high temperature nadic addition reaction. However, during the 300°C hold, the approach of ϵ'' to a constant value indicates that after 2 1/2 hours of this 3 hour hold in figure 1 the addition reaction achieves its completion level for 300°C. On the other hand the 9 day old PMR-15 resin does not achieve a constant value of ϵ'' indicating the reaction is not complete. This is do either to the moisture uptake and/or the formation of the short chains of nadimide during prolonged exposure to room temperature prior to cure, a fact which is supported by C^{13} data.

The changing position of the peaks in the ϵ'' high frequency values between 200°C and 300°C monitors the approach to the viscosity minimum prior to the onset of the high temperature

crosslinking reaction. Monitoring this viscosity minimum and fluidity in this region is critical to the question of when to apply pressure, good consolidation and the elimination of trapped volatiles and voids. The successive peaks, first for 5 KHz at 250 minutes, 250 KHz at 265 minutes and 1 MHz at 280 minutes tract the increase in fluidity as measured by the faster dipolar mobility relaxation time peaks observed at successively higher frequencies. In fact, in both figures 1 and 2 one can also see the subsequent buildup in viscosity (the successive lower frequency dipolar relaxation peaks) as the crosslinking reaction proceeds during the 300°C hold following softening. Most important is the observation that the high frequency 250 kHz to 1 MHz peaks can be used to detect and predict the future time of occurrence of the softening minimum.

Figure 3 is a plot of the RDA measured visosity and the relaxation time during the high temperature ramp. Using figure 3 the ϵ'' 100 kHz to 1MHz peaks can be used to qualitatively and quantitatively monitor the viscosity.

CONCLUSIONS

Measurements of the complex permittivity $\epsilon'' = \epsilon^* = \epsilon' - i\epsilon''$ over the 50 Hz to 1×10^6 Hz region can be used to monitor both the ionic mobility through σ and the dipolar mobility through the ϵ'' peaks. For a PMR-15 filament winding solution, the ionic mobility can be used to track solvent content, moisture viscosity - fluidity and the extent of completion of the imidization reaction. The high frequency 100 kHz to 1 MHz values of ϵ'' can be used to track and predict the viscosity minimum during the high temperature nadic crosslinking reaction and its approach to completion. Resin age and/or moisture uptake appears to lengthen the time needed for completion of the nadic crosslinking reaction.

ACKNOWLEDGMENT

This work was made possible through the support of the Astronautics Laboratory of the AirForce, Edwards, California and the National Aeronautics and Space Administration-Langley Research Center, Hampton, Virginia.

REFERENCES

1. R. E. Gluyas, NASA TM X-73448 (1976).

2. D. Kranbuehl, S. Delos and P. Jue, "Dielectric Properties of an Aromatic Polyimide", Polymer 27 11 (1986).

3. D. Kranbuehl, S. Delos, E Yi, and J. Mayer Proc. 2nd Int. Conf. on Polyimides SPE 469 (1985).

4. D. Kranbuehl "Cure Monitoring" in Encylopedia of Composites, Stuart M. Lee Editor VCH Publishers (in print).

5. D. Kranbuehl, S. Delos, M. Hoff, L. Weller, P. Haverty and J. Seeley., ACS Sym. Series, 367 100-119 (1988) and

ACS Div. Poly. Mats.: Sci. and Eng., <u>56</u> 163-168 (1987).

6. D. Kranbuehl, S. Delos, M. Hoff, L. Weller, P. Haverty, J. Seeley and B. Whitham, Nat'l SAMPE Sym. Ser., <u>32</u>, 338-348 (1987).

7. A. Loos, Dr. Dranbuehl and W. Freeman in <u>Intelligent Processing at Materials and Advanced Sensors</u>, Metallurgical Soc., 197-211 (1987).

8. D. Kranbuehl, M. Hoff, P. Haverty, A. Loos and T. Freeman, Nat'l SAMPE Sym. Ser., <u>33</u>, 1276 (1988).

* Inquiries regarding the FDEMS Sensor and instrumentation should be directed to D. Kranbuehl.

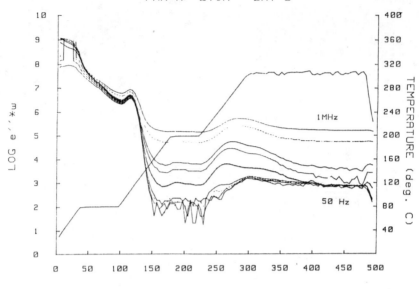

Figure 1.   Fresh PRM-15 ethonol solution: log (ϵ" times frequency) versus time (right scale); frequencies 50, 125, 250, 500, 5 x 10^3, 25 x 10^3, 50 x 10^3, 250 x 10^3, 500 x 10^3, 1 x 10^6 Hz.   Temperature (°C) versus time (left scale).

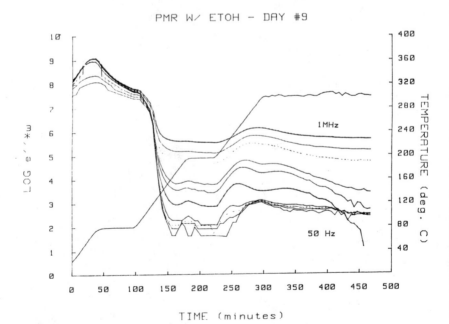

Figure 2.   Aged 9 day at room temerature PMR-15 ethanol solution.

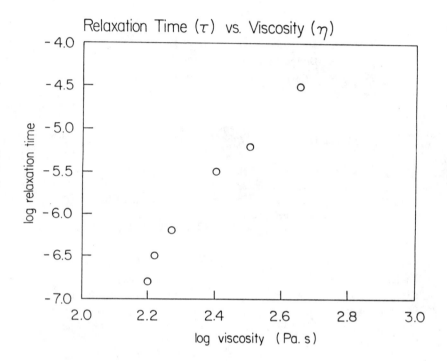

Figure 3. Log (relaxation time) versus log (viscosity Pa.s) during
200°C to 300°C ramp. Relaxation time = $\frac{1}{\omega}$ at ϵ'' (ω) peak.

PROCESS CHARACTERISTICS OF HIGH TEMPERATURE
POLYMERS AND COMPOSITES

Daniel A. Scola and John H. Vontell
United Technologies Research Center
East Hartford, Connecticut 06108

Abstract

The thermo–oxidative resistance of high temperature polyimides is an important property which has made these materials useful to the aerospace industry where temperatures in the region 288 to 350°C are required.

The thermal and rheological behavior of several high temperature polymers and graphite fiber/polymer prepregs was investigated. Specific examples of process problems of high temperature polymers will be cited.

1. INTRODUCTION

The application of graphite fiber/high temperature composite materials to aircraft engine components and other aircraft components necessitates a thorough understanding of these materials to insure performance with reliability and durability. For application in the temperature range 288–350°C (550–662°F), it is important that the process characteristics of the polymer system be understood, but of greater importance is the understanding of the process characteristics of the graphite fiber/ high temperature polymer composite system, (1,2,3). In this presentation, the process characteristics of several polymer and graphite fiber/high temperature polymer composites will be discussed. Properties of composites generated via the various process cycles will be compared.

2. EXPERIMENTAL

2.1 Thermal Analysis

Thermal analysis data was collected on a Dupont 9900 thermal analyzer equipped with a 912 Differential Scanning Calorimeter (DSC) and a 951 Thermogravimetric Analyzer (TGA). Both techniques used samples in powder form.

The DSC samples were analyzed at 10°C/min in open aluminum pans due to gas generation during heating.

The TGA samples were heated at a rate of 5 or 10°C/min depending on the thermal cycle. The particular heating rate is noted on the appropriate table of data.

2.2 Viscosity Determination

Rheology was performed on a Rheometrics 7700 series 2 Dynamic Spectrometer in both the parallel plate and torsional modes.

Parallel plate (25 mm) data was collected on RT compression molded discs (formed from powdered polymers) at a rate of 20 radians/sec and a strain of 1%.

Torsional data was collected on pretreated prepreg plies at a rate of 20 radians/sec and a strain of 0.5%.

The present temperature limitation of the instrument is 380°C.

2.3 Thermal Pretreatment

All thermal pretreatment of both neat polymers and prepreg was accomplished by using an air circulating Blue M oven.

2.4 Composite Fabrication

Composites were compression molded using a 1.5" x 5" open ended matched steel die with pressure and heat applied by a Tetrahedron platten press. Enough prepreg plies were stacked to achieve ~ 0.1" final thickness.

The Avimid N/T40R uniweave prepreg was obtained from Dupont while the PMR–II–30 prepreg was made at UTRC. The PMR–II–30 prepreg was fabricated by dry winding Celion 6K(u) fiber onto a drum followed by brush application of a PMRII–30/methanol solution to get a final solids content on the tape of ~ 38 wt %.

2.5 Optical Microscopy of Cross–Sections

A section of each composite was mounted perpendicular to the fiber direction, and polished for optical microscopy examination. Micrographs at 50x and 200x were taken to assess the quality of the composites for void content and fiber distribution.

3. DISCUSSION

The basic premise in this investigation is that the resin must be preimidized at some temperature to minimize gas evolution during the process steps–up to the final postcure temperature. Therefore, resin and prepreg samples were preimidized at three temperature/time conditions, namely 200°C/1 hr, 250°C/1 hr and 275°C/1hr. The chemical and

physiochemical behavior of these pretreated samples was investigated

3.1 Avimid N Studies

3.1.1 DSC Behavior

The DSC behavior of the thermally pretreated Avimid N resin is listed in Table 1. The DSC data reveals that as the pretreatment temperature increases, the softening temperature increases, an increase from 260°C after the 200°C pretreatment to 308°C after the 275°C pretreatment. This clearly shows that the higher imidization temperature increases chain stiffness which is most likely related to increased degree of imidization and increased molecular weight. The exotherm generated above 350°C but below 450°C for all pretreated samples suggests that additional reactions occur on continued thermal treatment. Above about 500°C, the exotherm is indicative of thermal decomposition.

3.1.2 TGA Behavior

Table 2 lists weight loss data during dynamic heating of the pretreated resin. The pretreated samples were heated to 400°C at 5°C/min and the weight changes which occur at specific temperatures in the process were noted. The weight loss at 200°C is due to absorbed moisture. A knowledge of the weight residue after correction for absorbed moisture at 343°C is important, because at this maximum temperature, the same temperature used in composite fabrication, it is a measure of how much material is retained, and lost.

The data clearly show that the 200°C or 250°C pretreated material undergoes an additional loss of material (2.2 to 2.5%) over this temperature range. However, the weight loss from the 275°C pretreated resin is only 0.45 wt%. This suggests that preimidization of the resin at 275°/1 hr would be a more favorable condition for composite fabrication because less volatiles would evolve at the cure and postcure temperatures. However, the ability to fabricate a composite from 275°C preimidized material must be demonstrated. This depends on the melt viscosity and flow properties of the material over the process temperature range from 250 to 343°C, and the ability to remove trapped air between prepreg plies.

3.1.3 Complex Viscosity of Avimid N/T40R Uniweave Prepreg

The complex viscosity of Avimid N/T40R uniweave prepreg was determined in the RDS Spectrometer in the torsional mode. Three plies of prepreg was used. The data are listed in Table 3.

The pretreatment temperature causes a gradual increase in the initial softening temperature accompanied by a gradual increase in the initial complex viscosity. The data shows the viscosity continues to decrease until the RDS Spectrometer's upper temperature limit of 380°C was reached. To simplify data interpretation the viscosities are compared at 340°C. The viscosities at 340°C are independent of the 200 and 250°C pretreatment temperatures. However, the highest pretreatment temperature (275°C) gave the highest viscosity (10^8 poise) at 340°C. This shows that increased pretreatment temperature causes chain extension reactions which influence the final rheological properties. This is evidence that reactions continue to occur during the post cure processing step required for composite fabrication.

3.1.4 Complex Viscosity of Pretreated Avimid N Resin

Two Avimid N resin specimens were measured in the RDS Spectrometer in the parallel plate mode. The specimens were fabricated as 1/8" x 1.0" discs at RT by pressing powder pretreated at 200°C for 1 hour. Then the complex viscosity of the discs were determined isothermally at 316°C (Fig. 1) and 360°C (Fig. 2). On heating the resin sample to 316°C, the minimum in the apparent viscosity (4.7 x 10^5 poise) is attained. However, during the isothermal hold at 316°C for one

hour, the apparent viscosity gradually increases to 8.5 x 10^5 poise.

On heating the resin sample to 360°C a viscosity minimum of 2 x 10^6 poise is attained. Further heating at 360°C for 1 hour caused a viscosity increase to 4.5 x 10^6 poise. The storage modulus, G', and loss modulus, G'', also show very gradual increases at the 360° hold. This viscosity data suggests that additional changes are occurring at the 316°C and 360°C holds. These changes most likely are derived from continued reaction, (imidization, chain extension, cross–linking) during the thermal holds. These changes also occur during composite processing and demonstrates the need to determine what causes these changes and how they can be controlled or eliminated before any elevated processing steps are attempted.

3.2 PMR–II Studies

3.2.1 DSC Behavior Of Pretreated PMR–II–13, PMR–II–30 And PMR–II–50 Resins

DSC data for pretreated PMR–II resins is shown in Tables 4, 5 and 6. The data clearly shows that for each resin system the increased pretreatment temperature increases the endothermic softening temperature, but has little or no influence on the exothermic temperatures, which are related to the cross–linking and gelation temperatures. Comparison of the PMR–II–13 pretreatment data (Table 4) with the PMR–II–30 and PMR–II–50 data (Tables 5 and 6) shows that the increased oligomer molecular weight causes an increase in the softening point of the preimidized prepolymer, for each pretreatment temperature. In fact, for 275°C/1hr pretreated PMR–II–30 and PMR–II–50 resins no softening points were observed. This suggests that this pretreatment condition may be extreme for further processing of the resin into a void free composite. However, softening temperature were observed in the 275°C/0.5hr pretreated PMR–II–13, PMR–II–30 and PMR–II–50 resins. The data shows that there is a critical temperature/time pretreatment condition above which it may not be able to process these resin systems. In all pretreatment cases, an exothermic reaction is observed which is an indication that these pretreated resin materials are undergoing gelation and cross-linking reactions.

3.2.2 TGA Behavior – Dynamic Heating And Isothermal Heating

The TGA data of pretreated PMR–II–30 resin heated dynamically from room temperature to 400°C at 5°C/min, is shown in Table 7. The wt. loss of 0.5 to 2.0% up to 200°C is due to absorbed moisture, and the quantity of absorbed moisture is dependent on the prevailing relative humidity of the laboratory air to which the samples are exposed. The weight loss at 371°C of the 200°C pretreated resin is substantial (6.4%). The data reveals that there is considerable decrease in the 371°C weight loss of the 250°C and 275°C pretreated resin samples relative to the 200°C pretreated resin sample (6.4% vs ~ 2.5 to 3.07). This is strong evidence that imidization reaction up to 200°C is incomplete and that even after the 275°C pretreatment temperature, volatiles are released. This shows the need for pretreatment of the resin or prepreg at the highest temperature possible, to eliminate or reduce off–gassing during the fabrication process. The ability to process pretreated resin or prepreg will be determined by the rheological characteristics of the pretreated resin. The DSC data (Table 5) suggests that the 275/1 hr treated sample may not be processable, but that the 275°C/0.5 hr treated samples may be processable based on the softening temperature.

The weight loss of pretreated PMR–II–13, PMR–II–30 and PMR–II–50 resin specimens was determined by TGA using the process cycles RT→ 250°C, hold, 1 hr, 250°C → 370°C hold 1 hr. This treatment could simulate a composite processing thermal cycle. The data is shown in Table 8. The weight loss up to 200°C is due to absorbed moisture. The increased pretreatment temperature from 200 to 250°C causes a decrease in weight loss at 371°C. Further increases in the pretreatment temperature up to 275°C cause no additional

loss in weight, for all the three resin systems investigated. As with the data generated by the dynamic heating cycle discussed above, the isothermal treatments reveal that at least a pretreatment temperature of 250°C is required to minimize volatile by–product evolution during processing up to 370°C.

3.2.3 Complex Viscosity of PMR–II–20/Celion 6K Prepreg

The complex viscosity data for the pretreated PMR–II–20/Celion 6K uniprepreg is shown in Table 9. The data reveals that both the minimum viscosity temperature and minimum viscosity increase with pretreatment temperature. This suggests that additional imidization occurs with increased temperature. The data suggests that 250 and 275°C pretreated PMR–II–20 prepreg is capable of additional processing into a composite.

3.3 Composite Fabrication Studies

Two materials Avimid N/T40R uniweave and PMR–II–30 were investigated further to apply the thermal analysis and rheology data to two composite fabrication cycles. The prepregs were pretreated at three levels 200°C/1 hr, 250°C/1 hr, and 275°C/1 hr and then subjected to the cycles (1) or (2) as indicated in Tables 10 and 11. The composite data in Table 12 for Avimid N/T40R reveals that cycle 1 with the various pretreatments did not successfully produce a void free composite. However, cycle 2 with the 275°C/1 hr pretreatment produced an acceptable composite.

The data for the prepreg material PMR–II–30/Celion 6K is listed in Table 13. In this system, cycle 1 with the 275°C/1 hr pretreated prepreg yielded an excellent composite with very few microvoids.

The Avimid N/T40R and PMR II–30/Celion 6K data show that the higher pretreatment temperature is conducive to the fabrication of composites with minimum voids. These composites are to be characterized for mechanical properties at 316°C and 370°. Data will be presented at a future conference.

4. CONCLUSIONS

Volatile released at high temperatures during polymer/graphite fiber composite fabrication increases the risk of void and blister formation in composites, thereby reducing quality and reliability and increasing costs due to poor composite yields. The treatment of the prepreg at an elevated temperature (250-275°C) before composite fabrication minimizes the probability of void and blister formation, and yields composites of excellant quality and reproducibility. The upper pretreatment temperature/time for Avimid N is 275°C/1hr, while for PMR-II-13, PMR-II-30 and PMR-II-50, it is 275°C/0.5hr.

These pretreatment conditions make the prepreg amenable to compression molding cycles, and particularly to Thermoclave® processing.

5. REFERENCES

1. Scola, D. A., Vontell, J. H., *A Comparison of the Thermo-Oxidative Stability of Commercial Graphite Fibers and Polymers for High Temperature Composite Application.* Antec '88 Proceedings, p. 1612-1616, Society of Plastics Engineers 46th Annual Tech. Conference and Exhibition, April 18-21, 1988.

2. Scola, D. A. and Vontell, J. H., *High Temperature Polyimides.* Chemistry and Properties Polymer Composites, Vol. 9, No. 6, Dec. 1988.

3. Scola, D. A., and Vontell, J. H., *Society of Plastics Engineers (SPE) Proceedings.* Antec '89, May 1-4, (1989).

6. ACKNOWLEDGMENT

The authors would like to acknowledge Stephen N. Seiser for his assistance in the thermal analysis.

7. BIOGRAPHIES

Dr. Daniel A. Scola received his B.S. degree from Clark University in 1952 and an M.A. degree in Chemistry from Williams College in 1954. His graduate studies were continued at the University of Connecticut where he received a Ph.D in Chemistry in 1958. Currently, Dr. Scola is a Senior Materials Scientist at United Technologies Research Center and Adjunct Professor of Chemistry in the Institute of Materials Sciences at the University of Connecticut. At UTRC, Dr. Scola is responsible for conducting research in advanced composite materials' including interfacial bonding studies, synthesis and evaluation of resin systems and composite materials evaluation.

Mr. John Vontell received a B.S. degree in Chemistry from the University of Hartford in 1984 and has taken graduate courses at the University of Connecticut in polymer science. Mr. Vontell has worked at UTRC for 14 years and is currently an Assistant Research Engineer responsible for supporting research in advanced composite materials.

TABLE 1. THERMAL (DSC) BEHAVIOR OF PRETREATED NR–1501B2 (AVIMID N) RESIN
(RT → 400°C, 10°C/min)

Pretreatment Condition	Endotherms		Exotherm °C
	Moisture Evolution°C	Softening°C	
200°C/1hr	-90	260	>350
250°C/1hr	-90	285	>350
275°C/1hr	-60	308	>350

TABLE 2. EFFECT OF AVIMID N RESIN PRETREATMENT TEMPERATURE ON WEIGHT LOSS DURING PROCESSING (TGA DATA)
(Dynamic Heating RT → 400°C, 5°C/min)

Pretreatment	Wt%[1] Loss @ 200°C	Wt% Residue[2] at 343°C	Wt%[2] Loss @ 343°C	Wt Loss On-Set Temp. °C
100°C/1hr	2.00	96.4	13.6	100
200°C/1hr	1.62	97.77	2.23	210
250°C/1hr	1.56	97.56	2.44	220
275°C/1hr	0.72	99.55	0.45	285

1. Assumed to be moisture.
2. After correction for moisture absorption.

TABLE 3. EFFECT OF AVIMID N/T40R PREPREG PRETREATMENT TEMPERATURE ON COMPLEX VISCOSITY
(RT → 380°C, 5°C/min)

Pretreatment	Temp @ initial softening, °C	Initial softening viscosity, poise	Temp @ midpoint of viscosity lowering °C	viscosity @ 340°C poise
200°C/1hr	170	3.3×10^8	200	5×10^7
250°C/1hr	220	3.5×10^8	280	4.4×10^7
275°C/1hr	250	5.9×10^8	305	1×10^8

TABLE 4. THERMAL (DSC) BEHAVIOR OF PRETREATED PMR–II–13 RESIN
(RT → 400°C, 10°C/min)

Pretreatment	Endotherms, °C		Exotherms °C
	Moisture Evolution[1]	Softening Temperature	
200°C/1hr	-75	210	265,>300
250°C/1hr	-75	230	275,>300
275°C/0.5hr	-75	250	>275
275°C/1hr	-75	250	>275

1. Absorbed moisture.

TABLE 5. THERMAL (DSC) BEHAVIOR OF PRETREATED PMR-II-30 RESIN
(RT → 400°C, 10°C/min)

Pretreatment	Endotherms, °C		Exotherm
	Moisture Evolution[1]	Softening Temperature	°C
200°C/1hr	-50	238	>300
250°C/1hr	-50	275	>300
275°C/0.5hr	-50	270	>300
275°C/1hr	-50	none observed	>300

1. Absorbed moisture.

TABLE 6. THERMAL (DSC) BEHAVIOR OF PRETREATED PMR-II-50 RESIN
(RT → 400°C, 10°C/min)

Pretreatment	Endotherms, °C		Exotherm
	Moisture, Evolution[1]	Softening Temperature	°C
200°C/1hr	-50	240	>300
250°C/1hr	-50	260	>300
275°C/0.5hr	-50	275	>300
275°C/1hr	-50	none observed	>300

1. Absorbed moisture.

TABLE 7. EFFECT OF PMR-II-30 RESIN PRETREATMENT TEMPERATURE ON
WEIGHT LOSS DURING PROCESSING (TGA DATA)
(Dynamic Heating RT → 400°C, 5°C/min)

Pretreatment	Wt%[1] Loss @ 200°C	Wt % Residue at[2] 371°C	Wt % loss @ 371°C	Wt Loss On-Set Temp. °C
200°C/1hr	1.68	93.54	6.44	220
250°C/1hr	2.03	97.34	2.66	265
275°C/1hr	0.54	97.65	2.35	260

1. Assumed to be moisture.
2. After correction for absorbed moisture.

TABLE 8. EFFECT OF PRETREATMENT TEMPERATURE ON WEIGHT LOSS DURING PROCESSING (TGA DATA)
(Process: RT→250°C, Hold 1 hr, 250°C→370°C Hold 1 hr)

Resin Material	Pretreatment	Moisture Content (200°C) Wt%	Wt% Residue[1] after 370°C/1hr	Wt% Loss[2] after 370°/1 hr
PMR–II–13	200°C/1 hr	1.0	92.18	6.82
	250°C/1 hr	0.7	90.95	8.35
	275°C/0.5 hr	0.5	92.45	7.05
	275°/1 hr	0.5	92.26	7.24
PMR–II–30	200°C/1 hr	0.5	93.57	6.43
	250°C/1 hr	1.0	95.33	4.67
	275°C/0.5 hr	0.8	94.67	4.53
	275°/1 hr	0.5	96.19	3.81
PMR–II–50	200°C/1 hr	0.5	94.58	4.92
	250°C/1 hr	0.5	95.66	3.84
	275°C/0.5 hr	0.25	97.48	2.27
	275°C/1 hr	0.25	97.43	2.32

1. Not corrected for evolved moisture.
2. Corrected for absorbed moisture.

TABLE 9. EFFECT OF PREPREG PRETREATMENT TEMPERATURE ON COMPLEX VISCOSITY PMR-II-20/CELION 6K PREPREG
(RT→380°C, 5°C/min)

Pretreatment	Temp., @ Initial Softening °C	Initial Softening Viscosity, Poise	Temp @ Minimum Viscosity °C	Minimum Viscosity, Poise
200°/1 hr	225	1.2×10^7	330	4×10^6
250°/1 hr	260	1.5×10^7	335	5×10^6
275°/1 hr	280	2.2×10^8	355	7×10^6

TABLE 10. COMPOSITE PROCESSING CURE CYCLES AVIMID N/T40R COMPOSITES

Cycle 1

RT → 250°C(482°F), 8.3°C(15°F)/min, hold 60 min, apply
1000 psi at 250°C
250°C(482°F) → 343°C(650°F), 5.5°C(15°F)/min,
hold 120 min, 1000 psi

Cycle 2

RT → 277°C (530°F), 11°C(20°F)/min, apply 1000 psi at 277°C
277°C(530°F) → 365°C(690°F), 5.5°C(10°F)/min, hold
120 min, 1000 psi

TABLE 11. COMPOSITE PROCESSING CURE CYCLES
PMR-II-30/CELION 6K(u) COMPOSITES

Cycle 1

RT → 250°C(485°F), 8.3°C(15°F)/min, hold 60 min, apply
1000 psi at 250°C
250°C(482°F) → 371°C(700°F), 5.5°C/min, hold 60 min,
1000 psi

Cycle 2

RT → 290°C(555°F), 11°C(20°F)/min, apply 1000 psi at 290°C
290°C(555°F) → 371°C(700°F), 5.5°C(10°F)/min, hold
120 min, 1000 psi

TABLE 12. EFFECT OF AVIMID N/T40R PREPREG PRETREATMENT
TEMPERATURE ON COMPOSITE QUALITY

Prepreg Pretreatment	Composite Fabrication Cycle	Quality Of Composite Based On Optical Microscopy
200°C/1 hr	1	continuous lge. voids between plies, no voids within bundles, poor
250°C/1 hr	1	large voids between plies no voids within bundles, poor
275°C/1 hr	1	large voids between plies, no voids within ply bundles, poor
275°C/1 hr	2	very few voids between plies, no voids within bundles, good

TABLE 13. EFFECT OF PMR-II-30/CELION 6K(u) PREPREG PRETREATMENT TEMPERATURE ON COMPOSITE QUALITY

Prepreg Pretreatment	Composite Fabrication Cycle	Composite Quality Based On Optical Microscopy Cross Section
200°C/1 hr	1	many voids between plies, poor
250°C/1 hr	1	some voids within bundles, fair
275°C/1 hr	1	very few voids between plies, excellent
275°C/1 hr	2	very few small voids between plies and within bundle, good

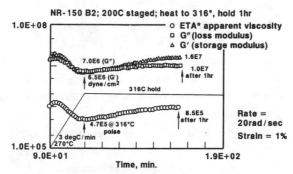

Figure 1. Process Characteristics of High Temperature Polymers and Composites

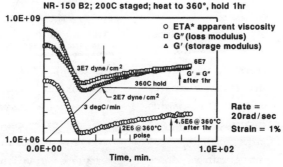

Figure 2. Process Characteristics of High Temperature Polymers and Composites

97

EFFECT OF -18 DEG. C STORAGE ON PMR-15 POLYIMIDE RESIN

Tuyet T. Vuong

Rohr Industries, Inc.

Riverside, California

Abstract

PMR-15 polyimide currently is being considered for use on aircraft in high temperature applications. Advancement of the resin matrix during storage and out-time could be a significant problem since the resin is stored in the monomer stage. A previously published paper (1) defined continuing advancement of the resin during exposure to room temperature. The purpose of this paper is to define the effect of -18 Deg.C storage.

Advancement of the resin matrix was detected by several analytical techniques. Aging of the resin resulted in increased viscosity and reduced resin flow. Voids started to develop and a significant reduction in room temperature interlaminar shear strength occurred after 25 months storage; however compression properties and elevated temperature properties were not affected.

1. INTRODUCTION

The thermosetting polyimide PMR-15, developed at the NASA Lewis Research Center (2) is being considered for a variety of high temperature advanced composite aircraft and aerospace structures.

The PMR resin systems are formulated, prepregged and stored in the monomer stage (A stage). (PMR is designated as polymerization of monomer reactants). The prepolymer (or imidization) and crosslinking reactions are thermally induced in situ during processing. The three monomers in PMR-15 are the 4-4' methylene dianiline (MDA), the dimethylester of 3,3', 4,4' benzophenone tetracarboxylic acid

(BTDE) and a reactive end-cap, the monomethyl ester of 5 norbornene 2,3 dicarboxylic acid (NE). A generalized reaction sequence for the system is shown in Figure 1.

Since the resin is stored in the monomer stage, its advancement during storage and out time has been of concern to users. An advancement of the resin during various storage conditions may cause a shift in the competing condensation reactions which occur during imidization. This could result in variations in molecular weight, molecular weight distribution of the prepolymers and crosslink density. Consequently, these variations will effect the processability, mechanical and thermal properties of cured laminates. Previous study was conducted to evaluate the influence of room temperature storage of up to 30 days, and that study revealed a high degree of advancement of the resin matrix. Laminate quality generally was good, but a definite reduction in resin flow was noted after 30 day exposure, and a small reduction in room temperature compression strength also occurred.

Since there have been controversies about stability of the material during freezer storage, a study was carried out to determine the effects of time

at -18 Deg.C storage. The specific objectives of this study were to determine the degree of advancement of PMR-15 in a prepreg form by chemical analyses and the effect of the observed advancement on processability and mechanical properties of cured laminates.

2. EXPERIMENTAL PROCEDURES

2.1 Conditioning of Samples
Celion epoxy sized carbon fiber C3K24X23, 8 harness satin weave fabric preimpregnated with PMR-15 resin was used in the study. The prepreg was stored for 12, 20 and 25 months at -18 Deg.C, in packs of 8 plies, in sealed bags. After storage, 6 ply test panels of 10" x 10" were laid up and cured after each exposure period. The remaining two plies were used for chemical characterization.

The panels were cured in the autoclave at 302 Deg.C (575 Deg.F) for 180 minutes and oven post cured at 315 Deg.C (600 Deg.F) for 10 hours.

2.2 Prepreg Characterization
Advancement of the resin matrix was monitored by Infrared Spectrophotometry (IR) and High Performance Liquid Chromatography (HPLC). Rheology of the materials was obtained using Dynamic Mechanical Analysis (DMA). Resin and volatile contents of the prepreg were determined by soxhlet extraction.

Infrared spectra were obtained on a Beckman IR 4230 spectrophotometer. The resin from the prepreg was solvent extracted with acetone and smeared onto a sodium chloride salt plate. A Waters Associates 244 Liquid Chromatograph equipped with a Hewlett Packard 1040A Spectrophotometric detector in combination with a data processor was used for HPLC analysis. Dynamic Mechanical Analysis was performed using a Dupont Dynamic Mechanical Analyser 982.

2.3 Laminate Evaluation

Quality of the cured panels was examined using standard metallographic procedures for micro-porosity and uniformity of composite structure. Resin, fiber, and void contents were determined by the standard acid digestion method (ASTM D 3171). Dynamic mechanical modulus was measured by DMA. Glass transition temperature was also obtained from the DMA.

The laminates were tested in compression and interlaminar shear at room temperature and 260 Deg.C (500 Deg.F). Interlaminar shear tests were performed using a three point fixture at a span to depth ratio of 3.5 to 1 and a cross head speed of 1.28 mm (0.05 inch)/min. Compression tests were performed with an one-inch gage length and a crosshead speed of 0.64 mm (0.025 inch)/min. A Rohr-designed compression test fixture was used with a mechanical gage Linear Variable Differential Transducer (LVDT) for recording strain. For elevated temperature testing, the load was applied when the specimens reached the required temperature.

3. RESULTS AND DISCUSSIONS

3.1 Prepreg Characterization
Resin and Volatile Contents
The resin and volatile contents of the prepregs are shown in Table 1. Resin content was determined by extraction of resin with acetone and was reported here as the percent of extracted resin weight divided by the original weight (wet resin content). All the samples recorded an average resin content of 44.8% except the 25 month storage sample had a 48.5% resin content. The total volatile content, which includes free solvent and reaction volatiles from the condensation reaction, was determined following processing at 600 Deg.F for 15 minutes. For the 12 and 20-month samples, a decrease in volatiles was noted which indicated that some condensation reaction has taken place. However, the volatile content of the 25-month sample was higher than expected, probably due to high resin content of the sample related to its location in the prepreg roll.

Infrared Spectrophotometry

Figure 2 illustrates the infrared spectra of a control and a 25 month storage sample. Only the portion of the spectra at wavenumbers below 2000 cm^{-1} is shown, since most of the indicative bands are found in this region. The carbonyl band at 1705 cm^{-1}, associated with the ester and/or acid groups, increased in absorption relative to 1725 cm^{-1} band. The cyclic imide band at 1765 cm^{-1} was observed as a shoulder on the ester band. Its presence indicated that imidization had occurred at this temperature. It is reported in the literature (3, 4) that the intensity of the band at 1380 cm^{-1} is related to imidization. A band at 1510 cm^{-1} was chosen as an internal standard since it showed no apparent change during imidization. The degree of imidization can be measured by the absorbtivity ratio of these two bands (3). The band at 1380 cm^{-1} increased slightly in intensity in comparison to the band at 1510 cm^{-1}. The band at 720 cm^{-1}, attributed to the imide carbonyl group (5), also increased with storage time. Thus, the IR analysis revealed that advancement of the resin occurred during storage. However, the technique is not sensitive enough for quantitative analysis. It can be concluded, however that chemical changes were occurring during storage.

High Performance Liquid Chromatography

The chromatograms, obtained by ion pair reverse phase, of the control, 12 – month and 25 – month samples are shown in Figure 3. The area percents of the monomers and reaction products are summarized in Table 2 and plotted in Figures 4 and 5. The results of the 30-day exposure at room temperature sample are also given for comparison.

The values recorded are based on the area percent under the HPLC curve, and are related to, but not exactly the same as the mole percent levels, since different products will absorb at different levels in the selected UV frequency. However, changes in concentration of a given product are directly comparable.

HPLC analysis clearly revealed the advancement of the resin matrix through decreases in the concentration of monomers and the appearance of various reaction products. MDA and NE were reduced significantly with storage (Figure 4), and an increase in their reaction products was noted. Figure 3 shows that the MDA, peaks Nos. 1 and 2, were reduced to about one half of their original concentration. The NE peak in the control originally was small, due to its low absorptivity. After 25 months storage, it became so small that the area was no longer integratable. The concentration of the monoadduct of NE-MDA, Peak No. 3, in the amide ester form, was reduced with storage time and converted to the more stable imide form, Peak No. 7, which increased rapidly with storage time, from 8 to 19 area percent after 25 months. The intermediate form of the NE-MDA-NE bis adduct, the amide-imide, Peak No. 20 increased slightly. The more stable, imide-imide, Peak No. 21, increased significantly. The mono-adduct is considered to be a normal step in the preliminary stages of the prepolymer formation. The formation of bis adducts is undesirable, because a skewed molecular weight distribution of prepolymers would result which would affect the flow during consolidation process.

The monoadducts of BTDE and MDA were formed slowly and continued to grow. The intermediate isomers of BTDE-MDA mono amides are shown as Peaks 8, 9 and 10 and are formed at a uniform rate, from 2 to 3.5 area percent. The two cyclic imides of BTDE-MDA are shown as Peaks 16 and 17 and increase slightly with storage time from 0 to 2 area percent. The triesters, Peaks No. 18 and

19, were not noticeably changed during storage.

The analysis indicated that the reaction between NE and MDA is much faster than the reaction between BTDE and MDA, at low temperatures. The advancement during freezer storage is much slower in comparison to exposure to room temperature. Exposure for 25 months at -18 Deg.C is equivalent to 15 days at room temperature.

Dynamic Mechanical Analysis

The rheology of the material vs. cure cycle is shown in Figure 6. Storage at -18 Deg.C only slightly affects the flow in the low temperature region, i.e. at the first step of the cure cycle. The prepreg is stiffer for the 25 month sample, as determined by the initial start point of the DMA curve.

3.2 Weight Loss During Processing

The weights of the panels were obtained before and after cure and postcure. The weight loss during cure decreased with storage, except for the 25-month sample as shown in Table 1. The weight loss represents the volatiles released from the condensation reaction plus the amount of resin through the bleeder plies. This serves as an indirect measure of resin flow. The data indicate that the fresh sample had better flow than the freezer storage sample. The 25-month sample had weight loss similar to the control sample. This is probably due to high resin content of this prepreg sample which results in higher volatile release and higher resin bleed. The weight loss during postcure appeared to be slightly increased with storage.

3.3 Cured Laminate Characterization

Microstructures

Microstructures of the polished cross section of the control, and 20-month cured laminates are shown in Figure 7. The photomicrographs illustrated that acceptable panels were obtained. However, large resin rich areas between fiber bundles were noted starting with the 20-month sample. Microvoids were noted in addition to resin rich areas in the 25-month sample. These observations, together with DMA and weight loss data indicate that long time storage reduced the resin flow.

Resin and Void Contents

Resin and void contents of the cured laminates were obtained by an acid digestion method. The results are shown in Table 1. Resin and void contents are slightly increased with storage time.

Glass Transition Temperature

Glass transition temperature was obtained from the dynamic mechanical analysis and the results are tabulated in Table 3. The glass transition shows a slight increase with storage.

Interlaminar Shear Tests

The results of the interlaminar shear (ILS) tests, determined at room temperature and 260 Deg.C, are tabulated in Table 3. The presented data are for an average of 5 to 7 specimens. A progressive reduction in room temperature (ILS) strength was observed, 11.5 ksi for control vs. 8.68 ksi for the 25 month samples, as shown in Figure 8. This trend is not evident when tested at 260 Deg.C.

Compression Tests

The compression strength results, tested at room temperature and 260 Deg.C are provided in Table 3 and Figure 9. The data are for an average of 6 to 7 specimens. The results of the tests indicated that storage of the prepreg at -18 Deg.C for up to 25 months, did not significantly affect compressive strengths of the PMR-15 composites. The analysis indicated that, even though the shear capability after a long storage period deteriorated, the resin still carries adequate compression loads.

4. CONCLUSIONS

4.1 Chemical Changes During Storage

A. Significant chemical changes occur during storage of PMR-15 at -18 Deg.C, as indicated by HPLC and IR analysis.

B. The reaction between NE and MDA is sufficiently rapid that virtually all of the NE was consumed after 12 months storage.

C. Although clearly detectable by HPLC, the reduction between BTDE and MDA is quite slow, and only a few percent of the original BTDE is consumed after 24 months storage.

D. For both of the esters, initial condensation is followed by imidization. However, the NE-MDA amide-ester is nearly 100% imidized, after 24 months, whereas a small amount of BTDE-MDA amide-ester produced is only partially imidized.

E. The NE-MDA-NE bis adduct also forms, during -18 Deg.C storage, and is a significant component in the 24 month storage sample. Like the mono-adduct, it mostly converts to the fully imidized form.

F. There was no detectable increase in BTDA triester concentration.

4.2 Physical/Rheological Changes

A. Storage of PMR-15 prepreg for 24 months at -18 Deg.C results in increased viscosity and reduced flow, as shown by weight loss during cure, and DMA analysis.

B. Slight increases in void content, after storage were noted, by void content measurement and photomicro analysis.

4.3 Mechanical Strength Changes

A. A significant reduction in room temperature interlaminar shear strength was noted after 24 months storage. However, 260 Deg.C shear strength, and compression properties at both room and elevated temperatures, were not affected significantly.

B. Since only thin laminates were fabricated, the influence of storage on thick laminates was not evaluated. However, general experience indicates that thick laminates are harder to fabricate, hence deterioration during storage probably will have a more significant influence on laminate quality. Further work is needed in this area.

C. Other areas not investigated were thermal aging and resistance to microcracking, after exposure to thermal cycling, and these parameters should be studied.

4.4 Overall Conclusions

A. The generally accepted storage limitation of 6 months at -18 Deg.C probably is consistent with the chemistry of PMR-15. However, any extension of prepreg service life by periodic requalification should be carefully evaluated with respect to a probable increased risk of failure. The economics associated with a scrapped part, compared to the cost of scrapping the prepreg, should be carefully considered, especially in view of the lack of a clear identification of the influence of storage on processibility, thermal resistance and micro-cracking.

B. Since this study was performed on standard prepreg containing 2-3% solvent, no information was generated on the role of solvent content on storage stability. However, limited test data, plus literature reports indicate better storage stability, for dry prepreg. Further definition of this parameter also is needed.

5. REFERENCES

1. T. Vuong, Proc. of the 32nd International SAMPE Symposium, 839 (1987).

2. T. T. Serafini, P. Pelvigs, and G. R. Lightsey, U. S. Pat, 3,745,149, July 10, 1973.

3. A. Werata, Jr., D. K. Hadad, "Analytical Techniques Applied to the Optimization of LARC-160 Composite Lamination". ACS Symposium Series 132.

4. D. Wilson, et al. "Polymerisation Mechanisms in PMR-15 Polyimide". 3rd International Conference on Polyimides.

5. K. L. Mittal, "Polyimide Synthesis Characterization and Application", Vol. 1, Plenum Press, New York, pp. 429-442.

BIOGRAPHY

Tuyet Vuong is a Senior Research Engineer at Rohr Industries, Inc. with twelve years experience in polymeric analytical techniques, polymer and composite properties and applications.

She received a B.S. in Chemical Engineering from the National Institute of Technology, Saigon - VN and an M.S. in Materials Engineering from the University of Wisconsin, Milwaukee.

6. ACKNOWLEDGEMENTS

The author wishes to thank the Rohr Industries Incorporation for their permission to publish this work. Thanks are also given to Dr. F. J. Riel for his technical discussion, to J. McGreavy for fabrication of the panels, and to the analytical and mechanical labs for carrying out the testing.

TABLE 1

PHYSICAL PROPERTIES OF PREPREG AND CURED LAMINATES
VS. FREEZER STORAGE TIME AT -18 Deg.C

SAMPLE	PREPREG		PROCESSING		CURED LAMINATES	
	RESIN CONTENT (%)	VOLATILE CONTENT (%)	WEIGHT LOSS DURING CURE (%)	WEIGHT LOSS DURING POST CURE (%)	RESIN CONTENT (%)	VOID CONTENT (%)
CONTROL	44.8	11.46	21.7	0.42	31.9	0.81
12 MONTHS	44.8	10.32	18.1	0.68	28.1	2.16
20 MONTHS	44.5	9.67	17.7	0.27	32.7	1.49
25 MONTHS	48.5	11.94	22.0	0.89	32.9	1.89
30 DAYS RT	44.0	9.13	17.6	0.60	33.5	0.63

TABLE 2

HPLC AREA PERCENT OF PMR-15 RESIN PRODUCTS
VS. PREPREG FREEZER STORAGE TIME AT -18 Deg.C

PEAK NO. [1]	IDENTITY	CONTROL	12 MOS @ -18 Deg.C	25 MOS @ -18 Deg.C	30 DAYS @ 75 Deg.F
1, 2	MDA isomers	27.12	21.0	20.53	16.29
3	NE-MDA amide ester	8.48	5.0	1.34	1.29
6	NE	1.08	0.5	-	-
7	NE-MDA imide	8.31	17.1	19.5	21.67
8, 9, 10	BTDE-MDA amide ester isomers	2.03	4.0	3.47	6.78
12, 13, 14	BTDE isomers	46.9	45.1	45.8	38.99
16, 17	BTDE-MDA imide	0.51	1.54	2.25	4.87
20	NE-MDA-NE amide-imide	1.95	2.06	1.71	-
21	NE-MDA-NE imide-imide	-	3.20	3.93	7.42

[1] - See Figure 3

TABLE 3
PROPERTIES OF CURED LAMINATES (0_6) VS. PREPREG FREEZER
STORAGE TIME AT -18 Deg.C

SAMPLE	TG	INTERLAMINAR SHEAR STRENGTH AT		COMPRESSIVE STRENGTH AT	
	DEG.C (DEG.F)	25 DEG.C MPA (KSI)	260 DEG.C MPA (KSI)	25 DEG.C MPA (KSI)	260 DEG.C MPA (KSI)
CONTROL	354 (669)	79.3 (11.5)	43.7 (6.34)	732 (106)	494 (71.6)
12 MONTHS	359 (678)	71.6 (10.4)	52.2 (7.57)	695 (101)	427 (61.9)
20 MONTHS	378 (712)	66.7 (9.68)	49.1 (7.12)	721 (105)	481 (69.7)
25 MONTHS	377 (711)	59.8 (8.68)	53.5 (7.76)	690 (100)	542 (78.6)
30 DAYS RT	351 (663)	75.8 (11.0)	42.9 (6.23)	664 (96.3)	469 (68.0)

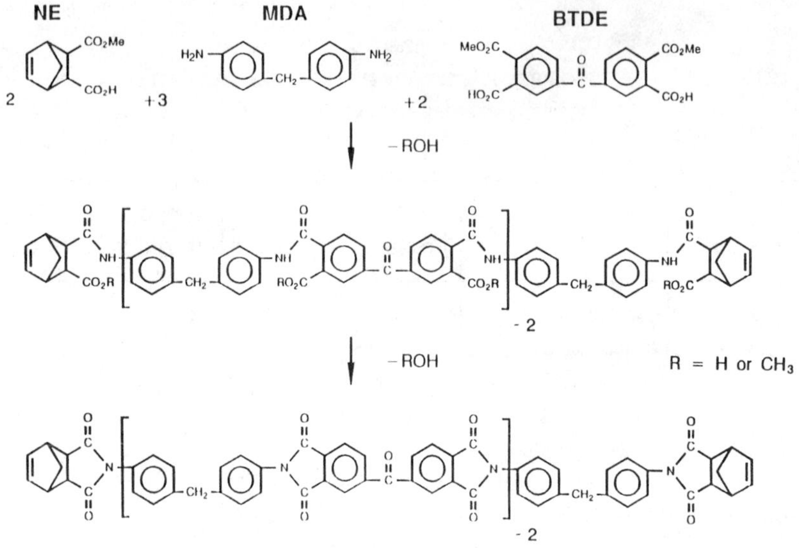

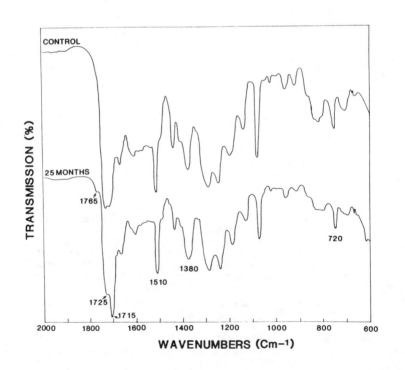

FIGURE 1

REACTION SEQUENCE FOR POLYIMIDE PMR-15 RESIN

FIGURE 2

INFRARED SPECTRA OF FRESH PMR-15 PREPREG

AND A PREPREG AFTER 25 MONTHS STORAGE AT -18°C

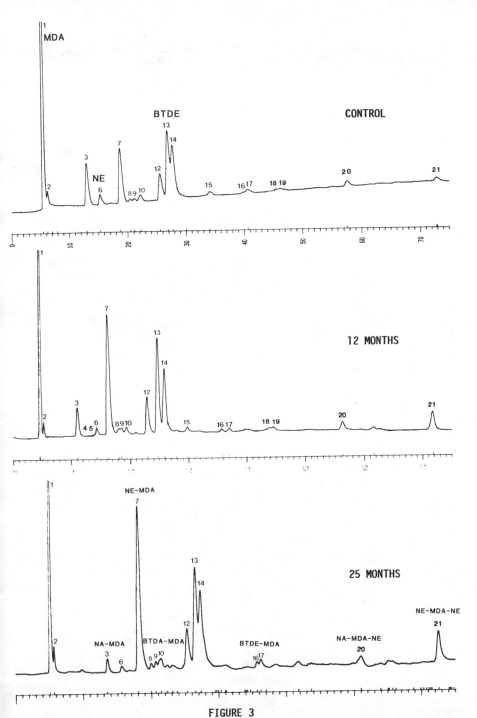

FIGURE 3

REVERSE-PHASE LIQUID CHROMATOGRAMS OF A FRESH PMR-15 PREPREG SAMPLE
AND SAMPLES AFTER STORED FOR 12 MONTHS AND 25 MONTHS AT -18°C

(SEE TABLE 2 FOR PEAK IDENTITY)

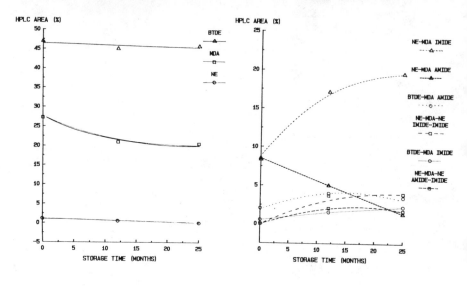

FIGURE 4
**PMR-15 MONOMER HPLC AREA PERCENT
VS. FREEZER STORAGE TIME AT -18 DEG.C**

FIGURE 5
**PMR-15 REACTION PRODUCT AREA PERCENTS
VS. STORAGE TIME AT -18 DEG.C**

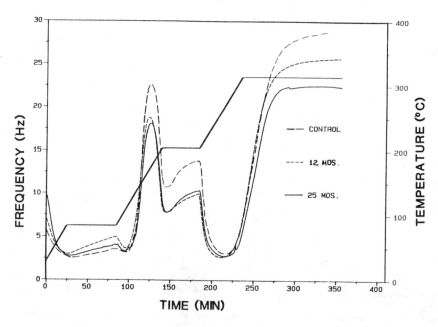

FIGURE 6

**DMA THERMOGRAMS OF PMR-15 PREPREG AFTER 0 MONTHS, 12 MONTHS AND
25 MONTHS FREEZER STORAGE TIME AT -18°C WITH CURE CYCLE**

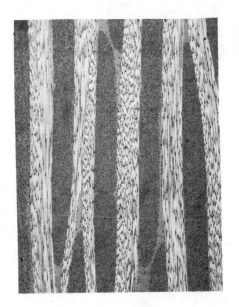 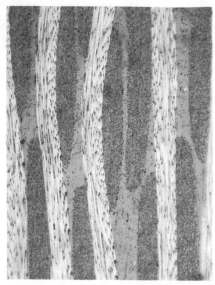

57.5X   CONTROL   57.5X   20 MONTHS

FIGURE 7

PHOTOMICROGRAPHS SHOWING MICROSTRUCTURE OF PMR-15 PANELS

FABRICATED FROM CONTROL PREPREG AND PREPREG AFTER FREEZER STORAGE

FOR 20 MONTHS AT -18°C.   THE EFFECT OF STORAGE ON RESIN FLOW IS DEPICTED

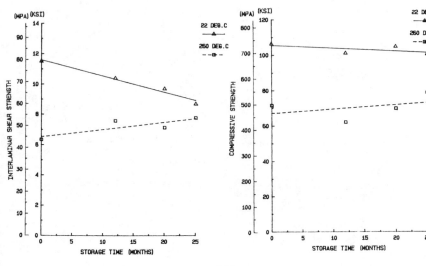

FIGURE 8
INTERLAMINAR SHEAR STRENGTH
VS. FREEZER STORAGE TIME AT -18 DEG.C

FIGURE 9
COMPRESSIVE STRENGTH
VS. FREEZER STORAGE TIME AT -18 DEG.C

COMPOSITE DEVELOPMENTS FROM FULLY IMIDIZED PMR-15 POWDER

Timothy Hartness
Debra Porter
BASF Structural Materials, Inc.
Thermoplastic Composites
Charlotte, North Carolina
and
Joseph P. Reardon
Dexter Composites
Cleveland, Ohio

Abstract

The ability to prepreg a fully
imidized PMR-15 that is then
consolidated without the
evolution of reaction volatiles
is a very significant
development. PMR-15, the most
widely used high-temperature
polyimide today, has several
severe limitations. The
traditional material is supplied
as a prepregging varnish. The
alcohol varnish contains three
monomers that are reacted after
prepregging, resulting in the
amic acid. One of the monomers,
Methylenedianiline, must be
handled with care due to its
toxic nature. Before curing, the
composition of the resin is
continually changing because of
monomer reactions that occur
during storage. Compositional
changes of the resin include
formation of soluble higher
esters, which severely affect the
processibility and properties of
the composition. These issues
are eliminated with the fully
imidized product form.

1. INTRODUCTION

One of the objectives of the
composites research and
development ongoing within
Thermoplastic Composites (TPC), a
division of BASF Structural
Materials, Inc., is to
investigate the feasibility of
using a fully imidized version of
PMR-15 as a matrix for
traditionally reinforced advanced
composites. PMR-15 [1], developed
at NASA Lewis Research Center
over seventeen years ago, is the
most widely used high temperature
polyimide for advanced
composites. It is manufactured
now by a number of suppliers.
The fully imidized PMR-15 used
for this study is manufactured by
the composite division of the
Dexter Corporation. The material
developed by NASA Lewis involves
the blending of three monomers in

anhydrous methanol. This solution is then used to impregnate the reinforcement which may be carbon, glass, or some other fiber. Fiber forms are primarily unidirectional tape or cloth. The polyimide is traditionally prepared from three monomeric components (See table I) which are mixed in a particular molar ration to achieve the required molecular weight of the final polymer (See table II). The composite processing of this polyamic acid oligomer is not straight forward. In a study by Darfler and Buyny[2] for the Hexcel Corporation several important observations and conclusions were made. The processing of PMR-15 is very dependent on the manufacturing technique as well as the part thickness. It is obvious that when autoclave processing a thick complex part several important considerations must be taken into account. The management of reaction volatile by-products that may result in void formation is most important. Some conclusions of the Hexcel study indicate that one must balance the effects of complete volatile removal against the risk of an increasing cross-linked resin. In addition, there seems to be a temperature regime in which void formation is diffusion controlled and one in which voids are flow controlled. It is most noteworthy that after fifteen years people are still reporting on how to process this resin system.

If one could develop the technology to take advantage of a fully imidized version of PMR-15 thereby eliminating these most complex issues then a considerable number of benefits could be achieved. The advantage of eliminating volatiles both from alchohol and water as a by-product are obvious. This elimination should result in greatly reduced voids in thick laminates as well as the requirement to precisely control viscosity by managing volatiles. The other major issue that is now receiving more attention, as environmental and health concerns are always important, is the exposure of the worker to methylene dianiline (MDA). In the traditional PMR-15 solvent product MDA is present at a level of 30 percent. Methylene dianiline is a suspected human carcinogen. The ability to greatly reduce or completely eliminate this agent from the work place in itself would be a significant contribution.

2. EXPERIMENTAL

2.1 Resin Preparation

Yungk and Watson first point out in January 1988 that oligomers with a single norbornenyl endcap were a common occurrence in imidized PMR-15 molding compounds[3]. The same phenomenon existed in PMR-15 prepregs from various vendors once the prepregs had been thermally imidized. Normally, of course, one would expect the oligomers in imidized PMR-15 powder to be endcapped at both ends. The fully imidized PMR-15 powder (HyComp M-100) being used in the new powder prepreg is manufactured in such a way as to minimize the occurrence of singly endcapped oligomers. The importance of minimizing these "fragments" is probably best illustrated in describing how Yungk and Watson discovered the phenomenon, identified the fragments in question, and showed the adverse impact on molded PMR-15 polyimide.

Imidized PMR-15 resin consists of oligomers formed by the reaction of 4,4"-methylenedianiline (MDA) and the dimethyl ester of 3,3',4,4'-benzophenonetetracarboxylic acid (BTDE), plus the monomethyl ester of 5-norbornene-2,3-dicarboxylic acid (Nadic ester or NE) as the endcap. The smallest normal oligomer is the bisnadimide. Beyond it, the oligomers grow in discrete increments by the addition of MDA-BTDE units (designed by N+1, 2, 3, ...).The standard method of analyzing for the distribution of oligomers is gel permeation chromatography (GPC). Yungk and Watson observed intermediate peaks in their chromatograms, except for a single batch of PMR-15 molding compound (Figure 1). To help identify these intermediate peaks, they isolated the fractions eluted from the chromatographic column and analyzed them by FTIR spectroscopy (Figure 2). They tentatively identified the intermediate species as oligomers terminated on one end by an anhydride group of BTDA unit (Figure 3)

Do such "anhydride fragments" pose a problem or should they be taken for granted in PMR-15? To answer this question, Yungk and Watson monitored the cure of a typical imidized PMR-15 by diffuse reflectance FTIR. Their results (Figure 4) showed that the unreacted anhydride groups break down under increasing temperature to generate carbon dioxide, which of course, would be a source of voids in the molded polyimide.

We postulate that the culprit in the formation of the "anhydride fragments" is the Nadic ester, because its reactivity towards MDA is greater than that of BTDE. Hence, minimizing the formation of "anhydride fragments" becomes a matter of properly manipulating the Nadic ester. Control is required in both stages of the formation of the imidized prepolymer, namely,
1) in the blending of the three monomers to form the PMR-15 precursor solution; and

2) in solvent removal and thermal imidization of the resin.

No additives are required and there is no modification of the stoichiometry. Common sense chemical technique suffices to produce what we term a low anhydride" imidized PMR-15 resin. Initial data indicate that the methodology developed by Dexter Composites (patent applied for) has been successful in greatly reducing the occurrence of anhydride fragments in imidized PMR-15. As a consequence, this low-anhydride imidized PMR-15 has become the material of choice for the production of the new powder prepreg.

2.2 Thermal Analysis

One of the primary objectives of this work were to develop the process criteria for the fully imidized PMR-15. The approach chosen was to characterize each lot of PMR-15 using DSC, TGA, and Rheometrics. The objective was to also learn if any of these techniques could be used in the quality control of the material. Consideration must be given to the fact that only a limited number of batches have been made and it was doubtful, based on this fact, that significant history could be established. Shown in Table 3 are the lots that were evaluated. Lot 3 was a small lab sample and also was an attempt to supply a low anhydride PMR-15 for evaluation in the program. The two following lots were larger batches of this version.

2.2.1 Differential Scanning Colorimetry (DSC)

An Omnitherm Data System was used for thermal analysis. This unit is similar to the DuPont 9900 unit and incorporates separate modules for both DSC and TGA analysis. Analysis using DSC incorporated the open pan method. Conditions are shown in Figure 5. As can be observed, there seems to be no significant differences between lots except Lot 3. In this lot, the onset of melt as indicated by an indotherm at approximately 175°C was somewhat early as compared to the other lots. This lot does not indicate the characteristic exotherm at approximately 235°C as shown by the other lots. Whether this is of any significance, is hard to say. All of the lots show the onset of crosslinking at approximately 300°C. This is supported by similar behavior observed in the Rheometrics. It is our judgement that additional lots must be analyzed before a decision could be made to use DSC as a QC tool. It is believed that useful information can be obtained so this technique will continue to be used. A more indepth study using DSC is warranted, but time has not allowed the study.

2.2.2 Thermal Gravimetric Analysis (TGA)

Samples were heated in air using a straight ramp at 10°C/min. Weight loss can be observed for all samples at approximately 175°C (Figure 6). This corresponds well to the indotherm observed in the DSC at the same temperature.

The significant weight loss observed at 325°C is thought to be cyclopentadiene. It is understood that the crosslinking of the prepolymer occurs via a ring opening process of the norbornene end-groups which incorporates cyclopentadiene into the polymer chain bridges. During the TGA analysis, the cyclopentadiene is free to escape rather than react under pressure as would normally occur. Again,

this technique will be used to help QC the material for any unusual volatile material which may help identify a bad lot of material.

2.2.3. Rheometrics

A Rheometrics Dynamic Analyzer (RDA-700) was used to characterize the viscosity of the various lots of PMR-15. Tests were run using the parallel plate mode. A heat ramp of 3°C/min was used with a frequency of 1 Rad./sec and a strain of 50%. A study was run to see if additional aging of the prepolymer at 204°C in air would effect the rheological behavior of the material. As shown in Figure 7, there was no significant change in the material after one hour. This was of interest in the case that drying may be required to remove moisture after prepregging. It is also understood that imidization occurs at approximately this temperature. In Figure 8 a comparison is shown between four lots of material. Significant differences can be observed between Lot 1, the early production lot and Lot 3 a small "low anhydride" batch. It is obviously desirable to have as low a viscosity as possible with no detrimental effects such as residual volatiles. Due to this desire, the low viscosity exhibited by Lot 3 was of much interest. Yet, at the same time, it should be noted that Lot 1 was also producing high quality low or zero void laminates. The results of this preliminary study indicates that a large window does exist for processing high quality laminates provided that high quality prepreg can be made with excellent fiber/resin distribution. It is hoped that future analysis of lots will help determine if this analytical technique can be use as a quality control criteria. It is certainly important in establishing a process window for the material.

2.3 Composite Processing

All composites were processed from either research prepreg or 3" wide production prepreg. The research prepreg is drum wound using a proprietary impregnation technique that results in a solventless powder prepreg. The carbon fiber used in this work was Celion G30-500, 12K, unsized. This fiber has been the standard for much of the PMR-15 evaluation in the past. All of the data generated to date has been compression molded. Based on the thermal analysis data a molding cycle was generated that can be used in either the press or autoclave (See Figure 9). One must allow sufficient time for the middle of a thick laminate to heat to the point that allows all moisture to be removed before pressure is applied. Thermal analysis indicates that no change will occur to the melt viscosity after one hour at 204°C. This is ample time for moisture removal even in a thick laminate. A good vent path is always a requirement in autoclave molding. The recommended molding cycle may need to be modified depending on the size of the part, it's condition regarding moisture content, etc. As can be seen though this molding cycle, it is very simple compared to the standard solvent based process. A standard free standing post cure at 316°C (600°F) is recommended as in the past. A post cure study was initiated to see if a normal glass transition (Tg) was being achieved in the material after post cure. A standard torson rectangular specimen was used for analysis in the Rheometrics Dynamic Analyzer (RDA-700). The results of the study are shown in Table 4. It appears that no increase in Tg occurs at 316°C after eight hours. Many studies show an increase in mechanical properties during thermal aging at 316°C so it makes sense to at least give the material a 24 hour post cure. Mechanical properties versus post cure time at 316°C will be completed in the future. A typical Rheometrics plot is shown in Figure 10. The composite sample was run after a 12 hour post cure in air at 316°C. G', G", and Tan Delta is plotted as a function of temperature.

2.4 Composite Properties

The primary objective of this initial program was to generate basic mechanical properties that compare to established literature values. All composites were fabricated from unidirectional tape either from drum wound or continuous 3" tape. Fabrication was accomplished using matched die molds. A polyimide (Kapton) peal ply was used on the top and bottom of the lay-up to assist in the composite removal. No bleeders or breathers were used during the processing. The cure cycle and post cure used was as shown in Table 9. A modified ASTM D790 test technique was used for 0° four point flexure. Rubber pads were used under the top loading pins to prevent local fiber damage. It has been established that mechanical properties often increase by approximately 25% versus standard flexure testing. This is especially true for thermoplastics where plastic deformation can occur at the loading surface. Tensile testing was accomplished using bonded glass epoxy tabs. All specimens were either strain gaged or an extensometer used to measure strain. Short beam shear testing was accomplished using a span-to-depth ratio of 4 to 1. Elevated temperature testing will be accomplished in the near future.

Mechanical properties to date are shown in Table 5.

3. ENVIRONMENTAL ISSUES

One of the major concerns that exists with the standard solvent system is the presence of free methylanedianiline (MDA). The monoymer is present at a level of approximately 30% of solids in the solution. The major concern is that MDA is a suspect human carcinogen. The common means of transport is through the skin, especially when a solvent such as methanol can be used as a transport medium. Work has been ongoing at BASF AG, the research headquarters in Ludwigshafen, West Germany, to try and detect any level of MDA in the fully imidized PRM-15. Three techniques have been used to date to detect MDA. The first method was high pressure liquid chromatography (HPLC). With this technique, no MDA has been detected with a detection level of 100 ppm. The second technique employed was thin layer liquid chromatography. With this technique, no MDA has been detected with a detection level of 15 ppm. The third technique used was liquid chromatography. With this technique no MDA has been detected at a detection level of 10 ppm. Additional testing is ongoing and will be reported at the meeting.

4. CONCLUSIONS

Based on initial studies, the data indicates that high quality laminates can be fabricated from fully imidized PMR-15 using a powder impregnation technique. Mechanical properties of laminates indicate excellent properties that are representative of literature values. The processing of fully imidized PMR-15 is quite simple as compared to the solvent based system. Thermal analysis indicates that representative Tg's are being obtained with typical post cures. Initial studies indicate that detectable levels of MDA are less than 10 ppm and offer a much safer product.

5. FUTURE WORK

The as reported work is understood to be an initial study with the necessity to initiate work to generate a much larger data base that includes long term thermal aging as well as other properties of interest. This initial study has been accomplished with unitape only. It is well understood that fabric prepreg makes up the majority of existing product now being fabricated. With this in mind, work is ongoing to develop a PMR-15 cloth product as well as towpreg for filament winding, braiding, etc.

6. ACKNOWLEDGMENTS

Recognition must go to the fine technical staff at TPC. Their work involved in the evaluation of PMR-15 is much appreciated.

7. REFERENCES

1. Serafini, T. T., Delvigs, P. and Ligthsey, G. R.: "Thermally Stable Polyimides From Solutions of Monomeric Reactants", Journal of Applied Polymer Science, Vol. 16, No. 4, April 1972.

2. Darfler, S. C. and Buyny, R. A.: "Cure Cycles for PMR-15, Effects of Imidization Times and Temperatures", pgs. 702-711, 31° International SAMPE Symposium. Vol 31, Anaheim, CA., April 7-10, 1986.

3. Yungk, R. and Watson, C., "PMR_15 Molding Compound

Mechanical properties to date are shown in Table 5.

3. ENVIRONMENTAL ISSUES

One of the major concerns that exists with the standard solvent system is the presence of free methylanedianiline (MDA). The monoymer is present at a level of approximately 30% of solids in the solution. The major concern is that MDA is a suspect human carcinogen. The common means of transport is through the skin, especially when a solvent such as methanol can be used as a transport medium. Work has been ongoing at BASF AG, the research headquarters in Ludwigshafen, West Germany, to try and detect any level of MDA in the fully imidized PRM-15. Three techniques have been used to date to detect MDA. The first method was high pressure liquid chromatography (HPLC). With this technique, no MDA has been detected with a detection level of 100 ppm. The second technique employed was thin layer liquid chromatography. With this technique, no MDA has been detected with a detection level of 15 ppm. The third technique used was liquid chromatography. With this technique no MDA has been detected at a detection level of 10 ppm. Additional testing is ongoing and will be reported at the meeting.

4. CONCLUSIONS

Based on initial studies, the data indicates that high quality laminates can be fabricated from fully imidized PMR-15 using a powder impregnation technique. Mechanical properties of laminates indicate excellent properties that are representative of literature values. The processing of fully imidized PMR-15 is quite simple as compared to the solvent based system. Thermal analysis indicates that representative Tg's are being obtained with typical post cures. Initial studies indicate that detectable levels of MDA are less than 10 ppm and offer a much safer product.

5. FUTURE WORK

The as reported work is understood to be an initial study with the necessity to initiate work to generate a much larger data base that includes long term thermal aging as well as other properties of interest. This initial study has been accomplished with unitape only. It is well understood that fabric prepreg makes up the majority of existing product now being fabricated. With this in mind, work is ongoing to develop a PMR-15 cloth product as well as towpreg for filament winding, braiding, etc.

6. ACKNOWLEDGMENTS

Recognition must go to the fine technical staff at TPC. Their work involved in the evaluation of PMR-15 is much appreciated.

7. REFERENCES

1. Serafini, T. T., Delvigs, P. and Ligthsey, G. R.: "Thermally Stable Polyimides From Solutions of Monomeric Reactants", Journal of Applied Polymer Science, Vol. 16, No. 4, April 1972.

2. Darfler, S. C. and Buyny, R. A.: "Cure Cycles for PMR-15, Effects of Imidization Times and Temperatures", pgs. 702-711, 31st International SAMPE Symposium. Vol 31, Anaheim, CA., April 7-10, 1986.

3. Yungk, R. and Watson, C., "PMR-15 Molding Compound

Characterization", High Temple
Workshop VIII, January 25-28,
1988 Riviera Beach, Fla.

        8. BIOGRAPHY

J. Timothy Hartness is a Group
Leader in the R&D Group at BASF
Structural   Materials,
Inc./Thermoplastic Composites
Division (TPC). He joined this
group in 1987 after working at
the University of Dayton Research
Institute on-site at the Air
Force Materials Laboratory since
1968.   His major effort is in
developing new composites.

Debbie Porter is a Composite
Engineer   in   R&D   at   the
Thermoplastic Composites Unit of
BASF Structural Materials, Inc.
She did her undergraduate and
graduate studies at the
University of Dayton in Dayton,
Ohio.

Joseph P. Reardon holds the Ph. D
in Physical Chemistry from The
American University, Washington,
D. C. He was a research chemist
and section head at the Naval
Research Laboratory from 1971 to
1979, where his work centered on
electrically conductive polymers,
the electrical properties of
carbon fibers, and the fire
safety of carbon fiber/epoxy
composites. He then joined Pure
Industries, Inc., where he served
as M&P Manager first in the
Carbon Division, and next in the
Tribon Bearing Division.   At
Tribon, he participated in the
introduction of polyimides for
various   high-temperature
bearing applications. He joined
Dexter Composites in April 1986
as a founding member of that
company. As Manager of Materials
and Process Development at Dexter
Composites, much of his effort
has been devoted to the
development of PMR-15 polyimide
bulk and sheet molding compounds.

TABLE 1

MONOMERIC COMPONENTS USED FOR THE FORMULATION OF PMR-15

NAME	STRUCTURE	ABBREVIATION	MOL WT
5-norbornene 2,3 dicarboxylic acid monomethyl ester		NE	196
4,4'-methylene dianiline		MDA	198
3,3',4,4' benzo-phenone tetra-carboxylic acid dimethyl ester		BTDE	386

TABLE 2

FORMULATED MONOMER RATIOS

Monomer	MDA	NE	BTDE
Molecular weight (1)	198	196	386
Molar ratio (2)	3.087	2.000	2.087
Weight ratio (1x2)	611.23	392.0	805.58
Normalised weight ratio (g of monomer/100 g of total monomers)	33.79	21.67	44.54

PMR-15 Prepolymer

120

Table 3

PMR-15 POWDER LOTS

LOT #1	100	Lbs.
LOT #2	<100	Lbs.
LOT #3	<5	Lbs.
LOT #4	110	Lbs.
LOT #5	390	Lbs.

Table 4

Post Cure Study

	Tg, C	
HRS @ 600 F	G' *	Tan ∂ Peak
0	337.7	379.5
4	359.8	384.7
8	367.4	391.8
1 2	362.6	387.4
1 6	364.4	389.9
2 0	364.0	388.8

* Intercept of first two linear portions of G' curve.

Post Cure Cycle

1. RT to 600 F @ 1 F/min.
2. Hold @ 600 F for t hrs.
3. 600 F to RT @ 1 F/min.

t = 0, 4, 8, 12, 16, 20

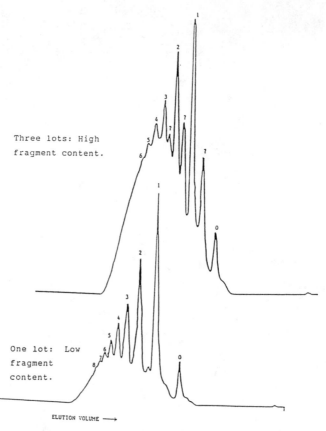

Three lots: High
fragment content.

One lot: Low
fragment content.

ELUTION VOLUME ⟶

Figure 1. Gel permeation chromatograms for imidized PMR-15 molding compounds. At bottom "normal" PMR_15. At top, PMR-15 showing intermediate peaks. (Data: Yungk and Watson)

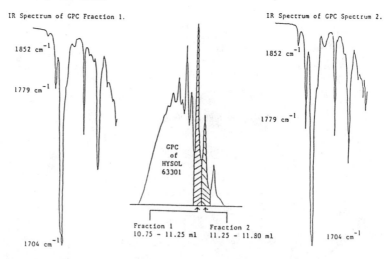

IR Spectrum of GPC Fraction 1.

1852 cm^{-1}

1779 cm^{-1}

1704 cm^{-1}

IR Spectrum of GPC Spectrum 2.

1852 cm^{-1}

1779 cm^{-1}

1704 cm^{-1}

GPC
of
HYSOL
63301

Fraction 1
10.75 - 11.25 ml

Fraction 2
11.25 - 11.80 ml

Figure 2. Isolation of GPC fractions for analysis by FTIR spectroscopy.
(Data: Yungk and Watson)

O
C
N
CH₂
N
C
O
C
O
C
O
C
O
C
O
C
O
O

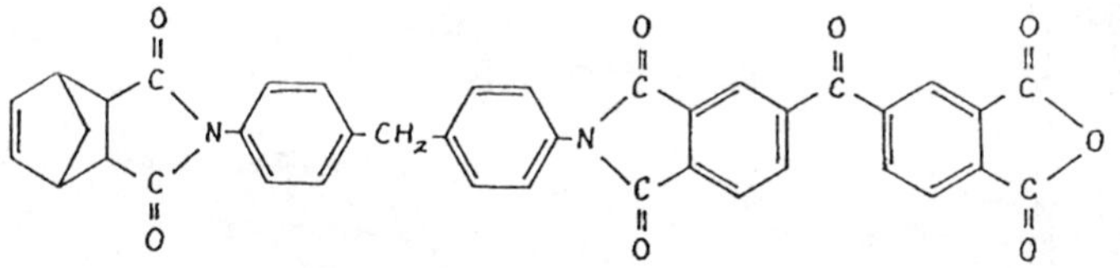

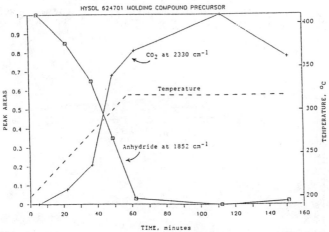

Figure 3. The suspected component of the lowest intermediate GPC peak (fraction 2 in Figure 2) the n = 1 anhydride fragment. The other intermediate peaks (N = 2, 3, 4, ...) have the analogous structure. (Data: Yungk and Watson.)

HYSOL 624701 MOLDING COMPOUND PRECURSOR
PEAK AREAS
TEMPERATURE, °C
CO2 at 2330 cm-1
Temperature
Anhydride at 1852 cm-1
TIME, minutes
1
0.9
0.8
0.7
0.6
0.5
0.4
0.3
0.2
0.1
0
400
350
300
250
200
0
20
40
60
80
100
120
140
160

Figure 4. Cure of a typical imidized PMR-15 resin as monitored by diffuse reflectance FTIR spectroscopy. (Data: Yungk and Watson)

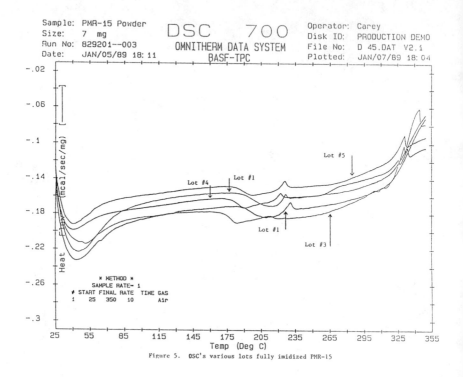

Figure 5. DSC's various lots fully imidized PMR-15

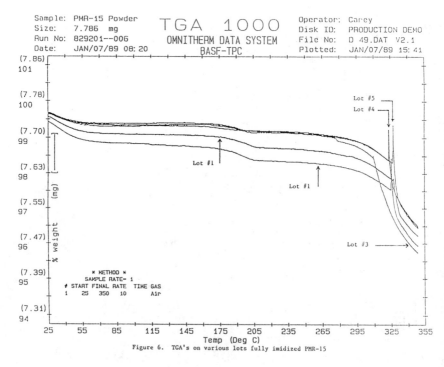

Figure 6. TGA's on various lots fully imidized PMR-15

PMR-15 (Lot# 3): With and without 60 min 206C prebake

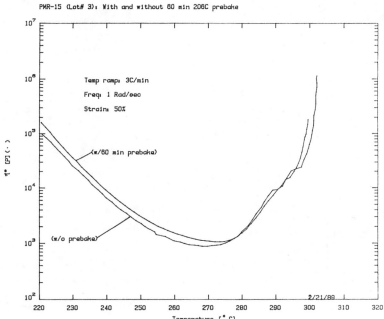

Temp ramp: 3C/min
Freq: 1 Rad/sec
Strain: 50%

(w/60 min prebake)

(w/o prebake)

2/21/89

Temperature [°C]

Figure 7. Parallel plate viscosity before and after aging at 206°C. PMR-15

PMR-15: 4 Lot comparison graph

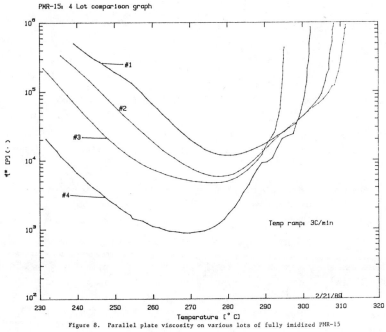

#1

#2

#3

#4

Temp ramp: 3C/min

2/21/89

Temperature [°C]

Figure 8. Parallel plate viscosity on various lots of fully imidized PMR-15

125

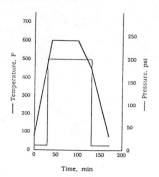

Compression Molding Cycle

1. Insert mold in press and apply 15 psi.
2. Heat from RT to 450 F at 10-20 F/min.
3. Apply 200 psi at 450 F.
4. Heat from 450 to 600 F at 10-20 F/min.
5. Hold 1 hr. at 600 F.
6. Cool from 600 to 450 F at 5 F/min.
7. Decrease pressure to 15 psi at 450 F.
8. Cool from 450 F to RT at 5-15 F/min.
9. Remove.

Post Cure

1. Standard post cure or 24 hrs at 600 F.

Figure 9. Cure cycle for compression molding of fully imidized PMR-15

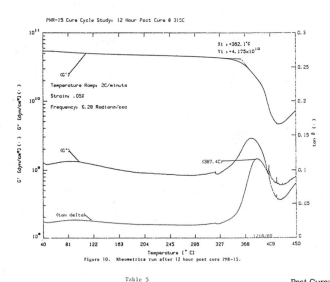

Figure 10. Rheometrics run after 12 hour post cure PMR-15.

Table 5

PMR-15

HYCOMP M-100/CELION G30-500

Post Cure: 13 hrs. @ 600° F

Void Content less than 1%.

TEST	STRENGTH, ksi	MODULUS, Msi	FIBER VOLUME	CONDITION
0° 4 pt. Flex @ RT	284	17.5	55	Mod. D790 No Postcure
	243	16.0	55	STD. D790 No Postcure
	295	19.2	55	Mod. D790 Postcure
90° 4 pt. Flex @ RT	6.87	1.38	55	No postcure
	6.23	1.02	55	Postcure
90° 4 pt. Flex @ 500° F	8.63	1.42	55	Postcure
0° Tensile @ RT	254	19.3	52	Postcure
90° Tensile @ RT	6.30	1.00	55	No Postcure
90° Tensile @ RT	6.75	1.15	55	Postcure
SBS @ RT	10.9		55	No Postcure
SBS @ RT	16.7		55	Postcure

126

34th International SAMPE Symposium
May 8-11, 1989

THE USE OF ORGANOFUNCTIONAL SILANES TO IMPROVE THE INTERFACIAL ADHESION OF POLYIMIDE RESIN SYSTEMS

Alfred D. Ulrich
Wallace G. Joslyn
PCR, Incorporated
8570 Phillips Highway, Suite 101
Jacksonville, FL 32256-8208

Abstract

Interest in the use of polyimide resins for a wide variety of high performance applications has been growing rapidly. Much research has centered around modifying the polyimide structure for improved performance. The use of organofunctional silanes is well recognized as a method of improving interfacial adhesion between organic resins and various reinforcements and fillers, thereby improving the end performance of finished parts.

This study looks at the use of a proprietary carboxyamide functional silane for improving the interfacial bond strength of polyimide resins to a variety of substrates, including glass, steel, aluminum, titanium, and silicon wafers. Data will be presented to illustrate the improvements possible through the use of organofunctional silanes in various types of polyimide resins, namely LARC-TPI and PMR-15.

1. INTRODUCTION

Polyimide resins have a host of unique properties which have resulted in a high level of interest within the materials science community. These properties include excellent thermal, dimensional, and oxidative stability; chemical and radiation resistance; toughness; and flexibility[1]. Applications include high temperature and aerospace composites and adhesives, multilayer printed circuit boards, and microelectronics as photoresist layers in the manufacture of computer chips. Polyimide films are used for insulation in electric motors and wire and cable applications. Mechanical parts such as bearings and seals are also constructed of polyimide resins.

Polyimide resins do have their limitations. Volatile by-products and water formation during cure cause processing problems, thus, requiring complex procedures which involve the use of autoclaves, vacuum bags, and/or long cure times at high temperatures and pressures. Proper part fabrication is, therefore, often difficult and expensive. Improved physical properties of composites, especially under conditions of heat, load, and thermal/humidity cycling, are also areas in which polyimides have demanded attention.

The beneficial attributes of polyimide resins are significant enough that a great deal of research has been done to overcome their limitations. The great majority of this research has centered on modifying the various types of polyimide resins and on improving the ultimate strength of the reinforcing fibers. Relatively little research has been done to explore methods of improving adhesion/performance in the resin/reinforcement interface region, which is the most susceptible area of a filled composite or laminate.

Organofunctional silane coupling agents are intended to improve the performance of composite systems by reacting across and bridging the interface between resin and reinforcement. Aminopropyl functional silanes, such as PCR Prosil^R 221 and Union Carbide A-1100, have long been the industry workhorses for a wide variety of different resin systems. Amino functional finishes were naturally extended to polyimide systems as interest in these resins grew. However, this type of functionality was not originally developed for use with polyimide resins and has its limitations with these resins. Amino functional silanes are quite reactive and gel readily when added directly to a polyimide resin. Additionally, the absolute strength values, while much better than those obtained without the use of a silane, could still be improved, especially under conditions of heat and humidity.

This paper explores the use of Prosil^R 9215, a proprietary carboxyamide functional silane developed for use with polyimide resin systems. The material is stable when blended into a polyimide resin and offers superior adhesion compared to standard amino silane. A brief review of silane chemistry is in order at this point to better understand the performance and characteristics of these different silane coupling agents.

Silane Chemistry

Organofunctional silanes are dual functional molecules which react across polymer/substrate interfaces. This results in a bridging effect which improves bond strength and results in improved physical properties of final parts, better hydrolytic resistance, and improved processing by allowing faster, more complete wet-out of surfaces.

Organofunctional silanes are generally comprised of a silicon atom with three attached alkoxy groups and an attached organic functionality specifically tailored for the intended resin system. The three alkoxy groups are easily hydrolyzed by water or moisture present on the surface of various reinforcements as illustrated by the following equation:

$$R-Si-(OCH_3)_3 + 3H_2O \longrightarrow$$
$$R-Si-(OH)_3 + 3CH_3OH \qquad (1)$$

where R is the organic functionality which differentiates the various silanes. R is gamma-aminopropyl for Prosil[R] 221.

The three silanol groups attached to silicon react readily with hydroxyl groups on the surface of reinforcements and with other silane molecules. This condensation reaction results in a cross-linked silane coating on the reinforcement surface. The organic functionality of the R group is oriented away from the surface and is available to react or graft into the resin matrix during the cure of the resin. This results in a chemically bonded bridge between the reinforcement and resin which is much stronger and more durable than the physical bonding that occurs without an organofunctional silane coupling agent.

The reaction of organofunctional silanes to the surface of reinforcements displaces surface moisture and eliminates surface hydroxyl groups. This alters the hydrolytic nature of these materials and makes the interface region much more resistant to degradation by water. Additionally, the organic coating on the surface allows organic resin to wet-out much easier, allowing for improved processing.

Organofunctional silanes can be applied by treating the reinforcement directly or by integrally adding the silane to the resin prior to use. When used as an integral additive, organofunctional silanes will migrate to interfaces due to the fact that their surface tension is generally less than that of an organic resin.

Both techniques for using silanes have their advantages and limitations. Pretreatment results in a more efficient use of silane, thus optimum performance is obtained at lower use levels.[2] However, pretreatment requires additional equipment. Integral addition eliminates a processing step and alleviates a source of variability. This is extremely beneficial in situations where processing costs or variations in performance are high. Additionally, it does not require the capital equipment necessary for treating the filler/reinforcement. It does however, require that the silane be stable when blended into the resin system.

2. EXPERIMENTAL

Treatment of Cloth. Silane was added to a 90% alcohol/10% water solution at such a level to provide a theoretical 0.1 wt.% deposition of silane. This solution was mixed for 30 minutes to allow the silanes to hydrolyze. Samples of heat-cleaned fiberglass cloth (Uniglass, Inc.) were then immersed in the silane bath, excess solution was removed, and the samples were allowed to dry at ambient conditions for 24 hours. The silanes were then heat-set at $100^{o}C$ for 10 minutes. The cloth used for the untreated control and Prosil[R] 9215 integral addition samples were prepared in the same way omitting the addition of silane.

Preparation of Laminates. Resin samples were uniformly weighed out and coated onto the surface of a fiberglass cloth in a thin layer. They were then B-staged according to the manufacturers' recommendations. This was repeated to allow for a sufficient amount of resin to be built up on the fabric without void formation. The plies of B-staged cloth were then clamped together under uniform pressure and cured according to the resin manufacturers' recommendations. The LARC-TPI was Durimid[R] 120 from Rogers Corp. The PMR-15 resin was obtained from Fiberite Corp.

Flexural Testing. Laminates were cut into 1/2-inch-wide specimens and tested using an Instron 1120 stress-strain machine according to ASTM-D790, with the exception that the 2- and 4 ply-specimens' thickness was less than specified. The results are the average of at least 2 laminates. Twelve specimens were tested, with the high and low values being eliminated from the calculations.

Lap Shear Testing. LARC-TPI resin was weighed out onto a 0.5 in. by 0.5 in. area of two unprepared subsrate panels. The samples were clamped together under uniform pressure and cured according to the manufacturers' recommendations. Lap shear strengths were then determined using an Instron 1120 stress-strain machine.

Silicon Wafer Testing. Silicon wafers were coated with a LARC-TPI resin by spin coating at 3500 rpm for 60 seconds. These samples were then tested as described in ASTM-D3359 after immersion in boiling water.

3. RESULTS AND DISCUSSION

Standard aminopropyltriethoxy silanes such as PCR Prosil^R 221 are reactive with polyimide resins even at room temperature. This is demonstrated visually in figure 1 where the vial with 7 phr of Prosil 221 (bottom) gelled solid 10 minutes after addition to a LARC-TPI polyimide resin. The top vial contains 7 phr of Prosil^R 9215, a carboxyamide functional silane 10 minutes after addition to the resin. The flow of the Prosil^R 9215 sample is clearly superior to that of the amino functional silane sample. The Prosil^R 9215 sample maintained its flow properties, showing no differentiation from the neat

resin even after 6 months' refrigerated storage.

The reaction kinetics for curing polyimides is often very sensitive as evidenced by the difficult processing parameters associated with them. The effects which a highly reactive primary amine may have on these systems is a valid question given the demonstrated reactivity of amino silanes in polyimide systems. A detailed study of these possibile effects is beyond the scope of this paper. However, there is evidence from field studies indicating that the use of Prosil^R 9215 as an integral additive to polyimide resin composites improves processing properties.

Table 1 compares the flexural strengths of 2-ply fiberglass/LARC-TPI laminates for a control containing no silane; Prosil 221 pretreated onto the fiberglass cloth; and Prosil 9215, both pretreated onto the fiberglass cloth and blended into the resin prior to processing. Flexural strengths as molded and strengths after 2 hours' exposure to boiling water are detailed.

Initial dry flexural strengths are depicted graphically in Fig. 2. The results indicate that the use of either silane improves physical strengths by over 100% compared to a control with no silane. Prosil 9215 pretreated onto the fiber-glass yielded a 20% improvement over standard amino silane. The standard deviation for these samples was between 7 and 8 MPa. The difference between silanes is slightly better than 2 standard deviations indicating that it is significant.

Integral addition of Prosil[R] 9215 provided approximately a 1 standard deviation improvement over the amino silane. This demonstrates that the use of Prosil[R] 9215 as a resin additive will provide at least equivalent, if not marginally superior, performance to standard amino silane without necessitating the extra pretreatment step. The fact that Prosil[R] 9215 worked better as a pretreatment is predictable based on previous studies comparing the two methods of silane use[2].

The interface region of a laminate or composite is generally the weakest portion. Water will migrate to this region and destroy the adhesive forces between resin and substrate. Therefore, accelerated aging in boiling water is an effective means of measuring the relative strengths of interfacial adhesion in laminates. This test is also useful for predicting performance in hot/wet

environments, long-term aging, and cycling under humid conditions.

The data from Table 1 comparing flexural strengths after 2 hours' exposure to boiling water is dipicted in Fig. 3. These results indicate that the use of amino functional silane will improve strength after aging by a factor of 4.5 compared to a control with no silane. Prosil[R] 9215 pretreated onto the fiberglass cloth, again, showed a 20% improvement over the amino silane. Likewise, the integral addition use of Prosil[R] 9215 showed a 20% improvement over Prosil[R] 221. The differences in strength was greater than 2 stand-ard deviations, which indicates the real strength improvement possible through the use of a silane specifically designed for use with polyimide resin systems.

Performance of these silanes was evaluated in PMR-15, an addition polyimide resin, to determine how it would compare with results obtained using a LARC-TPI resin. The results for both 2- and 4-ply laminates is detailed in Table 2. This data is depicted graphically in Figures 4 and 5. In both cases, the amino functional silane resulted in a 15% improvement in flexural strength compared to PMR-15 with no silane. The use of Prosil[R] 9215 pretreated onto the surface of the fiberglass cloth, however, yielded a 26% increase in flexural strength compared to the control. The average standard deviation of these samples was slightly greater than 8 MPa. Thus leading to the conclusion that the superior performance of Prosil[R] 9215 is significant.

Prosil[R] 9215, used as an integral additive, showed virtually no improvement compared to the untreated control in the 2-ply PMR-15 system. In the 4-ply system, it showed an improvement equivalent to that obtained by using Prosil[R] 221 as a pretreatment. This equivalent performance, compared with Prosil[R] 221, is the same level of improvement that the integral addition method showed for the LARC-TPI resin system.

There are two possible explainations for the apparent disparity of results between the 2- and 4-ply fiberglass/PMR-15 resin composites. The first is that it is due to experimental error. However, the consistency in standard deviations and the parallel results between the two resin systems casts doubt on this explanation. The second explanation is that Prosil[R] 9215 offers some processing advantages that become more pronounced as the number of plys of cloth is increased.

There are several factors which justify this second theory. First, silanes are surface-active agents. They are noted for their ability to improve resin wet-out. This is evidenced by the reduction in viscosity obtained by the use of silanes in filled composite systems. Silanes are attracted to other resin interfaces and could aid in the removal of volatiles and gases given off during the cure of PMR-15, by reducing surface tension at these interfaces. This effect may not be sufficient to result in noticeble differences for a 2-ply system, but become more pronounced for a 4-ply system, since volatiles would have to travel through more resin to to be eliminated from the part. Secondly, this principle was investigated by Arnold, et al.[3] who demonstrated that the inclusion of a polydimethyl-siloxane in a polyimide system will improve processing due to the low surface energy of the siloxane. Silanes surface energy are intermediate to that of the resin and siloxane. Therefore, it could conceivably act in a like manner. Third, field evaluations have indicated that Prosil[R] 9215 does, in deed, act as a processing aid in various polyimide systems.

Polyimide resins are used on a variety of substrates besides glass. Therefore, the performance of Prosil[R] 9215 was briefly examined with other substrates. Lap shear results comparing the integral addition use of Prosil[R] 9215 to untreated controls with no silane are depicted in Fig. 6. Prosil[R] 9215 demonstrated a 50% improvement on titanium, 100% improvement on cold roll steel, and 125% improvement on aluminum. This was at least a 3 standard deviation improvement in all cases.

This has significant implications in adhesive applications, implying that enhanced performance can be achieved without having to apply a separate primer to the substrate. These samples were prepared with no surface preparation to show the improvements possible in the worst case. It is recognized that the absolute strength values could be greatly increased by properly sandblasting and cleaning the surface with a suitable cleaner.

The adhesion of polyimide resins to silicon wafers is important for microelectronic applications. Normally, the adhesion promoter reauires a separate application and drying step. This is expensive considering the cost of cleanroom time. It is also an additional source of possible contamination. Eliminating processing steps is, therefore, very advantageous for this application.

Figure 7 is a photograph of the results of a cross-hatch adhesion test of a silicone wafer coated with a LARC-TPI after 10 minutes' immersion in boiling water. Figure 8 is a photograph of a similarly prepared silicon wafer, which contained 7 phr Prosil[R] 9214, after 72 hours in boiling water. Prosil[R] 9214 is a high-purity, low-ion version of Prosil[R] 9215 developed especially for microelectronic applications. These photographs dramatically show the improved performance in adhesion possible through the use of a properly designed and applied silane. They are visual evidence clearly supporting the data presented throughout this paper.

4. Conclusions

This paper demonstrates that Prosil[R] 9215, a carboxyamide functional silane developed specifically for use with polyimide systems, is superior to the use of conventional aminopropyltriethoxy silane for a variety of reasons. Unlike standard amino silanes Prosil[R] 9215 is stable when blended directly into a polyimide resin. This is advantageous in that it eliminates a processing step in adhesive and microelectronic applications.

The use of Prosil[R] 9215 as an integral additive results in physical property improvement that is equal if not marginally superior to that obtained by the use of an amino silane. However, it did not require the extra pretreatment step which the amino silane required. Additionally, the use of Prosil[R] 9215 as an integral additive gave indications that it improves processing more than could be achieved by the use of a silane pretreatment, this is supported in the literature.

Prosil[R] 9215, when used as a pretreatment onto the surface of a reinforcing material such as fiberglass cloth, improves physical strengths significantly, when compared to standard amino silane. This improvement was 20% in the case of LARC-TPI/fiberglass cloth laminates.

Prosil[R] 9215 maintained its physical strengths even under humid conditions. The physical strengths after 2 hours in boiling water for both pretreated and integral addition of Prosil[R] 9215 were 5.4 times greater than the control containing no silane. Comparatively, standard amino functional silane offered a 4.5X improvement under the identical conditions. This implies that the interfacial adhesion offered by the use of Prosil[R] 9215 is both stronger and more durable than that offered by conventional coupling agents.

5. References

1. Bystry-King, F.A., and King, J.J., "Polyimides" in Engineering Thermoplastics: Properties and Applications, Margolis, J.M. ed., 316-333, (1985).

2. Stafford, S.C., Ulrich, A.D., Canova, L.A., "Influence of Silane Addition Technique on Composite Preparation and Properties", 45th SPE ANTEC $\underline{33}$, 1250-3, (1987).

3. Arnold, C.A., et. al. "Structure Property Behavior of Polyimide Siloxane Segmented Copolymers", 32nd nat. SAMPE Symp. $\underline{32}$, 586-596, (1987).

6. Biographies

Alfred D. Ulrich joined the technical staff of PCR, Inc. in 1985 after receiving his B.S. in Chemistry from the University of Pittsburgh. Sicne that time he worked in the technical service and applications development laboratory on projects relating to the use of organofunctional silanes. He has co-authored several papers in the areas of; techniques for applying silanes, silanes for high performance reesins, and silanes for improving the hydrolytic performance of polymer composites. He is a member of both the Society of Plastics Engineers and SAMPE.

Wallace G. Joslyn is business development manager responsible for silanes at PCR, Inc. He has both a B.S. degree in chemistry and an M.B.A. He has 21 years of experience in silanes and silicones for specialty applications. His technical service and marketing responsibilities in the composites industry has resulted in an extensive knowledge base. He is a member of both the Society of Plastics Engineers and SAMPE.

TABLE 1

Flexural Strength Results
2-Ply Fiberglass/LARC-TPI Laminates

Silane	FLEXURAL STRENGTH MPa (psi)	
	Dry[1]	Wet[2]
None-Control	44.0 (6,380)	15.7 (2,270)
Prosil[R] 221 P.T.[3] (3-aminopropyl)	96.9 (14,000)	70.3 (10,200)
Prosil[R] 9215 P.T.[3] (Carboxyamide)	115 (16,700)	84.9 (12,300)
Prosil[R] 9215 I.A.[4] (Carboxyamide)	105 (15,200)	84.3 (12,200)

1. specimens were conditioned 48 hours at 72°F, 50% R.H.
2. specimens were conditioned 2 hours in boiling water
3. P.T.-silane was pretreated onto the fiberglass cloth
4. I.A.-silane was blended directly into the resin

TABLE 2

Dry Flexural Strength Results
2- and 4-Ply Fiberglass/PMR-15 Laminates

Silane	DRY FLEXURAL STRENGTH MPa (psi)	
	2 Ply	4 Ply
None-Control	123 (17,900)	161 (23,400)
Prosil[R] 221 P.T.[2] (3-aminopropyl)	141 (20,500)	188 (27,200)
Prosil[R] 9215 P.T.[2] (Carboxyamide)	153 (22,200)	203 (29,400)
Prosil[R] 9215 I.A.[3]	126 (18,300)	185 (26,800)

1. specimens were conditioned 48 hours at 72°F, 50% R.H.
2. P.T.-silane was pretreated onto the fiberglass cloth
3. I.A.-silane was blended directly into the resin

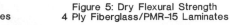

Figure 4: Dry Flexural Strength
2 Ply Fiberglass/PMR-15 Laminates

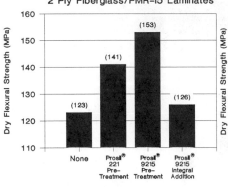

Silane

Figure 5: Dry Flexural Strength
4 Ply Fiberglass/PMR-15 Laminates

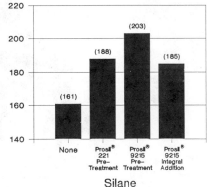

Silane

Figure 6: Lap Shear Strength
Durimid® 120 (LARC-TPI)

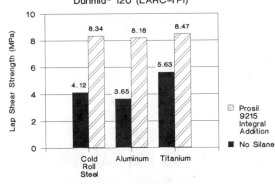

Substrate

FIGURE 7: Cross-Hatch Adhesion of
LARC-TPI on Silicon Wafer after
10 Minutes Immersion in Boiling
Water.

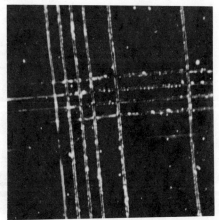

FIGURE 8: Cross-Hatch Adhesion of
LARC-TPI on Silicon Wafer after
72 hours Immersion in Boiling
Water.

137

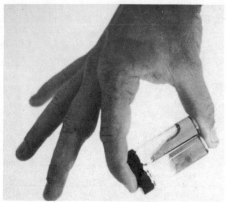

FIGURE 1: Gel Stability of LARC-TPI 10 Minutes After Addition of 7phr Silane; Prosil[R] 9215 (top) and Prosil[R] 221 (bottom).

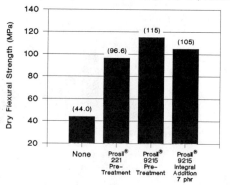

Figure 2: Dry Flexural Strength
2 Ply Fiberglass/Durimid® 120 (LARC-TPI) Laminates

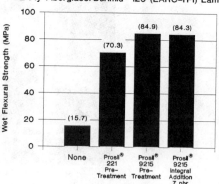

Figure 3: Wet Flexural Strength
2 Ply Fiberglass/Durimid® 120 (LARC-TPI) Laminates

SYNTHESIS, CURING AND PHYSICAL BEHAVIOR OF MALEIMIDE AND NADIMIDE
TERMINATED POLY(ARYLENE ETHER KETONE) NETWORKS

S. D. Wu, J. S. Senger, J. C. Hedrick, G. D. Lyle, D. H. Chen, M. Chen,
J. D. Rancourt and J. E. McGrath*
Department of Chemistry and
Science and Technology Center:
High Performance Polymeric Adhesives and Composites
Virginia Polytechnic Institute and State University
Blacksburg, VA   24061

*To whom correspondence should be addressed

Abstract

Maleimide and nadimide terminated
poly(arylene ether ketone) oligomers of controlled molecular weight
and end group functionalities were
synthesized by end-capping reactions of amine terminated
poly(arylene ether ketone) -
oligomers with maleic anhydride or
nobornene dicarboxylic anhydride
in chlorobenzene. The amine
terminated poly(arylene ether
ketone) oligomers of predictable
molecular weight were synthesized
via nucleophilic aromatic substitution, step polymerization of
bisphenol-A, m-aminophenol and
difluorobenzophenone (an activated
aromatic dihalide) in the presence
of potassium carbonate. A series
of nadimide terminated oligomers of
controlled molecular weights and
end group functionalities were
synthesized by bisphenol-A, m-
nadimidophenol and difluoro-
benzophenone in the presence of
potassium carbonate. The maleimide
and nadimide oligomers of designed
molecular weights were chain
extended and cross-linked through
a thermally induced free radical
reaction of maleimide and nadimide
end groups. The curing process and
the influence of cross-linking
density on physical and mechanical
properties of the cured neat
resins has been investigated by
thermal analysis and mechanical
testing. In particular, flexural
modulus and fracture toughness
values showed that very ductile
insoluble networks could be
generated which are candidates for
matrix resins and structural adhesive applications.

1. INTRODUCTION

The rapid growth of high performance composite materials is well
recognized. A well known advantage of composite materials over
metals is their high modulus to
weight ratio. Poly(arylene ether
ketones) and polyimides are
typically classified as high
performance structural materials
(1). The more familiar members of
this class of materials are the
semi-crystalline PEEK[R] 1, more
recently PEKK, 2 and the
commercially available thermoset
PMR-15, 3 (Scheme 1) (2,3). The
semi-crystalline poly(ether
ketone) systems have the important
advantages of excellent high energy
radiation resistance, good heat and
solvent resistance mainly due to
their molecular structure of the
aromatic ether and keto linkage and
the crystalline nature (4). Un-

fortunately, the modulus drops above the glass transition temperature, which reduces their mechanical performance. The high melting point of the crystalline structure requires the materials to be processed at higher temperatures than desirable. On the other hand, the aerospace industry continuously demands new classes of high performance thermosetting polymers as matrix resins and adhesives that have to serve for, at least, 200 hours at 371°C. The microelectronics industry has a need for adhesives which must withstand processing temperatures over 400°C for a few hours in an inert atmosphere (5). More demands for new materials are foreseeable in the application of dimensionally stable high-temperature polymeric materials as structural matrix resins. Generally, cross-linked polymers provide enhanced modulus above glass transition temperature, improved resistance to thermal degradation, to cracking effects by liquids and other harsh environments, as well as to creep, among other effects (6).

Early work in our laboratory has investigated the ketimine modified poly(arylene ether ketone) networks, involving condensation reactions of the terminal amine groups with the in-chain ketone groups, followed by the formation of ketimines and water (7). The previous synthesis on the maleimide terminated poly(arylene ether ketone) oligomers were carried out via end-capping reaction of amine terminated poly(arylene ether ketone) oligomers with maleic anhydride in a co-solvent of N-methyl pyrrolidone/N-cyclohexyl pyrrolidone (80/20) (8). One of our objectives herein was to select appropriate reaction conditions which would prevent or reduce any premature cross-linking reactions of the maleimide terminated poly(arylene ether ketone) oligomers. The main objective was to design polymeric matrix resins with good solvent and heat resistance, high fracture toughness, good dimensional stability and excellent high-

energy-radiation resistance. Our goals were to develop two new classes of high performance polymer networks by applying the experience and knowledge of PEEK, polysulfone, poly(arylene ether ketones) and PMR-15 polyimide. The first approach was to cross-link the designed maleimide terminated poly(arylene ether ketone) oligomers. The second approach was to cross-link nadimide terminated poly(arylene ether ketone) oligomers synthesized either by a two-step, end-capping route or by a one-step, direct polyetherification route.

This publication describes the synthesis of maleimide and nadimide terminated poly(arylene ether ketone) oligomers, the thermal curing process, and the physical properties of the cured systems characterized by thermal analysis methods such as differential scanning calorimetry, dynamic mechanical thermal analysis and thermogravimetric analysis. The low strain rate mechanical behavior and fracture toughness of the cured networks have also be investigated.

2. EXPERIMENTAL

2.1 Materials

Bisphenol-A (Bis-A) was received in polymer grade from Dow Chemical and was dried at 60°C under vacuum before use. The 4,4′-difluorobenzophenone purchased from Aldrich (or supplied by ICI) was recrystallized form diethyl ether (mp. 105-106°C). The m-aminophenol (Aldrich) was sublimed under vacuum at 120°C (mp. 122-123°C). cis-5-Norbornene-endo-2,3-dicarboxylic anhydride was sublimed under vacuum at 205°C (mp. 208°C). Maleic anhydride was sublimed under vacuum at 50°C (mp. 55-56°C). Anhydrous potassium carbonate (Fisher) was dried under vacuum at 100°C overnight. Chlorobenzene and N,N-dimethylacetamide (Fisher) were dried over calcium hydride and distilled under reduced pressure prior to use. Acetic acid (Fisher) was used as received.

2.2 m-Nadimidophenol

The starting reagents, m-amino-phenol (0.1 mole), cis-5-norbor-nene-endo-2,3-dicarboxylic anhydride (0.105 mole) and 100 ml acetic acid were transferred into a 200 ml one-neck round bottom flask with a magnetic stirrer and a condenser. The solution became homogenous and clear after stirring at room temperature for 30 minutes. It was heated to reflux for 3 hours, then cooled to room temper-ature. White crystals precipitat-ed out of the solution slowly at room temperature. The solution was filtered and the crystals stirred in hot water for 6 hours to remove any acetic acid, then filtered and dried in vacuum over at 100°C overnight. The white fine powder was sublimed under vacuum at 205°C (mp. 208°C).

2.3 Amine Terminated Oligomers

Procedures for the nucleophilic substituion step growth synthesis of the above mentioned oligomers have been well described elsewhere and will not be elaborated upon here (9). The molecular weights of the oligomers were controlled by varying the ratios of bisphenol-A and m-aminophenol according to Carother's equations (10). End group titrations of the amine group effectively confirmed the predicted values(9). Intrinsic viscosity values were determined in chloro-form. Infrared (FT-IR) measure-ments were conducted with a Nicolet MX-1.

2.4 Two-step Maleimide and Nadimide Terminated Oligomers

The titrated amine terminated oligomers (100 g, M_n = 5000) were added to a 3-neck 2000 ml round bottom flask equipped with a nitro-gen inlet, a stirrer, a thermo-meter and a condenser. Approx-imately 500 ml chlorobenzene were added into the flask to dissolve the oligomers. Either maleic anhydride (6.0 g) or norbornene dicarboxylic anhydride (10.0 g) was transferred into the flask after the oligomers were completely

dissolved. Then the solution was purged with nitrogen and stirred at room temperature for 4 hours and heated to 110°C for another 12 hours. The solution was next cooled to room temperature and coagulated in methanol. The end-capped oligomers were dried in vacuum at 80°C for 24 hours before redesolving in chloroform and precipitating from methanol. The oligomeric white powder was dried in vacuum oven at 90°C for 24 hours. Both infrared measurements and titration of potentially uncyclized maleamic acid groups suggested that the derivatization was quantitative.

2.5 One-step Nadimide Terminated Oligomers

For 5,000 molecular weight olig-omers, a 4-neck 500 ml round bottom flask was fitted with a Dean Stark trap, mechanical stirrer, thermo-meter and nitrogen inlet. Bisphenol-A (12.63 g), difluoro-benzophenone (13.09 g), m-nadimidophenol (2.49 g) and potassium carbonate (11.6 g) were added into the flask with 140 ml N,N-dimethylacetamide and 70 ml toluene. The reaction was refluxed at 145°C for 6 hours, then the toluene and water were drawn from the Dean Stark trap until the temperature reached 155°C. The reaction was allowed to proceed for another 8 hours. The solution was then cooled and filtered to remove the salts before it was acidified with a small amount of acetic acid. The filtrate was coagulated into a mixture of methanol/water (50/50) and dried in a vacuum oven at 90°C overnight. The dried oligomers were redissolved in chloroform, reprecipitated from methanol and dried in a vacuum oven at 90°C for 24 hours.

2.6 Differential Scanning Calorimetry

Glass transition temperatures were determined with a Du Pont 912 Dual Sample Differential Scanning Calorimeter, DSC. The baseline was checked for flatness at each heating rate and temperature calibration was achieved by using indium which has a melting point of $156.6°C$ and a known heat of fusion of 6.8 cal/gm. The heating rate was maintained at 10 or 20 K/min.

2.7 Dynamic Mechanical Analysis

The dynamic mechanical analysis of the precured and postcured male-imide terminated oligomers were conducted on a Polymer Laboratory DMTA. Samples (1.6 x 11.7 x 19 mm) cut from compression molded films were mounted on a dual cantilever clamp. The analyses were conducted at a heating rate of 4 K/min and at a frequency of 1 Hz. The storage moduli (ε') and tan δ were recorded.

2.8 Thermogravimetric Analysis

The thermogravimetric analysis of the polymers were conducted on a Perkin Elmer TGA-2 instrument at a heating rate of 10 K/min. The analysis was conducted in air. The TGA-MS analysis was conducted on a Perkin Elmer TGA-2 with Hewlett-Packard 5970 Series MSD. The sample was heated to $200°C$ at a heating rate of 20 K/min in argon.

2.9 Measurement of Mechanical Properties

Samples for stress strain measurements were cut from thin films of material using a die meeting ASTM Standard D-3368 (Microtensile). The powdery oligomers were preheated on a Pasadena Hydraulic Inc. hydraulic press at $160°C$ for 5 minutes, then pressed at $160°C$ for one minute under 10,000 psi guage pressure to form thin films. The thin films were cured at $190°C$, $220°C$, $250°C$, $280°C$, $316°C$ (for nadimide resins only) for a period of one hour at each temperature under 500 psi guage pressure and then quenched. The thickness of the films were originally controlled by a teflon sheet and was measured prior to testing. The samples were tested using a Model 1123 Instron Material Testing System at a cross-head speed of 0.1 in/min (0.25 cm/min).

2.10 Sample Preparation and Measurement of K_{IC}

Three point bend specimen were cut out using a scroll saw from a 3 mm sheet of material (specimen dimensions were 36 x 9 x 3 mm). The K_{IC} samples were notched and then pre-cracked by tapping a liquid nitrogen cooled razor blade into the notch. It was necessary to dip the specimen into the liquid nitrogen in order to start a precrack for the very ductile high molecular weight linear polymer. The measurements were performed on an Instron Testing Machine using a strain rate of 50 mm/min.

3. RESULTS AND DISCUSSION

Some characteristics and physical behavior of amine, maleimide and nadimide terminated poly(arylene ether ketone) oligomers shown in Tables 1-4. The molecular weights of amine terminated poly(ether ketone) oligomers were determined by the titration of the oligomer with a HBr titrant(9). The intrinsic viscosities of maleimide and nadimide terminated poly(ether ketone) oligomers were slightly higher (approximately 0.03-0.05 dl/gm) than the precursor amine terminated poly(ether ketone) oligomers. The glass transition temperatures increased significantly after curing. After curing, the maleimide or nadimide oligomers were converted into solvent resistant high molecular weight networks through thermally induced, free radical addition-polymerization of two or more maleimide or nadimide terminal groups. For example, cured films of bismaleimide and bisnadimide networks were extracted with hot tetrahydrofuran and less than 5% weight loss of soluble portions were observed.

The thermogravmetric analysis (TGA) data indicated that both maleimide and nadimide poly(ether ketone) networks showed no weight loss below $400°C$. The initial weight loss of a cured maleimide and nadimide terminated poly(ether ketone) with M_n = 10,000 g/mol. ("Mc") started at $470°C$ and $460°C$

(Figure 4 and Figure 5). The TGA-MS analysis of nadimide terminated oligomer (Mn=2,500 g/mol.) showed 2.5 weight percent loss (~60% by mole) due to the loss of cyclopentadiene intermediate.

The dynamic mechanic thermal analysis (DMTA) scans of the cured maleimide and nadimide terminated oligomers shown in Figure 6 and Figure 7 illustrate the β relaxation temperature (-80°C) and glass transition temperature (163-189°C). The strong β relaxation peak probably contributes to the observed highly ductile nature of the networks. Moreover, the storage moduli of the poly(ether ketone) networks above their glass transition temperatures were stable and in the "rubbery" region (logE′ = 5-7), at these crosslink densities. The loss moduli of cured poly(ether ketone) oligomers showed the same profile as the hydroquinone based semi-crystalline PEEK system, below their respective glass transition temperatures.

3.1 Stress-Strain Behavior

The stress/strain behavior of the maleimide and nadimide networks correlated well with the number average molecular weights (Mn) of the oligomers as shown in Figure 8 and Figure 9. The yield and ultimate elongation increased with increasing number average molecular weights of the oligomers. The cured 2.5K oligomers were only somewhat ductile (about twice the value of an epoxy control), but the cured 10K oligomers were very tough and ductile, which reflected the influence of number average molecular weight between cross-links (M_c) on the physical properties and mechanical performance. The constraint on the networks, as expected, decreased with increasing M_c. The 10K oligomers exhibited extensive amounts of plastic deformations and elongated to approximately 90% strain before failure.

3.2 Fracture Toughness Behavior

The critical stress intensity factor for mode I loading, K_{IC}, was used as the measure of fracture toughness for these materials. K_{IC} values were obtained from fracture tests on three point bend specimen and were calculated using the equation:

$$k = \frac{P \ S}{B \ W^{3/2}} \left[2.9\left(\frac{a}{w}\right)^{1/2} - 4.6\left(\frac{a}{w}\right)^{3/2} + 21.8\left(\frac{a}{w}\right)^{5/2} - 37.6\left(\frac{a}{w}\right)^{7/2} + 38.7\left(\frac{a}{w}\right)^{9/2}\right]$$

where:

-p – maximun load
-s – sample length
-B – sample thickness
-W – sample width
-a – initial crack length

The margin of error for the K_{IC} values were determined for one standard of deviation. A minimum of ten specimen were utilized.

The K_{IC} values, Table 4, showed that fracture toughness increases with the molecular weight of the oligomer used in the network. This was in agreement with the stress/strain behavior which showed the greatest amount of plastic deformation (strain at break) for the 10,000 "Mc" oligomeric network. Furthermore, the high molecular weight polymer control showed the highest toughness of the systems tested and was comparable to Bis-A based thermoplastic polycarbonate, as mentioned earlier.

Fracture toughness values presented here should, perhaps, be considered only semiquantitative, since difficulties were encountered in fabricating the thick sheets (6 mm or greater) required for specimens to precisely meet the requirements for plane strain fracture toughness testing. Nevertheless, it may be concluded that the crosslinked networks clearly showed excellent toughness.

4. CONCLUSIONS

A series of maleimide or nadimide terminated poly(arylene ether ketone) oligomers of controlled molecular weights and endgroup functionalities were synthesized by end-capping reactions of maleic anhydride or norbornene dicarboxylic anhydride with amine terminated poly(arylene ether ketone) oligomers in chlorobenzene. Another series of nadimide terminated oligomers were prepared by aromatic nucleophilic substitution, step growth polymerization of bisphenol-A and m-nadimidophenol end capper with 4,4′-difluorobenzophenone. The oligomers were thermally cured and converted into solvent resistant (THF insoluble) networks. The DMTA scans, TGA traces and coefficients of thermal expansion (CTE) indicated that the stiffness, thermal stability and dimensional stability of the networks were improved by comparison to the linear poly(arylene ether ketone) system. The fracture toughness K_{1C} values showed the networks to be very tough and ductile, even tougher than a polycarbonate control ($K_{1C} = 3.8 \pm 0.5$ MN/M$^{3/2}$). The materials are currently also being evaluated for processing with electromagnetic radiation. Further investigations of the coefficients of thermal expansion are in progress, as are co-cured toughened blends with simple BMI and PMR-15 type resins.

5. ACKNOWLEDGMENTS

The authors would like to thank the NASA Langley Research Center, Office of Naval Research and DARPA for the financial support of various portions of this research.

6. REFERENCES

1. Hergenrother, P. M., Wakelyn, N. T. and Havens, S. J., J. Polym. Sci.,: Pt. A.: Polym. Chem., 25, 1093(1987).
2. Chang, I. Y., SAMPE Symp 33, 194(1988).
3. Serafini, T. T., Proceedings of Conference on Aerospace Structural Materials, NASA SP-227(1970).
4. R. B. Rigby, "Engineering Thermoplastics", Ed. by Margolis, J. M., Marcel Dekker Inc., New York, New York(1986).
5. Schneier, B., "Handbook of Thermoset Plastics", Ed. by Goodman, S. H., Noyes Publication, Park Ridge, New Jersey(1986).
6. Collyer, A. A. and Clegg, D. W., "Mechanical Properties of Reinforced Thermoplastics", Elsevier Applied Science Publisher, New York(1984).
7. Mohanty, D. K., Senger, J. S., Smith, C. D. and McGrath, J. E., SAMPE Symp. 33, 970(1988).
8. Lyle, G. D., et. al., SAMPE Symp. 33, 1080(1988).
9. Lyle, G. D., Jurek, M. J., Mohanty, D. K., Hedrick, J. C. and McGrath, J. E., Polymer Preprints, 28(1), 77 1987; ibid, Polymer (London) accepted (1989).
10. Odian, G., "Principles of Polymerization", Wiley-Interscience, 2nd Ed., 86(1981).

7. BIOGRAPHIES

Shilain D. Wu received a B.A. in Chemistry from Chung-Yuan University in Taiwan in 1974. He then worked as an undergraduate research assistant in oxazoline chemistry under the direction of Dr. J. F. Hansen. He obtained a M.S. degree in Chemistry from the University of Florida under the direction of Prof. G. B. Butler in 1982. He entered the Ph.D. program at VPI & SU in 1982. His work has been in the area of liquid crystalline polymers, functionally terminated oligomers, high temperature polymers and block copolymer synthesis and modification under the direction of Prof. J. E. McGrath. Dr. Wu completed his Ph.D. in 1987 and is currently working as a Research Associate in Department of Chemistry and Science and Technology Center at Virginia Tech.

James S. Senger, a native of Towson, Maryland, received his B.S. in Chemical Engineering in 1983 and his M.S. in Chemistry in 1986 from Virginia Tech. His is currently studying toward his Ph.D. in Materials Engineerng Science from the same University. His current research interest is the mechanical behavior of high performance thermoplastic and thermoset systems.

Jeffrey C. Hedrick, A native of Alexandria, Virginia, received his B.A. in Chemistry in 1986 from the Virginia Polytechnic Institute and State University. He is currently studying toward his Ph.D. in Materials Engineering Science from the same university under the direction of Dr. J. E. McGrath.. His research interest involves the electromagnetic (microwave) processing of high performance thermoplastics.

Gregory D. Lyle, a native of Hendersonville, North Carolina, received a B.S. in chemistry and a B.S. in textile chemistry from N.C. State University. He entered the Ph.D. program in chemistry in 1983. His research at Virginia Tech has involved the synthesis and characterization of functionally terminated engineering thermoplastics.

Ming Chen received his B.S. in Chemistry from Taiwan Normal University in 1975 and his M.S. in Industrial Chemistry from Taiwan Tsing Hua University in 1978. He joined Chung Shan Institute of Science & Technology before he was accepted as a graduate student at University of Florida in 1984. In 1985 he entered the Ph.D. program in Material Engineering Science at VPI & SU under the direction of Dr. T. C. Ward. His research interest involved microwave processing and characterization of polymers.

Dr. David Hsein-Pin Chen received his undergraduate education in chemistry at Fu-Jen Catholic University, Taiwan in 1974. He was a doctoral candidate in an area of natural product synthesis in 1980, before he transfered to the University of Southern California. He finished his Ph.D. work in polymer science in 1986. He is currently a research associate for Prof. J. E. McGrath. His specialties involve both synthesis of polymers and monomers and characterization in thermal analysis and mechanical properties.

Dr. James D. Rancourt is a Research Scientist in the Department of Chemistry at Virginia Tech. He earned a Ph.D. in this department in 1987. Previously, Rancourt was employed by Albany International Research Company, Dedham, MA.

James E. McGrath was born and raised in Easton, New York. He received his B.S. in Chemistry from Siena College in 1956. He was employed in cellulose fiber and film research by ITT Rayonier in Whippany, NJ until October 1959. At that time he joined the research division of the Goodyear Tire and Rubber Co. where he conducted research on synthetic rubbers. He obtained an M.S. degree in Chemistry from the University of Akron in 1964 and Ph.D. in Polymer Science from the same university in 1967. Professor McGrath joined the Union Carbide Corporation in August of that year and became a chemistry department faculty member at VPI & SU in September 1975. Dr. McGrath was the Chairman of the Polymer Division of the American Chemical Society in 1986 and in November of 1986, was chosen as the first Ethyl Chaired Professor of Chemistry. In September of 1987, Dr. McGrath became the first Director of the newly established Materials Institute. Dr. McGrath led a group of 19 faculty in chemistry and engineeeing who were awarded a National Science Foundation Science and Technology Center on "High Performance Polymeric Adhesives and Composites". He assumed the Directorship of this newly established center in February 1989. Professor McGrath has written or edited six books and has over 200 contributions in the literature, including 24 U.S. patents. He is a frequent consultant to industry and government.

Scheme 1

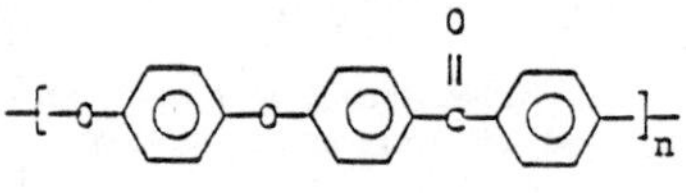

1

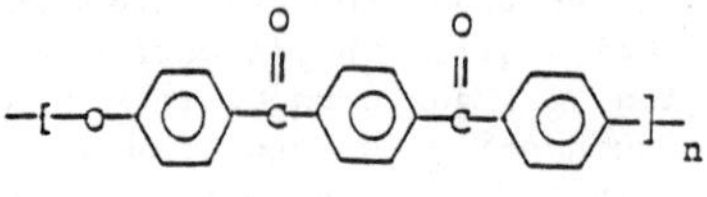

2

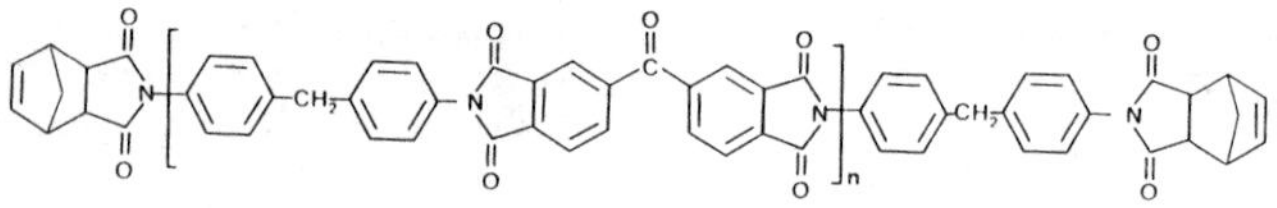

3

Table 1.

Characteristics of Amine Terminated
Poly(ether ketone) Oligomers

sample number	$<M_n>$ Target	$<M_n>$ Titrated	$[\eta]_{25°C}^{CHCl_3}$ (dl/g)	Yield (%)
1. NH$_2$PEK2.5K	2,500	2,600	0.11	77
2. NH$_2$PEK5.0K	5,000	5,100	0.24	89
3. NH$_2$PEK7.5K	7,500	7,400	0.29	96
4. NH$_2$PEK10K	10,000	10,000	0.35	98

Table 3.

Characteristics of Nadimide Terminated
Poly(ether ketone) Oligomers Synthesized by a
One-step Route

sample number	$[\eta]_{25°C}^{CHCl_3}$ (dl/g)	T_g (°C) uncured	cured T_g (°C) DSC	DMTA	TMA
1. NIPEK2.5K	0.15	133	174	186	185
2. NIPEK3.8K	0.28	140	170	177	177
2. NIPEK5.0K	0.38	146	163	170	168
3. NIPEK7.5K	0.47	153	162	163	167

Table 2.

Characteristics of Maleimide Terminated
Poly(ether ketone) Oligomers

sample number	$[\eta]_{25°C}^{CHCl_3}$ (dl/g)	T_g (°C) uncured	cured T_g (°C) DSC	DMTA	TMA
1. MIPEK2.5K	0.13	135	164	176	169
2. MIPEK5.0K	0.30	143	158	168	167
3. MIPEK7.5K	0.32	146	160	168	166
4. MIPEK10K	0.40	152	159	165	165

Table 4.

Characteristics of Nadimide Terminated
Poly(ether ketone) Oligomers Synthesized by a
Two-step Route

sample number	$[\eta]_{25°C}^{CHCl_3}$ (dl/g)	T_g (°C) uncured	cured T_g (°C) DSC	DMTA	TMA	K_{IC} MN/M$^{3.2}$
1. NIPEK2.5K	0.15	130	174	189	190	1.59 ± 0.16
2. NIPEK5.0K	0.29	132	160	170	170	3.17 ± 0.25
3. NIPEK7.5K	0.32	146	159	169	170	3.77 ± 0.23
4. NIPEK10K	0.37	149	162	—	—	4.42 ± 0.37

Figure 1. Synthesis of Maleimide Terminated Poly(arylene ether ketone) Oligomers

MI - PEK OLIGOMERS

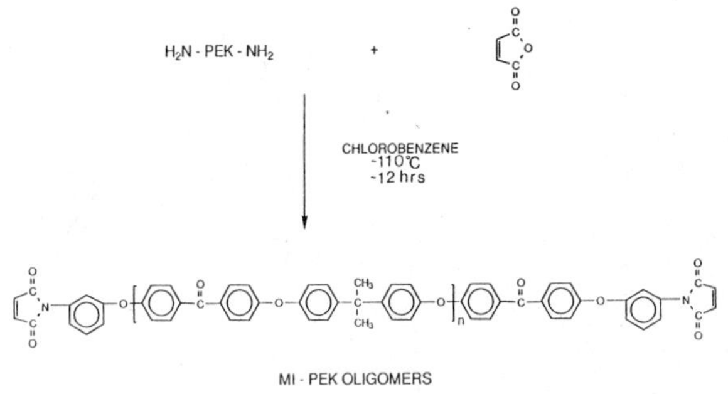

Figure 2. Synthesis of Nadimide Terminated Poly(arylene ether ketone) Oligomers Synthesized via a Two-step Route

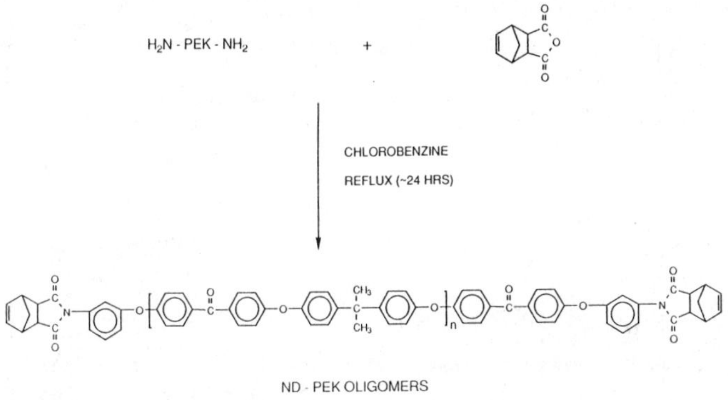

ND - PEK OLIGOMERS

Figure 3. Synthesis of Nadimide Terminated Poly(arylene ether ketone) Oligomers Synthesized via a One-step Route

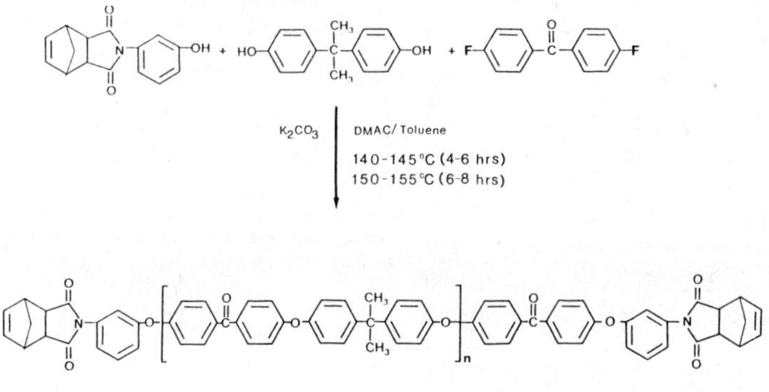

147

Figure 4. TGA Traces of Cured Maleimide Terminated Poly(arylene ether ketone) Oligomers

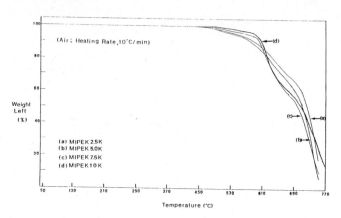

Figure 5. TGA Traces of Cured Nadimide Terminated Poly(arylene ether ketone) Oligomers Synthesized by a Two-step Route

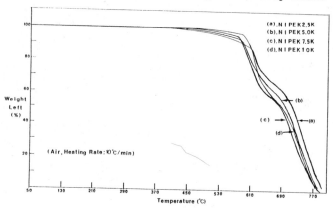

Figure 6. DMTA Scans of Cured Maleimide Terminated Poly(arylene ether ketone) Oligomers

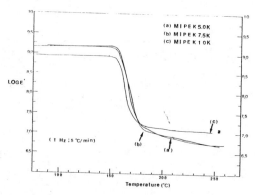

Fig. 10

Fig. 7 DMTA of Cured Nadimide
    Oligomers

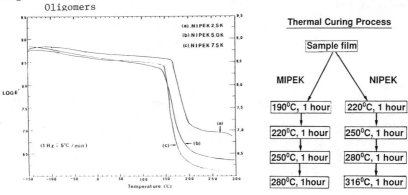

Figure 8. The Stress-strain Behavior of Cured Maleimide
Terminated Poly(arylene ether ketone) Oligomers

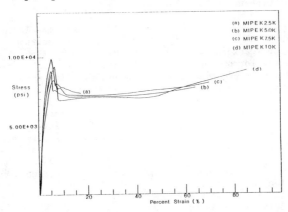

Figure 9. The Stress-strain Behavior of Cured Nadimide Terminated
Poly(arylene ether ketone) Oligomers Synthesized by a Two-step
Route

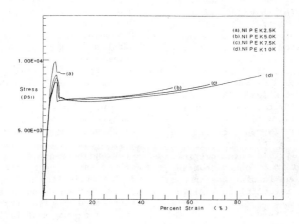

LONG-TERM DEGRADATION OF FIBROUS SILICA COMPOSITES

W.H. Wheeler, J.F. Creedon, and Y.D. Izu
Lockheed Missiles and Space Company, Inc.
Sunnyvale, California

Abstract

Rigidized, lightweight fibrous silica, with or without other fiber additives, has performed well as thermal protection for the Space Shuttle Orbiter, and for a variety of electronic applications. Recently, the behavior of these composites under extended high temperature exposure was investigated, and limitations were established. Mechanisms contributing to the limitations are discussed.

1. INTRODUCTION

All thermal protection systems (TPS) used in space applications are weight critical. A rigidized fibrous silica insulation (LI-900) was developed as a lightweight 0.14 g/cc (9 pcf) reusable TPS material system, and is currently in use on the Space Shuttle Orbiter. More critical areas are protected by a stronger silica material (LI-2200) with a density of 0.35 g/cc (22 pcf), and by another insulation called FRCI. The FRCI system is a combination of silica and aluminoborosilicate fibers, resulting in greater strength and slightly higher operating temperature, 1316°C (2400°F) versus 1260°C (2300°F) for LI-900. Density is 0.19 g/cc (12 pcf). A more recent insulation development, called HTP, contains silica and alumina fibers plus finely divided boron nitride. This material is stronger than any of the previous insulations at equal density, and is useful to 1427°C (2600°F).

The promising properties of HTP prompted a material request for evaluation as an automotive gas turbine (AGT) insulation. The material was reported to possess superior performance characteristics over all previously evaluated insulation. Cyclic testing was utilized to simulate AGT operation at idle 1093°C (2000°F) and acceleration 927°C (1700°F). Since several thousand hours of operation would be required, and since long term stability was never previously of interest, a program was conducted to assess its performance at temperatures up to 1093°C (2000°F).

2. EXPERIMENTAL PROCEDURE

Blocks of uncoated HTP-12 0.19 g/cc (12 pcf), FRCI-12, LI-900 and LI-2200 were weighed and measured and flexural test bars were cut. The blocks were than placed in a kiln at 1093°C (2000°F). The HTP-12 block was removed, weighed and measured, and test bars cut after 66 hours. No shrinkage was noted, and flexural strength was slightly higher. Similar measurements were made at 500, 1000, and 2000 hours on HTP-12 and on LI-2200. The FRCI-12 block was badly cracked at 500 hr. The LI-900 block was tested at 1000 and at 2000 hr. Results of flexural strength testing are shown in Figure 1. Linear shrinkage is shown in Figure 2. The all-silica materials increase in density and show strength increase with time, but their linear shrinkages are much higher than those

of HTP. As will be discussed later,
their strengths also drop dramatically at 4000 hr.

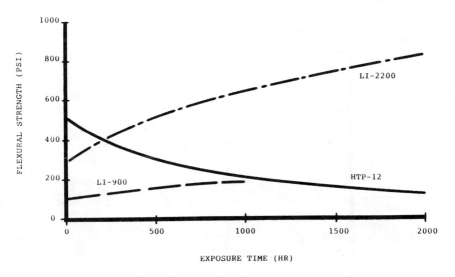

FIGURE 1. LONG TERM STABILITY OF FIBROUS CERAMIC COMPOSITES AT 2000°F

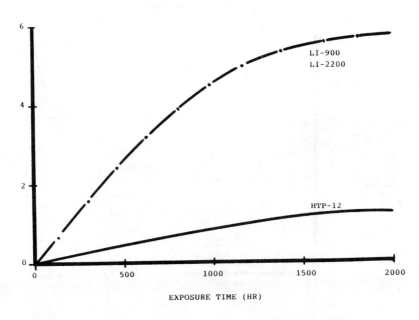

FIGURE 2 SHRINKAGE OF FIBROUS CERAMIC COMPOSITES AT 2000°F

Samples submitted for X-ray diffraction (XRD) analysis confirmed suspicions that crystallization was responsible for cracking and strength loss. A more detailed analysis was conducted on 0.24 g/cc (15 pcf) HTP-15 wherein flexural and XRD measurements were made at 135, 183, 233, 303, 404, 543, 830, and 1000 hr. Flexural strength data are shown in Figure 3. Crystallization data are shown in Figure 4 where a dramatic increase is noted above 400 hr.

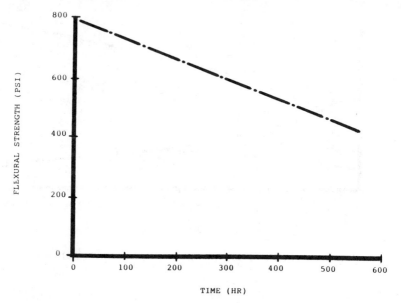

FIGURE 3   EFFECT OF TIME AT 2000°F ON FLEXURAL STRENGTH OF HTP-15

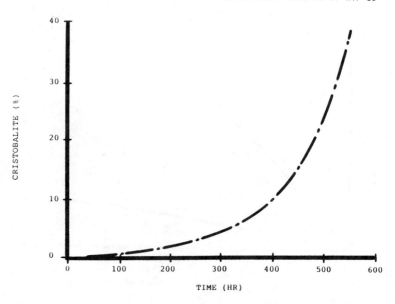

FIGURE 4   CRYSTALLIZATION OF HTP-15 AT 2000°F

152

Crystallization rate appears to follow a cube root function. Weight loss measurements indicate a gradual, linear loss with time, believed due to sublimation of B_2O_3. This may be seen in Figure 5.

Typical specimen cracking is shown in Figure 6.

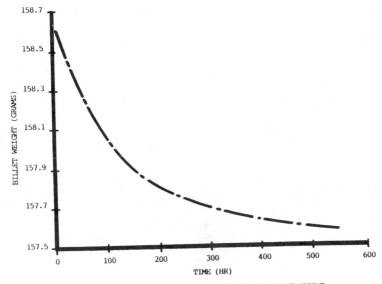

FIGURE 5 EFFECT OF TIME AT 2000°F ON HTP-15 BILLET WEIGHT

FIGURE 6. HTP-12 EXPOSED FOR 1100 HOURS AT 2000°F

The cracks originate at the surface and gradually propagate inward. At 2000 hr LI-2200 had surface cracks, but the interior was crack free and showed no strength loss. At 2000 hr LI-900 was crack free, but was badly cracked at 4000 hr throughout the specimen.

During development of HTP it was concluded that a minimum amount of B_2O_2 (added as BN) was required to preclude crystallization of silica in contact with alumina. The curve of BN content versus crystallization is shown in Figure 7. Standard HTP contains 2.85% BN which inhibits crystallization of silica over the 100 mission Shuttle lifetime of 15 hr at 1260°C (2300°F). Boron nitride was selected because of its slow and uniform oxidation at the HTP firing schedule at 1288°C (2350°F) for 90 min. The TGA curve of Figure 8 shows oxidation weight gain for BN, and it is clear that slow but significant oxidation occurs at 1093°C (2000°F).

The rate at 816°C (1500°F) is much less, and this was demonstrated in that HTP-12 and FRCI-12 blocks exposed to that temperature for 2000 hr showed no decrease in strength over their initial values.

Boron nitride used in HTP fabrication is typically 99.5% purity. To assess the importance of purity level, a 99.9% BN and single crystal platelets of B_4C were evaluated. Strength loss versus time was not significantly altered.

High temperature evaporation of B_2O_3 was suspected as being responsible for HTP and FRCI crystallization. In an attempt to measure the BN conversion and subsequent B_2O_3 evaporation rate, a platinum crucible was filled with 3.2 g of BN and placed in a kiln at 1093°C (2000°F). Periodic removal and weighing yielded the curve shown in Figure 9.

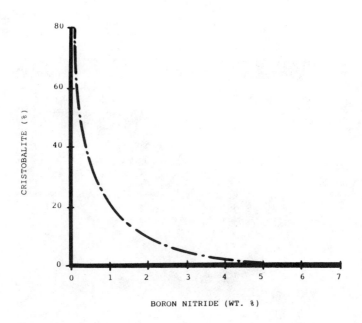

FIGURE 7   INFLUENCE OF BORON NITRIDE ON CRYSTALLIZATION OF HTP COMPOSITE

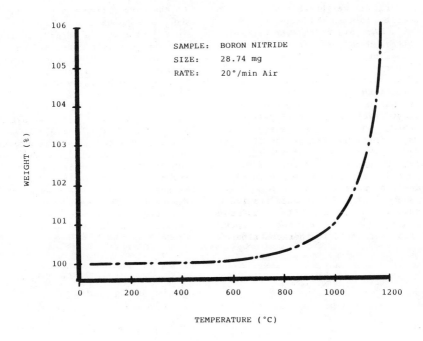

SAMPLE: BORON NITRIDE
SIZE: 28.74 mg
RATE: 20°/min Air

FIGURE 8   TGA OF BORON NITRIDE

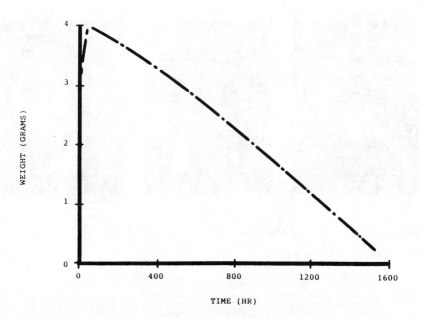

FIGURE 9   LONG TERM STABILITY OF BORON NITRIDE AT 2000°F IN AIR

The initial weight gain at 66 hr is attributable to oxidation of BN to B_2O_3. At this point, the crucible contained BN particles in clear B_2O_3 liquid. As time was further increased, the evaporation rate of BN was greater than the conversion rate of BN to B_2O_3. The same slope was maintained to about 600 hr, after which BN was completely converted, and a slightly steeper slope was maintained through depletion of B_2O_3. The 0.5 g remainder after 1500 hr was analyzed using XRD, and most of the impurities previously analyzed were present in significant amounts, although no quantitative analysis was made. This illustrates a fractional distillation of impurities that could further contribute to the crystallization process. The B_2O_3 loss mechanism is illustrated in Figure 10. The BN/B_2O_3 in the pre-test specimen continued to oxidize BN to 600 hr where BN is mostly depleted and evaporation of B_2O_3 at 1000 hr is evident in the photomicrograph.

Crystallization of all-silica composites (LI-900 and LI-2200) is believed due to the sluggish reaction potential for amorphous silica to convert to cristobalite at temperatures above 1000°C (1832°F). This is shown in the phase diagram of Figure 11. The reaction was observed to occur with LI materials between 2000 and 4000 hr at 1093°C (2000°F).

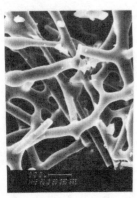 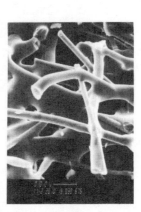 

BEFORE TEST   600 HOURS   1000 HOURS

FIGURE 10 MICROSTRUCTURE (1000X) OF HTP-15 SUBJECTED TO 2000°F

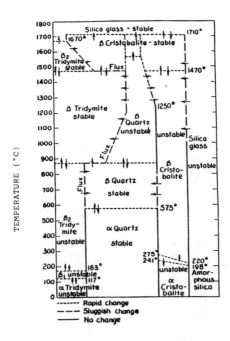

FIGURE 11   STABILITY RELATIONS OF SILICA
MATERIALS (FROM "PHASE DIAGRAMS
FOR CERAMISTS" JACS VOL 30, NO.
11, PART II, NOV 1947)

3. CONCLUSIONS

The evaporation of B_2O_3 to below the levels required to inhibit crystallization of silica in two-fiber systems (HTP and FRCI) is responsible for limiting long-term stability of these insulations at temperatures above 816°C (1500°F). Stability at 1039°C (2000°F) is limited to a few hundred hours.

Longer high temperature stability is realized with all-silica systems, but is limited to about 2000 hr due to the sluggish inversion to cristobalite at that temperature.

Fibrous crystalline ceramics appear more attractive for meeting long-term stability requirements at temperatures of 1093°C (2000°F) or above.

4. BIOGRAPHY

W. H. Wheeler is a Staff Engineer, Materials & Processes Engineering Department, Space System Division, Lockheed Missile & Space Co. (LMSC). He received his B.S. and M.S. degrees in Ceramic Engineering from the Virginia Polytechnic Institute. For the past 16 years he has been involved in development of lightweight fibrous composites and coatings for thermal protection, and for a wide variety of dielectric, electronic, and other space applications. Mr. Wheeler has been the key technical person in the development of advanced ceramic composite material systems at LMSC.

J. F. Creedon is a Materials & Processes Engineering Specialist for the Astronautics Division, Lockheed Missiles and Space Co. He has a BSCE degree from Northeastern University and has completed graduate work at Brooklyn Polytechnic Institute, University of Michigan and UCLA. For the past 14 years he has been involved in the development and production of thermal protection system materials. Mr. Creedon has been a principal technical investigator in the development of advanced materials and processes for the Lockheed ceramic fiber composite insulation system.

Y.D. Izu is Supervisor of the Materials & Processes Engineering Laboratories, Space System Division, Lockheed Missile and Space Co. He holds a B.S. -Chemical Engineering from Stanford University. He has been involved in and directed many of the laboratory developmental efforts since the early Lockheed concept of ceramic bonded ceramic fibrous composite materials for lightweight, insulative thermal protection systems. Mr. Izu has served as Task Leader in various Lockheed and government-contracted programs concerning ceramic and organic composite materials development.

34th International SAMPE Symposium
May 8-11, 1989

THERMOPLASTIC FILAMENT WOUND PARTS
DEMONSTRATING PROPERTIES IN CRUSH TUBE AND
TORQUE TUBE APPLICATIONS

M. W. Egerton and M. B. Gruber
E. I. Du Pont Composites Division

Abstract

Thermoplastic filament winding is a viable alternative to thermoset filament winding bringing both conversion cost and property advantages. High throughput in-situ consolidation of thermoplastic impregnated tow material is a key to low cost processing. A comparison of in-situ consolidated and post consolidated thermoplastic parts will be made along side conventional autoclaved epoxy systems. The comparisons will center on data bases generated on torque tubes and crush tubes fabricated using carbon, Kevlar* aramid, and fiberglass reinforcing fibers. The thermoplastic resin system of primary interest is DuPont's amorphous nylon known as J2.

1. INTRODUCTION

Filament winding is a process by which fibers are placed in a predetermined orderly path to form a given shape or part. By combining these fibers with a resin or binder a structure possessing unique properties can be obtained. Current manufacturing techniques incorporate either a thermosetting or thermoplastic resin system as the binder.

Thermoset systems have been used in the trade for many years and have established their value in making light weight, strong composite structures. This technology has repeatedly been applied to applications such as rocket motor cases, pressure pipes, structural beams, and rotor blades. An established engineering data base exists for the more commonly used thermosetting systems which in combination with laminate theory can be used to accurately predict the performance of a given part.

Thermoplastic resin systems have recently entered the filament winding arena bringing with them the potential for lower processing cost, more ductile damage tolerant systems, increased temperature ranges, and improved handling and storage characteristics. These materials, however, are so new to continuous fiber reinforced composites that established data bases do not exist . At this time only rough estimates can be made as to how a part will perform.

* DuPont Registered Trademark

In this paper two data bases will be discussed that have been generated with thermoplastic resin systems in mind. These two data bases are comprised from several hundred data points and are focussed at establishing the properties of in-situ consolidated filament wound thermoplastics tubes verses post consolidated thermoplastic and thermoset filament wound tubes. These data bases are not complete in nature but can be used to show general trends relative to material systems and processing techniques.

Several interesting side lines are also presented that will help fill in or support property trends that thermoplastic resin systems have shown. A complete engineering data base does not exist at this time for thermoplastic composite tubes. The crush tube and torque tube data bases presented here only scratch the surface in developing the needed engineering data to reliably design a part using thermoplastic composite materials.

2. FEED MATERIALS USED

Many different fiber and resin systems are currently used to make composite tubes. After selecting a fiber and resin there are various material forms available and processing techniques that can be used. The number of variables becomes staggering. Guidelines and assumptions must be made to narrow these variables down to a workable number.

Reinforcing fibers for composites will generally fall in one of three classes, metallic, organic or inorganic. The data bases

presented here have primarily been centered on continuous carbon, Kevlar* aramid, and fiberglass reinforcing fibers which represent two of the above three classes.

The resin systems available are far too numerous to list and fall into two basic categories, thermosetting and thermoplastic. The differentiating factor between these categories is that thermosetting systems undergo a non-reversible chemical curing process in forming a part whereas thermoplastic systems undergo a reversible melting and solidification process.

Two basic thermosetting systems have been incorporated into the databases for comparison purposes. These include Fiberite's 948 phenolic 250°F cure system designed with a wide processing window for sporting goods manufacture, and Shell's Epon® 9405/9470 350°F cure system designed for high performance composites.

The thermoplastic resins evaluated include low melt temperature polymers such as Hytrel* polyester elastomer and Surlyn* ionomer, moderate melt temperature polymers such as J2 amorphous nylon and PETG, and high melt temperature polymers like PEEK. The majority of work has centered on DuPont's J2 amorphous nylon and various forms of PET due to their low cost, reasonable temperature limits, and high volume potential.

Fiber and resin systems may be combined before or during the winding process. In general, filament winders like to separate the impregnation and the filament winding steps

* DuPont Registered Trademark

to simplify processing variables. This is done by using prepreg materials that have the resin distributed among or around the continuous reinforcing fibers in tow form.

Thermoset prepreg materials have been commercial for several years and are manufactured by various wet impregnation techniques yielding one basic form of tow. Thermoplastic prepregs, however, are available in several forms. These include powder impregnated yarns, comingled yarns, melt impregnated yarns and slit tape to name a few.

Each form of thermoplastic feed material has its benefits and drawbacks and may find rightful niches in the market. It is not the intention of this paper to pass judgement on the feed material for all applications. In selecting which type of feed material to use, cost, damage tolerance, uniformity of matrix distribution, fiber volume control, consolidation rate, guiding ability and tensioning ability must all be taken into account.

Most of the thermoplastic parts referred to in this paper have been fabricated using forms of melt impregnated tow. The tow, consisting of several thousand unidirectional filaments fused together by a thermoplastic resin, can have a prespecified width and thickness which can be tailored to specific processing needs. In general the tow width can be 1 - 6 mm (.05 -.25 inches), with a thickness of 0.1 - 0.4 mm (.005 - .015 inches). Note that these tows are made very thin in order to give excellent flexibility overcoming the stereotype that thermoplastic prepregs are boardy in nature.

3. PROCESSING TECHNIQUES USED

The thermoset tubes described in this paper were processed by one of two methods. The first method is called "wet filament winding" and is accomplished by pulling dry continuous fiber bundles through a resin impregnation bath just prior to the filament winding step. This is shown pictorially in Figure 1. The second method is to use a thermoset prepreg tow and wind the part directly, as shown in Figure 2. Both methods usually require oven or autoclave post consolidation steps for high quality parts.

Figure 1. Typical Wet Filament Winding.

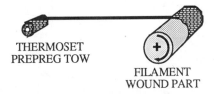

Figure 2. Typical Thermoset Prepreg Filament Winding.

The thermoplastic tubes described in this paper were also processed by one of two methods. The first method is called "in-situ consolidation" and is the process of using a thermoplastic prepreg material and adding heat and a consolidating force in the filament winding step. The result is a finished part directly off the winder that requires no oven or autoclave post consolidation. This process is shown pictorially in Figure 3. Additional information about the in-situ consolidation process and its potential impact is available (1). The second method would be to directly wind or hand lay up a thermoplastic prepreg, with or without heat, and post consolidate it in an oven or autoclave as you would a thermoset system.

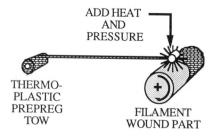

Figure 3. Typical Thermoplastic Filament Winding.

4. TORQUE TUBE GEOMETRY & LAY UP

In order to evaluate new materials, material forms, and processing techniques for filament wound thermoplastic structures, and compare them against existing thermoset structures, it was necessary to fabricate a "standard" test specimen. Finding the existing "standard" tests, including pressure bottles and various ring tests, to be very limiting it was necessary to develop a new standard (2,3).

Due to the ease of manufacture, relatively small amount of material required and applicability to real parts a "torque tube" design was selected as the "standard" of choice. Each tube has a 2.79 cm (1.1 inch) inside diameter, 3.18 cm (1.25 inch) outside diameter and is 30.5 cm (12 inches) long, as shown in Figure 4. The most efficient fiber orientation for a tube in pure torsion is to place the fibers at ±45°. This ensures that each fiber is either in pure tension or pure compression as shown in Figure 5.

5. TORQUE TUBE PROPERTY COMPARISON

There has been a great amount of work done to apply fiber reinforced composite technology to drive shafts in automobiles, helicopters, tanks and various other vehicles (4,5,6). The work has been very successful to date. It is important to note that the results provided here have not been optimized for drive shaft applications. These results are provided strictly for comparing various materials and processing techniques in a generic ±45° lay up under torsional load.

Each tube was fabricated, cut to 30.5 cm (12 inches) in length, fitted with epoxy end tabs and placed in pure torsion, at a rate of ~6000 in-lbs per minute, until failure. Two basic types of failure were noted, a compressive or buckling type of failure as shown in Figure 6, or a tensile failure as shown in Figure 7.

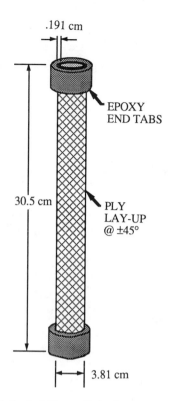

Figure 4. Typical Torque Tube Geometry.

.191 cm

EPOXY
END TABS

30.5 cm

PLY
LAY-UP
@ ±45°

3.81 cm

Figure 6. Torque tube section showing compressive failure.

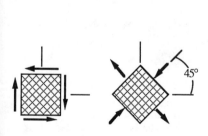

Figure 5. Stress Elements Showing Principal Stresses at ±45° For A Tube in Pure Torsion.

45°

Figure 7. Torque tube section showing tensile failure.

163

Viewing the torsional results shown in Table 1, cross referencing them against the material properties shown in Table 2, and dialing in the failure mechanism and trends established for each material system, the following conclusions can be drawn:

1) Thermoplastic matrixes exhibited equal or better performance than epoxy in both Kevlar* and carbon torque tubes. No comparison was made in fiberglass.

2) In select cases in-situ consolidation of thermoplastic tubes demonstrated up to a 25% improvement, in torsional break strength, over post consolidated thermoplastic tubes due to improved fiber alignment and reduced fiber wave.

3) Resin systems with low modulus and high elongation, such as Hytrel* and Surlyn*, while being very flexible will provide poor lateral support to fibers in compression. This results in buckling compressive failures, similar to that in Figure 6, and low torsional break strengths.

4) Resin systems with tensile modulus ≥1730 MPa (250 ksi) provide adequate lateral support to fibers to prevent compressive buckling failures in torque tubes.

5) Torque tubes show a high degree of sensitivity to the interfacial bond strength between the polymer and fiber. This bond strength is a measure of the compatabily of the sizing material with both the fiber and polymer.

* DuPont Registered Trademark

TABLE 1

Kevlar* Torque Tube Properties

Resin System	Mean Torque For 3 Tubes (Nm)	Max. Torque For 1 Tube (Nm)
J2 (I)	253	263
Epoxy^2 (P)	252	287

Fiberglass (E) Torque Tube Properties

Resin System	Mean Torque For 3 Tubes (Nm)	Max. Torque For 1 Tube (Nm)
Hytrel* (I)	69	81
Hytrel* (P)	75	83
Surlyn*(I)	76	83
Surlyn*(P)	105	113
PETG+(I)	395	413
PETG+(P)	352	384
PET+(I)	247	303
J2+ (I)	323	329
J2+ (P)	((279))	280

Carbon (AS4) Torque Tube Properties

Resin System	Mean Torque For 3 Tubes (Nm)	Max. Torque For 1 Tube (Nm)
J2+ (I)	560	583
J2+ (P)	446	606
PEEK (P)	((648))	683
Epoxy^2 (P)	((528))	602

*	- DuPont Registered Trademark.
(( ))	- Indicate mean value is based on 2 tubes.
+	- Indicates the addition of carbon black to the system.
(P)	- Indicates oven or autoclave post consolidation
(I)	- Indicates consolidation during filament placement
2	- Indicates the use of Fiberite 948-A1 epoxy.

TABLE 2

Thermoplastic Matrix Properties

Resin System	Tensile Strength (MPa)	Tensile Modulus (MPa)	Break Elongation (%)
Hytrel* [1]	28	50 [f]	560
Surlyn* [2]	28	260 [f]	490
PETG+ [3]	48	1720	225
PET [4]	69	2830	50
J2+ [5]	103	3170	25
PEEK [6]	103	3790	11

Thermoset Matrix Properties

Resin System	Tensile Strength (MPa)	Tensile Modulus (MPa)	Break Elongation (%)
Epoxy 948 [7]	49	4140	1
Epoxy Epon [8]	83	2950	9

* - DuPont Registered Trademark.
f - Substitution of Flexural Modulus
+ - Addition of carbon black to the system.
1 - DuPont Design Handbook " Hytrel* Polyester Elastomer"; properties for Hytrel* grade 4056; E-52083
2 - DuPont Product Guide "Surlyn* Ionomer Resins"; properties for Surlyn* grade 9950; E-68761.
3 - Eastman Kodak Kodar*** PETG Copolyester 6763; ECP 4159
4 - Neat resin properties for PET change dramatically based on additives. An average value has been used.
5 - DuPont Preliminary Data Sheet for "J-2 Polymer Thermoplastic Resin Impregnated Tapes and Fabrics"; E-89563-1.
6 - Taken from "PEKK as a New Thermoplastic Matrix for High Performance Composites" by I. Y. Chang
7 - Published property data for Fiberite's 948A1 resin system are not available. Values for Fiberite's 934 epoxy have been substituted.
8 - Shell Technical Bulletin SC:856-86R for EPON® 9405 /9470 epoxy.

6. CRUSH TUBE GEOMETRY & LAY UP

The use of torque tubes as a standard for evaluating materials and processing techniques in filament winding is invaluable. A test was needed, however, that was more sensitive to void content. Fiber reinforced composites placed in pure compression are much more sensitive to void content and minor flaws than those placed in tension. This led to the use of crush tubes as a standard.

The crush tube geometry that was selected is based on earlier work at NASA and Bell Helicopter (7,8,9). Each tube has a 3.81 cm (1.5 inches) inside diameter, 4.32 cm (1.7 inches) outside diameter, is 10.2 cm (4 inches) long and has a 45° bevel on one end. A typical crush tube is shown in Figure 8. Consistent with the earlier torque tube work a fiber lay up of ±45° was selected.

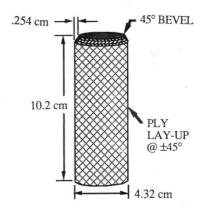

Figure 8. Typical Crush Tube Geometry.

7. CRUSH TUBE PROPERTY COMPARISON

There have been a fair number of feasibility studies done looking at fiber reinforced composite tubes as energy absorbing structures for crash worthiness in automobiles, helicopters, aircraft and various other vehicles. The work has shown very favorable results to date. The majority of the published work has been done with thermoset systems, while limited data is available on thermoplastic systems. The objective of this previous work was to modify the material system and fiber lay up as needed to maximize the energy absorbed per unit weight (7,8,9,10).

It is important to note that the fiber lay up used in the work presented here has not been optimized to gain maximum energy absorption. These results are provided strictly for comparing various materials and processing techniques in a generic ±45° lay up under static and dynamic axial loading conditions. Figure 9 depicts two dimensional stress elements showing the non-optimal fiber loading for a ±45° crush tube under axial load conditions. The resulting stresses in the fiber direction are both compressive and shear. Pure compressive loading would be preferred.

Each tube was fabricated, cut to 10.2 cm (4 inches) in length, beveled on one end, placed between flat plates and crushed in either a static mode at 5.08 cm/min (2 in/min) or dynamic mode at 4.88 m/s (16 ft/s). Two basic types of failure were noted, an accordion or buckling type of failure as shown in Figure 10, or a tearing mushroom failure as shown in Figure 11.

Figure 10. Crush tube showing accordion or buckling failure.

Figure 11. Crush tube showing mushroom or tearing failure.

From both the static and dynamic tests a graph of load verses crush length will result. See figure 12. The key points of interest on the graph are the peak load, the average load and the deviation from the average. The idea is to maximize the average load while minimizing the peak load and the deviation from the average. The ideal would be a perfectly square graph with a high, repeatable, average load. The area under the graph represents the amount of energy

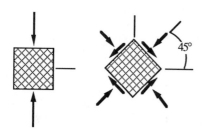

Figure 9. Stress Elements Showing Non-Optimal Fiber Loading For ±45° Crush Tubes.

expended in crushing a tube. If the energy expended is divided by the weight of the tube a normalized value with the units of KJ/Kg is obtained.

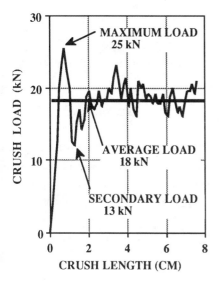

Figure 12. Typical Plot of Load Verses Crush Length Under Static Load Conditions

Viewing the crush tube results shown in Table 3, cross referencing them against the material properties shown in Table 2, and dialing in the failure mechanism and trends established for each material system, the following conclusions can be drawn:

1) Thermoplastic matrixes exhibited equal or better performance than epoxies in Kevlar*, fiberglass and carbon crush tubes under both static and dynamic load conditions.

2) Insitu-consolidated thermoplastic tubes demonstrated 60% - 90% of the static crush properties of post consolidated thermoplastic

tubes. This would indicate that crush tube performance is highly sensitive to, and inversely proportional to, void content. Note that in-situ consolidated thermoplastic tubes have shown 2% - 5% voids, whereas, post consolidated thermoplastic tubes have <1% voids.

3) Resin systems with low modulus provide poor lateral support to fibers in compression. This results in premature buckling failures at the fiber level and low energy of absorption values for the tube. Resin systems with tensile modulus ≥3170 MPA (460 ksi) provide the necessary lateral support to prevent premature fiber buckling in crush tubes.

4) Fibers with good tear resistance and relatively low compressive strength, like Kevlar*, will tend to exhibit accordion or buckling failures as shown in Figure 10. This failure mode does not necessarily indicate low energy of absorption values and does tend to yield the best post crush integrity of the material systems tested.

5) Tearing or mushroom type failures, shown in Figure 11, are indicative of well consolidated tubes made from high modulus resins and fibers that are good in compression. Generally speaking, a mushroom type failure involves much fiber breakage and will result in high energy of absorption values.

6) In all cases the dynamic crush mode seemed to yield equal or slightly lower energy of absorption values than the static mode. Typically the dynamic values would

* DuPont Registered Trademark

be 80% - 100% of the static values. For all intensive purposes the crush rate seemed to have little effect on energy absorbed.

TABLE 3

Kevlar* Crush Tube Properties

Resin System	Static Energy of Absorption (KJ/Kg) Avg. For 3 Tubes	Dynamic Energy of Absorption (KJ/Kg) Avg. For 3 Tubes
PETG (I)	29	-
PETG (P)	33	-
J2 (I)	42	49
J2 (P)	55	45
Epoxy[1] (P)	((43))	36
Epoxy[2] (P)	41	((32))

Fiberglass (E) Crush Tube Properties

Resin System	Static Energy of Absorption (KJ/Kg) Avg. For 3 Tubes	Dynamic Energy of Absorption (KJ/Kg) Avg. For 3 Tubes
PETG+ (I)	26	28
J2+ (I)	30	30
J2+ (P)	52	(38)
Epoxy[1] (P)	56	42

Carbon (AS4) Crush Tube Properties

Resin System	Static Energy of Absorption (KJ/Kg) Avg. For 3 Tubes	Dynamic Energy of Absorption (KJ/Kg) Avg. For 3 Tubes
J2+ (I)	58	60
J2+ (P)	70	59
Epoxy[1] (P)	(50)	(54)
Epoxy[2] (P)	50	50

* - DuPont Registered Trademark.
( ) - Indicate mean value is based on 1 tube.
(( )) - Indicate mean value is based on 2 tubes.
+ - Indicates the addition of carbon black to the system.
(P) - Indicates oven or autoclave post consolidation
(I) - Indicates consolidation during filament placement.
1 - Indicates use of Shell Epon 9405/9470 epoxy.
2 - Indicates the use of Fiberite 948-A1 epoxy.

8. COMMENTS

This paper has shown that in both torsional and compressive applications thermoplastic composites will perform equivalent to if not slightly better than thermoset composite systems. The potential for high performance in-situ consolidated thermoplastics is also shown.

The value of both torque tubes and crush tubes for material and process evaluations is well documented. There is a need for these two individualized tests in that each test is sensitive to different criteria. For example, the torque tube test will load fibers along their principal axis' showing a high degree of sensitivity to the interfacial bond strength between the polymer and each individual fiber. The crush tubes are much more sensitive to void content as fiber movement or buckling will start on the microscopic level at the location of a void.

The torque tube and crush tube results presented here compliment the necessary engineering data bases needed to allow reliable design with thermoplastic composites.

9. ACKNOWLEDGEMENTS

The authors would like to thank the combined efforts of the entire Composites Division at E. I. DuPont for their efforts in researching, manufacturing, testing, and documenting this work in thermoplastic filament wound torque tubes and crush tubes. Donna Dietert's contribution's in machining and testing of samples was invaluable. The guidance provided by Jim Cronkhite from Bell Helicopter and Marilyn Wardle from DuPont's Material Test Center are especially appreciated.

10. REFERENCES

1. Egerton, M. W. and Gruber, M. B., "Thermoplastic Filament Winding Demonstrating Economics and Properties Via In-Situ Consolidation," 33rd International SAMPE Symposium, March, 1988.

2. ASTM D 2585-68, "Preparation and Tension Testing of Filament Wound Pressure Vessels."

3. ASTM D 2344-76, "Apparent Interlaminar Shear Strength of Parallel Fiber Composites By Short-Beam Method."

4. Spencer, B. E., "Composite Drive Shafting Applications," 32nd International SAMPE Symposium, April, 1987.

5. Wright, C. C. and Baker, D. J., "Progress Report III of Cooperative Program for Design, Fabrication and Testing of High Modulus Composite Helicopter Shafting," Technical Report ARLCD-TR-79028, June 1980.

6. McGee, J., Spencer, B. and Shy, D., "Feasibility Study on The Design of Reinforced Plastic Components for LVTP (7) Vehicle Shafts," AMMRC-TR-84-27, May, 1983

7. Farley, G. L., "Energy Absorption of Composite Materials," NASA Technical Memorandum 84638, March, 1983.

8. Farley, G. L., "Energy Absorption of Composite Material and Structure," 43rd Annual Forum of the American Helicopter Society, May, 1987.

9. Cronkhite, J. D., et al., "Investigation of Crash Impact Characteristics of Composite Airframe Structures," USARTL-TR-79-11, September, 1979.

10. Kindervater, C. M., "Crash Impact Behavior and Energy Absorbing Capability of Composite Structural Elements," 30th National SAMPE Symposium, March, 1985.

BIOGRAPHIES

Ken Egerton is a Research Engineer with E. I. Du Pont Company working for the Composites Division at the Chestnut Run Site in Wilmington, Delaware. He received a Masters Degree in Mechanical Engineering, specializing in robotics, from Bucknell University in 1984. His current efforts are centered in the areas of advanced composite processing techniques for thermoplastic and thermosetting matrixes. Ken received the DuPont Market Director's Award for outstanding contributions to the Textile Fibers Department and is the author of three papers on Composite Processing and Properties.

Mark Gruber is a Research Engineer with E. I. Du Pont Company working for the Composites Division at the Chestnut Run Site in Wilmington, Delaware. He received a Masters Degree in Mechanical Engineering, specializing in Composites, from The University of Delaware in 1981. His current efforts are centered around developing new fabrication techniques for thermoplastic materials. Mark is the author of six articles on Composites and holds a patent in Thermoplastic Tape Laydown.

LONG DISCONTINUOUS ORDERED FIBER STRUCTURAL PARTS

Steven J. Medwin
E. I. Du Pont
Engineering Development Laboratory
Wilmington, Delaware

Abstract

Long discontinuous, ordered fiber composite materials were used in the fabrication of contoured structural parts. The material consisted of AS4 graphite fibers reinforced in a J2 amorphous nylon thermoplastic matrix. Destructive and non-destructive inspection techniques were used to determine final fiber placement. These were then compared to a computer model of this process with very good agreement. This novel thermoforming process and the parts made by it will be discussed. In addition, the economics of this system will be compared with the current hand layup technique.

1. INTRODUCTION

In weight critical applications, graphite composite materials can provide a highly desirable combination of structural properties provided the orientation of the fibers is precisely controlled during the fabrication of the part. To obtain this control, each part must be hand laid up ply by ply until the desired thickness and fiber orientation is achieved. If the resin is a thermoset, the part must then be cured in an autoclave. If the resin is a thermoplastic, then a press is typically used for final consolidation instead of an autoclave, but the labor intensive hand layup procedure is still required. A new process is needed that improves the economics of these critical parts while maintaining the required properties.

Some alternatives to hand layup of complex, contoured shapes are available. Xerkon has developed a soft stitched "fiber form" that is resin impregnated in a proprietary process[1]. Alcoa/Goldsworthy has patented a process called pulforming that can form complex thermoset parts[2]. Microdot Aerospace is developing a roll forming process for continuous fiber reinforced thermoplastic resin systems[3]. However each of these

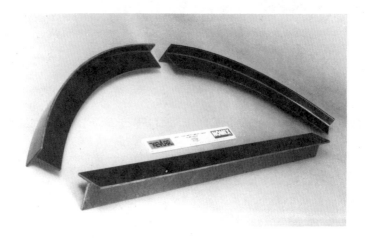

FIGURE 1. PHOTOGRAPH OF FORMED AND UNFORMED "T" SHAPES

processes has its limitations. Long discontinuous ordered fiber (LDF) stretch forming is a new approach that could be the ideal combination of economics and performance. Thermoplastic LDF materials offer the advantage of thermoforming while maintaining at least 90% of the continuous fiber material properties[4].

Initially a straight stock shape is formed in the desired cross section and then thermoformed into the required final contour. The economics are attractive since the stock shape can be produced efficiently and the final part can be contoured automatically with minimal labor. And most significantly, the fibers can be precisely controlled during forming to follow the curves as required.

This process has been demonstrated on a lab scale by forming T cross section parts with an inner radius of 61 cm (24 in) and an included angle of 60° from AS4/

J2 material (see Figure 1). This paper will review the fiber placement in these sample parts, the general process required to form them, the formed part inspection and the economics of this technique.

2. FIBER PLACEMENT

The key to the success of stretch forming is the precise control over the fiber placement. During the forming process, the fibers must never be compressed - they must always be kept in tension. If fiber compression happens, then the laminate will wrinkle and the properties will drop off. Also the angular relationship between the fibers must be maintained. This precise control is typically achieved by clamping both ends of the unformed part, heating up the portion between the clamps and then carefully forming the stock shape to the desired curvature. The general forming concept is shown in Figure 2.

* Kevlar and Nomex are Du Pont Registered Trademarks for their aramid fibers.

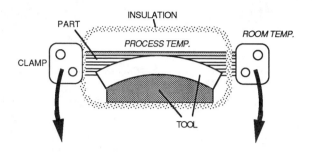

FIGURE 2. GENERAL STRETCH FORMING CONCEPT

The motions are such that the 0° fibers follow the tool contour while the 90° fibers become radial (see Figure 3). At any section through the part, the 90° fibers remain perpendicular to the 0° fibers.

By forming in this manner, a strain gradient is established from the inner part curve to the outer part curve. The forming process is designed so the inner curve has a minimal amount strain to insure that the fibers don't go into compression. This amount of strain is established by how far the neutral axis is offset from the inner curve.

Since the ±45° fibers traverse this gradient, they end up with a slight bow directed toward the center of curvature. This can be seen in the diagonals in Figure 3. However, at any local point in the curved beam, these fibers maintain the ±45° orientation.

The overall effect of the stretch forming on the fibers is shown in Figure 4. This sequence shows half of a part being formed.

This sequence was generated by an animated computer model of the stretch forming process developed on an Apple Macintosh computer. For any given geome-

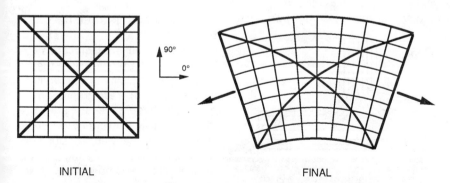

INITIAL

FINAL

FIGURE 3. FIBER POSITION IN STRETCH FORMED PART

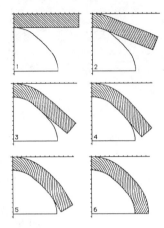

FIGURE 4. STRETCH FORMING
SEQUENCE

try, the 0°, 90° or ±45° fibers may be observed during the actual forming. The above sequence shows the -45° ply during various steps in the process. Notice the gentle arc that forms in these fibers as the part is shaped. This arc is a signature visible in radiographs that differentiates a stretch formed part from a hand layup part.

3. PROCESS DEVELOPMENT

The fabrication process starts with the straight stock shape. This stock shape is formed from

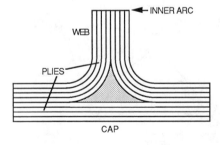

FIGURE 5. STOCK SHAPE LAYUP

individual plies of LDF prelam material. A variety of techniques can be used to form this shape (see Figure 5).

The stock shape is consolidated in separate tooling and trimmed to the length required for the particular part. It is then clamped into the stretch forming machine and the center heated to the process temperature. The stock shape is then formed to the desired part contour using the general approach previously described.

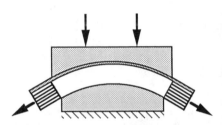

FIGURE 6. COOLING UNDER PRESSURE

Once the full part is formed, the whole part is then cooled down while maintaining pressure (Figure 6). This technique was used with demonstration tooling to fabricate a number of contoured T parts.

4. PART INSPECTION

Several inspection techniques were utilized to determine the formed part quality. Ultrasonic scans (C-scan), radiographs and photomicrographs were made of the formed and unformed parts. The C-scans showed no significant signal loss indicating good consolidation and no voids. However this did not yield any fiber placement information and this was critical for demonstrating the stretch forming technique.

FIGURE 7. RADIOGRAPH WITH OVERLAY OF MODEL

Radiographs were taken of the formed and unformed parts with Du Pont NDT 30 radiographic film (an ultra fine grain, very high contrast film designed for maximum resolution and image quality). This is a new film, developed for composites inspection, which is sensitive enough to view the fibers without the need for markers.

These fiber images were separated into 0°, ±45° and 90° overlays and then digitized. The absolute angles of these fibers were converted to an angle relative to its position around the arc of the

part. Figure 8 shows the results of this relative fiber angle analysis versus position. The discrete groupings of the fibers into 90°, 45°, 0° and -45° angles from the -20° arc position to the +20° arc position can readily be seen.

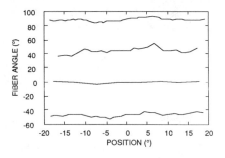

FIGURE 8. FIBER ANGLE VS. POSITION

These relative angles were then compared to the theoretical location as determined by the computer model. As a control, this was also done for a hand layup thermoset part and an unformed, thermoplastic stock shape. The results, summarized in Table 1, show that stretch forming achieved fiber placement comparable to the thermoset control.

TABLE 1

SUMMARY OF FIBER ANGLE VS. DEVIATIONS

FIBER ANGLE	THERMOPLASTIC UNFORMED	THERMOPLASTIC STRETCH FORMED	THERMOSET HAND LAYUP
0°	±0.9°	±3.2°	±3.2°
90°	±2.7°	±4.3°	±3.3°
45°	±4.1°	±5.4°	±4.2°
-45°	±2.3°	±3.8°	±1.8°

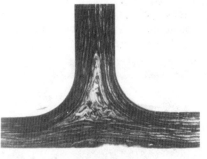

| UNFORMED | FORMED |

FIGURE 9. PHOTOMICROGRAPHS OF FILLER AREA AT 3.5X

In addition to the radiographic analysis, cross sections were made of the formed and unformed parts. Photomicrographs of these cross sections are shown for comparison in Figure 9. The first photograph shows the unformed, straight stock shape. The second photograph shows a part after stretch forming. These photos and radiographs clearly show that stretch forming is a technically viable process for controlling fiber placement.

5. ECONOMIC EVALUATION

An economic evaluation of the stretch forming process was done and compared with the current commercial, hand layup technique.

A semi-automatic stretch forming manufacturing process was assumed. The example part was a 0.64 kg (1.4 lbs) contoured T shape made from graphite fibers in J2 resin. Additional assumptions were a production rate of 1000 parts per year, 20% equipment utilization and 1 year tooling amortization. The results, normalized for total material cost, are summarized in Table 2.

The difference is dramatic. A stretch formed part would cost 34% of a hand layup part. The major difference here is in labor costs. For this contoured T section, the labor can be reduced from 49 hours per part to 2 hours per part.

TABLE 2

SUMMARY OF ECONOMIC ANALYSIS

	THERMOSET HAND LAYUP	THERMOPLASTIC SEMI-AUTOMATIC	COST RATIO
TOTAL MATERIAL	1.0X	0.8X	80%
COST OF MANUFACTURE	15.6X	4.2X	27%
COST + 20% NROI	22.5X	7.6X	34%

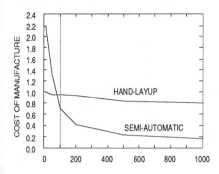

FIGURE 10. COST OF MANUFACTURE
VS. NUMBER OF PARTS

An economic advantage is still
available at quantities as low as
100 parts per year, as seen in Figure 10. This graph shows the normalized cost of manufacture for a
hand layup part versus a semi-
automatic, stretch formed part.

6. CONCLUSIONS

A cost effective method for forming high quality contoured structural shapes made from long discontinuous fiber composite
material has been demonstrated.
Precise placement of the fibers is
possible by stretch forming a
thermoplastic stock shape. Several contoured T cross section
parts were made by this technique. Radiographs and photomicrographs show the final fiber position and were compared to a
computer model with good agreement. An economic analysis
showed significant cost savings
compared to the current hand lay-
up technique.

7. REFERENCES

1. Xercon product literature
   (1986).
2. W.B. Goldsworthy, "Pulforming
   - The Changing Shape of Composites", Plastics & Rubber
   Weekly, Nov.15, 1986, p22-23.
3. Advanced Materials, Vol. 10,No.
   11, (July 1988).
4. R. Okine, D. Edison and N. Little,
   "Properties and Formability of
   a Novel Advanced Thermoplastic Composite Sheet Product",
   SAMPE Engineering Series, Vol.
   32, p. 1413 (1987).

8. ACKNOWLEDGMENTS

The author would like to acknowledge the following Du Pont Company people for their contributions to this program: Mike
Agreen, Dick Baker, Dale Bre-
thauer, Debbi Connor, Bob Cooper,
Joe Collingwood, Tom Dewey, Har-
ry Ladd, Frannie Vincent-Messick,
Dave McKee, Rich Okine, Andy Per-
rella, Jim Pratte, Nancy Smith,
Darwin Wall and Mark Williams.

9. BIOGRAPHY

Steven J. Medwin is a Development
Engineer in the Engineering Research and Development Division
(Engr Dept) at E. I. Du Pont Company. He is currently working on the
technology required to form Du
Pont's LDF composite materials.
He joined Du Pont in 1978 after
receiving his M.S. in mechanical
engineering from University of
Pennsylvania and his B.S. in mechanical engineering from Cornell
University.

MESOPHASE PITCH-BASED CARBON FIBER PRODUCTION PROGRAM

Mr Dennis S. Hager
DPA Title III Program Office
Wright-Patterson AFB, Ohio 45433
and
Mr Donald L. Schmidt
Materials Consultant
Universal Energy Systems, Inc.
Dayton, Ohio 45432

Abstract

The Defense Production Act (DPA) Title III Program Office operates under the Defense Production Act of 1950 for the purpose of creating or expanding domestic production capacity for materials deemed critical to the national defense. In July 1988 a Title III contract (USAF Contract Number F33733-88-C-1004) was awarded to Amoco Performance Products to maintain a domestic production supply of high modulus pitch-based carbon yarn for use as reinforcements in advanced composite materials utilizing thermosetting resin, thermoplastic resin, metal and carbon matrices.

1. INTRODUCTION

A strong and responsive U.S. industrial base is key to maintaining a credible deterrent to war, and to meet military needs during times of surge and mobilization. Many basic industries important to the production of defense systems and hardware have systematically declined over recent years, thus depriving the Unites States of industrial capabilities critical to national security.

A proactive approach to reducing foreign dependency and developing new domestic sources for advanced materials is being implemented through Title III of the DPA. The specific purpose of these programs is to increase domestic production capabilities for materials in all forms, from basic materials through fully formed materials that can be applied directly to critical Department of Defense (DOD) weapons systems and items. Title III accomplishes this goal by providing domestic industries with incentives to establish new or expanded capacity.

The Government's commitment to building domestic production capability through Title III is based on two important factors. First, it reduces the nation's growing dependence on off-shore sources for its supply of critical materials. Secondly, it provides for a stable supply of new high-technology materials, for which a commercially viable production capacity has not yet been developed.

Critical defense applications often use the highest performance material available to maximize systems effectiveness. Such materials tend to be of a speciality nature. Costs are routinely high, production quantities are low and single sources are often encountered. Industrial uses are typically stymied because of costs and availability considerations. Since these high performance materials are essential to weapons systems, continued availability of quality material remains a primary concern of the DOD.

The DPA was originally passed in 1950 as emergency legislation. It has been extended regularly every two or three years due to a congressional mandate to meet national defense needs. Since the renewal in 1985 of the Title III program, multi-million dollar purchase commitment contracts have been awarded.

2. TITLE III PROGRAMS

2.1 Project Criteria

Each project must meet four criteria which are certified to Congress before a contract can be executed. Except during periods of declared national emergency, the President must make a determination that:

(a) the material is essential to the national defense
(b) without Title III, U.S. industry cannot reasonably be expected to provide the production capacity in a

timely manner.

(c) Title III is the most cost effective, expedient and practical alternative method for meeting the need, and (d) the U.S. national defense demand for the material is equal to or greater than the output of current domestic industrial capacity.

In addition to these requirements, the DOD has added the following criteria:

(a) the project must be accomplished through purchase or purchase commitment (b) the material must be used by more than one Service, and (c) the product must meet a specification agreed to by the Government and the contractor prior to contractor award.

2.2 Project Life Cycle

The life cycle of each Title III project occurs in six stages, all of which are complex and involve a great deal of coordination. These steps are:

a. Identification of a capacity shortfall
b. Project analysis and structuring
c. Project advocacy

d. Project approval
e. Project execution
f. Project administration

Ultimately, DOD program managers will coordinate their program schedules with Title III deliveries and require their contractors to use materials produced under Title III contracts. (1)

3. MESOPHASE PITCH-BASED CARBON FIBERS

3.1 Historical Development

In 1965, low cost carbon fibers were produced from inexpensive, synthetic isotropic pitches. Further studies revealed that commercial pitches, coal tars, petroleum asphalts and other synthetic organic pitches were also suitable precursors. Fiber tensile strengths were about 1.0 GPa (145 ksi) and the Young's moduli were on the order of 35-69 GPa (5-10 Msi). Hot stretching the pitch fibers during the initial stages of carbonization was found to greatly increase fiber strength and modulus, but this process was not commercialized. In the early 1960's, research on pitches resulted in a dramatic discovery that greatly impacted the future of pitch-based carbon fibers. It was found that pitches while still in the liquid state could form an intermediate, high oriented, optically aniso-tropic liquid crystal phase (mesophase) when heated above 350°C (662°F). This research lead to the development of mesophase pitch based (MPP) carbon fibers. The first commercial product was sold in 1973 as spun filament mat. Continuous filament yarns were sold later in 1974. The fibers had a tensile strength of 1.4 GPa (200 ksi), moduli of 35-207 GPa (5-30 Msi), elongation over 1.0%, and a diameter of 10 microns. Within a short period of time, fiber tensile strengths were upgraded to 2.46 GPa (348 ksi) and the Young's modulus increased to 380 GPa (55 Msi). MPP carbon fibers with a Young's modulus of 517 GPa (75 Msi) were sold in 1975, and, 724 GPa (100 Msi) carbon fibers were produced in 1982. More recently, developmental quantities of 897 GPa (130 Msi) MPP carbon fibers have been made available to the industry. Today, continuous MPP carbon fibers are marketed in the moduli range of 172-897 GPa (25-130

Msi). Prices range from $66/kg ($30/1b) to $4950/kg ($2250/1b) depending upon strand filament count and fiber modulus. The most common strand count is either 2000 or 4000 filaments, although 500 and 1000 filaments/strand materials are also available in some grades. MPP carbon fibers in mat form presently cost about $55/kg ($25/1b) to $62/kg ($28/1b). Woven fabrics are also available in various styles.

3.2 Manufacturing Process

The production of MPP carbon fibers is a long and complex series of processing steps, some of which are carried out at extreme conditions. Process details are prop-rietary, but much information has been published in techni-cal articles and patents. Figure 1 illustrates the basic processes, which were obtained from the published literature.

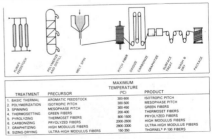

Figure 1. MPP Carbon Fiber Manufacturing Process.

MPP carbon fibers have been produced domestically since the mid-1970's. The first U.S. plant was built by the Union Carbide Corporation (later sold to the Amoco Performance Products, Inc.) at Greenville, S.C. It has a nominal carbon fiber capacity of 227,000/kg (500,000 pounds) a year. MPP carbon fibers are presently manufactured by two U.S. sources and about three foreign sources. Domestic production levels are in the tens of thousands of pounds annually, and most of the MPP carbon fibers produced is of the lower modulus and low cost type. HM and UHM MPP carbon fibers are presently manufactured in the hundreds of pounds per year. U.S. capacity now exceeds demand, but accelerated composite developments in the U.S will significantly increase domestic consumption.

3.3 UHM Carbon Fiber Properties

UHM carbon fibers are distinguished from other carbon fibers in a number of important characteristics. They have very high carbon contents, outstanding Young's modulus (stiffness), very high thermal conductivity and high dimensional stability along the fiber axis. They are also slightly more resistant to oxidation than other types of carbon fibers. On the other hand, UHM carbon fibers are characterized by low fracture strains, moderate strengths, and relatively high costs.

Figure 2 illustrates the axial Young's modulus of various carbon fibers along with data on ceramic fibers and metallic materials.

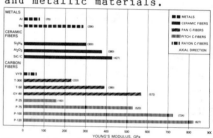

Figure 2. Young's Modulus of Carbon and Metallic Fibers.

The axial thermal expansion coefficient of MPP carbon fibers are shown in Figure 3 along with data on ceramic fibers and typical structural metals.

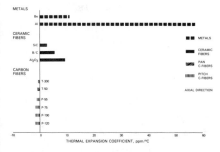

Figure 3. Thermal Expansion
Coefficient of Various
Fibrous Materials.

Structural metals are shown
to have relatively high expansion coefficients.
Ceramic fibers exhibit lower
thermal expansion properties,
but MPP carbon fibers have
very desirable low expansion
coefficients. Values are actually slightly negative up
to about 400°C (752°F).

The axial thermal conduc-
tivity of MPP carbon fibers
is also unique. Figure 4
presents the thermal conduction properties of various
structural and heat dissipa-
tive metals along with applicable data for various
carbon fibers.

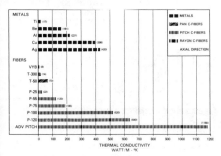

Figure 4. Thermal Conduc-

tivity of Various Fibrous
Materials.

When normalized for density
differences (important in
aerospace applications), the
specific thermal conductivity
of the 120 Msi MPP carbon
fibers were over six times
that of copper. MPP carbon
fibers with even higher conduction values 1130 Watt/m-°K
(653 Btu/ft-hr°F) have been
produced in laboratory quantities.

The tensile strengths of MPP
carbon fibers are adequate
for most applications, but
lower than most competitive
PAN-based carbon fibers.

The fracture strains of MPP
carbon fibers are typically
low. See Figure 5.

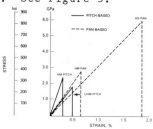

Figure 5. Fracture Strain of
High Strength, High Modulus
and Ultra-High Modulus Carbon
Fibers.

Low modulus MPP carbon fibers
have elongations-at-break
values of 0.9 to 1.03%. High
modulus MPP carbon fibers
have significantly lower
break elongations, ie., 0.27

to 0.55%.

MPP carbon fibers, like all carbon fibers, are susceptible to oxidizing environments. Oxidation in hot air becomes significant at about (316°C 600°F) and increases with oxidizing specie concentration and temperature. Protective coatings have been developed to extend the lifetimes of carbon fibers during high temperature oxidation.

The cost of MPP carbon fibers is volume sensitive. Although the precursor material for MPP carbon fibers is quite inexpensive, the cost of the finished yarn can be quite high. In general, low modulus MPP carbon fibers are low in costs. The price of 4K yarn 172 GPA (25 Msi) is only $30/lb. Intermediate modulus MPP yarn 380 GPa (55 Msi, 4K) sells for about $43/lb. High and ultra-high modulus MPP carbon yarns (2K, 724 GPa, 100 Msi) sells for $950/lb, and, ultra-high modulus MPP carbon yarn (2K, 827 GPa, 120 Msi) is priced at $1250/lb.

MPP carbon fiber production is expected to grow significantly in the next few years. As the production base expands, improved fiber quality and lower cost products should be realized. Additional physical forms of MPP carbon fibers will likely be develped and provide considerable benefits to the users. Additional improvements are also anticipated in fiber properties. The Young's modulus is already approaching that of single crystal graphite (1000 GPA, 145 Msi), and thus little further improvement will be possible. Fiber tensile strength, on the other hand, should increase significantly as new and novel pitch purification processes are developed and implemented in the manufacturing scheme. Laboratory experiments have already demonstrated that MPP carbon fibers can be produced with a tensile strength of 4.0 GPa (580 ksi). Fiber thermal conductivity, which is already unequaled by all other types of fibers, will be further increased by improved control of orientation (graphite layer plane alignment), crystallinity (crystalline size and perfection) and defects (surface and internal flaws). The attainment of these goals, however, will be heavily dependent upon the development of additional technology and volume usage of the fibers.

4. TITLE III CARBON FIBER PROGRAM

DOD's documented need for lighter weight, stiffer, stronger structural materials has grown significantly in the past several years with carbon fibers offering one of the most versatile solutions to this need. Carbon fibers have emerged as a class of high modulus reinforcement material which can be utilized in thermosetting resin, thermoplastic resin, metal and carbon matrice composite materials.

The Title III carbon fiber program was competitively bid in early 1988. On July 25, 1988, a $7,879,200 Air Force contract (F33733-88-C-1004) was awarded to the Amoco Performance Products, Inc., Ridgefield, CT. Figure 6 shows the overall program plan (1).

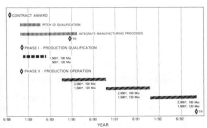

Figure 6. MPP Carbon Yarn Program Plan.

4.1 Phase I

Phase I involves the production qualification of the precursor pitch, the manufacturing processes and the fibrous end products. A primary source of starting decant oil will be qualified, which is capable of yielding high modulus yarns by spinning the pitch mesophase into yarns and subsequently graphitizing into 100 and 120 Msi moduli yarns. A total of 2,000 pounds of 100 and 120 Msi moduli material will be produced during an 18 month production demonstration effort and purchased by the Government. Phase I material will be production qualification material and therefore will be allocated to qualified Government and industry agencies in exchange for their test results. The independent test results will be compiled with the contractor test results and then compared by the Government to the contract material specification to determine acceptability of as-produced material. See Table 1.

FIBER PROPERTY	P-100 MIN	P-100 MAX	P-120 MIN	P-120 MAX
Modulus (Msi)	105	115	120	— —
Tensile Strength (ksi)	325	— —	325	— —
Yield (g/m)	0.30	0.34	0.30	0.36
Density(g/cc)	2.13	— —	2.13	— —
Elongation (%)	0.3	— —	0.25	— —
Size—If Approp (wt/o)	0.5	1.00	0.5	1.00
Twist — If Approp (t/in)	0.65	1.00	0.65	1.00

Table 1. Production Specifications for MPP Carbon Fiber/Yarn.

A determination of material acceptability will be the main criteria for Government approval for the contractor to proceed into Phase II. The production of this yarn will utilize different qualified sources of petroleum pitch to assure that the end products are insensitive to variable source materials. The yarn material will be furnished with either a metal matrix, epoxy or thermoplastic compatible sizing, thus addressing composite manufacturer's fabrication requirements.

4.2 Phase II

Phase II will be a full-scale production effort where the Government will commit to purchase, over a three year period, the difference between what the contractor sells on the open market and the agreed upon purchase com-

mitment quantities. The annual purchase commitment quantities are for 2,000 pounds of 100 Msi moduli and 1,500 Msi moduli materials (for a total of 10,500 pounds), thus establishing a qualified production rate capacity of 3,500 pounds/year. The contractor will be judged by their ability to adhere to approved marketing and quality assurance program plans.

5. APPLICATIONS

Defense and space applications require carbon fibers with high thermal stability, high modulus, low thermal expansion, high thermal conductivity and low density. High modulus and ultra-high modulus MPP carbon fibers are ideal for these applications, but to date, only several applications have been completed. Many more new applications are under development in space, missile and flight vehicle componentry.

5.1 Space Structures

Space structures encounter large thermal gradients as they pass in and out of the sun, or encounter man-made thermal or optical threats.

One very challenging area for the materials engineer is the development of very large, ultra-lightweight space structures. The high stiffness, low thermal expansion coefficient, low density and low outgassing characteristics of MPP carbon fibers lend themselves to these applications. Organic (thermosetting and thermoplastic) matrix and metal (aluminum, copper and magnesium) matrix composites in thin gages are being developed for tubular truss structural and special purpose components. Other potential applications include space station struts, communication antenna reflectors, optical support structures, weapons platform structures, and others.

5.2   Thermal Management Componentry

Many space, missile and aircraft system components operate at or near their temperature limits, and thus, the rapid transfer and dissipation of heat is essential to maintaining safe operating conditions. Highly efficient heat sinks based on high thermal conductivity composites have been developed

for these high heat load applications. Systems benefits have included increased reliability, reduced weight (less insulation) increased survivability in a laser environment, and selection of adjacent materials with a lower maximum operating temperature. Major uses are expected in electronic devices where rapid increases in heat flux generated per unit area are being experienced as chip sizes become smaller. Avionic circuit board substrates, in particular, should benefit from the highly conductive, low expansion MPP carbon fiber containing composites. Other applications of interest include: heat pipes, space thermal radiators, and various heat sinks.

5.3   Heat Protective Components

Defense, space and energy applications often encounter extremely high temperatures for a transient period of time. Various heat protective composites utilizing carbon fibers have been developed and used successfully in missile nosetips, rocket motor throats, aircraft brake discs and others. Rayon-based and PAN-based carbon fibers have been the most widely used, although MPP carbon fibers have found specialty uses. In these applications, the high carbon content, high fiber density, high stiffness and high thermal conductivity of the MPP carbon fibers were favored over other competing carbon fibers.

5.4 Flight Vehicle Structures

Most flight vehicle structures are stiffness limited, particularly control surfaces. MPP carbon fibers offer great promise for composite uses because of their superior stiffness properties. Composite control surfaces for very high velocity aircraft, transatmospheric flight vehicles and maneuvering re-entry bodies are envisioned.

5.5 Modified Carbon Fibers

The properties of UHM carbon fibers can be altered greatly by intercalation, coating or inclusion of a second phase in the fiber. Thermal electrical and mechanical properties of UHM MPP carbon fibers were shown to change significantly with bromine intercalation, and the brominated carbon fibers were suggested for potential applications like electromagnetic interference (EMI) shielding, conductive composite space structures, aircraft de-icing and lightning strike tolerant aircraft structures.

5.6 The Outlook

Applications developments utilizing high modulus MPP carbon fibers have progressed slowly, to date, because of uncertain fiber availability, high fiber costs, available physical forms, limited fabrication experience and an incomplete design data base. The assured availability of high modulus MPP carbon fibers over the next few years should stimulate the composite industry toward increased usage of these high performance carbon fibers.

6. SUMMARY

A multi-million dollar, Defense Production Act Title III project has been initiated to maintain and expand domestic production capacity for ultra-high modulus carbon yarns. A manufacturing capacity of 3,500 pounds per year is expected to be demonstrated during 1990. As fiber production increases, it is anticipated that fiber properties will improve, fiber quality will increase and fiber costs may decrease. These positive factors should stimulate the aerospace industry toward continued and higher fiber usage of MPP carbon yarns.

7. BIOGRAPHY

Mr Dennis S. Hager is the chief materials engineer for the Department of Defense's DPA Title III Program Office, responsible for technical management of over 50 million dollars worth of structural and electronic material production programs. Mr Hager began his career with the US Air Force Wright Aeronautical Laboratories where he was involved with structural research and development efforts dealing with high temperature materials and their coatings. Mr. Hager graduated from Wright State University in 1981 with a BS in Materials Engineering. In addition, he received his MS in Mechanical Engineering from the University of Dayton in 1985.

Donald L. Schmidt is an internationally recognized authority on ablative and carbon-carbon composites, and, a multi-client materials consultant for various government agencies. He retired in 1987 from the AF Materials Laboratory, Wright-Patterson AFB, OH where he was a supervisory Materials Engineer with responsibility for the AF Thermal Protection and Structural Materials area. While in government service, he was awarded two AF Meritorious Civilian Service Medals and numerous other awards including a $10,000 scientific achievement award for the conception and successful development of missile carbon-carbon nosetips. He has authored over 100 technical publications on high temperature materials, and, he is on the Technical Advisory Board of the SAMPE Quarterly.

8. REFERENCES

1. Anon., "The Defense Production Act Title III Program", AFSC Booklet, 1987.

34th International SAMPE Symposium
May 8-11, 1989

GRAPHITIZATION OF VAPOR GROWN CARBON FIBERS

Karren K. Brito, Applied Sciences,Inc., 800 Livermore, Yellow Springs, OH 45387
and
David P. Anderson & Brian P. Rice, University of Dayton Research Institute,
300 College Park, Dayton,OH 45469-0001

Abstract

Carbon fibers grown by chemical vapor deposition have been annealed to 2200, 2500, 2700, 2800 and 2900°C. These and as-grown fibers have been studied using SEM and x-ray diffraction of intact fibers. These fibers appear as cylinders on a small scale, but on a larger scale they appear branched and complex in shape, and also vary widely in their dimensions. Annealing causes the surface of the fiber to change in appearance, from smooth to corrugated, and causes the concentric layers to separate and crack. The x-ray diffraction shows that in the annealing process the growth of crystallites in the direction of the fiber axis lags behind the growth of crystallites perpendicular to the axis. The x-ray patterns indicate a very high degree of graphitization in the fibers annealed to 2700, 2800 and 2900°C.

1. INTRODUCTION

Fibers produced by chemical vapor deposition have a common morphology of concentric graphene layers parallel to the fiber axis creating the appearance of tree rings in the fiber cross-section. CVD fibers have large aspect ratios, and are easily converted to graphite fibers by a heat treatment. The CVD fibers can be classified by their dimensions and morphology. Dresselhaus[1] has used the microscopic appearance of these CVD carbon fibers to classify them as straight, vermicular or coiled. This work has focused on the so-called straight fibers.

Previous studies[2,3] have shown that heat treatment of these fibers dramatically affects their physical and chemical properties. In this study the morphological changes caused by heat treatment are characterized by examining the macroscopic and microscopic morphology of many straight CVD carbon fibers before and after various heat treatments.

2. EXPERIMENTAL

CVD fibers were grown in a batch process by catalytic pyrolysis of methane. The fibers were divided into six batches; one batch was kept as-grown and the five others were annealed at different temperatures. Heat treatment or annealing was done in a sealed Astro furance, Model 1000 under an argon atmosphere. The temperature was raised to a maximum of 2200, 2500, 2700, 2800 or 2900°C, held for 15 min. and allowed to cool before removing the fibers.

The diameter of the individual fibers was measured by a laser diffraction technique[4]. This method offers the advantage of detecting multiple fibers that appear as single fibers under visual inspection.

The x-ray diffraction experiments used ~2 mm fiber bundles. The bundles had been aligned with tweezers and attached to a holder with amorphous cyanoacrylate glue which drew the fibers together by a wicking action. The diffractometer was a Blake Industries system using a Huber 4-circle goniometer, CuKα radiation, a graphite incident beam monochromator, with a Vax-730 minicomputer controlling and storing the scintillation detector responses and motor commands.

The diffraction data was transferred to a mainframe computer for analysis[5]. This data includes intensity corrections for absorption, polarization, and incoherent scattering. Nonlinear least squares curve fitting of the symmetrical reflections to gaussian distributions were performed to accurately determine their positions and integral breadths. D-spacings were calculated from the peak positions using Bragg's Law[6] and the crystallite sizes were calculated using the Scherrer equation[7], from integral breadths corrected for instrumental broadening. Asymmetrical two-dimensional reflections were measured by hand and crystal sizes determined according to Warren and Bodenstein[8].

Computer plots of some of the data in the figures have been normalized to a maximum intensity of either the (10,0) or (11,0) reflections and vertically displaced for clarity in displaying scans of several samples in the same figure.

This x-ray technique of mounting an aligned fiber bundle in a diffractometer allows more complete information to be obtained than techniques employing either flat-film photography or ground fiber powders. Not reported before in x-ray of carbon fibers (although recognized for the electron diffraction[9]) is the need to tilt the fibers to obtain the maximum intensity from the off-axis 3-D crystal reflections. The off-axis three-dimensional crystal reflections can be observed quite clearly by tilting the fibers at an angle from the vertical equal to the angle the crystal normal makes with the fiber axis (i.e., ~15° for the (10,1) and ~20° for the (11,2) reflections). This tilting occurs in flat-film photography by coincidence; approximately correct for the (10,1) when using CuKα and for the (11,2) when using MoKα radiation.

At greater orientation of the graphene planes parallel to the fiber axis, a decrease in intensity of the off-axis reflections is expected in a meridional scan[9] and was in fact observed in the samples heat treated to a higher temperature.

The SEM photomicrographs were obtained on a JEOL 840 at 10kV using Polaroid Type 55 postive/negative film. The uncoated fibers (mounted in small bundles) were sufficiently conductive to avoid surface charging.

3. RESULTS AND DISCUSSION

3.1 Macroscopic Morphology and Statistical Distribution

These fibers appear straight in SEM micrographs but on a larger scale a more complex morphology is observed. Visual inspection of many fibers has revealed that many are multiple fibers and that many branch. Attempts to obtain a statistical distribution of lengths in a batch have been frustrated by the difficulty of clearly defining the length of a branched fiber. The dense growth of fibers and their branching leads to entanglement. Additionally, the fibers seem fragile at the branch points and manipulating them, to separate individual fibers and to align them with a calibrated grid, causes breakage. One batch yielded an average of about 1 cm for the length of the straight fragments that could be clearly separated. The range of fiber lengths in a single growth batch is large, and the distribution is not a normal distribution, with many short fibers occurring for each long fiber. Yet long fibers (10 - 25 cm) are a regular occurrence.

Fibers grown under the same conditions or even side-by-side do not have the same diameter. In some low magnification SEM micrographs, several fiber diameters can clearly be seen. Visually the diameter of a single fiber appears to diminish from the base to the tip. Multiple diameter measurements on a fiber 23 cm long showed that it diminished from 40 μm at the base to 18 μm at the tip. The measurement of all fiber diameters in a small aliquot gave a statistical distribution that is a broad asymmetrical peak, skewed towards the thick fibers. The value of the median changed with growth conditions; the larger its value the broader the peak.

3.2 Scanning Electron Microscopy

Figures 1 -12 are SEM micrographs of the six different fiber preparations. The tree ring morphology is clear in all of the cross-sections which includes a range of diameters. The as-grown fiber has a compact, cohesive structure with layers ~1μm thick. As the maximum temperature of the heat treatment increases, the layers appear to separate and crack; voids and flaws are obvious in the annealed fibers.

On this scale the longitudinal appearance of the fibers is straight and the occurrence of the multiple fibers is evident. Some fibers show periodic fluctuations in diameter; others have a uniform diameter. Both types of fibers occur in all batches examined. The outer surface of the as-grown fibers is relatively smooth. Annealing causes the outer surface to wrinkle. As the maximum temperature of the heat treatment increases the wrinkles deepen, giving the impression that the outer layer is too big for the fiber. All fibers, even those treated at 2900°C, maintain a circular cross-section.

3.3 X-ray Diffraction

X-ray data is presented in Figures 13-16, and variables calculated from the data are presented in Table 1. Both the uppermost curve in Figure 13 and the D-spacing between the graphene planes in Table 1 clearly indicated that the as-grown fibers have no graphitic structure. The empirical graphitization index, g_p, which is based on the difference between the turbostratic and ideal graphite has a negative value because turbostratic graphite is not a good model for the as-grown fibers. The diffraction pattern of the as-grown fiber is indicative of a low modulus fiber. Heat treatment to 2200°C causes significant graphitization as evidenced by the well defined but asymmetrical peaks for (00,2), (00,4), (10,0), and (11,0) reflections, and a large jump in g_p which now equals 23%. Yet the calculation, from the (10,0) or (11,0) lines, of the average crystallite dimensions in the graphene layer, L_a ,indicate that only two-dimensional crystallites are present.

With further increases in the maximum temperature of the heat treatment, the (11,0) line (at $2\theta = 77.47°$) becomes symmetrical, narrows, and increases in intensity indicating a loss of disorder, an increase in crystallite dimensions and an increase in the number of crystallites. The growth in crystallite size is confirmed by the increase in L_a. At 2500°C the (11,2) line appears as do three dimensional crystallites as indicated by the values for L_a calculated from the (11,1) or (10,1) lines. Table 1 shows that the crystallite growth parallel to the fiber axis is much slower than the growth of crystallites perpendicular to the fiber axis. The overall

diffraction pattern now corresponds to a high modulus fiber.

At 2700°C the (11,2) reflection is well defined at both $\chi = 90$ and 70 (see Figures 13 and 15), but at higher temperatures the intensity of this reflection differs. At $\chi = 70$ the peak narrows and increases in intensity while at $\chi = 90$ the peak diminishes (see Figure 16). Our interpretation of this phenomenon is that the first crystallites that grow in the direction of the fiber axis are misaligned, then at higher heat treatment temperatures the crystallites align with the axis.

Our data are easily interpreted by a model of the graphitization process developed from TEM data[10]. The first step of graphitization envisioned by this model is an increase in alignment between the graphene planes, producing isolated columnar crystallites. At higher temperatures the columnar crystallites connect, and L_a begins to increase, but the resultant structure is zigzagged or wavy ribbons of graphene layers. At even higher temperatures the graphene layers straighten by disappearance of twist and tilt boundaries.

Our observations agree with this model except that these different steps in the graphitization process occur at significantly higher temperatures . It is probable that the graphitization process is sensitive to more variables than just the maximum temperature reached.

4. CONCLUSIONS

X-ray examination of the small scale morphology indicates a high degree of crystalline perfection usually associated with high modulus fiber and other desirable physical properties. These findings seem to contradict the large scale observation of separated layers, cracks and voids in the fiber.

The empirical graphitization index is based on the D-spacing in the sample, and since we have observed that the D-spacing approaches the value for ideal graphite before the crystallites align in the direction of the fiber axis, it seems to overestimate the graphitic nature of the CVD fiber.

5. Anderson,D., "X-ray Analysis Software: Operation and Theory involved in Program 'DIFF' ",Technical Report AFWAL-TR-85-4079,June 1985; U.S. Air Force Materials Laboratory, Wright-Patterson Air Force Base, OH 45433

6. Scherrer,P., Gottinger Nachrichten, 2, 98 (1918).

7. Alexander, L.E., X-ray Diffraction Methods in Polymer Science, Wiley-Interscience, 1969, Chapter 7.

8. Warren, B.E., Bodenstein, P., Acta Cryst. 20, 602 (1966).

9. Fourdeux. R., Perret, R., and Ruland, W., J. Appl. Cryst., 1, 252 (1968).

10. Guigon, M., Oberlin, A., Desarmont,G., Fibre Sci. Technol. 20, 55 (1984) and 20, 177 (1984).

5. BIBLIOGRAPHY

1. Dresselhaus, et al., Graphite Fibers and Filaments, Springer-Verlag, 1988, p. 19.

2. Brito.K.K., Hagerhorst, J., Lake, M., Proceed. Am. Pys. Soc., March 1988.

3. Lake, M., Hickok, J.K., Brito, K.K., and Lin, R.Y., Proceed. Am. Phys. Soc. March 1989.

4. Gilliar, W., Bickel, W.S., Videen, G. and Hoar, D., Am. J. Phys., 55, 555 (1987).

6. BIOGRAPHIES

Karren K. Brito is Research Chemist for Applied Sciences, Inc. working on the development of cabon fibers and films by chemical vapor deposition. She has previously served on the faculties of Antioch College, Ecole Polytechnique (Paris), and Universidad del Zulia (Venezuela), specalizing in fast chemical kinetics. She received her Ph.D. from State University of New York at Buffalo in physical chemistry.

David P. Anderson is a Polymer Reseacher Scientist at the University of Dayton Research Institute working on the morphology of advanced composite materials. His current work is specifically directed at determining the structures of composite components by wide-angle x-ray diffraction both individually and in the composite itself. He received a Bachelor's degree in chemistry fron the University of Connecticut in 1973 and his Ph.D. in polymer science and engineering in 1981 from the University of Massachusetts. He gained industrial research experience between degrees and at DuPont prior to joining UDRI.

Brian Rice is a Research Engineer at the University of Dayton Research Institute specializing in the processing and characterization of advanced composite materials. He received his BS degree in chemical engineering in 1986 from Ohio State University and is currently working on a MS in materials science at the University of Dayton.

TABLE I : Graphitization in CVD fibers that have been heated treated to different temperatures.
All parameters are derived from x-ray diffraction data.

Crystallite sizes, nm^2

Annealing Temperature	D-spacing, nm^1	L_c, (00,2)	L_a, (10,0)	L_a, (10,1)	L_a, (11,0)	L_a, (11,1)	Crystallographic density, gcm^{-3}	g_p^3
As-grown	0.34990	2.2	---	---	---	---	2.17	-68%
2200°C	0.34206	21.8	21.7	---	24.6	---	2.22	23%
2500°C	0.33770	38.1	33.9	4.1	30.5	6.8	2.25	73%
2700°C	0.33697	39.4	30.3	11.7	43.1	11.2	2.26	82%
2800°C	0.33663	40.4	38.1	14.9	45.7	15.0	2.26	86%
2900°C	0.33590	36.5	39.9	15.7	42.6	20.5	2.26	94%

1. D-spacing calculated from (00,2) reflection

2. Calculated from the reflection indicated at $\chi = 90$.

3. The empirical graphitization index calculated from

$$g_p = \frac{(0.3440 - \text{D-spacing observed})}{(0.3440 - 0.3354)}$$

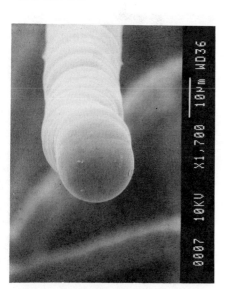

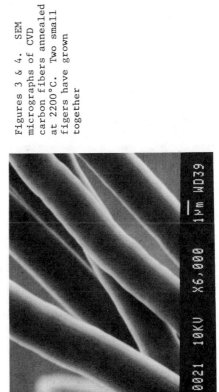

Figures 1 & 2.SEM micrographs of as-grown fibers. Notice the cohesive layers in the large dia-meter fiber.

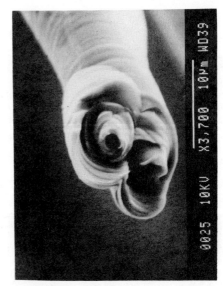

Figures 3 & 4. SEM micrographs of CVD carbon fibers annealed at 2200°C. Two small figers have grown together

197

Figures 5 & 6. SEM micrographs of CVD fibers annealed at 2500°C. The separation of the layers and the surface wrinkles are evident in this thin fiber.

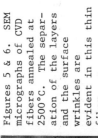

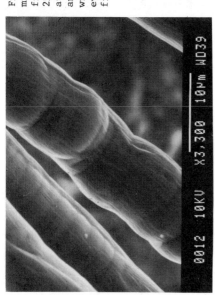

Figures 7 & 8. SEM micrographs of CVD fibers annealed at 2700°C. Two fibers appear to have grown together and many separations of the layers are evident.

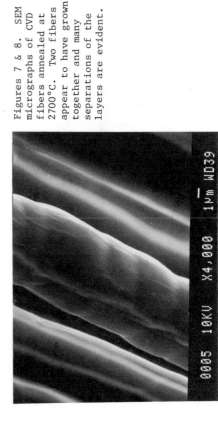

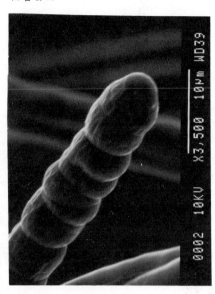

Figures 9 & 10. SEM micrographs of CVD fibers annealed at 2800°C.

Figures 11 & 12. SEM micrographs of CVD fibers annealed at 2900°C.

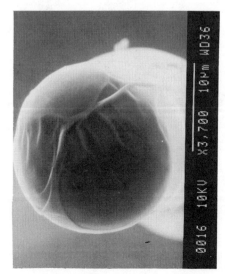

199

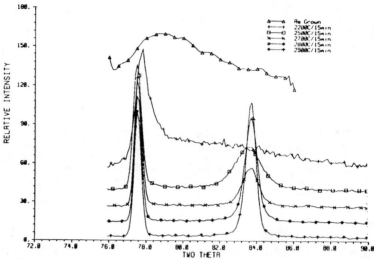

Figure 13. The x-ray reflections (11,0) and (11,2) at χ = 70 of CVD fibers that have been heat treated to 2200, 2500, 2700, 2800 and 2900°C and untreated fibers. Note that (11,2) reflection appears at 2500°C and its intensity increases as the annealing temperature increases.

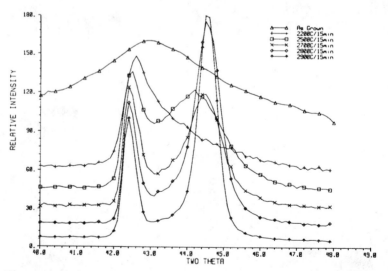

Figure 14. The x-ray reflections (10,0) and (10,1) at χ = 75 of CVD fibers that have been heat treated to 2200, 2500, 2700, 2800 and 2900°C and untreated fibers.

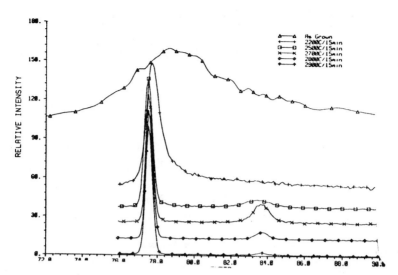

Figure 15. The x-ray reflections (11,0) and (11,2) at $\chi = 90$ of CVD fibers that have been heat treated to 2200, 2500, 2700, 2800 and 2900°C and untreated fibers. Note that the (11,2) reflection has its maximum intensity for the fibers annealed at 2700°C.

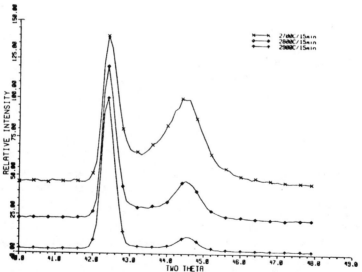

Figure 16. An enlargement of Figure 15 with only the fibers annealed at 2700, 2800 and 2900°C. The decrease of the intensity of the (11,2) is clarified.

HELTRA:HIGH PERFORMANCE CARBON FIBRE SPUN YARNS TAILORED TO
MEET WIDE RANGING ADVANCED MATERIAL REQUIREMENTS

R J Coldicott

T Longdon

Courtaulds Research

Advanced Composites

Coventry, UK

Abstract

By innovatively modifying fibre handling techniques and processes, an original range of high performance carbon yarns has been developed. The Heltra process produces staple yarns from a range of high modulus, intermediate modulus and high strain carbon fibres, which can be supplied treated for specific applications with epoxy size, PTFE, graphite and metal. These yarns offer the advantage of ultra fineness (as low as 0.1k equivalent) and suitability for a very wide range of processing techniques, including weaving, braiding, knitting and stitching. Since this unique process converts comparatively heavy continuous filament tow into fine staple yarns, the method is a very economic route to fine yarns and lightweight drapeable fabrics. With the degree of consistency and staple length distribution being close to that predicted by theory, the process results in a highly consistent yarn with minimal fibre damage. These yarns have exciting applications in the area of carbon/carbon composites. The use of a staple spun yarn with high tensile strength significantly increases interlaminar shear strength over continuous filament, with almost zero shrinkage compared to staple spun OPF. In conventional composite applications, there is an exceptionally high translation of tensile properties from the continuous tow to the yarn.

1. INTRODUCTION

The manufacture of carbon fibre for high performance composite applications has been established for over 25 years. A number of suppliers now produce a wide range of continuous filament tows from both PAN and pitch-based fibre routes. Typically these tows contain from 12000 (12k) down to 1000 (1k) filaments, and are presented to the composite manufacturer in the form of UD tapes or biaxial woven fabrics. In the latter case textile weavers have had to develop specialised techniques for handling and processing these very stiff fibres. Moreover, the production costs for continuous carbon tows rise steeply as the number of filaments in the tow is reduced: 1k tows are extremely expensive, and very few materials are available below 1k (fig.1). To overcome this problem Courtaulds have applied their textile expertise to develop a method for the production of very 'fine' spun staple carbon yarns for high performance end uses. Carbon yarns down to 100 filaments (0.1k) have been spun, permitting

the production of very lightweight, thin UD and woven materials for composite manufacture. The yarns process well on textile machinery. The Heltra process produces 100% carbon yarns, Grafitex, for use in thermoset composite production. The technique is also used to spin Filmix yarns, intimately blended carbon (and other reinforcement fibres) with thermoplastic fibres (PEEK, PEI, PPS), for the production of advanced thermoplastic composites. The current paper describes the Grafitex range of yarns, their properties and some of their applications. The Filmix yarns are described in a further paper presented at the current SAMPE symposium.

2. TECHNOLOGY

2.1 Heltra

The Heltra process, by innovatively modifying fibre handling and processing techniques, converts continuous filament tow to staple yarn.

A staple spun yarn consists a series of individual fibres that are placed to form a continuous overlapping assembly, being bound together by twist, which prevents fibre slippage by increasing the interfibre friction. An original range of high performance yarns has been developed, which include Grafitex, 100% carbon yarn. In spite of the discontinuity and twist in the fibre, there is a high translation of tensile properties from the continuous filament carbon tow to the Grafitex carbon yarn. Results of epoxy impregnated tow tests are presented in table 1 and confirm that up to 97% of the tensile modulus and 84% of the tensile strength are retained. When a yarn is twisted the angle of twist, and hence the angle of orientation of the individual fibres, is best described in terms of a twist factor. This twist factor is the product of the twist level (turns/m) and the square root of the linear density (tex$^{1/2}$). By combining composite theory for the orientation dependence of Youngs Modulus with the yarn twist factor, the dependence of modulus on twist factor can be determined for impregnated yarns. Fig 2 shows this theoretical curve together with a series of tested moduli for a range of differing twist factor Grafitex yarns. These results show that composite theory can be applied to a textile yarn structure.

Another unique feature of a staple spun yarn when compared to a continuous filament tow is the presence of fibre that protrudes from the main body of the yarn in the form of little hairs. The degree of hairiness is dependent on the twist of the yarn, a yarn with low twist possessing a greater degree of hairiness than one with high twist. This feature appears to offer an attractive increase in interlaminar shear strength when in composite form.

2.2 Grafitex

Since this process converts comparatively heavy continuous filament tow into fine staple yarns, the method is a very economic route to fine yarns. Singles yarns as fine as 50 filaments have been produced, giving a total of 100 filaments for a 2-ply yarn, 6.5 tex/59 denier. Whilst these carbon yarns offer the advantage of ultra fineness they also remain eminently suitable for the wide range of processing techniques; weaving, braiding, knitting and stitching, possessing a more textile like quality than conventional high performance fibre tows.

Although yarns produced by the Heltra process are made up of discontinuous fibres, the mean staple length of the fibres is about 100mm (approx. 4"), which is well above the critical length associated with composite materials. In fact the degree of consistency and staple length distribution are very close to those predicted by theory, fig. 3 & fig. 4, resulting in a highly consistent yarn with minimal fibre damage.

General yarn properties; tenacity, elongation, consistency, and hairiness, are given in table 2 for Grafitex yarns of differing count and twist.

The Grafitex carbon yarn variables include:

- source fibres, from a range of high modulus, intermediate modulus and high strain carbon;
- mass per unit length;
- number of plies;
- twist of both the single and plied yarn;
- coating, which can include epoxy sizes, PTFE, graphite and metal;
- hairiness.

These can all be tailored to suit specific applications, and current work involves the characterisation of all these yarn variables.

3. APPLICATIONS

3.1 Carbon/Carbon Composites

Carbon/carbon composites are materials that consist of carbon fibre embedded in a carbon matrix system. The aim is to combine the advantages of fibre reinforced composites such as high strength, stiffness and toughness with the refractory properties of structural ceramics. While these materials are chemically inert and biocompatible, possess good thermal stability, have a high resistance to thermal shock, and, most importantly, exhibit high strength and stiffness at high temperatures, the carbon matrix is unfortunately very brittle. This results in poor interlaminar properties and may result in the 'dusting out' of the matrix under fatigue loading.

Continuous filament carbon fibre tow gives excellent warp tensile performance, but has this design limitation of weak interlaminar properties. Previously known spun staple materials such as spun oxidised PAN fibre markedly increase interlaminar shear strength but at the cost of a 60% loss in tensile performance, whilst exhibiting high shrinkage in carbonisation (typically 35%). Recent independent research has demonstrated that Grafitex carbon yarns offer increases of over 70% in interlaminar shear strength while retaining nearly 70% of tensile strength, and exhibiting low shrinkage in carbonisation (typically 5%). This is a result of the hairy structure the yarn possesses, effectively providing additional 'through the thickness' reinforcement in the matrix. Continuing development is also producing yarns for ablative and friction applications as well as investigating carbon braided tubes as a novel building block for carbon/carbon structures.

3.2 Motorsport

An epoxy sized Grafitex plain weave fabric of $140g/m^2$ (4.1 oz/yd^2) has been used to successfully construct a fairing, seat and petrol tank for a Formula 1 motorcycle. The primary requirements were those of stiffness and light weight, since the components where fabricated from a single ply of fabric. There is additionally a need for damage tolerance in such a structure, and whilst the single carbon skin performed without problem it is expected that a blend of carbon/kevlar will be used in subsequent developments to enhance this aspect. The Heltra process can easily produce a blended carbon and kevlar yarn to maintain the single ply arrangement which is favoured, due to the weight constraints.

The Tyrrell Formula 1 Grand Prix team has been using a nose cone constructed from woven kevlar and braided glass fibre tubes during the past season. Whilst this structure has shown excellent energy absorption characteristics, recent tests have shown that Grafitex braided tubes exhibit even greater energy absorption. In fact this particular yarn yielded a higher value than a continuous filament carbon tow. Consequently there has been a great deal of interest shown in this by the Formula 1 fraternity, as a Grafitex crash box would not only give a reduction in weight but would also increase safety for the driver.

3.3 Medical

Designers have recognised the advantages of carbon fibre reinforced composites in medical applications for a while, where high strength and stiffness combined with light weight and good fatigue resistance are supplemented by the low absorption of X-rays. This has allowed radiographers to reduce the patients exposure to radiation whilst obtaining better images. Carbon fibre X-ray patient support couches have been manufactured for the past 15 years, being stiff enough to support people in cantilever with very little deflection, and hence allowing access to the patient from almost any angle. With ultrafine fabrics now being available through the utilisation of Grafitex yarns, other applications in the radiological field are being found. X-ray film cassettes can be fabricated from a knitted Grafitex structure, and mammography plates can also be constructed from these fine carbon yarns.

3.4 Composite Tooling

With the advent of high performance epoxy thermoset matrix systems composite component manufacturers have been given the opportunity to construct their tooling from materials which are directly comparable with those that are used in the component, offering a better match in thermal expansion, and the ability to construct tools without incurring costly and time consuming machining. These advantages of prepreg tooling can be increased by using Grafitex yarns, where the ultrafine fabrics can improve the surface finish, and the increased interlaminar shear properties of Heltra yarns reduce the likelihood of delamination.

3.5 Packing Yarns

The packing yarn industry has witnessed a substantial increase in the usage of both carbon and oxidised PAN fibres with the demise of asbestos. Consequently Heltra has developed a range of packing yarns from both fibre types that possess significant advantages over continuous filament tows in that the yarns are easier to braid, they have better bulk packing characteristics due to their circular cross-section, and they have a greater ability to absorb lubricants and coatings.

3.6 Conductive Yarns

The conductive properties of carbon can be increased by coating with metallic films, and nickel coated carbon fibres have been processed to form yarns that can be woven into conductive fabrics for use in EMI shielding applications. For increased electrical conductivity, carbon yarns can be plied with copper wire.

4. CONCLUSIONS

The ability to produce fine staple yarn from relatively heavy continuous filament carbon tows without a significant reduction in tensile property translation has been demonstrated, together with significant increases in interlaminar properties in certain applications.

The process enables yarns to be constructed for specific applications, with predetermined properties, that can then be manipulated using the wide range of processing techniques. These facts will be of great interest to engineers and designers, who will be able to appreciate the flexibility and performance advantages that these products provide.

BIOGRAPHY

Tony Longdon received his BSc degree in Chemistry from Imperial College in 1973. His past work has included the development of fibre processing techniques and textile materials for industrial and engineering applications. He is a Scientific Associate with Courtaulds Research, responsible for work on textile-related composites.

Robert Coldicott was awarded his Bsc degree in Physics by Leeds University in 1987. He is a Research Scientist with Courtaulds Research, and has worked on the resin transfer moulding of knitted structures and the development of novel high performance spun yarns.

TABLE 1

Property Translation - Resin Impregnated Tow Test

Material	Tensile Strength	Tensile Modulus	Fibre Density
Continuous Filament 12K tow	4.2 GPa (610 KSI)	235 GPa (34.1 MSI)	1.80 g/cm^3 (0.065 lb/in^3)
Grafitex 80 Tex 2-ply Yarn	3.5 GPa (512 KSI)	228 GPa (33.1 MSI)	1.80 g/cm^3 (0.065 lb/in^3)
% Retained	84	97	100

TABLE 2

General Yarn Properties

Yarn M.U.L.	Twist	Tenacity (cN/tex)	Elongation (%)	Consistency (CV%)	Hairiness $\Sigma 3$
44 tex	8tpi	70.7	1.1	12.1	4300
44 tex	9tpi	75.2	0.9	12.3	608
44 tex	13tpi	61.9	1.0	12.3	155
88tex	5tpi	65.1	1.0	8.5	3956
88tex	9tpi	61.2	0.9	8.4	429
88tex	13tpi	35.2	1.1	8.3	255
176tex	4tpi	77.7	1.5	6.8	4882
176tex	7tpi	59.6	1.4	6.8	654
176tex	9tpi	55.7	1.3	6.8	208

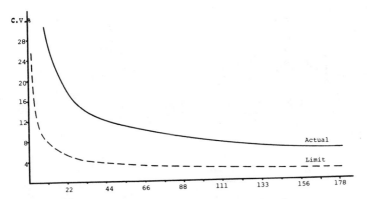

Figure 3. Limit and Actual Irregularities of Grafitex Yarn

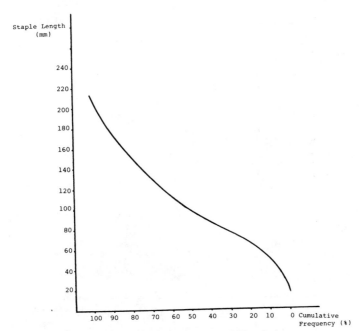

Figure 4. Staple Length Distribution of 88tex 2-ply
Grafitex Yarn

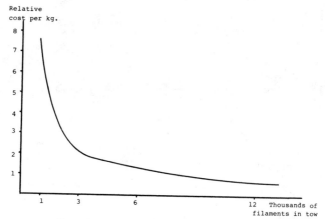

Figure 1. Carbon Tow Size vs Relative Production Cost

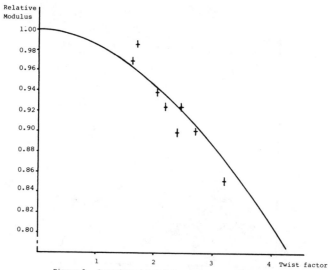

Figure 2. Dependence of Modulus on Twist Factor for Impregnated
Yarns Together With Tested Modulii

DEVELOPMENT OF ORGANIC FIBER-REINFORCED
COMPOSITE MATERIALS
Dr. Benjamin C. Tobias
Mechanical Engineering Department
Footscray Institute of Technology
Footscray, Victoria, Australia

Abstract

The organic fibers were extracted from abaca plants which are dominantly found in tropical parts of the world under the banana family. These natural fibers are the end product of processed abaca plants. They are part of the plant's fibro-vascular system. This investigation was intended to determine the mechanical properties of the multicelled fiber in four test configurations, the matrix used, and the fabricated composite lamina. Fiber's relative mechanical properties were compared and evaluated to be suitable as reinforcement in plastic. Its strength was found to be as high as those found in some synthetic fibers. Single strand fiber properties were used in the micromechanics analysis of 60% long abaca fiber reinforced/modified epoxy lamina. The resin dominated properties were void and hygrothermally degraded resulting in a reduction of less than 10% from room temperature dry properties. Actual Weibull strength of composite decreased 3% from theoretical strength attributed to a mixed mode of interfacial bond between fiber and matrix as observed in initial fractographic study of fractured surfaces. Abaca fiber reinforcement greatly improved the resin properties.

1. INTRODUCTION

Today, the commercially known fiber-reinforced composites have been made of synthetic fibers. These fibers play an important role in the development of new materials. Starting with glass and nylon in the 1930s together with carbon, boron, and kevlar fibers in the 1950s, they comprised the major constituent in composite technology. The success of these fibers as reinforcement in plastics opens new avenues of research including the development of fine ceramic fibers reinforcement in metals and ceramics. (1) However, the emergence of this class of composites also led to the deviation of further development in plant fibers composites. In fact, some plant and vegetable fibers were used in commercial high performance composites in early aircrafts, pneumatic tires, and automotive timing gears. (2)

The fibers and the matrix maintain their own properties. However, when these constituents are combined into a composite material it will have distinctive properties which neither the fibers nor the matrix can achieve alone. Fibers are the main load carrying constituent whereas the matrix serves the fibers in a capacity as a load transfer medium, keeping the fibers in desired position, and protecting .it from detrimental effects of the environment.

The development of abaca fiber-reinforced composite materials requires knowledge of both fibers and matrix properties which are necessary in the theoretical and actual design consideration of composite materials.

2. THE ABACOM

Attention is focused on developing an abaca fiber reinforced modified epoxy composite materials, ABACOM. The constituents used were 60% long abaca fibers and a mixture of thermosetting resins.

2.1 Fiber

The fibers were extracted from the abaca plants (Musa Textilis). They are classified as leaf fibers among the plant and vegetable fibers. The plant grows 6m (20ft) high and has large oblong leaves. It consists of 12 to 30 stalks radiating from the central root system. Each of the stalks is 2.7-6.7m (9-22ft) tall with a trunk 10-20cm (4-8 inch) wide at the base. The sheaths forming the stalk expand into the overhanging leaf structure (p.501 of ref. 2). It is the outer sheaths that contain the valuable fibers which run lengthwise in the sheaths.

When the plant is about two years old it bears blossoming flowers indicating the most favourable condition for fiber processing. The stalk is cut down and the outer fiber bearing layer of each successive leaf stem is stripped off in the form of ribbons or tuxies.(3) The tuxies are scraped to remove the pulp and other waste materials, leaving the cleaned fibers which are then dried. The fibers vary in color and strength relative to the sheaths locations in the stalk. Outermost sheaths contain short, strong, and discolored fibers, which are in contrast with the inner sheaths. It has a chemical composition of 70.2% cellulose,

21.8% hemi-cellulose, 0.6% pectins, 5.7% lignin, 1.5% water soluble compounds, and 0.2% fats and waxes, and a chemical analysis of 63.72% cellulose, 11.83% moisture, 1.02% ash, 21.83% lignin and pectin, and 1.6% extractives by percentage weight (p. 500 of ref. 2). These natural fibers are multicelled and are not readily split into the components cells. It ranges from 1.8 tó 3.4m (6-11ft) in length, and 0.01 to 0.28mm (0.0004-0.011 inch) in width. The cells are composed of microfibrils which are groups of parallel cellulose chains. Individual cells or ultimate fibers have an average length of 6mm (0.24inch) and an average diameter of 0.024mm (0.0009 inch), (p. 501 of ref. 2). It contains spiral molecules that are parallel to one another which accounts for its low percent elongation (p. 499 of ref. 2).

2.2 Matrix

The major thermosetting resins used in conjunction with fiber reinforcement are the epoxy resins which has the advantage of being cured at room temperature with negligible liberated volatiles during curing.[4] The embedding expoxy resin can be modified to suit its particular application. Its outstanding properties of low shrinkage, excellent adhesion, high resistance to detrimental effects of the environment, and ease of application for casting and encapsulation are the underlying factors in choosing epoxy as a starting resin of the matrix used in ABACOM. This matrix of solid thermosetting resin is a mixture of 616ml Araldite D, 247ml Thiokol, and 137ml Hardener LC136LV. Mixture of Araldite D and Hardener LC is ideal for large room cured casting where low exotherm is essential.[5] Foremost, the mixture was dictated by the type of application, service environment, and cost in the development of ABACOM. Araldite D, an epoxy type of polymer was the starting material. This was thoroughly mixed with Thiokol and Hardener for enhancement of polymerization or curing reaction at room temperature in a short time.

2.3 Composite Lamina

The main requirement of fiber-reinforced composite's development is for the fiber to have better strength and stiffness compared with the resin. Composite strength is determined by the strength of the reinforcing fibers and the nature and strength of the bond between the fibers and the matrix. Fiber-matrix interface plays a significant role in the mechanical properties of the lamina through stress transfer. In the development of composite lamina the long abaca fibers are incorporated into the modified epoxy matrix to form the composite material.

2.4 Composite Fabrication

The sheet mould was first treated
with a release agent (wax). A
coating of liquid modified epoxy
resin was brushed on the surface of
the mould. The abaca fibers which
were in direct contact with each
other were placed and laid
longitudinally over the mould. The
fibers were worked into intimate
contact with the mould surface by
hand and compressive action as
schematically shown in Figure 1.

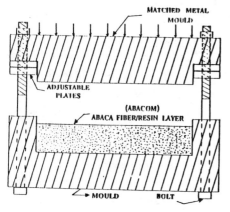

FIG. 1. Schematic diagram of ABACOM
thin sheet fabrication

Additional fibers and resin were
added in building up the lamina in
accordance with the constituents
relative volume fractions and sheet
geometry. The quantity of abaca
fibers needed in the lamina required
compression to bring the lamina
into its desired thickness of
5mm (0.2 inch). In this connection,
a matched metal mould is pressed
against the impregnated fibers.

This procedure also eliminated
bubbles formation in the resin.
Curing reaction initiated and
proceeded at room temperature for
24 hours. The mould was designed
to produce a composite lamina of
400 x 400 x 5mm (16 x 16 x 0.2 inch).

3.   EXPERIMENTATION

There were three main approaches
in the experimental determination
of strength, modulus, and percent
elongation. One involving the
fibers of four different fiber test
geometries, i.e., single fiber,
single yarn, single strand, and
three strand. The other two tests
were tension test of the matrix
and undirectional tension test of
the lamina and failure investigation of fractured surfaces.

3.1 Specimen

Nine tension test specimens were
prepared from the fibers, five from
the resin mixture, and thirteen
from the fabricated lamina. A
great deal of information was
available for standardized tension
test of the fiber and resin but not
for the composite lamina because of
the non-synthetic fiber used.

3.1.1 Fibers

All test specimens were selected
at random from the abaca 5mm
(0.2 inch) diameter Manila rope.
Tension tests were made possible
by designing special moulds at the
fiber ends for grip attachment
shown in Figure 2.

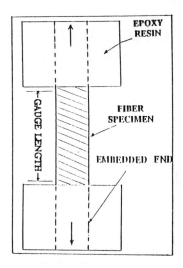

EPOXY RESIN

GAUGE LENGTH

FIBER SPECIMEN

EMBEDDED END

FIG. 2. Abaca fiber tension specimen with embedded ends for wedge action grips

Fiber ends were embedded into the epoxy resin. A gauge length of 50mm (2 inch) was used in all specimens with the following geometry: single fiber, average cross section, 0.11 x 0.269mm (0.0004 – 0.011 inch); single yarn (thread of twisted fibers), 2mm (0.08 inch) diameter; single strand (two twisted yarns), 3mm (0.12 inch) diameter; and three strand (three twisted strands), 5mm (0.2 inch) diameter.

3.1.2 Matrix

The specimens were rough cut with a bandsaw from a solid modified epoxy resin sheet specially made for this purpose. The rough sides were surface finished with descending grades of emery paper. Test and specimen geometry were made in accordance with ASTM D638 designations.

3.1.3 Lamina

Undirectional tension specimens were rough cut with a bandsaw from the fabricated composite lamina and the sides were finished similar to the matrix. Having no known standard tension test of fiber-reinforced composite materials with fiber modulus less than 20 GPa (ASTM D3039) and with natural fibers reinforcement for that matter, tension specimens with the same dimensions as the matrix were used instead.

3.2 Equipment and Procedure

Tension test and fracture analysis were conducted through the facilities at Footscray Institute of Technology and Royal Melbourne Institute of Technology. The uniaxial strength, modulus, and per cent elongation were determined by static tension test using the INSTRON machine in accordance with ASTM D2256, and Australian Standard AS 1504 designations for the fibers, and ASTM D638 for the matrix. The tensile specimen was held in the INSTRON by wedge action grips and pulled at crosshead speed of 50mm/min. A load–displacement diagram was obtained for each test. Fractographic study of fractured surfaces was done using the scanning electron microscope.

3.2.1 Specific Gravity of Abaca Fibers

Lack of information about other fiber physical properties made it necessary to include in this investigation the determination of its specific gravity which was measured using the immersion weighing system as specified by ASTM D792. Samples were approximately 38 grams in weight, and were weighed to three significant figures with an analytical balance. Water was used as immersion fluid. Comparison of weights in air before and after immersion indicated absorption of water by all ten specimens. Hence, values were read immediately after immersion with a sinker. An average specific gravity of 0.938 was calculated.

4. DATA ANALYSIS

It was necessary to compliment the large variation of experimental data as observed particularly for the fibers and composite lamina. The statistical nature of the fibers and resin properties led to some variations in fiber strength, and the composite strength taking into account the combined influence of both constituents. Instead of assuming a normal distribution of data, the variation has been realistically represented using the Weibull distribution.[6,7] Weibull normal probability plot was utilized in plotting the data points. A best fit curve was drawn through the data points which turned out to be closed to linear indicating an approximate normal distribution (p. 348 of ref. 6). Figure 3 shows a typical result for composite lamina. The extreme points on such a plot usually dev-

iates from the straight line. However, this deviation at the tails are normally disregarded (p. 348 of ref. 6).

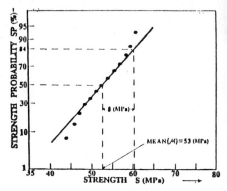

FIG. 3. Strength of ABACOM normalized in Weibull's probability plot.

From the plot, the mean value of strength corresponding to 50% probability scale level and standard deviation corresponding to an increment level between 50% and 84% have been estimated.

5. THEORETICAL ANALYSIS

For fibers to have the same length and cross-section, the tensile failure of the fibers will precipitate a tensile failure of the composite. The non-resin and resin dominated mechanical properties have been evaluated using the micromechanics design equations.[8] Single strand properties were utilized in the theoretical design of composite lamina because the results under this test are more accurate measure of strength and elongation as discussed in ASTM D2256. Substituting the following values:

fiber strength (S_{ft}) 94.4MPa (13.7ksi), fiber modulus (E_{f11}) 1578MPa (220ksi), fiber volume fraction (k_f) 0.6, matrix strength (S_m) 30MPa (4.4ksi), matrix modulus (E_m) 61.8MPa (9ksi), void (k_v) 5% resin glass transition temperature (T_{GD}) 160°C (320°F), moisture (M_m) 1%, and ambient temperature (T_o) 25°C (77°F) into the equations for the non-resin dominated strength and modulus, and the resin dominated transverse strength the following are obtained:

Longitudinal strength, S_{C11T}

$$S_{C11} \cong k_f \ S_{ft} \qquad (1)$$
$$\cong 56.64 \text{ MPa (8.2ksi)}$$

Longitudinal modulus, E_{C11}

$$E_{C11} = k_f \ E_{f11} + k_m \ E_m \qquad (2)$$
$$= 976.92 \text{ MPa (141.8ksi)}$$

Transverse tensile strength void degraded and dry, S_{22} (dry)

$$S_{C22 \ (dry)} = [1 - (k_f \ 1/2 - k_f)$$
$$(Em/E_{f22}) \ ] \ S_{MTV} \quad (3)$$
$$= 16.5 \text{ MPa (2.4ksi)}$$

where:

$$S_{MTV} = [1 - [4 \ k_V/(1-k_f \ \pi]^{1/2} \ ] \ S_m \qquad (3a)$$

Transverse tensile strength void and hygrothermally degraded, $S_{C22(hy)}$

$$S_{C22(hy)} = [1-(k_f \ 1/2 - k_f)$$
$$(E_{md}/E_{f22})] \quad S_{MTVH} \ (4)$$
$$= 15.44 \text{ MPa (2.2ksi)}$$

where:

$$E_{md} = (Em) \ [T_{GW} - T)/T_{GD} - To] \ ^{1/2} \qquad (4a)$$

$$S_{MVTH} = (S_{MTV}) \ [T_{GW} - T)/T_{GD} - To]^{1/2} \qquad (4b)$$

$$T_{GW} = (0.005M_m^2 - 0.10M_m + 1.0) \ T_{GD} \qquad (4c)$$

These results illustrate how various strength and other mechanic -al properties are interrelated and it also provides a quantitative view of micromechanics strength behavior of the abaca fiber-rein- forced composite.

6. RESULTS AND DISCUSSION

Figure 4 delineates a typical load- displacement diagram of the fiber. It exhibits a knee portion which does not represent a property of the fiber. It is caused by taking up of slack, seating of specimen, and interaction of twisted fibers. This portion of the curve was compensated in determing the correct values of properties by giving the corrected zero point on the displacement axis. The curve is a hookean type with a linear portion to some point then non-linear up to the point of initial breaking of the fiber.

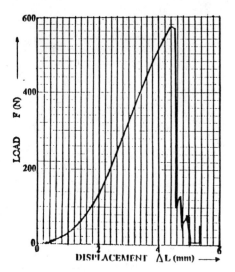

FIG. 4. Typical load-displacement diagram of Abaca fiber (single strand).

Loading ends as designed for INSTRON wedge action grips satisfied the test requirement because of the absence of fiber pullout in the resin, fibers fractured within the gauge section, and attaining a minimum breaking load of 1.7N (0.38lb) for 5mm (0.2 inch) diameter three strand which confirmed with the result specified in AS 1504. Maximum fiber mean breaking load of 158000g (348lb), was obtained from Figure 5 which was then converted to tenacity defined as the breaking load per denier (g/denier).

Denier as defined is weight in grams of 9000m (29,520 ft) of the specimen. This was determined and found to be 154800g (341lb) for the 5mm (0.2inch) diameter three strand, 51600g (114lb) for 3mm (0.12 inch) diameter single strand, and 25800g (11.7lb)

for 2mm (0.08 inch) diameter single yarn. Hence, knowing the tenacity, and average specific gravity of the fibers, its equivalent strength in MPa was calculated using the equation, Strength (MPa) = tenacity (g/denier) x density (g/cm^3) x 88.3 (p.542 of ref 4.).

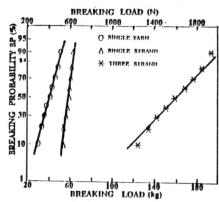

FIG. 5. Breaking load of abaca fiber relative to its lay out as normalized in Weibull's plot.

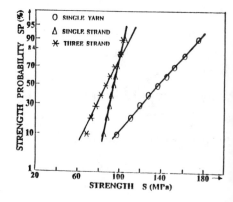

FIG. 6. Strength of abaca fiber relative to its lay out as normalized in Weibull's plot.

Figure 6 delineates the fibers relative strength (MPa) of 91.6MPa (13.3ksi) for single strand in particular can be obtained. The curves in Figure 5 and Figure 6 dep -ict contrasting results. As delineated, the three strand shows the lowest strength and initial modulus (evaluated as tenacity per elongation) in spite of its high breaking load compared with the other configurations. This was expected considering the high denier value of the three strand. Figure 7 shows the strength of the fibers at different tension test configuration. As the number of strands increases the fiber strength decreases. This kind of result has also been generally observed in synthetic fibers (p.20 of ref. 7).

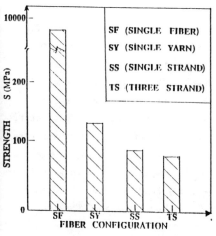

FIG. 7. Comparison of fiber strength with fiber lay out.

Tensile test results of resin mixture differed with the unmodified epoxy. An average strength of

30MPa (4.4ksi) was obtained out of the mixture showing a 25% decrease from the minimum value given for unmodified Araldite D plus Hardener LC. The reduction can be attributed to the addition of Thiokol and other test variables. However, the fibers strength and modulus are still considerably higher compared with the given value for the unmodified resin. The resin also shows a hookean stress-strain curve with large plastic deformation. In particular, the modulus of elasticity was calculated corresponding to a specified extension of 1% gauge length.

Figure 8 delineates the relative properties of the fibers, matrix, and composite lamina. As shown, the composite properties fall between the fibers and the matrix. Specific -ally, matrix failure strength is less than the fiber strength. On the other hand, the fiber failure strain is lower than the matrix strain. These results are also generally observed in synthetic fiber reinforced composite (p.76 of ref. 7). Attaining high values of strength, 53MPa (8ksi) and modulus, 1514MPa (220ksi) for the composite lamina satisfied the composite design of greatly improved plastic properties. Accordingly, the strength and modulus of plastics can significantly improve when reinforced by reinforcing fibers (p.230 of ref. 4).

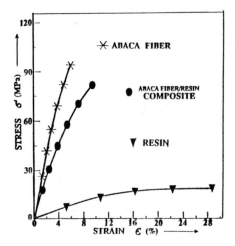

FIG. 8. Effects of Abaca fiber reinforcement on the mechanical properties of modified epoxy matrix.

The transverse tensile strength given in Equation 4 is a resin dominated property with hygrothermal effects. From this equation, a reduction of 7% compared with dry room temperature (Equation 3) is evident. Hygrothermal condition promotes this small further reduction from void degraded transverse strength as a result of nominal bonding at fiber matrix interface, and the differences of actual resin properties and the neat resin properties.

Correlating the results, actual composite strength decreased 6% from micromechanics strength (Equation 1) which is influenced greatly by the fiber content. It shows a small variation between experimental and theoretical result, an attribution to relatively good stress transfer between fibers and matrix in the presence of moderate interfacial bond as observed in initial fractographic studies of fractured surfaces. In essence, composite failure is characterized by combined mechanism. Some fibers showed clean surfaces, and others exhibited surfaces coated with thin layers of resin, evidence of debonding and absence of fiber-matrix debonding respectively. Thin cracks were observed between fiber and matrix, and lear impressions were also observed in the matrix from which the fibers were pulled out an indication of cohesive failure in the matrix.

7. CONCLUSIONS

Development of ABACOM encompasses very promising results and from which the following conclusions appear warranted: 1. Abaca fibers have strength and stiffness that approach that of some known synthetic fibers. 2. Abaca fibers have superior strength but moderate stiffness compared with other natural fibers. 3. Resin mixture constituent used in the fabrication of lamina is adequate to give inter--facial bonding. 4. There is good theoretical and experimental correlation in abaca fiber-reinforced composite material. 5. Abaca fiber reinforcement considerably improved the matrix properties. 6. The composite material is relatively easy to fabricate and very safe to work with at room temperature. 7. With the availability of inexpensive fibers, the developed composite materials can economically compete against other materials in the market today.

8. REFERENCES

1. Bunsell, A.R., A Journal of the Science and Technology of Engineering Materials. Institute of Metals and Materials Australasia. Vol. 11 (1988), pp.78-84.

2. Grayson, M., Encyclopedia of Composite Materials and Components, John Wiley and Sons, N.Y., 1983, pp.373-375.

3. The New Encyclopedia Britannica, 15th Edition, Encyclopedia Britannica, Inc., Vol. 1, 1988, p.6.

4. Chanda, M., Roy, S.K., Plastic Technology Handbook, Marcel Dekker, Inc., N.Y., 1987, pp.189-232.

5. CIBA-GEIGY Australia Ltd., Plastic Department, Instruction Sheet.

6. Collins, J.A., Failure of Materials in Mechanical Design Analysis Prediction Prevention, John Wiley & Sons Inc., N.Y., 1981, pp.344-351.

7. Mallick, R.K., Fiber-Reinforced Composites Materials Manufacturing and Design, Marcel Dekker, Inc., N.Y., 1988, pp.180-184.

8. Weeton, J.W., et al, Engineers Guide to Composite Materials, American Society for Metals, Metals Park, Ohio, 1987, pp.3.3-3.22.

9. BIOGRAPHY

Benjamin C. Tobias BSME, MSME, Ph.D.; Lecturer of Mechanical and Materials Engineering; born July 27, 1946, Philippines; education: BSME (Silliman University), MSME & Ph.D. (Oregon State University); Instructor of Engineering, 1971-1975, Assistant Professor of Mechanical Engineering, 1978-1980, Silliman University; Lecturer of Metallurgy & Materials Engineering, 1987, Royal Melbourne Institute of Technology; Lecturer of Mechanical Engineering, 1987, Footscray Institute of Technology; registered professional; active involvement in applied and basic research of energy systems and materials; design consultant; address: Footscray Institute of Technology, P.O. Box 64, Footscray, Victoria, Australia, 3011.

CYANATE ESTERS - AN EMERGING FAMILY OF VERSATILE COMPOSITE RESINS

D. A. Shimp, J. R. Christenson and S. J. Ising
Hi-Tek Polymers, Inc.
9800 E. Bluegrass Parkway
Louisville, KY 40299

Abstract

The development of a family of six cyanate-functional thermosetting resins is described, each member molecularly tailored to meet processing and performance needs of advanced circuit board substrates and structural composites. Relationships of monomer chemical structure to viscosity (140 cps to crystalline), homopolymer Tg (240-290°C), elongation at break (3-6%, dielectric constant (2.6-3.1), inherent flame retardancy, moisture absorption (1-3%) and other key properties are developed. Comparisons with multifunctional epoxies and toughened bismaleimides demonstrate several advantages of the ring-forming cyanate esters with respect to processing characteristics, toughness properties, ease of alloying with high Tg thermoplastics, adhesion, elimination of brominated flame retardants, hydrophobicity and reduction of dielectric loss properties over a broad frequency range.

1. INTRODUCTION

Cyanate ester resins are bisphenol derivatives containing the ring-forming cyanate (-O-C≡N) functional group. Chemically, this family of thermosetting monomers (see Fig. 1) and their prepolymers are esters of bisphenols and cyanic acid which cyclotrimerize to substituted triazine rings upon heating (Fig. 2). Conversion, or curing, to thermoset plastics forms three-dimensional networks of oxygen-linked triazine rings and bisphenol units, correctly termed polycyanurates. Because no leaving groups or volatile byproducts are formed during cure, the cyclotrimerization curing reaction is classified as addition polymerization.

Five distinctive structural features of polycyanurates contribute to unique performance characteristics:

- Single atom ring linkages (↑Tg)
- 67% -O- linkage (toughness)
- Low X-link density (toughness)
- Balanced dipoles-short moment (↓Dk)
- Absence of active H (↓H_2O abs.)

2. NEW COMPOSITE REQUIREMENTS

The principal end uses for cyanate esters are as matrix resins for printed wiring board (PWB) laminates and structural composites. The 1980's have brought major changes in the performance requirements of high speed logic circuits, RF/microwave telecommunication switches, radar and military IC packages:

- Higher circuit density intensifies problems with heat generation and impedance matching in high speed devices. Lower dielectric constant (Dk) and dissipation factor (Df) are advantageous.
- Faster signal speed is achieved by selecting insulating resins and substrate reinforcements

with lower Dk values.

- Surface mounting of chip packages requires reduction of substrate thermal expansion coefficients and introduces resin compatibility problems (microcracking) with low CTE reinforcements such as Kevlar®
- Higher reliability translates to improved dimensional stability (↑resin Tg), lower moisture absorption (less moisture effects on Dk and Df), increased thermal stability during processing and solder repair, and reduced potential for conductor corrosion (halide ion generation).

In the last ten years, aerospace composites have evolved into damage-tolerant primary and secondary structures utilizing blends, or alloys, of thermosetting and thermoplastic resins. Applications in radome construction and aircraft with reduced radar signatures seek resins with "microwave transparency", approached via the reduction of dielectric constant and dissipation factor values. Newer, more attractive processes for less costly production of structural composites, i.e. filament winding, resin transfer molding and pultrusion, require low viscosity resins which do not sacrifice matrix performance.

3. MONOMERS

Bisphenol A dicyanate, the precursor of Triazine A resin, was commercially introduced in the mid 1970's by Bayer AG. Mitsubishi Gas Chemical (BT resins) and Hi-Tek Polymers (AroCy™ resins), under license to Bayer, currently produce higher purity grades of this monomer. Hi-Tek Polymers developed and introduced under the AroCy trademark four structural variants utilizing novel bisphenol precursors to achieve greater hydrophobicity, reduced dielectric loss properties, inherent flame retardancy and a low viscosity liquid physical state. Dow Chemical Co. has introduced XU 71787, a cycloaliphatic modified cyanate ester resin designed to lower dielectric loss properties and moisture absorption. Table 1 associates monomer chemical structures with physical state and homo-

polymer features.

With reference to the Fig. 1 model, these structural modifications encompass:

- o-Methylation (AroCy M)
- Thio (-S-) linkage (AroCy T)
- Fluorocarbon linkage (AroCy F)
- Asymmetric linkage (AroCy L)
- Cycloaliphatic linkage (XU 71787)

4. PREPOLYMER RESINS

Partial homopolymerization of dicyanate monomers to 30-50% conversion levels forms amorphous prepolymer resins ranging in physical state from tacky semisolids to friable solids. Prepolymers of the AroCy B, M and F series are soluble in MEK laminating solvent. Unlike the series of difunctional bisphenol epoxy resins, which vary from liquids to hard resins via backbone extension, cyanate ester prepolymers develop cured-state properties which are identical to those of cured dicyanate monomers. In essence, the homopolymerization reaction can be interrupted at any degree of conversion up to ~55% and resumed after formulation or fiber reinforcement. Thus prepolymers provide a versatile means of adjusting resin molecular weight and associated rheological properties over a broad range without changing cured-state properties. Table 2 compares properties of some commercially available prepolymers.

5. REACTION CHEMISTRY

Cyanate ester monomers and prepolymer resins are generally polymerized via cyclotrimerization to polycyanurates, but can also undergo thermally reversible additions to active hydrogen compounds and will co-react with epoxide functionality to form commercially useful disubstituted oxazoline structures. These reactions and their acceleration with catalysts will be discussed in more detail.

5.1 Cyclotrimerization/Catalysis

The formation of substituted triazine rings (cyanurates) via the cyclic addition of three aryl cyanates (Fig. 2), involves a series of step-growth reactions. High purity monomers require the addition of two catalysts:

- An active hydrogen source such

as nonylphenol (2 to 6 phr).

- A soluble coordination metal compound, e.g. zinc octoate or cobalt acetylacetonate, which "gathers" cyanate groups into ring-forming proximity.

Metal concentrations of 5 to 300 ppm are typical. Carboxylates (high activity) and acetylacetonate chelates (latent activity) of zinc, copper and cobalt are preferred metal catalysts. Predissolving the transition metal compounds in nonylphenol facilitates their incorporation into hot melt formulations.

5.2 Epoxy Co-Reaction

Cyanate esters function as curing agents for epoxide resins through a combination of oxazoline ring formation and catalysis of epoxide homopolymerization (Fig. 3). Cyanurate rings formed by cyanate trimerization appear to be the catalytic species. As little as 35 weight % of unsubstituted aryl dicyanates or their prepolymers will completely convert 65% glycidyl ether type epoxy resins at 177°C.

6. PROCESSING AND CURING

Figure 4 plots viscosity versus temperature for a number of monomers, prepolymers and BT blends, illustrating the wide selection offered the formulator with respect to fiber wetting speed, tack/drape properties and flow control in pressure molding operations. The compatibility of AroCy L-10 liquid monomer with cyanate ester (CE) prepolymer resins and epoxy resins (Fig. 5) is an even more versatile tool for adjusting rheological properties to specific composite processing requirements. Recent patent literature indicates growing interest in utilizing the good processing characteristics of CE's to improve hot melt processibility of bismaleimides and allylnadicimides.

6.1 Tp Resin Modification

Compatibility with a number of amorphous thermoplastic (Tp) resins including copolyesters (MEK soluble), polysulfones, polyethersulfones, polyarylates and polyetherimides offers another route to flow control as well as major improvements

in fracture toughness. Thermoplastics available in powder form, such as Udel P-1800 or Victrex 5003P, are amenable to dissolving neat in AroCy L-10 liquid monomer or molten dicyanates with heat and agitation. Granular or slab-form thermoplastics require dissolving in mutually compatible solvents, generally chlorinated hydrocarbons, with subsequent removal of solvent for hot melt filming of unidirectional prepregs.

6.2 Unidirectional Prepreg

Semisolid prepolymers such as AroCy B-30 and M-30 are filmed in the manner of TGMDA/DDS epoxy formulations at temperatures ranging from 60 to 90°C. Latent catalysts, preferably copper, zinc or cobalt acetylacetonates at levels providing from 20 to 200 ppm as metal, are first dissolved in 2 to 6 phr nonylphenol and added under agitation to the warm prepolymer. Impregnation of unidirectional carbon fiber is achieved by working the release film-sandwiched prepreg with heated pressure rollers on a heated stage. Formulations containing up to 25% polysulfone thermoplastic have produced quality prepreg using processing temperatures in the range of 100–145°C.

6.3 Fabric Impregnation

Woven fabrics used to reinforce PWB laminates and structural composites are conveniently impregnated from MEK prepolymer solutions. Varnishes are catalyzed with 0.5-1.0% bisphenol (hydroxyl source) and manganese or zinc octoates at concentrations providing from 5 to 100 ppm metal. Tower drying conditions are similar to those employed for FR-4 epoxy, but cyanate esters may be processed at faster line speeds in the absence of tail solvents and generally higher varnish solids.

6.4 Curing

Cyanate ester homopolymers develop Tg's in the 240–290°C range and require post curing at temperatures of 225–250°C to develop full cure. Two formulation techniques which can provide a satisfactory degree of cure (≥85% conversion) or full cure at conventional press/clave temperatures of 177°C (350°F) are:

- Increasing nonylphenol concentration to 5-7 phr.
- Modification with 55-65% epoxy resin.

Conversion of homopolymers is conveniently monitored by FTIR (ratio of cyanate to methyl absorbances), DSC (residual heat of reaction) or correlation with Tg.

7. CURED RESIN PROPERTIES

Comparisons are made with three representative competitive matrix systems:

TGMDA/DDS: blend of 69.2% tetra functional epoxy resin, 7.6% Epi-Rez SU-8 and 23.2% DDS.
BMI-MDA: a toughened bismaleimide prepared by reacting 2.5 mols BMI with 1.0 mol methylene dianiline.
BMI-DAB: a toughened bismaleimide prepared by reacting 1.0 mol BMI with 0.87 mol o,o'-diallylbisphenol A.

7.1 Mechanical Properties

Table 3 demonstrates the generally superior strength, extensibility and fracture toughness properties of CE homopolymers. Within this series the least hindered structure (AroCy L) provides maximum toughness properties, illustrating the benefit of rotational freedom around ring couplings. Figure 6 locates the position of several matrix resin families in a trade-off plot of Tg versus toughness. Relative positions are unchanged when fracture toughness is substituted for tensile elongation. The most extensible CE homopolymer (6% elongation at break) is derived from an ether-linked bisphenol dicyanate, Hi-Tek Polymers' experimental product ESR 288. Ten to fifteen percent higher modulus values for tetrafunctional epoxy and bismaleimide matrices reflect higher cross link densities and reduced segment rotational freedoms.

7.2 Moisture Conditioning Effects

As a class, CE homopolymers absorb less water at saturation than epoxy and bismaleimide resins (Fig. 7). The cyanurate ester linkage is very resistant to hydrolysis, withstanding hundreds to thousands of hours immersion in boiling water. Figure 8 demonstrates the exceptional resistance to moisture plasticization of the o-methylated AroCy M homopolymer. In general, the hydrocarbon bulk of a dicyclopentadienyl bisphenol linkage (XU 71787) and the cyanurate shielding effect of o-methylation (AroCy M) are equally effective structural modifications for maximizing the hydrophobic nature of CE homopolymers.

7.3 Thermal Properties/Flammability

Tg values range from 233 to 289°C, depending on the test method and CE structure. Lower values for the cycloaliphatic modified XU 71787 can be attributed to increased segment distance between crosslinks while its higher DMA modulus probably reflects less rotational freedom within the bisphenol linkage. TGA onsets of rapid degradation for CE homopolymers (400 to 431°C) are significantly higher than for reference matrix systems. See Table 4.

High char yields in polymers are associated with inherent flame retardancy attributed to low saturated hydrocarbon content. Vertical bar ignitions (UL 94 test) support self-extinguishing ratings for AroCy F, AroCy T, AroCy M and BMI-MDA. Eliminating the need to incorporate brominated additives conveys several advantages to inherently flame retardant thermosets:

- Increased thermal stability
- Reduced corrosion potential
- Lower dielectric loss characteristics
- Lower coefficients of thermal expansion
- Higher Tg

7.4 Electrical Properties

Perhaps the most unusual characteristic of CE homopolymers is their low dielectric loss properties. While chemical compositions include appreciable percentages of electronegative elements (11.5% oxygen and 10% nitrogen for AroCy B), their symmetrical arrangement around electropositive carbon creates balanced dipoles of short moments which store surprisingly little electromagnetic energy. Dielectric constants decrease slightly with frequency increases into the giga-hertz (10^9 Hz) range, with flat response to temperatures up to 200°C. The multivalent transition metal cations and bulky carboxylate anions used as cure catalysts make no measurable contribution to electromagnetic field energy storage (Dk) or to its dissipation into heat (Df). Relatively low levels of absorbed moisture maintain these desirable dielectric loss properties even after days immersion in boiling water.

Figure 9 ranks CE homopolymers and reference matrix resins for dielectric constant measured dry and after 48 hours water boil. REX 360, Hi-Tek Polymer's experimental CE homopolymer, measures only 2.7 after moisture conditioning. The family range is 2.5 to 3.1 dry, 2.7 to 3.6 wet, well below epoxy resin, bismaleimide and polyimide values.

7.5 Miscellaneous Properties

Chemical resistance of CE homopolymers is satisfactory for exposure to degreasers, etchants, strippers and other chemicals used in the manufacture of printed wiring boards (Fig. 10). Two-week immersion of castings in jet fuel, MEK and Skydrol hydraulic fluids (latter at 160°F) has no significant effect on DMA tensile storage modulus. While caustic solutions can slowly etch unsubstituted polycyanurates, modification with epoxy resin or use of the o-methylated AroCy M resins will provide long term alkali resistance.

Adhesion of copper conductor foil to PWB laminates is exceptional, equaling 130°C Tg epoxy-dicy FR-4 resins at room temperature while maintaining ≥8 lb/inch peel strength to well above 200°C. See Section 8 for comparison of peel strength data.

7.6 Thermoplastic Alloys

Several amorphous thermoplastic (Tp) resins with Tg values in the 170-300°C range, such as polyether-imide, polysulfone, polyethersulfone and certain asymmetric polyimides, are soluble in dicyanate monomers but phase separate during the curing process. Figure 11 illustrates the exponential increase in fracture toughness associated with formation of co-continuous phases when Tp con-centrations exceed ~15%. Figure 12 compares SEM photomicrographs of casting fracture surfaces showing the reduction in node size and improved interfacial adhesion achieved with end-group-reactive thermoplastic (Victrex 5003P polyether-sulfone). Performance advantages associated with graftable, i.e. hydroxyl or aromatic amine terminated, Tp's are solvent resistance and higher strain-at-break values.

8. PWB LAMINATE PROPERTIES

To meet the escalating demands on PWB substrates described in Section 2, laminating resins must provide lower Dk/Df values, reduced moisture absorption, higher Tg, reduction of corrosive ion sources, greater thermal stability, inherent flame retardancy and higher conductor peel strengths. Processing characteristics (impregnation, lamina-ion, drillability, resistance to degreasers, strippers, etchants, and molten solder) must equal or improve on those of FR-4 epoxy.

Figure 13 illustrates the significant reductions in E-glass laminate dielectric constant which can be achieved with CE homopolymers relative to epoxies and polyimides. When reinforced with lower dielectric loss fibers such as quartz or Kevlar , CE's can provide Dk values approaching 3.0 at resin contents typical of multilayer laminates (70 ± 5 volume %).

Cyanate ester peel strengths are the equivalent of FR-4 at room temperature but are maintained at high values up to molten solder temperatures. Elimination of damage to multilayer boards during field repair is an important benefit.

The highest category of self-extinguishing flammability rating, V-0, is achieved with AroCy F or AroCy T laminates (Fig. 14) minus the disadvantages accompanying formulation with brominated additives (see section 6.3). AroCy M and BMI-MDA polyimide laminates are rated V-1, satisfactory for most military applications.

Key properties of E-glass lami-nates prepared with comparable resin volume contents are summarized in Table 5, demonstrating major advantages for cyanate ester resins relative to epoxy and polyimide laminating resins.

9. STRUCTURAL COMPOSITES

In contrast to the widely publicized electrical grade laminate development, few publications provide any data on CE-carbon fiber composites. A University of Washington paper by E. Woo describes the impregnation of unidirectional AS-4 tapes with CE resin containing up to 25% of dissolved thermoplastic resin (injection molding grade polysulfone). Eventually, the adaptation of custom synthesized, lower molecular weight Tp oligomers with reactive end groups (ref. US 4,656, 208) to toughening cyanate esters may prove a more efficient alloying approach.

Moisture conditioned short beam shear strength data (Fig. 15) indicates 150°C service temperature is a reasonable design goal for bisphenol A dicyanate based matrices. Hot-wet flexural modulus values of CE homopolymers (Fig. 8) suggest a higher service temperature, estimated at 170°C, may be achievable for the more hydrophobic AroCy M resins.

The use of cyanate esters for radome construction and other applications requiring microwave transparency is predictable from their success in related low dielectric loss PWB laminates. The recent availability of a low viscosity dicyanate monomer should facilitate the use of cyanate esters in high speed composite-forming processes, particularly filament winding and resin transfer molding.

10. REFERENCE

This preprint paper is a condensation of the chapter on cyanate ester resins prepared for a SAMPE monograph edited by Clayton May.

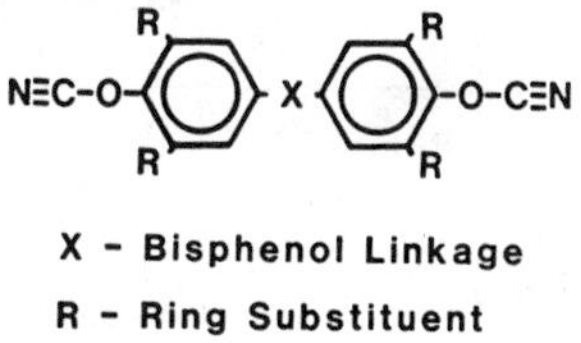

X - Bisphenol Linkage

R - Ring Substituent

FIG. 1
Chemical structure model for dicyanate monomers.

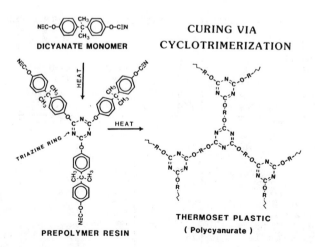

FIG. 2
Homopolymerization of dicyanates.

227

TABLE 1 - COMMERCIALLY AVAILABLE DICYANATE MONOMERS

CHEMICAL STRUCTURE / PRODUCT DESIGNATION	PHYSICAL STATE	KEY MONOMER / HOMOPOLYMER FEATURES
N≡C-O-⟨⟩-C(CH₃)(CH₃)-⟨⟩-O-C≡N AROCY B-10	Crystalline m.p. 79°C Den. 1.259	• Least Expensive • Most Extensive Data Base • Prepolymers MEK Soluble
N≡C-O-⟨⟩(CH₃)(CH₃)-CH(H)-⟨⟩(CH₃)(CH₃)-O-C≡N AROCY M-10	Crystalline m.p. 106°C Den. 1.197	• Dk 2.75 • H₂O Abs. 1.4% • V-1 Flamm. Rating • Prepolymers MEK Soluble
N≡C-O-⟨⟩-S-⟨⟩-O-C≡N AROCY T-10	Crystalline m.p. 94°C Den. 1.395	• V-0 Flamm. Rating • Most Solvent Resistant
N≡C-O-⟨⟩-C(CF₃)(CF₃)-⟨⟩-O-C≡N AROCY F-10	Crystalline m.p. 86°C Den. 1.497	• Dk 2.66 • V-0 Flamm. Rating • Prepolymers MEK Soluble
N≡C-O-⟨⟩-C(CH₃)(H)-⟨⟩-O-C≡N AROCY L-10	Liquid 140 cps @ 25°C Den. 1.180	• Low Viscosity Liquid • Excellent Reactive Dil. • B-10 Cured Properties
N≡C-O-⟨⟩-⟨⟩-⟨⟩-O-C≡N XU 71787.00L	Semisolid 700 cps @ 85°C	• Dk 2.8 • H₂O Abs. 1.4% • MEK Soluble

Note 1 - AroCy monomers supplied by Hi-Tek Polymers.
Note 2 - XU 71787.00L supplied by Dow Chemical Co. contains 0.2 mol fraction of trisfunctional oligomer (Ref.6).

TABLE 2 - COMMERCIAL[*] CYANATE ESTER PREPOLYMER RESINS

Typical Properties	AroCy B	AroCy M	AroCy T	AroCy F
SEMISOLIDS:				
Product No.	B-30	M-30	T-30	
Cyanate Equiv. Wt.	200	218	240	
Mol. Wt., Mn/Mw	560/1310	490/2300	690/2800	
Viscosity, cps, 82°C	450	3,100	16,700	
HARD RESINS:				
Product No.	B-50	M-50		
Cyanate Equiv. Wt.	278	262		
Mol. Wt., Mn/Mw	1100/12000	920/5500		
Viscosity, cps,149°C	3,600	700		
MEK SOLUTIONS:				
Product No.	B-40S	M-40S		F-40S
Cyanate Equiv. Wt.	232	243		284
Mol. Wt., Mn/Mw	730/2650	660/2870		820/2100
% Nonvolatile	75	65		75
Viscosity, 25°C, cps	190	85		100

*AroCy is a trade name of Hi-Tek Polymers.

1.

$3 \ R\text{-}O\text{-}C\equiv N \longrightarrow$

CYANURATE

Cyclotrimerization

2.

$R\text{-}O\text{-}C\equiv N \ + \ R'\text{-}CH\text{-}CH_2 \longrightarrow$

OXAZOLINE

Co-reaction

3.

$n \ R'\text{-}CH\text{-}CH_2 \ \xrightarrow{R''OH} \ H \overset{R'}{(O\text{-}CH\text{-}CH_2)_n} OR''$

Polyetherification

FIG. 3
Blends of epoxide and cyanate ester resins
undergo three reactions.

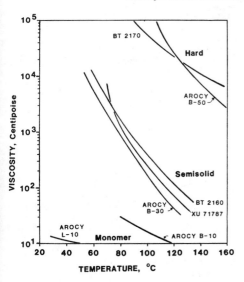

FIG. 4
Melt viscosity profiles of cyanate ester
monomers, prepolymers and BT blends

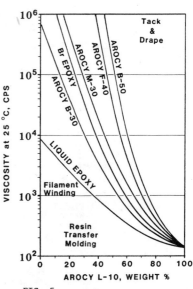

FIG. 5
Viscosity reduction of cyanate
ester prepolymers and epoxy
resins with AroCy™ L-10 liquid
monomer.

TABLE 3 - MECHANICAL PROPERTIES OF UNREINFORCED CASTINGS

PROPERTY (25°C)	A R O C Y					XU 71787	Epoxy TGMDA DDS	BMI-MDA	BMI-DAB
	B	M	T	F	L				
Flexure									
Strength, ksi	25.2	23.3	19.4	17.8	23.5	18.2	14.0	10.9	25.5
Modulus, msi	0.45	0.42	0.43	0.48	0.42	0.49	0.55	0.50	0.53
Ult. Strain, %	7.7	6.6	5.4	4.6	8.0	4.1	2.5	2.2	5.1
Izod Impact									
ft-lb/in notch	0.7	0.8	0.8	0.7	0.9	NA	0.4	0.3	0.5
G_{IC}, in-lb/in	0.8	1.0	0.9	0.8	1.1	0.35	0.4	0.4	0.5

NA - Not available in literature.

Tg - STRAIN TRADE-OFFS IN THERMOSETS

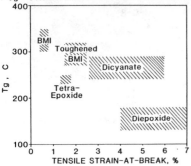

FIG. 6
Relationship of Tg and tensile
elongation-at-break for several
families of thermoset resins.

Cured Resin	10% H₂SO₄	10% Acetic	20% NaOH	Clorox	MEK
AROCY B (Bis A type)	1.1	1.3	(2.0) Etch	1.0	4.3
50% AROCY B 50% DIEPOXIDE	0.9	1.0	0.5	0.6	7.7
DIEPOXIDE + AROMATIC DIAMINE	1.9	1.8	1.1	0.2	7.2
VINYL ESTER	1.0	1.1	0.7	0.7	Disint.
BISMALEIMIDE	0.9	1.0	(4.6) Etch	(9.0) Etch	0.7

FIG. 10
Chemical resistance (changes in weight and
appearance) of castings immersed in representative chemicals for 30 days at 50°C.
Bracketed numbers signify weight loss due
to surface etching.

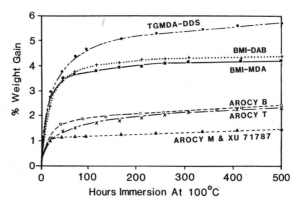

FIG. 7
Water absorption of 0.125 inch thick castings
immersed at 100°C.

FLEXURAL MODULUS (WET) VS. TEMPERATURE
(48 hour water boil)

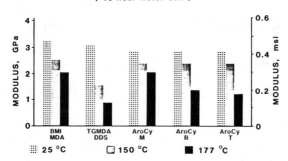

FIG. 8
Flexural modulus comparisons of bismaleimide,
epoxy and CE homopolymers conditioned 48 hours
in boiling water. Bars heat soaked 3 minutes
prior to testing.

TABLE 4 - THERMAL PROPERTIES OF UNREINFORCED CASTINGS

PROPERTY	A R O C Y					XU 71787	Epoxy TGMDA DDS	BMI-MDA	BMI-DAB
	B	M	T	F	L				
HDT, °C									
Dry	254	242	243	238	249	NA	232	>270	266
Wet(a)	197	234	195	160	183	NA	167	262	217
DMA									
Tg, °C	289	252	273	270	258	244	246	320	288
E', GPa									
at 25°C	1.62	1.61	1.41	1.42	1.34	1.75	1.97	1.65	1.90
at 200°C	1.30	1.07	1.10	1.04	1.01	1.32	1.13	1.30	1.35
TMA									
Tg, °C	257	244	270	265	259	223	210	297	263
CTE, ppm/°C	64	71	68	54	64	68	67	62	63
(40 to 200°C)									
TGA									
Onset, °C (air)	411	403	400	431	408	405	306	369	371
Char % (N₂)	41	48	46	52	43	32	31	48	29
Flammability(b)									
1st Ignition	33	20	1	0	1	>50	>50	1	>50
2nd Ignition	23	14	3	0	>50	–	–	5	–

(a) Conditioned 64 hours @ 92°C and >95% RH.
(b) UL-94 test procedure; seconds to extinguish flame after each ignition
    of a vertical bar.
NA - Not available in literature.

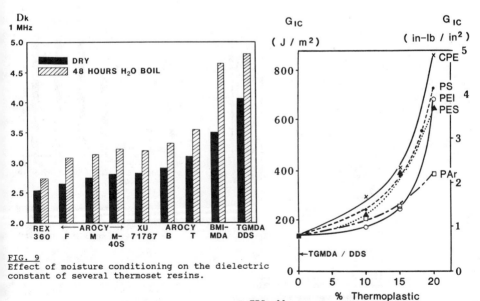

FIG. 9
Effect of moisture conditioning on the dielectric
constant of several thermoset resins.

FIG. 11
Effect of thermoplastic resin and con-
centration on fracture toughness of
AroCy B castings. CPE (copolyester),
PS (polysulfone), PEI (polyetherimide),
PES (polyethersulfone), PAr (polyarylate).

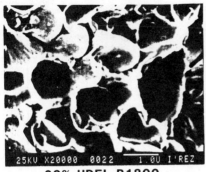 

20% UDEL P1800   **20% VICTREX 5003P**

CHLORO	– Tp TERMINATION –	PHENOLIC
15 Minutes	– $MeCl_2$ Soak –	700 Minutes
3.8 in–lbs/in^2	– G_{lc} –	2.8 in–lbs/in^2
22.4 ksi	– Flexure Strength –	25.5 ksi
0.42 msi	– Flexural Modulus –	0.43 msi
6.9%	– Flexural Strain –	10.1%

FIG. 12
Contribution of reactive (Victrex 5003P) and unreactive
(Udel P-1800) Tp resins to morphology and properties of
80/20 AroCy L-10/Tp alloys. Note effect on interfacial
adhesion in fracture plane.

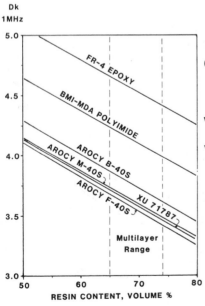

FIG. 13
Dielectric constant of E-glass laminates
is a function of resin selection and resin
volume.

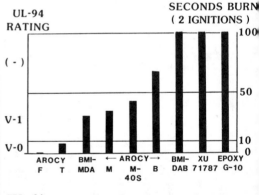

FIG. 14
Flammability of non-brominated E-glass laminate
Laminate thickness is 0.060 inch (8ply); resin
content is 55 ±2% by volume. Rating (–) means
burn time exceeds self-extinguishing requiremen

TABLE 5 - SUMMARY OF E-GLASS LAMINATE PROPERTIES AT
EQUAL RESIN VOLUME CONTENT*

Resin	Dk, 1 MHz Volume % 70	55	Df (10⁻³)	DMA Tg °C	TGA Onset °C	Flamm. Rating UL-94	Peel Str. lb /inch 25°C	200°C	Pressure Cooker (Min.)
CYANATE ESTER:									
AroCy F-40S	3.5	3.9	2	290	400	V-0	11	9	120
AroCy M-40S	3.6	4.0	2	290	415	V-1	12	10	>120
XU-71787	3.6	4.0	3	255	426	**	8	6	>120
AroCy B-40S	3.7	4.1	3	290	405	**	12	10	120
POLYIMIDE:									
BMI-MDA	4.1	4.5	9	312	400	V-1	9	6	>120
EPOXY:									
FR-4	4.5	4.9	20	145	300	V-0	12	4	45

* Except for Dk measurements on 55 and 70 volume % resin laminates,
tests were performed on 55 volume %, 0.060 inch, 8 ply laminates.
** Burn times exceed self-extinguishing classifications.

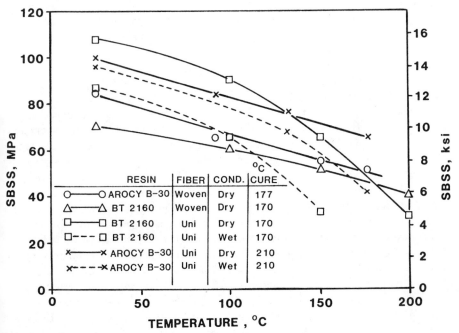

FIG. 15

Short beam shear strength of unidirectional and woven carbon
fiber composites as a function of resin, cure temperature
and moisture conditioning. Maximum cure temperatures were
limited to those employed commercially for TGMDA/DDS epoxy.

233

VINYL ESTER RESINS: VERSATILE RESINS FOR COMPOSITES

Larry T. Blankenship, Mary N. White, Paul M. Puckett

Dow Chemical U.S.A.

Freeport, Tx

Abstract

Vinyl esters are thermosetting resins based on the reaction of epoxy resins with ethylenically unsaturated monocarboxylic acids and containing styrene as a copolymerizable diluent. These resins, which combine the superior thermal, mechanical and chemical resistant properties of epoxies with the rapid curing and ease of processing of unsaturated polyesters, have long been recognized as the premium resin for fabrication of industrial fiber reinforced plastic (FRP) parts in demanding corrosion resistant applications. In addition, their excellent elevated temperature performance, high elongation, and fatigue resistance attributable to the epoxy backbone, however, make them favored candidates for new structural composite applications with either glass or carbon fiber reinforcements. This paper describes the synthesis, structures, and typical properties of vinyl ester resins as castings and as laminates. Structure-property correlations and resin curing characteristics both at ambient and elevated temperatures are illustrated. Recent developments in material characterization, rapid processing, and applications in corrosion-resistant equipment and transportation fields are reviewed.

1. CHEMISTRY

Vinyl ester resins are produced by esterification of a multifunctional epoxy resin with an unsaturated monocarboxylic acid, usually methacrylic or acrylic acid, in the presence of a polymerization inhibitor. The resinous product is dissolved in styrene to give a low viscosity liquid thermoset which can be cured by radical polymerization. Copolymerization of styrene with the terminally unsaturated vinyl ester (VE) resin produces a three dimensional network that is free to elongate under mechanical or thermal stresses along the entire length of the epoxy backbone, thus providing high elongation, fatigue resistance, and thermal resistance (1-3). Major manufacturers and sellers of vinyl ester resins include Dow Chemical (DERAKANE*), Ashland Chemical (Hetron), Koppers (Atlac, Dion), and Interplastic Corporation (Co-Rezyn).

Trademark of The Dow Chemical Company.

2. STRUCTURE-PROPERTY RELATIONSHIPS

The properties of vinyl ester resins depend upon:
1) the epoxy resin structure which determines mechanical and thermal properties, and affects corrosion resistance;
2) the unsaturated acid which affects reactivity and chemical resistance;
3) the diluent monomer which affects viscosity, reactivity, and chemical resistance.

The bisphenol A backbone (Figure 1) of the general purpose corrosion resistant vinyl ester resin provides high modulus, strength and chemical resistance. Increasing the molecular weight of the base epoxy reduces crosslink density, and produces tougher, more impact resistant polymers with better caustic resistance, although the heat distortion temperature (HDT) is decreased. Most commercial vinyl ester resins used in composites are methacrylates which are more resistant to basic hydrolysis due to steric hindrance by the methyl group, although fast curing acrylate VE resins have been developed for ultraviolet curable photoresists and adhesives. Since the methacrylate groups occur only at each end of the vinyl ester resin molecule, the equivalent number of ester linkages is lower than in a typical polyol/ maleate or fumarate based polyester, improving flexibility, toughness, and caustic resistance. The hydroxyl groups along the backbone promote wetout and adhesion to glass fibers and fillers. The addition of styrene as a polymerizable diluent provides viscosity control, acts as a crosslinker during polymerization, and improves resistance to polar solvents and caustic. Chemical resistance data for specific vinyl ester resins can be obtained from various manufacturers (4).

Typical liquid and casting properties of vinyl ester resins are summarized in Table 1, and compared to those of cured epoxy resins having similar structure. The increased functionality of an epoxy novolac as the base for a VE resin results in a higher crosslink density which increases the Tg of the cured resin and improves resistance to solvents. Vinyl ester resins based on tetrabromobisphenol A have fire retardant properties, and exhibit greater fatigue resistance (5). [Note: All vinyl ester resins are organic materials and will burn under the right conditions of heat and oxygen supply.] A brominated novolac epoxy resin based vinyl ester resin can be used when heat resistance is also needed. Modification with carboxy-terminated acrylonitrile butadiene rubber improves impact resistance and adhesive strength. Carboxyl functional vinyl ester resins produced by addition of maleic anhydride can be thickened with divalent metal ions. This type of resin has been developed primarily for sheet molding and bulk molding compounds.

Table 1. Typical Properties of DERAKANE* Vinyl Ester Resins

	Vinyl Ester Resins				Epoxy resins Cured with Methylene Dianiline	
(Epoxy base)	DERAKANE 411-45 (Bisphenol A)	DERAKANE 470-36 (Novolac)	DERAKANE 510C (Brominated)	DERAKANE 8084 (Rubber Mod.)	Bisphenol A Epoxy	Novolac Epoxy
Liquid Properties						
Viscosity, cs	450	200	350	450		
Specific gravity	1.04	1.07	1.15	1.05		
25 °C Gel time, min.	28	12	12	40		
82 °C Gel time, min	12	13	12	15		
Clear Casting Properties						
Tensile strength, MPa	82.7	75.8	76.1	69.0	70.3	75.8
Tensile modulus, GPa	3.4	3.5	3.9	3.2	2.9	2.8
Elongation, percent	6.0	3.0	6.0	10.0	4.0	3.0
Flexural strength, MPa	124.0	138.0	124.0	117.0	93.1	106.9
Flexural modulus, GPa	3.1	3.8	3.6	3.0	2.7	3.1
HDT, °C	102	144	110	80	160	190
Barcol hardness	35	40	40	30		
Rockwell hardness					106	112

The following methods were used to determine properties: Kinematic viscosity, 25 °C, D 2515; Density, D 4052; gel time (25 °C), 1.83 phr HiPoint 90 (Witco), 0.3 phr cobalt naphthenate (6 % cobalt), D 2471; Tensile properties, D 638; Flexural properties, D 790; Heat deflection temperature (HDT), D 648; Barcol hardness, D 2583. The 82 °C gel time was performed as specified by The Society of Plastics Institute.

*Trademark of the Dow Chemical Company

3. FORMULATION AND CURE

3.1 Formulation

Vinyl esters are formulated and processed using many of the same techniques as used by the unsaturated polyester industry. Peroxides are added to provide a source of radicals to initiate polymerization. Other additives include fillers to reduce polymerization shrinkage and lower cost, thixotropic agents to modify flow and prevent sagging in vertical lamination, wetting agents, internal mold releases, and a wide variety of fiber reinforcements.

3.2 Elevated Temperature Cure

Heat-activated free radical initiators such as benzoyl peroxide, t-butyl peroctoate and t-butyl perbenzoate are used when vinyl ester resins are cured in heated molds during filament winding, pultrusion or resin transfer molding (RTM). The choice of initiator is based on the activation temperature of the peroxide and required cycle time of the process (6). Single initiators are effective over relatively narrow temperature ranges, and it is common to blend catalysts to modify the cure profile. Recent reports describe fast curing systems for RTM (7) and selection of initiators based on DSC thermal analysis (8,9).

3.3 Ambient Temperature Cure

For ambient cure applications, promoters must be added to resin formulations to induce decomposition of peroxides forming free radicals at rates sufficient for curing. Cer-

tain metallic soaps and tertiary amines are especially effective (10). The most common system is methyl ethyl ketone peroxide (MEKP) promoted with cobalt naphthenate (CoNap), and optionally including N,N'-dimethyl aniline (DMA) as an accelerator. If a sufficient reaction exotherm is achieved, green strength develops rapidly; however, postcuring is often desirable for optimum properties. A strong exotherm which can result in cracking or decomposition of a thick part may be minimized by using fillers or a less reactive catalyst such as cumene hydroperoxide. An alternative system which gives fast cures and is less sensitive to moisture effects is benzoyl peroxide and dimethyl aniline. [Safety Note: Promoters and accelerators must never be mixed directly with peroxide catalyst, since rapid decomposition or explosion could occur (11-13).]

4. COMPOSITE PROPERTIES

The most commonly used reinforcement for vinyl ester composites is Type E fiberglass, but graphite, aramid, olefin and ceramic fibers may also be used. Typical engineering properties of unidirectional glass reinforced vinyl esters are shown in Table 2. Flexural and tensile properties are relatively uniform among resin types, and compare favorably to amine cured bisphenol A diglycidyl ether (DGEBA) mechanical properties. Differences are observed in matrix glass transition temperature, and compressive and shear properties. The latter properties are dominated by interphase structure, adhesion, and fracture mechanisms.

TABLE 2. MECHANICAL PROPERTIES OF UNIDIRECTIONAL GLASS COMPOSITES

RESIN MATRIX	DERAKANE* 411C-50	DERAKANE 470-36	DERAKANE 8084	DERAKANE 510C-350	D.E.R* 383 / DACH
SPECIFIC GRAVITY	1.845	1.837	1.869	1.928	1.86
GLASS CONTENT (wt%)	69.3	70.0	68.1	67.1	66.4
TENSILE					
Strength (MPa)	883.6	780.9	840.3	922.0	815.1
Modulus (GPa)	38.2	40.0	39.5	40.3	36.3
Elong. %	2.42	2.02	2.16	2.37	2.40
Poisson Ratio	0.30	0.30	0.27	0.28	0.29
FLEXURAL					
Strength (MPa)	1260	1374	1196	1270	1102
Modulus (GPa)	39.1	37.7	39.1	38.0	33.5
COMPRESSIVE					
Strength (MPa)	612.6	936.7	770.4	934.6	271.7
Modulus (GPa)	35.8	38.1	37.0	39.3	31.4
IN-PLANE SHEAR					
Strength (MPa)	140	110	135	141	110
Modulus (GPa)	4.1	4.3	4.0	5.9	5.2
INTERLAMINAR SHEAR					
Strength (MPa)	68	73	59	75	68

Unidirectional E-glass reinforced plaques (8 ply, 70 weight percent glass, 0.125" thick) wound on a flat-plaque filament winder and compresssion molded.
VE Resins : CertainTeed 660-11 roving (250 yield)
            Postcured 2 hours @ 155 °C, oven cool
Epoxies   : CertainTeed 670-12 roving (225 yield)
            Postcured 2 hours @ 180 °C, oven cool
D.E.R. 383 = Bisphenol A type liquid epoxy resin, EEW = 176-183.
DACH = 1,2-Diaminocyclohexane curative
*Trademark of The Dow Chemical Company

The lower polarity of the vinyl ester network reduces moisture absorption relative to the epoxy and permits a higher percent retention of properties in hot/wet service. Table 3 shows hygrothermal properties of VE and epoxy-amine composites reinforced with woven carbon fiber. The advantages in compressive strength and Tg for the dry epoxy system disappear when the systems are moisture saturated. Structural composites made from this VE resin should perform similarly to many epoxy-amine systems when used in applications at 200 °F/wet.

5. APPLICATIONS

Due to higher cost than polyesters, vinyl esters are used in applications that require their superior corrosion, thermal, and fatigue properties. Hand layup and sprayup techniques are frequently combined with filament winding to manufacture corrosion resistant tanks, piping, ducts, and fittings of virtually all sizes (14). Aggregate and sand mixtures with vinyl ester resins form strong, chemically resistant polymer concrete used in waste handling applications (15). High volume automated fabrication methods such as pultrusion, resin transfer molding, and compression molding also make good use of the low viscosity and adjustable cure of vinyl ester resins in production of composites for automotive, industrial and military applications (16). Corrosion resistance, parts consolidation, design flexibility, and reduced cost are driving forces in their selection.

6. NEW DEVELOPMENTS

6.1 Resins

Vinyl esters have participated in the interplay of materials, processing, and performance that has been characteristic of the composites industry during the 1980's, and should continue to do so with growth of composites applications in the 1990's. More versatile resin systems will extend the achievable range and balance of processing and composite properties. These resins can originate from blending or alloying of existing resins or polymers (17-19), replacement of part of the vinyl ester backbone with other polymeric structures such as silicone (20), isocyanates and urethanes (21-24), or hydrocarbons (25,26), or replacement of styrene with alternate monomers (27). Hybrid systems based on free radical and urethane chemistry have already reached commercialization (28).

6.2 Processes and applications

Reactive processing by simultaneous polymerization and molding is increasingly important for economical, high volume production of composite parts. Processes include compression molding, injection molding and pultrusion (29-32). Computer modeling and simulation of these processes has seen significant activity (33).

Automotive structural parts continue to be a main objective of development efforts by the FRP industry because of the large potential volume and the small current share in vehicle construction. Plastic parts

TABLE 3. HOT / WET PROPERTIES OF
GRAPHITE REINFORCED COMPOSITES

RESIN MATRIX CONDITION	DERAKANE* 510C-350 RTD / 200W		TACTIX* 123/H31 RTD / 200W	
TENSILE				
Strength (Mpa)	902.5	733.4	850.1	768.4
Modulus (GPa)	71.3	69.2	68.5	63.6
Elong %	1.4	1.1	1.2	1.2
FLEXURAL				
Strength (MPa)	916.4	590.9	881.5	521.1
Modulus (GPa)	70.6	73.3	63.6	60.1
COMPRESSIVE				
Strength (MPa)	569	433	673	458
INTERLAMINAR SHEAR				
Strength (MPa)	60	35	59	35

Composite panels were prepared via RTM techniques using 8 plies of 8 harness satin weave AS-4 fabric which produced panels of 58% fiber volume. The cure schedule was 1 hour at 200 °F followed by 3 hours at 350 °F. Composite samples were moisturized at 185 °F/95% relative humidity until constant weight was achieved.

TACTIX 123 = Bisphenol A type liquid epoxy resin, EEW 172-176.
TACTIX H31 = Aliphatic Amine.
RTD = tested at ambient temperature before moisture saturation
200W = tested at 200 °F following moisture saturation

*Trademark of The Dow Chemical Company

gain access to the automotive industry only if they offer a technical advantage at equivalent (or lower) cost. This economic efficiency is achieved via improvements in processing technology.

In SMC this has been achieved by use of rapid curing resin systems, high speed parallel presses, improved sheet composition uniformity for consistent processing, near zero shrinkage for dimensional accuracy, and improved surface quality of the molded parts. Oil pan sumps and valve covers for diesel trucks take advantage of VE's inherent strength, stiffness and dimensional stability, and heat distortion temperature. Bumper beam supports with oriented glass fibers are gaining acceptance. Very large parts including a pickup bed box are being prototyped (34).

Transfer molding of thermoset resins has been receiving increased attention by the automotive, aerospace, and defense industries. Process advantages such as smooth surfaces on both sides, molding of complex shapes with tight dimensional tolerances, precise fiber placement, and elimination of styrene emission from the closed process are pertinent. Higher pressure injection techniques and improvements in resin and initiator chemistry are beginning to blur the distinction between SRIM and RTM processes. The development of cost effective preforming techniques using vacuum formed or thermoformed glass mats have enabled cycle time to be reduced while at the same time improving the quality of the molded part. New applications are emerging in the automotive industry for vehicle body parts produced in small

series, and high stress assemblies where parts consolidation is possible (35).

6.3 Materials Science

The application of advanced characterization techniques to vinyl esters has improved understanding of processing properties, polymerization kinetics, structural and morphological properties of the polymers, matrix / reinforcement interface properties, and final performances and structural properties of the composites. Thermal and spectroscopic methods have been used to study gelation and curing (36-41). Various nondestructive test methods including acoustic emission, NMR imaging and radioisotopic methods, and fracture mechanics methodologies have been used to investigate effects of laminate structure, damage, and enviromental aging on structural composites and matrix materials (42-51). New methods have been developed to investigate interfacial effects in composites (52).

6.4 Regulatory Effects

Regulation of the handling of volatile organic compounds has added to costs in the manufacture and use of styrene-containing vinyl ester and unsaturated polyester resins. OSHA has reduced the permitted exposure level of styrene from 100 ppm to 50 ppm, and more rigorous regulations have been enacted in California where styrene content of resins will be limited to 35% unless styrene emissions are rigorously controlled. An excellent source of information about regulations concerning styrene is the Styrene Information and

STRUCTURAL CHARACTERISTICS

BISPHENOL A VINYL ESTER

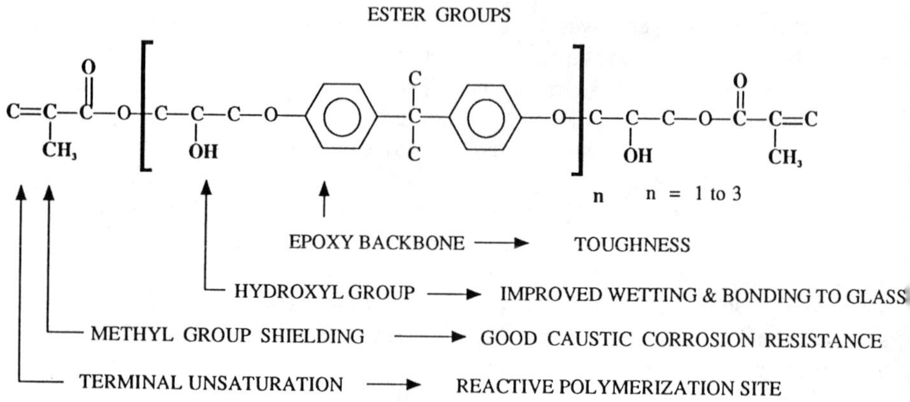

FIGURE 1

Research Center (SIRC) Bulletin (53). On the other hand, new applications for vinyl ester resins have arisen as federal and state regulations aimed at reducing pollution are implemented, for example, lining or construction of underground fuel storage tanks (54) and renovation of sewer lines to prevent ground water contamination (55).

7. SAFETY CONSIDERATIONS

Manufacturers' literature, Material Safety Data Sheets from suppliers, and current OSHA guidelines should be consulted for safe handling and storage of all resins and chemicals. Notice: The information in this article is presented in good faith, but no warranty is given, nor is freedom from any patent to be inferred.

8. REFERENCES

1. Anderson, T.G, and Messick, V.B. In "Developments in Reinforced Plastics-1"; Pritchard, G., Ed.; Applied Science Publishers: London, 1980; Chapter 2.

2. Launikitis, M.B. In "Handbook of Composites"; Lubin, G., Ed.; Van Nostrand Reinhold: New York, 1982; p. 38.

3. Zaske, O.C. In "Handbook of Thermoset Resins"; Goodwin, S.H., Ed.; Noyes Publications: Park Ridge, New Jersey, 1986; Chapter 4.

4. Corrosion Resistance Guide, Form No. 296-320-87R, Resins Products, The Dow Chemical Company, Midland, MI 48674. Other manufacturers include Ashland Chemical Company, Columbus, OH and Koppers Company, Inc., Pittsburg, PA.

5. Barron, D.L. and Kelley, D.H. Corrosion 88, NACE, 1988, Paper 175.

6. Kamath, V.R. and Gallagher, R.B. pp. 121-144 of ref. 1.

7. Babbington, D., et al. In "How to Apply Advanced Composites Technology"; Proc. Fourth Ann. Conf. on Advanced Composites, ASM International, 1988, 269-280.

8. Werner, R.I. and Kusibab, Z. 38th Ann. Conf., RP/C Inst., SPI, 1983, Session 6-G

9. Bladergroen, W. and Milleville, B. 43rd Ann. Conf., RP/C Inst., SPI, 1988, Session 23-C.

10. Barton, J. and Borsig E. "Complexes in Free-Radical Polymerization"; Polymer Science Library 6, Jenkins, A.D., Ed.; Elsevier: New York, 1988; Chapter I.3.

11. Fabricating Tips, Form No. 296-315-1283, The Dow Chemical Company, Resins Products, Midland, MI 48640.

12. Organic Peroxides: Their Safe Handling and Use. Bulletin 30.40, Lucidol Div., Pennwalt Corp.

13. Organic Peroxide Safety and Handling. Bulletin 1-200, Akzo Chemie America, Noury Chemicals.

14. Mallinson, J.H. "Corrosion-Resistant Plastic Composites in Chemical Plant Design"; Marcel Dekker: New York, 1988.

15. Craigie, L.J., Hagemeier, T.G. and Drummond, C.L. 42nd Ann. Conf., RP/C Inst., SPI, 1987, Session 16-D.

16. Kircher, K. "Chemical Reactions in Plastics Processing"; MacMillan: New York, 1987; 11-63.

17. Woelfel, J.A. U.S. Patent 4,489,184, 1984.

18. Shigeki, B., Yoshimasa, N. and Yoshihiro, O. U.S. Patent 4,708,982, 1987.

19. Roland, P. Eur. Pat. Appl. EP 235772, 1987.

20. Rao, B.S., Madec, P.J. and Marechal, E. Makromol. Chem., Rapid Commun. I, 703-707 (1986).

21. Lewandowski, R.J., et al. 30th Ann. Conf., RP/C Inst., SPI, 1975, Section 6-B.

22. Hefner, R.E. and Messick, V.B. U.S. Patent 4,719,268, 1988.

23. Bristowe, W.W. EUR Pat. Appl. EP 132295, 1985.

24. Cheung, M.F., et al. Ind. Eng. Chem. Prod. Res. Dev., 25(2), 296-302 (1986).

25. Lamont, M.J. and Nelson, D.L. U.S. Patent 4,594,398, 1986.

26. Lopez, J.A. and Uzelmeir, C.W. U.S. Patent 4,357,456, 1981.

27. Howard, R.D. and Sayers, D.R. 4oth Ann. Conf., RP/C Inst., SPI, 1985, Session 2-A.

28. Plastics Technology, Dec. 1988, p.19.

29. Meyer, R.W. "Handbook of Pultrusion Technology"; Chapman and Hall: New York, 1985.

30. Meyer, R.W. "Handbook of Polyester Molding Compounds and Molding Technology"; Chapman and Hall: New York, 1987.

31. Kamal, M.R. and Ryan, M.E. In "Injection and Compression Molding Fundamentals"; Isayev, A., Ed.; Marcel Dekker: New York, 1987; Chapter 4.

32. Tucker, C.L. Chapter 7 of Ref. 31.

33. Mangaraj, D., et al. "Reactive Processing of Polymeric Materials, Vol. III. Models of Reactive Processes". Battelle: Columbus, Ohio; 1988.

34. Phipps, J.J. and Miskech, P. 44th Ann. Conf., RP/C Inst., SPI, 1989, Session 18-C.

35. Johnson, C.F., et al. In "ADVANCED COMPOSITES III: Expanding the Technology", Proc. Third Ann. Conf.

on Advanced Composites, ASM International, 1987, 197-217.

36. Buck, H.J, Blankenship, L.T. and Bryan, P.C. 44th Ann. Conf., RP/C Inst., SPI, 1989, Session 4-E.

37. Han, C.D. and Lee, D. J. Appl. Polym. Sci., 34, 793-813 (1987).

38. Huang, Y.J. and Lee, L.J. AIChE Journal, 31(10), 1585-1593 (1985).

39. Batch, G. and Macosko, C. ANTEC'88, Ann. Tech. Conf. of the Soc. Plast. Eng., 1039-1047 (1988).

40. Gonzalez-Romero, V.M. and Macosko, C.W. J. Rheology, 29, 259-272 (1985).

41. Yang, Y.S. and Lee, L.J. Polymer Process Eng., 5(3-4), 327-356 (1987).

42. Summerscales, J. and Short, J. In "Non-Destructive Testing of Fibre-Reinforced Plastic Composites. Vol. 1"; Summerscales, J., Ed.; Elsevier: New York, 1987; Chapter 7.

43. Paci, M., Del Vecchio, E. and Campana, F. Polymer Bull. 15, 21-27 (1986).

44. Kranbuehl, D.E. In "Developments in Reinforced Plastics-5", Pritchard, G., Ed.; Elsevier: New York, 1986; Chapter 6.

45. Day, D.R., et al. 42nd Ann. Conf., RP/C Inst., SPI, 1987, Session 22-E.

46. Newaz, G. Compos. Sci. Technol., 24(3), 199-214 (1985).

47. Shih, G.C. and Ebert, L.J. Compos. Sci. Technol., 28(2), 137-61 (1987).

48. Craigie, L.J., et al. Corrosion 85, NACE, 1985, Paper No. 201.

49. Berliner, L.J., Wan, X. and Fujii, H. J. Polym. Sci.: Polym. Let. Ed. 24, 587-595 (1986).

50. Marshall, J.M., Marshall, G.P. and Pinzelli, R.F. CHEMTECH 1983, 426-432.

51. Lo, S.K., Luizzi, J.M., and O'Hearn, T.P. 43rd Ann. Conf., RP/C Inst., SPI, 1988, Session 19-C.

52. Caldwell, D.L. and Cortez, F.M. 43rd Ann. Conf., RP/C Inst., SPI, 1988, Session 24-A.

53. SIRC Bulletin, Styrene Information and Research Center, 1825 K Street, NW, Suite 210, Washington, D. C. 20006.

54. Craigie, L.J., Svatek, M.J. and White, M.N. Materials Performance, 25(9), 34-40 (1986).

55. Johnson, D., et al. 43rd Ann. Conf., RP/C Inst., SPI, 1988, Session 8-C.

9. BIOGRAPHIES

Larry T. Blankenship is a Research Leader in the Resins Research Department of The Dow Chemical Company. He received his B.A. in Chemistry from Rice University in 1970 and his M.A. in Chemistry from the University of Texas at Austin in 1973. Prior experience includes polyol and isocyanate development for urethane foam applications. His current research is development and application of epoxy and vinyl ester systems for structural composites.

Mary N. White joined the Texas Division of The Dow Chemical Company in 1981. After three years in the Organic Products Department working with various types of polymers, she joined Resins Research to investigate corrosion-resistant vinyl ester resins. She holds a B.S. in Chemistry from Northwestern (OK) State College and a Ph.D. in Chemistry (Biochemistry) from the University of Texas at Austin.

Paul M. Puckett joined The Dow Chemical Company in 1984 where he has worked on the synthesis and characterization of ablative thermoset polymers, and low temperature curing resins and adhesives for composite repair. His current research is development of liquid thermoset systems for resin transfer molding. He holds a B.S. degree in chemistry and mathematics from Harding University, and a Ph.D. in chemistry from Texas A&M University.

245

THE STATUS OF HIGH TEMPERATURE POLYMERS
FOR COMPOSITES - LIKELY CANDIDATES

Daniel A. Scola

United Technologies Research Center

East Hartford, Connecticut 06108

Abstract

Several commercial high temperature polymers have emerged within the last four years for application in the aerospace and electronic industries. Each material has its own temperature capability, processing characteristics, and unique applications. The temperature capabilities, processing chemistry, and composite mechanical properties at 316°C and above, will be discussed and compared.

1. INTRODUCTION

The application of graphite fiber/high temperature composite materials to aircraft engine components and other aircraft components necessitates a thorough understanding of these materials to insure performance with reliability and durability. For application in the temperature range 287–343°C (550–650°F), it is important that the process characteristics of the polymer system be understood, but of greater importance is the understanding of the process characteristics of the graphite fiber/high temperature polymer composite system. In this presentation, the chemistry, properties and process characteristics of several polymer and graphite fiber/high temperature polymer composites will be discussed. The materials which appear to be emerging as candidates for application within the next five years will be reviewed.

2. DISCUSSION

2.1 Candidate Polymer Materials

2.1.1 High Temperature Thermoplastic and Thermoset Polymers

There are two general types of commercial polymers: thermoplastics which are derived from a condensation reaction and addition–type crosslinked polyimides, which are derived from preformed imide monomer or oligomers, such as bismaleimides or the Reverse Diels–Alder (RDA) PMR polyimide types, illustrated by PMR–15 and the acetylene terminated polyimide illustrated by MC–600 or IP–600.

2.1.2 Thermo–Oxidative Stability of Candidate Polymers

The polymer materials which are candidates for application in advanced composites in the temperature region 287–343°C (550–650°F) are listed in Table 1. One of the key issues with respect to long term applications at temperatures of 316°C or above is to what extent do these materials resist thermo–oxidative degradation? The thermo–oxidative stability of these materials was reported by Scola and Vontell (1,2) in 1988. The ranking established for the polymers isothermally aged at 316°C in air (100cc/min)

246

that several polymers are available for use at 316°C in adhesive applications.

2.1.4 Mechanical Properties of Isothermally Aged Composites

The question of what the long term stability of these materials under these conditions remains to be answered for selection of a material system for continuous 316°C service. Long term aging data for a few high temperature polymer composite systems is listed in Tables 5 through 9. Considering the number of years these polymers and fibers have been evaluated for advanced composite applications, there is not a vast body of data available to make a judicious selection of the best materials for 316°C long term use. For long term use at 316°C, only one composite system has been studied thoroughly, and this is PMR-15/ Celion 6K. For this system several aging studies for up to 2000 hours at 316°C, discussed below, have been conducted.

2.1.4.1 316°C Mechanical Properties of 316°C Isothermally Aged Composites

The 316°C shear and flexural properties of high temperature polymer/graphite fiber composites after isothermally aging at 316°C for up to 3000 hours are listed in Tables 5 & 6 .(11) It is apparent that limited data is available. However for continued use at 316°C for 1000 hours, it is clear that several composite systems are available. These are PMR-15/Celion 6K, Larc 160/Celion 6K (PI03), and NR-150B2/E-glass cloth. Two composite systems, PMR-15/Celion 6K(u) and Avimid-N/ /HMS are capable of being used for 1600 hours at 316°C, and only Avimid-N/Celion 6K is capable of use for 3000 hrs at 316°C.

The PMR-15 resin system was investigated with several graphite fiber materials to determine the influence of fiber thermo-oxidative stability on long term use of composites at 316°C. (11) The order of thermo-oxidative stability of the graphite fibers investigated (1) is T40R(unsized)> G40-700(unsized)=G40-700(epoxy sized)>

T300R(unsized)>IM6(unsized)>AS4(unsized)> Celion 6000(unsized)= Celion 6000(epoxy).

Based on the 316°C shear and flexural strength data (11), the useful lifetime of Celion 6K (unsized) or epoxy sized/PMR-15, and G40-700 (unsized)/PMR-15 composites is 1600 hrs at 316°C in flowing air (100cc/min), while for the other composites systems investigated, namely G40-700(epoxy sized)/PMR-15, T40R(unsized)/ PMR-15 and IM6(u)/PMR-15 the lifetime is about 1200 hours. It is apparent that the thermo-oxidative stability of the fiber at 316°C does not influence performance in a composite on aging at this temperature. Apparently, the PMR-15 matrix offers a protective cover for the fibers in the composite. Degradation of the composites occur mostly from oxidation of the surface inward, and to a much lesser extent via the interface.

2.1.4.2 316°C Mechanical Properties of 335°C Isothermally Aged Composites

The RT and 316°C shear properties of 335°C isothermally aged Celion 6000/ PMR-15 composites are listed in Table 7. (20) The data clearly shows that this composite system exhibits good 316°C strength retention after 1000 hours aging at 335°C.

2.1.4.3 350°C Mechanical Properties of 350°C Isothermally Aged PMR-15/Graphite Fiber Composites

The influence of graphite fiber on the flexural properties of PMR-15 composites which contained various fiber materials and which were aged at 350°C in flowing air (100 cc/min) is illustrated in Table 8. (21)

This data clearly reveals that after aging for 520 hours, the Celion 6000 (unsized or PI sized) graphite/PMR-15 composites are superior to the other PMR-15/ graphite fiber composites tested. The composites contained the graphite fibers Thornel 300(u), AS4(u), Fortifil-5(u) and Panex 30(u). With the exception of the PMR-15/Panex 30(u) composite material, all composites tested exhibited good 350°C flexural and shear strength (53 to 118 ksi respectively) and after aging for 250 hours under these conditions, with the Fortifil 5(u) composite system exhibiting the best flexural strength (118 ksi at 350°C) of the systems evaluated.

2.1.4.4 371°C Mechanical Properties of 371°C Isothermally Aged Composites

The 371°C flexural and shear strengths of Celion 6000/PMR–15 and N–phenyl modified PMR–15 composites after aging at 371°C in air for 100 hours are shown in Fig. 4. (22) The data shows that the Celion 6000/PMR–15 and Celion 6000/N–phenyl modified PMR–15 composites are capable of being used at 371°C for 100 hours. These composites exhibited flexural and shear strengths ranging from 43 to 58 ksi and 3.5 to 4.0 ksi, respectively at 371°C after aging from 100 hours in an air circulating oven.

Recent investigations (4,5) on the thermo–oxidatively stable PMR systems shown in Table 9 reveals tht composites containing these modified PMR–15 resins exhibit excellent 371°C flexural strengths (60 to 90 ksi) after aging for 200 hours in 4 atmospheres of air at 371°C.

3. CONCLUSIONS

3.1 Relative Ranking of High Temperature Polymers for CompositeApplications

3.1.1 Thermo–Oxidative Stability

In terms of their thermo–oxidative stability in air for 1500 hrs at 316°C, the polymers can be rated as follows: based on the 1988 and present study Sixef®–44=Avimid–N(NR–150B2)>>>PPQ> Durmid 500P>L–20N=PMR–15>Larc TPI>>>IP600=L–30N>PBI

3.1.2 Long Term Composite Mechanical Properties at 316°C

From the available long term mechanical property aging data at 316°C and above, composite systems containing the polymers listed below can be ranked as follows:

Avimid–N>PMR–II–30>PMR–15>IP–600 or MC–600.

3.1.3 Material Costs

In terms of material costs, the polymers can be ranked as follows: PMR–15<IP–600<<Avimid N<<<PPQ<L–20N = L–30N = Sixef®–44.

3.1.4 Overall Ranking for 316°C or Above Applications

If one considers the available data for thermo–oxidative stability, processing, long term 316°C mechanical properties, and costs, the polymer materials can be ranked as follows: PMR–15>Avimid–N>PMR–II–30.

BIOGRAPHY

Dr. Daniel A. Scola received his B.S. degree from Clark University in 1952 and an M.A. degree in Chemistry from Williams College in 1954. His graduate studies were continued at the University of Connecticut where he received a Ph.D in Chemistry in 1958. Currently, Dr. Scola is a Senior Materials Scientist at United Technologies Research Center and Adjunct Professor of Chemistry in the Institute of Materials Sciences at the University of Connecticut. At UTRC, Dr. Scola is responsible for conducting research in advanced composite materials' including interfacial bonding studies, synthesis and evaluation of resin systems and composite materials evaluation.

REFERENCES

1. Scola, D. A., Vontell, J. H., *A Comparison of the Thermo–Oxidative Stability of Commercial Graphite Fibers and Polymers for High Temperature Composite Application*, Antec '88 Proceedings, p.1612–1616, Society of Plastics Engineers 46th Annual Tech. Conference and Exhibition, April 18–21, 1988.

2. Scola, D. A. and Vontell, J. H., *High Temperature Polyimides, Chemistry and Properties Polymer Composites*, Vol. 9, No. 6, Dec. 1988.

3. Serafini, T. T., Vannucci, R. D. and Alston, W. B., *Second Generation PMR Polyimides*, NASA TM X–71894, 1976.

was as follows: Avimid N (NR-150B2)>PPQ= PMR-15>Larc TPI = IP600 > Eymyd L-20N = Eymyd L-30N > PBI. The reproducibility of such measurements due to material, process chemistry and measurement variables (such as material purity and history, the fabrication process, the imidization process, the final post-cure temperature and temperature and airflow control) must be questioned in data of this nature. Therefore, these studies were repeated with these questions in mind. A comparison of the thermo-oxidative stability of the two studies are shown in Figs. 1 & 2.

There are several significant aspects of these results: (1) the history of the material appears to affect the thermo-oxidative stability, (2) There is fairly good reproducibility of the thermo-oxidative stability (TOS) for most of the polymers, namely Avimid N, Larc TPI, and PMR-15, but poor reproducibility for IP-600, (3) In terms of ranking the polymers for TOS at 316°C for 1500 hours, the most recent study (Fig. 3) suggests the following order: Sixef®-44=Avimid-N > Durimide 500P > L-20N = PMR-15 > Larc TPI >>> IP-600 = L-30N.

Although, Sixef®-44 shows better TOS than Avimid-N, the differences in weight loss after 23 weeks (3864 hrs) are relatively minor (5.5% Vs 8.9%). The better TOS of Eymyd L-20N over Larc TPI, PMR-15 and Eymyd L-30N is not understood because from a molecular structure point of view, the presence of diphenylether units in the backbone structure of L-20N and L-30N is expected to lead to similar TOS stability. Moreover, L-20N is not expected to have better TOS than the other polymers because bond scission of the C-0-C unit between phenyl rings occurs readily because of the tendency to form a stable phenoxy-free radical. The TOS of chemically imidized L-20N and L-30N will be repeated in future studies. Therefore, it is apparent that sample history has a profound effect on the TOS of a polymer.

The TOS of the second generation PMR polyimides (3) were recently evaluated by Vannucci (4,5) for high temperature 371°C

(700°F) applications (Table 2, Fig. 4). The PMR-II compositions, PMR-II-13, PMR-II-30, and PMR-II-50 appear to hold the greatest promise for 371°C applications. Vannucci showed (4,5) that PMR-II-50, which contains the lowest concentration of nadic end-cap (aliphatic content), exhibited the lowest weight loss, and hence highest thermo-oxidative stability (Table 3). It is also apparent that a low NE content (approximately 5%) in a PMR resin does not necessarily mean that the PMR composition will have good thermo-oxidative stability.

2.1.3 Adhesive Properties of Candidate Polymers

Some indication of the bonding characteristics of these resin materials is listed in Table 4 for available tensile lap shear strength data.

The data shown on Table 4 reveals that for the polymers investigated, room temperature adhesion of these polymers to aluminum or titanium adherends which have been properly surface treated is good to fair. For Larc CPI, adhesion at room temperature is excellent. For structural applications the elevated temperature adhesion tests are carried out below the Tg of the polymers. Therefore, a direct comparison of the adhesive characteristics of several polymers at 316°C, is listed in Table 4. The data reveals that at 316°C, adhesion to titanium for most systems is approximately 1300 psi (8.6 MPa), approximately 50% of the room temperature adhesive strength. In some cases, long term aging at 316°C could improve these values. However, whether or not these bond strength values are adequate for long term application at 316°C must be determined for the specific application. The low value of 0.27 psi at 316°C for Larc TPI is due to measurement above its Tg's which is 250°C. When Larc TPI, Larc CPI and m-PPQ were tested below their Tg's, adhesive bond values of 2.1 ksi and 2.8 ksi were attained. These materials obviously can not be used at 316°C in structural applications for extended time periods. Assuming bond strength values of 1.3 ksi are adequate for specific structural applications, it can be seen

4. Vannucci, R. D., *PMR Polyimide Compositions for Improved Performance at 371°C*, SAMPE Quarterly 19(1), 31–36, Oct. 1987.

5. Vannucci, R. D., and Cifani, D., *Proc. of 20th International SAMPE Technical Conference*, SAMPE 20, Sept. 27–29, 1988.

6. Scola, D. A., Vontell, J. H., United Technologies Research Center, unpublished work.

7. Kuhbander, R. J., *SAMPE 33*, 1582–1592 (1988).

8. Rogers Corp Data Sheet on Durimid 100 and 120.

9. Hergenrother, P. M. and Havens, D. J., *SAMPE 33*, 451–463 (1988).

10. Hergenrother, P. M., *SAMPE Quarterly*, 3(1) (1971).

11. Scola, D. A., and Vontell, J. H., *Society of Plastics Engineers (SPE) Proceedings*, Antec '89, May 1–4 (1989).

12. Gibbs, H., *Section 2–D, In Proceedings of the 28th Annual Technical Conference*, Reinforced Plastics/Composites Institute, Society of the Plastics Industry, 1973.

13. Gibbs, H., Section 11–D, in *Proceedings of the 29th Annual Technical Conference*, Reinforced Plastics/Composites Institute, Society of the Plastics Industry, 1974.

14. *NR–150B2 (Avimid N)*, DuPont NR–150B2 Data Sheet, E.I. DuPont de Nemours & Company, April 1976.

15. *Thermid MC–600*, Data Sheet 26283, National Starch and Chemical Corporation, Feb 1985.

16. Hergenrother, P. M., NASA Langley Research Center, private communication (1987).

17. Luipold, D. A., *SAMPE 30*, 876–888 (1985).

18. Spigelman, P. P., Aldrich, D. C., and Wanglutal, R. F., paper #871834 SAE Aerospace Tech. Conference and Exhibition, Long Beach, CA, Oct. 5–8, (1987).

19. Monsanto, Co., Product Technical Bulletins, Nos. 5042 and 623A.

20. Scola, D. A., 27th National SAMPE Symposium, SAMPE 27, 623(1982).

21. Scola, D. A., Polymer Science and Technology Series, *Molecular Characterization of Composite Interfaces*, Vol . 27, 423–444 (1985).

22. Pater, R. H., *Proceedings of the National Tech. Conf. (Nantec) of SPE*, pp 127–130, Sheraton Bar Harbor, Fla., Oct. 21–27, (1982).

TABLE 1. CANDIDATE POLYMERS FOR HIGH TEMPERATURE COMPOSITE APPLICATIONS

Thermoplastic
Sixeff®-44
Avimid-N (NR-150B2)
Polyphenylquinoxaline (m-PPQ)
Durimid 500-P (Larc TPI), Rogers
Larc TPI (Mitsui Toatsu)
Skybond 701
Eymyd L-30N
Eymyd L-20N

Thermoset
PMR-15
PMR-II-30, -50
Thermid 600

TABLE 2. COMPOSITIONS OF PMR RESINS INVESTIGATED[1]

Resin	Diester	Diamine	n	FMW	Wt% NE
PMR-15	BTDE	MDA	2.09	1500	21.8
PMR-30	BTDE	MDA	5.2	3000	10.9
PMR-50	BTDE	MDA	9.3	5000	6.5
PMR-75	BTDE	MDA	14.5	7500	4.4
PMR-MD-64	BTDE	BDAF/PPDA	9.0	6400	5.1
PMR-MD-60	BTDE	BDAF/PPDA	9.0	6000	5.4
PMR-II-13	HFDE	PPDA	1.67	1270	25.2
PMR-II-30	HFDE	PPDA	5.0	2980	10.9
PMR-II-50	HFDE	PPDA	9.0	5050	6.5

[1]Refs. 4, 5.

TABLE 3. THERMO-OXIDATIVE STABILITY OF PMR-15 AND PMR-II COMPOSITIONS BASED ON WT. LOSS AT 371°C, 1 AND 4 ATMOSPHERE[1]

Resin	Wt.% NE Present	Wt.% Loss After	
		300 hrs/1 atm.	75 hrs/4 atm.
PMR-15	21.8	18.0	18.2
PMR-30	10.9	12.0	14.0
PMR-50	6.5	13.0	13.0
PMR-75	4.4	16.5	13.8
MD-64	5.1	16.0	17.0
MD-60	5.4	12.2	14.0
PMR-II-13	25.2	13.0	12.3
PMR-II-30	10.9	8.0	6.4
PMR-II-50	6.5	5.5	5.0

[1]Refs. 4, 5.

TABLE 4. TENSILE LAP SHEAR STRENGTH OF HIGH TEMPERATURE ADHESIVES

Material	Adherend	Tensile Lap Shear Strength ksi (MPA)	
		RT	Elevated Temp., °C
PMR-15[1]	Aluminum[6]	4.5(30.9)	2.2(15.1) 316°C
PMR-15[2]	Titanium[7]	2.3(15.8)	1.8(12.3) 316°C
Thermid 600[2]	Titanium[7]	2.8(19.5)	1.3(8.6) 316°C
PBI[2]	Titanium[7]	3.1(21.2)	1.3(8.8) 316°C
Larc-13[2]	Titanium[7]	2.3(15.7)	1.3(9.4) 316°C
Avimid N (NR-150B2)[2]	Titanium[7]	2.3(15.7)	1.4(9.6) 316°C
IP-600[2]	Titanium[7]	2.4(16.9)	1.4(9.6) 316°C
Larc-TPI[2]	Titanium[7]	2.9(19.9)	0.27(1.9) 316°C
Durimid[3]	Titanium[7]	4.3(29.7)	2.1(29.7) 232°C
Larc-CPI[4]	Titanium[7]	6.3(43.3)	2.8(19.5) 232°C
m-PPQ[5]	Titanium[7]	4.7(32.3)	2.8(19.5) 260°C

[1]Ref. 6   [3]Ref. 8   [5]Ref. 10
[2]Ref. 7   [4]Ref. 9   [6]Phosphous acid anodized 2024.
                              [7]Plas-Jel 107 surface treated.

TABLE 5. SHEAR PROPERTIES OF HIGH TEMPERATURE POLYMER/GRAPHITE FIBER COMPOSITES AFTER ISOTHERMAL AGING

Composite System	Unaged	316°C Shear Strength, ksi (MPa)			
		Aged 400 hr 316°C	Aged 1000 hrs 316°C	Aged 1600 hrs 316°C	Aged 2000 hrs 316°C
PMR-15/Celion 6K(u)[1]	7.7(53.1)	–	6.77(46.7)	5.74(39.6)	2.63(16.3)
NR150B2/E-glass cloth[2]	3.4(23.4)	–	3.90(26.9)	–	–
Thermid MC-600/HTS[3]	8.0(55.1)	–	–	–	–
m-PPQ/HMS[4]	3.4(23.4)	–	1.65(11.4)	–	–
Larc 160/Celion 6K (P103)	8.1(56)	8.4(57.9)	7.3(50)	5.4(37)	–
PMR-15/Celion 6K (epoxy)[5]	8.8(61)	8.1(55.9)	9.7(67)	7.5(52)	–

[1]Ref. 11   [3]Ref. 15   [5]Ref. 17
[2]Refs. 12, 13, 14 [4]Ref. 16

TABLE 6. FLEXURAL STRENGTH OF HIGH TEMPERATURE POLYMER/GRAPHITE FIBER COMPOSITES AFTER ISOTHERMAL AGING

Composite System	Unaged	316°C Flexural Strength, ksi (MPa)				
		Aged 500 hr 316°C	Aged 1000 hrs 316°C	Aged 1600 hrs 316°C	Aged 2000 hrs 316°C	Aged 3000 hrs 316°C
PMR-15/Celion 6K (u)[1]	125(862)		141(872)	120(817)	70(483)	–
Larc 160/Celion 6K (PI03)[2]	132(910)	134(924)	144(993)	108(745)	–	–
Avimid N/HMS[3]	98.6(680)	109(751)	–	–	–	82.6(570)
Avimid N/E-glass cloth[4]	35(241)	–	43(296)	–	–	–
Thermid MC-600/HTS[5]	148(1020)	130(896)	83(572)	–	–	–
m-PPQ/HMS[6]	56(386)	49(337)	36(248)	–	–	–
Skybond 700/181 glass cloth[7]	–	29(200)	20(138)	11(76)	–	–

[1]Ref. 11   [3]Refs. 13, 18   [5]Ref. 15   [7]Ref. 19
[2]Ref. 17   [4]Ref 13   [6]Ref. 16

TABLE 7. EFFECT OF ISOTHERMAL AGING AT 335° (635°F) OF CELION 6000/PMR-15 COMPOSITES[1]
(In flowing air, 100 cc/min)

Isothermal Aging at 335°C(635°F) hours	Flexural Properties			
	RT		316°C(600°F)	
	psi	Mpa	psi	MPa
0	17,850	123.3	5120	35.3
70	16,700	115.3	6130	42.3
100	16,400	113.3	6270	43.2
200	15,600	107.7	6640	45.8
500	14,450	99.8	6330	43.6
1015	10,850	79.9	5750	39.6

[1]Ref. 20

TABLE 8. FLEXURAL PROPERTIES OF ISOTHERMALLY AGED PMR-15 COMPOSITES[1]
(350°C, 1000 cc/min airflow)

Fiber/PMR-15 Composite System	350°C Flexural Properties		
	Unaged Strength Ksi(MPa)	After 250 hrs Strength Ksi(MPa)	After 520 hrs Strength Ksi(MPa)
Celion 6000 (u)	39(268)	54(372)	61(421)
Thornel T-300 (u)	53(365)	53(363)	12(831)
Celion 6000 (PI)	40(276)	95(655)	43(287)
AS4(u)	43(297	68(469)	18(124)
Fortafil 5(u)	55(379)	118(314)	32(221)
Panex 30 (u)	57(393)	25(172)	Completely degraded

[1]Ref. 21

TABLE 9. FLEXURAL PROPERTIES OF ISOTHERMAL AGED GRAPHITE/PMR-II TYPE COMPOSITES[1]

Composite System	Aged 200 hrs, 4 atm of air at 371°C 371°C Flexural Strength ksi (MPa)
Celion 6K/MD-60	83(572)
T40R/MD-60	75(517)
Celion 6K/PMR-II-30	88(607)
T40R/PMR-II-30	90(621)
Celion 6K/PMR-II-50	60(414)

[1]Refs. 4, 5

253

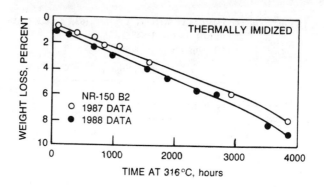

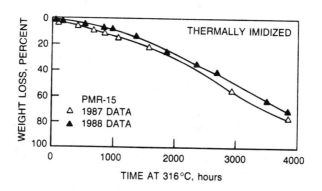

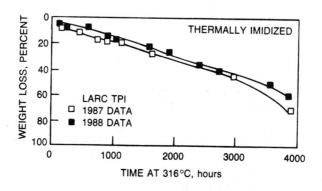

FIG. 1 THERMO-OXIDATION STABILITY OF HIGH TEMPERATURE POLYMERS AT 316°C IN FLOWING AIR (100 cc/min)

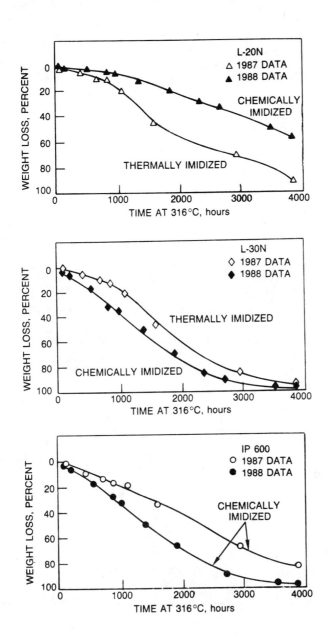

FIG. 2   THERMO-OXIDATIVE STABILITY OF HIGH
TEMPERATURE POLYMERS AT 316°C
IN FLOWING AIR (100 cc/min)

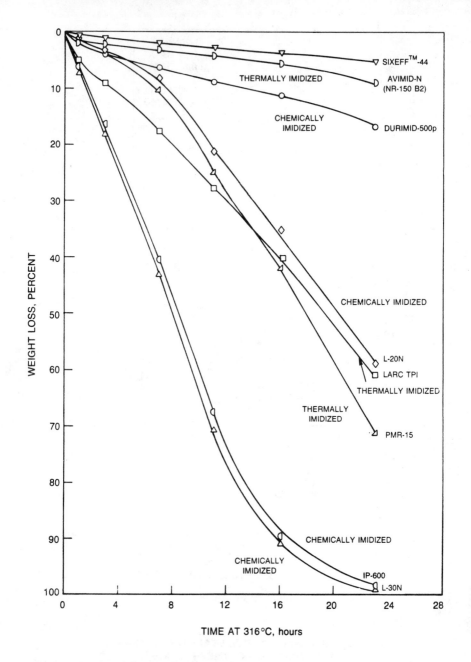

FIG. 3 THERMO-OXIDATIVE STABILITY OF HIGH TEMPERATURE POLYMERS AT 316°C IN AIRFLOW (100 cc/min)

NE⁅MDA-BTDE⁆$_n$MDA-NE

PMR

NE⁅PDDA-HFDE⁆$_n$PDDA-NE

PMR-II

NE⁅BDAF/PPDA-BTDE⁆$_n$BDAF-PDDA-NE
    2 / 3
        PMR-MD 64

NE⁅BDAF/PPDA-BTDE⁆$_n$ BDAF-PDDA-NE
    1 / 1
        PMR-MD-66

WHERE

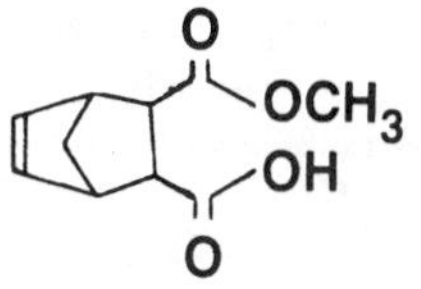

NE

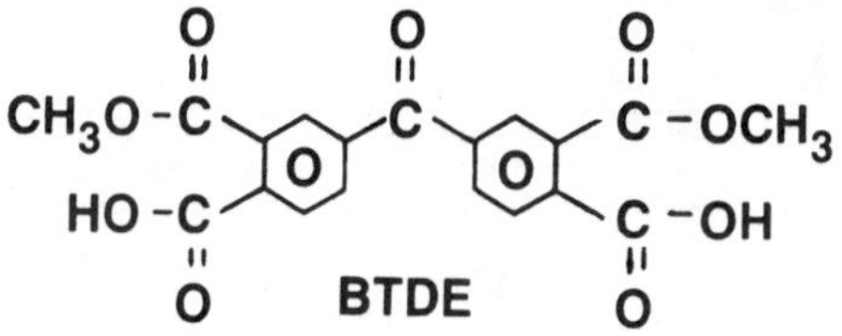

BTDE

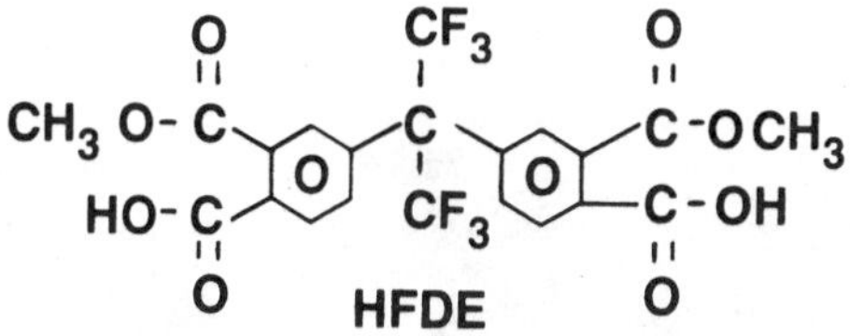

HFDE

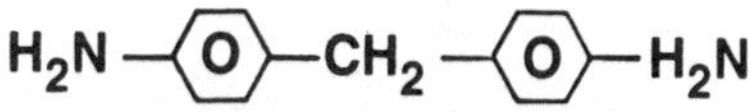

4, 4'-MDA

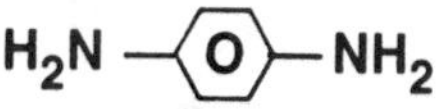

PPDA

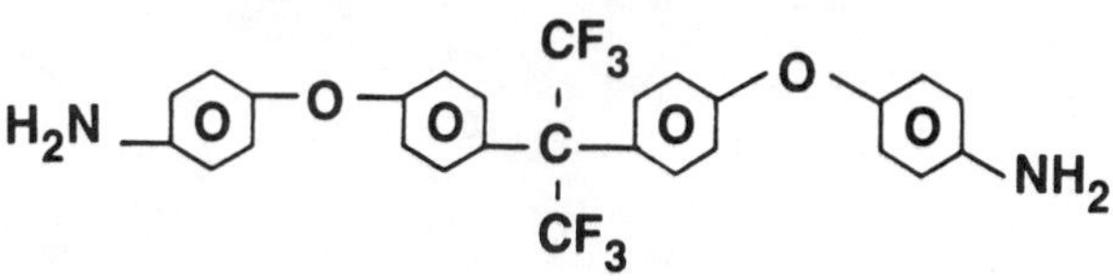

4-BDAF

are in the condensed imide structure

FIG. 4   SCHEMATIC OF PMR RESIN COMPOSITES

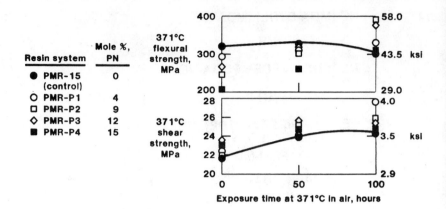

FIG. 5   371°C MECHANICAL PROPERTIES OF CELION 6000/N-PHENYLNADIMIDE
          MODIFIED PMR-15 POLYIMIDE COMPOSITES (REF. 22)

977 - A FAMILY OF NEW TOUGHENED EPOXY MATRICES

G.R. Almen[*], R.M. Byrens[*], P.D. MacKenzie[*], R.K. Maskell[*],
P.T. McGrail[+], M.S. Sefton[+]
[*]Fiberite, 2055E Technology Circle, Tempe, Arizona 85284
[+]ICI PLC, Wilton Materials Research Centre, Wilton,
Middlesbrough, Cleveland, TS6 8JE, U.K.

Abstract

In previous papers ICI/Fiber-
ite have demonstrated the
potential of epoxy/thermoplas-
tic alloys for primary
structural aerospace applications. This joint research
program has now culminated in
the development and commercialization of a family of new
damage tolerant epoxy resin
systems. The members of the
977 family have been specifically designed to meet the
required balance of toughness
and hot/wet mechanical
strength at a variety of
different service temperatures.

1. INTRODUCTION

The chemistry of epoxy resins
is well established. These
materials offer a diverse
range of properties, such as
good chemical resistance,
exceptional adhesion, and low
shrinkage. Epoxies are
currently employed in a host
of differing industrial and
commercial applications.
However, the following
discussion will be solely
concerned with the use of
epoxy resins as matrices for
advanced fiber reinforced
composites. More specifically,
the ensuing discussion will
deal only with continuous
carbon fiber reinforced epoxy
resin systems for primary
structural aerospace applications. Primary structural
implies here, applications
with critical load bearing
requirements. This clearly
excludes the use of rubber/-
elastomeric modified epoxies
and is thus beyond the scope
of this paper.

A considerable variety of
epoxy resins are currently
commercially available.

Despite this fact, new "epoxy backbones" continue to be developed. These developments reflect a growing need for materials with increased damage tolerance and higher service temperature performance. The crosslink density of a cured epoxy resin largely determines its glass transition temperature (T_g); which clearly has some bearing on its ultimate service temperature. Unfortunately, highly crosslinked thermosets are characteristically brittle materials. Thus it appears at first sight that the goals of increased damage tolerance/- toughness and increased service temperature performance are mutually exclusive.

A good deal of effort has been expended recently in the area of thermoplastic blends and alloys. Blending offers a means of combining the desirable attributes of a number of different polymers into a single material. In a similar vain, blends of thermosets and thermoplastics have been studied, in a joint ICI/Fiberite research program, as potential matrices for primary structural applications.

2. DISCUSSION
The following discussion describes, in general terms, the concept of thermoset/- thermoplastic alloys, a brief review of morphological options, and finally an introduction to the ICI/Fiber- ite 977 family of new toughened epoxy matrices.

As mentioned previously, blending presents an oppor- tunity to combine the attractive qualities of two or more polymers into an unique system. In terms of thermo- set/thermoplastic alloys; the objective here is to retain the chemical resistance, modulus, and handleability characteristics of epoxy resins; in combination with the inherent ductility associated with thermoplastic matrices. In addition to the aforementioned properties; the intention here is that the system should process like a conventional thermosetting resin. Processability is largely related to resin viscosity. The incorporation of significant amounts of thermoplastic, into for example an epoxy, will clearly have a deleterious effect upon both the viscosity of the resultant blend and hence the processability of the system.

Processability is obviously linked to the amount of

thermoplastic incorporated into the system. Not surprisingly, the more thermoplastic incorporated, the more damage tolerant the blend becomes and the more difficult the system is to process. Clearly there is a balance between toughness and processability. The viscosity of a thermoset/-thermoplastic blend is not solely dependant upon the quantity of thermoplastic incorporated: the molecular weight of the thermoplastic also plays an important role. For a given thermoset/thermoplastic blend; more thermoplastic can be incorporated by lowering the molecular weight of the thermoplastic component; hence improved toughness can be achieved whilst maintaining the same blend viscosity/processability. The quantity and the molecular weight of the thermoplastic incorporated are undoubtedly important. However, the modulus of the thermoplastic is also an important parameter. The modulus of the thermoplastic should ideally be complimentary to that of the thermoset. This implies that the choice of thermoplastic is essentially limited to that of high T_g engineering thermoplastics.

The above discussion has largely concerned the

toughness versus processability issue. However, blend toughness is not solely dependent upon the amount of incorporated thermoplastic. The resultant morphology of the cured alloy is also a key factor. The term morphology, as it pertains to this discussion, is used to describe the spacial arrangement of the thermoset and thermoplastic phases upon completion of cure. Generally, four distinct morphological options are observed:

a. Homogeneous
Single phase

b. Particulate
Thermoset continuous
Thermoplastic discontinuous

c. Co-continuous
Thermoset continuous
Thermoplastic continuous

d. Phase Inverted
Thermoset discontinuous
Thermoplastic continuous

The co-continuous and phase inverted morphology options are typically only observed for thermoset/thermoplastic blends where the amount of thermoplastic exceeds 15-20%. It is interesting to note that phase inverted systems can be achieved even when the thermoplastic is very much the minor component. In a previous paper (1) it was shown that there is a distinct advantage in terms of toughness in developing a co-continuous morphology.

The kinetics and thermodynamics of the phase separation process for a thermoset/-thermoplastic alloy are extremely complex. Obviously the nature of both the thermoset and thermoplastic (backbone and molecular weight) are important. Perhaps surprisingly, the nature of the thermoplastic end groups play a crucial role in determining morphology. That aside, reactive end groups are essential for providing good chemical resistance in the cured alloy. The function of the thermoplastic end groups in determining morphology, toughness, and solvent resistance will be addressed in a later publication.

It should be evident from the above discussion that thermoplastic "design" and subsequent synthesis were key elements in this joint ICI/Fiberite toughened thermoset program. This research/development effort has resulted in the commercialization of the ICI/Fiberite 977 family of new toughened epoxy resin systems.

The family contains a proprietary thermoplastic; designed specifically to meet the key parameters of morphology (toughness), modulus, processability, and chemical resistance of the resultant thermoset/thermoplastic blend. The proprietary thermoplastic is manufactured on full scale ICI Victrex production equipment.

The objective of this thermoset/thermoplastic blending technology is to combine good hot/wet performance, characteristic of first generation epoxy matrices, with toughness (typically associated with thermoplastic materials). The ICI/Fiberite 977 family has been specially designed to meet the requirements of hot/wet mechanical strength and toughness at different service temperatures (Table 1). The resin systems 977, 977-2, and 977-3 have been targeted for three distinct aerospace markets: commercial aircraft, military transport/helicopter, and fighter aircraft respectively.

3. COMPOSITE MECHANICAL PROPERTIES

The majority of the composite mechanical properties referred to in this paper relate to

977-2/IM7. It should be noted that X77 and X77-3 (see Table 5) are currently developmental: their "transition" to the production items 977 and 977-3 respectively, is expected in the near future.

Composite mechanical performance for 977-2/IM7 is given in Tables 2 and 3. The system shows excellent translation of fiber properties; even at sub-ambient conditions. Matrix dominated properties, such as in-plane shear and 0° compression, are also very good. Of particular note is the good retention (74% of room temperature value) of in-plane shear modulus after hot/wet conditioning at 220°F. Compression after impact (1500 in.lb./in.) values typically range from 38-44 ksi; depending on cure cycle. A typical first generation epoxy generally gives ca. 20 ksi under similar testing conditions. Comparative solvent/fuel resistance data (977-2/IM7 and Hercules 3501-6/IM7) are presented in Table 4.

In summary, 977-2/IM7 combines the hot/wet performance of standard first generation epoxies with the toughness typically exhibited by thermoplastic composites.

Mechanical data for the developmental members of the family, X77 and X77-3, are given in Table 5. 977-2/IM7 is also included as a comparison. The balance of hot/wet performance versus toughness can clearly be "tailored" to provide a family of resins for a variety of service temperature applications. Further mechanical data will be presented at a later date.

4. CONCLUSION

It has been demonstrated that the incorporation of a thermoplastic can provide an opportunity to significantly toughen an inherently brittle thermoset matrix. This thermoset/thermoplastic blending technology allows toughness and hot/wet performance to be combined in one material system. A proprietary ICI thermoplastic has been designed, synthesized, and evaluated in a number of epoxy formulations. This joint ICI/Fiberite Composite Materials research program has resulted in the development and commercialization of the new 977 family of toughened epoxy matrices. These thermoset/-thermoplastic alloys fulfil the requirements, of toughness (co-continuous morphology), modulus, processability, and chemical resistance, for primary structural aerospace applications at a variety of different service temperatures.

5. ACKNOWLEDGEMENTS

The authors would like to thank their associates at both Fiberite Composite Materials and ICI Wilton for their contribution to this work.

6. REFERENCES

1. Sefton, M. et al, "Semi-Interpenetrating Polymer Networks as a Route to Toughening of Epoxy Resin Matrix Composites", 19th International SAMPE Technical Conference, (1987), 19, 700.

7. BIOGRAPHIES

Greg Almen received his B.S. in chemistry in 1982 from the Institute of Technology at the University of Minnesota, MN. Since that time he has been employed by ICI/Fiberite Composite Materials.

Rick Byrens graduated with a B.S. in chemistry from the University of California, Irvine in 1982. Mr. Byrens spent two years as a project engineer for Programmed Composites, and in 1984 became Production Manager of their Materials subsidiary. In 1986 he joined the Technical Service Group of ICI/Fiberite Composite Materials, where he has concentrated on new products and processes; dealing predominantly with toughened epoxies.

Dr. Paul MacKenzie graduated with a Ph.D. in organic chemistry from King's College, London. He joined ICI's New Science Group in 1984. After three years research at Wilton, he was seconded to ICI/Fiberite Composite Materials, where he is currently a research chemist.

Currently Dr. Rob Maskell is Research Manager of the Composite Materials Research Group within ICI/Fiberite Composite Materials. In 1980, upon completion of his D.Phil. studies at the University of Sussex, he joined ICI. Following several years of experience in organic/polymer research, he was seconded to his present position in the U.S.A.

Dr. P.T. McGrail is a Research Associate with ICI. He is leader of the Composite Materials and Interfaces Group within the Materials Science Group at Wilton, England. He read chemistry and completed his Ph.D. at Sheffield University. He has extensive

experience in the areas of
polymer chemistry and film
manufacture and coating.

Dr. Mark Sefton graduated from
Manchester University in 1982.
He spent a year at Harvard
University as a Henry Fellow
before returning to Manchester
to complete his Ph.D. studies;
graduating with a Ph.D. in
physics. In October 1985, he
joined ICI and has since been
researching into toughened
thermoset composites.

977 FAMILY PROPERTY TARGETS*

RESIN SYSTEM	CAI (ksi)	0° COMPRESSION	APPLICATION
977	45	150 ksi at 180°F/wet	COMMERCIAL AIRCRAFT
977-2	40	180 ksi at 180°F/wet	MILITARY TRANSPORT/ HELICOPTER
977-3	35	180 ksi at 220°F/wet	FIGHTER AIRCRAFT

*INTERMEDIATE MODULUS CARBON FIBER

TABLE 1

266

IM-7/977-2

Composite Mechanical Properties - Dry

Mechanical Property	-75°F	RT	190°F	220°F	250°F
0° Tensile Strength, ksi	429	409			
Tensile Modulus, msi	25.9	25.1			
90° Tensile Strength, ksi		10.9			
Tensile Modulus, msi		1.1			
0° Compression Str., ksi		234	225	217	214
Compression Mod., msi		22.8	23.0	21.4	22.7
Short Beam Shear Str., ksi		16.3	13.5	12.7	11.4
In-Plane Shear Strength, ksi		15.8	15.3	14.6	14.1
Shear Modulus, msi		0.80	0.72	0.68	0.69
Comp. Interlaminar Shear, ksi		12.4	9.7		
0° Flexural Strength, ksi		235	212		
90° Flexural Strength, ksi		22.4	19.1	17.9	16.9
Open-Hole Tensile (1), ksi		72			
Open-Hole Tensile (2), ksi	113	124			
Open-Hole Comp. (3), ksi		48	42		38
Open-Hole Comp. (2), ksi		62	51	50	49
Compression After Impact, ksi		38-44			

Notes:
(1) Used [+45,0,-45,90]s lay-up
(2) Used [±45,0,0,90,0,0,±45,0]s lay-up (50/40/10)
(3) Used [+45,0,-45,90]2s lay-up
(4) All of the above data was generated using 145-155 g/m2 material. Laminates used were between 56-60% Fiber Volume, and the resulting data was not normalized.
(5) Compression after Impact Specimens were impacted and tested per BMS 8-276.

TABLE 2

IM-7/977-2

Composite Mechanical Properties - Wet

Mechanical Property	180 (1)	190 (1)	190 (2)	220 (1)
0° Compression Str., ksi	192	185	206	175
Compression Mod., msi	22.2	21.6	22.7	22.6
Short Beam Shear Str., ksi	12.3	11.8	12.6	10.0
In-Plane Shear Strength, ksi	14.5	14.1	15.3	13.9
Shear Modulus, msi	0.67	0.64	0.63	0.59
0° Flexural Strength, ksi				
90° Flexural Strength, ksi		15.3	18.0	
Open-Hole Comp. (4), ksi	38			
Open-Hole Comp. (3), ksi		49.6	51.2	

Notes:
   (1) Wet Condition = 2 week immersion in 160°F water.
   (2) Wet Condition = 24 hour water boil.
   (3) Used [±45,0,0,90,0,0,±45,0]s lay-up (50/40/10)
   (4) Used [+45,0,-45,90]2s lay-up
   (5) All of the above data was generated using 145-155 g/m2 material. Laminates
used were between 56-60% Fiber Volume, and the resulting data was not normalized.

TABLE 3

SOLVENT/FUEL RESISTANCE COMPARISON
977-2 vs. 3501-6
(BOTH WITH HERCULES IM-7 FIBER)

IN-PLANE SHEAR AFTER MEK IMMERSION @ RT

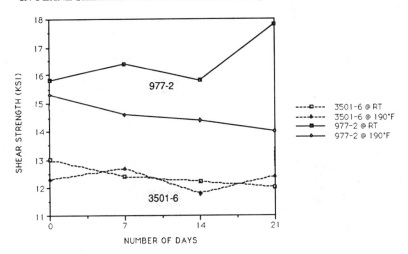

IN-PLANE SHEAR AFTER JP-4 IMMERSION AT 180°F

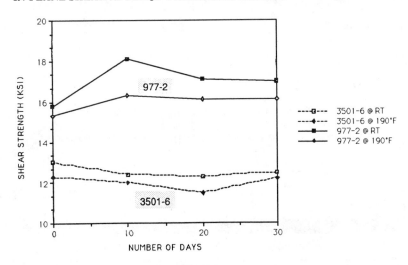

TABLE 4

Composite Mechanical Properties

Mechanical Property	X77/IM7	977-2/IM7	X77-3/IM7
0° Tensile Strength, ksi, (RT)	387	409	397
Tensile Modulus, msi, (RT)	22.3	25.1	24.2
0° Compression Strength, ksi			
RT	206	234	232
180°F	189	----	----
180°F/wet[1]	180	192	182
220°F/wet[2]	----	----	173
Compression After Impact,[3] ksi	46.0	38-44	33.3

Notes:
(1) Wet condition = 2 week immersion in 160°F water
(2) Wet condition = 1 week immersion in 160°F water
(3) Compression after impact specimens were impacted and tested per BMS 8-276

TABLE 5

TRANSVERSE REINFORCEMENT METHODS FOR
IMPROVED DELAMINATION RESISTANCE

David A. Evans, J. S. Boyce,
Foster-Miller Inc.
350 Second Avenue
Waltham MA. 02254

Abstract

The delamination resistance of fiber composites can be improved by transverse reinforcement. Stitching can provide this reinforcement, but lowers the in-plane properties and requires access to both sides of the layup. Two methods have been developed which insert fibers without removing or damaging the layup. The fibers are placed vertically from inner to outer ply. These transverse fibers resist delamination with minimal loss of in-plane strengths. We describe an insertion method that uses ultrasonic energy, and a transfer method which uses forces generated by the normal cure process. Panels of AS4/3501-6 were reinforced transversely and tested. Delamination resistance is markedly improved with little change of in-plane properties.

1.   INTRODUCTION

In recent years the aerospace industry has increased its dependence on advanced structural composites. Composite structures offer a variety of properties which are not available in their metal counterparts. On a strength-to-weight basis, organic matrix composites are leading materials. They offer the design engineer a multitude of new options as well as invaluable weight savings in the design of aerospace structures.

Polymer composites are laminated layers of aligned fibers in a resin matrix. The lamination produces interply areas between each layer which are mainly resin. The properties orthographic to the laminate, which depend on the interply layer, are weak in comparison to the in-plane properties of composites. The weak interply region is an area where cracks propagate easily. Structural failure can often be traced to interply cracking. Cracking sometimes originates at holes or edges of the laminate where out-of-plane stresses occur.

Cracks are also often started by impact events. Three types of impact damage can be described. The low speed impact of a stone being thrown up from a runway, or the careless dropping of a wrench onto a composite panel can cause invisible crack damage. The surface damage is often not significant enough to be detected visually. The majority of the damage is to the internal structure of the laminate. The presence of these cracks severely reduces the compressive strength of the laminate and can lead to early delamination and failure. High speed impacts from ballistic fragments cause similar damage within the component, but cause more visible damage at the surface.

The third type of damage applies to aircraft fuel tanks such as "wet wings." A ballistic fragment penetrates one side of the fuel tank and decelerates rapidly, imparting most of its energy into the fluid. The shock wave in the fluid, known as hydraulic or hydrodynamic ram, can severely damage the the fuel tank [1].The hydrodynamic ram causes severe

deformation of the skins and internal stiffeners can become detached. Composite structures are thought to be particularly vulnerable to this type of damage.

1.1 Potential Solutions

The cracking in all the impact damage modes is propagated through the weak interply layer. It is essential to confine delamination to the area of impact to improve the "after impact" strength of composite panels. Two approaches are possible. The toughness of the interply layer can be improved to blunt the crack, or the out-of-plane strength can be increased to resist the forces propagating the crack.

Methods to increase the toughness of the interply layer usually modify the bulk of the resin or interleave a tough layer instead of the interply layer [2]. Unfortunately, these modifications alter all the properties of the composite and a new design database is required.

The transverse strength of the laminate is increased by adding fibers in that direction. The transverse fibers are added by 3-D weaving, stitching or needling, or short fiber insertion. 3-D weaving requires that a complete component be fabricated in one piece and cannot be applied to composites made by the more common hand layup procedure. The single piece weaving has similar volumes of fiber in each plane and almost always has redundant yarns.

Stitching or needling through the uncured laminate are methods which confine delaminations and improve post-impact strength (3,4). Unfortunately, all of these methods damage the main reinforcements (especially when these are graphite). Stitching or needling also requires placing the uncured laminate in a sewing or needling machine (5). This creates handling problems and practically limits application to flat laminates. In another investigation, laminates were prepared by stitching dry fabric layers and injecting resin into a mold containing the stitched preform. Results from this investigation show that up to 25 percent of the in-plane strength is sacrificed for a 40 to 60 percent improvement in impact damage (6).

Huang, Richey and Deska (7) embedded short steel wires at 45 degree orientations into laminates of graphite-epoxy. Using steel wires of 0.3mm (0.013 in.) diameter at 1.5mm (1/16 in.) spacing, Huang et. al. measured a 40 percent increase in short beam shear strength. Uhl (8) inserted boron fibers and tufts of graphite fibers into laminates and increased the delamination resistance, but reduced the in-plane strength.

These transverse reinforcements increase the delamination resistance but, for various reasons, decrease the in-plane strengths. Some methods of adding transverse fibers need a new process. A method is required which will insert sufficient fibers without these drawbacks.

2.   OBJECTIVES

The methods we have developed were designed to replace stitching as a means of adding transverse fibers to a laminate. Both programs sought to increase the survivability of military aircraft by controlling the damage during ballistic impact. The delamination from lower energy impacts will also be less if this objective is met. The process must be effective in cost and performance to be accepted and used. This leads to further objectives:

a) There must be no great loss of in-plane properties. Stitching causes a loss of 25% of the properties of a laminate. We set a target of 5% maximum loss.

b) The new process must fit within the current vacuum bag/autoclave method for composites. No extra steps should be allowed and the process should not be complicated.

c) The process should be completed without removing the layup from the mold tool. The new process should only require single-sided access to the layup.

d) The new process should be capable of inserting a small and controlled amount of fiber through the laminate. Effective transverse reinforcement requires less than 5% fiber inserted orthographically.

We have developed two distinct methods which meet these objectives. One method transfers fibers from a preform into the laminate. In the other process, fiber yarns are inserted into the cold laminate. Both methods warm the resin to ease the new fibers into the laminate.

3. FIBER TRANSFER

The program to develop a fiber transfer method started with the concept of a tape that could be laid over the component(Figure 1). Fibers are transferred from the tape into the layup during cure. The autoclave pressure provides the force to transfer the fibers. Our original concept, fibers embedded in a B-staged resin matrix, could not support the fibers during transfer. A medium was needed that would provide support while it slowly collapsed.

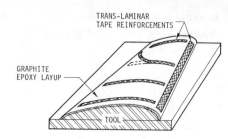

Figure 1 Z-Direction Tape is Applied to The Layup.

The transfer of the fibers is best accomplished when the matrix resin of the layup is at a low viscosity. This lowers the force needed to transfer the reinforcing fibers and reduces the damage to the in-plane fibers. Thus we needed a medium with enough rigidity to resist 100 psi at room temperature, but the medium had to collapse under the same pressure at a higher temperature. A foam is the only material form that has such low compressive strengths and several thermoplastic foams show a gradual loss in strength at higher temperatures. Our final concept, using foam, is shown in Figure 2.

A foam layer is embedded vertically with boron fibers. The foam is covered on the top with a layer of steel shim and beneath with a release layer. This foam assembly is placed onto the layup where transverse reinforcement is needed. A normal vacuum bag is formed over the layup and the foam preform. At room temperature the foam supports the autoclave pressure. The foam begins to collapse as the temperature increases. An epoxy system requires the foam to collapse between 200 and 250°F. The autoclave pressure is trans- ferred to the ends of the boron fibers by the steel shim. The foam supports the boron fibers and prevents buckling. The fibers are pushed into the laminate. As the foam collapses it increases in density and continues to support the fiber. The fibers are driven all the way through the laminate.

After cure the collapsed foam is stripped from the laminate leaving a stubble of boron fibers. This stubble is removed to leave a laminate with transverse reinforcement.

Initial tests proved the concept and led into characterization tests. Foam preforms were prepared with boron fibers every 1.5mm (1/16 inch) across the foam. These preforms were used to prepare test specimens. The effectiveness of the boron fiber in arresting crack propagation was measured by the Double Cantilever Beam Cleavage Test. This test showed that there is a 3-5 fold rise in the critical strain energy release rate , G_{IC}, when a laminate is transversely reinforced. A typical load curve for a reinforced specimen is superimposed on the load curve for an unreinforced specimen in Figure 3. The figure graphically depicts the sudden increase in toughness when the crack reaches the reinforced region.

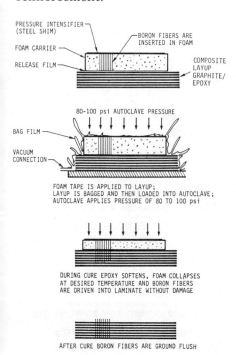

Figure 2 Z-Direction Fibers by Transfer.

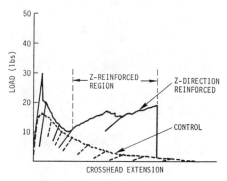

Figure 3 Load Curves for DCB Tests with Z-Direction Reinforcement

The DCB specimens were opened after testing and the surfaces examined by Electron Microscopy to determine the mode of failure of the boron fibers.

Eighty percent of the boron fibers failed in tension. The remaining fibers had an adhesive failure with the matrix resin and were pulled out of the laminate. Also noted in the micrographs was the position of the graphite fibers; most had moved aside to allow penetration of the boron fibers. No broken graphite fibers were seen which could be attributed to the boron penetration. Two typical Electron Microscope Micrographs are shown in Figure 4, where all these features can be seen.

The effects of transverse reinforcement on the tensile and shear strengths were measured. Tensile strength and interlaminar shear strengths showed no significant difference in reinforced and unreinforced laminates. Table 1 summarizes all the results of the initial testing.

Table 1 Summary of Results of Fiber Transfer.*

Test	Control	Z-Reinforced Specimens*
DCB -G_{IC} in-lb/in^2	1.2	4.2
Tensile Strength Ksi	272	289
Tensile Modulus Msi	23.5	23.1
ILS Ksi	9.15	9.08

*All testing used AS4/3501-6 UD, with transverse boron fibers at 1/16 inch

4.   FIBER INSERTION

This program began with the insertion of conventional metal staples into a laminate. The staple was eased in after heating the laminate with an ultrasonic horn. The metal staples increased the crack propagation resistance of the laminate. Bag pressure pushes the staple over, leaving it cured into the laminate at an angle. PPS/carbon fiber staples also heeled over in the cured laminate. Nylon12/glass fiber staples behaved differently. The nylon/glass staples damaged the laminate less and remained sub-stantially perpendicular to the plies. The Nylon12 showed signs

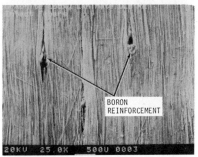

Figure 4 SEM Micrographs of Z-Reinforced Laminates

f softening during insertion and was more securely bonded to the laminate than either metal or PPS staples. All the staples inhibited delamination: the crack propagation from an impact is limited. Figure 5 shows the extent of delamination in AS4/3501-6 panels with and without staples.

NYLON/GLASS STAPLE

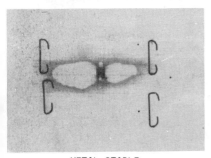

METAL STAPLE

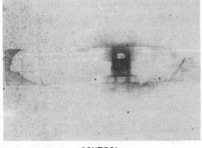

CONTROL

Figure 5 X-Radiographs of Stapled Panels after 30 in-lb Impact

4.1 The Spike Concept

The staple has two problems that prevent it from meeting our objectives. The legs of the staple must be clinched and therefore the layup must be removed from the mold. The legs and crown of the staple are driven into the plies during cure and produce a wrinkle (Figure 6). The wrinkle lowers the in-plane strength (9).

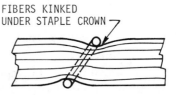

Figure 6 Staple Crown and Legs Cause Wrinkled Fibers

A staple mechanically clamps the laminate and prevents the movement needed to spread the crack. Remove the clinched legs and crown of the staple and one has a spike through the laminate. The transverse strength of laminate with spikes is proportional to the bond shear strength to the spike. This bond strength is insufficient to break the spike.

A fiber-reinforced spike is a yarn coated with a rigid binder. A fiber-reinforced spike has the shear strength of the bond between the matrix resin and binder polymer. The strength of this spike can be increased if the binder is removed and each individual fiber is bonded with the

277

matrix resin. We have developed spikes with a binder of rigid polymer that is soluble in the matrix. During cure the binder is washed off the fibers in the spike and replaced by matrix resin. Thus the transverse fibers are as securely bonded as the main fibers. Delamination spreads only when all the individual fibers have been fractured.

These reinforced spikes were inserted into the laminate by pushing them from a close-fitting cylinder with a plunger. The laminate was heated rapidly by applying an ultrasonic horn. The cylinder was then applied to the warm spot and the spike was driven in. This process only worked with very thin laminates.

We investigated the temperatures produced by the ultrasonic horn and found there was a large difference between the temperatures of the upper and lower plies. Figure 7 shows this difference for a 16-ply laminate. The ultrasonic energy is apparently converted into heat energy in the upper plies and little energy reaches the lower plies.

4.2 Hollow Needle Insertion

There was no way to heat through the laminate without causing other damage, therefore we developed a hollow needle to insert the fiber-reinforced spike.

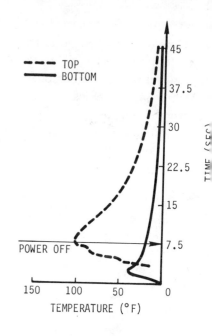

Figure 7 Ultrasonic Heating of a 16-Ply Graphite/Epoxy Laminate

An ultrasonic horn was modified by drilling a hole through to the end. The tip of the horn was modified by inserting a 0,5mm (.020 inch) tube into it. A coated fiber was fed down the horn into the tip. The tip is driven into the layup. The ultrasonic vibration allows it to enter easily by a combination of cutting and displacement of the layup fibers. The horn is withdrawn while the fiber is held still in the layup. The fiber is cut above the layup (Figure 8).

The fiber has to be "pushed" during this sequence, hence it requires some rigidity. S-2 glass fiber (37 1/0) was coated with about 17% polysulfone to make it rigid enough to be used in this

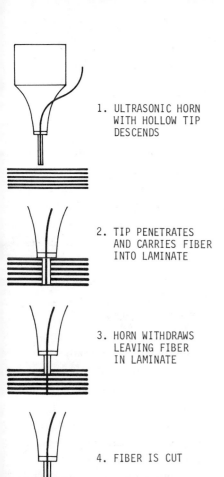

1. ULTRASONIC HORN WITH HOLLOW TIP DESCENDS

2. TIP PENETRATES AND CARRIES FIBER INTO LAMINATE

3. HORN WITHDRAWS LEAVING FIBER IN LAMINATE

4. FIBER IS CUT

Figure 8 Translaminar Fibers by Insertion.

process. This coated fiber is approximately 0.45mm (.018 inch) in diameter. The polysulfone also met our previous requirement for a soluble binder; it dissolves in 3501-6 in 30 minutes at 250°F. Figure 9 shows a broken S-2 glass bundle after it has failed in a graphite/epoxy DCB specimen. The photomicrograph shows that the graphite fibers (in the plane of the photograph) are only slightly disturbed by the transverse fiber. The S-2 glass yarn (end-on to the viewer) is broken in random lengths, indicating that the load was borne by individual fibers.

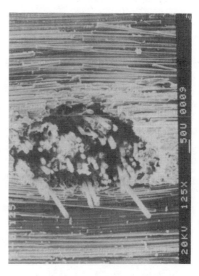

Figure 9 Photomicrograph of Broken S-Glass Bundle in DCB specimen

4.3 Test Results

The hollow needle insertion met our objectives. We have tested the effect of these fiber insertions on delamination and in-plane strengths. The delamination behavior was measured with the Double Cantilever Beam specimen to NASA RP-1092. Tensile strength, compressive strength and in-plane shear strength were measured to ASTM D 3039, D 3410 and D 3518 respectively. The Compression Strength after Impact was measured to NASA RP-1092.

The S-2 glass fibers were inserted in laminates of AS4/3501–6 in rows at 1/4 and 3/8 inch spacing. The rows were either aligned or offset by a half-pitch (staggered). The results of this testing are shown in Table 2.

Table 2. DCB Test Results.*

Spacing (in).	Fiber Geometry	G_{IC} (in.-lb/in.^{2})
3/8	Straight	3.2
3/8	Staggered	3.4
1/4	Straight	4.6
1/4	Staggered	6.7

*AS4/3501-6 Reinforced with S-2 Glass Insertions

The 1/4 inch staggered configuration will have the largest effect on in-plane properties; this configuration was used for all the reinforced tensile, compressive and shear specimens. The results of this testing are shown in Table 3. The results showed that the in-plane strengths are only slightly reduced by this method of transverse reinforcement. The average reduction was around five percent for a five-fold increase in fracture toughness.

The compression strength after impact testing demonstrated the ability of transverse fibers to contain impact damage. The ultrasonic scans in Figure 10 show a large reduction in damage area .

5.   CONCLUSIONS

We have developed two successful methods for the transverse reinforcement of laminates. One method inserts large fibers and the other inserts yarns. In both methods we have succeeded in increasing the delamination resistance without seriously affecting the in-plane properties. The methods do not fracture and distort the fibers of the laminate. The reinforcing fibers extend from inner to outer surfaces without a loop across the laminate.

Table 3 In-plane Tests of AS4/3501-6   Z-Reinforced with S-2 Glass.

Test	Layup Direction	Direction of Test	Result	
			Control	Reinforced
Tensile Strength	Cross-ply	0 degree	48 Ksi	47 Ksi
Tensile Strength	All 0 deg	90 degree	5.58 Ksi	4.47Ksi
Compressive Str.	Cross-ply	0 degree	65.4 Ksi	60.4 Ksi
Compressive Str.	Cross-ply	90 degree	50.9 Ksi	44.7 Ksi
Compressive Str.	All 0 deg.	0 degree	143Ksi	131 Ksi
Compressive Str.	All 0 deg.	90 degree	30.6 Ksi	27.3 Ksi
Shear Strength	±45 deg.	0 degree	11.95.Ksi	12.77 Ksi

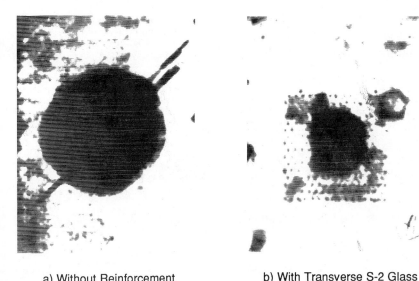

a) Without Reinforcement

b) With Transverse S-2 Glass

Figure 10 Ultrasonic Scans of Impacted Panels. - AS4/3501-6

Further testing will determine the effects of ballistic impacts on panels with stiffening elements. The stiffeners will be attached with transverse reinforcements. We expect the reinforced panels to exhibit better damage tolerance.

A hand held device was developed for the insertion method (Figure 11). This device can insert local transverse reinforcement on a lay-up but requires positioning by hand. The basic device should be mounted on a robot, or a tape-layer, for the automatic insertion of transverse fibers.

Both methods can be used with other fibers. The transfer method requires a large diameter fiber, or a bundle of fibers with a binder. The method has already been applied to preforms for carbon-carbon moldings. Transverse reinforcements such as silicon carbide, boron and rods of pultruded graphite have been inserted into phenolic panels. Figure 12 shows a panel with graphite

Figure 11 Hand-Held fiber Insertion Device

rods. The Z-direction reinforcement will provide transverse strength in carbon-carbon moldings.

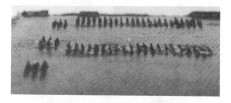

Figure 12 Graphite Rods (.018")
Transferred Into Phenolic-Carbon.

6. REFERENCES

1 Jacobson, M.J., R.M. Heitz, J.R. Yamane, "Survivable Composite Integral Fuel Tanks, Volume 1 Testing and Analysis," AFWAL-TR-85-3085 Northrop Corporation, January 1986.

2 Kreiger, R.B., "An Adhesive Interleaf to Reduce Stress Concentrations between Plies of Structural Composite," Proceedings 32nd SAMPE Symposium, April 6-9, 1987.

3 Sun, C.T., L. Miller, "The Use of Stitching to Suppress Delamination in Laminated Composite," ASTM STP-876.

4.Sawyer, J.W., "Effect of Stitching on the Strength of Bonded Composite Single Lap Joints," AIAA Journal 23,11 pp. 1744-1748 December 1985.

5 Forsch, H.H., European Patent 0 027 107, "Method of Fastening a Composite Substructure and Structure," assigned to Grumman Aerospace Corp.

6 Dexter, B.H., J.G. Funk, "Impact Resistance and Interlaminar Fracture Toughness of Through Reinforced Graphite/Epoxy," AIAA paper 86-1020-LP May 1986.

7 Huang, S.L., R.J. Richey and E.W. Deska, "Cross Reinforcement in a Gr/Ep Laminate," Winter Annual Meeting of the American Society of Mechanical Engineering," December 10-15, 1978.

8 Uhl, D. T.,"3-D Reinforcement Processing," Final Report for Period October 1985 to December 1986, AFWAL-TR-88-4004, General Dynamics Fort Worth.

9 Boyce, J.S. and R.R. Wallis, "Translaminar Reinforcement of Organic Matrix Composites," AFWAL-TR-86-3053, Oct 1986.

7. ACKNOWLEDGEMENTS

These programs are SBIR contracts. The transfer method is funded by Naval Weapons Center, China Lake. The insertion method is funded by Flight Dynamics Laboratory, AFWAL, WPAFB.

We are grateful for the help of Dr. R. S. Sandhu at AFWAL in testing the compression strength after impact. The Foster-Miller staff who have helped include Dan Bullock, Randy Wallis, Lucy Elandjian and Tom Fusco.

STRENGTH SUBSTANTIATION OF THE ALL COMPOSITE AIRFRAME
(A MATERIALS DATA BASE APPROACH)

Ric Abbott and Ann L. Kolarik
Beech Aircraft Corporation
Wichita, Kansas

ABSTRACT

Beech Aircraft has completed
Federal Aviation Administration
certification of the all-composite
Starship 1 business airplane. This
paper describes development of the
data base for graphite/epoxy
thermoset materials along with the
tests and analysis methods used to
satisfy Federal Aviation
Regulations (FAR Part 23) and the
special conditions pertaining to
composite certification.

1. MATERIAL QUALIFICATION

A selection of fiber and resin
systems was required to produce a
wide spectrum data base. Multiple
vendors were desired to eliminate
supply problems in production.
Different areal weights and weaves
of material were tested and
certified to allow for flexibility
in design of the aircraft
structure. The material
qualification program established
the lamina properties for each
format certified. The current test
matrix for qualifying woven
materials consists of testing for
modulus and strength for tension
and compression in the 0° and 90°
direction. Tests are performed in
Cold/Dry, RT/Dry, RT/Wet and
Hot/Wet environments. This matrix
has been revised since the original
material qualification testing. It
is now based on recent MIL-HDBK-17

committee recommendations but
includes an increased number of
tests in the first batch tested.
The tests are performed according
to ASTM D 3039-76 and ASTM D 695.
Figure 1 shows sample results of
the nine different lamina
properties obtained for each
material qualified.

E_x	18.72 MSI
E_y	1.31 MSI
E_s	0.81 MSI
ν_{xy}	.274
X_t	307.8 KSI
X_c	221.8 KSI
Y_t	6.54 KSI
S_{45}	21.09 KSI
t	.010 in.

FIGURE 1
SAMPLE LAMINA PROPERTIES
RT/DRY HITEX/E7K8 280 TAPE

2. MOISTURE EXPOSURE

All materials and assemblies
certified met minimum requirements
at severe environmental conditions
along with room temperature
requirements. The effects of long
term exposure to environmental
elements was an area of limited
published information. A
comprehensive survey of ground
environments at 158 Air Force bases
in the U.S. and overseas was
reviewed.

The moisture conditioning environment chosen represents the average relative humidity of the most humid month at Andersen Air Base, Guam: 85% relative humidity, plus a 2% margin, used to set the conditioning chambers.

The moisture conditioning process consists of exposing all graphite/epoxy specimen to 87% relative humidity. To accelerate the process the temperature in the conditioning chamber was raised above ambient. Assemblies which include various adhesives, foam cores and honeycomb cores were elevated to 140°F. Those specimen that are laminate only are exposed to 160°F. The advantage of this process is that the entire specimen becomes saturated whereas hot water immersion encourages the surface of the specimen to be over saturated. Figure 2 shows a typical percent moisture gain plot.

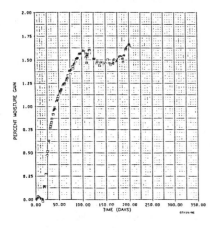

FIGURE 2
PERCENT MOISTURE GAIN

3. MAXIMUM TEMPERATURE

The maximum structural temperature occurs from solar heating when the aircraft sits on the runway. During July, Death Valley, California has the highest expected ambient temperature, (116°F) as well as the highest solar radiation, (310 BTU's/sq ft/hr). Solar soak tests were conducted with an ambient temperature of 91°F producing a skin temperature of 125°F. Adjusting the surface temperature for the 116°F ambient requirement results in a skin temperature of 150°F. By controlling the colors used to paint the airplane, the upper surface temperature will remain below the qualification tested temperature of the laminating resin (180°F).

4. STRUCTURAL LOADING ENVIRONMENTAL EXTREMES

It is important to evaluate the aircraft's external loading with the appropriate environment. Various laminates, because of their location on the aircraft and the applied external load condition, will not be exposed to critical loads combined with Hot/Wet conditions. The aircraft is assumed to become conditioned while stationed on the runway and cools during take-off and flight. Therefore, a separate external loads analysis was performed for cases considered Hot/Wet. For example, the pressure cabin maximum internal pressure occurs at 41,000 ft; therefore, it is not a Hot/Wet case.

5. LAMINATE ANALYSIS

The lamina properties of individual materials were determined from the qualification test results. Two resins, three fibers and various formats were originally qualified.

To assist the stress engineer in laminate analysis, integrated software was developed. The Laminate Analysis Software Package (LASP) is based on analysis detailed in Reference 1. LASP was used to create the laminate's stacking sequence from lamina properties. Also, the material property cards required for NASTRAN were created by LASP. The finite element model was then run to determine the internal loading of the structure. These loads (Fx, Fy, S) are then applied to the designed laminate via LASP. The stress and strain on each individual ply may be investigated.

If any ply has failed the particular mode (tension, compression or shear) was automatically determined and shown in the output. This provides the stress engineer immediate feedback of the failure mode and allows for re-evaluation of the laminate prior to any static testing. Furthermore, when no single ply fails due to the specified loading, the margin of safety of the laminate may be determined for strength.

Another part of the software package developed was Sandwich Panel Analysis: Impact/Delamination, (SPAID), to determine the stability behavior of panels under compressive and shear loads, in the virgin and damaged states.
The damage can be either a delamination or impact damage with resin damage at multiple ply interfaces. Reference 2 is the detailed description of the modeling techniques and verification of this software package. The basic panel stability analysis is based on the procedures outlined in MIL-HDBK-23. SPAID output is the load required to fail the defined panel, no matter what the initial condition of the panel. The margin of safety is then determined for the buckling modes.

These analysis procedures are followed to evaluate laminates at room temperature condition and at the appropriate severe environment.

6. LAMINATE VALIDATION

Laminate material properties vary due to processing, material variability and manufacturing variability. Variations also occur in sheet metal. To determine the applicability of the graphite/epoxy data base in substantiation of ultimate load margins of safety, comparisons were made of the coefficient of variation (COV) of the graphite/epoxy materials and a typical aluminum (7075-T73) from MIL-HDBK-5. With the variation in tensile strength and thickness of 7075-T73 the COV is 11.1%. The Beech graphite/epoxy data base has

83% of its COV's equal to or better than 11.1%. The presence of honeycomb core in co-cured panels tends to increase COV values slightly. This was not a serious concern because honeycomb panels tend to fail due to instability prior to the material failure.

MIL-HDBK-17 defines B-Basis allowables as: "At least 90 percent of the population of values is expected to equal or exceed the B-Basis mechanical property allowable, with a confidence of 95 percent." Using this approach, the lamina strength properties in the graphite/epoxy data base automatically allows for material variabilities.

As mentioned, the laminate stiffness predictions are based on the classical laminated-plate theory defined in Reference 1. Comparisons of calculated tension and compression stiffness properties to test values are shown in Figure 3 for typical laminates.

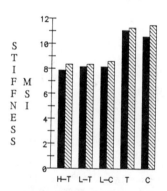

■ EXPERIMENTAL RESULTS

▨ THEORETICAL RESULTS

FIGURE 3
STIFFNESS COMPARISON
H - Hoop
T - Tension
L - Longitudinal
C - Compression

The accuracy of laminate strength prediction is dependent on first ply failure criterion, (that load which causes the weakest ply(s) to fail within the laminate). First ply failure criterion is a classical analysis method; it is not a condition that can be readily duplicated by test. The validity of first ply failure was checked using both mean and B-Basis lamina strength allowables. Laminate failure values determined by test, were also mean and B-Basis values. Figure 4 details the first, second and third ply calculated failure for mean and B-Basis data of a typical skin (37%/26%/37% layup) compared to mean and B-Basis test results.

are reasonably applicable to laminate strength calculations when B-Basis lamina properties are used.

When compression instability is analyzed, the first ply failure criterion does not apply. The compression instabilities are divided into three categories: 1) column buckling, 2) panel buckling and 3) local crippling.

Figure 5 shows schematics of these three conditions for a honeycomb panel. Column buckling is a one dimensional buckling in the direction of the applied load.

Panel buckling is a two dimensional buckling in the direction of the applied load and transverse to the applied load. Local crippling is buckling in a small portion of the panel with the rest of the panel remaining intact.

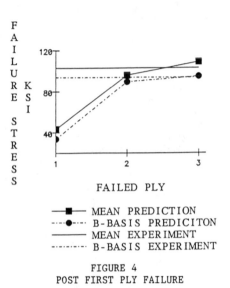

FAILED PLY

- ■─ MEAN PREDICTION
- ●─ B-BASIS PREDICITON
- ── MEAN EXPERIMENT
- ─── B-BASIS EXPERIMENT

FIGURE 4
POST FIRST PLY FAILURE

The conclusion from this validity check was that first ply failure is not allowed at or below limit load. This corresponds with the limit load requirements in metallic aircraft. Metallic parts must withstand limit load without detrimental yielding. If the part yields prior to limit load the resulting load carrying capability, after unloading, has been altered. When first ply failure is allowed below limit load a similar redistribution occurs after initial loading. First ply failure is allowed between limit and ultimate load as long as the remaining plies have load carrying capability and catastrophic failure does not occur. The validity check also confirmed that B-Basis predictions

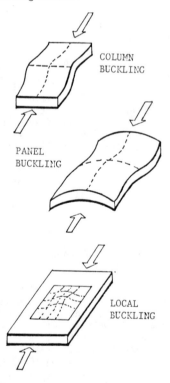

FIGURE 5
BUCKLING CONDITIONS

Column buckling analysis was found to give the best failure predictions for compressive loading for panels with a high aspect ratio: greater than 1.5. The boundary conditions were considered to be simply supported. Panel buckling analysis was more accurate for low aspect ratio panels: =1.0. Local crippling analysis yielded very high failure loads and was never found to be the failure mode for the specified panels.

The shear buckling predictions are conservative in comparison to test data. It is assumed that buckling coincides with complete panel failure. However, post test inspection of the shear buckling panels shows evidence of buckling and material strength failure.

It was difficult to determine whether shear buckling or material failure was the primary failure mode. It implies that the panel buckled first then, in the post buckling regime, failed the material and then the panel failed. This would account for the conservative predictions shown in Figure 6 because the analysis methods deals with only one failure mode.

7. DAMAGE EFFECTS

Reference 3 details the FAA special conditions applied to the Starship airframe. Special conditions are new regulations required by the FAA to ensure a level of safety in a newly designed airplane equivalent to that envisioned by the original regulation base. The special conditions on composite certification includes taking into account the capability of the structure after damage has been inflicted.

The threshhold of detectability (TOD) damage level is the energy level at which damage is just visible to the naked eye on the surface of the structure. Therefore, for laminates of different thickness or equal thickness but different stacking sequences the TOD energy level will be different. The important thing

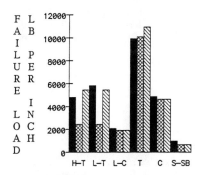

EXPERIMENTAL RESULTS

1st PLY FAILURE

2nd PLY FAILURE

FIGURE 6
ANALYSIS PREDICTIONS VS.
THEORETICAL RESULTS
H - Hoop
T - Tension
L - Longitudinal
C - Compression
S - Shear
SB - Shear Buckling

to remember is that the amount of damage created is the driver, not a fixed energy level to create the damage.

TOD energy levels, for typical panels, were determined by dropping a steel weight on panels at various energy levels. Each drop area was inspected to determine the energy required to create barely visible damage. The SPAID software verification testing for TOD panel failure set the stress allowables for typical laminate definitions.

To comply with FAA Special Condition No. 5a (Reference 3) the TOD failure stress was established as the design allowable. Initially, using the TOD stress level as the design allowable was considered a rather severe criterion. This means carrying extra weight in the aircraft. However, it was determined through flaw growth testing that laminates designed to TOD impact allowables continue to have limit load capability when puncture damage is present. This makes the structure damage tolerant. If the structure has non-visible damage the load can be carried due to the TOD stress allowance. Figure 7 details the reduction in failure stress of a typical compression panel with various levels of damage.

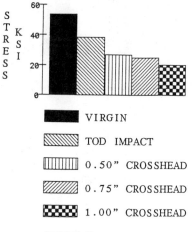

VIRGIN

TOD IMPACT

0.50" CROSSHEAD

0.75" CROSSHEAD

1.00" CROSSHEAD

FIGURE 7
FAILURE STRESS VARIATION

8. FULL SCALE VERIFICATION

After completing analysis software verification the process extended to full scale aircraft structure. Strain gage data and deflection data from the full scale static test articles were compared to the finite element model data. When discrepancies existed the detail modeling was modified to more closely represent the structure, particularly the tested structure with its specific restraints and loading conditions. Since the material properties were known and verified the material property cards were not altered.

Due to the limitations of the strain gage system, strain data read during static tests automatically have a tolerance of ± 75 μ in/in. Furthermore, strain data below 300 μ in/in is inaccurate due to electronic chatter of the connection wires. With this information the criterion was set that the models were considered tuned when model strains were within 10% of test gage

data over 1000 μ in/in and within ± 75 μ in/in of test gage data below 1000 μ in/in. With accurate NASTRAN models the applied loads may be altered to represent any external load condition.

The FAA voiced a concern about the specific effect of temperature and moisture on internal strain and the ability to calculate the internal loads under Hot/Wet conditions. An investigation was undertaken to determine if strain was induced in the structure while being conditioned. As shown in Figure 8 low levels of strain were induced when the structure's temperature was increased from ambient to 185°F. Similarly, once the structure is stabilized at the increased temperature and moisture is added, strain is once again induced. However, as shown in Figures 8 and 9 the induced strain is a fraction of the maximum strain recorded during static testing. When the moisture conditioned structure was repeatedly loaded with the same load case, but under different temperatures (seven in all), the strain gage traces had the same slope, within the gage tolerance as shown in Figure 10.

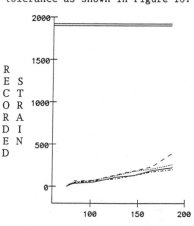

TEMPERATURE IN DEGREES F

MAX TEST STRAIN

FIGURE 8
TEMPERATURE INDUCED STRAIN

288

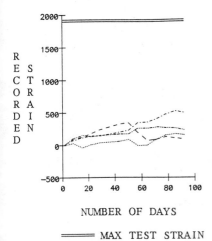

NUMBER OF DAYS

══════ MAX TEST STRAIN

FIGURE 9
MOISTURE INDUCED STRAIN
ARTICLE STABILIZED AT ELEVATED
TEMPERATURE

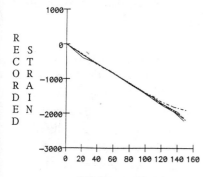

PERCENT OF LOAD

FIGURE 10
STRAIN TRACES OF CONDITIONED
TEST ARTICLE

9. CONCLUSION

The important result from the
Starship program was that the
structural strains, deflections and
failure loads could be accurately
predicted for any external load case
and environmental condition. Use of
an accurate materials data base for
lamina properties enables accurate
full scale structural analysis.

10. REFERENCES

1. Tsia, S.W. and Hahn, T.H.,
   Introduction to Composite
   Materials, Technomic Publishing
   Co. Inc., 1980

2. Kassapoglou, C., Jonas, Paul J.,
   and Abbott, Ric, "Compressive
   Strength of Composite Sandwich
   Panels After Impact Damage: An
   Experimental and Analytical
   Study", Journal of Composites
   Technology & Research, Vol. 10,
   Summer 1988, pp 65-73.

3. Federal Register Vol. 51, No.
   153, Docket No. 012CE, Special
   Conditions No. 23-ACE-11, Dated
   August 8, 1986.

ACKNOWLEDGEMENTS

The authors would like to thank the
management of Beech Aircraft
Corporation for their cooperation
and support during the writing of
this paper.

FATIGUE AND FRACTURE TOUGHNESS PROPERTIES AS A
FUNCTION OF SECTION THICKNESS FOR
BETA ANNEALED TI-6AL-4V, ELI

D. E. Turner
Boeing Military Airplanes
P.O. Box 7730, K96-50
Wichita, Kansas 67277

Abstract

Presently, Boeing practices
restrict procurement of Ti-6Al-4V
(Ti-6-4) in the beta annealed (BA)
condition to a maximum section
thickness of 3 inches to insure
acceptable fatigue properties.
This report presents the fatigue
and fracture toughness response
of BA sections of Ti-6-4, extra
low interstitial (ELI) grade up
to 7 inches thick to demonstrate
the feasibility of increasing BA
section thickness and maintaining
damage tolerance properties. Two
heats of Ti-6-4, ELI were step
forged to 3, 5, and 7 inches, beta
annealed, and characterized via
tension, fatigue, fracture toughness and crack growth rate tests.
Test results indicate that fatigue
and fracture toughness properties
comparable to the baseline, 3 inch
thick sections of BA Ti-6-4,
ELI are realized for 1) sections
up to 7 inches thick that are
water quenched from the BA
temperature and 2) sections up to
5 inches thick that are air cooled
from the BA temperature.

1. INTRODUCTION

Beta annealed Ti-6-4 possesses
excellent fracture toughness and
high strength, making it an
attractive material for aerospace
structural applications. In this
capacity, fatigue life is also a
prime concern. The use of BA
Ti-6-4 for Boeing engineering
designs of structural components
which are fatigue critical is
restricted to a maximum section
thickness of 3 inches. The
following limitation was imposed
because of the unavailability of
fatigue data from material greater
than 3 inches thick and indications
that fatigue life degrades with
increasing alpha platelet size (1).
As a result, large structural

components of BA Ti-6-4 requiring forged block sizes in excess of 3 inches underwent costly intermediate processing. Starting forged blocks of mill annealed material were first machined to within 3 inches thick, followed by beta annealing, chemical milling and final machining to net shape. Additional costs were incurred for fixturing rough machined parts to eliminate distortion from the BA heat treatment, shipping components to various facilities which could accommodate the large sizes for intermediate processing and mechanical testing of coupons from each heat treat load to verify a proper beta anneal heat treatment.

The objective of this investigation is to determine the upper limit in section thickness of Ti-6-4, ELI which can be annealed per Boeing Material Specification (BMS) 7-269 (2) to yield acceptable fatigue and fracture toughness properties. This determination is to be based on mechanical property data from 3, 5, and 7 inch thick BA material, with 3 inch thick Ti-6-4, water quenched or fan air cooled from the BA temperature, as the baseline.

2.0 PROCEDURE

Ingots from two heats of Ti-6-4, ELI per MIL-T-9047 were step forged to provide 3, 5, and 7 inch thick segments. Each step forging was sectioned into five 18" X 20"

blocks to net two 3 inch thick, two 5 inch thick and one 7 inch thick pieces. Blocks of equal thickness were beta annealed at 1875 F in the same furnace run per BMS 7-269. Hold times ranged between 20 and 32 minutes. Blocks were either water quenched in an agitated brine solution or fan air cooled from the BA temperature. After the BA, all blocks were mill annealed at 1375 for 3 hours, followed by a furnace cool to 900F.

The 10 BA blocks were prepared for metallurgical and mechanical property evaluations. Two compact tension specimens, our tensile specimens, and eighteen fatigue specimens were machined per block. Fatigue and fracture toughness specimens were located mid-thickness and positioned such that the critical test area was representative of material that experienced the slowest cooling rate in the block. Locations of tensile specimens were selected to expose any variation in mechanical tensile properties due to variable cooling rates within a block.

Room temperature tensile tests were conducted per ASTM E8 in an MTS 20 KIP loading machine. Room temperature, constant-amplitude, low cycle fatigue tests were conducted per ASTM E606. Stress ratios, R, of +0.50, +0.05, and -1.0 were used at maximum stress levels of 75% and

90% of yield strength (YS). The maximum stress level for each series was calculated by averaging the YS from mid-thickness tensile specimens. Tests were conducted on a MTS 20 KIP loading machine at a frequency of 11 hertz. Fatigue tests were terminated by specimen failure or after an accumulation of 2 million cycles.

Room temperature fracture toughness tests were conducted per ASTM E399 using compact (T) (L-T) specimens with a chevron notch. All pre-cracking and static loading were carried out on an MTS 100 KIP loading machine at 3 and 4 hertz, respectively. An estimated K_{IC} value of 100 $_{KSI}(in)^{1/2}$ was used to determine specimen dimensions. Compact tension specimens from 3 inch thick forged block measured 7.2" X 7.5" X 3.0". Compact tension specimens from 5 and 7 inch thick forged block measured 8.4" X 8.75" X 3.5"

The standard test method for measurement of room temperature fatigue crack growth rates was conducted per ASTM E647. Compact tension specimens, salvaged from spent fracture toughness specimens, measured 0.25" X 2.4" X 2.5". The test procedure was conducted on an MTS 20 KIP loading machine at a frequency of 10 hertz and a stress ration of +0.50. Specimens were precracked to 0.525". Load limits

were 1.83 and 0.91 KIPs. Front and rear crack lengths were monitored with a 50X power lens and averaged. Accumulated cycles were recorded at approximately 0.04 inch increments of crack growth.

3.0 RESULTS AND DISCUSSION

An identification scheme of three alphanumerics is employed to designate block thickness (3,5,7), cooling method (W=water quench, A=fan air cool), and heat number (1,2) in the following discussion. (i.e. 3W1 is a 3 inch thick block water quenched from the BA temperature, from heat 1.)

3.1 Metallurgical Evaluation

All blocks exhibited microstructures of 100 percent transformed beta, verifying that the BA temperature of 1875 F was above the beta transus for both heats of material. Micro-structures representing the three thicknesses of block show a slight decrease in prior beta grain size with decreasing block thickness. This variation in grain size might derive from either the forging process or the BA thermal treatment.

During hot forging, material sub-jected to the severest amount of deformation has the largest number of nucleation sites for dynamic recrystallization. The result is that this material will have the smallest initial grain size, as it the case for the 3 inch thick forged block.

During the BA thermal treatment, the larger the block thickness, the greater the time needed for block centers to attain the BA temperature. These extended periods above the beta transus may be sufficient for noticeable degrees of grain growth resulting in the largest prior beta grain size, as is the case for the 7 inch thick forged block.

Comparing microstructures from blocks of like thicknesses that were subjected to different cooling rates from the BA temperature, differences are noted in prior beta grain size and alpha colony size. Alpha colony size is notably smaller in both 5 and 3 inch thick blocks that were water quenched as opposed to fan air cooled. The faster cooling rate of a water quench results in a higher driving force or alpha phase nucleation. The more alpha colonies that nucleate, the smaller will be their size at impingement with adjacent colonies as the transformation goes to completion.

Prior beta grain sizes are larger in fan air cooled specimens than in water quenched counterparts of like thickness. This phenomenon may result from longer residence times of air cooled block centers at temperatures above the beta transus, allowing time for grain growth.

Based on microstructural features at surface and center locations, block thicknesses up to at least 7 inches appear to have adequate cooling rates during the water quench to give acceptable Widmanstatten transformation product throughout. For the lesser thicknesses of 3 and 5 inches, both water quenching and fan air cooling from the BA temperature give adequate cooling to insure through-thickness Widmanstatten product.

3.2 Mechanical Tests

Tensile test results of mid-thickness specimens giving yield strength, ultimate tensile strength, percent elongation, and percent reduction in area are summarized in Figure 1. Specimens from heat 1 showed consistently higher strengths than counterpart specimens from heat 2. Within the same heat, specimens from blocks subjected to the same cooling method showed a slight decrease in ultimate tensile and yield strengths with increasing block thickness. Specimens from blocks that were water quenched exhibited consistently higher ultimate and yield strengths over specimens from like thicknesses that were fan air cooled. The average elastic modulus for blocks from both heats was 17.0×10^6 psi.

Fracture toughness test results are given in Figure 2. Values presented are averages of duplicate specimens from each block. Specimens from equivalent block thicknesses showed enhanced fracture toughness performance if air cooled rather than water quenched. General trends indicate increasing fracture toughness with increasing block thickness. All specimens failed to meet the precracking requirement of K(max)) E$\leq$ 0.002 per ASTM E399. In addition, all specimens from the 3 inch thick block of heat 1 failed to meet the static fracture requirement of P(max)/P$_Q$ $\leq$ 1.10. Thus, the fracture toughness test results are reported as K$_Q$ values.

The fatigue behavior of blocks from heats 1 and 2 are essentially identical. Fatigue results of material from heat 1 only will be used to illustrate trends. Results are summarized in Figures 3 through 5. Three inch thick blocks, both water quenched and air cooled, provide the baseline for evaluation of fatigue life of the remaining blocks.

The stress ratio of R=+0.50 is the least severe loading condition examined. Test results for maximum stress levels of 75% YS and 90% YS are shown in Figure 3. Fatigue performances of all blocks at these loading conditions are comparable. Specimens cycled at maximum stresses of 75% YS are considered to demonstrate infinite fatigue life, sustaining 2 million cycles without failing. The premature failures of

a single specimen from 3A1 and 5A1 can most likely be attributed to data scatter, since both sets of sister specimens from heat 2 sustained 2 X 10^6 cycles. The fracture faces of these prematurely failed specimens were examined with optical and scanning electron microscopes. No anomolous features were noted which may have contributed to the shortened fatigue life.

As the maximum stress level at R=+0.50 is increased to 90% YS, the average fatigue life is reduced for all blocks. The 3W1 specimens show the best performance at this higher stress level. Fatigue life of specimens from the remaining blocks are consistent with fan air cooled baseline specimens (3A1) and show a high degree of reproducibility.

At R=+0.05, the beta annealed materia exhibits a reduction in damage tolerance compared to R=+0.50. See Figure 4. Overall fatigue performance at R=+0.05 is consistent among the three thicknesses and cooling rates, showing acceptable fatigue life relative to the baseline specimens.

At R=-1.0, the most severe loading condition, fatigue performance of all blocks is further degraded. See Figure 5. Fatigue life cycles are reduced from the R=+0.05

condition by an order of magnitude. The response of all blocks to cycling at maximum stress levels of 75% YS and 90% YS correspond well with the baseline specimen performance.

These observed trends in fatigue response are consistent with specimens from heat 2 that were cycled at identical loading conditions. Only at R=-1.0 and a maximum stress level of 90% YS does all material from heat 2 show consistent reductions in fatigue life from sister specimens of heat 1. Fatigue life at these conditions, however, maintain the same order of magnitude for both heats.

The results of crack growth rate tests show excellent agreement between fan air cooled and water quenched specimens from blocks of equal thickness. A representative crack growth rate curve for each beta annealed block thickness is presented in Figures 6 through 8. Results indicate that the crack growth rates are insensitive to the variations in beta annealed block thickness and cooling methods examined in this investigation.

The crack growth rate data generated in this series of tests was compared against published da/dN versus stress intensity factor, K, curves for beta annealed Ti-6-4, given in the Damage Tolerant Design Handbook, MCIC-HB-01 (3). For K values

greater than 20 ksi(in)$^{1/2}$, generated data compares well with published data. However, at K values less than 20 ksi(in)$^{1/2}$, generated data indicated improved damage tolerance over the MCIC data, exhibiting slower crack growth rates.

4.0 CONCLUSIONS

A. No degradation in tensile strength or fracture toughness properties was noted for BA Ti-6-4, ELI up to 5 inches thick (air cooled) and 7 inches thick (water quenched) relative to the baseline material, 3 inch thick BA Ti-6-4, ELI.

B. Fatigue life of BA Ti-6-4, ELI block up to 5 inches thick (air cooled) and 7 inches thick (water quenched) is comparable to the fatigue performance of the baseline, material.

C. No degradation in crack growth rate response as a function of BA Ti-6-4 block thickness or cooling rate was evident over the thickness range of 3 to 7 inches.

5.0 REFERENCES

(1) Eylon, D., and Pierce, M., Met Trans. A, 1976, vol.7A, pp. 111-121.
(2) BMS 7-269, Titanium Alloy 6A1-4V Forgings, Beta Annealed, Boeing Material Specification.
(3) Damage Tolerant Design Handbook- Part 2, Jan. 1975, MCIC, Columbus, Ohio, p. 8.4-50.

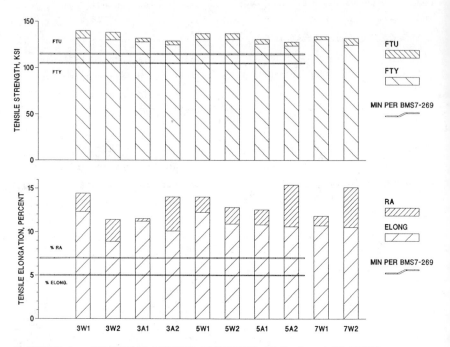

FIGURE 1. MECHANICAL TENSILE PROPERTIES OF 3, 5 and 7" THICK
BETA-ANNEALED TI-6-4, ELI

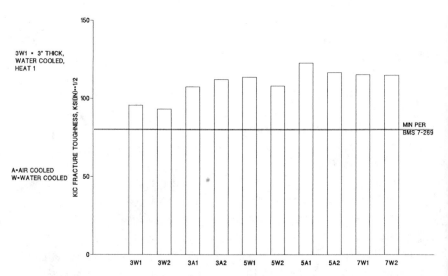

FIGURE 2. FRACTURE TOUGHNESS OF 3, 5 and 7" THICK BETA-ANNEALED
TI-6-4, ELI

CONSTANT AMPLITUDE, LOW-CYCLE FATIGUE TESTS
CYCLES TO FAILURE

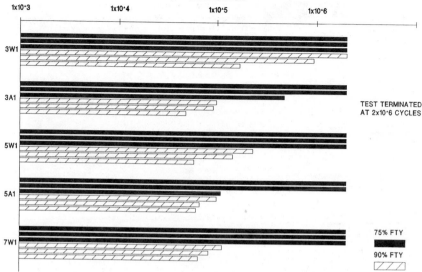

TEST TERMINATED
AT 2x10⁻6 CYCLES

75% FTY

90% FTY

FIGURE 3.   FATIGUE LIFE OF BA TI-6-4, ELI, HEAT 1, R=+0.50

CONSTANT AMPLITUDE, LOW-CYCLE FATIGUE TESTS
CYCLES TO FAILURE

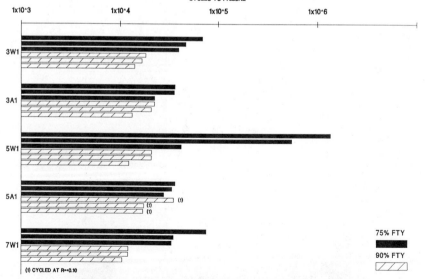

75% FTY

90% FTY

(t) CYCLED AT R=+0.10

FIGURE 4.   FATIGUE LIFE OF BA TI-6-4, ELI, HEAT 1, R=+0.05

CONSTANT AMPLITUDE, LOW-CYCLE FATIGUE TESTS

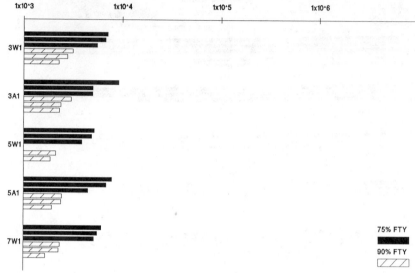

FIGURE 5.   FATIGUE LIFE OF BA TI-6-4, ELI, HEAT 1, R=-1.0

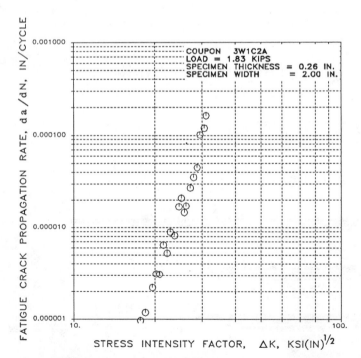

FIGURE 6.   CRACK GROWTH BEHAVIOR OF 3" THICK BETA-ANNEALED
TI-6-4, ELI

298

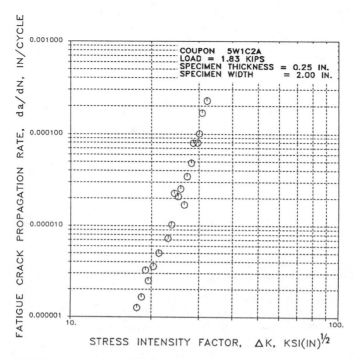

FIGURE 7.   CRACK GROWTH RESPONSE OF 5" THICK BETA-ANNEALED
TI-6-4, ELI

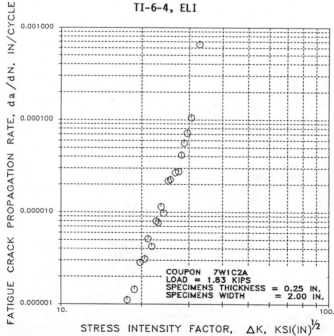

FIGURE 8.   CRACK GROWTH BEHAVIOR OF 7" THICK BETA-ANNEALED
TI-6-4, ELI

THERMOPLASTIC COMPOSITE FIGHTER FORWARD FUSELAGE

Robert B. Ostrom
Stephen B. Koch and Debra L. Wirz-Safranek
Composite Development Center
Lockheed Aeronautical Systems Company

ABSTRACT

A thermoplastic composite fighter forward fuselage manufacturing demonstration article was designed, fabricated, and assembled as part of the Lockheed Aeronautical Systems Company Composites Development Center independent research and development program on thermoplastic composites. The project objective was the development and demonstration of engineering and manufacturing technology for thermoplastic fuselage structure. The demonstration article is representative of a section of a generic fighter forward fuselage. The design includes most of the primary structural components typical of fighter fuselage structure and incorporates a variety of structural concepts. Several thermoplastic composite material systems were used in fabricating the component parts. A number of fabrication subcontractors, in addition to the Composites Development Center, and a variety of manufacturing approaches were employed in the fabrication. These included various tooling approaches, forming and consolidation methods, and joining techniques. Final assembly of the demonstration article was performed at the Composites Development Center. The program resulted in a significant step forward in the determination of manufacturing methods for the production of efficient and cost-competitive thermoplastic composite primary structure.

1. INTRODUCTION

A thermoplastic composite fighter forward fuselage manufacturing demonstration article has been designed, fabricated, and assembled as part of the Lockheed Aeronautical Systems Company (LASC) independent research and development program on thermoplastic composites. The objective of this program was the development and demonstration of engineering and manufacturing technology for thermoplastic composite primary fuselage structure. The program was conducted at

LASC's Composite Development Center (CDC). In addition to the fabrication facilities at the CDC, a number of major subcontractors were employed in the fabrication effort. These included ICI's Composite Structures Group, Alcoa's Composite Manufacturing Technology Center, Composites Horizons Inc and Programmed Composites Inc, along with several specialty fabrication and tooling subcontractors.

The forward fuselage demonstration article is a generic representation of primary forward fuselage structure projected for use in future advanced fighter aircraft. The selected fuselage segment is approximately 122 cm (48 in.) long and 137 cm (54 in.) in diameter, is complex contoured, and represents a relatively lightly loaded region forward of the crew compartment. Although lightly loaded, the selected segment addresses most of the engineering and manufacturing challenges of primary fuselage structure.

The demonstration article, illustrated in Figure 1, contains ten major sub-assemblies:

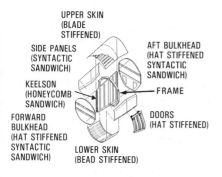

Figure 1. Forward fuselage demonstration article

upper and lower stiffened skins, left and right side panels, forward and aft bulkheads, keelson, intermediate frame, and two access doors. Configuration of these components was selected to allow examination of a wide range of tooling, fabrication, and assembly methods. The selected structural concepts included: a blade-stiffened complex contoured upper skin, a beaded corrugation-stiffened complex contoured lower skin, syntactic sandwich side panels, hat-stiffened syntactic sandwich bulkheads with integral flanges, honeycomb sandwich keelson, curved 'T' and 'J' section frames and curved hat-stiffened access doors.

The use of several different fabricators in addition to the CDC allowed a variety of

manufacturing approaches to be demonstrated. A range of 'dry' thermoplastic prepreg material systems were used to produce structural components on several different high temperature tooling systems. The tooling systems incorporated advanced tooling materials and unique tool designs. Replicates of each part were fabricated using different forming and consolidation methods. These processes ranged from labor intensive hand forming and autoclave consolidation, to double diaphragm forming/consolidation which can produce a consolidated component from a loosely stacked lay-up every 30 minutes. A number of different joining technologies were surveyed and development efforts centered on the methods having the most potential for success on this program. A summary of composite materials, tooling materials, forming and consolidation methods, and joining and assembly techniques used in the program is shown in Figure 2. This approach allowed a comprehensive evaluation of thermoplastic composite applications for primary fighter structure.

2. MATERIALS

Five intermediate service temperature thermoplastic materials were used on this program. APC-2/AS4 unitape, made from ICI's PEEK semi-crystalline polymer, is a composite material suitable for continuous 120°C (250°F) service applications for primary aircraft structure. Cypac 7005/ Apollo 43-600 unifabric, made from GEs PEI amorphous polymer, and PAS-2/AS4 unitape, made from Phillips' PAS amorphous polymer, are both suitable for 150°C (300°F) service structural applications. The matrix resins in APC-HTA/IM8 unitape and Radel-C/T650-42 unitape are amorphous

THERMOPLASTIC MATERIALS	FORMING/CONSOLIDATION METHODS
Cypac 7005/Apollo 43-600 Unifabric APC-2/AS4 Unitape APC-HTA/IM8 Unitape Radel-C/T650-42 Unitape PAS-2/AS4 Unitape	Press Forming Single Diaphragm Forming Autoclave Consolidation Double Diaphragm Forming/Consolidation • Superform Process (Alum. Diaphragms) • Diaform Process (Polymeric Diaphragms)
TOOLING	JOINING & ASSEMBLY
Steel Aluminum Monolithic Graphite Castable Ceramic Integrally Heated Laminated Ceramic Soluable Mandrels	Mechanical Fasteners Adhesive Bonding Dual Polymer Bonding Co-consolidation

Figure 2. Materials and fabrication methods

polymers suitable for 175°C (350°F) service applications. The processing temperatures of these materials ranged from 340°C (645°F) to 390°C (735°F). This spectrum of thermoplastic resins allowed an assessment of the effect of processing temperature on producibility. The inclusion of a unifabric material allowed a comparison of the formability of woven fabric to unitape. These 'dry' pre-pregs are boardy and have no tack. A 'dry' material offers the potential processing advantage of eliminating the need to extract solvents during processing and drastically shortening cycle times. Processing cycles for 'dry' thermoplastic composites can be on the order of 15 to 30 minutes.

3. TOOLING MATERIALS AND APPROACHES

Several tooling systems were used to define the tool surfaces of the individual components. The materials that showed the most promise for high temperature processing of thermoplastic composites included three types of ceramic materials: castable ceramic (Thermosil 120), castable filled ceramic (Oxy Chem), and integrally heated laminated ceramic (Comtool). The

Thermosil and Oxy Chem tools were processed in an autoclave for both temperature and pressure application. The Comtool ceramic tool was integrally heated and was processed in a pressure vessel. Other tooling systems used on the program included steel, aluminum and monolithic graphite materials.

3.1 Castable Ceramic Tools

Thermosil 120 castable ceramic material was used to fabricate Cypac 7005/Apollo IM side panels, a forward bulkhead, an upper and a lower skin. Its advantages included room temperature castability, relatively short tool fabrication times, low cost, and coefficient of thermal expansion (CTE) comparable to quasi-isotropic carbon fiber reinforced laminates. Thermosil 120 has several drawbacks: poor mechanical strength, surface porosity, low thermal conductivity, and high weight.

Female mold dies were cast on REN-450 masters numerical control machined using CADAM®* data. The master and ceramic mold die for the forward bulkhead are shown in Figure 3. The ceramic was reinforced with short stainless

---

* CADAM is a registered trademark of CADAM, Inc.

Figure 3.　REN-450 master with female Thermosil 120 forward bulkhead tool

steel fibers to improve the strength of the material; inclusion of these fibers did not significantly change its thermal characteristics. A photograph of a typical forward bulkhead is shown in Figure 4.

Attempts to seal the porous surface of the tool using sodium silicate were unsuccessful. A sheet of Kapton film was used as a barrier film against the mold surface. The tools were either bagged to a thin tool sheet, envelope bagged with Kapton bagging film or, for the largest tool, bagged to a five-sided welded thin steel box.

The Thermosil 120 tools required modifications in the process cycle used for steel and aluminum tools because of its poor thermal conductivity. The maximum autoclave temperature was increased to more rapidly heat the part and a steel baffle directed the hot autoclave gas onto the part surface.

These modifications made it possible to heat the part without heating the tool and to shorten the process cycle from 13 to 5 hours.

Thermosil 120 has potential for use in an integrally heated tooling system. Thermosil 120's low coefficient of heat transfer makes it a good choice for integrally heated tooling. Placement of heaters at the tool surface takes the best advantage of Thermosil's insulating characteristic. Rapid heat up and cool down cycles can be achieved by minimizing the amount of heat lost to the tool and to the pressure vessel.

3.2 Castable Filled Ceramic Tools

Oxy Chem tools were used to fabricate lower skins and doors from Cypac 7005/Apollo IM, Radel-C/T650-42, PAS-2/AS4, and APC-2/AS4 prepregs. A lower skin co-consolidated assembly is shown in Figure 5. An Oxy Chem ceramic lower skin tool is shown in Figure 6. These thin shell tools (approximately 1.6 cm (0.6 in.) thick) have the decided advantages of light weight,

Figure 5.　Lower skin assembly

Figure 4.　Forward bulkhead assembly

Figure 6.　Oxy Chem thin shell filled ceramic lower skin tool

a smooth vacuum tight molding surface, and high thermal conductivity. The drawbacks in comparison to Thermosil 120 are increased cost (approximately five times) and higher CTE (approximately two times that of quasi-isotropic carbon fiber reinforced laminates).

Comtek XS is a filled ceramic fabricated by Occidental Chemical Company by a proprietary process which requires room temperature vacuum mixing and casting. The filler improves tensile strength, thermal conductivity, and lowers the CTE of this ceramic material to 9 x 10^{-6} cm/cm/°C (5 x 10^{-6} in./in./°F).

The higher initial tool cost of Oxy Chem tools can be offset for larger production runs by the ease of handling and bagging and shortened autoclave process cycle times. The vacuum tight tool surface allowed bagging directly to the tool surface which greatly simplifies the bagging process for autoclave fabrication. The high thermal conductivity and thin shell construction resulted in heat-up rates from 5-10°C/min (10-20°F/min). Oxy Chem tools are recommended for future applications in high temperature autoclave processing.

3.3 Integrally Heated Laminated Ceramic Tools

Comtool's electrically heated laminated carbon fiber/ceramic matrix tool system was used to fabricate an upper skin from APC-2/AS4. Comtool's integral heating offers tremendous reduction in process cycle time and costs associated with bagging by allowing the use of lower temperature films and sealants. A Comtool is shown in use in Figure 7. Comtool's other advantages include a CTE which closely matches that of the carbon fiber thermoplastic parts being

Figure 7. Typical Comtool with insulation in place.

fabricated. Its main disadvantage is mold surface porosity leading to the same limitations as Thermosil 120 with respect to bagging.

This thin, 1.0 cm (0.4 in) thick, carbon fiber reinforced ceramic tool is typically fabricated on a carbon epoxy pattern at 120°C (250°F) in an autoclave. The tool fabricated for this program was made using the same REN-450 master used to cast a Thermosil 120 upper skin tool. An upper skin assembly is shown in Figure 8.

A 390°C (735°F) heat up and cool down process can be reduced to 1 hour and 45 minutes with the Comtool heating approach. The laminate and tool were envelope bagged, surrounded with insulation, and placed in an unheated pressure vessel. The part was heated using the integral heating in the tool, pressure was

Figure 8. Upper skin assembly

applied, and the assembly was allowed to cool under pressure. Since the pressure vessel atmosphere remained cool, the insulated assembly was vacuum bagged with low temperature nylon film and sealants which greatly reduced the costs associated with bagging both by simplifying the task as well as reducing the actual material costs.

This tool/fabrication process offers tremendous reduction in autoclave bottlenecks, process cycle times and associated costs, and is highly recommended for future applications.

4. FORMING/CONSOLIDATION PROCESSES

The boardiness of the 'dry' prepregs requires pressure in order to force the plies to conform to a curved tool surface. Since the materials also have no tack, the plies do not stick together or to the tool surface unless they are taken up above the forming temperature. Approximate forming temperatures are 260°C (500°F) for Radel-C; 230°C (450°F) for Cypac 7005 and PAS-2; 360°C (680°F) for APC-2. Forming temperature is defined as the temperature at which the resin softens sufficiently to allow the materials to form to the desired contour and tack to the adjacent plies. If processed below these temperatures, the plies will return toward their original condition and flatten out when the pressure is released. These materials are best formed to the proper shape by heating them above the forming temperature, then applying pressure to form them and hold them in shape until cooled below this critical temperature. Consolidation requires heating to the processing temperature which is generally 30-110°C (50-200°F) above the softening temperature. The processing temperature is loosely defined as the point of minimum viscosity below the degradation temperature of the resin.

Several forming and/or consolidation processes were used. The processes considered most promising for cost-effective production of primary fighter structure are discussed in detail in the following section. Rubber press forming is a viable production forming process which has great potential for preforming detail parts that are subsequently co-consolidated into an assembly. Autoclave consolidation is still the best method for producing large parts. Double diaphragm processing allows the forming and consolidation of parts in one operation and has the potential to fabricate thermoplastic composite parts cost-effectively.

4.1 Double Diaphragm Processing

Double diaphragm processing is based on vacuum forming of thermoplastics. Double diaphragm processing of thermoplastics combines the forming and consolidation operations in one step. A major advantage of the double diaphragm process is that both surfaces of the composite part remain in tension throughout forming which reduces wrinkling.

Three variations of double diaphragm processing were employed on this program. Both metals and polymers were used as diaphragm materials. The first and most developed method is metallic diaphragm processing. This is best known as the Superform™ process. The process uses Supral® aluminum diaphragms and a tool maintained at the processing temperature of the thermoplastic. The second and third processes use polymeric diaphragms. These are included, collectively, in the Diaform™ process. The second process is essentially identical to the Superform process but with Upilex diaphragms. The third uses Upilex diaphragms with a tool maintained at a constant temperature below the forming temperature of the thermoplastic resin.

The general process for all three variations follows. An unconsolidated composite lay-up was placed between two elastic diaphragms. The diaphragms were clamped to a vacuum ring and a vacuum was drawn between the diaphragms. The diaphragm/lay-up stack was heated to the processing temperature and positive pressure was applied to force the part against the tool. The diaphragms stretched and slid past the composite part. Although the carbon fiber reinforcement restricted stretching along the fiber in each ply, the lay-up deformed by inter-ply slippage and lateral fiber movement.

4.1.1 Metallic Diaphragm Forming

The Superform process was used to successfully form and consolidate a side panel, an aft bulkhead, a corrugated inner skin for a lower skin assembly, and components for the frames from APC-2/AS4 prepreg. The Superform process has been used extensively in other programs for the production of high quality fully consolidated APC-2 parts. The Superform process is jointly patented by ICI and ALCAN. The Supral patent is held exclusively by ALCAN.

Since Supral is strain rate sensitive, forming steps are on the order of 20 minutes depending on the degree of elongation required and the temperature at which the process is performed. Slow forming allows the composite plies to slip past each other without wrinkling. The stiffness of the aluminum diaphragms also prevents the material from deforming out of plane. However, slow forming and the stiffness of

the diaphragms results in significant fiber wash, especially in plies where the fibers are normal to the bend radius. Additional development is necessary to minimize thinning in the bend radii due to fiber wash.

Another limitation of this process is the temperatures required for superplastically deforming the aluminum. Most of the high service temperature thermoplastic resins being evaluated process best below 370°C (700°F). Below 380°C (715°F), the elongation of the Supral aluminum decreases by 50-100 percent, limiting the applicability of the Superform process for these materials to gently contoured part configurations. The Superform process is mainly recommended for thermoplastic materials which can be processed above 380°C (715°F). Figure 9 shows a curved frame segment fabricated using the Superform process.

4.1.2 Polymeric Diaphragm Forming

The Diaform process was used to fabricate a forward bulkhead and a side panel using APC-2/AS4 material. The type of Upilex diaphragms used have an elongation of 250-300 percent at temperatures from 315-425°C (600-800°F). Upilex, 0.13 mm (0.005 in.) thick, has a lower modulus than

Figure 9. Superform-processed frame segment

Supral 1.3 mm (0.050 in.) thick. Greater care must be exercised with the Diaform process to keep the composite material in tension during forming to reduce out-of-plane deformations.

The forward bulkhead was formed using a tool heated to the processing temperature of the APC-2 material. Since the Upilex is not strain rate sensitive, the forming can be completed in a shorter time (1 minute versus 20 minutes required for the Superform process). The short forming time coupled with the greater flexibility and lower modulus of Upilex resulted in less fiber wash, compared with similar components made using the Superform process. Due to facility limitations, the part and diaphragms could only be loaded at room temperature. The large thermal mass of the tool required three hours to heat up to the 390°C (735°F) processing temperature. Modification of the equipment to be able to preheat the tool to the processing temperature and then load the part/diaphragm stack would result in a total process cycle on the order of two hours.

The side panel was fabricated using a tool maintained at a constant temperature below the forming temperature of the thermoplastic. This variation has the potential to produce fully formed and consolidated parts at a rate of one part every 15 to 30 minutes. Figure 10 shows the completed Diaform-processed side panel. The process utilizes vacuum forming techniques that have been well developed in the plastics industry with unreinforced commercial grade thermoplastic resins. The basic concept is to heat the unconsolidated composite ply stack under vacuum between two Upilex diaphragms in an infrared oven. This stack is quickly transferred into the forming press. A

Figure 10. Diaform-processed side panel

pressure box is closed around the material and positive air pressure is used to force the part against the tool.

The side panel geometry required the material to bend in two directions simultaneously, resulting in compression wrinkles (See Figure 11). Slowing down the forming processes minimizes these wrinkles. There is, however, a limit to the amount the process can be slowed due to the use of a cooler tool. The part will cool to the metal tool temperature within seconds and the material will not form below the forming temperature. A thermoforming technique often used in the plastics industry will overcome this problem. The technique is plug-assist thermoforming which forces a

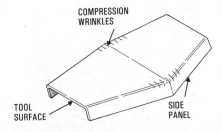

Figure 11. Wrinkling of Diaform-processed APC-2 side panel

male plug into the composite ply stack to form one bend before positive air pressure is applied to complete the forming of the part (See Figure 12). This technique requires a double action thermoforming press that allows the pressure box to be closed and the tool or male plug moved independently.

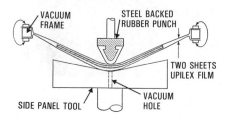

Figure 12. Plug-assisted Diaform process

4.2 Press Forming

A rubber punch tooling concept was used to press form details. The tool design combined the benefits of matched metal molds and rubber hydroforming techniques commonly used in metal forming. A press setup with a rubber punch tool is illustrated in Figure 13.

This tooling method was shown, in this and other programs, to be an acceptable production approach to press forming thermoplastic matrix composites into relatively simple shapes including angles, hats, C-channels, Zs and pans. The press

forming process used an infrared oven to heat the laminate to the processing temperature. The hot laminate was transferred to the press tooling. The female tool was heated to just below the forming temperature to minimize part chill during forming. The press was closed and pressure applied. Pressure was held for 30 seconds and then released. Press process time from start to finish was eight minutes per part.

Press forming techniques were used to form PAS-2 and Cypac 7005 lower skin corrugations. The beads were formed one at a time. After applying pressure to form a bead, the pressure was released and the material was indexed to the next bead location.

Press forming process was used to form Radel-C hat section door stiffeners. The hat sections were curved to approximately a 30 cm (12 in.) radius which presented some challenges in forming them without wrinkles. Initially, the mismatch between the radius at the top of the hat and the bottom of the flange made the material lock in at either end first (See Figure 14). As the middle of the hat was formed the unsupported composite plies were placed in compression resulting in severe wrinkling. The radius on the rubber punch was reduced to start the forming of the hat in the middle curved section first, allowing the material to

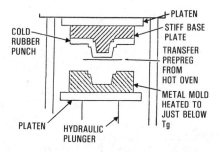

Figure 13. Rubber punch tool in press

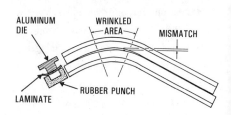

Figure 14. Rubber press forming of hat section door stiffeners

remain in tension as the ends of the hat section were formed. This approach successfully formed curved hat sections suitable for subsequent autoclave co-consolidation.

5. JOINING AND ASSEMBLY

A variety of joining and assembly methods were demonstrated. Adhesive bonding, dual polymer bonding and co-consolidation were used to join formed details into component assemblies. Dual polymer bonding and co-consolidation are most promising for assembly of thermoplastic structural components. Mechanical fasteners as well as adhesive bonding were also used to assemble the components into the forward fuselage assembly. The use of these joining techniques successfully eliminated 73 percent of the fasteners which would otherwise have been required to assemble the demonstration article.

5.1 Co-consolidation

A number of elements and sub-assemblies were co-consolidated. All of the 'T' sections for the frames and upper skin stiffeners were fabricated by co-consolidating two 'L' sections. Upper skin blade stiffeners were co-consolidated to upper skins. Hat section door stiffeners were co-consolidated to door skins. Corrugated inner skins were co-consolidated to lower outer skins.

Due to the lack of any sharp contours, upper skin 'T' stiffeners were fabricated straight and formed to contour during co-consolidation. This allowed the use of a single set of tools to fabricate the 'T' stiffeners. Tooling was required to hold the vertical blades straight as they were heated to process temperature during co-consolidation.

A corrugation-stiffened lower skin and several hat stiffened access doors were co-consolidated using Caremold disposable mandrel material. Caremold is a dissolvable mandrel material developed by Composites Horizons for use up to 425°C (800°F). Caremold combines low shrinkage and low CTE with ease of casting. It was, however, necessary to use a barrier film to prevent the resin from flowing into the porous surface of the mandrel. A co-consolidated door assembly is shown in Figure 15.

Figure 15. Co-consolidated door assembly

5.2 Dual Polymer Bonding

Keelson skin-to-core and doubler-to-skin bonding operations were carried out using dual polymer bonding techniques. This process was developed as a method for joining APC-2 parts without using thermoset adhesives. The concept is to use a thermoplastic adhesive with a bonding temperature lower than the softening point of the APC-2 laminate. A PEI film was used and the bond process was performed at 270°C (520°F) and 100kPa (30 psi). The pressure for the skin-to-core bond was applied using a vacuum bag. The skin-to-doubler bond was made using heated steel bars to apply pressure to the doublers. The entire set of five pairs of doublers were bonded two at a time within 30 minutes using this technique. Lap shear test results indicate this process has potential as a joining process.

Some development was needed to use this process with the amorphous resins being considered for 175°C (350°F) service temperature structures due to the differences between semi-crystalline and amorphous polymers. The amorphous polymers do not melt, but soften above their glass transition temperature (T_g) whereas semi-crystalline polymers generally remain boardy above their T_g up to their melt temperature. A keelson was successfully fabricated using the dual polymer bonding process with HTA/IM8 skins. Figure 16 shows the APC-2 keelson assembly.

One lower skin assembly was joined using the dual polymer bonding process. The low processing temperature combined with a fully formed Supral inner diaphragm caul sheet eliminated the need to support the

Figure 16. Keelson honeycomb sandwich assembly

beaded corrugations during the joining process.

5.3 Assembly

Assembly of the demonstration article was done in a floor assembly jig and an elevated work platform. The floor assembly jig was used to assemble the internal structure of the article. The keelson was attached to the bulkheads and the side panels were bonded in place while the parts were held in position by the floor jig. The skins and the doors were fitted to the structure in the elevated platform. The majority of the fasteners used in the final assembly were Eddy Bolt IIs manufactured by Voi Shan. The Eddy Bolt II is a threaded fastener which has a collar that deforms at a preset torque level.

The forward bulkhead was located in the floor jig. The keelson which had separate angles that formed the aft and upper flanges and integral forward and lower flanges was placed in the jig. The keelson and forward bulkhead were fastened together. The aft bulkhead was located in the assembly jig. The aft keelson angles were located to the aft bulkhead, bonded to the keelson, and fastened to the aft bulkhead. This keelson design allowed it to be adjusted to fit. The straight mid-frames were bonded to the side panels in the floor jig at the proper location. The side panels were bonded to the forward and aft bulkheads. Figure 17 shows the partially assembled demonstration article in the floor assembly jig. The assembly was transferred to the elevated platform. Separate fixtures were used to bond the frames to the upper and lower skins. The upper skin, the lower skin and the doors were installed in the elevated skin fitting jig. The finished demonstration article is shown in Figure 18.

Figure 17. Partially assembled demonstration article in the floor assembly jig

Figure 18. Assembled forward fuselage demonstration article

6. CONCLUSIONS

Design, fabrication, and assembly of the full-scale forward fuselage demonstration article served as the focal point for the integrated development of a wide range of manufacturing technologies required for the application of thermoplastic composites to fighter fuselage structure. In all areas of fabrication - tooling, forming, consolidation and joining - significant developments were made, vital lessons were learned, and competing methodologies and techniques were evaluated. The result has been a significant step forward in the determination of manufacturing methods for the production of efficient and cost- competitive thermoplastic composite primary structure.

BIOGRAPHIES

Robert B. Ostrom is Group Engineer, Advanced Concepts and Materials Applications, at Lockheed Aeronautical Systems Company in Burbank, California. He holds a Bachelor of Science degree in Engineering and a Master of Engineering degree from the University of California, Los Angeles, and a Master of Science degree in Aerospace Engineering from the University of Southern California. He has thirty years experience at Lockheed in the development of structural analysis methods and their application in the design of aircraft structures, with the last eleven years in the area of composite structures.

Stephen B. Koch is a Materials and Processes Engineer at Lockheed's Composite Development Center. He received a Bachelor of Science degree in Mechanical Engineering in 1983 from Rensselaer Polytechnic Institute. He has two years experience in the design and stress analysis of composite structures and three years experience in materials and processes development of thermoplastic composites.

Debra L. Wirz-Safranek is a Senior Manufacturing Research Engineer at Lockheed's Composite Development Center. She received a Bachelor of Science degree in Chemistry in 1979 from Humboldt State University, California. She has nine years experience in the development and application of composite manufacturing methods for aircraft structure.

DIELECTRIC CURE MONITORING—A CRITICAL REVIEW

Peter R. Ciriscioli and George S. Springer

Department of Aeronautics and Astronautics
Stanford University, Stanford, California 94305

Abstract

Tests were performed to evaluate the usefulness of dielectric techniques in monitoring the cure of thermoset matrix composites. Using a Micromet Instrument Eumetric System II microdielectrometer, signals related to the permittivity and loss factor of the material were recorded during the cure of Fiberite T300/976 and Hercules AS/3501-6 graphite epoxy composites. From the data, values of the ionic conductivity were deduced by both the Day and the Kranbuehl methods. The ionic conductivities thus obtained were compared to viscosities, rates of cure, and degrees of cure calculated by chemical kinetic models. It is shown that the Day and Kranbuehl methods a) yield similar ionic conductivities, and indicate the times at which the viscosity is minimum and the degree of cure is nearly complete, b) as yet, cannot provide either the viscosity, the degree of cure, or the rate of cure as a function of time throughout the cure process. Some practical aspects of cure monitoring are also discussed.

1. INTRODUCTION

In recent years, considerable efforts have been made to monitor in real time the curing process of thermoset matrix composites. As part of these efforts, various cure monitoring methods have been proposed, of which the dielectric technique appears to be the most promising. This technique consists of three major steps:

1) Measurement of a signal related to some dielectric property of the material.

2) Conversion of the measured signal to the actual value of the dielectric property.

3) Conversion of the experimentally determined dielectric property to the viscosity and degree of cure of the material.

Of these three steps, the first two are well in hand; the technology is available for sensing the appropriate signals, and models exist for converting these signals to dielectric properties.[1--12] However, most problems regarding the third step have not yet been resolved. Contrary to frequent belief, current dielectric techniques cannot provide either of the two most important cure parameters, viscosity and degree of cure, during the entire cure process. They only give partial information regarding these parameters, namely the time at which viscosity is minimum and the time at which cure becomes complete.

The primary objectives of this paper are to review the dielectric cure monitoring techniques, to show clearly the type of information which can be obtained by such techniques, and to point out the area in which further research is needed in order to make the dielectric technique a complete cure monitoring tool. In addition, practical aspects of the measurement technique are discussed which have been found to aid in the acquisition of high quality data.

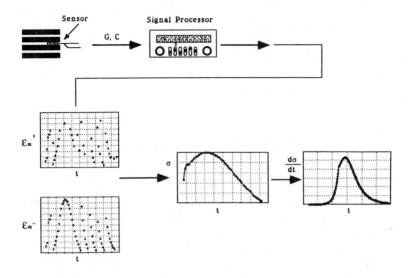

Figure 1. Schematic of the test procedure.

2. EXPERIMENTAL PROCEDURE

A thorough evaluation of the different types of dielectric methods, as well as their application in practice, require that all aspects of the methods be understood fully. Unfortunately, it is difficult to gain comprehensive overviews of the different methods from the widespread information presented in numerous papers which, on occasion, contain omissions and misprints. Therefore, a review is given of the dielectric cure monitoring technique, in general, and of the Day[4--7] and Kranbuehl[8--14] methods, in particular. Attention is focused on the latter two methods because these are the most commonly used in conjunction with commercially available equipment.

2.1 General Considerations

During cure the capacitance and conductance of the material are recorded. From these data, the value of the ionic conductivity is deduced. The procedures by which these tasks are achieved are outlined below.

The sensor is placed at the location where the cure is to be monitored (Figure 1). In placing the sensor, two important considerations must be borne in mind. The sensor a) must not be in contact with conducting fibers, and b) must be in good contact with the resin. To isolate the sensor from the fibers, the active face of the sensor is covered by a non-conducting insulator. To ensure good contact with the resin this insulator must be fully permeable to the resin, because low permeability reduces sensor-resin contact resulting in poor data. Application of pressure to the material being cured may enhance contact between the sensor and the resin.

From the recorded values of the capacitance C and the conductance G, the "measured" permittivity ϵ'_m and loss factor ϵ''_m are calculated by[8,9,15]

$$\epsilon'_m = \frac{C}{C_o} \qquad \epsilon''_m = \frac{G}{C_o 2\pi f} \qquad (1)$$

where f is the frequency and C_o is the capacitance of air. Obviously, a low value of ϵ'_m ($C \to C_o$ and $\epsilon_m \to 1$) indicates poor contact between the sensor and the resin. The subscript m denotes values deduced directly from the measured data. The measurements are performed at several different frequencies, as discussed subsequently.

The actual permittivity ϵ' and the loss factor ϵ'' are related to the ionic conductivity σ, relaxed permittivity ϵ_r and unrelaxed permittivity ϵ_u by the following expressions[15--17]

$$\epsilon' = \epsilon_u + \frac{\epsilon_r - \epsilon_u}{1 + (\omega\tau)^2} \qquad (2)$$

$$\epsilon'' = \frac{\sigma}{\omega\epsilon_o} + \frac{(\epsilon_r - \epsilon_u)\omega\tau}{1 + (\omega\tau)^2} \qquad (3)$$

ω is the angular frequency ($\omega = 2\pi f$), τ is the dielectric relaxation time, and ϵ_o is the permittivity of free space ($\epsilon_o = 8.854 \times 10^{-12}$ Farads/meter).

Electrode polarization of the sensor may affect the measurement. Hence, the "measured" values of the permittivity and loss factor (ϵ'_m and ϵ''_m) may differ from the actual values of these parameters (ϵ' and ϵ''). Polarization effects can be taken into account by appropriate correction factors, denoted by SF_1 and SF_2, in the following manner

$$\epsilon'_m = \epsilon' \cdot (SF_1) \qquad (4)$$

$$\epsilon''_m = \epsilon'' \cdot (SF_2) \qquad (5)$$

In expressions (2)–(5) above, the ionic conductivity σ is of interest. Therefore, the next step is to extract σ from these expressions. The two most commonly used methods of obtaining σ were proposed by Day and his workers[4--7] and by Kranbuehl and his colleagues.[8--14] These two methods are discussed next.

2.2 Kranbuehl Method

In the Kranbuehl method the frequencies are found for which sensor electrode polarization and dipole effects are negligible and ionic effects dominate. Then, $SF_2 = 1$ and from Eqs. (3) and (5) we have

$$\epsilon''_m = \frac{\sigma}{\omega\epsilon_o} + \frac{(\epsilon_r - \epsilon_u)(\omega\tau)}{1 + (\omega\tau)^2} \qquad (6)$$

This equation can be rearranged to yield

$$\epsilon''_m\omega = \frac{\sigma}{\epsilon_o} + \frac{(\epsilon_r - \epsilon_u)(\omega^2\tau)}{1 + (\omega\tau)^2} \qquad (7)$$

The second term on the right hand side of the equation is negligible when the following inequality is satisfied

$$\frac{(\epsilon_r - \epsilon_u)(\omega^2\tau)}{1 + (\omega\tau)^2} \ll \frac{\sigma}{\epsilon_o} \qquad (8)$$

At frequencies where the condition expressed by Eq. (8) is satisfied, the ionic conductivity is related to the loss factor by the expression (see Appendix)

$$\epsilon''_m\omega \simeq \frac{\sigma}{\epsilon_o} = \text{constant} \qquad (9)$$

σ may be calculated from Eq. (9) using the measured value of ϵ''_m. To insure that the inequality of Eq. (8) is satisfied and that Eq. (9) is valid, the measurements must be performed at a number of different frequencies, $\omega_1, \omega_2, \omega_3, \ldots$. Those data are valid for which the product $\epsilon''_m\omega$ has the same value

$$(\epsilon''_m\omega)_1 = (\epsilon''_m\omega)_2 = \cdots = \text{constant} \qquad (10)$$

Unfortunately, the correct frequencies which satisfy the above criterion are not known, a priori. Therefore, the measurements must be performed over a wide frequency range, with the anticipation and hope that there will be at least two frequencies for which the $\epsilon''_m\omega$ products are equal.

In addition to ionic conductivity, Kranbuehl and his co-workers utilized dipolar mobility and changes in the magnitudes of ϵ' and ϵ'' to monitor cure.[10] As yet, these data do not yield information on the absolute values of viscosity and degree of cure.

2.3 Day Method

The Day method also utilizes the loss factor in determining the ionic conductivity. Equations (3) and (5) give

$$\epsilon''_m = (SF_2)\left[\frac{\sigma}{\omega\epsilon_o} + \frac{(\epsilon_r - \epsilon_u)\omega\tau}{1 + (\omega\tau)^2}\right] \qquad (11)$$

Under those conditions where both the correction factor SF_2 is unity and the second term in the bracket is negligible Eq. (11) becomes

$$\epsilon''_m = \frac{\sigma}{\omega\epsilon_o} \qquad (12)$$

Thus, Eq. (12) can be used to calculate the ionic conductivity when the following conditions are satisfied

$$\frac{\sigma}{\omega \epsilon_o} \gg \frac{(\epsilon_r - \epsilon_u)\omega\tau}{1 + (\omega\tau)^2} \qquad (13)$$

$$SF_2 = 1 \qquad (14)$$

The second term on the right-hand side of Eq. (13) is a maximum when $\omega\tau = 1$. For this value of $\omega\tau$ the inequality of Eq. (13) becomes

$$\frac{\sigma}{\epsilon_o \omega} \gg \frac{\epsilon_r - \epsilon_u}{2} \qquad (15)$$

Equations (12) and (15) give

$$\epsilon_m'' \gg \frac{\epsilon_r - \epsilon_u}{2} \qquad (16)$$

Equation (16) is one of the requirements of the Day method. In addition, SF_2 must be equal to unity (Eq. 14). Day et al.[7] introduced the following expression for SF_2

$$SF_2 = \frac{1 - \frac{1}{R}}{1 + \left(\frac{1}{R}\frac{\epsilon''}{\epsilon'}\right)^2} \qquad (17)$$

R is a constant which depends on the geometry of the sensor and the material being tested.[7] It is evident that SF_2 becomes unity when the following conditions are satisfied

$$SF_2 = 1 \quad \text{when} \quad R \gg 1 \quad \text{and} \quad R \gg \epsilon''/\epsilon' \qquad (18)$$

In practice R is usually large and the first inequality is satisfied.[18] By noting that $\epsilon_m'' = (SF_2)\epsilon''$ (Eq. 5) and $SF_2 = 1$, the second inequality may be written as

$$\epsilon_m'' \ll \epsilon' R \qquad (19)$$

Practical limits for ϵ_m' and ϵ_m'' can now be established. According to Day,[18] for many common polymeric materials the values of ϵ_r range from 2 to 25 and for ϵ_u from 1 to 5. With these values the lower and upper limits of ϵ' are (see Eq. 2)

$$\epsilon' > 1 \quad \text{and} \quad \epsilon' < 25 \qquad (20)$$

Correspondingly, the lower and upper values of ϵ_m'' are (see Eqs. 16, 19, and 20)

$$\epsilon_m'' \gg 12 \quad \text{and} \quad \epsilon_m'' \ll R \qquad (21)$$

The upper limit on ϵ_m' is obtained by combining Eqs. (4) and (20)

$$\epsilon_m' < 25\,(SF_1) \qquad (22)$$

Day[7] proposed the following expression for SF_1

$$SF_1 = \frac{1 + \frac{(\epsilon''/\epsilon')^2}{R}}{1 + \left(\frac{1}{R}\frac{\epsilon''}{\epsilon'}\right)^2} \qquad (23)$$

As seen from Eq. (23) the lowest value of SF_1 is one. Hence, the inequality in Eq. (22) is always satisfied when the following condition is met

$$\epsilon_m' < 25 \qquad (24)$$

As was noted previously, the lowest value of ϵ_m' is one (see Eq. 1). Thus according to the Day method, during the measurements the following conditions must be satisfied

$$R \gg 1$$
$$1 < \epsilon_m' < 25 \qquad (25)$$
$$12 \ll \epsilon_m'' \ll R$$

When the conditions expressed by these inequalities are met, the ionic conductivity can be obtained from the expression (see Eq. 12)

$$\sigma = \omega \epsilon_o \epsilon_m'' = 2\pi f\, \epsilon_o \epsilon_m'' \qquad (26)$$

As in the Kranbuehl method, it is not known a priori which frequencies satisfy the inequalities in Eq. (25). Therefore, the measurements must be performed at a number of frequencies covering a wide range with the hope that for at least one of the preselected frequencies the requirements of Eq. (25) are satisfied.

Finally, it is emphasized that when using an instrument which is preprogrammed for the Day method only those data in the data file can be used which are within the limits of Eq. (26). All other data must be discarded.

315

In the Micromet Instruments Eumetric System II with a low conductivity sensor the upper limit of ϵ_m'' is approximately 1000.

3. RESULTS

The procedures described in the previous section yield the ionic conductivity σ. First, we wish to examine what differences, if any, are there in the ionic conductivities given by the Day and the Kranbuehl methods. Second, we seek to examine the relationships between the ionic conductivity and the viscosity and the ionic conductivity and the degree of cure.

For these reasons, dielectric measurements were performed with Fiberite T300/976 tape and Hercules AS/3501-6 fabric graphite-epoxy composites. Six inch long, 6 inch wide, and 0.10 in thick laminates were fabricated. A Micromet instruments low conductivity sensor was placed at the midthickness, 1 inch from the edge of each laminate. The sensor was connected to a Eumetric System II microdielectrometer. The output of the dielectrometer was displayed on the screen and stored on the hard disk of an IBM AT computer.

The laminate was vacuum bagged and cured in an autoclave at a pressure of 100 ± 5 psia. During cure the temperature at the location of the sensor (as measured by the sensor itself) the permittivity, and the loss factor were measured at five frequencies. The data are shown in Figures 2 and 3.

The Kranbuehl method requires that $\epsilon_m'\omega$ be constant (Eq. 10). Hence we plotted $\epsilon_m'\omega$ versus time (Figure 4). At none of the frequencies between 1 Hz and 10 KHz did the data satisfy the $\epsilon_m''\omega =$ constant condition for the entire time of the test. For each frequency, this condition was satisfied for only a limited time. Data which did not meet the $\epsilon_m''\omega =$ constant requirement are not included in Figure 4.

The ionic conductivities deduced from the data by the Day method are shown in Figure 5. For comparison the ionic conductivities given by the Kranbuehl method are also included in Figure 5. The Day and the Kranbuehl methods yield similar ionic conductivities. More importantly, both methods predict the times at which the ionic conductivity σ is maximum and the rate of change of ionic conductivity $d\sigma/dt$ is zero. Further-

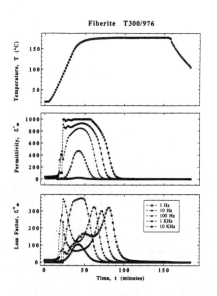

Figure 2. Test results for Fiberite T300/976.

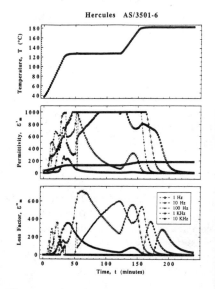

Figure 3. Test results for Hercules AS/3501-6.

more, the two methods yield nearly the same time at which σ is maximum, and also give nearly the same time at which $d\sigma/dt$ is zero.

Next, we examine the relationships between the rate of cure and the rate of ionic conductivity and between the viscosity and the ionic conductivity. To this end we calculated the rate of cure $d\alpha/dt$ and the viscosity μ by the chemical kinetics given in Table 1. The measured values of the temperatures were used in the calculations.

The calculated values of the viscosity and the rate of cure are shown at the bottom of Figures 6–9. For comparison, in the top of these figures we included the inverse of the ionic conductivities (Figures 6, 7) and the rates of ionic conductivity (Figures 8, 9). The inverse ionic conductivities were plotted because this parameter is proportional to viscosity.[6,9] The rates of ionic conductivity were obtained by numerical differentiation of the ionic conductivity versus time data of Figure 5.

The following important observations can be made from Figures 6–9.

1) The ionic inverse conductivity σ is not directly related to the viscosity (Figures 6, 7).

2) The ionic conductivity σ does indicate the time at which the viscosity reaches its minimum value, in as much as σ is a maximum at approximately the same time at which the viscosity is minimum (Figures 6, 7).

3) The rate of ionic conductivity $d\sigma/dt$ is not directly related to the actual rate of cure $d\alpha/dt$ (Figures 8, 9).

4) The rate of ionic conductivity $d\sigma/dt$ does indicate the time at which cure reaches completion $(d\alpha/dt \rightarrow 0)$ in as much as $d\sigma/dt$ approaches zero at about the same time as the rate of cure (Figures 8, 9).

3.1 Degree of Cure

Finally, we made an attempt to relate directly the ionic conductivity to the degree of cure. The degree of cure α can be expressed in terms of the area under the rate of degree of cure $d\alpha/dt$ versus time t curve. Thus, with reference to Figure 10, the degree of cure is

$$\alpha = \frac{\text{Area up to time } t}{\text{Total area}} = \frac{A^\alpha}{A_T^\alpha} \quad (27)$$

We now define an ionic degree of reaction σ^* which is obtained from the rate of ionic reaction $d\sigma/dt$ versus time curve in a similar manner

$$\sigma^* = \frac{\text{Area up to time } t}{\text{Total area}} = \frac{A^\sigma}{A_T^\sigma} \quad (28)$$

The ionic degrees of reaction were calculated by numerical integration of the $d\sigma/dt$ versus time t curves in Figures 8 and 9. The results thus obtained are given in Figure 11. In these figures we also included the degree of cure values calculated by the kinetics equations in Table 1. The α and σ^* values are similar, indicating a relationship between the degree of cure and the ionic conductivity. However, this procedure is impractical for actual cure monitoring because it requires a prior knowledge of the ionic conductivity as a function of time. This information, of course, is unavailable. Such information could be obtained prior to the actual test by calibration. Unfortunately, there is no assurance that the predetermined values of the ionic conductivity will prevail during the actual test.

Although this procedure is inadequate for determining α in practice, the result is sufficiently promising to lead one to believe that practical means of determining the values of α and μ are feasible.

4. CONCLUDING REMARKS

For emphasis, the major conclusions are recapitulated below:

1) In tests, the limiting conditions (detailed in this paper) must be strictly observed.

2) The limiting conditions are affected by the frequency. Unfortunately, the proper frequency is not known a priori. Therefore, each test must be performed at different frequencies. The use of a broad

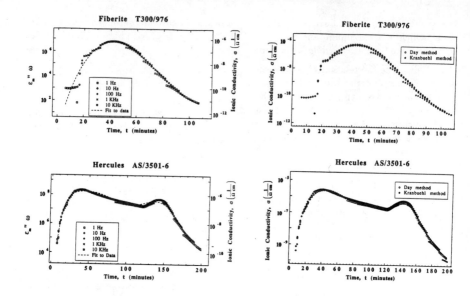

Figure 4. The ionic conductivity deduced from the data by the Kranbuehl method.

Figure 5. The ionic conductivities deduced from the data by the Day and Kranbuehl methods.

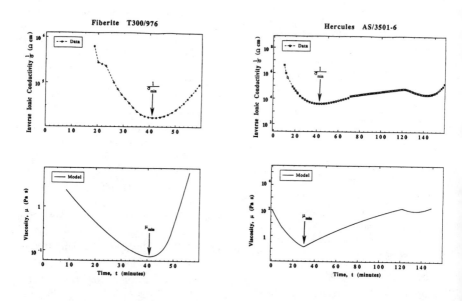

Figure 6. Top: The inverse ionic conductivity deduced from the data. Bottom: The viscosity calculated by the model in Table 1.

Figure 7. Top: The inverse ionic conductivity deduced from the data. Bottom: The viscosity calculated by the model in Table 1.

Table 1

DEGREE OF CURE AND VISCOSITY
OF HERCULES 3501-6 AND FIBERITE 976 RESINS[19,20]

	976 $0 < \alpha < 1.0$		3501-6 $0 < \alpha \leq 0.3$	3501-6 $0.3 < \alpha < 1.0$
A_1 (min^{-1})	2.64×10^5		2.101×10^9	1.960×10^5
A_2 (min^{-1})	4.23×10^5		-2.014×10^9	0
ΔE_1 (J/mol)	6.25×10^4		8.07×10^4	5.66×10^4
ΔE_2 (J/mol)	5.68×10^4		7.78×10^4	
B	1.0		.47	0
a	1.03		1.0	0
b	1.22		1.0	0
c	0		1.0	1.0
d	0		1.0	1.0
H_u	530		474	474
H_T/H_u	$0.0044\,T - 1.1$	$T < 480\,K$	1.0	1.0
	1.0	$T \geq 480\,K$		
μ_∞ (Pa S)	1.06×10^{-6}		7.93×10^{-14}	7.93×10^{-14}
U (J/mol)	3.76×10^4		9.08×10^4	9.08×10^4
K	18.8		14.1	14.1

$$\frac{d\alpha}{dt} = \frac{H_T}{H_u}(K_1 + K_2\beta^a)(B - \beta)^b(1 - \beta^d)^c$$

$$\beta = \frac{H_u}{H_T}\int_o^t \frac{d\alpha}{dt}\,dt$$

$$K_{1,2} = A_{1,2}\exp(-\Delta E/RT)$$

$$\mu = \mu_\infty \exp(U/RT + \kappa\alpha)$$

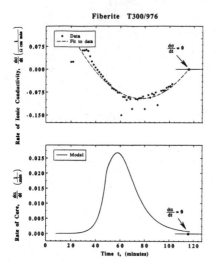

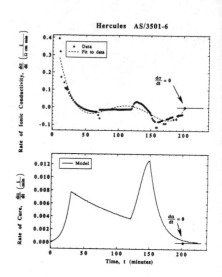

Figure 8. Top: Rate of ionic conductivity deduced from the data. Bottom: The rate of degree of cure calculated by the model in Table 1.

Figure 9. Top: Rate of ionic conductivity deduced from the data. Bottom: The rate of degree of cure calculated by the model in Table 1.

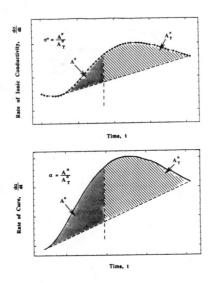

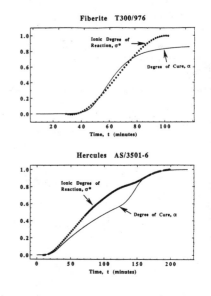

Figure 10. Illustration of the procedure for calculating the ionic degree of reaction σ^* and the degree of cure α. A^σ and A^α are the areas up to time t, while A_T^σ and A_T^α are the total areas.

Figure 11. Symbols: Ionic degree of reaction deduced from the data. Solid line: The degree of cure calculated by the model in Table 1.

range of judiciously selected frequencies enhances the possibility, but does not guarantee that the proper frequencies were used in the test.

3) Although the Day and Kranbuehl methods differ in detail, they provide nearly identical ionic conductivity values.

4) The ionic conductivity data indicate the times at which the viscosity is minimum and at which cure is near completion.

5) The ionic conductivity data do not provide the values of either the viscosity or the degree of cure at any time during the processing.

The results in this paper show that dielectric measurements yield some useful information about the cure process but, as yet, do not provide the viscosity or degree of cure histories during the entire cure. Nonetheless, the results are encouraging in that they give further evidence of a relationship between the ionic conductivity and the viscosity and degree of cure. To determine the absolute values of viscosity and degree of cure it might be necessary to take into account additional parameters such as temperature, dipolar mobility, and rates of permittivity, loss factor, and ionic conductivity. Further research along these lines may prove useful and seems warranted.

5. ACKNOWLEDGMENTS

The authors wish to thank Micromet Instruments, Inc. for their grant of a Eumetrics II microdielectrometer cure monitoring system. They are also grateful to Drs. David Day and David Kranbuehl for their many helpful comments.

APPENDIX

Kranbuehl and his co-workers[9] start with the Johnson and Cole expression[15]

$$\epsilon'' = \frac{\sigma}{\omega\epsilon_o} + \frac{\epsilon_r - \epsilon_u}{1 + (\omega\tau)^2}$$
$$- C_o Z_o \cos\frac{n\pi}{2}\omega^{-(n+1)}\left(\frac{\sigma}{\epsilon_o}\right)^2 \qquad (A.1)$$

where $Z = Z_o(i\omega)^{-n}$ is the electrode impedance induced by the ions, and n is a constant having a value between zero and one. For pure d. c. conductance $n = 0$ and Eq. (A.1) becomes

$$\epsilon'' = \frac{\epsilon_r - \epsilon_u}{1 + (\omega\tau)^2} + \frac{\sigma}{\omega\epsilon_o}\left(1 - \frac{C_o Z_o \sigma}{\epsilon_o}\right) \quad (A.2)$$

According to Kranbuehl et al.[9] the d. c. ionic component of ϵ'' is $\sigma/\omega\epsilon_o$. This is identical to Eq. (9) in the text.

REFERENCES

1. Senturia, S. D. and Sheppard, N. F. "Dielectric Analysis of Thermoset Cure," *Advances in Polymer Science, 80*, 3–47 (1986).

2. Senturia, S. D., Sheppard, Jr., N. F., Lee, H. L., and Marshall, S. B. "Cure Monitoring and Control With Combined Dielectric/Temperature Probes," *Materials and Processes—Continuing Innovations,* Society for the Advancement of Materials and Processes Engineering, *28,* 851–861 (1983).

3. Chang, S. S., Mopsik, F. I., and Hunston, D. L. "Correlation of Cure Monitoring Techniques," *The Nation's Future Materials Needs,* Society for the Advancement of Materials and Processes Engineering, *19,* 253–264 (1987).

4. Day, D. R. "Thermoset Cure Process Control for Utilizing Microdielectric Feedback," *Materials: Pathways to the Future,* Society for the Advancement of Materials and Processes Engineering, *33,* 594–602 (1988).

5. Day, D. R. "Sensor Development for PMR15 Cure Monitoring and Control," *Advanced Materials Technology '87,* Society for the Advancement of Materials and Processes Engineering, *32,* 1472–1479 (1987).

6. Day, D. R. "Cure Control: Strategies for Use of Dielectric Sensors," *Materials Sciences for the Future,* Society for the Advancement of Materials and Processes Engineering, *31,* 1095–1103 (1986).

7. Day, D. R., Lewis, T. J., Lee, H. L., and Senturia, S. D. "The Role of Boundary Layer Capacitance at Blocking Electrodes in the Interpretation of Dielectric Cure Data in Adhesives," *Journal of Adhesion, 18*, 73–90 (1985).

8. Kranbuehl, D., Delos, S., Yi, E., Mayer, J., Hou, T., and Winfree, W. "Correlation of Dynamic Dielectric Measurements With Viscosity in Polymeric Resin Systems," *Advance Technology in Materials and Processes,* Society for the Advancement of Materials and Processes Engineering, *30,* 638–659 (1985).

9. Kranbuehl, D. E., Delos, S. E., and Jue, P. K. "Dielectric Properties of the Polymerization of an Aromatic Polyimide," *Polymer, 27,* 11–18 (1986).

10. Kranbuehl, D., Haverty, P., Hoff, M., Hoffman, R. D., and Godfrey, J. J. "Dynamic Dielectric Analysis for Nondestructive Cure Monitoring and Process Control," *42nd Annual Conference, Composites Institute,* The Society of the Plastics Industry, Session 22-D, 1–5 (1987).

11. Kranbuehl, D. E., Delos, S. E., Hoff, M. S., Weller, L. W., Haverty, P. D., Seeley, J. A., and Whitham, B. A. "Monitoring Processing Properties of High Performance Thermoplastics Using Frequency Dependent Electromagnetic Sensing," *Advanced Materials Technology '87,* Society for the Advancement of Materials and Processes Engineering, *32,* 338–348 (1987).

12. Kranbuehl, D., Hoff, M., Haverty, P., Loos, A., and Freeman, T. "Insitu Measurement and Control of Processing Properties of Composite Resins in a Production Tool," *Materials: Pathways to the Future,* Society for the Advancement of Materials and Processes Engineering, 1276–1284 (1988).

13. Kranbuehl, D., Delos, S., Hoff, M. S., and Weller, L. W. "Dynamic Dielectric Analysis: A Means for Process Control," *Materials Sciences for the Future,* Society for the Advancement of Materials and Processes Engineering, *31,* 1087–1094 (1986).

14. Kranbuehl, D., Haverty, P., Hoff, M., and Hoffman, R. "Monitoring the Cure Processing Properties of Unsaturated Polyesters In-Situ During Fabrication," Society of Plastics Engineers 46th Technical Conference Proceedings, 955–959 (1988).

15. Johnson, J. F. and Cole, R. H. "Dielectric Polarization of Liquid and Solid Formic Acid," *the Journal of American Chemical Society, 73,* 4536–4540 (1951).

16. Debye, P. *Polar Molecules,* Chemical Catalog Co., 94–98 (1929).

17. Cole, K. S. and Cole, R. H. "Dispersion and Absorption in Dielectrics," *Journal of Chemical Physics, 9,* 341–345 (1941).

18. Day, D. R. Private communication, December 1988.

19. Dusi, M. R., Lee, W. I., Ciriscioli, P. R., and Springer, G. S. "Cure Kinetics and Viscosity of Fiberite 976 Resin," *Journal of Composite Materials, 21,* 243–261 (1987).

20. Lee, W. I., A. Loos, and G. S. Springer. "Heat of Reaction, Degree of Cure and Viscosity of Hercules 3501-6 Resin," *Journal of Composite Materials, 16,* 510–520 (1982).

THE EFFECT OF PRESSURE ON THE IMPREGNATION OF

FIBERS WITH THERMOPLASTIC RESINS

T.-W. Kim and E.-J. Jun

Korea Institute of Machinery and Metals,Changwon,Korea

and

W. I. Lee

Seoul National University,Seoul,Korea

Abstract

Effect of process variables on the impregnation of thermoplastic resin into continuous unidirectional fiber tows was investigated. A model to predict the degree of impregnation as a function of time, impregnation pressure, impregnation temperature and tow size was proposed. For the model it was assumed that the radial inward flow of resin through the fiber tow is governed by Darcy's law and the permeability is constant. Experiments were performed to evaluate the validity of the model. Toray T300 graphite fiber bundles and PolyEtherEtherKetone (PEEK) resin were used for the experiments. Pressure and temperature were applied to fiber tows surrounded with resin powder in a mold. After a predetermined time, the sample was taken out and the degree of impregnation was measured from the microphotographs of the cross-sections of samples. Experiments were performed for different impregnation conditions such as impregnation time, pressure, temperature and tow size. Experimental data agreed well with the prediction by the model.

1. INTRODUCTION

Thermoplastic resins as matrix material for advanced composites have many advantages over thermosetting counterparts. However, the viscosity of thermoplastic resin is extremely high and thus is hard to flow.

The high viscosity imposes many problems in the manufacturing process of composites. One of the major difficulties is the impregnation of resin into reinforcing fibers. Along with poor dispersion of fibers in the thermoplastic matrices, impregnation has been a major problem in the manufacturing process of thermoplastic composites.

Many semi-crystalline thermoplastics such as PEEK have no effective solvent and thus solution dip method in prepregging is not applicable for this class of materials. Moreover, since these thermoplastics usually have very high melting point which is close to the decompsoition temperature, reducing viscosity by raising process temperature has not been successful.

Lee and Springer[1] proposed a model describing the impregnation process in the absence of pressure. In order to speed up the impregnation, pressure must be applied. In this case, the mechanism of resin impregnation is totally different from the model by Lee and Springer[1].

Therefore the objective of this study is to find out the effect of pressure on the impregnation of fiber bundles with thermoplastic resin matrices.

2. MODEL

Impregnation is accomplished by surrounding the fiber tow with the matrix and let the polymeric matrix penetrate into the fiber. One way to accelerate the impregnation process is to apply pressure. If the fibers in the tow are perfectly straight and parallel to each other as in the ideal case, the fiber bundle will collapse inward leaving no room for the resin to penetrate as pressure is applied. In the real situation, however, individual fibers are not perfectly straight. Rather it is wavy in nature. Therefore as the bundle collapses inward by the applied pressure, physical contacts between the fibers will take place at some points. In between these contact points there exist rooms for the resin to pass through. The rooms between the fibers which is directly related to the permeability of the fiber bundle represents the resistance for resin flow.

If we assume that Darcy's law[2] can be applied for the radial flow of the resin,

$$V_r = - \frac{K}{\mu} \frac{dP}{dr} \qquad (1)$$

where V_r is the radial velocity of the resin, K is permeability, P is applied pressure and r designates the radial position (Fig.1). The rate of mass flow through the radial position r is

$$\dot{m} = \rho(-V_r)(2\pi r)\epsilon \qquad (2)$$

where ϵ is the porosity of the fiber bundle. Equations (1) and (2) give

$$\frac{\dot{m}}{2\pi\rho\epsilon} \frac{dr}{r} = \frac{K}{\mu} dP \qquad (3)$$

The pressure at $r = r_o$ is the applied pressure, i.e., P_o. Integrating Eq.(3) from r_o to r_f yields

$$\frac{\dot{m}}{2\pi\rho\epsilon} \ln(\frac{r_f}{r_o}) = - \frac{K}{\mu} (P_o - P_a) \qquad (4)$$

where r_f is the location of the resin front where the pressure is the atmospheric pressure P_a. The mass flow rate can be expressed in terms of dr_f/dt as

$$\dot{m} = 2\pi\rho r_f \epsilon (- \frac{dr_f}{dt}) \qquad (5)$$

Equations (4) and (5) yield

$$r_f \ln (\frac{r_f}{r_o}) dr_f = \frac{K}{\mu}(P_o - P_a)dt \qquad (6)$$

Integrating Eq.(6) along with the initial condition $(r = r_o$ at $t = 0)$ gives

$$t = \frac{\mu r_o^2}{4K(P_o - P_a)} \{ 2(\frac{r_f}{r_o})^2 \ln(\frac{r_f}{r_o}) + 1 - (\frac{r_f}{r_o})^2 \} \qquad (7)$$

The degree of impregnation D_{imp} can be defined as the ratio between the total number of fibers and the number of impregnated fibers. If we assume that fibers are distributed uniformly, the degree of impregnation can be expressed as

$$D_{imp} = \frac{\text{Area Impregnated}}{\text{Tow Area}} = \frac{\pi r_o^2 - \pi r_f^2}{\pi r_o^2}$$

$$= 1 - (\frac{r_f^2}{r_o^2}) \qquad (8)$$

Substituting Eq.(8) into Eq.(7), we finally obtain the degree of impregnation as a function of time, applied pressure, viscosity, initial bundle radius and permeability.

$$t = \frac{\mu r_o^2}{4K(P_o - P_a)} \{ 2(1 - D_{imp}) \ln \sqrt{(1 - D_{imp})} + D_{imp} \} \qquad (9)$$

Equation (9) provides a relationship between the degree of impregnation and the process variables in the impregnation process, namely impregnation pressure, temperature, tow size and time.

3. EXPERIMENTAL

Tests were performed to evaluate the validity of the model. In these tests Toray T300 graphite fiber tows (3K, 6K, 12K) were impregnated with PEEK 150P polymer. Prior to the tests the sizing was removed from the fibers by the following procedure. The fibers were immersed in methylethylketone (MEK) for 24 hours, then were washed with fresh MEK in an ultrasonic cleaner for 30 minutes. This procedure was repeated. After the second treatment with fresh MEK the fibers were dried in a vacuum oven at 80 ° C for two hours. A fiber tow, treated in the above manner, was placed in a cavity of a matched die mold (Fig.2). The mold was made of steel and nickel was plated on the mold surface. The mold was filled with PEEK 150P powder to make the fiber tow surrounded by resin. The mold then was placed in a hot press and heated to the test temperature with no pressure applied. The mold was held at the test temperature for approximately 10 minutes with no pressure applied to reach the thermal equilibrium. Once the mold reached the test temperature, pressure was applied. After a preset period of time the mold was removed from the hot press and cooled to room temperature. The impregnated tow was removed from the mold, was cut perpendicular to the fibers. Microphotograph of the tow cross-section was taken. The number of impregnated fibers in the tow was counted from the microphotograph and the degree of impregnation was calculated by the expression

$$D_{imp} = \frac{\text{Number of Impregnated Fibers}}{\text{Total Number of Fibers}} \quad (10)$$

This process was repeated for different pressures (2 atm, 4 atm, 5 atm and 10 atm), different temperatures (370 ° C, 380 ° C, 390 ° C and 400 ° C), different tow sizes (3K, 6K and 12K) and different duration of time (5,10,20 and 30 minutes). The data are shown in Fig.3-6.

The degree of impregnation was also calulated by the model (Eq.9) for the test conditions. The following value and expression were used for the radius r_0 and the resin viscosity μ

$$r_0 = 300 \ \mu m \qquad \text{for 6K tow}$$

$$\mu = 1.13 \times 10^{-10} \exp \left(\frac{19123}{T \ (^\circ K)} \right) \ Pa \cdot sec \qquad (11)$$

where T is temperature. The value of K was determined by fitting a selected data point (Pressure = 10atm, Temperature = 370 °C, Tow size = 6K, Time = 10min, see Fig.6) to Eq.(9).

$$K = 1.2 \times 10^{-14} \ m^2 \qquad (12)$$

The results of the calculations by the model are presented in Fig.3-6. As can be seen the agreement between the model and experimental data is good , and this lends support to the validity of the model.

4. CONCLUDING REMARKS

A model is developed to predict the effect of pressure and other process variables on the impregnation of fiber tows. As the model incorporates the effect of pressure, it supplements the result obtained by Lee and Springer for the impregnation process in the absence of pressure[1]. The model presented here can be employed in analyzing and optimizing the impregnation process of thermoplastic matrix composites.

5. REFERENCES

1. Lee, W.I. and Springer, G.S., "A Model of the Manufacturing Process of Thermoplastic Matrix Composites," Journal of Composite Materials, Vol.21, pp.1017-1055 (1987).

2. Happel, J. and Brenner, H., Low Reynolds Number Hydrodynamics, Noordhoff International Publishing Company, 1973, pp.389-404.

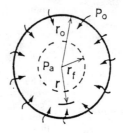

Fig.1 Geometry of the Model.

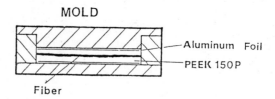

Fig.2 Schematic of the Mold Used in the Impregnation Tests.

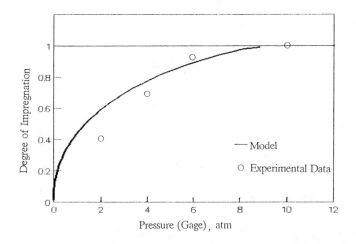

Fig.3 Degree of Impregnation as a Function of Pressure (Gage). T = 370°C, Tow Size = 6K and Impregnation Time = 30 m in. Experimental Data and Result of the Model.

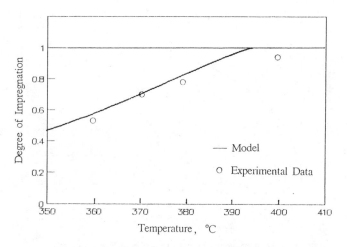

Fig.4 Degree of Impregnation as a Function of Temperature. P = 10atm (gage), Tow Size = 6K and Impregnation Time = 10 min. Experimental Data and Result of the Model.

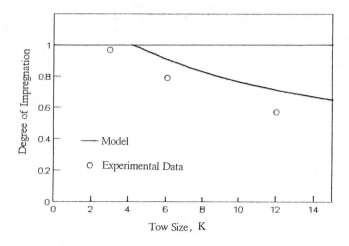

Fig.5 Degree of Impregnation as a Function of Tow Size. P = 10atm(gage) ,
T = 370°C and Time = 20 min. Experimental Data and Result of the
Model.

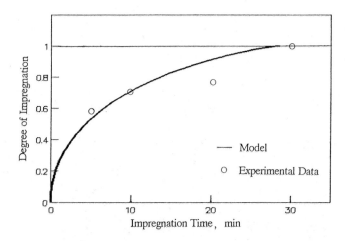

Fig.6 Degree of Impregnation as a Function of Time. P = 10atm(gage),
T = 370°C and Tow Size = 6K. Experimental Data and Result of
the Model.

ECONOMIC COMPARISON OF ADVANCED
COMPOSITE FABRICATION TECHNOLOGIES
Susan Krolewski
IBIS Associates
Cambridge, Massachusetts
and Timothy Gutowski
Massachusetts Institute of Technology
Cambridge, Massachusetts

Abstract

The acquisition of manufacturing equipment is frequently justified in terms of direct labor savings.
Indirect benefits such as higher quality, shorter response time and flexible
capacity can, however, lead to a
higher market share and more substantial profits. In this paper, the
basic framework for a quantitative
method for justifying automated
technologies for composites fabrication is presented. The economic benefits of standalone replacement as
well as less tangible benefits such as
quality improvements and process
flexibility will be discussed.

1. Introduction

The superior strength and
stiffness to weight ratios of advanced
composites have led to performance
improvements in aircraft and other
aerospace vehicles. The high material
and manufacturing costs, however,
have limited their use to applications
in which performance is critical. For
example, since replacement of conventional structures by composites on
the Boeing 737 resulted in a substantial increase in cost, it was decided to
use the original materials for some
parts for which tooling, design and
certification already existed [1].

Traditionally, the acquisition
of equipment has been justified in
terms of direct labor savings. Higher
quality, reliable delivery, shorter lead
times and flexible capacity are, however, important strategic advantages.
These indirect benefits can lead to a
higher market share and a more substantial increase in profit for the firm.
The majority of automation justifica-
tion techniques in the literature are
very qualitative and rely on subjective ratings to measure quality and
process flexibility. In this paper, the
basic framework for a more quantitative method [2] for justifying automated technologies in terms of cost,
process flexibility and quality is pre-

sented. Current composite fabrication technologies are evaluated and desirable characteristics of new equipment are identified.

2. Economic Implications

Generally, the first step in justifying the acquisition of a manufacturing technology is an economic comparison with the present system. Traditionally, it has been assumed that the manufacturing cost has three components: (1) direct material, (2) direct labor and (3) manufacturing overhead. Overhead consists of indirect labor or material, depreciation of factory machinery and buildings, and factory administration and supervision. These expenses are accumulated into a single burden rate which is multiplied by direct labor hours to determine the overhead cost component. With the advent of more complex and expensive automation equipment, this type of accounting does not always provide a fair evaluation of competing approaches.

Due to the higher depreciation costs of automated systems, overhead frequently represents the largest component of the manufacturing cost and is not necessarily proportional to the direct labor hours. This is particularly important when manufacturing methods with different levels of automation are compared. A more expensive system may consume more overhead resources, but appear more cost effective since it may use less direct labor hours. Overburdened labor rates may give the impression that the elimination of people is cost

effective despite large capital investment in equipment. In this paper, a modified approach is taken to compare manufacturing technologies. Equipment depreciation as well as material, labor and tooling are considered direct costs.

An economic model was developed to compare the direct cost of fabricating a flat composite part by hand layup to that of alternative automated procedures. These processes included (1) manual production with automated cutting, (2) robotic transfer with automated cutting, (3) tape layup, (4) pultrusion, (5) filament winding with autoclave and oven cure and (6) resin transfer molding (RTM). The objective was to determine the production volumes at which alternative methods were able to compete with manual production and identify factors which contribute to this cost savings. The analysis is based on the present worth method.

The model is based on information in the literature, government reports and design guides and has been compared with industrial experience to validate its accuracy. It is assumed that the capital investment in equipment is borrowed at ten percent interest rate and is depreciated over an eight year period. Labor costs are based on part cycle time, the learning curve and the degree of skill required. Manual cycle times are based on time studies performed by Northrop [3]. Simple models based on process physics are used to determine automated cycle times. Material costs are based on data from material suppliers. Tooling costs are a function of the part area, the tool lifespan and the production requirements.

Figure 1 shows the fabrication costs for a 12 inch by 48 inch, 24 ply, 4.1 pound part by each process as a function of annual production volume. In general, the manufacturing cost is higher at low production volumes since the equipment depreciation is spread over a smaller number of parts. For these low production volumes, typical of the aerospace industry today, the automated prepreg processes are not competitive with manual layup of prepreg since the reduction in direct labor does not offset the capital investment in equipment. The wet processes are, however, able to successfully compete due to low equipment and material costs.

A breakdown of the costs for each manufacturing method for an annual production rate of 5,000 parts is shown in Figure 2. With the exception of RTM, which utilizes expensive preform fibers, the wet processes offer substantial reduction in material costs. In addition, equipment costs for pultrusion and RTM are substantially lower. At this production volume, the automated prepreg methods give a slight decrease in material costs due to reduction in raw material scrap but require a greater investment in equipment.

Figure 3 shows the breakdown of cycle times for each process for batch production of over 1,200 parts. All the automated methods offer a decrease in cycle time with RTM and

pultrusion offering the most substantial reduction. Note that, with the exception of RTM and pultrusion, each of these processes requires an additional six hour cure cycle. The reduction in cycle time by the automated prepreg methods is primarily achieved by eliminating the compaction process which accounts for over 30% of the manual cycle time. Only a 25% and 50% decrease in layup time is realized by tape layup and robotic transfer. The winding time is longer than that required to manually cut and layup the prepreg.

The automated prepreg methods do not breakeven with manual production until very high volumes. Although tape layup breaks even at 30,600 lbs, after producing 41,000 lbs it is no longer cost effective due to the need for parallel tape layup machine. Automated cutting and robotic transfer breakeven at 72,900 and 42,400 lbs, respectively. These volumes are extremely high in comparison to usage of composites today. A new market study [4] estimates the annual production as 3.0, 1.0, .4 and 6.0 million lbs of prepreg for hand layup, machine assisted layup, pultrusion and filament winding, respectively.

3. System Issues

Two important issues related to process flexibility are the firm's response time to new orders and its ability to produce parts in small batches. There is an inherent trade-off between equipment utilization and the ability of a firm to response to random orders. Although low equipment utilization will increase manufacturing costs, it generally will shorten response time and the level of work-in-progress inventory. The optimal operating point for a given firm will depend on its manufacturing strategy. Companies which chose to compete on low cost will maximize equipment utilization; firms which compete on response time will tend to operate below capacity and sacrifice potential cost savings.

To quantify the tradeoffs between response time, work-in-progress inventory and manufacturing cost, the response of the manufacturing system was simulated to determine the effect of downtimes and randomly arriving orders on waiting times in queues and equipment utilization. The response time of an unbalance manufacturing line is limited by the workstation with the highest cycle time. As indicated by cycle times in Figure 3, there is a substantial mismatch in processing rates between stations for each of these methods. This is especially true for methods which use the automated cutting systems and for manual methods when lot sizes are small. More balanced operation can be achieved by using multiple machines at some of the workstations. This added capacity will decrease response time and work-in-progress inventory and decrease manufacturing cost if demand increases. Adjusting the capacity of the autoclave reduces the mismatch in processing rates for this station.

The processing rate of the autoclave is dependent on its capacity. As the autoclave capacity increases the production rate increases until it reaches a maximum and levels off. The response time decreases with increasing capacity until it reaches this optimal operating point and then begins to increase again. If the capacity is too high, the autoclave is idle while waiting for parts and the response time increases. If the capacity is too low, the autoclave workstation will be the bottleneck and will limit the system production rate and increase the response time. The results show that the optimal autoclave capacity is achieved by matching the throughput of the autoclave to that of the weakest link of the system. For these machine layouts, the capacities are below the potential capacity for typical size of autoclave.

Layouts with one machine per workstation have very high response times and are only capable of producing rather low production volumes. For this type of layout, the response time is very sensitive to the production volume; small decreases in volume drastically decreases the response time and increases the cost. Manual production experiences a less severe increase in cost than the alternative methods since at these production volumes the labor costs are less than equipment costs. When the workstations are balanced, the response time verses manufacturing curve is very steep since the response time is very sensitive to production volume but the cost increases dramatically with increasing demand.

332

Since a large price is paid for a minimal improvement in response time, operating below capacity does not offer much of a competitive edge in this case.

A comparison of the different methods shows that the alternative methods decrease the cycle time and therefore the response time. The addition of an automated cutting system to hand layup operations results in a decrease in response time combined with a large increase in cost. The use of transfer robots results in lower response times, but larger production volumes are necessary to compete on a cost basis. Only tape layup offers a substantial decrease in response time, primarily due to decreased cycle time, without large increases in cost at lower production volumes.

Since the wait in the autoclave queue can add to the response and throughput times and the optimal autoclave capacity is in some cases quite low, the use of individual heated tools to replace the autoclave was investigated. When any layout is operating at its maximum capacity, the response times are almost identical since the autoclave capacity matches the capacity of the weakest link. As the utilization decreases for each layout, the response time is slightly lower for the system with individual tools since the wait for the autoclave has been eliminated. An advantage of individual tools is a decreased throughput time. There may also be a cost savings since a substantial investment in tooling could be made to offset the 1.2 million dollar investment in the autoclave.

Since lot sizes are small in the aerospace industry, it is important to consider the costs associated with the learning curve, reprogramming, setup and retooling. As batch sizes become smaller, the learning curve results in significantly longer average cycle times and possible increases in labor force and equipment needs. Methods with the highest degree of manual labor experience the most dramatic change in cycle time as batch size varies. The cycle time for manual production decreases by 85% as batch sizes increase from 20 to 1220 parts. The decrease in cost for manual production and automated cutting systems is nearly an order of magnitude as batch sizes increase from 10 parts to 1000 parts. Robotic transfer, tape layup, and filament winding experience cost reductions in proportion to their manual labor content of 57.5%, 54.9%, and 71.7%, respectively. As batch size decreases, the breakeven points can decrease by over 90%.

4. Quality Issues

Although quality is a difficult criteria to quantify, it is particularly important for the comparison of wet processes and prepreg layup techniques. According to Ishikawa [5], the true quality of a product is related to its ability to satisfy the customer's requirements. The quality problem can be formulated as a control problem. Inability to control a process results in inconsistent product quality and inhibits automation. Process variability decreases the flexibility by increasing setup times since more time is required to adjust system parameters to produce consistent quality parts each time processing conditions change.

The inputs to the system are the process parameters such as pressure, temperature, equipment positions and rates and human abilities which the manufacturer would like to control in order to produce consistent quality parts. The process outputs such as void content and fiber volume fraction can be thought of as microscopic properties which effect the product properties and dimensions and, depending on the user's requirements, the true quality of the part. Limitations on these outputs due to physical constraints on the process affect the level and consistency of quality. The outputs of the process can be used to define substitute quality characteristics, such as material strength, surface quality and tolerances, which can be related to customer satisfaction.

Statistical data or knowledge of process physics can be used to determine the input/output relationships. A high quality process can compensate for variability, although the highly coupled nature of the many of these systems complicates the control problem. In manual production, multiple layers of inspection can be viewed as a crude control system which detects errors after a task is performed and attempts to compensate by rework and adjusting parameters to prevent future errors. Discrete events such as failing to remove backing paper, bag breakage and wrinkling can be evaluated by the use of human reliability models and equipment failure statistics.

Table 1 summarizes the processing limitations for each alternative method. Manual production and automated cutting methods are able to produce the broadest range of part geometries with reasonable accuracy, high fiber volume fractions and low void content. Current automated prepreg layup methods have more restrictions on part geometry. Although fiber volume fraction, void content and accuracy of pultruded parts are comparable, the part geometry is very restricted. In comparison to prepreg methods, filament winding has lower fiber volume fractions, higher void content and more restricted part geometries. Fiber volume fraction is lowest for RTM but more complex geometries and 3-D fiber structures are possible.

Since quality is dependent on requirements of the user, an example is needed to illustrate the effect of true quality on manufacturing cost. For a given set of customer requirements, the substitute quality characteristics were specified in terms of maximum deflections for a given applied load and the ability to withstand a given interlaminar shear moment. The requirements were satisfied by the properties of a $(0°/90°)_{6S}$ laminate fabricated from prepreg materials. To produce parts which would also satisfy these constraints by RTM and filament winding, the thickness of the part must be increased in order to compensate for lower fiber volume fractions, higher void contents and inferior resin properties and thereby satisfy the customer's requirements. Pultrusion cannot meet these specs without an order of magnitude increase in thickness.

Figure 4 compares the manufacturing costs for these parts for an annual production volume of 5,000 parts. Although the non-prepreg methods are still more cost effective than prepreg methods, the relative cost savings is substantially less. Filament winding with oven cure is the most cost effective process in this example due to its low equipment costs and ability to produce cross ply components. Although the equipment and labor for RTM are still low, the material costs are comparable to those of prepreg methods. Filament winding offers a cost competitive alternative without the substantial increase in weight necessary to meet the user's requirements for the other processes.

The economic comparison indicated that the capital investment in alternative prepreg layup methods cannot be justified on labor savings alone assuming that the manual and machine assisted prepreg layup methods have similar error rates. Since costs for correcting poor quality can exceed 30% of the total process cost in

the composites industry [6], more consistent quality may give the machine assisted methods an advantage.

Due to the complex and tedious nature of the layup process, there are many opportunities for error including missing or extra plies, incorrect fiber orientation, and failure to remove the prepreg backing paper and variability due to differences in human skill and fatigue. Human error models, based on information theory, can help to quantify the error rate. According to Ayres [7], as part complexity and required level of precision increases, the ability of human workers with an inherently large error rate to produce quality products is greatly impaired. Automated equipment is far more reliable than humans since they have an a priori probability of error per opportunity at least an order of magnitude lower than humans.

Since data was not available to determine the relative error rate for each process, it was assumed that automated methods have the same number of opportunities for error per task but that the error rate per opportunity is an order of magnitude less and that the error rate for a method is a related to the amount of manual cycle time that is automated. Based on cycle times for a 4 ft^2, 24 ply part, the cost for correcting quality are 30%, 25.7%, 8% and 8% for manual production, automated cutting, robotic transfer and tape layup, respectively. Figure 5 gives the cost for producing this part adjusted for quality related costs. Comparison to Figure 1 shows that the breakeven points for the prepreg methods are substantially lower. If automated methods are able to decrease the error rate as they have in other industries, the cost savings can be substantial.

5. Concluding Remarks

The results of the economic analysis stress the strong influence of material costs on the cost effectiveness of composite fabrication techniques. Methods which use neat resin and fibers benefit from a substantial materials cost reduction over those which utilize prepreg materials. In addition, since these methods generally have lower equipment costs and cycle times, they are able to compete with manual production even without a savings in material costs.

There are, however, tradeoffs between cost effectiveness, geometric constraints and quality characteristics for raw material methods. Although pultrusion is the most cost effective method and produces high quality parts, it is limited to constant cross sections and unidirectional fiber orientation. Filament winding offers more flexibility in fiber orientation at a higher cost. RTM offers lower cycle times, but the need for fiber forms can increase materials costs and there are limitations on maximum attainable fiber volume fraction.

Unless machine assisted prepreg methods can reduce quality related costs or produce more complex parts, these technologies are only marginally cost effective. This agrees with a recent study [8] which concluded that despite the 6 lb/hr production rates, tape layup equipment was not competitive with automated ply cutting system and manual layup. For simple parts, these methods compete by eliminating the need for compaction between plies and reducing the scrap. Since there is not a large decrease in layup cycle time, it appears that some forms of intermediate automation which increase the efficiency or quality of the manual procedure may be more appropriate. Ink-jet ply location marking/ inspection and semi-automated compaction systems have been successfully utilized by Boeing [9] to increase productivity.

Each of the alternative methods reduce the cycle time and therefore the throughput of the system and the work-in-progress inventory costs. For the machine assisted prepreg layup methods, there is a substantial mismatch in the capacities of workstations resulting in a bottleneck at the "slowest" workstation which dominates the response time. If process flexibility is desired the emphasis should be placed on developing more balanced equipment lines. Perhaps a more appropriate breakdown of tasks is necessary or less expensive slower equipment in high capacity workstations such as automated cutting. Autoclave capacities which optimize response time are low in comparison to the size of the typical autoclave. The use of individual heated tools would reduce response and throughput time by eliminating the wait in the autoclave queue and possibly the labor intensive autoclave preparation and compaction procedures.

Although this work focused on specific methods, many generalizations can be drawn which serve as guidelines for the design of new manufacturing technologies. Since a high level of integration and low assembly costs enable composite structures to successfully compete with other materials, part complexity is an important issue. More complex parts require more manual labor and, therefore, are attractive targets for automation. Much of the equipment technology was borrowed from other industries and does not have the operating characteristics suitable for composites applications. In contrast, raw material methods which simplify the amount of information in the part are able to compete economically. These methods are constrained to a reduced set of geometries in which the part complexity or information content is low resulting in low equipment costs and cycle times.

Equipment design is, therefore, a key area of improvement. There is a strong need for new equipment designed for composites applications which will enable the production of complex geometry parts and take advantage of the repetitive nature of composite parts. An example of this is the modular design adopted by Airbus [10] for the horizontal stabilizer. The basic module can be repetitively produced by layup robots and special tools to facilitate automation. It was claimed that this method can produce more complex parts at a substantially faster rate than manual fabrication and at the same cost of an equivalent aluminum structure.

Perhaps a better solution would be to replace the basic module with a shape that could be economically produced by a form of pultrusion, filament winding or resin transfer molding and use these basic modules to produce more highly integrated structures. Another approach may be to produce the basic microstructure by simplified cost effective methods and then use a forming process to give the part gross geometric complexity. This would be analogous to the stamping of steel parts.

Further research is required to gain a better understanding of raw material processes in order to implement these ideas. The high material costs and high level of integration for composite structures require consistent quality parts. There are several process related issues which restrict the quality of raw material processes. High quality parts could be produced at low cost by filament winding if void formation could be eliminated without the use of autoclave cure. Low viscosity resins and better resin impregnation techniques are necessary to produce parts for markets which require high fiber volume fractions. To produce complex parts, a better understanding of the deformation process is necessary.

References

1 McLane, R., "Economic Issues in Composites Manufacturing", Proceedings of the American Society for Composites, September 1988.

2 Krolewski, Susan, "An Economic Based Model to Evaluate Advanced Composite Fabrication Technologies", Ph. D. Thesis. M.I.T., February 1989.

3 LeBlanc, D.J. et al., *Advanced Composites Cost Estimating Manual*, Volume 1, AFFDL-TR-76-87, Northrop Corporation, Aircraft Division, 1976, p 16.

4 McDermott, J., "Assessing the Advanced Composites Market", *Advanced Composites*, April/May 1988, p 52.

5 Ishikawa, K., *What is Total Quality Control?*, Prentice Hall, 1985.

6 Margolis, J., "Composite Fabricating Economics", *Composites in Manufacturing*, v 4, n 1.

7 Ayres, R., "Complexity, Reliability and Design: Manufacturing Implications", *Manufacturing Review*, v 1, n 1, March 1988.

8 "Automating Composites Fabrication", *American Machinist and Automated Manufacturing*, November 1987.

9 McLane, R., "Economic Issues in Composites Manufacturing", Proceedings of the American Society for Composites, September 1988, p 23.

10 Sarh, B., "Robotic Applications to Automated Composite Aircraft Component Manufacturing", SME Technical Paper, MF85-506. 1985

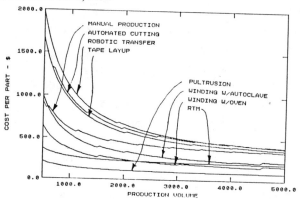

Figure 1 Fabrication Costs for a 24 Ply 4.1 lb Laminate

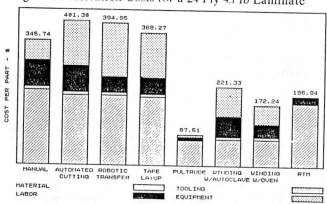

Figure 2 Cost Breakdown for an Annual Production Volume of 5,000 Laminates

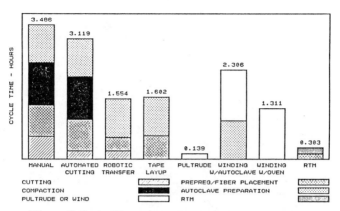

Figure 3 Cycle Times for a 24 Ply 4.1 lb Laminate

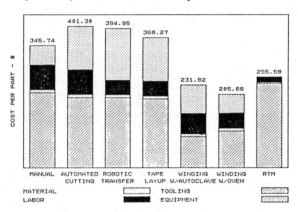

Figure 4 Breakdown of Part Cost

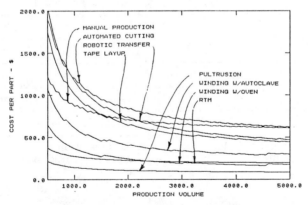

Figure 5 Part Cost Adjusted for Quality Related Costs

Table 1 Process Limitations

	hand layup and autocutting	tape layup and robotic transfer	pultrude	filament winding	RTM
V_F	62%	62%	60%	60% 49.4-57.5%	47.4%
V_V	<1%	<1%	<1%	.5-5% .5%!, 3-8%	
fiber structure	2-D	2-D	1-D roving 2-D mat	2-D	3-D
inside radii	1/4"	difficult	1/32" roving 1/16" mat	1/8"	1/4"
minimum thickness	.060"	.060"†	.040" roving .060" mat	.010"	.080" .100"
maximum thickness	no limit	no limit†	3.0" roving 1.0" mat	2.0"	.5"
tolerance	±.005"	±.005"†	±.005"	±.010"	±.010"
corrugation	yes	yes	yes	concave only	yes
molded holes	large	large‡, no*	no	no	no
contours	yes	<±30°	longitudinal	concave only	yes
hat section	yes	yes†	yes	no	yes
cylinders	yes	difficult	yes	yes	yes
bosses	yes	yes†	no	no	difficult
ribs	no	no†	longitudinal	no	difficult [113]
hollow section	no	no	longitudinal	longitudinal	no

† based on hand layup data   ‡ robotic transfer only
* tape layup only   ! wound prepreg cured in autoclave

THE GENERAL DEFORMATION BEHAVIOR OF
A LUBRICATED FIBER BUNDLE

Z. Cai and T. Gutowski
Laboratory for Manufacturing and Productivity
Massachusetts Institute of Technology
Cambridge, MA 02139, U.S.A.

ABSTRACT

This paper addresses the equilibrium deformation behavior of a lubricated bundle of aligned fibers subjected to a state of homogeneous complex stress. We review the observations for the deformation of the fiber bundle and propose a continuum mechanics model which identifies the elastic and viscous modes of response. The elastic deformation of the fiber bundle is analyzed and the stress-deformation relation is established. Experiments on deformation behavior under various load conditions are performed.

INTRODUCTION

During the processing of polymer based composites, loads are applied to shape and consolidate the composite. For advanced composites, the fiber volume fraction V_f is usually high (≥ 0.5). Therefore, the deformation behavior of the fibers has an enormous effect on the overall processing behavior of the composite. How the load is carried by the composite and partitioned between the fiber bundle and the resin will have important effects on the composite microstructure [1,2]. For example, low resin pressure can lead to voids in the composite [3], whereas axial compressive stresses can lead to buck-

ling and wrinkling of the fibers [4,5]. The purpose of this paper is to present a continuum mechanics framework for the viscoelastic deformation behavior of a lubricated aligned fiber bundle in the drained state. We will then explore the elastic response of the material in greater detail.

OBSERVED BEHAVIOR

We first summarize some of the observed deformation behavior of fiber bundles and aligned fiber composites. We assume the coordinate system for a nominally aligned fiber bundle as shown in Fig. 1. The bundle is transversely isotropic in the 2-3 plane. We are concerned with the deformation behavior of this fiber bundle to complex but homogeneous states of stress. Furthermore, the fiber bundle is in the "drained" state, in which fibers are lubricated but the lubricant carries no load (i.e. the pressure in the resin p_r is negligible). Following is the list of observed deformation behavior of this system.

1) $\sigma_{11} \geq 0$. When pulled along the fiber axis, the bundle behaves in a linear elastic manner [6].

2) $\sigma_{11} \leq 0$. Confined fiber bundles may support small compressive axial loads and then buckle [4,5]. We assume that they behave linear

elastically up to the buckling
load.

3) $\sigma_{22}=\sigma_{33}\leq 0$. This is a type of
"hydrostatic" compression in the 2-
3 plane. Fiber bundles have been
shown to support these kind of
loads elastically with a strong
non-linear response. For loads in
the range of the pressures applied
during processing, the stiffness of
the fiber bundle is usually well
below 1/100 of the transverse
modulus for the fiber. Note that
in general this is a difficult
stress to apply. If the two
stresses are not exactly equal,
some viscous slipping effects can
be noted [1,2].

4) $\sigma_{23}\neq 0$. This shearing mode occurs, for example, when $\sigma_{22}\neq\sigma_{33}$.
Cogswell [8] has observed this
deformation mode for thermoplastic
composites and found that there is
a yield stress on the order of
10^3Pa followed by a region where
the slip velocity is proportional
to the shear stress. He observes
that the composite viscosity,
$\eta\approx 30\eta_{TP}$ where η_{TP}=shear viscosity
of the thermoplastic resin. There
is also some evidence of deformation hardening at large strains.
This is probably due to fiber
entanglement [7,8].

5) $\sigma_{22}\leq 0, \sigma_{33}=0$. This is a squeezing flow deformation mode which
probably leads to a viscoelastic
response. From measurements which
we have conducted on graphite epoxy
prepregs heated to 38°C (100°F), we
were able to describe the gross
spreading behavior assuming shear
deformation in the core and using a
non-Newtonian power law viscosity
[7]. Whether shear actually does
take place in the core as opposed
to slipping at the boundary depends
on the presence of resin rich
layers and needs to be confirmed.

6) $\sigma_{12}\neq 0$ and/or $\sigma_{13}\neq 0$. This shearing mode has also been observed by
Cogswell [8] for thermoplastic composites. He has observed a yield
stress at about 10^3Pa followed by
viscous slip where $\eta\approx 30\eta_{TP}$.

DEFORMATION BEHAVIOR ANALYSIS

Based on the above observations we
proposed the following continuum
mechanics model which captures many
of the major features described
above. The key to this development
is to subdivide the stress into
those components which cause
elastic response and those which
cause a viscous response. We start
by defining the stress carried by
the fiber bundle as follows,

$$\sigma_{ij} = P_{ij} + \tau_{ij} \qquad (1)$$

Here P_{ij} is called the "cylindrical" state of stress, where

$$P_{11} = \sigma_1$$
$$P_{22} = P_{33} = \frac{1}{2}(\sigma_{22} + \sigma_{33})$$
$$P_{ij} = 0 \quad \text{where } i \neq j$$
$$(2)$$

τ_{ij} is called the "deviatoric"
stress, it is simply defined as the
difference between the fiber stress
and the cylindrical stress,

$$\tau_{ij} = \sigma_{ij} - P_{ij} \qquad (3)$$

These are related to the total
stress carried by the composite T_{ij}
by,

$$T_{ij} = \sigma_{ij} - p_r \delta_{ij} \qquad (4)$$

Where δ_{ij} = Kronecker delta (δ_{ij}=1,
i=j; δ_{ij}=0, i≠j), and p_r=resin
pressure. However, for our discussion in this paper we assume p_r=0.
The partitioning of stress as shown
in equation (1) allows us then to
propose that the composite will
respond elastically to states of
stress $p_{ij}\neq 0$, and viscously to
states of stress $\tau_{ij}\neq 0$. The proposed constitutive equations are
most conveniently written in contracted form as,

$$P_i = C_{ij} \epsilon_j \quad (i,j = 1,2) \qquad (5)$$

$$\tau_i = \eta_{ij} \dot{\gamma}_j$$
$$(i,j = 1,2,\ldots,6) \qquad (6)$$

where

$$\epsilon_1 = \frac{\partial u_1}{\partial x_1}$$

$$\epsilon_2 = \frac{1}{2} \left(\frac{\partial u_2}{\partial x_2} + \frac{\partial u_3}{\partial x_3} \right)$$

(7)

Note that these strains are written in terms of Eulerian strains. In the axial direction this will not introduce any large errors since the strains are small. In the transverse direction, however, either the incremental form, or the fiber volume fraction V_f, which accounts for the stretch or contraction of the material, must be used since the deformation is large. The term $\dot{\gamma}_{ij}$ are the usual rate of deformation tensor terms as given in [9,10,11]. Note that there only two important stresses shown in equation (5) which will induce elastic responses. Our present work will concentrate on evaluating the stiffness terms C_{ij} quantitatively.

FIBER BUNDLE ELASTIC BEHAVIOR

In order to describe the nonlinear deformation behavior of the fiber bundle, an incremental form of the fiber deformation will be used,

$$\Delta \epsilon_i = [S_{ij}(\sigma_o, \epsilon_o)] \, \Delta \sigma_j$$

$$(i,j = 1,2)$$

(8)

where the usual form of stress and strain are used, and S_{ij} terms are the compliance in different directions and the subscript "o" refers to the reference state. This expression is physically identical to (5). Here S_{11} is the longitudinal compliance of the fiber bundle, S_{22} is the transverse bulk compliance, and S_{12} and S_{21} reflect the coupling between the longitudinal stress and the transverse deformation and vise versa. These are so-called "coupling terms" which are related to the Poisson ratio effect. According to the energy balance, $S_{12}=S_{21}$, so that there are only three independent terms. Note that we also have the relation between $\Delta \epsilon_2$ and V_f, which is the

fiber volume fraction,

$$\Delta \epsilon_2 \approx -\Delta V_f / V_f$$

(9)

where V_f refers to the reference state. We also assume $V_f \approx A_f$, which is the cross section fiber area fraction.

The estimation of S_{22} was done extensively in our previous work [1,2]. The basic assumption was that the fiber bundle responded to the transverse loads by bending between multiple contact points which were resulted from either the waviness of the fiber or the misalignment of the fibers during the process. S_{22} was found to be a function of V_f, and can be expressed as,

$$S_{22} = \left(\frac{\sqrt{V_a}}{\sqrt{V_f}} - 1 \right)^5 \div$$

$$\left\{ A_s \frac{\sqrt{V_a}}{\sqrt{V_o}} \left[2.5 - 0.5 \frac{\sqrt{V_f}}{\sqrt{V_a}} - 2 \frac{\sqrt{V_o}}{\sqrt{V_f}} \right] \right\}$$

(10)

where A_s is the spring constant which is equal to 4.1×10^2 Pa (0.06 psi), V_a is the available fiber volume fraction and is equal to 0.85, V_o is the fiber volume fraction under which fibers carry no load, and is equal to 0.5 [2]. S_{22} decreases with the increase of V_f, and reaches zero when V_f approaches V_a. This relation is plotted in the Fig. 2. The test arrangements used for measuring transverse deformation of the fiber bundle is shown in Fig. 3. Test results supported this compliance relation.

The term S_{11} would be equal to $1/(E_f V_f)$ if all fibers in the bundle were perfectly aligned and straight. Because of the waviness and misalignment of fibers, the stiffness is reduced. By using the energy method [12], we can obtain the elongation of a single waved fiber under the axial tension load, as shown in Fig. 4,

$$\frac{\Delta L}{L} = \frac{P}{E_f A} \left(1 + \frac{4}{Lr^2} \int_0^L y^2 \, dx \right)$$

(11)

where P is the load applied to the fiber in the axial direction, E_f is the fiber stiffness, L is the length of the fiber, A is the cross section area, and $y=f(x)$ is the curve shape. Here the second term in the parenthesis is the contribution of the waviness. Apparently we can use E_{eq} instead of E_f in the expression and choose E_{eq} as,

$$E_{eq} = \frac{E_f}{1 + \frac{4}{Lr^2} \int_0^L y^2 \, dx}$$

(12)

In a real fiber bundle, there are thousands of fibers with different kinds of curve shapes. In order to simplify the analysis, we assume the curvature form for a fiber as $y=f(x)=(a/2)[1-\cos(2\pi x/L)]$, where a is the magnitude of the curvature, and a uniform distribution of the parameter a between 0 and c, where c is a constant. With these assumptions, we can derive the average stiffness of a fiber bundle to be $E_b = R(V_f E_f)$, where R is the reduction factor based on the magnitude of c. From the experiment observation, about half of the fibers were straight or almost straight, while the other half were with some kind of curvature, and the constant c was about equal to r, the fiber radius, which was 4×10^{-6} m [1,13]. Under these conditions, the expectation of E_b can be derived [14], and the reduction term R was about o.86 around the fiber volume fraction of $V_f=0.5$. Experiments on measuring term S_{11} were performed by using uncured prepreg tapes. Strain gages were bonded on to the specimen ends which were cured by special arrangement, as shown in Fig. 5. Tensile tests were conducted on the Instron test machine. Test data of stress versus strain are plotted in Fig. 6. The fiber volume fraction of the specimens were around $V_f=0.5$. The stress and strain relation was found to be almost linear and the reduction factor of

the stiffness was about 0.83. This was very close to the analytical estimation. As the fiber volume fraction goes higher, this reduction number will increase and approach to 1 for $V_f=V_a$. In many practical cases a constant of 0.9 is probably suitable to be used as the reduction factor if the variation of the fiber volume fraction is between 0.5 to 0.8.

The determination of term S_{12} was mainly on the experimental basis. In the experiments, the ends of the fiber bundle were confined and a force transducer was placed against the ends of the fiber bundle. While the transverse compression load was being applied, the induced longitudinal force was monitored. This is shown in Fig. 7. Under this test condition, we had $S_{12} = -(\sigma_1/\sigma_2)S_{11}$, since there was no ϵ_1. In the experiment, the total force in the x direction was measured as F_t, and the cross section area was A_x, so that we had $\sigma_1=F_t/A_x$. From that we had,

$$S_{12} = -S_{11}(F_t/A_x)/\sigma_2$$

(13)

By using the energy method and statistical analysis on curved fibers [12,14], we can estimate the induced force F_t, which is related to V_f. In the experiment, F_t was picked up by the force transducer, σ_2 was derived from the Instron load cell output, and S_{11} was determined by V_f. S_{12} can then be calculated from the test data. However, F_t was found with variations from sample to sample, as shown in Fig. 8, which resulted from the variation of sample conditions and the disturbance of test operations. The test results clearly showed that F_t was indeed related to V_f. Therefore from (13) we knew S_{12} was a function of V_f. To simplify the analysis, a power function of V_f was suggested to express the term S_{12},

$$S_{12} = C \, (V_f)^d$$

(14)

Here C and d were considered as constants. By using nonlinear least square curve fitting based on the test data, we obtained,

344

$$S_{12} = 0.0156 \ (V_f)^{-5.94} \ / \ E_f$$

(15)

where E_f is the modulus of the fiber which is equal to 234×10^9 Pa (34×10^6 psi). The test data and the proposed function are plotted in Fig. 9. The large variation of the test data resulted from both the variation of the fiber bundle specimen conditions and the disturbance in handling fibers during the test process.

With all these compliance terms are determined, we establish a general model for the elastic deformation of a fiber bundle under the process conditions. These terms are all functions of the fiber volume fraction V_f so that V_f is a key factor in determining the fiber bundle deformation behaviors.

CONCLUSIONS

In this work the deformation behavior of a lubricated and well aligned fiber bundle was summarized. The deformation of the fiber bundle was treated as the summation of the elastic deformation and the shear effect. A quantitative analysis of the elastic deformation of the fiber bundle was derived. Experiments were performed to verify the analytical estimations. This result can be used in the analysis of various composite processing techniques, such as filament or tape winding, resin transfer molding, and pultrusion.

ACKNOWLEDGEMENT

This work was supported by Charles Stark Draper Lab in Cambridge, Mass, and the MIT/Industry Composite Polymer Processing Program whose members were Boeing, DuPont, Lord, and Alcoa.

REFERENCES

1. Gutowski, T.G., Kingery, J., and Boucher, D. "Experiments in Composites Consolidation: Fiber Deformation", *Proceedings of the Society of Plastics Engineers 44th Annual Technical Conference*, Boston, May 1986, p.1316-1320.

2. Gutowski, T.G. et al. "Consolidation Experiments for Laminate Composites", *J. Composite Materials*, Vol.21, June 1987, p.650-669.

3. Kardos, J.L. et al. "Void Formation and Transport During Composite Laminate Processing", in *Composite Materials: Quality Assurance and Processing*, Ed. C.E. Browning, ASTM STP 797, 1983, p.96-109.

4. Soll, W.E. "Behavior of Advanced Thermoplastic Composite Part", S.M. Thesis, Dept of M.E., MIT, 1987.

5. Soll, W.E. and Gutowski, T.G. "Forming Thermoplastic Composite Part", *SAMPE Journal*, May/June 1988.

6. Adams, D.F. and Odom E.M. "Testing of Single Fiber Bundles of Carbon/Carbon Composite Materials", *Composites*, Vol.18, No.5, November 1987, p.381-385.

7. Gutowski, T.G. et al. "The Mechanics of Composites Deformation During Manufacturing Processes", *Proceedings of the American Society for Composites*, First Technical Conference, Dayton, Ohio, Oct. 1986, p.154-163.

8. Cogswell, F.N. and Groves, D.J. "The Melt Rheology of Continuous Fiber Reinforced Structural Composite Materials", *Proc. Xth Internat. Congr. Rheol.*, Sydney, August 1988.

9. Bird, R.B., Amstrong, R.C., and Hassager, O. *Dynamics of Polymeric Liquids*, Vol. 1, Wiley, 1977.

10. Middleman, S. *Fundamentals of Polymer Processing*, McGraw-Hill, 1977.

11. Tadmor, Z. and Gogos, C.G.
Principles of Polymer Processing,
Wiley, 1979.

12. Timoshenko, S.P. and Gere,
J.M.,*Mechanics of Materials*,
Brooks-Cole, 1972, p.354-368.

13. Kingery, J."Composite Process
Modeling: Consolidation of Aligned
Fiber Assemblies", S.M. Thesis,
Dept. of M.E., MIT, June 1985.

14. Larsen, R.J. and Marx, M.L. *An
Introduction to Mathematical
Statistics and its Applications*,
Prentice-Hall, 1986, p.133-143.

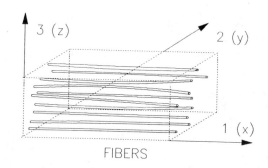

Fig. 1. Illustration of a fiber bundle and the coordinates

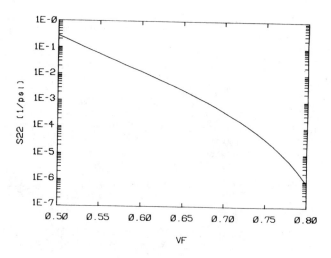

Fig. 2. Compliance term S_{22} versus fiber volume fraction V_f

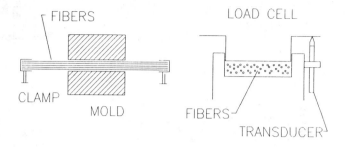

Fig. 3. Test device for measuring compliance term S_{22}

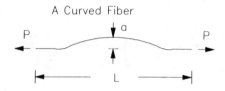

Fig. 4. Illustration of tension load on a single fiber

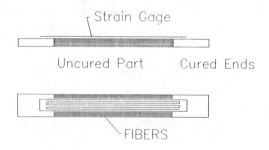

Fig. 5. Test arrangements for measuring compliance term S_{11}

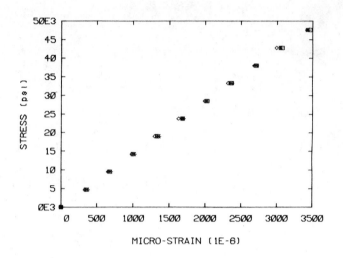

Fig. 6. Test results on stress-strain relation in axial direction
(Sample V_f=0.5, E_f=234×10^9Pa)

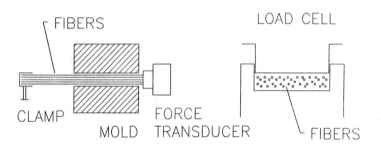

Fig. 7. Test arrangements for measuring compliance term S_{12}

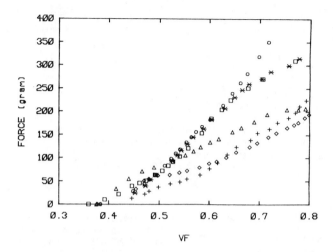

Fig. 8. Test results of S_{12} term measurement -- induced force in the
axial direction while loaded in the transverse direction
(Sample: 0.076m (3 inch) wide, 4 plies, original ply thickness
1.8×10^{-4}m (0.007 inch)

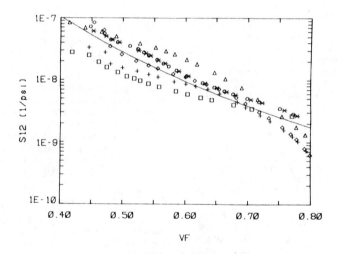

Fig. 9. Teat data and curve fitting of S_{12} term vs. V_f

EFFECT OF ANNEALING ON THE PROPERTIES
OF CARBON FIBER REINFORCED PEEK COMPOSITE

CHEN-CHI M. MA [*] , SHIH-WEN YUR[*]
CHING-LONG ONG[**] AND MING-FA SHEU[**]

[*]Institute of Chemical Engineering
National Tsing Hua University
[**]Material Research and Developing Center/CSIST
P.O. Box 8876-1-10 , Taichung
Hsin-Chu, Taiwan, Republic of China 3004

ABSTRACT

This study investigates the effect of annealing temperature,time on the crystallinity, thermal stability, change of Tg , dynamic viscoelasticity and flexural strength, ect. of PEEK/C.F. composite. DSC, WAXR, and RMS were utilized in this research. It was found that the structure of PEEK/C.F. changed after annealed. Crystallinity, Tg, and flexural strength increase with the increasing of annealing time and temperature. The incorportion of carbon fiber in the PEEK matrix enhances the effect of annealing,and reduces the annealing time.

I.INTRODUCTION

Annealing process influences the properties of composite materials,specially the crystalline polymer based matrix. Annealing time, temperature,cycles of processing , ect. affect the crystallinity, interface between fiber and matrix, and dimensional stability of finished part of composite.

The annealing effects include recovery, recrystallization , and grain growth(1). Nguyen(2) studied the morphology change of PEEK after annealing by FTIR. Gunilam et al (3,4) studied annealing effect by using DSC. X-ray diffraction method can be utilized to determine the crystallinity and structure of spherulite. D. J. Blundell(5) used wide angle X-ray diffraction method to measure the crystallinity of APC-2. From the ratio of h110/hc, one can obtain the crystallinity of composite. DSC,WAXR and RMS were utilized in this research to investigate the effect of annealing on the properties of carbon fiber reinforced PEEK composites.

Crystallization behavior affects the properties of semicrystalline resin and its composites, including mechanical properties,chemical resistance, dimensional and thermal stability,interface between fiber and matrix, etc. Effects of the type of fiber, fiber contents, thermal history and process condition on the crystallinity of semicrystalline PEEK composite were discussed.

II.EXPERIMENTAL

1. Materials

(1) PEEK film : 5 mil thick, I. C. I. Co. ,

U. K.

(2) Carbon fiber woven cloth (3K) : #3101, 200g/m^2,Toho, Japan.

2. Processing of composite

PEEK film and carbon fiber were laminated by using film stacking method. Specimens were preheated at 390°C for 20 minutes, then were compressed at 200 psi for 20 minutes, and cooled under pressure. The finished samples were annealed in a chamber at various temperatures and times.

3. Test methods and Instruments

(1) Flexural strength : ASTM D790-81 method, Instron 1123 type, U. S. A.

(2) Crystallinity : wide angle X-ray diffraction (WAXR), Shimadzu X-ray diffractometer Model XD-5, JAPAN.

(3) Dynamic mechanical properties : Rheometric Mechanical Spectrometer RMS 605,Rheometrics Co. , U. S. A.

(4) Thermal properties : Differential Scanning Calorimeter DSC-II, PERKIN ELEMER, U. S. A.

III.RESULTS and DISSCUSSION

1.Effect of annealing on the crystallization :

Figures 1 and 2 show DSC heating scans of specimens with various fiber contents which had been annealed at different temperatures. It was found that PEEK/C.F. composite was still partially amorphous just after laminated. It can be crystallized and showed exothermic behavior during the DSC heating scan. However,this phenomenon disappears after annealed. Effect of annealing on the samples at such process was illustrated in Figures 1 and 2 . Crystallization behavior can be characterized by two peaks in the figures.The peak of lower melting temperature is related to the morphology of spherulite , and can be explained in term of the recrystallization phenomenon as described by Tung and Dynes(6). When the annealing temperature rised , the activity of polymer molecules increased. Hence,the arrangement of molecules in the spherites structure will be better and the crystallinity will be increased, the melting temperature will be increased as well.

Figure 3 illustrated the effect of annealing temperature on PEEK/C.F. composites by WAXR. Quenched amorphous sample and a series of samples which have been annealed at various temperatures were investigated.There are three prominent diffraction peaks were observed. The highest peak is the (110) plane reflection at 2 =18.9^o , peak height is defined as h110. The crystallinity of carbon fiber reinforced PEEK composites was characterized by the height hc at 2 = 25° above the horizonal baseline extrapolated backward from 2 =38 . The X-ray diffraction curve of PEEK/C.F. composite is similar to the curve of APC-2 studied by Blundell

(5). The crystallinity of PEEK/C.F. was obtained from the ratio of h110/hc. As shown in Figure 4 ,the higher the annealing temperature,the higher the crystallinity.

2. Effect of annealing time on the thermal stability and crystallinity:

Figures 5 and 6 show the effect of annealing time on the DSC thermograms of PEEK/C.F. composites with various fiber contents. Thermal stability , melting temperature and the crystallinity of PEEK/C.F.increase with the increasing of annealing time. Figures 7 and 8 show the WAXR diffraction curves and the crystallinity of PEEK/C.F. composites as function of annealing time, respectively. PEEK/C.F. composite possesses higher crystallinity when it was annealed at Ta=250°C after 40 min.Furthermore, the crystallinity of PEEK/C.F. will be increased slightly for a longer annealing time.

3. Effect of carbon fiber contents on the annealing :

Figure 9 shows the DSC scans of composite with various fiber contents annealed at Ta=250°C for 20 min. Figure 10 illustrates the effect of carbon fiber content on the DSC thermograms of PEEK/C.F. composites at Ta =250°C for 10 hours. The higher the carbon fiber content,the higher the melting temperature which is correlated to the perfect structure at the annealing condition. This phenomenon is more significant by enhancing the annealing temperature (as shown in Figures 11 and 12).

It is shown that carbon fiber will accelerate the annealing effect on PEEK/C.F. and decreases the annealing time at the same condition.

4. Effect of annealing on the dynamic viscoelasticity and mechanical properties :

Figures 13 and 14 show the effect of annealing on the dynamic viscoelasticity of PEEK/C.F. at various temperatures.At here,temperature of tan was analogized to Tg (7). Dynamic shear moduli of PEEK/C.F. composite increased with the increasing of annealing temperature. The Tg of PEEK/C.F. composite is also shifted to higher temperature by rising the annealing temperature. The annealed composites show better mechanical properties at higher annealing temperature as shown in Figure 15. However , the effect of annealing temperature on the flexural strength is insignificant as shown in figure 16.

Figures 17 and 18 show the dynamic viscoelasticity properties of PEEK/C.F. composites that had been annealed at Tc=250° C at various times. The dynamic moduli and Tg increased by prolonging the annealing time ,which is also similar to the effect of the annealing temperature.The longer the annealing time , the more completely the residual stress released , and the higher the flexural strength will be as can be seen in Figure 15.

IV.CONCLUSIONS

1. The higher the annealing temperature, the higher the crystallinity of

PEEK/C.F. composite.

2. Prolonging annealing time shows the effect on PEEK/C.F. composites which is similar to the rising of annealing temperature, and will increase the crystallinity of PEEK/C.F. composite.

3. Carbon fiber accelerates the annealing effect on PEEK/C.F. and decreases the annealing time at the same annealing condition.

4. Dynamic viscoelasticity, Tg , flexural strength of PEEK/C.F. composites were affected by annealing. They are increased by rising the annealing temperature or prolonging the annealing time.

V. REFERENCES

1. R. E. Mehta and J. P. Bell, J. Poly. Sci. Poly. Phys. Ed. , 11, 1793 (1973).

2. H. X. Nguyen and H. Ishida, J. Poly. Sci. Part B , 24, 1079 (1986)

3. Gunilam K. Ostberg and James Seferis, J. Appl. Polym. Sci. , 33, 29 (1987).

4. D. J. Kemmish and J. N. Hay, Polymer , 26, 905 (1985).

5. D. J. Blundell, SAMPE Quarterly, 16(4), 22 (1985).

6. G. M. Tune and P. J. Dynes, J. Appl. Polym. Sci. ,33, 505 (1987).

7. L. E. Nielsen, " Mechanical Properties of Polymer and Composite" Marcel Dekker, Inc. New York, Vol.1 , P.139 ,1974.

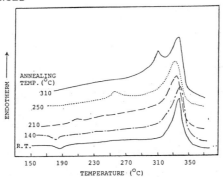

FIGURE 1. Effect of annealing temperature on the DSC thermogram of PEEK/C.F. composite, annealing time was one hour (carbon fiber content : 25% wt.).

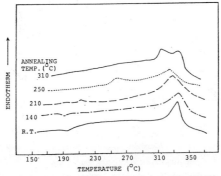

FIGURE 2. Effect of annealing temperature on the DSC thermogram of PEEK/C.F. composite, annealing time was one hour (carbon fiber contant: 60% wt.).

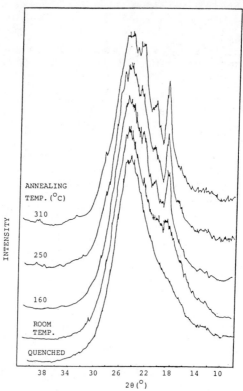

FIGURE 3. Effect of annealing temperature on the X-ray
diffraction of PEEK/C.F.composite , annealing
time was one hour (carbon fiber content:60% wt.)

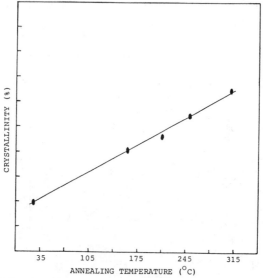

FIGURE 4. Effect of annealing temperature on the crystallinity of PEEK/C.F. composite obtained
from X-ray measurement.(annealing time=1 hr)

354

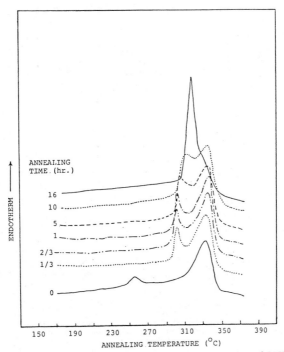

FIGURE 5. Effect of annealing time on the DSC thermogram of PEEK neat resin at $T_a=300°C$ after annealed one hour.

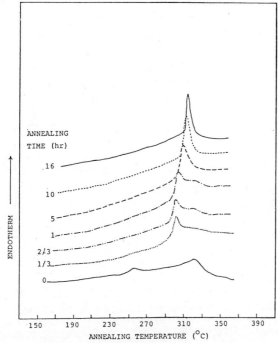

FIGURE 6. Effect of annealing time on the DSC thermogram of PEEK/C.F. composite at Ta= 300°C after annealed one hour (carbon fiber content : 60% wt.).

355

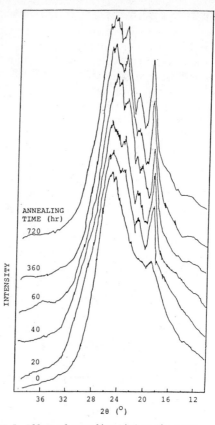

FIGURE 7. Effect of annealing time on the X-ray
diffraction of PEEK/C.F. composite at
Ta = 250°C. (carbon fiber content: 60% wt.)

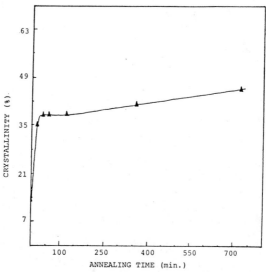

FIGURE 8. Effect of annealing time on the crystallinity of
PEEK/C.F. composite. (Ta = 250°C)

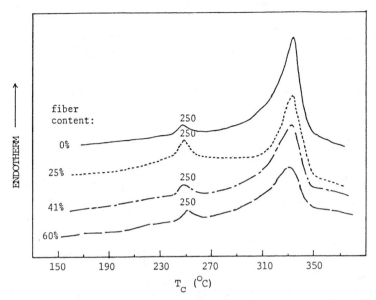

FIGURE 9. Effect of carbon fiber content on the DSC thermogram of PEEK/C.F. composites at T_a = 250°C for 20 min.

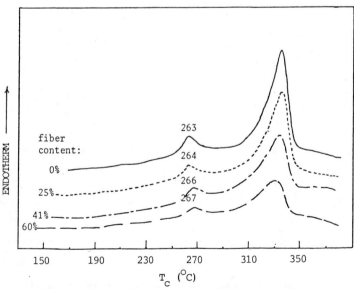

FIGURE 10. Effect of carbon ifber content on the DSC thermogram of PEEK/C.F. composites at T_a = 250°C for 12 hours.

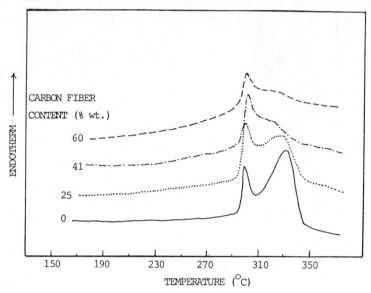

FIGURE 11. Effect of carbon fiber content on the DSC thermogram of PEEK/C.F. composite which has been annealed at $T_a = 250^{\circ}C$ for one hour and then annealed at $T_a = 300^{\circ}C$ for 20 min.

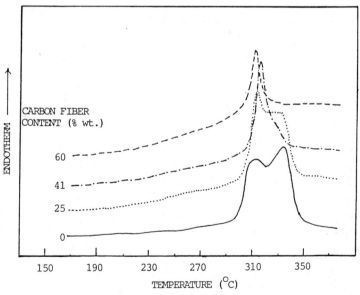

FIGURE 12. Effect of carbon fiber content on the DSC thermogram of PEEK/C.F. composite which has been annealed at $T_a = 250^{\circ}C$ for one hour first and then annealed at $T_a = 300^{\circ}C$ for 10 hours.

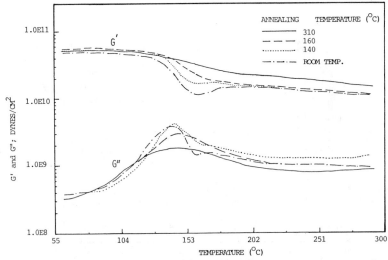

FIGURE 13. Dynamic storage modulus (G') and loss modulus (G") versus temperature of
PEEK/C.F. composite annealed one hour (1 Hz., carbon fiber content : 60% wt.)

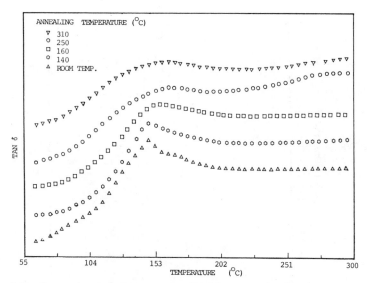

FIGURE 14. Damping factor (tanδ) of PEEK/C.F. composite annealed at various temperatures
(1 Hz., carbon fiber content : 60% wt.)

359

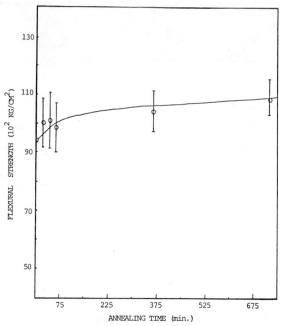

FIGURE 15. Effect of annealing time on the flexural strength of
PEEK/C.F. composite (carbon fiber content : 60 % wt.).

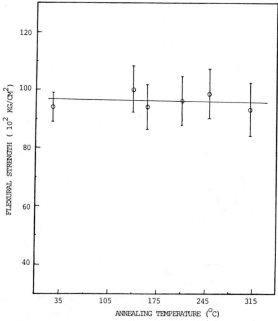

figure 16. Effect of annealing temperature on the flexural strength of
PEEK/C.F. composite (annealing time 1 hr. fiber content: 60 % wt.)

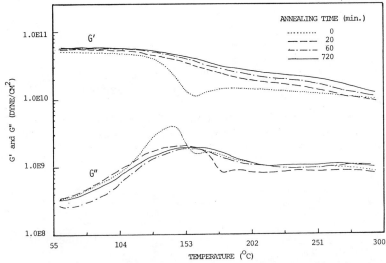

FIGURE 17. Dynamic storage modulus (G') and loss modulus (G") of PEEK/C.F. composite annealed at various times (1.0 Hz. carbon fiber content: 60% wt.)

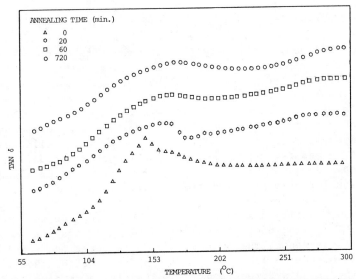

FIGURE 18. Damping factor (tan δ) of PEEK/C.F. composite versus temperature at verious times (1.0 Hz. carbon fiber content : 60 % wt.)

REPLACING COMPOSITE HAND LAYUP TEMPLATES WITH A SIMPLE PROJECTION SYSTEM

Scott Blake
Assembly Guidance Systems, Inc.
400 Fifth Ave, Waltham, MA 02154

Abstract

Hardware templates used to provide patterns and assembly information for assemblers performing hand layup can be completely replaced by a vector scanning laser projection system. This projection system can provide sharply defined, accurately registered graphics on complex curved tooling and materials. Significant time and cost savings can be achieved through the implementation of this system. The CAD interface and registration sensing system can provide additional functions which are useful for monitoring assembly, quality assurance inspections, engineering, and other departments. The system and its operation are described, and a comparison with hardware templates is made.

1.0 INTRODUCTION

The benefits of using composite materials in aircraft structures are partially offset by high fabrication costs. A significant reduction in fabrication and quality assurance costs would allow the benefits of composite materials (reduced weight, better performance, corrosion immunity) to be applied to a wider range of structures. Hand layup of prepreg has proven to be a reliable but costly way to produce composite structures. Most available automation techniques, which eliminate manual layup, do not yield justifiable cost savings. [1] These automation techniques can often not be used effectively on complex curved parts.

This paper describes a laser based projection system which can lower the cost of producing composite parts. This system can replace hardware template tooling used in hand layup with a much faster method of providing assembly information.

A significant cost of producing hand laid composite structures is contained in the production and use of templates used by the assemblers. These [2] templates are used to guide the positioning of the composite plies.

2.0 CURRENT METHODS

The current method of providing patterns, measurements, and instructions to assemblers of composite structures involves mechanical templates. Costs and problems associated with mechanical templates are:

* time, space, skills, equipment and materials required to produce the template. It is often necessary to make a tool to make a tool.

* storage space for templates (templates are the same size as the parts they produce). Some parts require many templates.

* training requirements for assemblers in decoding assembly sequences from the templates

* cumbersome, time consuming, labor intensive handling of the templates. Each ply of material requires a complete cycle of:

1. template removal from storage,
2. registering the template on the tool,
3. deciphering the current instructions,
4. marking references from these instructions,
5. and removal of the template to temporary storage.

* long term storage of the templates when the part is not in production

* time, space, skills, equipment and materials required to modify templates

* the templates are cumbersome to the point where they are often not used to verify that proper assembly has taken place.

2.1 Examples of Assembly Problems

Problems related to current production techniques are well documented. The US Army's Advanced Composite Airframe Program evaluated fabrication problems in a 500 part production run. Forty percent of these parts were found to be non-conforming. "Human error such as mislocated plies, mistrimming, or wrong materials accounted for 36% of the non-conformities." [3]

3.0 THE PROPOSED SOLUTION

The proposed system provides a major enhancement of the manual layup process. Manual layup is a proven and reliable production method. Improving this well understood method is more likely to provide immediate and long term cost savings than elaborate attempts at full automation. It will be very difficult to eliminate manual labor from composites production before computers and robots achieve major breakthroughs in reasoning, vision, and tactile capabilities.

A simple laser projection system can be configured to provide assemblers with all template information directly on a part being assembled. This information includes shapes, measurements, and instructions. This projection system can work on parts of all sizes and shapes and eliminates the need to produce, store, or handle hardware templates which provide layup information and measurements for assemblers producing composite parts.

Costs are reduced by:

* eliminating the production of hard template tooling (saving critical time and materials)

* eliminating storage space for templates during production, saving space on the shop floor

* eliminating handling operations (saving large amounts of time)

* eliminating the need for assemblers to decipher the template which contains information for as many steps as possible on one tool. A simpler presentation of instructions reduces confusion and chance for error.

* eliminating the need for storage space when the part is not in production

* reducing time, training, skill, facilities, and material requirements to modify production routines.

* providing additional references to enhance quality assurance inspections. These instantly available references will allow inspectors to verify proper assembly in areas where this is not convenient with mechanical templates.

3.1 System Description

Traditional template hardware can be completely replaced with a system which uses vector scanned laser light to project assembly instructions and layup patterns directly onto tooling or work in progress. The assembly instructions may take the form of text, or layup patterns and fiber alignments, shown with dots or lines. These assembly instructions and layup patterns are used by assemblers and QA inspectors.

A vector scanning laser system can achieve this function because:

* Laser light is well columnated, presenting a sharply defined dot of light at any distance from the projector. This allows sharply defined light to be easily observed on a highly curved surface.

* Laser light is bright enough to be seen on dark material in the ambient light of a production environment.

* CAD data can be used to electronically generate all layup patterns. Engineering CAD data can be transmitted to the laser system with standard computer communications techniques.

* The system provides instantaneous, preprogrammed instructions delivered by a computer.

Figure 1. shows a all components in a complete workstation.

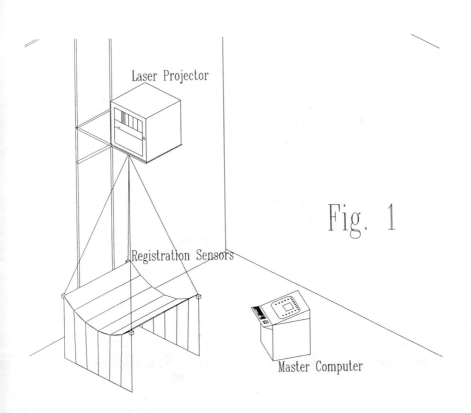

Laser Projector

Registration Sensors

Master Computer

Fig. 1

The main components in this system are:

* THE MASTER COMPUTER, which acts as the user interface (control panel for operators) and creator of the messages and patterns which make up a production routine. The user interface at the assembler level may be nothing more than a bar code reader, CRT or alphanumeric display, and buttons to advance or reverse the routine. The master controller can use floppy or hard disk storage for production routines and any other data generated or recorded by the system. A graphics tablet or tracker ball may be used to manually enter template data.

* THE LASER PROJECTOR: The projector must be mounted with a clear sightline to any part of the tool that will display information. Multiple projectors can be registered and synchronized using overlapping fields to cover extreme contours or very large areas.

The projector incorporates a slave computer which contains the production routines (a production routine is a complete set of layup patterns and instructions) downloaded from the master computer. The projector controller, once loaded from the master computer, allows a projector to function independently. This permits multiple workstations functioning from one master computer.

The projector also contains the scanner amplifiers, beam blanking controller, laser power supply, and laser safety interlock electronics.

The projector must be mounted at a distance above the work of at least 1.5 times the maximum dimension projected. (Example: a 10' part requires that the projector be at least 15'above the work)

* REGISTRATION SENSORS WHICH ATTACH TO THE TOOL. (Four shown here attached to the corners of the tool.) These sensors attach to registration pins, and are removed before the assembly is sent into the autoclave for cure. These sensors provide data on the relative position of the projector and the tool. The projector controller uses data from the registration sensors to adjust the patterns which are displayed, ensuring accurate display of layup patterns.

3.2 PROOF OF CONCEPT TEST RESULTS

In test situations, the vector scanned laser system has proven easy to use, comfortable to observe, and capable of providing all necessary functions required to replace template tooling. The actual operation of the system, at the assembler level, requires no more than simple button pushing. Routines are selected and then advanced or reversed one step at a time.

The images displayed by the system are readable on dark prepreg material, in the ambient light of production areas, well within the safety limits set by American regulators concerning exposure to laser light (Center for Devices and Radiological Health). The projected images can be varied in brightness (always staying below safety regulation limits) and may be comfortably observed over long periods without eye fatigue. Vector scanned laser light has been used to project usable guide images on tooling, dark colored graphite, glass, and honeycomb.

Obstruction of the projected images by the assembler does not hamper the layup process. There are enough points or lines of light displayed to ensure that either the majority of information can be seen no matter where the assembler stands, or with small pieces, that small changes in position of the assembler eliminate shadow problems. The tool itself presents much more of an obstruction to an assembler. The assembler must often move back and forth around corners to position and smooth out plies.

4.0 THE ECONOMIC IMPLICATIONS
   OF THE PROPOSED SOLUTION

A comparison is made between traditional template tooling and a system using vector scanned laser light. Two examples are used to provide projected costs, where cost models are available. The assumptions for the examples are:

* a medium sized, complex curved tool which is 4' by 6', with 40 pieces in the layup kit (plies and honeycomb)

* a large sized, complex curved tool which is 5' by 12', with 80 pieces in the layup kit (plies and honeycomb)

* each ply has 6 scribe marks (eyebrows in each template) per ply

* both tools require 2 physical templates, one for plies before honeycomb, and one for plies laid up over honeycomb.

* templates are stored on end in a special rack on wheels, which is located with easy access to the tool.

* A total labor rate of $52.65/hr. based on the following assumptions:

  * labor rate: $15/hr.   [4]

  * benefits: 30%   [5]

  * correction factor: accounting for fatigue, delays, and personal time: .35   [6]

* Overhead rate: 2.00

* Template handling time:
H=0.000107A $^{0.7701}$

Where: H=hours per template,
A=Area in inches   [7]

* Shop floor space rate:
$28/sq. ft.   [8]

4.1 Template Storage

Assuming that templates are
stored on end in a special
rack on wheels which is
located with easy access to
the tool:

Medium Hardware Template
Storage: $1,680/yr

Medium laser template Storage:
$448/yr

Percentage Saved with Laser
System = 73%

Large Hardware Template
Storage: $4,480/yr

Large Laser Template Storage:
$448/yr

Percentage Saved with Laser
System = 90%

Note: the storage cost for
patterns on the laser system
is unrelated to the number of
patterns being stored. The
space required by the system
remains constant. The cost
listed here is the complete
cost for storage of all
patterns (many thousands)
which the machine may display.

4.2 Template Handling

Medium Hardware Template
Handling Time $291/part

Medium Part Laser Pattern
Selection and Laser Equipment
Setup Time $42/part

Percentage Saved with Laser
System = 85% (Hours and
dollars)

Large Hardware Template
Handling Time $1,242/part

Large Part Laser Pattern
Selection and Laser Equipment
Setup Time $86/part

Percentage Saved with Laser
System = 93% (Hours and
dollars)

4.3 Summary of quantifiable cost savings with laser projection

Storage Space Cost:

Medium Part   Large Part
73%   90%

Template Handling Time
(Hours and dollars)

Medium Part   Large Part
85%   93%   [9]

Fabrication represents 72% of
the cost in finished composite
materials. The savings of 70%
- 90% at key production stages
will significantly reduce the
finished part cost.   [10]

4.4 Other Primary Benefits of the Proposed Solution

Savings which were not quantified in the preceding economic model, but represent areas for significant cost reduction include:

* the cost of producing and storing printed documentation to be used by the shops to create templates.

* the cost of machining or mocking up the tooling required to make the template.

* the cost of laying up the template.

* the cost of producing the markings and reference holes in the hardware template.

* the cost of storage when the part is not in production

* the cost of custom revisions in templates

Laser Templates have costs associated with generating production routines, but even the most cumbersome, complex project will cost significantly less than the hardware template production methods.

Laser templates can be produced through manual digitization or directly from CAD data. Manual digitizing is fast and simple, utilizing editing utilities which make it easy to trace patterns. The time required to trace a pattern and enter text is usually a few minutes. The skill required is less than that required for machining curved surfaces. Changes are easily accomplished either through software or manual entry.

The practice of putting as many patterns as possible onto one hardware template increases the opportunity for error. The assembler must locate "eyebrow" scribe holes from hundreds of possible locations in a small area.

As the complexity and amount of information in a manufacturing operation increases, there is a corresponding increase in the probability of incorrect information. In [11] template use, incorrect information results in errors made by the assembler. When discovered before cure, they require costly rework. If errors are not recognized until after cure, the part may have to be scrapped. Any reduction in these "incorrect information" errors will result in a cost savings.

5.0 THE EFFECTS OF A LASER PROJECTION SYSTEM ON PRODUCIBILITY, COSTS, AND LEAD TIME

When designing a component, the ease of production will have a direct impact on cost. The availability of a computer based replacement for hardware tooling has a positive effect on many of the steps involved in designing and producing parts. Producibility, costs, and lead time are favorably affected in critical areas such as:

* transmitting and implementing specifications
* design detail
* inspection requirements
* process specs
* design team to manufacturing team coordination
* production planning

Many complicated problems associated with producibility are simplified with the proposed software based laser projection system. Equipment availability is simplified because one entire category of tooling (the templates) is transmitted electronically or on disk, eliminating production, storage, and moving requirements for assembly guidance information. This simplification also reduces tooling requirements, since electronic creation of layup patterns can be done more quickly in CAD than through CAD plus machine shop fabrication of templates.

Risk is reduced in prototype or early stage production because hardware tooling is much more expensive to produce and modify. The laser assembly guidance tooling is created quickly and is easily modified.   [12]

This unrestrictive, standardized process reduces the need for special tooling,

simplifies shop flow and scheduling, and provides quality enhancements. The issue of template tooling life is effectively eliminated.

5.1 Secondary Benefits of the Proposed Solution

Secondary benefits resulting from the laser based projection system fall into two categories:

* Functions which might be accomplished by templates

* New capabilities not related to templates

The ability to display a tolerance range with inner and outer boundaries is a template-like function which is not easily accomplished on large parts.

Another template-like function is the projection of "see through" information. Internal structures are sometimes not the exact size and shape that CAD data defines. The real world shape and size of manufactured internal structures can be quickly digitized and projected on outer pieces to assure proper drilling and fastening.

The laser projection system employs a powerful set of microprocessors, registration sensing equipment, a laser, and a communications link at the assembly area. This equipment is idle much of the time and can support additional functions.

Simple functions which are of real value in productivity enhancement include:

* monitoring labor distribution and operator presence

* more detailed assembler assistance

* immediate record of completions

* convenient data collection directly from assemblers

* historical analysis [13]

This data can yield refined schedules and identify problems within the production cycle.

More advanced, future functions which can be supported by the basic hardware in the laser projection system include:

* Control of video documentation of proper ply placement

* Automatic checking for proper ply placement

* Automatic checking for foreign objects which can cause delamination.

6.0 CONCLUSION

A computer and laser based projection system provides many significant benefits which will reduce costs in the manufacture of composite parts. The enhancement of a proven method (hand layup) will simplify implementation of this change in production method. The positive effect which this system has on producibility, lead time, and cost will promote the application and benefits of advanced composites.

REFERENCES

1. Susan Krolewski and Timothy Gutowski, "The Effect of the Automation of Advanced Composite Fabrication Process on Part Cost", SAMPE Quarterly, October 1986, v18, n1, p43.

2. Boeing Commercial Aircraft Co., Optical Layup Tool, Video Tape # 6569, February 1988.

3. Wolf, Bartlett, and Good, "Structural Technology Advancements for Rotorcraft", p1004, U.S. Army Aviation Research and Technology Activity, Presented ath the 43rd Annual Forum and Technology Display of the American Helicopter Society, St. Louis, MO, May 1987

4. Employment Hours and Earnings, United States, 1909-1984. Volume II, Bulletin 1312-12, U.S. Department of Labor, Bureau of Labor Statistics, March 1985, p324.

5. Ostwald, Philip, Cost Estimating, Prentice Hall, Inc., New Jersey, 1984, p47.

6. Ostwald, Philip, p32.

7. Northrop Corporation, "Advanced Composite Cost Estimating Manual", AFFDL-TR-76-87

8. Thomas Klahorst, "How to Justify Multimachine Systems", American Machinist, September 1983.

9. Blake, Scott. "Laser Guidance for Prepreg Layup", Automated Composites 88, The Plastics and Rubber Institute in association with The British Composites Society and the United States Air Force (European Office for Aerospace R&D), 1988.

10. "Fabrication 70 percent of cost for advanced composites", Advanced Composites, page 12, July/August 1988.

11. Robert Ayres, "Complexity, Reliability, and Design: Manufacturing Implications", Manufacturing Review, vol 1, no 1, March 1988.

12. Hyatt, Donald G., "Design Producibility at MDHC", Composites in Manufacturing 8 Conference Reading, Society of Manufacturing Engineering, January 9, 1989.

13. Eastwood and Long, "Computer-controlled Manual Assembly", Manufacturing Engineering, Pg. 89-92, November 1988.

BIOGRAPHY

Scott Blake has worked with vector scanning laser systems since 1973. He began work in this field at the MIT Center for Advanced Visual Studies. Mr. Blake was the Special Projects Manager for Image Engineering Corp. before founding Assembly Guidance Systems, Inc. Mr. Blake has provided consulting service for other applications of scanned laser systems in North and South America, Europe, and the Middle East. He is President of Assembly Guidance Systems, Inc. in Waltham, Mass, producing laser projection systems to replace templates in aerospace composites production.

34th International SAMPE Symposium
May 8-11, 1989

PRODUCTION IMPLEMENTATION OF FULLY AUTOMATED,
CLOSED LOOP CURE CONTROL FOR ADVANCED COMPOSITE STRUCTURES

Sean A. Johnson
Nancy K. Roberts
Advanced Manufacturing Technology and Advanced Technology
General Dynamics/Pomona Division

Abstract

Economics of advanced composite part production requires development and use of the most aggressive cure cycles possible without sacrificing quality. As cure cycles are shortened and heating rates increase, tolerance windows for process parameters become increasingly narrow. These factors are intensified by condensation curing systems which generate large amounts of volatiles. Management of the situation requires fully automated, closed loop process control and a fundamental understanding of the material system used for the application. No turnkey system for this application is currently available. General Dynamics Pomona Division (GD/PD) has developed an integrated closed loop control system which is now being proofed in production. Realization of this system will enable cure time reductions of nearly 50 percent, while increasing yield and maintaining quality.

1. INTRODUCTION

The traditional approach to process control has relied on empirical trials to arrive at a process. Availability of modern "in situ" cure monitoring techniques, most notably dielectric rheometry, has made possible four new basic approaches to process control.

1.1 Quality Assurance Method

The Quality Assurance (QA) approach is outlined in Figure 1. This approach has been standard practice in the elastomer raw material industry for years.

The limitations of the QA technique are such that it cannot promote improvement of finished part quality or reduced raw material cost. Neither does it address process adaptation to best use material which may be at the extremes of the property windows.

1.2 LDPT Method

The LDPT (laboratory determination/production translation) method (Figure 2) is very similar to the QA method, but has one major advantage: rheological determinations performed on test samples are used to adjust production process cycles in response to differences observed.

The LDPT method also shares one of the biggest shortcomings of the QA method: lack of correlation between the laboratory and production cure situations.

1.3 Mathematical Model Method

This method would represent the ideal situation for closed loop cure control (Figure 3). Potential benefits are great: process equipment heat and pressure inputs are redefined at each moment throughout the cure cycle to force part rheological, temperature, and pressure profiles to conform to the predetermined ideal. Each part produced shares identical states of cure, internal stress distributions, volatile and porosity contents, etc. Barriers to implementation of such a system are enormous. All rheological and transport relationships for the material system, tooling, and processing equipment/control system must be known. Diffusion coefficients, matrix-fiber interactions, reaction kinetics, material and tool heat capacities and thermal conductivities, control system transfer functions, and process equipment response must all be expressed in a functional relationship and synthesized to provide an overall mathematical model for the system. Complex ge-

ometries and solvent/volatile generation reactions also greatly complicate system solution.

1.4 Event Based Method

The event based closed loop cure control method (Figure 4) combines features from both the LDPT and Mathematical Model methods; minimizing unfavorable points, but preserving most of the advantages. Event based control is directed to adapting the cure cycle to accommodate rheological variations observed, rather than forcing part rheology to strictly conform to a predetermined profile. This approach precludes the need for an extremely complex control system and algorithms, exhaustively detailed information on resin transport constants and kinetics, and the need for mathematical representation of tool geometry.

The basic (optimized) cure profile is originated and refined heuristically (e.g., by an experimental method such as steepest ascents). A sensitivity analysis is then performed to define the effects of variation in important input parameters. Sensitivity analysis output is used to define time/temperature tolerances (windows) about the major control points in the cure cycle. The end result is a real-time adaptable cure cycle with built-in flexibility with respect to material, tooling and processing equipment, and part configuration.

2. METHODOLOGY

Realization of event based closed loop control is dependent upon a well defined methodology involving a systematic series of steps that address the physiochemical properties of the material from prepreg to finished parts.

2.1 Behavior/Chemistry

The first, and perhaps most critical, step in establishing a closed loop cure control system is understanding the material. For event based control one must know the chemical reactions occurring and reaction products generated as functions of temperature, kinetics, rheological characteristics versus thermal profile used, and any special behavior known to be associated with the system (e.g., brickdust formation in polyimides and crystalline transitions in thermoplastics).

The closed loop control system used at GD/PD is being implemented for a material system based on Monsanto Skybond® 703 polyimide resin. The resin system consists of BTDA esters, MDA, and low molecular weight oligomers in an NMP solvent. During reaction the system generates ethanol and water. Significant amounts of high boiling NMP solvent are also retained within the matrix and given up during the mid and latter stages of cure. This is further complicated by the existence of an alternate reaction mechanism which increases volatile generation[1].

The rheology of this system is affected greatly by the evolution of reactive and nonreactive volatiles. Ideally, the morphology of the rheological profile resembles the curve shown in Figure 5 (for the temperature profile depicted). Evolution and retention of volatiles can affect the curve morphology in many ways. Understanding the causes and effects of changes in rheology curve morphology is the first step in determining closed loop control strategy for a given system.

2.2 Process Optimization

Once basic material behavior is understood, the central issues of process optimization and control strategy may be addressed. In the authors' application, the main strategic concern was the protracted time period during cure that volatiles are released. First, water and ethanol are produced as reaction products and peak during the critical minimum viscosity segment of the cure cycle. Unfortunately, as production of these volatiles tapers off, NMP solvent begins to dissociate from the matrix and strongly volatilize[2].

Timing and extent of volatile generation dominated cure control strategy. Other important factors were: sorting out volatile generated effects from mechanical effects on the dielectric rheology profile, range of lot-to-lot variability in prepreg, correlation of observed dielectric events with actual physical events occurring within the laminate during cure, minimization of laminate process time, finished part quality, and basic capabilities of factory process equipment.

Laboratory dielectric comparisons between well vented and volatile diffusion restricted test specimens during cure verified that volatiles add to (superpose with) the mechanical viscosity contribution of the overall dielectric profile, but do not substantially alter basic morphology. Capacitance ratios (which are very good indicators of volatile generation timing and relative magnitude) also verified this conclusion. All other strategic considerations had to be considered as a group during the optimization.

The approach taken to the optimization/control problem at GD/PD involved establishing a basic set of axioms regarding the nature of the optimum cure cycle and then scaling up from laboratory through to full production.

Original assumptions were first tested in the laboratory on flat panels. Panels were C-scanned, X-rayed, and tested for mechanical properties. Process parameters were systematically varied until an optimum cycle was defined. Experiments were designed based on the method of steepest ascents. An interesting result of the panel process optimization was the discovery that the the polyimide could be successfully processed without intermediate dwells and at heating rates higher than the factory process equipment could accommodate.

The cycle developed for panels was verified and refined on sub-scale tooling in the laboratory. Sub-scale parts were of approximately the same thickness and cross-section as full scale parts, but were scaled down approximately 1:4 in the z-axis direction. Size of the sub-scale parts was designed such that laboratory manufacture and handling was expedient, and so that edge effects could be taken into account and evaluated, while leaving ample unaffected material on the interior for mechanical property verification. Maximum heat up rates investigated were automatically limited to rates attainable by factory equipment.

The optimum process cycle that emerged from the sub-scale part evaluation was the basis for the production phase-in of the optimum cycle for full scale parts. Since geometry varied little from sub-scale parts to full scale parts, process adjustments required were minimal.

Definition of cure cycle event windows was performed at each stage of process development and implications for control system hardware and software were evaluated.

3. HARDWARE/SOFTWARE DEVELOPMENT

Closed loop control (CLC) system hardware and software

development was performed in parallel with process optimization and development.

3.1 Hardware

CLC system hardware is based upon and centered around the Micromet Eumetrics System II Microdielectrometer. Figure 6 shows overall system integration.

The parts for which the CLC system is being developed are compression molded in matched metal die tooling. The porous parallel plate (P3) sensor is inserted into a specially designed sensor/tab area attached to the part. After cure the tab is machined off (no foreign objects are allowed in the part). Each dielectric sensor also has an independent thermocouple input for the channel. Sensor and thermocouple data is relayed to the dielectrometer multiplexer via a shielded cord. Dielectric data is reduced in real time by the system microcomputer and communication with the press controller is accomplished via a customized interface.

Dielectric cure monitoring was selected for in situ cure measurement because it is the most mature technology. The Micromet system was selected as the heart of the GD/PD CLC system for several reasons: (1) frequency ranges are more than adequate to describe cure phenomena for organic composites of interest; (2) hardware is configured as a "black box" system, software driven and controlled, well suited for factory envi-

ronments; (3) essential customer support functions are excellent in all aspects and (4) availability of uniform, precalibrated sensors that cover all conductivity ranges of interest.

3.2 Software

Software is the key to real-time operation for all cure control systems. The basis for dielectrometer control and data reduction functions in the GD/PD CLC system is the basic operational software (BOS) supplied by Micromet with the dielectrometer.

In order for the CLC system to operate efficiently, the artificial intelligence (AI) software elements must be nested within the BOS. The AI elements include the cure event recognition and control action algorithms.

Cure event recognition is accomplished by determining the first and second derivatives of the conductivity. In order to prevent control functions from being triggered by spurious signals, the conductivity signal is averaged across frequencies within each cycle. A moving average of a number of cycles (number determined by the control system designer) is also performed to further reduce noise effects and provide a degree of curve smoothing.

Figure 7 illustrates how the software determines cure events and how the principle of "event windows" applies to cure control. Since there are conceivably any number of combinations of maxima, minima, and inflection points which could be significant to a given material system cure; the software must be able to recognize each of these features.

In the authors' application, it was desired to accommodate three distinct cure events. The first, minimum viscosity is shown in Figure 7a. This corresponds to a first derivative of zero and a negative second derivative.

The second event represented is "gelation." It is taken as the inflection of the conductivity curve subsequent to minimum viscosity, where the second derivative changes sign. The rationale for assigning this as the gel point is convenience. This may or may not represent a change in the reaction rate within the material; this depends on prevailing thermal conditions, resin kinetics, and volatiles/solvents present. What it does represent is a relatively constant, distinguishable event (subject to the conditions noted above) that occurs after minimum viscosity and before end of cure. If a required control action does not coincide with the gelation point, a clock can be started to trigger the control action at a subsequent time.

Cure event three is the end of cure. It is the point at which the magnitude of the slope of the conductivity curve falls below a critical value. This signals that

further change (e.g.; resin crosslinking, volatile egress, or a combination of the two) is no longer occurring at a significant rate.

The windows serve two functions. First, they isolate the specific cure event in "time/temperature space," so that possible pre-occurrences or re-occurrences of specified values of first and second derivatives do not trigger erroneous control actions. Secondly, they provide fail-safes for the specific events. Control system response to specific cure events cannot be triggered below the minimum time/temperature values. Conversely, they must be triggered above the maximum window values. This prevents control system response "pre-triggers" and missed triggers in case of an equipment malfunction.

The cure events and windows shown are specific to the authors' application. However, software operation is flexible so that any type of cure event, time/temperature setting, and control action may be designated for the three windows. Figure 8 details the AI/BOS integration logic and provides additional insight into operation of the event windows.

A critical aspect of the software development was "industrial hardening." This mainly addresses prevention of tampering with control system parameters on the factory floor and what the system will do if a major component fails. To address these concerns the AI/BOS software was modified to incorporate: (1) authorization levels accessible via passwords, (2) redundant operation if a dielectric sensor or channel should fail, (3) default operation to maximum time/temperature window settings if all redundant sensors fail, and (4) a routine to check thermocouple operation and disregard the input if found to be erroneous.

The resultant CLC software is the product of inputs from both GD/PD and Micromet. Both companies independently envisioned the approach to cure event recognition described herein: use of first and second derivatives to describe cure events, time/temperature windows for fail-safes, and averaging within and across cycles to reduce noise and curve smooth. Micromet provided an initial version addressing these needs. GD/PD completed the concept of multiple cure events, added industrial hardening, and provided software for determination and communication of control action to process equipment.

4. SUMMATION

Results and progress, current activity, and needs for further development are addressed in this section.

4.1 Sub-scale/Laboratory

The sub-scale definition phase provided the optimum cycle that is currently in transition to the factory. Fully functional operation of the software developed was

verified in the laboratory on sub-scale parts. Figure 9 is an example of output from an optimum cycle variation run with the full-up CLC control system.

Vertical lines represent points at which the CLC software recognized cure cycle events and triggered control actions. The first line marks the minimum viscosity event. A pressure increase from 40 to 350 psi was triggered. The second line marks the gelation event. No cure control action was taken at this point. The third line marks the end of cure event. Again, no cure control action was taken; however, typically cool-down would be initiated at this point. Detecting end of cure directly from the part would reduce cure time in this instance by approximately 40 minutes. Although only the pressure was varied in this instance, any cure parameter could be controlled.

Operation of the sub-scale press in the laboratory via the CLC system is accomplished by digital communication between the computer and the press controller. However, in the factory communication is accomplished by analog methods. The microcomputer sends a conditioned voltage signal through a digital/analog interface to specify press controller setpoints. Capability of the CLC system to communicate properly in this mode was also verified in the laboratory. Toggling between the digital and analog modes is accomplished by setting a flag in the software.

The laboratory also proved to be the ideal arena to study tooling modification effects. The critical issue of venting was able to be addressed by fitting and removing damns to the sub-scale tooling. This proved the importance of insuring adequate venting without the need to perform full factory trials, saving large amounts of time and money.

4.2 Factory

Given that the cure cycle and basic CLC system were proven in the laboratory, the main consideration for factory implementation was correlation of rheological properties versus position in the part. In production only one position is sampled, and volatile egress from that position is unrestricted versus the bulk of the part.

Laboratory trials verified that rheological correlations for diffusion restricted areas versus unrestricted areas were repeatable and consistent. Figure 10 is a correlation run in the factory environment. Two parts are run in one press load, material in both cavities is from the same lot and roll of material. Channels 1 and 5 (CH1, CH5) are the unrestricted tab positions. CH2/CH6, CH3/CH7, and CH4/CH8 are the correspondent pairs from each part with respect to position. The 3/7 pair is the most restricted position, with 2/6 and 4/8 being successively

less restricted. Note that the rheology reflects the retained volatiles extremely well. Figure 10 reflects a non-optimum cure cycle and restricted venting situation.

The current factory phase-in stands at the point of optimum cycle proofing on full scale equipment, and final verification of hardware and communication reliability.

5. ACKNOWLEDGEMENTS

The authors gratefully acknowledge the contributions of Micromet Instruments Inc., William Provine, Chris Cuciak, Linda Panson, Wayne Anderson, and Robin Lee.

6. REFERENCES
1. Johnson, S. A. and Roberts, N. K.; "Chemical Behavior of Graphite/Polyimide Composite Material During Cure Utilizing Dielectric and Gas Chromatographic Analysis;" 19th International SAMPE Tech. Conference; 1987.
2. Johnson, S. A. and Roberts, N. K.; "New Insights into Chemistry and Processing of Condensation Curing Graphite/Polyimide Composites;" 32nd International SAMPE Symposium; 1987.

7. BIOGRAPHIES

Sean Johnson is a Manufacturing Development Specialist and is the Composites Group Leader in Advanced Manufacturing Technology at GD/PD.

Nancy Roberts is a Senior Research Engineer and is project manager for Advanced Composites in the Advanced Technology section at GD/PD.

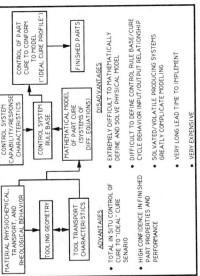

FIGURE 1. QUALITY ASSURANCE INSPECTION METHOD OF CURE CONTROL

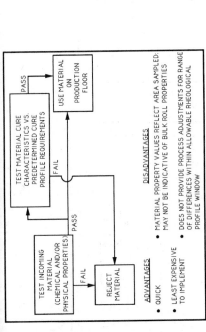

FIGURE 2. LABORATORY METHOD OF DETERMINING PRODUCTION CYCLES

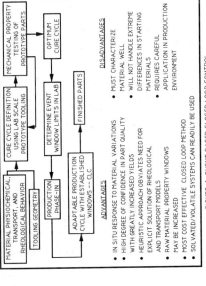

FIGURE 3. MATHEMATICAL MODELING APPROACH

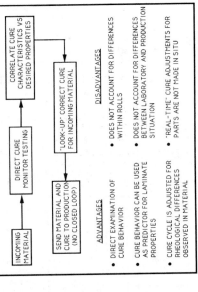

FIGURE 4. EVENT BASED CLOSED LOOP CONTROL

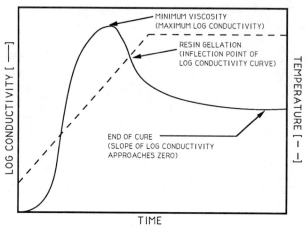

FIGURE 5. MORPHOLOGY OF A TYPICAL RESIN CURE CURVE

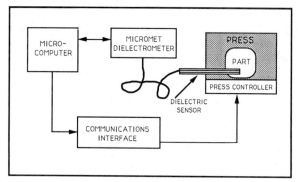

FIGURE 6. HARDWARE SYSTEM SCHEMATIC

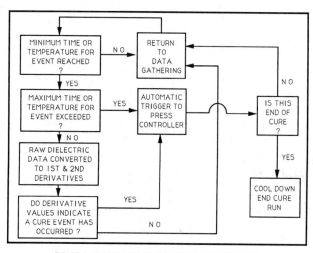

FIGURE 8. CLOSED LOOP CONTROL SOFTWARE OPERATION

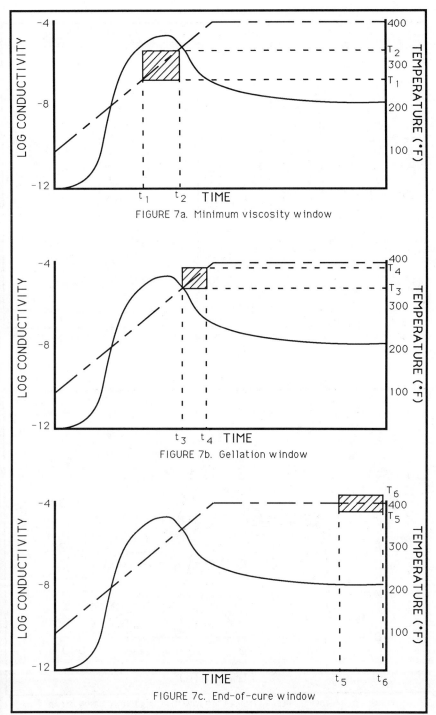

FIGURE 7a. Minimum viscosity window

FIGURE 7b. Gellation window

FIGURE 7c. End-of-cure window

FIGURE 7. CLOSED LOOP CONTROL WINDOWS

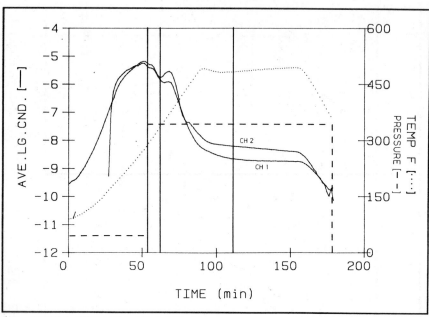

FIGURE 9. FULLY AUTOMATED CLOSED LOOP CONTROLLED SUB-SCALE PART DEMONSTRATION

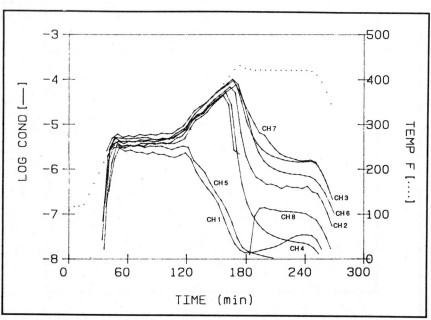

FIGURE 10. FACTORY CORRELATION OF RHEOLOGY WITH RESPECT TO POSITION IN PART.

34th International SAMPE Symposium
May 8-11, 1989

USING ELECTRIC FIELDS TO CONTROL FIBER ORIENTATION
DURING THE MANUFACTURING OF COMPOSITE MATERIALS

Gerald Mark Knoblach
FMC Corporation
Naval Systems Division
P.O. Box 59043
Minneapolis, MN 55459-0043
(612) 337-3054

Abstract

There are two main problems with using electric fields to orient fibers. The first is that the forces are too small to align fibers in the high viscosity resins in common use, and the second problem is that high concentrations of fibers cause dielectric breakdown. The process outlined in this paper overcomes these problems by aligning the fibers while they sink through a low viscosity fluid. The fibers settle out of this fluid to form a mat of fibers with the desired orientation. This mat is then processed into the final part by appling heat and pressure. The problem of wetting the fiber mat with the matrix is accomplished by actually aligning prepreg rods.

Plates of uniaxial aligned 1.6 cm (.625 in), graphite fibers in a nylon matrix were produced by the proposed process. On average 68% of the fibers were within $\pm 10^\circ$ of perfect alignment, 84% were within $\pm 20^\circ$, and 91% were within $\pm 30^\circ$. Tensile tests were conducted on these plates, plates of randomly aligned 1.6 cm (.625 in) fiber and plates of manually uniaxial aligned 1.6 cm (.625in) fiber. Electrically aligned material was 170% stronger and 130% stiffer than randomly aligned material, and was 63% as strong and 59% as stiff as manually aligned material. Plates with two dimensional alignment patterns, such as radial patterns and bolt hole reinforcement patterns, were also produced.

The results demonstrate that electric fields can be used to effectively control fiber orientation. Areas for further research, as well as possible techniques for producing 3-D alignment patterns, are also discussed.

1. INTRODUCTION

Even though advanced fiber composite materials have been around for over two decades, their applications have remained rather limited. This is largely due to the lack of an inexpensive mass production process that takes full advantage of the fibers' stiffness and strength. Current manufacturing processes can be divided into two main categories; those which randomly orient fibers, and those which attempt to align the fibers along the critical stress directions.

Random orientation processes fail to take full advantage of the fibers' stiffness and strength, and are thus uneconomical except for inexpensive fibers, such as glass. Another drawback is that these processes are only capable of producing parts with low volume fractions of fibers. However, the advantage these processes do have is the ability to produce a large variety of shapes with a high degree of automation.

Processes which orient fibers take full advantage of the fibers' properties, but either produce a limited variety of shapes (pultrusion, filament winding) or require extensive amounts of labor (hand lay-up). A better manufacturing process is necessary if advanced fiber composite materials are ever to be used extensively for nonspecialized applications.

2. USING ELECTRIC FIELDS TO ALIGN FIBERS

2.1 Design of the Alignment Process

The ideal manufacturing process for composite materials would be able to use any fiber-matrix system, be able to control fiber orientation throughout the part, be fully automated, and be fast enough for mass production. Many problems arise in designing such a process because many factors are coupled together. For example, it would be impossible to electrically align conducting fibers quickly in normal resins because the viscous drag is too great compared to the relatively weak electronic forces. The electric forces could be increased by using a higher voltage electric field, but only to the point of causing dielectric breakdown in the fluid. To design a process for general application it was necessary to uncouple these factors and solve each problem individually.

The ability to control variations in fiber orientation is achieved most easily by using chopped fibers. At first it would seem that using chopped fibers would sacrifice some of the advantages of the fibers' strength and stiffness, however, this need not be the case. If long enough fibers are used, the average stress in the discontinuous fibers approaches the average stress in continuous fibers. Therefore, a composite part made from long chopped fibers will have basically the same properties as a part made from continuous fibers. The chopped fiber composite

part may actually be superior to the continuous fiber part if the chopped fibers can be better oriented along the stress lines than continuous fibers.

The problem of aligning fibers in high viscosity resin systems is uncoupled and solved by aligning the fibers in a low viscosity alignment fluid. After the fibers are aligned, the alignment fluid is removed without destroying the fiber orientation. This results in a mat of fibers with the desired orientations. A low viscosity fluid reduces the alignment time for fibers to a fraction of a second even when using relatively weak electric fields.

Another problem with using an electric field to align fibers is the fiber-fiber interactions when the fiber concentration is not infinitely dilute. Not only do the fibers physically bump into each other, but conductive paths also form which short out the electric field. Since the final part could be as great as 65% fibers by volume, the fiber-fiber interactions are a major problem. A solution to this is to have the fibers be denser than the alignment fluid so that they sink. This way the fiber concentration can be very low as the fibers sink through the electric field and increase only when the fibers settle on the mold, forming a mat of fibers with the desired orientation. This mat is built up layer by layer until the desired thickness is obtained. The fiber orientation of each layer and even within each layer can be varied by changing the electric field orientation. The concentration of fibers in the suspension is simply controlled by the rate at which fibers are added and the rate at which they sink.

The major problem remaining to be addressed is how to completely wet the fiber mat with the matrix material without destroying the fiber orientation. This problem can be solved by aligning slender prepreg rods which already contain the matrix material. These rods are made by cutting prepreg tow to the desired fiber length. Thus, once a mat of these aligned rods is obtained, the mat is simply compressed and cured to form the final part.

2.2 Alignment Fluid Selection

The alignment fluid must meet many requirements to produce good results. The fluid must be an insulator or else it will short out the electric field. The fluid must also have a low viscosity and a density slightly less than the density of the prepreg rods. A high dielectric strength is necessary to prevent excessive arcing and since some arcing is likely to occur anyway, the fluid should have a high flash point. The nonflammability requirement can be relaxed if the process is carried out in an oxygen free environment or if the apparatus is designed so that the arcing can only occur below the surface of the liquid where no oxygen is present. A low vapor pressure is helpful when removing the fluid from the fiber mat. Also, the fluid must not react chemically with the matrix material or the fibers. Since the fluid is a key part of the manufacturing process it should be inexpensive and nontoxic. For the purpose of development a transparent fluid is necessary to allow observation of the fibers.

Many liquids meeting these requirements are available. Composites with specific gravities of 1.4 to 1.6 can be aligned in halogenated hydrocarbons solvents such as freons and 1,1,1 trichloroethane. Composites with specific gravities in the .9 to 1.2 range can be aligned in light weight mineral oils and low viscosity silicone oils. Ideally a mixture of two or more fluids would allow for precise control of the density over a large range.

2.3 Fiber and Matrix Selection

The only requirement of a fiber-matrix system for use with this process is that either the fiber or the matrix must be fairly conductive. A logical choice would be graphite fibers, which are between 1 and 10 percent as conductive as copper. Prepreg rods of nonconducting ceramic fibers in a metal matrix would also readily align in electric fields. Alignment of nonconducting fibers in nonconducting matrix systems can also be achieved in a couple of different ways: nonconducting fibers (glass and Kevlar) could be coated with a conductive coating such as ion vapor deposited aluminum; the prepreg rods could be a mixture of conducting fibers and nonconducting fibers; or the prepreg rods could be sprayed with a conductive coating. This coating could be removed from the aligned mat with solvents prior to compression and curing if desired.

2.4 Electrode Configurations

Many complexities are encountered when designing electrode configurations, even for simple uniaxial fiber alignment. Voltage applied to two parallel plates will produce a parallel electric field capable of uniaxially aligning fibers. However, since the fibers are conducting they will distort the field. If the electrode plates extend fully to the bottom of the alignment tank the mat of conductive fibers will short out the field. For this reason it is best to collect the fiber mat on a conductive bottom, in order to intentionally short out the electric field on the bottom so that the fibers already aligned will not be affected by subsequent changes in field orientation. If the plates are stopped short of the bottom to prevent shorting, distortion occurs, as shown in figure 2-1. This distortion causes fibers to stand on end near the plates.

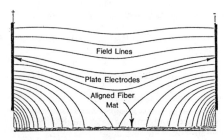

Figure 2-1: Field distortion caused by a conducting bottom.

387

An improvement is to use plates of resistive material. The resistive plates will act like voltage dividers, which will gradually lower the field strength from full strength at the top, to zero at the bottom, producing a parallel field as shown in figure 2-2. Distortions also

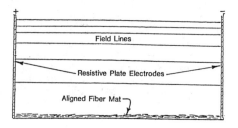

Figure 2-2: Field with resistive plate electrodes.

occur because infinite plates are not used. These edge effects can be reduced by extending the plates beyond the actual alignment region.

It must be recognized that even an initially distortion free field will be distorted by the conducting fibers during alignment. A major problem encountered during previous research was that individual graphite fibers that failed to bond to the prepreg fibers stayed suspended in the fluid (1). These short fibers would build long fibers by fibration. This is where the positive end of one fiber-dipole attracts the negative end of another fiber-dipole, thus forming a long fiber dipole which repeats the process over and over until one long chain of fibers forms. Shorter fibers near the middle of the long fiber chain remain unaligned since the long fiber chain shorts the field in that area. A conductive path eventually forms between the electrodes causing arcing and shorting out the entire field.

2.5 Final Processing of Fiber Mats

Once the aligned mat has been formed the alignment fluid is drained and the mat is heated to evaporate any of the remaining fluid. If a thermoplastic matrix is used the mat can then be heated

to the transition temperature in order to melt the rods together. This allows the mat to be handled easily without worry of destroying the alignment. The mat is now placed in a oven to dry the matrix for the required time. Then the mat is placed on the mold. Finally, pressure and heat are applied to the part the same as if the fibers had been manually laid up. Compression molding, vacuum bag molding or an autoclave may be used to apply the pressure and heat.

3. THEORY

3.1 Qualitative Analysis of Fiber Alignment in Electric Fields

Conducting rods align in an electric field because the field induces a dipole in the rod. The Coulomb force between the ends of the rods and the field cause electric torque which aligns the rod parallel to the field lines. This electric torque is balanced by a hydrodynamic torque which results from the viscous drag on the rotating rod. Since the time for a dipole to form is extremely short, alternating current fields can be used. Alternating current fields have the advantage of eliminating electrophoresis effects, which would force the rods toward one electrode if a direct current field were used.

3.2 Equations of Motion for Conducting Rods in Electric Fields

Electrohydrodynamic theory was first developed in the late 1960's by Melcher and Taylor (2). A detailed derivation of the governing equations for aligning a conductive rod suspended in a fluid can be found in the references (3),(4).

The equation of motion for conducting rods suspended in a nonflowing insulating fluid in the presents of an electric field is:

$$\log \tan \varnothing = \frac{1}{\eta} \left\{ 8\pi\varepsilon_o K\, E^2\, P(q, r_e)\, t \right\} \qquad (1)$$

In this equation, $\varnothing$ is the angle the fiber forms with the field lines; ε_0 is the permitivity constant; K is the dielectric constant of the fluid; E is the applied field strength in V/m; η is the dynamic viscosity of the fluid in Kg/m-s; t is the time in seconds; and $\varnothing(0) = \pi/4$. $P(q,r_e)$ is a non-dimensional function of q, the ratio of the particle dielectric constant to the fluid dielectric constant and r_e, the aspect ratio of the rod. Since conducting rods are assumed and conducting materials have a dielectric constant of infinity, q is assumed to be infinite.

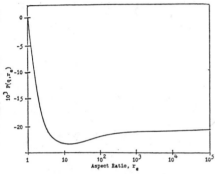

Figure 3-1: Plot of $P(q,r_e)$ for infinite q.

The equation (1) can be rearranged to yield the expression for the time necessary for a rod to align from an initial angle of $\varnothing_i$ to an final angle of $\varnothing_f$.

$$t = \frac{\eta\left[\log\left(\tan\varnothing_f\right) - \log\left(\tan\varnothing_i\right)\right]}{8\pi\varepsilon_0 K\, E^2 P(q,r_e)} \quad (2)$$

It should be noted from this equation and the plot of $P(q,r_e)$, that alignment time is only a weak function of the aspect ratio for values above 50. When examining the functional dependence of this equation it must be pointed out that the dielectric constant of the fluid, K, is not inversely proportional to the alignment time, because $P(q,r_e)$ is dependent on K. For small values of q, $P(q,r_e)$ is greater and thus results in longer alignment times. Note that alignment time is directly proportional to the fluid viscosity and inversely proportional to the square of the electric field strength.

3.3 Numerical Calculations of Alignment Time

Assuming an initially random distribution of rods the time for some given percentage of rods to align within a certain angle $\varnothing$ can be found from the previous equation to be:

$$t_{5^\circ}^{90\%} = \frac{-4.28\,\eta}{8\pi\varepsilon_0 K\, E^2 P(q,r_e)} \quad (3)$$

The standard case of a conducting rod with an aspect ratio of 35, in an electric field of 26,250 volts per meter was evaluated for three fluids: epoxy resin, 1,1,1 trichloroethane, and air. The results are displayed in table 3-I.

Table 3-I: Alignment time in various fluids.

Align Fluid	Visc [cs]	Dielec Const	Time to Align 90% of fibers within 0=5° [sec]
Epoxy	0.54	3.6	185.0
Trich	0.0012	3.4	0.428
Air	1.8×10^{-5}	1.0	0.022

Note: $P(q,r_e) = -0.023$ (for a rod with an aspect ratio = 35:1)

The results of these calculations point out how drastically the alignment time can be reduced if a low viscosity fluid is used. It takes 425 times longer for a fiber to align in epoxy resin than in trichloroethane. The alignment time can be reduced by another factor of 20 if air is used as the fluid. These results point out that a mass production process using an electric field to align the fibers is indeed possible if a low viscosity alignment fluid is used.

3.4 Stress Distribution in Discontinuous Fibers

Theoretically, a chopped fiber composite can have the same properties as a continuous fiber composite if long enough fibers are used (5).

389

Since the longer a fiber is the harder it is to align and process; the optimum fiber length must be determined. The important parameter is the average fiber stress (6). If fibers at least 50 critical lengths long are used the average fiber stress will approach that of continuous fibers and there will be virtually no sacrifice in stiffness or strength of the final part. In reality this estimate may be slightly low since the analysis does not account for stress concentrations at the fiber ends.

3.5 Similarity of Stress and Electric Fields

Using electric fields to align fibers with stress fields has a sound basis in theory since both fields are governed by the analogous equation:

$$\frac{\partial}{\partial x}\left(K_x\frac{\partial\Theta}{\partial x}\right) + \frac{\partial}{\partial y}\left(K_y\frac{\partial\Theta}{\partial y}\right) + \frac{\partial}{\partial z}\left(K_z\frac{\partial\Theta}{\partial z}\right) = -q^B + q^S \quad (4)$$

Where for a stress field Θ is the displacement vector, constants K_x, K_y, K_z are the material stiffness matrix, q^B is the body forces and q^S is the externally applied forces. For an electric field Θ is the voltage vector, constants K_x, K_y, K_z are the conductivity matrix, q^B is the internal current sources and q^S is the externally applied current.

Since the fields are analogous it should be fairly simple to create an electric field that has the same orientations throughout the part as the stress field will have in the finished part.

An example of how this would work is to imagine a three dimensional part. Now imagine a mold with the same shape as this part except expanded by a factor of ten in every direction. Now this mold is filled with chopped prepreg rods evenly dispersed in a nonconducting fluid of the same density. Then this mixture is electrically stressed in the same manner the final part will be stressed by externally applying current to the load bearing surfaces of the part. This will create an electric field with the same

field lines as the stress field will have when external forces are applied to the bearing surfaces of the final part. The conducting rods will form dipoles and align with this field. Now imagine that the fluid could be removed from the mold and the mold shrunk down to the size of the final part without destroying the rods' orientations. Curing this block of aligned prepreg rods would result in a part with the reinforcing fibers perfectly aligned with the stress lines throughout the part, thus making the most effective use of the reinforcing fibers. Note that all the alignment was done automatically without the use of finite element methods to determine stress directions.

It may in fact be possible to place two types of prepreg rods in the mold, one with conductive, strong, expensive fiber such as graphite, and the other with nonconductive, weaker, less expensive fiber such as glass. Now when the dispersion is electrically stressed the graphite rods will be drawn to the most highly stressed areas and aligned, and the glass rods will be displaced to the relatively unstressed areas where they will remain randomly aligned since they are not affected by the electric field. In this way, a part of hybrid material is formed in which the electric field automatically uses the strongest fibers in the most highly stressed areas. Thus, in theory, electric fields seem to be the ideal way of aligning fibers for the automatic production of composite parts.

4. Experimental Apparatus and Methods

4.1 Apparatus

The general setup is diagramed in figure 4-1. A chute with inside dimensions of 15.25 cm (6 in) square and 69 cm (27 in) tall was constructed of .64 cm (.25 in) Plexiglas sheet. This chute had a flange at the the bottom that was bolted to the base. A rubber gasket provided a liquid-tight seal between this flange and the base.

A drain in the base was connected to valves A and B as shown. Valve B was connected through a filter to a gear pump and also to valve A.

Valve A went to the alignment fluid. The pump output was connected to a shower head which hung above the chute. By closing valve B the pump would fill the chute with the alignment liquid. Once the proper level was obtained, valve A was

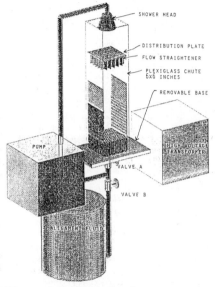

Figure 4-1: Diagram of apparatus.

closed and valve B was opened, this allowed the pump to circulate the fluid through the chute. This produced a downward fluid velocity in the chute of 8 cm/s (3 in/s). Inside the bottom of the chute was placed metal screen to collect the prepreg rods. At the top, about 15.24 cm (6 in) into the chute a flow straightener was fixed. A Plexiglas distribution plate was placed on the straightener. The plate had 6.4 mm (.25 in) holes in a grid pattern so that each hole was centered over a flow straightener chute. Two voltage supplies were used. One was a 5,800 VAC 60 cycle at 5 mA transformer and the other was a Sorenson 0-120 KVDC at 5 mA variable power supply.

4.1.1 Parallel Plate Electrodes

A diagram of the parallel plate

electrodes used to produce uniaxial alignment patterns is shown in figure 4-2. To approximate the

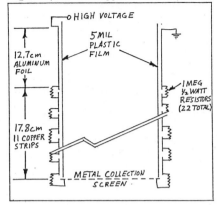

Figure 4-2: Parallel plate electrodes.

effect of resistive plates, printed circuit board material with ten 2.5 cm (1 in) wide copper strips connected by 1 meg ohm resistors were used. These plates were connected to the collection screen with 1 meg ohm resistors also. Each of the plates were insulated with 5 mil plastic film.

4.1.2 Rod to Plate Electrodes

Top views of the two single rod to plate electrode configurations are shown in Figure 4-3. The plates were made by attaching aluminum foil to the insides of the chute.

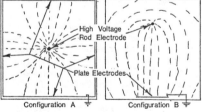

Figure 4-3: Top view of (a) radial, and (b) bolt hole alignment pattern electrode configurations

The rod electrode was made by soldering six 10 meg ohm resistors end to end. Both the rod and plates were connected to the collection screen. The rod was insulated and the plates were not insulated. Configuration A produced a radial alignment field and configuration B produced a field simulating the stress field created in a bolt hole loaded in tension.

4.2 Alignment Fluid Characteristics

Dow Corning 245 Silicone Fluid was selected as the alignment fluid. The 245 Fluid is a volatile, crystal clear liquid, with a flash point of 77°F. It evaporates leaving no residue. It has a viscosity of 2.5 cst at 25°F and a specific gravity of .956. It is also nontoxic, odorless, and inexpensive.

4.3 Properties of Prepreg Rods

The prepreg rods used were Hercules AS4 graphite fibers in a Nylon 12 matrix. The rods were obtained in their final, 1.6 cm (.625 in) long, chopped form from Polymer Composites, Inc. The rods were approximately 3 mm (.12 in) in diameter and were 25% graphite by volume. The specific gravity of the rods was tested to be 1.20. A thermoplastic matrix was preferred for ease of storage and final processing. Graphite-PEEK and Graphite-Ryton prepreg material were also available in .12 mm (.005 in) thick sheets, but the graphite- nylon material was chosen because of reduced lead time and cost.

4.4 Experimental Procedure

4.4.1 Alignment of Prepreg Rods

The chute was filled with alignment fluid to a level 5 cm (2 in) above the distribution plate. The pump was turned off, then valve A closed and valve B opened. Voltage was applied to the electrodes. Enough prepreg rods to produce a plate of the desired thickness were placed on the distribution plate. The pump was turned on. Fluid from the shower head vigorously mixed the region above the distribution plate causing rods to fall one by one through the many holes. As the rods sank they passed through the electric field, aligned then settled on the bottom screen.

Once all the rods had been aligned

the pump and voltage supply were turned off. Valve A was opened to drain the fluid. Next the chute was carefully removed from the base, and the collection screen was removed from the chute without destroying the fiber orientation. The aligned mat was now ready for final processing.

4.4.2 Processing of Aligned Mats

Once the aligned mat was removed from the chute a heat gun was used to melt the rods together. This evaporated any remaining alignment fluid and made it possible to store the mat without worry of destroying the fiber orientation. To begin final processing, each mat was dried at 150°F for at least 2 hours. The dried mat was then placed in the hardened steel mold and heated to 470°F. The mold was maintained at this temperature for at least 15 minutes to ensure that the heat had fully penetrated the thickness of the plastic. The mold was then placed in a hydraulic press. Force was applied to the mold in order to compress the mat to a pressure of 3.4 MPa (500 psi). After the mold had cooled to 120°F the mold was quenched with water. The pressure was then removed, the mold opened and the finished plate removed.

4.4.3 Tensile Tests

Tensile tests of the plates were conducted in accordance with ASTM D 3909. Most plates were .18 to .25 cm (.07 to .10 in) thick. Two samples from thicker plates (approximately 1 cm thick) were also tested according to ASTM D 638. The tests were performed with a computer controlled MTS tensile test machine.

5. Experimental Results and Observations

Using the apparatus, five uniaxial plates were produced with the electric field on and three randomly aligned plates were produced with the electric field off. In addition two plates were produced by manually aligning the prepreg rods. Two plates with continuous uniaxial fibers were also produced for comparison. All the plates were 15.24 cm (6 in) square. Table 5-I lists information on all the test plates produced. Densities of the test plates were consistent within 5%.

5.1 Observations and Problems

Interactions between the prepreg rods and the electrodes tended to reduce the number of rods that fall near the electrodes. This resulted in aligned mats that were thick in the middle and thin near the electrode plates. If electrodes with no insulation were used, the

Table 5-I: Data on plates produced

SAMPLE	ALIGNMENT METHOD	APPLIED VOLTAGE	MASS gr	THK mm	DENSITY g/ml
A	// PLATE	12KVDC	63	2.3	1.174
B	// PLATE	16KVDC	55	2.0	1.165
C	// PLATE	12KVDC	65	2.4	1.172
D	// PLATE	12KVDC	77	2.8	1.180
E	// PLATE	12KVDC	--	7.6	--
F	RANDOM	0	65	2.3	1.194
G	RANDOM	0	70	2.6	1.152
H	RANDOM	0	--	9.1	--
I	MANUAL	--	50	1.9	1.128
J	MANUAL	--	48	1.8	1.164
K	CONTINUOUS	--	74	2.6	1.206
L	CONTINUOUS	--	60	2.2	1.157
M	CONTINUOUS	--	68	2.4	1.213
N	RADIAL	25KVDC	119	4.3	1.180
O	BOLT HOLE	25KVDC	106	3.9	1.175

positive end of the dipoles would be attracted to the electrode. Then as the rod touched the electrode it became the same charge as the electrode and is propelled away from the electrode. Insulated electrodes were then tried. The prepreg rods were attracted as before, but now due to the insulation they could not short to the electrode plate so they just stuck to the electrode. The uneven thickness of the aligned mats was not a serious problem, because when the mats were compressed during final processing, rods from the thicker middle flowed toward the edges. This did not affect the alignment pattern.

Observed processing rates were as follows: It took 8 seconds for a prepreg rod to sink to the bottom of the chute. Rods were fully aligned in approximately 4 seconds. Using the apparatus described, a layer of rods equivalent to approximately a 2.5 mm (0.1 in)

thick final part could be aligned in 1.5 minutes. This is equivalent to laying down 2.5 cm (1 in) of aligned fibers every 15 minutes. No attempt was made to optimize this rate, thus increased rates should not be difficult to achieve.

5.2 Alignment Results

Tracings of each side of every aligned mat were made before and after final processing in order to determine fiber orientations. The results are compiled in Table 5-II.

Table 5-II: Alignment Results

UNIAXIAL SAMPLES	FIBERS ALIGNED WITHIN		
	$\pm 10^{\circ}$	$\pm 20^{\circ}$	$\pm 30^{\circ}$
A	75%	87%	93%
B	67%	83%	92%
C	65%	82%	90%
D	67%	84%	91%
AVERAGES	69%	84%	92%
RANDOM SAMPLE G	11%	21%	34%

The orientation did not change when the mats were compressed and processed into the final plates. Note that the random mat results were close to the theoretical angular distribution of 11%, 22%, and 33% in each angular range. The overall average for electrically aligned mats was 69% within $\pm 10^{\circ}$, 84% within $\pm 20^{\circ}$, and 91% within $\pm 30^{\circ}$. From these results it is evident that an electric field can be used to effectively uniaxially align conducting prepreg rods.

5.3 Tensile Test Results

Results of the tension tests are summarized in Table 5-III. Of the two manually aligned plates produced one was soaked in the alignment fluid for 8 hours and one was not exposed to the fluid. The tensile properties of these plates were nearly identical which proves that the alignment fluid did not affect the results.

Comparison of the uniaxial samples

Table 5-III: Tensile test results

	AV. ULT. STRESS (MPa)	AVERAGE MODULUS (GPa)
ELECTRICALLY ALIGNED AXIAL	66.2	11.0
THICK SAMPLE	77.6	N/A
ELECTRICALLY ALIGNED TRANS	19.3	2.7
RANDOMLY ALIGNED	25.1	5.0
THICK SAMPLE	37.7	N/A
MANUALLY ALIGNED AXIAL	106.2	18.8
CONTINUOUS FIBER PLATE	193.7	15.9

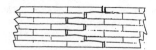

Manually Aligned Sample

Electrically Aligned Sample

Figure 5-1: Failure mode of samples

shows that electrically aligned plates had an ultimate stress 2.5 times that of randomly aligned plates. The modulus was 2.2 times higher for the electrically aligned material. The electrically aligned material was 67% the strength of the manually aligned samples and 59% the stiffness. These results prove that electric alignment of fibers can greatly improve physical properties over random alignment and even approach the properties of manually aligned material to a large degree.

These results are low, however, when compared to the results of continuous fiber samples. The reason for the large difference in properties can be found by examining the failure mode of chopped fiber samples (figure 5-1). The samples did not fail due to fracture of the graphite fibers, but due to failure of the nylon matrix seams between the fiber ends. Because the prepreg rods were essentially the same thickness as the samples and all the fiber ends line up, seams of unreinforced matrix resulted. The theory that material with short fibers 50 times the critical length will be as strong as continuous fiber material

is only true if the fiber ends are not lined up with each other. Thus comparisons between short fiber results and continuous fiber results are not valid.

The problem with the seams would be greatly reduced if prepreg rods of a smaller diameter had been used. Smaller diameter rods would increase the overlapping, thereby increasing the strength. The electrically aligned sample strength was very sensitive to misaligned rods. This is because the rod diameter was essentially the same as the sample thickness and the transversely aligned rod would be the weak link in the chain thereby severely limiting the material properties. If thinner rods were used a few misaligned rods would not be significant and with the increased overlap the material properties would more closely approach those of the manually aligned short fibers and the continuous fiber materials.

To test the reasoning that more overlaps would increase material properties, two plates (one randomly aligned and the other electrically aligned) 4 to 5 times thicker than the other samples were produced. Due to time constraints only one sample from each plate was tested. The random sample had an ultimate strength of 37.7 MPa (5.5 ksi) which was a 52% improvement over the thin sample average. The aligned sample showed an improvement of 17% over the average thin sample strength. Failure in these samples still occurred along the seams. However, the improvements in strength support the reasoning

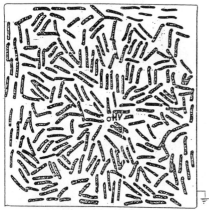

Figure 5-2: Tracing of radial alignment pattern.

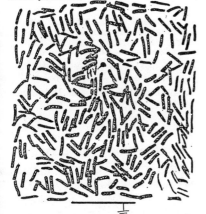

Figure 5-3: Tracing of bolt hole alignment pattern.

that thin prepreg rods would yield results more closely approaching those of continuous fiber material.

5.4 Single Rod to Plate Electrodes

Tracings of the aligned mats resulting from the two electrode configurations are shown in figures 5-2 and 5-3. In figure 5-2 the radial alignment of rods near the center is apparent. Near the edges the rods aligned parallel to the plates due to surface tension effects between the rods and the plates. This radially aligned mat was processed into a plate, but was never tested. The bolt hole stress pattern in figure 5-3 shows a definate uniaxial alignment between the rod and the plate electrodes where the field was strongest, and a rather

random alignment in the corners where the field was weakest. A sample with the dimensions shown in figure 5-4 was machined from this plate using the location of the rod electrode as the hole center. A similar sample was also machined from a plate of continuous, uniaxial fiber material. These samples were tensile tested by clamping the one end in the jaws and bolting a fixture to the end with the hole. In the continuous fiber sample the material above the hole sheared out, whereas in the electrically

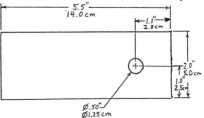

Figure 5-4: Dimensions of bolt hole samples.

aligned chopped fiber sample a tension crack formed at the hole. The aligned sample withstood twice the stress of the continuous sample. This dramatic improvement proves, that even with the thick prepreg rods, complex orientation patterns are producible and result in a genuine improvement of a part's properties.

6. CONCLUSIONS AND RECOMMENDATIONS

This research has proved that conductive prepreg rods can be aligned with electric fields to produce parts with material properties approaching those of manually aligned uniaxial composites. These results, coupled with the fact that the process formed aligned mats at rates of 4 inches per hour as compared to rates of hours per inch with hand lay-up methods, indicates the high potential of this process. Unlike any other manufacturing process for composites this process can produce parts with a wide variety of geometries, control the fiber orientation throughout the part, operate with virtually any fiber-matrix system, and operate fully automatically at rates far exceeding those of manual processing. More research is needed before this process can be applied to a wide variety of parts. With the current knowledge, production of parts with fairly simple alignment patterns should be possible. Although to make this process truly universal, another electrode configuration is needed. One that can produce a wide range of alignment patterns and has the ability to change the pattern without physically inserting and removing electrodes. Electrode configurations are the area needing the most research, and there are many good possibilities that have not been tried.

More research is also necessary on the type of voltage used to power the electrodes. What are the advantages of AC over DC fields? What is the best frequency? Does the wave form shape matter? What is the optimum voltage? Possibly current sensing devices could be used to detect when shorting starts to occur and then signal the field to pulse in such a way as to reduce the shorting.

Different types of materials need to be tried to gain more experience. What is the best prepreg rod diameter? The best length? How can nonconducting fiber matrix systems be made conductive for processing? If denser metal matrix prepreg rods are used, what alignment fluid should be used? Can stronger, more conductive fibers be drawn to highly stressed areas by stronger electric fields, thereby leaving less conductive fibers in the areas of low stress when a hybrid, two fiber system is used? More tensile test data from parts of a different materials is needed.

Although many questions remain, the research performed proves that the process does work. Fibers were aligned. Parts were produced. A significant improvement in material properties for both simple uniaxial alignments and more complex alignments was demonstrated. And no barriers to further improvements were identified.

Referances

1. Knoblach, Gerald M. Using Electric Fields to Control Fiber Orientation During Manufacture of Composite Materials. Bachelor's thesis, Massachusetts Institute of Technology, June, 1985.

2. Melcher, J.R. and G.I. Taylor. Electrohydrodynamics: A Review of the Role of Interfacial Shear Stresses. Annual Review of Fluid Mechanics 1:111-146, 1969.

3. Arp, P.A., R.T. Foister, and S.G. Mason. Some Electrohydrodynamic Effects in Fluid Dispersions. Advances in Colloid and Interface Science 12(4):295-356, March, 1980.

4. Okagawa, A., R.G. Cox and S.G. Mason. Particle Behavior in Shear and Electric Fields. Journal of Colloid and Interface Science 47(2):536-567, May, 1974.

5. Hayashi, T., K. Kawata, S. Umekawa (editors). Progress in Science and Engineering of Composites. The Japan Society for Composite Materials, 1982.

6. Agarwal, B.D. and L.J. Broutman. Analysis and Performance of Fiber Composites. John Wiley & Sons, 1980.

Biography

Gerald Knoblach, a native of Minnesota, graduated from the Massachusetts Institute of Technology in 1985 with a B.S. in Mechanical Engineering. He is currently working toward his M.S. in Electrical Engineering at the University of Minnesota. Gerald is currently employed as a design and research engineer at FMC Corporation in Minneapolis.

ACOUSTIC MONITORING OF COMPOSITE MATERIALS
DURING THE CURE CYCLE

Susan S. Saliba
University of Dayton
Research Institute
Dayton, Ohio

Tony E. Saliba, Ph.D.
University of Dayton
Dayton, Ohio

John F. Lanzafame
University of Dayton
Dayton, Ohio

Abstract

In-situ sensors are essential to monitoring physical and chemical changes in a process, thus allowing automatic control and optimization of the manufacturing process. The feasibility of using an Acoustic Ultrasonic Sensor to monitor the cure of Hercules IM6/3501-6 (Graphite/Epoxy) was studied. The acoustic signal characteristics reflect changes in the viscosity of the resin. The effects on the acoustic response curve of moisture, vacuum, laminate thickness, prepreg to bleeder ratio, ply orientation sequence, and degree of prepreg advancement were investigated. Results indicated that moisture had only a slight effect on the response curve. Vacuum release during a run shifted the response curve, but did not alter the shape of the curve. The addition of plies lowered the response curve without altering the time required to reach the minimum viscosity. Prepreg to bleeder ratio, and ply orientation sequence had no significant effect on the response curve. A general correlation relating the actual viscosity to the acoustic reading was developed. Another correlation relating degree of cure obtained from Differential Scanning Calorimetry (DSC) to the acoustic signal was obtained.

1. INTRODUCTION

In the autoclave/vacuum bag fabrication of composites, knowledge of the time-temperature-viscosity profile is critical since the sequence of devolatilization, fiber compaction, and resin flow occurring during cure is dependent on the viscosity profile of the resin. Therefore, a monitoring system which determines changes in the physical state of the thermosetting resin, such as gelation and vitrification, and could relate its signal to viscosity, is desired.

The objective of a monitoring system is two fold:

(1) To provide a curve, such as viscosity versus time and temperature, based on the response of the material. This curve would determine the time for the application of pressure, thereby leading to an optimally compacted final product.

(2) To provide parts that have consistent properties from run to run by using the response curve of the material given by the cure monitor. The cure monitor would be integrated into an on-line control system. It would send the time-temperature-acoustic reading

profile to a process control unit where correlation would be made to specific properties, such as viscosity of the curing material. Based on the time-temperature-acoustic reading profile, the control system would determine the projected product quality and have the ability to constantly adjust parameters, such as temperature, during the run yielding a higher quality product.

The major objectives of this work are to use an acoustic-ultrasonic monitor to determine the acoustic response of graphite/epoxy (IM6/3501-6) which occurs when ultrasonic pulses are propagated through the prepreg stack during specific cure cycles. Effects of different cure cycles, laminate thickness, vacuum release, absorbed moisture, bleeder plies, ply orientation sequence, and prepreg exposure at room temperature on the response curve were studied. DSC was used to determine the degree of cure of the matrix resin at various stages in the cure cycle, where the degree of cure indicates the extent of polymerization of the resin system. In addition, the actual viscosity was determined for each cure cycle utilizing a Rheometrics instrument. A general correlation relating the viscosity to the acoustic reading was developed. An additional correlation relating degree of cure obtained from DSC to the acoustic signal was obtained.

II. Experimental Procedure and Materials

Apparatus
The apparatus used in this study was an Advanced Cure Monitor (ACM) 101 developed by Applied Polymer Technology, Inc. [1] The ACM 101 was designed to measure both acoustic emission and wave propagation properties of a composite material during cure. It artificially generates signals in systematic repetition so that the properties of the material may be assessed by analyzing resultant stress waves. Using a broadband ultrasonic transducer, the pulser sends ultrasonic pulses into the composite material. Each pulse produces stimulated stress waves that resemble acoustic emission events. The receiving transducer (acoustic emission transducer) relays the signals back to the Acoustic Emission (AE) section where they are electronically processed. Both of the transducers are piezoceramic crystals composed of lead zirconate titanate. An oscilloscope displays the amplified signal received by the AE sensor. Both temperature and acoustic monitor reading are acquired via an IBM PC equipped with a data acquisition board. A schematic of the apparatus is presented in Figure 1.

Procedure
Graphite/Epoxy composite samples consisting of eight-ply laminates with a stacking sequence of $[0/90]_{2s}$ were utilized in the majority of the experiments. For each experiment, the laminate was placed on an aluminum test fixture directly above the receiving sensor. The ultrasonic transducer was placed on the laminate directly above the AE sensor. The system was then vacuum bagged and placed in an oven. A schematic of the layup is presented in Figure 2. For the majority of the experiments, both vacuum and pressure (11 psi) were applied to the laminate during the cure cycle. The application of pressure caused effective coupling of the transducer to the laminate resulting in efficient propagation of sound waves through the laminate.

III. Results and Discussion

For each of the experimental runs, plots of acoustic ultrasonic response and temperature versus time were constructed. Figure 3 represents a typical experimental plot. For comparison purposes, the minimum point on the curve was noted as well as any definite plateau occurring during the run. Since it is known that Hercules 3501-6 cures at 350°F, experiments were conducted with an ultimate temperature of 350°F. Figure 4 illustrates the average response

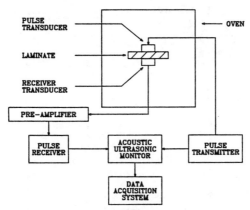

Figure 1. Acoustic Monitoring Apparatus Schematic Diagram.

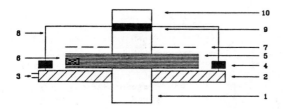

1 Acoustic Emission Transducer

2 Base Plate of Sample
  Holder Fixture

3 Vacuum Port

4 High Temperature Sealant

5 Prepreg Layup

6 Thermocouple

7 Release Film – Porous Teflon

8 Vacuum Bag – Nylon 66

9 High Temperature Sealant

10 Utrasonic Transducer

Figure 2. Typical Bagged Sample Layup.

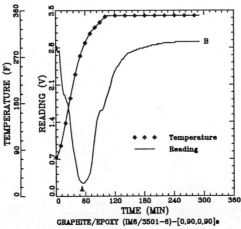

GRAPHITE/EPOXY (IM6/3501-6)-[0,90,0,90]s

Figure 3. Typical Acoustic Response Curve.

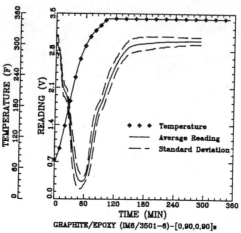

GRAPHITE/EPOXY (IM6/3501-6)-[0,90,0,90]s

Figure 4.   The Average of Four 350-Hold Curves Plus One
Standard Deviation.

curve and standard deviation
resulting from all of the 350°F
heat and hold cure cycles. This
average response curve was used as
a baseline for comparison of
results from other test runs. The
individual effects of cure cycle,
laminate thickness, vacuum release,
absorbed moisture, number of
bleeder plies, ply orientation and
prepreg exposure time at room
temperature on the acoustic
ultrasonic response curve were
studied. Details of each of these
variables have been discussed by
Shappert[2]. Only those variables
which affected the response curve,
including cure cycle, laminate
thickness, moisture, and vacuum
release will be discussed.

Effect of Different Cure Cycles
Many different cure cycles were
used to investigate the changes in
the acoustic response curve due to
the temperature profile. As
expected, acoustic response curves
generated from cure cycles which
did not reach the final cure
temperature of the resin differ
from those cure cycles with 350°F
as the final temperature. Figure
5 illustrates an acoustic response
curve for a cure cycle of 150°F-
hold 5 minutes, 250°F-hold.
Comparison of this curve with
that of Figure 4 (350°F-hold)
illustrates this point. The curve
in Figure 5 goes through the

standard minimum value, indicating
minimum viscosity, as the
temperature is increased. It does
not, however, achieve an ultimate
plateau, indicating a completely
cured material. In contrast, all
of the response curves obtained for
cure cycles with 350°F as the
ultimate temperature level out and
remain constant. Figure 6
illustrates a multiple step cure
cycle more indicative of a typical
autoclave cure cycle. It is
observed in these figures, that the
minimum reading reaches lower
values as the temperature is
increased from each hold position.
In addition, the rate of reading
increase is higher for higher
temperatures than for lower
temperatures.

Effect of Laminate Thickness
In order to observe the effect of
laminate thickness on the response,
experiments were run using the
350°F heat-and-hold cure cycle for
8 ply, 16 ply, 32 ply, and 64 ply
laminates. The response curves for
each laminate thickness is illustrated in Figure 7. Theses
curves illustrate the significant
effect that laminate thickness has
on the response curve. As the
number of plies increases, both the
minimum point on the response curve
and the ultimate plateau value
decreases. The curves flatten out
at the minimum point illustrating

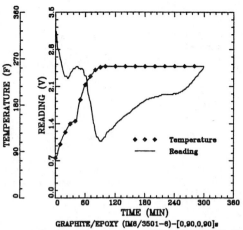

Figure 5. Acoustic Response Curve for a 150-Hold, 250-Hold Cure Cycle.

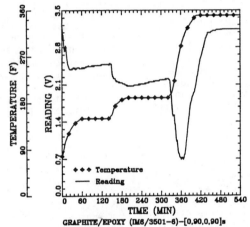

Figure 6. Acoustic Response Curve for a Three Step Cure Cycle.

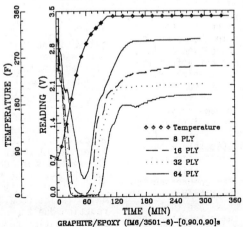

Figure 7. Effect of Laminate Thickness on Acoustic Response Curve.

the limited sensitivity of the monitor. An increase in the laminate thickness increases the probability of sound absorption, increasing the attenuation. Since one would expect the signal transmission levels to be progressively reduced with increasing laminate thickness, the results illustrated in Figure 7 are consistent.

Other factors besides thickness however, affect signal attenuation. These include the resin, fiber, and void content of the laminate. The resin and fiber content influence the acoustic transmission efficiency by virtue of the relative acoustic attenuation of resin versus fiber and the dispersive effect of the small diameter fibers in the laminate. The porosity level in the laminate affects signal attenuation by virtue of its relatively low transmission efficiency and the scattering effect of the voids within the laminate. Thus, in interpreting the effect of laminate thickness on response curve level, one must consider these other factors as well.

Effect of Vacuum Release
The effect of vacuum release on the acoustic response curve was studied. Figure 8 illustrates the response curves for an experiment where (1) the vacuum was applied during the entire run, (2) the vacuum was released after 40 minutes, and (3) the vacuum was released after 70 minutes. No significant change in the response curve minimum occurred, indicating that the vacuum does not affect the time or temperature at which resin viscosity reaches a minimum. The differences in the ultimate response values for each curve can be attributed to the variations in compaction between laminates. The cured laminate exposed to a vacuum release after 70 minutes had a density of 1.478 g/cc. This density, while low by comparison to structural grade graphite/epoxy laminates, was higher than that obtained for the laminate where the vacuum was applied during the

entire run, indicating lower void content resulting in the higher signal levels observed in Figure 8. The response curve observed for the laminate exposed to a vacuum release after 40 minutes is within the standard deviation observed earlier in Figure 4.

Effect of Moisture
Uncured prepreg was exposed to humidity in order to study the effect of absorbed moisture on the acoustic response curve. Samples were placed in a humidifier at room temperature for various periods of time ranging from 1 day to 2 weeks and then cured. A sample from each prepreg stack was analyzed using a DuPont Moisture Analyzer. Those samples with a moisture content less than 0.05 wt.% were considered dry and used as the reference condition. Figure 9 illustrates the change in the acoustic response curve as the moisture level in the laminate is increased from 0.05 wt.% to 0.61 wt.%. Using the minimum on the response curve as the reference point, an increase in prepreg moisture content decreased this minimum value. The time to reach the minimum value is not altered significantly by the presence of moisture. It has been shown in previous work[3] that the BF_3 catalyst in 3501-6 resin reacts slowly with water to form ethyl-ammonium tetrafluoroborate and hydroxy fluoroborates. The hydroxy fluoroborates are ineffective catalysts and are insoluble in epoxy systems. Thus, exposure to moisture can result in reduced catalytic activity and subsequent decrease in reaction rate of the prepreg material. Dynamic mechanical results in studies conducted by Stark et al. [4] showed a decrease in the secondary peak, due to the T_g, in a tan δ curve for samples of 3501-6 resin exposed to moisture, indicating a lower extent of crosslinking for the system. In addition, the primary peak, due to the T_g, disappeared when water was added which indicates a higher extent of reaction due to water-initiated etherification reaction. This

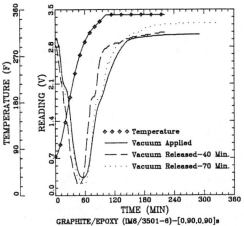

GRAPHITE/EPOXY (IM6/3501-6)-[0,90,0,90]s

Figure 8.   Effect of Vacuum Release on the Acoustic Response Curve.

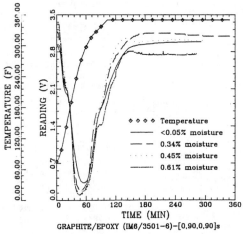

GRAPHITE/EPOXY (IM6/3501-6)-[0,90,0,90]s

Figure 9.   Effect of Moisture on Acoustic Response Curve.

would be expected to lower the viscosity of the resin and is, therefore, felt to be a major reason for the observed decrease in the acoustic response curve.

Other factors influencing these acoustic response values are density, per ply thickness, and degree of resin advancement. For example, the laminate with a moisture content of 0.45 wt.% had a much lower density and higher per ply thickness than the other laminates having absorbed moisture, indicating a higher void content and less compaction. Therefore, a

decrease in the acoustic signal is probable and would add to the effect of the absorbed moisture.

The same changes in the acoustic response curve are observed in both the laminates having increased moisture contents and those with different degrees of resin advancement. Since aging a laminate to a higher moisture content simultaneously results in longer "out-time" at room temperature, the higher moisture content sample may also be in a more advanced cure state at the start of cure. Therefore, distinguishing between the two effects is difficult.

Acoustic Reading and Viscosity Correlations

Acoustic response values and actual dynamic viscosity data determined using Rheometrics were correlated using the Multiple Correlation Program developed by Compuserve. This program allows for user modification of the terms in the proposed fit equation in order to minimize the standard error of estimate and achieve the best possible fit. Application of this program resulted in the following sixth order equation:

$$\ln(\eta) = -0.947455 + 2.05801\ A - 3.40531\ A^2 + 2.59695\ A^3 - 0.989526\ A^4 + 0.182794\ A^5 - 0.0129603\ A^6 \qquad (1)$$

with a standard error of estimate of 0.087771

where:

η: Dynamic Viscosity (kg/m sec),
A: Acoustic Attenuation (V).

This equation was then applied to various cure cycles, and the actual viscosity was compared to that predicted by the above correlation. Figures 10 and 11 illustrate this comparison for two-step cure cycles. The standard error estimates between predicted and measured viscosity ranged from 0.0605 to 0.1071 as various cure cycles were used. The standard error estimates are well within the acceptable level.

A similar procedure was followed in order to correlate the acoustic response of the system with the degree of cure predicted using Lee's model[5]. The degree of cure values generated by this method were then correlated with the acoustic response for all of the runs used and fit to an equation using the Multiple Correlation Program. The best fit resulted in the following fifth order equation:

$$\text{Degree of Cure} = -3.79259 + 12.5502\ A - 12.1504\ A^2 + 5.12825\ A^3 - 0.995542\ A^4 + 0.073545\ A^5 \qquad (2)$$

with a standard error of estimate of 0.35943.

The accuracy is considerably less than that for the viscosity fit, which is to be expected, since the acoustic attenuation in the frequency range used is more reflective of viscosity changes.

IV. Conclusions and Recommendations

A general correlation relating viscosity to acoustic-ultrasonic reading has been developed and tested. In addition, the effects of ply thickness, absorbed moisture, vacuum release, and cure cycles on the acoustic response curve were determined.

Conclusions

The development of this correlation illustrates both the feasibility and limitations of using acoustics to monitor the changes in the matrix resin which occur during the cure of a composite material.

A viable procedure for correlating viscosity values with acoustic reading was developed. An acoustic cure monitor can now be used in-situ to provide real-time readings indicative of the composite state of cure. Through a computer program which utilizes the general correlation, these readings can be converted to viscosity continuously throughout the entire cure cycle. A process control system, containing control criteria, can be developed to adjust process parameters, such as temperature and pressure, based on the values of viscosity determined. This would yield optimally compacted composite parts. Based on the results found when studying the effects of various chemical and physical parameters on the acoustic response curve, laminate thickness and cure cycle, as a minimum, must be taken into account in establishing the control criteria, in order to ensure product quality.

Laminate thickness had a significant effect on the acoustic response curve. The greater the number of plies, the lower the

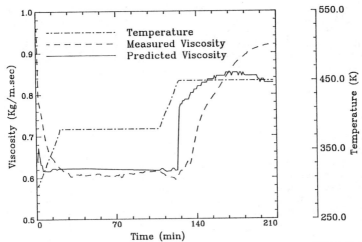

Figure 10. Comparison of Predicted and Actual Viscosity for 225°F Hold, 350°F Hold Cure Cycle.

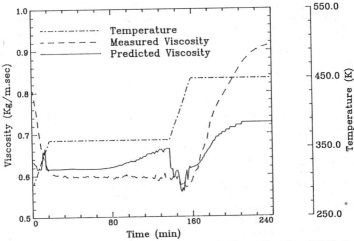

Figure 11. Comparison of Predicted and Actual Viscosity for 190°F Hold, 350°F Hold Cure Cycle.

acoustic response curve. A significant difference was observed between results obtained with 8-ply laminates and those with 64-ply laminates. No significant alteration of the acoustic response curve was noted when the vacuum was released at various times during the cure cycle. An increase in moisture content lowered the acoustic response curve slightly. Unequivocal conclusions as to the effects of some of the variables studied on the acoustic response behavior during cure could not be reached because the effect of differences in the physical properties of the cure laminates (void content, per ply thickness, fiber content) contributed to the differences in acoustic response and could not be separated out within the scope of this investigation.

Recommendations
Additional experimentation should be conducted by monitoring the

laminates in an autoclave. Use of an autoclave would allow for the application of much higher pressures (85-100 psi) than those applied in the oven. The higher pressures would achieve higher compactions and lower void contents, altering the acoustic response curves.

The effect of emissions on the acoustic response curve should be studied. Further experimentation should be completed to study the effect of porosity and/or fiber content level on the response curves for laminates of the same number of plies so as to permit distinguishing between thickness effects and porosity/fiber content effects.

The apparatus used to contain the laminate during cure, and hold the transducers, should be redesigned to accommodate various shaped composites. A viable alternative to the existing transducers might be a transducer which could be implanted in the prepreg stack. This would increase the capability of the monitor and would make it more appealing to the industrial community as a feasible means of in-situ monitoring.

References

1. Applied Polymer Technology, Inc., Acoustic Ultrasonic Monitor Operating Manual, 1984.
2. Shappert, S. E., "Acoustic Monitoring of Composite Materials During the Cure Cycle," Master's Thesis, University of Dayton, Dayton, OH, July 1986.
3. Sanjana, Z.N., et al., "Effect of Aging and Moisture on the Reactivity of a Graphite Epoxy Prepreg", Polymer Engineering Science, Vol. 21, No. 8, pp. 474-482, June 1981.
4. Stark, E.B., et al., "Moisture Effects During Cure of Higher-Performance Epoxy Matrices", Journal of Applied Polymer Science, Vol. 30, pp. 1717-1731, 1985.
5. Lee, W., et al., "Heat of Reaction, Degree of Cure, And Viscosity of Hercules 3501-6 Resin", Journal of Composite Materials, Vol. 16, pp. 510-520, Nov., 1982.

Biography

Susan S. Saliba is a Materials Research Engineer for the University of Dayton Research Institute. Her primary area of research is failure analysis of composite materials. She received a B.S. in Chemical Engineering from Auburn University in 1984 and a M.S. in Materials Engineering from the University of Dayton in 1986.

Dr. Tony Saliba is an Assistant Professor of Chemical and Materials Engineering at the University of Dayton. His research areas center around composite materials process modeling and control using both conventional and artificially intelligent systems. He received a Ph.D. in Materials Engineering from the University of Dayton in 1986.

John Lanzafame is a graduating senior in Chemical and Materials Engineering at the University of Dayton. His honors thesis research included the use of acoustic monitoring to study the cure characteristics of BMI composite materials.

IN-PROCESS RIM ANALYSIS WITH MICRODIELECTRIC SENSORS

David D. Shepard, Huan L. Lee, and David R. Day
Micromet Instruments, Inc.
University Park
26 Landsdowne Street, Suite 150

Abstract

Conventional thermoset reactions are studied dynamically by classical laboratory
techniques such as FTIR. However, these
methods are not very useful for high speed
systems such as RIM where gelation can
occur within 3 seconds and cure is complete by 30 seconds. Recently developed
Microdielectric sensors and associated electronics can be operated with high sampling
rates so that a measurement is recorded
every 10 milliseconds. This paper will first
review recent developments in microdielectric data reduction and high speed measurement capabilities. Several examples of in-
mold RIM dielectric data will be presented.
Critical points in the RIM reaction, such as
time for resin to reach the far recesses of the
mold, end of cure, and de-mold will be
described utilizing the dielectric response.
Finally, several methods for process control
utilizing the microdielectric response are
proposed.

1. INTRODUCTION

Dielectric measurements have been used to
monitor the reactions of a wide range of
polymeric materials. Thermosetting resin
systems are particularly well suited for
dielectric cure monitoring since the materials undergo a large change in dielectric
properties during reaction. While dielectric
analysis has been in use for over 50 years
(1), only in recent years has the technology
been advanced far enough to make in-
process use feasible. Microelectronic
technology now enables the fabrication of
integrated circuit dielectric sensors (2)
which are extremely sensitive and can
function at low frequencies (down to 0.001
Hz).

One of the major advantages of microdielectrometry is that the measurements can be
made both in the laboratory and in the
production environment with the same
equipment. This forms a bridge between
the sensitive and vital laboratory equipment
and the heretofore limited process control

instrumentation; the clock, thermometer, and pressure gauge.

The monitoring of Reaction Injection Molding systems is an ideal application for microdielectrometry since the microdielectric sensors can be easily implanted into a RIM mold. The RIM systems undergo a large change in dielectric properties as they go from liquids in the unreacted state to highly cross-linked solids in the cured state. However, the extremely short cure times of RIM systems (commonly less than 5 seconds gel time) require rapid acquisition and processing of the dielectric data. In normal operation, the microdielectrometer requires between 8 to 10 seconds to make a complete dielectric measurement. Through software manipulation, this time was reduced to 1 to 1.5 seconds per measurement; however this was still not sufficient to detect the material behavior near the viscosity minimum and the onset of cure.

In order to increase the rate of data acquisition, new hardware and software was developed which is capable of making a dielectric measurement every 8.3 milliseconds. This paper will discuss dielectric curing data of RIM systems collected through the microdielectrometer with the Fast Measurement Software and with the new "Ultra Fast" hardware and software.

2. BACKGROUND

The dielectric properties of a material can be measured by monitoring its response to an oscillating electric field. The two dielectric properties measured, the permittivity

and the loss factor, result from dipole motion and ionic conduction. Permittivity changes during typical polymerization are only a function of dipole motion. As a reaction proceeds, the motion of dipoles is hindered and the permittivity decreases. The usual change in permittivity ranges from a factor of 3 to 6.

The dielectric loss factor is influenced by both dipole motion and ionic conduction. The dipole motion contribution is relatively small throughout typical polymerization processes. The ionic conduction contribution results from the motion of ionic impurities in the material. As little as 1 part per million of impurities will produce significant conduction levels (3). Since ionic conduction is essentially a measure of the mobility of ions in the resin, it can be correlated with viscosity prior to gelation and to degree of cure after gelation. It must be noted that gelation is not a dielectric event; it is merely a step on the continuum from an uncured to a cured state. The correlation is strong because ionic mobility and, therefore, conduction, usually changes by several orders of magnitude during the course of the polymerization process. Further, since the ionic conduction term is inversely proportional to frequency, it can always be made to dominate the loss factor if measurements are made at a low enough frequency. Loss factor is thus very sensitive to the degree of polymerization throughout the entire reaction. Implicit in this view is the assumption that the concentration of the ions does not change as the viscosity of the resin changes. Since ionic impurities generally do not enter into the polymerization reaction, this assumption is valid.

Normally during dielectric cure monitoring, multiple frequencies are monitored and the ionic conductivity is extracted from the multi- frequency loss factor data. In monitoring RIM systems, the need for rapid data acquisition allows only a single frequency to be monitored. Therefore, data should be collected at a low enough frequency to ensure that the conductivity term dominates the loss factor equation during the region of interest.

3. DIELECTRIC MEASUREMENTS

The measurements reported in this paper were made with a Eumetric System II Microdielectrometer manufactured by Micromet Instruments, Inc. Low Conductivity Integrated Circuit sensors featuring a built-in thermal diode for temperature recording were used to monitor all dielectric responses (see Figure 1). The microdielectrometer is capable of simultaneous and independent measurements of both permittivity and loss factor at frequencies ranging from .005 to 10,000 Hz. The instrument is driven by an IBM PC or equivalent using software provided by the manufacturer.

During normal operation, the microdielectrometer makes measurements every 8 to 10 seconds. During this time the microdielectrometer generates an excitation signal at a given frequency, measures the change in gain and phase of the response signal (which is a function of the dielectric properties of the material), converts the gain and phase data into permittivity and loss factor measurements, takes a temperature reading, and transmits the data to the computer for plotting and storage.

Dielectric measurements taken with the Fast Measurement Software record dielectric and temperature data every 2 to 3 seconds or only dielectric measurements every 1 to 1.5 seconds, depending on the operating rate of the computer. This increased sampling rate is obtained by storing the raw gain, phase, and temperature data in the microdielectrometer memory until the test is completed. The gain and phase data is then converted to permittivity and loss factor and transmitted along with temperature to the computer for data storage. The data may then be viewed and manipulated through the plotting program.

The "Ultra Fast" measurement option takes 1200 measurements during a user selectable period from a minimum of 10 seconds to a maximum of 200 seconds. The 1200 measurements are distributed evenly throughout the selected testing time (10-200 seconds). This translates into one data point every 8.3 milliseconds at its fastest sampling rate or every 0.167 seconds over the longest run time. These sampling rates are achieved by using analog signal processing to obtain continuous gain and phase data which are measured and stored in the microdielectrometer. Upon completion of the run the data is converted to permittivity and loss factor and transferred along with temperature to the computer for storage.

The dielectric data discussed in this paper were obtained in heated RIM molds by taping a Low Conductivity Integrated Circuit Sensor in the desired location so that the 14 inch lead extended out of the mold. After closing the mold, the sensor was connected to the microdielectrometer interface by connector cables. Dielectric measurements were initiated just prior to the injection of the resin into the mold. This ensures the capture of the entire cure.

4. DISCUSSION

The 100 Hz loss factor data obtained during the curing of a relatively slow curing RIM system in a 104 C (220 F) mold is shown in Figure 2. The measurements were made using the Fast Measurement Software so that data points were collected approximately every 3 seconds. The sharp increase in the loss factor data after about 10 seconds indicates the point at which the resin made full contact with the sensor. The loss factor then increased gradually until it reached its viscosity minimum (loss factor maximum) after about 30 seconds. The onset of reaction is indicated by the rapid decrease in the loss factor resulting from decreased ionic mobility as cross-linking occurs. After about 80 seconds had elapsed, the rate of decrease in the loss factor lessens as the rate of reaction decreases. For the remainder of the cure the slope of the loss factor is near zero which normally indicates that the cure is complete. However, the loss factor level is relatively low at the end of cure and may be significantly affected by dipole influences. When this occurs the loss factor data

is no longer conductivity dominated and is not as sensitive to any additional cross-linking that may occur. To maximize the conductivity contribution to the loss factor and the sensitivity to the end of cure, measurements should be taken at frequencies lower than 100 Hz.

The 100 Hz loss factor data obtained from a sensor located in the flash portion of a shear mold is shown in Figure 3. No temperature data was recorded which enabled the Fast Measurement Software to obtain data points every 1.5 seconds. The resin made contact with the sensor at what appears to be a point just past the viscosity minimum (loss factor maximum) of the resin. The loss factor then decreased rapidly as curing occurred and began to level after 30 seconds. Once again, the loss factor level at the end of cure is relatively low and conductivity may not be dominant. Data should be taken at a lower frequency if the true end of cure is to be monitored. It is interesting to note that the resin system is near its viscosity minimum when it flashes out of the mold. However, the infrequent sampling of data points in relation to the cure time prevents much information from being obtained about the viscosity minimum region of the resin system. Data about this region would be useful in adjusting the resin formulation or mold conditions in order optimize filling the mold and reducing flash.

The 100 Hz loss factor data collected during the curing of a polyurethane/urea resin system is shown in Figure 4. Data points were taken every 3 seconds with the Fast

Measurement Software. In this experiment, a data point was obtained just before the resin reached its viscosity minimum (loss factor maximum). After the second data point, the loss factor decreased rapidly as the reaction began. Evidently the onset of cross-linking occurred just after the material reached the sensor location. The time from resin contact with the sensor at a specified mold location to the onset of cure at that location provides valuable information on the filling of the mold. While the data from this experiment follows the curing portion of the curve very well, the viscosity minimum is defined by only three points. It is desirable to sample data more rapidly in order to obtain more complete information about the material behavior near the viscosity minimum.

The "Ultra Fast" Measurement Option (Figure 5) was developed in order to collect more data points in the viscosity minimum region of RIM reactions. In Figure 6, data points at 1000 Hz were collected every 28 milliseconds with this option during the reaction of a polyurethane/urea RIM system. Both the permittivity (E') and Log Ion Viscosity, a value calculated from the loss factor data, are shown for a sensor near the back corner of the mold (a dead area not near a resin inlet port). Since data collection was initiated before injection, the permittivity is near 1 (for air) and Log Ion Viscosity is not detected for the first few seconds. When the resin contacts the sensor, the permittivity jumps to nearly 20 and the Log Ion Viscosity appears on scale. Although the permittivity can be used to monitor resin contact and initial cure, it is not sensitive to the later stages of cure. The Log Ion Viscosity (the inverse of conductivity) is related to actual viscosity before gelation and rigidity after gelation. This value increases rapidly as the resin makes contact with the back of the mold where the sensor is located. An initial decrease in viscosity might be expected close to the mixing chamber since the resin temperature is increased from 71 C (160 F) to 88 C (190 F) as it enters the mold. However, the reaction appears to dominate immediately and resin viscosity is increasing by the time it reaches the back of the mold. Although the viscosity minimum was not observed in this experiment, the rapid collection of data points clearly indicates the resin was increasing in viscosity by the time it made contact with the sensor. With slower data collection, up to three seconds of data may be missed once resin contact occurs. After about 2 to 3 seconds, the rate of increase in Ion Viscosity slows markedly but continues to increase until the part is demolded. This shows that additional reaction is occurring.

Figure 7 shows the comparison of the the Ion Viscosity data from Figure 6 (at 1000 Hz) with data collected on an identical cure at 100 Hz. The two curves superimpose showing that the data are dominated by ionic movement (conductivity) rather than static dipoles. Thus, either frequency is acceptable for monitoring the viscosity minimum region as well as the end of cure.

The mix ratio of the components in a RIM system is critical in obtaining a good part.

To determine if changes in the mix ratio could be detected through dielectric measurements, experiments at different mix ratios were performed using a polyol/isocyanate RIM system. Indices of 70, 90, 110, and 130 were used where 110 represented the optimum mix ratio and a lower index indicated less isocyanate. Duplicate experiments were performed at indices of 90, 110, and 130 and the loss factors plotted in Figure 8. Data points were collected approximately every 60 seconds using the Fast Measurement Software and the first point for each experiment has been adjusted on the plot to have the same approximate starting time. The data show that the experiments at the 110 optimum index had the lowest loss factor during the reaction. As the index deviated from the optimum, the loss factors trended toward higher levels. The reproducibility of the 110 index experiments was very good. However, some differences were observed within the 90 and 130 index experiments. The Permittivity data suggested that it may be very sensitive to changes in mix ratio; however, the permittivity values from run to run may be the result of air trapped near the sensing surface. Any trapped air could possibly be eliminated by adjusting the location of the sensor or through the use of a reusable, flush-mounted in-mold sensor. The use of an in-mold sensor may enable dielectric measurements to be used to economically determine the optimum mix ratio of isocyanate-polyol RIM systems and to monitor this ratio during production.

5. CONCLUSIONS

The curing of Reaction Injection Molding (RIM) systems can be monitored through microdielectrometry. Fast Measurement Software which can sample data points every 1.5 seconds is well suited to monitoring the end of cure but may miss valuable information near the viscosity minimum of the resin. A new "Ultra Fast" measurement module which can obtain data points as often as every 8.3 milliseconds can monitor entire RIM reactions from resin contact with the dielectric sensor through demolding. Dielectric measurements may be useful in determining and monitoring the mix ratio of RIM systems.

6. REFERENCES

1. R. Kienle and H. Race, Trans. Electrochem. Soc., 65, 87(1934)

2. S.D. Senturia, N.F. Sheppard Jr., H.L. Lee, S.B.Marshall, SAMPE J.,19, 22(1983)

3. A.R. Blythe, "Electrical Properties of Polymers," Cambridge University Press, Cambridge, UK (1979)

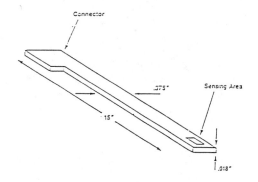

Figure 1: Diagram Of Microdielectric Sensor

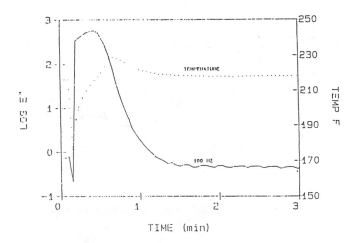

Figure 2: Loss Factor Data From Relatively Slow Curing RIM System

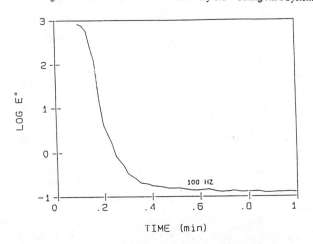

Figure 3: Loss Factor Data From Flash Portion Of RIM Mold

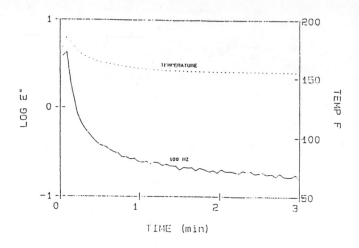

Figure 4: Loss Factor Data From Curing Of Polyurethane/Urea Resin System

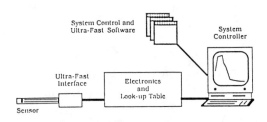

Figure 5: Block Diagram of the Ultra-Fast Measurement System

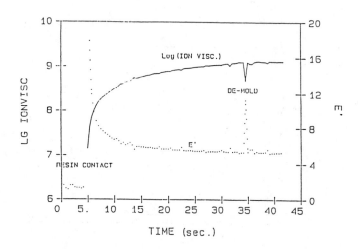

Figure 6: Ion Viscosity And Permittivity Data From Polyurethane/Urea Resin
System Cure Using "Ultra Fast" Module

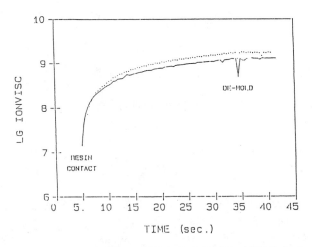

Figure 7: Comparison Of Ion Viscosity Data At 100 And 1000 Hz During Polyurethane/Urea Cure

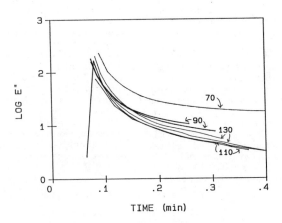

Figure 8: Loss Factor Data of Various Mix Ratios of Polyol/Isocyanate RIM System.

34th International SAMPE Symposium
May 8-11, 1989

MONITORING AND MODELING THE CURE PROCESSING PROPERTIES
OF RESIN TRANSFER MOLDING RESINS

D. Kranbuehl, M. Hoff,
D. Eichinger, and R. Clark
Department of Chemistry
College of William and Mary

A. Loos
Department of Engineering Science and Mechanics
Virginia Polytechnic Institute and State University
Blacksburg, Virginia 24061

ABSTRACT

Resin transfer molding, RTM, of advanced fiber architecture materials promises to be a cost effective process for obtaining composite parts with exceptional strength. A measurement technique has been developed for monitoring the impregnation and cure processing properties of RTM resins. Frequency dependent electromagnetic sensors (FDEMS) were used to directly monitor resin viscosity both in a testing environment and during processing in the mold. The effects of the cure cycle and resin aging on the viscosity during cure were investigated using the sensor. Viscosity measurements obtained using the sensor are compared with the viscosities predicted by the Loos-Springer cure process model.

1. Introduction

Resin transfer molding of advanced fiber architecture components promises to be a cost effective process for fabricating composite parts of exceptional strength. Resin transfer molding (RTM) is a closed mold process which is different from conventional prepreq processing in that the graphite or glass cloth and the resin are combined in the mold to form the composite. As such the technique eliminates many problems involving prepreq preparation, storage and layup. Most important however, the RTM process permits the use of three dimensionally stitched fabrics, textile revited plys, which significantly enhance the compression after impact strength.

The RTM process, on the other hand, replaces the single step cure process with a two stage impregnation and cure process. As a result there are a large number of material parameters that must be observed, known and/or controlled during the resin transfer molding process. Of particular importance is control of the viscosity both during impregnation and cure. In-situ sensors which can observe these processing properties both prior to infiltration and within the RTM tool during the fabrication process are essential.

This paper will discuss recent work on the use of two high performance MY 720 resins, Hercules 8551-2 and 3501-6, as resin transfer molding resins. Frequency dependent electromagnetic sensing (FDEMS) techniques are used to monitor the RTM process both in the laboratory and in the RTM tool. The objective is to use these sensing techniques to address problems of RTM scaleup for large complex parts and to develop a closed loop, intelligent, sensor controlled RTM fabrication process.

2. Experimental

Frequency dependent electromagnetic measurements (FDEMS) were made with a Dek Dyne sensor-multiplexed instrument package* which uses a Hewlett Packard 4191A LF Impedance Analyzer controlled by a PC computer workstation. Measurements at frequencies from 50 to 1×10^6 Hz were taken at regular intervals throughout the cure cycle and converted to the complex permittivity $\epsilon* = \epsilon' - \epsilon''$. Using the Dek Dyne multiplexed system, measurements on multiple samples were made simultaneously side-by-side

in temperature controlled processing tools.

Dynamic mechanical measurements were made using a Rheometrics RDA dynamic rheometer at 1.6 Hz and used to compute the magnitude of the complex viscosity.

Measurements were made on two MY 720 resins provided by the NASA Langley Research Center, 3501-6 and 8551-2 manufactured by Hercules, Inc.

3. Theory

Measurements of capacitance, C, and conductance, G, were used to calculate the complex permittivity $\epsilon* = \epsilon' - \epsilon''$ where:

$$\epsilon' = \frac{C \text{ material}}{C_o}$$

and

$$\epsilon'' = \frac{C \text{ material}}{C_o 2\pi f}$$

at each of 10 frequencies between 50 Hz and 1 MHz.

This calculation is possible when using the Dek Dyne probe whose geometry independent capacitance, C_o, is invariant over all measurement conditions. Both the real and the imaginary parts of $\epsilon*$ have an ionic and dipolar component. The dipolar component arises from diffusion of bound charge or molecular dipole moments. The dipolar term is generally the major component of the dielectric signal at high frequencies and in highly viscous media. The ionic component usually dominates $\epsilon*$ at low frequencies, low viscosities and/or higher temperatures.(1-3)

417

Analysis of the frequency dependence of $\underline{\epsilon}^*$ in the Hz to MHz range is, in general, optimum for determining both the ionic mobility-conductivity, σ, and a mean dipolar relaxation time, τ. These two parameters are directly related on a molecular level to the rate of ionic translational diffusion and dipolar rotational mobility and thereby to changes in the molecular structure of the resin which reflect the reaction rate, changes in viscosity and the degree of cure.

Results and Discussion

Figure 1 and Figure 2 are plots of the loss factor of the Hercules 8551-2 and 3501-6 resins during identical multiple ramp-hold cure cycles. The values of ϵ", measured at 10 frequencies from 50 to 1×10^6 Hz, are multiplied by the frequency. As previously discussed, the overlapping ϵ" times frequency lines indicate the frequencies and time - temperature periods during cure where ϵ" is dominated by ionic diffusion and where the ionic conductivity $\sigma(\text{ohm}^{-1}\text{cm}^{-1}) = 8.84 \times 10^{-14}$ $\omega\epsilon$". The non-overlapping high frequency ϵ" lines, 125 kHz to 1 MHz, exhibit a series of peaks during heat up for both resins. A similar series of peaks is observed as full cure is approached for the 8551-2 resin during the final hold temperature. These high frequency peaks in ϵ" can be used to measure the time of occurrence of a particular relaxation time $\tau = \frac{1}{\omega}$ at the ϵ" (ω) peak. These relaxation times are a characteristic of the WLF preglass (T_g to $T_g + 50°C$) region.

The magnitude of σ and the time of occurrence of particular values of τ can be used to

qualitatively monitor the viscosity. Quantitative measurement is also possible through simultaneous viscosity measurements, thereby calibrating σ and τ with the viscosity for a particular resin system. Figure 3 is a plot of the 3501-6 resin viscosity as measured quantitatively by σ, σ having been correlated with viscosity through simultaneous σ - viscosity measurements. Also shown is the calculated viscosity using the Loos-Springer model (4). The agreement between the FDEMS measured viscosity and the model predicted viscosity is good.

Figures 4 and 5 show the ϵ" values for an 8551-2 resin left at room temperature for 20 days and the 3501-6 resin left at room temperature for 15 days.

For the 8551-2 resin, the 20 day old sample, exhibits much less flow, as seen by lower values of ϵ" and σ throughout the initial ramp and hold The time of occurrence of particular values of τ associated with each ϵ" (ω) peak requires a slightly higher temperature during the initial ramp indicating the increase in Tg with reaction advancement as the resin ages. The magnitude of the second viscosity minimum, ϵ" overlapping line maximum, during the ramp to 177° is also a decade lower due to age. The approach to Tg, full cure, as seen by the ϵ" peaks and the gradual drop in ϵ" during the final hold temperature is nearly identical for the aged and fresh 8551-2 resin, indicating little effect of resin age on the cure process during the final hold at 177°.

Similar affects are observed for the 3501-6 fresh and 15 day aged sample. In light of the shorter out time, the 3501-6 appears to show a greater loss in flow during the initial ramp and hold temperatures with exposure to room temperature.

Figure 6 is a plot of the FDEMS ϵ'' sensor measured viscosity for the 3501-6 resin aged 30 days and the Loos-Springer Model calculated viscosity.

We now turn to using the FDEMS sensor to examine the MY 720 resin impregnation and cure properties during the single step resin transfer molding impregnation and cure fabrication procedure. An 8 ply graphite 8 harness satin weave was used. Figure 7 shows that the resin layer was placed at the bottom of the mold and sensors were placed on top of the first, second, fourth, and top ply.

In this initial study, we focused on using the sensor to monitor and measure the impregnation process. Current work is focusing on using this information to develop an optimum time-temperature cycle for impregnation and cure for each resin.

Figures 8 and 9 show the output of the sensor at the first and top layers of the TGDDM graphite resin transfer molding run. As shown by the increase in ϵ'', sensor 1 was wet out after 45 minutes, 60°C, into the process cycle. The top sensor was wet out approximately ten minutes later at 70°C. Following impregnation, the $\epsilon''(\omega)$ properties of the resin at the bottom layer and the top layer show markedly different values. Throughout the cure process the resin at the top sensor appears to exhibit a lower ionic mobility. The cure process is not uniform due to the time for impregnation. The results suggest that reducing the time to impregnation will reduce the variation between the cure process across the bottom to top ply.

Finally, in Figures 10 and 11, we show the results of a sensor controlled run in which the sensor was used to control the cure process using criteria similar to those used in controlling the autoclave cure of a 1 inch thick 3501-6 graphite prepreg reported on last year (5,6)

As seen in Figures 10 and 11, the sensor controlled RTM run reduces the impregnation time from 40 minutes to 15 minutes, produces a far more uniform cure from the bottom to the top ply, and reduced the total cure time as indicated by the approach of $\frac{d\epsilon''}{dt}$ to 0, by approximately 60 minutes.

CONCLUSIONS

Frequency dependent electromagnetic sensing techniques (FDEMS) provide a rapid sensitive convenient technique for monitoring the effects of resin exposure to room temperature on the flow properties of MY-720 epoxies used for resin transfer molding. Use of the sensor to control the RTM cure cycle can significantly reduce fabrication time and increase the uniformity of cure in the tool. The agreement between the FDEMS ϵ'' sensor measured viscosity and the predictions of the Loos Springer model is good. The sensors provide a convenient in-situ technique for measuring in the tool the impregnation process and uniformity of cure at various positions during the resin transfer molding process.

REFERENCES

1. D. Kranbuehl "Cure Monitoring" in _Encylopedia of Composites_, Stuart M. Lee Editor VCH Publishers (in print).

2. D. Kranbuehl, S. Delos, M. Hoff, L. Weller, P. Haverty and J. Seeley., ACS Sym. Series, _367_ 100-119 (1988) and ACS Div. Poly. Mats.: Sci. and Eng., _56_ 163-168 (1987).

3. D. Kranbuehl, S. Delos, M. Hoff, L. Weller, P. Haverty, J. Seelely and B. Whitham, Nat'l SAMPE Sym. Ser., _32_, 338-348 (1987).

4. A. Loos andG. Springer J. of Composite Materials _17_, 135-165 (1983).

5. A. Loos, Dr. Kranbuehl and W. Freeman in _Intelligent Processing at Materials and Advanced Sensors_, Metallurgical Soc., 197-211 (1987).

6. D. Kranbuehl, M. Hoff, P. Haverty, A. Loos and T. Freeman, Nat'l SAMPE Sym. Ser., _33_, 1276 (1988).

*   Inquiries regarding the FDEMS Sensor and instrumentation should be directed to D. Kranbuehl.

This work has been made possible through support from a NASA Langley Research Center Grant.

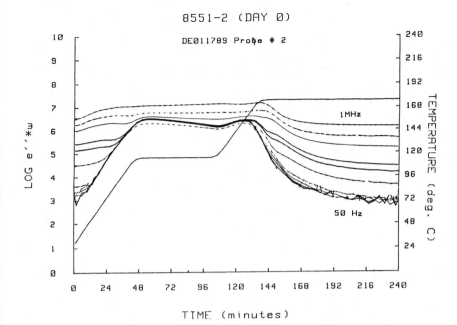

Figure 1.   Log (ϵ'' x ω) vs. time for 8551-2 during a multiple ramp-
hold cure cycle.

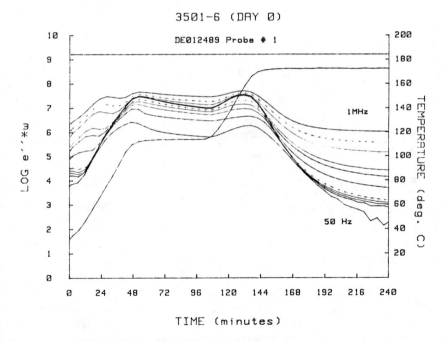

Figure 2.   Log (ϵ'' x ω) vs time for   3501-6 during a multiple ramp-
hold cure cycle.

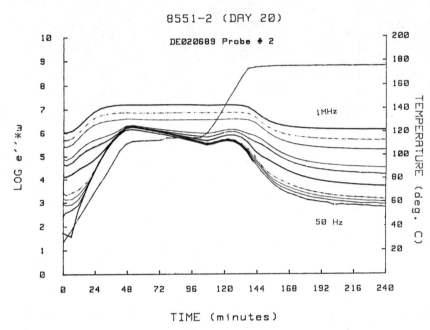

Figure 3. Log (ϵ" x ω) vs time for 8551-2 aged 20 days at room temperature during a multiple ramp-hold cure cycle.

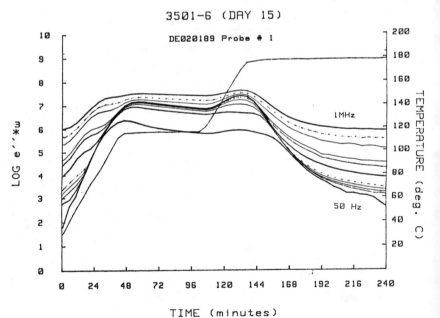

Figure 4. Log (ϵ" x ω) vs. time for 3501-6 aged 15 days at room temperature during a multiple ramp-hold cure cycle.

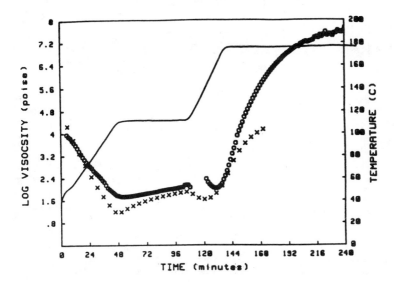

Figure 5. A comparison of the FDEMS predicted viscosity and the Loos-Springer Model predicted viscosity for 3501-6 during a multiple ramp-hold cure cycle.

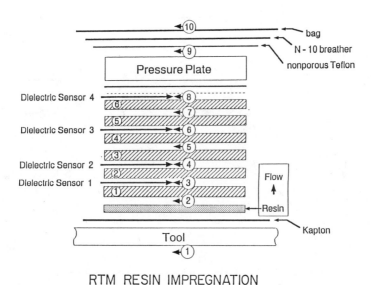

RTM RESIN IMPREGNATION

Figure 6. A diagram of the in-situ monitoring of the infiltration and cure processes in an RTM tool.

3501-6 RTM GRAPHITE 2 PLIES

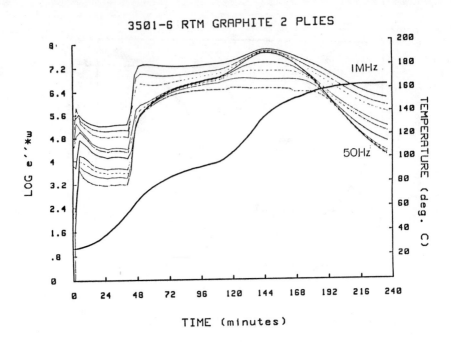

TIME (minutes)

Figure 7. <u>In-situ</u> monitoring of the infiltration and cure processes,
2 plies from the bottom, using 3501-6 and an 8 ply cloth
layup.

3501-6 RTM GRAPHITE 8 PLIES

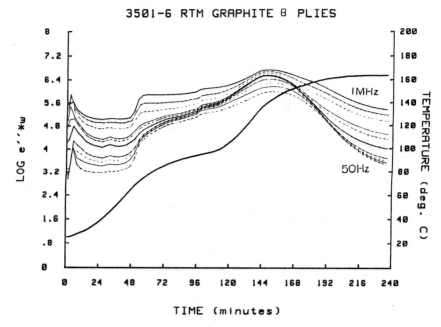

TIME (minutes)

Figure 8. <u>In-situ</u> monitoring of the infiltration and cure processes,
8 plies from the bottom, using 3501-6 and an 8 ply cloth
layup.

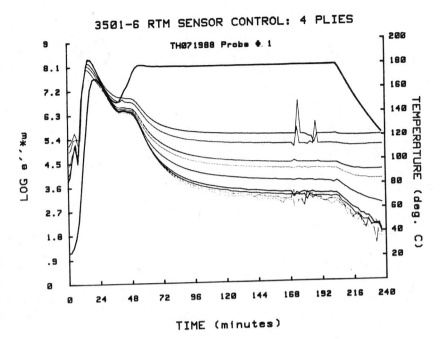

Figure 9. Sensor output (ϵ" ω vs. time) used to control the pressure temperature cycle, 4 plies from the bottom, in a 16 ply cloth layup.

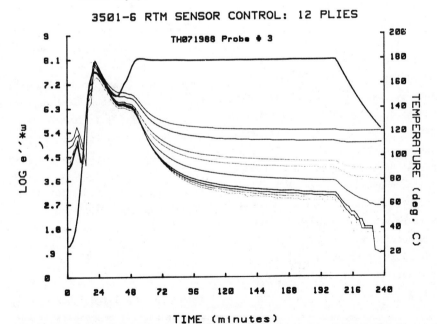

Figure 10. Sensor output (ϵ" ω vs. time) used to control the pressure temperature cycle, 12 plies from the bottom, in a 16 ply cloth layup.

A NONLINEAR PROCESS CONTROLLER
FOR CURING A THERMOSET COMPOSITE

Albert S. Tam, Timothy G. Gutowski
Laboratory for Manufacturing and Productivity
Massachusetts Institute of Technology
Cambridge, MA 02139

ABSTRACT

The manufacturer's recommended cure
cycle for a thermoset composite is
usually determined empirically for
each new resin system. Because the
cycle is fixed, it is unable to account for material, part, or process
variations, or else is overly conservative and hence inefficient.
Ideally, each individual cure is
monitored and modified by a controller in real-time. This paper presents a control strategy which can
handle both the nonlinear system dynamics and the presence of modeling
error inherent in the cure process.
Performance is simulated for the
compression molding of a Hercules
AS4/3501-6 flat laminate. The controller cures the laminate to a
specified fiber volume fraction
within given time limits. It displays good robustness to process
changes and model uncertainties.
Results indicate that the important
parameters are the size of the part
and its initial moisture content.

1. INTRODUCTION

For every new thermoset resin system, the material supplier must empirically determine an appropriate
cure cycle. Since it usually does
not take into account such aspects
as part geometry, laminate thickness, material variations, or process fluctuations, the recommended
cure cycle is necessarily conservative and is sub-optimal for many
cases. The lack of feedback measurement during processing also makes
it uncertain whether the part has
been properly cured.

Because of the large inherent value
of each part (from both labor and
material), an improperly cured part
incurs a large cost. As a result,

the need to directly monitor the advancement of the resin during the cure is being recognized. Currently, the dielectric technique is most commonly used (6,10,11). Several researchers have also tried to model the individual process components, including the cure kinetics, resin flow, compaction, and void formation (1,2,4,9,13,14). From these models, one can devise improved strategies for tailoring the cure cycle.

Recently, research has progressed to the next logical step, which is to combine the in-process measurements with the mathematical models and individually control each cure cycle. An expert system approach has been implemented at Wright-Patterson AFB (7). This method is mainly a temperature control which tries to prevent excessive exotherms during the autoclave curing of a thick section laminate. A second technique has been to use the dielectric measurements along with knowledge about the outgassing of volatiles to determine the optimal time for pressure application (16). However, these control methods only address individual components of the cure process.

sa
This paper presents a control technique which integrates the components of resin cure, compaction, resin flow, and void formation. It is a closed loop strategy, which simply means that measurements of critical parameters are obtained during the process and compared with

the desired values. A controller uses the error to determine an appropriate control action to modify the cure cycle *in-situ* (Figure 1). What remains is to choose a proper controller formulation to guarantee good performance and stability.

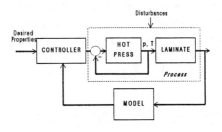

Figure 1. Schematic representation of the closed loop control system.

The controller requires a mathematical model of the process physics, both to evaluate the measurements and to know how the system will respond to changes in commands. A major problem is that the dynamics of the cure process are highly nonlinear and are not well handled by classical controller formulations. Moreover, a certain amount of error is inevitable in the models and is worsened by possible material and process variations. The sliding mode formulation was chosen for its particular ability to handle these concerns.

2. MODEL DEVELOPMENT

To test the viability of this control concept, we chose a well modeled process—the compression molding of a Hercules AS4/3501-6 flat laminate. This process contains many aspects of the general cure problem, and a good understanding of the underlying physics has been achieved and is available in the literature.

Following standard control formulation techniques, we first identify the state variables x_i and control efforts u_i:

$$
\begin{aligned}
x_1 &\equiv V_f, & u_1 &\equiv p, \\
x_2 &\equiv \alpha, & u_2 &\equiv T_{in}, \\
x_3 &\equiv T_{part},
\end{aligned}
\qquad (1)
$$

where V_f is the fiber volume fraction of the part, α is the degree of cure of the resin, T_{part} is the temperature of the part, p is the applied pressure, and T_{in} is the applied temperature. These state variables are sufficient to completely describe the system status during the process.

The system dynamics may then be described in standard form as:

$$
\begin{aligned}
\dot{\underline{x}} &= \underline{f}(\underline{x}) + g(\underline{x})\underline{u}, \\
\underline{y} &= \underline{h}(\underline{x}),
\end{aligned}
\qquad (2)
$$

where $\underline{x}$ is the state vector, $\underline{y}$ is the output vector, and the dot indicates differentiation with respect to the time, t.

We obtain the dynamics of the consolidation from Gutowski's model (5) and the cure kinetics from Lee's model (8). The corresponding elements of the $\underline{f}$ and g matrices are:

$$
\underline{f}(\underline{x}) =
\begin{bmatrix}
-(3S_{xx}\sigma x_1)/(\mu a^2) \\
f_2(x_2, x_3) \\
-x_3/\tau
\end{bmatrix},
\qquad (3a)
$$

$$
f_2 =
\begin{cases}
(K_1 + K_2 x_2)(1 - x_2)(B - x_2) & 0 < x_2 \leq 0.3 \\
K_3(1 - x_2) & 0.3 < x_2 \leq 0.5,
\end{cases}
\qquad (3b)
$$

$$
K_i = A_i \exp(-\Delta E_i/(Rx_3)), i = 1..3,
\qquad (3c)
$$

$$
g(\underline{x}) =
\begin{bmatrix}
(3S_{xx}\sigma x_1)/(\mu a^2) & 0 \\
0 & 0 \\
0 & 1/\tau
\end{bmatrix},
\qquad (4)
$$

$$
\underline{u} =
\begin{bmatrix}
u_1 \\
u_2
\end{bmatrix},
\qquad (5)
$$

where S_{xx} is the permeability of the fiber bed, a is half the length of the part, σ is the fiber stress, μ is the viscosity of the resin, τ is the heat transfer lag, B is an empirical constant, A_i are the pre-exponential factors, ΔE_i are the activation energies, and R is the universal gas constant. Both S_{xx} and σ are nonlinear functions of V_f.

The outputs of interest are the fiber volume fraction and degree of cure, so the output vector is:

$$
\underline{y}(\underline{x}) = \underline{h}(\underline{x}) =
\begin{bmatrix}
x_1 \\
x_2
\end{bmatrix}.
\qquad (6)
$$

428

In addition, Lee provides a relationship between the resin viscosity, degree of cure, and the part temperature:

$$\mu(\alpha, T_{part}) = \mu_\infty \exp((U/(RT_{part}))+K\alpha), \qquad (7)$$

where U is the activation energy and μ_∞ and K are empirical constants. The viscosity couples the cure kinetics to the compaction dynamics.

We have two available control inputs, p and T_{in}, and two main variables of interest, V_f and α. The system is controllable in the sense that we can affect all the desired output variables with the given control efforts. Not included in these dynamics is the irreversibility of the process. V_f must be monotonically increasing since resin cannot be sucked back into the part once it is squeezed out. Also, for a thermoset system, the degree of cure must be monotonically increasing.

To control void formation, we must look at a third quantity, the mean resin pressure p_r, given by:

$$p_r = p - \sigma(V_f). \qquad (8)$$

Dave (1) has found that to suppress the predominant water-based voids in a graphite/epoxy system, we need to maintain a minimum pressure in the resin given by:

$$p_v > 4.962 \times 10^3 \\ * \exp(-4892/T_{part})(RH)_0, \qquad (9)$$

where p_v is the void suppression pressure in atmospheres (absolute), and $(RH)_0$ is the initial equilibrium relative humidity of the part. Unfortunately, this criterion is independent of part size; the minimum pressure required tends to squeeze the resin out of smaller parts much faster than larger parts. Here, we are faced with a possibly unstable situation: resin loss resulting from the void suppression requirement leads to a *lower* resin pressure since more load is supported by the fibers.

3. MIMO SLIDING MODE CONTROL

The control strategy used is based on the sliding mode control concept. This method is popular in robotics and avionics because of the highly nonlinear dynamics of those systems. The full mathematics of the multi-input-multi-output (MIMO) design and proofs of its stability and performance are beyond the scope of this paper; for a detailed treatment, please refer to Utkin (15), Slotine (12), and Fernandez and Hedrick (3). Here, we present the underlying equations from which application of standard sliding mode design follows.

We first define the errors e_i between the measured outputs y_i and the desired output values y_{id}:

$$e_i = y_i - y_{id}(t), \quad i=1,2. \tag{10}$$

We next chose "sliding surfaces" S_i in state space; these surfaces describe where we would like the states to be. The controller then calculates the efforts required to drive the system to these surfaces and keep it there. We define each surface in terms of the errors so that being on the surface means that the system is tracking the desired trajectory:

$$S_1 = e_1 + \lambda_1 \int_0^t e_1 d\tau,$$

$$\tag{11}$$

$$S_2 = \dot{e}_2 + \lambda_2 e_2,$$

where λ_i are chosen to give desired response dynamics on the surface.

The control efforts are now calculated to ensure that the surfaces are "attractive", meaning that whenever the system state is not on the surface, the control will drive the states toward it:

$$u_1 = -[\ \eta_1 \mathrm{sgn}(S_1) + f_1 + \lambda_1 e_1$$
$$- \dot{y}_{1d}] \ / \ g_{11}(\underline{x}), \tag{12}$$

$$u_2 = -\left[\ \eta_2 \mathrm{sgn}(S_2) + \frac{\partial f_2}{\partial x_2} f_2 - \frac{\partial f_2}{\partial x_3} \frac{x_3}{\tau} \right.$$
$$\left. + \lambda_2(f_2 - \dot{y}_{2d}) - \dot{y}_{2d} \right] \frac{\tau}{\dfrac{\partial f_2}{\partial x_3}}, \tag{13}$$

where η_i are non-negative control gains chosen to ensure the "attractiveness" condition.

A major benefit of using a sliding mode controller in this application is its robustness to modeling errors. As long as we have an idea where the modeling errors occur, and we can place bounds on their magnitudes, we can compensate for them in the controller. The primary modeling error occurs in the empirical expression for the viscosity, which in turn greatly affects the compaction dynamics. The value of K in Eq. 7 is accurate to within 10%, resulting in a much larger uncertainty in both $f_1(\underline{x})$ and the first control gain, $g_{11}(\underline{x})$. With this information on the error, we can calculate a new (time-varying) η_1 to ensure that the sliding surface is still "attractive".

Another attribute of this control strategy is its ability to track a given trajectory. We design these trajectories to maintain the desired resin pressure and enhance void suppression ability. We only examine the cure process up until the gel point ($y_2=0.5$), after which no more flow is possible. A power-law path is selected for y_2, allowing a moderate temperature build-up. The path for y_1 is chosen to apply pressure up until gelation, but not squeeze so hard that the desired compaction is reached too early and the applied pressure drops:

$$y_{1d}(t) = \begin{cases} V_0, & t \leq t_s \\ V_0 + (V_{fd}-V_0) \\ \quad *(1-\exp(-(t-t_s)/\tau_c)), \\ & t > t_s \end{cases} \quad (14)$$

$$y_{2d}(t) = 0.5(t/t_{gel})^n, \quad n \geq 1, \quad (15)$$

where V_0 and V_{fd} are the initial and desired fiber volume fraction, respectively, t_{gel} is the desired time to reach gelation, t_s is the time to start compaction, and τ_c is a suitably chosen time constant.

4. SIMULATIONS RESULTS

The nonlinear computer simulation package SIMNON was used to determine the performance of the closed loop system. The specifications were to achieve gelation and the desired fiber volume fraction within a reasonable time. The resin pressure was to be kept above the necessary void suppression pressure throughout the process. The system parameters used for the simulation were obtained from the models cited above.

The command trajectory for the degree of cure was parabolic, with a time limit of one hour to gelation.

Compaction was set to begin after approximately 12.5 minutes. The command for fiber volume fraction was calculated as a first order response to a step input with four time constants elapsing until gelation time. We simulated the compaction of two different part lengths: 1.524E-1 m. (6 in.), and a=3.048E-1 m. (12 in.).

Figure 2 shows the results for the larger part, V_{fd}=0.70, and no modeling errors. The sliding mode gains η_i and λ_i were all set at 1. Both the fiber volume fraction and the degree of cure tracked the desired trajectory perfectly. The pressure plot shows the applied pressure and the void suppression pressure difference, Δp, given by

$$\Delta p = p_r - p_v \quad (16)$$

where p_v is the minimum pressure needed to suppress voids at the cur-

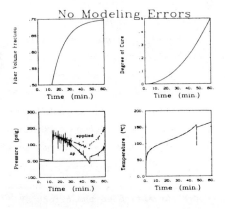

Figure 2. Simulation results for long part with no modeling errors.

431

rent part temperature. Here, we
have assumed the worst moisture
case, with $RH_0=100\%$. For voids to
be suppressed, Δp must be positive,
ideally throughout the cure.

The required control efforts were
certainly within the capabilities of
a typical hot press. The temperature did not exceed the hold temperature for this resin of $177^{\circ}C$. Although Δp was negative for a short
time, it was well positive at gelation and void growth should be suppressed.

A problem arose for the smaller
part. The command trajectories were
still followed, but the void suppression criterion was not met.
The solution was to introduce a
saturation limit into the control
laws, bounding the applied temperature to make sure the available
resin pressure was greater than the
needed void suppression pressure.
The results of the simulation with
this restriction imposed are shown
in Figure 3. Both the compaction
and void suppression were satisfactory, but the resin still had not
reached gelation after 80 min. The
temperature ceiling means the resin
takes longer to cure, so that though
the final degree of compaction had
been reached, the resin had not gelled and could still flow.

We next investigated the effect of
the modeling errors. The possible
error in viscosity means $g_{11}(\underline{x})$ and

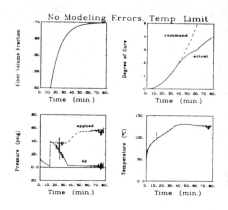

Figure 3. Simulation results for short part with
no modeling errors, but with a temperature limit
imposed.

$f_1(\underline{x})$ may vary up to 80%. The controller was modified to ensure the
sliding surfaces were still "attractive." No problem existed if the
actual viscosity was higher than
predicted, since the controller
could simply apply more pressure. In
fact, the smaller part could be
cured, though the time to gel took
80 min. instead of 60 min. (Figure
4). However, if the actual viscosity was lower, then squeezing
harder caused more resin to flow, in
turn causing a large drop in resin
pressure. Even for the larger part
size, the void suppression ability
was questionable (Figure 5).

To handle the worst possible case,
that is, worst moisture content,
small part size, and viscosity lower
than modeled, the commanded fiber
volume fraction was increased to
0.75. Also, a first order filter

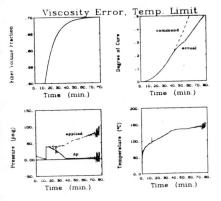

Figure 4. Simulation results for short part with actual viscosity higher than modeled.

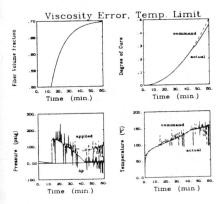

Figure 5. Simulation results for long part with actual viscosity lower than modeled.

was introduced between the calculated control pressure and the actual applied pressure to account for the mechanical response of the hot press. Figure 6 shows the simulation results for this worst case scenario. Both compaction and gelation were achieved within 60 min.

and the void suppression criterion was met. The required control efforts were also reasonable.

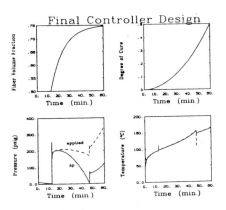

Figure 6. Final controller design for the worst case scenario: small part, 100% RH, viscosity lower than modeled.

5. CONCLUDING REMARKS

The sliding mode controller design provides excellent control over the cure cycle necessary to cure a part to a certain fiber volume fraction. It is able to handle both the cure kinetics and the compaction dynamics together. In addition, the ability to follow tailored command trajectories enhances the ability to suppress voids. The imposed control effort restrictions do not compromise system performance and introduce no instabilities. From the simulations, it is apparent that the small, moist parts pose the greatest problems. However, the controller can overcome these problems by either compacting to a higher fiber volume fraction or by taking longer to cure the part. In this manner, the control scheme can tailor the cure cycle and make parts not previously possible using the standard cure cycle.

In terms of implementation, the controller assumes full state feedback. The fiber volume fraction is obtainable by measuring the part height. The degree of cure and the part temperature are both obtainable by using a microdieletric sensor available from Micromet Instruments, Inc. (Cambridge, MA). The viscosity and hence degree of cure may also be reconstructed by measuring the rate of change of the part height over time. Though these measurements may be noisy, the dynamics of our system is slow enough that most of the noise can be filtered out, either with suitable signal processing or a Kalman filter in the controller. Likewise, the sliding mode controller requires a significant amount of calculations, but again, with currently available microprocessors, the computation time should be insignificant with respect to the required system bandwidth.

This work has demonstrated that the sliding mode method can handle both the nonlinearity and modeling uncertainty in the cure process. Although the case we considered was relatively simple physically, it was highly complex mathematically. Further research will address the addition of exotherm control in thicker

parts as well as application to distributed systems such as autoclave molding.

6. REFERENCES

1. Dave, R., Kardos, J.L., and Dudukovic, M.P., "Process Modeling of Thermosetting Matrix Composites: A Guide for Autoclave Cure Cycle Selection," Proceedings of ASFC, First Technical Conference., Oct 7-9, 1986, p. 137.

2. Dusi, M.R., et. al., "Predictive Models as Aids to Thermoset Resin Processing," in Chemorheology of Thermosetting Polymers, C. May, Ed., ACS Symposium Serial #227, 1982-3, p. 301.

3. Fernandez, B., and Hedrick, J.K., "Control of Multivariable Non-Linear Systems by the Sliding Mode Method," International Journal of Control, 46, Sept. 1987, p. 1019.

4. Ford, C.G., et al., "Advanced Composite Production Cure Cycles Based on Prepreg Rheology," 31st International SAMPE Symposium, April 7-10, 1986, p. 1300.

5. Gutowski, T.G., et.al., "Consolidation Experiments for Laminate Composites," Journal of Composite Materials, 21, June 1987, p. 650.

6. Kranbuehl, D.E., "Electrical Methods of Characterising Cure Processes in Resins," in Developments in Reinforced Plastics-5, G. Pritchard, Ed., Elsevier Applied Science Publishers, Ltd., NY, 1986, p. 181.

7. LeClair, S., et al., "Qualitative Process Automation for Autoclave Curing of Composites," AFWAL-TR-87-4083, May, 1987.

8. Lee, W.I., et al., "Heat of Reaction, Degree of Cure, and Viscosity of Hercules 3501-6 Resin," Journal of Composite Materials, 16, Nov. 1982, p. 510.

9. Loos, A.C. and Springer, G.S., "Curing of Epoxy Matrix Composites," Journal of Composite Materials, 17, March 1983, p. 135.

10. Senturia, S.D., et al., "In-situ Measurement of the Properties of Curing Systems with Microdielectrometry," Journal of Adhesion, 15, 1982, p. 69.

11. Sheppard, N.F., et al., "Microdielectrometry," Sensors and Actuators, 2, 1982, p. 263.

12. Slotine, J., "Sliding Controller Design for Nonlinear Systems", International Journal of Control, 40, 1984, p 421.

13. Springer, G.S., "Modeling the Cure Process of Composites," 31st International SAMPE Symposium, April 7-10, 1986, p. 776.

14. Tang, J.M., et. al., "Effects of Cure Pressure on Resin Flow, Voids, and Mechanical Properties," Journal of Composite Materials, 21, May, 1987, p. 421.

15. Utkin, V.I., "Variable Structure Systems with Sliding Modes", IEEE Transaction on Automatic Control, AC-22, April 1977, p. 212.

16. Yokota, M.J., "In-Process Controlled Curing of Resin Matrix Composites," SAMPE Journal, July/Aug., 1978, p. 11.

DIMENSIONAL STABILITY AND PROPERTY GRADIENTS
IN THICK SMC SECTIONS

Hua-tie Kau

Laurie A. Petrusha

Polymers Department

General Motors Research Laboratories

Warren, MI   48090

Abstract

The dimensional stability of SMC cylinders composed of cured R-25 and R-50 pastes were investigated. A significant amount of dimensional change was found for these samples when they were annealed. To identify the source of the phenomenon, three techniques: infrared spectroscopy (IR), differential scanning calorimetry (DSC), and mechanical spectroscopy, were employed to determine the physical and chemical properties of the sample as a function of location in the sample. The results showed that there is a gradient in the degree of cure. Furthermore, we found a gradient in the major transition temperature (Tg). These property gradients could be related to the potential dimensional instability of the material. But, the direction in the degree of cure gradient is opposite to that of the gradient in the mechanical properties, and does not agree with the observed pattern of deformation. In light of this, we consider it likely that the dimensional instability may be physical and associated with stress relaxation.

1.   INTRODUCTION

Sheet molding compound (SMC) is the leading material for automobile exterior and structural composite parts. This reinforced material is composed of chopped glass fibers and a styrenated polyester thermoset matrix with calcium carbonate filler and is fabricated into parts using a compression molding process. During the molding operation, the compound flows and solidifies into the desired shape under pressure and heat.

The solidification is caused by a crosslinking polymerization reaction of the resin. Several aspects of the curing reaction profoundly influence the molding operation. The curing process determines not only the molding cycle and therefore the production rate, but also the surface and mechanical quality of the molded parts. Finally, the residual stresses generated in a cure cycle usually are detrimental to the mechanical strength and durability of SMC. Thus, it is imperative to both determine and control the thermal and mechanical histories of the material during the cure cycle and to analyze the chemical and physical properties of the material after it has been cured.

In our previous investigation of the curing behavior of SMC, we constructed a cure reactor to determine the chemical transformations by recording the temperature rise along the centerline of cylindrical SMC paste samples and to determine the physical transformations by following the concomitant mechanical behavior in a cure cycle.[1] As a by-product we also obtained from each experiment a cured sample with a well documented cure history. With these samples, we were able to investigate the relationship between the properties of the as-cured SMC and the processing conditions in the cure cycle.

Furthermore, because of the thermal gradient and the propagation of the curing reaction during the curing process, we were interested not only in the overall properties but also in the variations of the properties within each sample. The presence of property gradients in the sample would have several important consequences. First of all, this would turn the material itself into a composite and the effective properties could be very different from a material of uniform properties.[2,3] Mallick and Raghupathi[4] have found that the mechanical properties of SMC plaques are affected by the molding conditions and have shown that the flexural strength of SMC plaques is not uniform and increases with the length of the molding time. They attributed such a change in the mechanical properties to a difference in the degree of cure, a, for the molded samples.

Next, perhaps even more importantly, the nonuniformity in some properties could culminate in internal stresses and become a precursor to a potential imbalance in the material. Residual stresses in SMC have been observed and found to affect the properties of SMC. Marker and Ford[5] reported that in molding disk-shaped SMC plaques, the region away from the center had a different curing history from the region close to the center because of flow. They detected residual stresses in the plaque along the radial direction. This was shown

437

by cutting the plaques into an outer ring and a center disk and inspecting the dimensional changes. They observed an expansion of the outer ring and a shrinkage of the inner disk and concluded that the outer ring was under compression and the disk was under tension. Residual stresses are even more probable in thicker sections. Pusatcioglu, Hassler, Fricke, and McGee[6] have shown, by birefringence, that a gradient of residual stresses can be detected in cured SMC resin. They also contended that this gradient was in good agreement with a thermal gradient that, based on their computations, exists during the cure.

While the issues of property gradients and internal residual stresses have been addressed and been associated with the nonuniformity of the thermal and curing history, detailed information is still rather incomplete. In particular, the extent of property variations has not been adequately determined for SMC. And, except for a few noted cases, neither the levels nor the sources of the residual stresses have been definitively determined. In this work, we first devised a technique to qualitatively detect the internal instability in the as-cured SMC paste. Then, we investigated the causes of the stresses by analyzing the variations in composition and properties of the as-cured samples

and then correlated that with the dynamic curing behavior of the SMC pastes.

2. EXPERIMENTAL

The experimental procedure consisted of two principal steps: the curing experiment that produced the as-cured samples and the subsequent series of tests that characterized the properties of the as-cured samples.

2.1 Materials and Paste Compounding

The SMC pastes were based on two formulations, R-25 and R-50 (Table I). The R-25 paste contains a higher amount of filler, 60 wt%, as opposed to an R-50 with 32 wt%. In addition, the R-25 resin has a low profile thermoplastic ingredient with a weight concentration normally at a ratio of 60 to 40 between the polyester and the low profile resin. The R-50 paste does not contain low profile additives. The materials were used as received.

The R-25 paste was mixed in a laboratory Ross mixer (7.5 L) according to established steps by preparing the acidic and alkaline mixtures separately before combining them together into the final paste. The R-50 paste was mixed in one package in a 3.8 L (one gallon) paint can using a drill press. After mixing, the pastes were degassed and sealed in

438

60 mL syringes. These paste samples in the syringes were stored in desiccators saturated with styrene vapor to prevent the loss of styrene monomer.

Curing Experiment

The curing experiments were conducted in a cure reactor. The design and function of the reactor apparatus have been described in a previous paper.[1] For each curing experiment, a cylindrical paste sample (Figure 1) was cured in the reactor with a wall (mold) temperature set at 150°C under a set pressure of 3.5 MPa using a 500 kN PHI hydraulic press. The overall dwell time was about 15 minutes for each run. After the curing reaction, the sample cooled to the mold temperature in the reactor and then was removed from the reactor and allowed to cool to room temperature under ambient conditions.

Differential Scanning Calorimetry (DSC)

Thermograms of the as-cured samples were obtained with a thermal analyzer (DuPont 1090) equipped with a dual sample DSC cell (Dupont 985). The sample size was less than 10 mg and the tests were run using hermetically sealed pans at a heating rate of 10°C/min from room temperature to 250°C under a stream of nitrogen at a flow rate of 50 mL/min.

Infrared Spectroscopy

The infrared spectra of the as-cured sample were obtained with a fast Fourier transform infrared spectrometer (Nicolet 20DX FTIR). The specimens were prepared by first grinding the sample with a pestle and mortar and then pressing them into disks using KBr powder (Harshaw Chemical). The concentration of the cured paste in KBr was about 3% and the disks were very thin and weighed only about 70 mg.

Mechanical Spectroscopy

The dynamic mechanical properties of the as-cured samples were determined using a Rheometrics Mechanical Spectrometer (RMS Model 605). Small cylindrical rod specimens, 3 mm in diameter and 25 mm in length, were machined from the as-cured samples. A rod testing fixture was used for the measurement. The tests were run using the dynamic mode with a strain of 0.1% and a strain frequency of 1 rad/s. Each test swept over a range of temperatures from room temperature to about 250°C at 5°C intervals. It took about two hours to complete a run.

3. RESULTS AND DISCUSSION

In SMC, the curing reaction is an essential part of the molding process and several aspects of the relationship between the curing reaction and molding conditions have been studied.[7-9] The reaction takes place concomitant with heat conduction into the material through the reactor or mold walls and the properties of the molded product usually reflect the effect of the complex physical and chemical transformations that take place during the curing process. From the dynamic response data, we noted that during the curing experiment, heat was transferred from the reactor wall into the center of the paste sample, while, at the same time, a reaction front propagated into the sample with a result that thermal expansion and volume shrinkage occurred during the curing period.[1,10] This sequence of processes is likely to influence the properties of the cured sample and induce property gradients in the radial direction of the as-cured cylindrical sample.

Internal Stability in Cured SMC Paste

A test was devised, which has been named the "pacman test," and used to detect the potential dimensional instability in the cured cylinders. In this test a 3 mm thick disk was cut from the middle of the as-cured sample with a diamond saw. Next, a slit, about 1 mm wide, was cut along the radial direction of the disk as depicted in Figure 2. These specimens were then subjected to thermal annealing to achieve an equilibrium state, while the dimensions of the slits were measured periodically using a feeler gauge. We found that the dimensions of the slits had changed during annealing. Thus, it is evident that the as-cured material was not initially stable.

Furthermore, the dimensional changes are significantly different depending on the location along the radial axis of the disk. The dimension of the slit close to the center increases by about 5%, while the dimension of the slit near the outer region decreases by nearly 10%. The combination of an expanded inner dimension and contracted outer dimension turns the slit into an inside out pie-shaped gap instead of a regular pie-shaped gap. From the shape of the slit, it is clear that the inner region has a higher potential to shrink than the outer region, at least in the relative sense. Of course, because of interactions, it is impossible to determine the deformation in absolute terms.

As noted earlier, the possibility of dimensional instability is well known for SMC and has been reported in several papers.[4-6] But, our findings are still significant for two reasons. First of all, these results show that the dimensional instability could be rather important, as evidenced by the large magnitude of the change over the small size of the specimen. Second, we may have determined some new characteristics related to the dimensional instability.

Property Gradients

The results from the "pacman tests" not only confirm the severity of the potential instability in the cured material, but also suggest complex and probably multiple causes for such phenomena. While normally it has rarely been possible to be exact regarding the sources, two likely types of factors are well known. In general, one is related to the chemical properties of the material and the other is related to the physical properties.

These factors become a matter of concern for dimensional instability in an SMC part when the properties are not uniformly distributed. To assess the probable causes that · result in dimensional instability, we carried out a series of experiments aimed at determining the degree of cure, composition, and the mechanical properties of SMC.

Reaction Gradient. The variation in chemical conversion, or degree of cure, was ascertained using DSC by determining the amount of reactive monomer still in the as-cured product.[11,12]

The amount of undercure was found to be a function of the location along the radial direction in the as-cured samples, as indicated by the residual heats of reaction for specimens at different locations. In Figure 3 we show the thermal curves of specimens from the outer, middle, and center regions of the SMC sample cylinder for the R-25 paste (reference Figure 1). The curves are different with the specimen that was farthest away from the centerline of the cylinder having the most pronounced residual heat of reaction. Similar results were also obtained for the R-50 paste.

A gradient of cure in the sample can cause dimensional instability when the sample undergoes further curing and an uneven curing shrinkage can occur, as was observed in the annealing experiment. But, the importance of this contribution to the observed dimensional change in the "pacman test" remains to be determined.

Composition Gradient. Since the DSC results clearly show a gradient of chemical conversion in the as-cured cylindrical samples, it was then of interest to further find out if there is a corresponding variation in the chemical composition. Infrared spectroscopy was used to obtain further information on the chemical composition of the sample. This method has been used for SMC by several other researchers.[11-12] However, the application of this technique to SMC resins is still rather empirical at the present time and there is little agreement among the researchers regarding the bands to be selected for the study of the curing reaction.

441

We have obtained infrared spectra using FTIR for the as-cured sample. Our results for the specimens from different locations are not conclusive, and they could neither lend support to the DSC results nor provide additional information with respect to the composition of the sample.

Mechanical Property Gradient. The overall mechanical properties of a thermoset could become rather complicated in the presence of a property gradient, and the mechanical properties are usually related to the degree of cure or the chemical conversion in a complex fashion.[14] In particular, Mallick and Raghupathi[4] have reported a higher flexural and interlaminar shear strength for thick SMC plaques with a longer mold opening time, i.e., a longer dwell time. In addition they also found a difference in the flexural strength, depending on which side of the specimen was facing up in the bending test, for plaque samples cut in half through the center plane. These observations suggest a stiffer SMC with better cure and variable mechanical properties is possible due to a different extent of cure.

Since there is a gradient in the degree of cure in the sample cylinder, we expected to find a corresponding gradient in the mechanical properties in the sample. In order to determine the

mechanical properties of the sample as a function of distance from its centerline, we adopted a technique to determine the dynamic mechanical properties using small rod specimens (1.25 mm in diameter and 25 mm in length). The dimension of the specimen is therefore sufficiently smaller than that of the as-cured cylinder. The shear modulus is plotted against temperature in Figure 4a for the R-25 sample. Obviously, the material becomes softer as it is heated, as indicated by a gradual decrease of the shear modulus with the temperature, before a large transition at about 150°C when the shear modulus begins to drop significantly.

The dynamic mechanical behavior is basically the same for the specimens from different locations of the sample cylinder. But, as we will discuss in a moment, the major transition temperature for these specimens could be shifted on the temperature scale as a consequence of modifications in the organic matrix. Such a shift is common for materials with a different degree of cure, with the highest transition temperature for the completely cured material.[14] Therefore, a shift is expected in the transition temperature since the DSC data show a gradient in the degree of conversion. As shown in Figures 4a, however, the dynamic mechanical properties data for the R-25 paste do not show this effect. Because of the scatter in the data,

442

it is difficult to determine if there are any changes in the transition temperature.

One way to increase the accuracy of the mechanical measurements is to increase the amount of polymer in the formulation. Thus, the same set of experiments was carried out for an R-50 sample which does contain a greater concentration of polymer, 70 vs. 30 wt%.

In Figure 4b we show the shear modulus for this sample as a function of temperature for specimens from different locations. The curves in the figure show with little doubt that the transition temperature of the samples depends on the location in the sample, ranging from 150°C for the center region specimen to 160°C for the outer region specimen. The result that the outer region has a higher transition temperature is rather unexpected in light of the lower degree of cure in that region. On the other hand, such a gradient in the transition temperature agrees with the observed deformation of the slit in the "pacman test" in terms of a stress relaxation process in the material. It is conceivable that if the material in the outer region solidified slightly earlier than the inner region material, then there will be stresses built up in the inner region when it began to shrink as a result of the crosslinking reaction. A consequence stemming from such a solidification sequence would be a lower density material near the center region, since the shrinking of the material as a result the crosslinking process is somewhat inhibited. When there is a density difference, even a minute amount, there could be a significant shift in the transition temperature, according to the concept of free volume in such a material. Such a scheme would explain the potential instability in the material as a result of frozen-in residual stresses, with the inner region under tension and the outer region under compressive forces, in full agreement with the result of the "pacman test."

4. CONCLUDING REMARKS

The mechanical instability or the residual stresses observed in this study are a result of variations in the properties of the material caused by thermal conduction. Therefore, it is expected that such stresses would be most likely to develop as the dimension of the material in the heat conduction direction increases. Indeed, we have demonstrated that in the thick cylinder sample (25 mm), the internal stresses are quite prominent. However, the sample dimension is probably close to the upper bound of the thickness of fabricated parts used in SMC applications. Most of the parts are designed to be substantially thinner, e.g., 3 mm. Thus, while it is important to bear in mind that in general the molded parts

443

may not be entirely free from potential instability, the amount of internal stress in such parts is probably not as severe if they are molded properly.

Nevertheless, we found that the "pacman test" was relatively simple to run and provided useful information on the potential dimensional instability of SMC materials. Therefore, it may be worthwhile to consider this test for other formulations of interest since instability can have a strong influence on the performance of the material.

5. ACKNOWLEDGMENTS

The authors would like to thank Mr. Ed Hagerman for valuable discussions.

6. REFERENCES

1. Kau, H. T. "An Experimental Study of the Dynamics of the Curing Process of Sheet Molding Compound (SMC) Paste," Proceedings of 46th SPE ANTEC, pp. 971-975, Atlanta, GA, April 18-21, 1988.

2. Broyer, E. and Macosko, C. W., "Heat Transfer and Curing in Polymer Reactive Molding," AIChE J., Vol. 22, No. 2, pp. 268-276, March 1976.

3. Timoshenko, S. and Young, D. H., Elements of Strength of Materials, 4th edition, D. Van Nostrand Company, Princeton, NJ, 1962.

4. Mallick, P. K. and Raghupathi, N., "Effect of Cure Cycle on Mechanical Properties of Thick Section Fiber-Reinforced Poly/Thermoset Moldings," Polymer Eng. and Sci., Vol. 19, No. 11, pp. 774-778, August 1979.

5. Marker, L. F. and Ford, B., "Flow and Curing Behavior of SMC during Molding," Modern Plastics, Vol. 54, pp. 64-70, 1977.

6. Pusatcioglu, S. Y., Hassler, J. C., Fricke, A. L. and McGee, Jr., H. A., "Effect of Temperature Gradients on Cure and Stress Gradients in Thick Thermoset Castings," J. of Appl. Polym. Sci., Vol. 25, pp. 381-393, 1980.

7. Lee, L. J., " Curing of Compression Molded Sheet Molding Compound," Polym. Eng. and Sci., Vol. 21, No. 8, pp. 483-492, Mid-June 1981.

8. Adabbo, H. E., Rojas, A. J. and Williams, R. J. J., "Critical Parameters for Thermoset Curing in Heated Molds," Polymer. Engr. and Sci., Vol. 19, No. 12, pp. 835-840, September 1979.

9. Barone, M. R. and Caulk, D. A., Int. J. Heat and Mass Transfer, Vol. 22, p. 1021, 1979.

10. Kau, H. T., (unpublished data).

11. Fan, J. D., Huang, Y. J. and Lee, L. J., "Fast Cure of Polyester Sheet Molding Compounds," Technical Papers, ANTEC, pp. 1331-1335, May 1986.

12. Han, C. D. and Lee, D. S., "Analysis of the Curing Behavior of Unsaturated Polyester Resins Using the Approach of Free Radical Polymerization," J. Appl.Polym. Sci., Vol. 33, pp. 2859-2876, 1987.

13. Box, G. E. P., Hunter, W. G., and Hunter, J. S., Statistics for Experimenters: An Introduction to Design, Data Analysis and Model Building, John Wiley and Sons, New York, 1978.

14. Nielsen, L. E., Mechanical Properties of Polymers, Reinhold, New York, 1962.

TABLE I

Formulation of SMC Paste

Ingredients	Major Components	Composition (wt%)	
		R-25	R-50
Unsaturated Polyester	Polyester/Styrene	22.4	64.5
Low Profile Agent	PMMA/Styrene	15.5	--
Filler	Calcium Carbonate	60.0	32.4
Lubricant	Zinc Stearate	1.6	1.6
Catalyst (Curing Agent)	t-Butyl Perbenzoate	0.21	--
Catalyst (Curing Agent)	t-Butyl Percotoate	0.21	0.65
Thickener	Magnesium Oxide	0.27	1.0

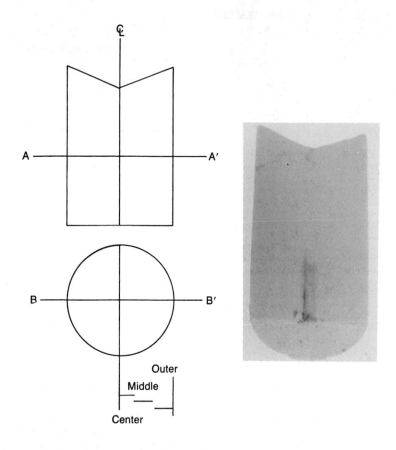

Figure 1.   Photograph of the cross-section of an as-cured SMC and the coordinates for the as-cured SMC sample.

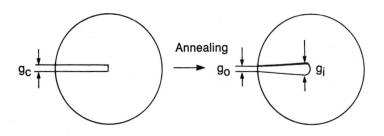

Figure 2.   Schematics of the changes in the gap during the "pacman test."

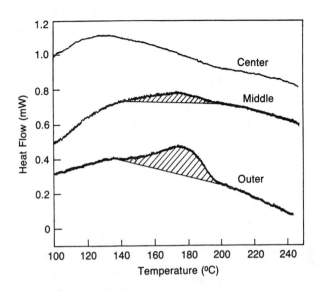

Figure 3. DSC thermograms for R-25 SMC samples at different locations.

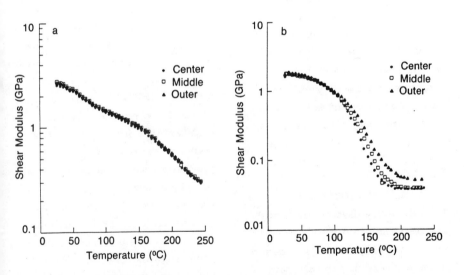

Figure 4. Shear modulus of SMC paste as a function of temperature for specimens from different locations: (a) R-25 and (b) R-50.

RAPID LOW-TEMPERATURE CURE
PATCHING SYSTEM FOR FIELD REPAIR
George T. Sivy
ITW Adhesive Systems
30 Endicott Street
Danvers, Massachusetts

ABSTRACT

A new field repair patch that cures within 1 hour at room temperature is described. The patch forms high strength bonds to metals, thermoplastics, and composites with little or no surface preparation. Under medium load, the patch has good resistance to humidity and temperature. Commonly used solvents and fluids have very little effect on the repair. Shelf-life is 1 year+ when stored at or below room temperature.

1. INTRODUCTION

From the early days of air travel, the need for field repair of damages incurred during service has been a necessary part of aircraft maintenance. Back then, a roll of simple duct tape was able to provide the speedy repairs to keep the Fokker D's and Sopwith Camels flying. As aircraft evolved and wood and cloth were replaced with advanced composites, metals, and plastics, the requirements and techniques of field repair have become more demanding, more complex and more time consuming. However, the notion of a "duct tape" for speedy repair of today's modern aircraft and other apparatus remains most appealing. Such a material would permit field repairs with little or no equipment, without disassembly, significantly reduce downtime and may, for example, provide aircraft a means for restricted flight to a repair depot. When reviewing the numerous and diverse articles devoted to field repair, a consensus among authors is seen regarding the requirements for field level repairs.

1. Repairs can be performed without disassembly.

2. Field-level skills required.

3. Can be performed in a limited control environment.

4. Repairs are temporary (some

may be permanent).

5. Minimum repair Q.C.
6. Materials and processes can be different from the original.
7. Adhesives or other chemicals can be storable at normal temperatures for at least one year.

These criteria strongly convey the motive for field repair: urgency. Obviously, the criteria are the same for battlefield repair; but these types of repairs are considered very urgent and very temporary.

Current field repairs fall into four categories:

1. Bolted metal or composite plate.
2. Bonded metal or composite plate.
3. Wet lay-up or patch.
4. Resin injection.

Each of the above is suitable for certain types of repairs but is generally limited to external surfaces and mechanisms. Internal repairs such as repairs to hydraulic lines, fuel lines, radiators, etc., could be made with these methods; however constraints imposed due to confined spaces and potential flammability severely limit their use. Accordingly, cold cure repair systems for these "under the hood" repairs may comprise a 5th category.

At first glance it would seem that bolting metal or composite patches over a damaged area would be the easiest and most reliable method. (Psychologically, it is certainly the most assuring). However, one must carefully consider the stresses introduced by drilling holes and the stress concentrations around mechanical fasteners. These considerations are obviated by adhesively bonding the patches, but the metal or composite must still be tailored to cover the damaged area. This may not always be possible, particularly in a battlefield setting. Resin injection is limited to edge delamination of composites and usually does not work for repairing a blister.

Wet lay-up patches or prepregs offer the most versatility and are the simplest to use. Many systems from a variety of manufactures are available; all have certain advantages and disadvantages, foremost, curing temperatures and conditions.

The elevated-temperature cure adhesives or prepregs afford, in many cases, permanent structural repairs. However, the procedures involved, although considered fast and simple, require a heat source, maybe a vacuum assist, and usually take several hours for full cure. Further limitations are realized when one considers potential heat damage to other areas during cure cycle and the detrimental effect of sorbed moisture (composite repair) during any vacuum bag cure cycle.

The cold bond repair adhesives or patches are usually limited to use at temperatures less than 180°F. However, and most important in the context of battlefield repair, they are fast and the interim repair may be sufficient to allow for restricted operation back to the repair depot. Many of the current adhesives are used on a flexible scrim but must be mixed and applied to the scrim by the user. Furthermore, these patches or adhesives generally do not adhere to the more sophisticated thermoplastic composites. Finally, many of the adhesives or prepregs require refrigeration to maintain their shelf life, usually limited to 6 months, after which they must be retested for integrity.

A new single-component no-mix, flexible patching system now exists. These adhesive-impregnated patches make it possible to effect repairs to metals, composites, and advanced thermoplastics at room temperature in less than one hour with little or no maintenance equipment.

2. PANEL PATCH REPAIR SYSTEM

The new Panel Patch Repair System consists of fiberglass cloth impregnated with an advanced generation acrylic adhesive, all contained in a plastic-lined aluminum pouch. Sufficient spray-on activator is provided. The fiberglass cloth normally supplied is a 19 oz/yd, 33 mil plainweave with 20 ends/in. Other styles and thicknesses of cloth are also used. Shelf life is 1 year + at 72°F.

Application has been simplified, and in most cases repairs can be completed in 10 minutes or less. Little or no surface preparation is required, but users may wish to prepare the damaged areas according to their standard operating procedures (e.g. solvent wipe, sanding, abrading, etc.). Once the patch has been cut to the desired size, the adhesive is activated by merely spraying on the activator. The activated patch is placed over the damaged area, groomed, and treated with additional activator. The spray-on activator eliminates the clumsy and untidy hand-mixing and applying to scrim material and requires no special measuring for proper mix ratio as required for most two-component repair adhesives. The patch hardens in less than 15 minutes at 72°F.

The mainstay of this new patching system is an advanced generation methacrylate adhesive. The suitability of these new adhesives for rapid repair follows from a consideration of the following general characteristics:

- Fast, ambient temperature cure
- Broad compatibility
- Tolerance for surface contamination.
- High bond strength
- Excellent environmental durability.

Also, the free-radical cure chemistry of these adhesives makes them more responsive to heat acceleration than are epoxies.

Generally speaking, the methacrylate adhesives offer a blend of the high strength of epoxies with the high impact and peel strength of urethanes – but without the disadvantages of either. The data in Table 1 illustrate this point.

In the context of field repair, the service temperature range of the methacrylates is usually much wider than many ambient cure epoxy adhesives as shown in Table 2.

The broad substrate compatibility of methacrylate adhesives further distinguishs this class from epoxy and urethanes. This compatibility includes coated and uncoated metals, thermoplastics, thermosets, many new polymer alloys, and the "superplastics" such as Kevlar® composites, P(I-A)'s and others.

When these superior performance characteristics are married to the convenience of a flexible fiberglass carrier, the notion of a "duct tape" for repair of modern aircraft and other military/commercial hardware is realized.

2.1 Performance

Table 3 lists several general properties of Panel Patch as a function of plies used.

The patch has been evaluated on several substrates and affords excellent adhesion to many materials commonly employed in military and commercial aircraft and other hardware. Table 4 lists some of these materials.

Although intended primarily as a field-repair system, the patch exhibits good durability even under moderate load. Figure 1 shows that even at 40°C and 100% R.H., 70% of the original load is maintained.

Durability of the patch after exposure to harsh environments is excellent. Table 5 shows the results of immersion tests in several commonly encountered fluids.

The foil of ambient cure adhesives for field repair has long been their poor hot-strength. Current cold cure adhesives afford only 10% of their room temperature properties on short term exposure to temperatures greater than 180°F. Referring back to Table 2, one can see that the Panel Patch adhesive is capable of maintaining greater than 50% of its room temperature strength for a period of time at 200°F! However, when this adhesive is tested as the patching system, the hot strength under the same conditions drops to 30%. The hot strength performance of Panel Patch is shown in Figure 2. Also plotted in Figure 2 are the hot strength data for a variation of Panel Patch. This system, as can be seen, maintains about 60% of its R.T. strength at 200°F. This variation is in the final stages of development and will be discussed later.

An important property of a repair patch is its ability to withstand moderate velocity impacts occurring on a relatively small area of film. An instrumented drop dart impact test was employed to measure Panel Patch's ability to withstand such impacts. Briefly, in this test, a freely falling dart of specified shape is passed through an anchored sample of material. The velocity of the dart after passing through the material is then determined by photoelectric speed traps. The corresponding kinetic energy is then compared to that of a dart that does not pass through the material. The kinetic energy that is lost to the film is used as an index of impact resistance.

Table 6 shows the impact resistance of Panel Patch as a function of number of plies. As a comparison, data for a sheet molding compound (SMC) and an aramid·composite are shown.

These data show that for the same thickness, Panel Patch is comparable to fiber-reinforced epoxy composites in terms of its ability to withstand a rapid impact. Furthermore, at the maximum load the patch undergoes a ductile failure in contrast to the brittle failure of many epoxy matrices. This ductile failure is less likely to form cracks or other stresses that may propagate into and damage surrounding areas.

Finally, as previously mentioned, most repair adhesives or prepegs require refrigeration to maintain shelf-life. Many of these materials are limited to 6 months and must be periodically tested to assure their integrity. Panel Patch now offers the advantage of a 1 year shelf life at room temperature with little or no loss of performance. This unique property is illustrated in Figure 3. Refrigeration would also augment the 1 year shelf life.

3. CURRENT DEVELOPMENT WORK

Throughout this discussion, we have included data for other generations of Panel Patch currently being developed and tested. Immediate emphasis is being placed on the bonding of the high-performance thermoplastics composite materials such as those listed in Table 4. Concurrently, a variation of Panel Patch, capable of maintaining 60% of strength at 200°F is under final development. The direction of future activity in these and other areas will be greatly influenced by military and commercial needs and applications.

References

1. Chen, L., Jang, B., Hwang, L., Hawkes, J., and Zee, R. ANTEC '88, 1626 (1988).

Biography

George T. Sivy received his Ph.D. in Polymer Science from the Pennsylvania State University in 1982. As a member of ITW/Devcon, he has been involved with diverse adhesive systems for both OEM and MRO applications. With ITW Adhesive Systems, his emphasis has been on development and application of advanced methacrylate technology for the efficient bonding and repairing of old and new engineering materials.

TABLE 1

	Methacrylate	Epoxy	Urethane
Lap Shear (ASTM D1002)	20–27 MPa (3000–4000 psi)	20–27 MPa (3000–4000 psi)	7–14 MPa (1000–2000 psi)
"T" Peel (ASTM D1876)	53–88 N/cm (30–50 pli)	9–18 N/cm (5–10 pli)	53–88 N/cm (30–50 pli)
Impact (Modified ASTM D3998)	4–5.25 J/cm^2 (20–25 ft–lb/in^2)	0.5–1 J/cm^2 (3–5 ft–lb/in^2)	3–5 J/cm^2 (15–25 ft–lb/in^2)

TABLE 2

	Tensile Shear Strength MPa (psi)	
Test Temperature °C (°F)	Panel Patch Adhesive	Typical Ambient Cure Epoxy Adhesive
–40(–40)	30(4300)	˜30(4300)
–30)–20)	31(4500)	--
–17(0)	33(4750)	--
23(75)	28(4100)	29(4200)
93(200)	16(2300)	<3.5(500)

2024–T3 Al Adherends, acid etched.

ASTM D1002

TABLE 3

Flexural Strength (ASTM D790). . . . . 130 MPa (19,000 psi)
Flexural Modulus . . . . 2 x 10^3 MPa (2.95 x 10^5psi)

Tensile Strength (ASTM D638) . . . . . 70 MPa (10,150 psi)
Tensile Modulus . . . . 690 MPa (100,000 psi)

Average Thickness . . . . 1 ply: 1.9 mm (0.075 in.)
                                       2 ply: 3.7 mm (0.145 in.)

Hardness (Shore D) 70

Coefficient of Thermal Expansion . . . 11.5 x 10^{-5} cm/cm/°C   23°C to 90°C
                                       (6.4 x 10^{-5} in/in/°F   73°F to 194°F)

TABLE 4

| | Adhesive Tensile Shear Strength | |
| | MPa (psi) | |
	2 Ply	3 Ply
Aluminum 2024T3, abraded	12.5 (1800)	16.5 (2300)
Titanium, abraded	12.5 (1800)	16.5 (2300)
CR Steel, abraded	12.5 (1800)	16.5 (2300)
Graphite/Epoxy composites	12.5 (1800)	N.T.
Kevlar®*/Epoxy composites	10 (1450)	N.T.
PEEK (glass-filled)	5.8 (850)	N.T.
Poly(amide-imide)	5.2 (750)	N.T.
Polysulfone	6.7 (960)	Substrate failure

ASTM D3528 Type A

454

TABLE 5

Solvent Resistance
Immersed 2 weeks @ 42°C

Fluid	% 24 hr. Strength Retained
Hydraulic Oil	100
Anti-freeze	82
Distilled Water	100
Sea Water	93
Jet Fuel (A)	98
*Unleaded Gasoline	81
100% RH	84

Abraded Al/Al, ASTM D3528, Type A
*2 months @ 74°F

TABLE 6
*Dart Impact Comparison

Fiber/Matrix	Thickness Mil (in)	Total Energy Absorbed J (in lb)	Maximum Load @ Failure KN (lb (f))
1 Ply Panel Patch	1.6 (0.062)	10.5 (93)	1.5 (336)
2 Ply Panel Patch	3.7 (0.145)	37.3 (330)	3.0 (683)
3 Ply Panel Patch	5.4 (0.211)	64.7 (572)	4.3 (970)
Aramid/Epoxy[1]	1.3 (0.05)	13.0 (114)	1.0 (229)
Graphite/Epoxy[1]	1.1 (0.04)	9.3 (81)	1.0 (229)
Glass/Epoxy[1]	1.9 (0.076)	14.0 (124)	1.5 (341)
Sheet Molding Compound	2.7 (0.106)	23.7 (210)	2.8 (633)

Dart Speed: 3.35m/sec, except 1: 4.53 m/sec.

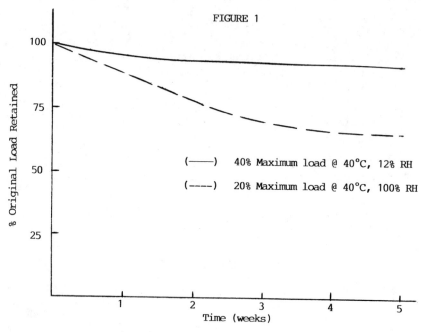

Figure 1. Stressed Aging of Panel Patch.
          Al/Al ASTM D3528 Type A Lap Joints in Stress Rings

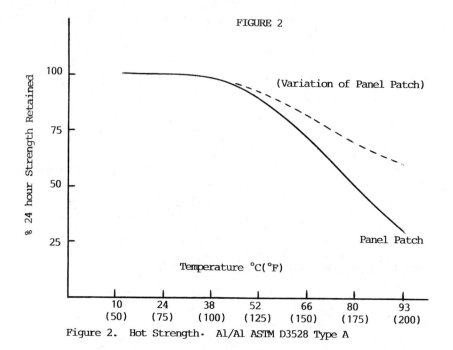

Figure 2. Hot Strength. Al/Al ASTM D3528 Type A

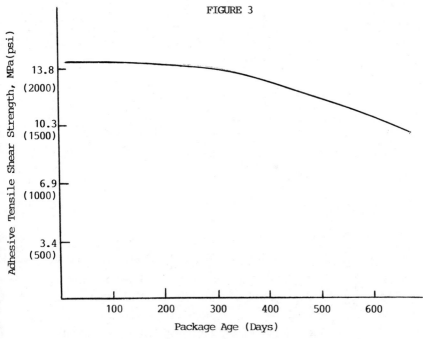

Figure 3.   Shelf Life.   Tested ASTM D3528 Type A Al/Al

THE REPAIR OF THERMOPLASTIC COMPOSITES AFTER IMPACT

Ching-Long Ong, Ming-Fa Sheu, Yie-Yih Liou
Chung-Shan Institute of Science and Technology
P.O. Box 90008-11-12
Taichung, Taiwan, R.O.C.

Abstract

The most two attractive properties of advanced thermoplastic composites are the high impact resistance and the reformability. In order to utilize these advantageous properties, the repair of the thermoplastic composite subjected to impact has been studied.

The materials are Gr/PPS (PolyPhenylene Sulfide) and Gr/PEEK (Poly-Eether Ether Ketone) laminates with a particular lay-up sequence. The specimens were impacted by the instrumented drop weight tester, and then detected by Ultrasonic C-Scan to measure the damage size. Compression after impact (CAI) test was conducted to assess the residual properties, i.e., damage tolerance. Then, the repair methods including the thermo-reforming and patch-thermo-reforming were applied and compression test was conducted again to determine the strength recovery. Results were represented by quantitative relationship between impact
energy level, damage area, residual compression strength, and strength recovery. Based on these results, it was concluded that Gr/PEEK had the best performance including the smallest damage area, highest residual strength and strength recovery.

1. INTRODUCTION

Advanced thermoplastic composite is a rather newly developed materials. With the advantageous properties, e.g., no cold storage required, reformability and high impact energy, thermoplastic composites have attracted many studies on their physical and mechanical properties. Among the thermoplastics, Gr/PEEK and Gr/PPS are more interested, especially their crystallization behavior [1]-[3] and mechanical properties [4]-[6].

For the compression strength after impact, Brink and Spamer[7] investigated the Gr/PEEK, Gr/PPS, and AS-4/3501-5A composites of quasi-isotropic specimens. In addition, Moore and Prediger[8] worked on the impact failure mode investigation. In this study, the Gr/PEEK, Gr/PPS and Gr/Epoxy composites of a particular stacking sequence for an aircraft structure were chosen for the investigation of the impact behavior and repair efficiency. First, the damage area and residual compressive strength were measured to evaluate the damage tolerance. Furthermore, the impact damaged thermoplastic specimens were repaired by thermo-reforming or patch-thermal-reforming, and the compression strength was tested to determined the strength recovery after repair.

2. EXPERIMENTAL

2.1 Material

Three prepreg materials, namely AS-4/PEEK, AS-4/PPS, and T-300/Epoxy used are listed in Table 1. The lay-up sequence is $[90/0_3/45/0/-45/0]_s$ and the specimen size is 6"x4". In addition, the curing or thermoforming procedures and the resultant resin content are listed in Table 2 while their mechanical properties are in Table 3.

2.2 Impact Test

The impact tester is the instrumented drop weight RDT-5000 of Rheometric Inc. with the dart impact head consisted of a 0.5" hemispherical steel tip (Figure 1). The impact energy were 0-180, 0-260, and 0-80 in-lb for AS-4/PEEK, AS-4/PPS, and T-300/Epoxy respectively.

2.3 Compression Test

The impacted and the repaired specimens were compressively tested in Zwick 1474 universal test equipment with cross-head speed 0.05"/min. To avoid buckling in compression test, specimen is guided with steel sheet in the compression fixture as shown in Figures 2 and 3. The compression strength is calculated with the following equation:

$$\sigma_C = \frac{F}{wt}$$

Here σ_C and F are the compression strength and the fracture load respectively, and w and t are width and thickness of the specimen respectively.

2.4 Non-Destructive Inspection

The damage areas of the impacted specimens were detected by S-80 water injection C-Scan ultrasonic tester of Auto Mation Company. The internal damages were recorded as Figure 5 and areas were measured.

2.5 Repair of the Impacted Thermoplastic Specimens

Two repair methods have been tried.

(1) Thermo-Reforming

The impacted specimens were reformed by its original thermoforming procedure, and then ultrasonic scanned to determine the internal flaws. In addition, the compression strength was measured.

(2) Patch-Thermo-Reforming

The impacted specimens were repaired with a 4-layer 0° AS-4/PEEK patch on one side over the damaged area (Figure 4). The specimen and the patch were consolidated with the original thermoforming procedure.

3. RESULT AND DISCUSSION

3.1 Impact Energy and Damage Area

The impact resistances in terms of penetration energy of the three composite systems, namely AS-4/PEEK, AS-4/PPS, and T-300/Epoxy, with the same stacking sequence and specimen thickness are 180, 260, and 80 in-lb respectively. Figure 5 shows the damage area detected by C-Scan at 40 in-lb impact energy. The resultant damage areas at different normalized impact energies, i.e., the impact energy per thickness, for the three materials are shown in Figure 6. Figures 5 and 6 reveal that AS-4/PEEK has smallest damage area at all impact energy levels. On the other hand, AS-4/PPS has largest damage area. That is due to the low interlaminar shear strength (see Table 3). Therefore, the impact induced crack can propagate more easily and produce larger delamination damage over T-300/Epoxy and AS-4/PEEK.

3.2 Damage Area and Residual Compression Strength

The compression strength after impact and its normalized ones with different damage areas are shown in Figures 7 and 8. From the slopes of the curves, it is apparent that the thermoplastics have slower compression strength decrease with increasing damage area than that of the thermosets. Therefore, thermoplastics has better damage tolerance. Figure 7 shows the lower compression strength of AS-4/PPS at zero damage, i.e., no impact, than those of AS-4/PEEK and T-300/Epoxy. This result is due to the lower compression

strength and in-plane shear strength of AS-4/PPS as presented in Table 3. In Figure 8, at the same damage area, the decrease of residual compression strength is in the order of T-300/Epoxy > AS-4/PEEK > AS-4/PPS. This order can be explained by the compressive fracture mechanism. Since the high interlaminar fracture toughness of AS-4/PEEK[9]-[11], there is no delamination occur at low impact energy. However, in order to absorb the energy, the transverse shear crack may happen in the resin matrix. At higher impact energy, fibers take the impact load and break at their limit. On the other hand, AS-4/PPS has low interlaminar fracture toughness as depicted in Figure 6. Delamination would be the main fracture mechanism and absorb most of the impact energy. In addition, T-300/Epoxy is a thermoset composite with more brittle matrix. During the impact, delamination, matrix cracking, and fiber breakage may happen at the same time. From the above fracture mechanism discussion and using the anti-buckling protection at the fixture during compression test, AS-4/PPS has lower decreasing rate of compression strength since the fibers take the compressive load. On the other hand, for AS-4/PEEK, higher impact energy is required to have the same damage area, and the matrix cracking and fiber breakage will occur with large effect on the compressive load path. Therefore, AS-4/PEEK has higher compression strength decreasing. Furthermore, lower impact energy is required to have the same damage area for T-300/Epoxy, but the material is severely damaged. Therefore, T-300/Epoxy has highest compression strength decreasing.

3.3 Impact Energy and Residual Compression Strength

The residual compression strength after different impact energy is shown in Figures 9 and 10. The curves of AS-4/PEEK and AS-4/PPS depict slower compression strength decreasing than T-300/Epoxy, i.e. they have better impact resistance. In addition, after the penetration with 0.5" diameter impactor, the retention of compression strength is 80%, 70%, and 55% for AS-4/PEEK, AS-4/PPS, and T-300/Epoxy, respectively.

Accordingly to Figure 10, after the same impact energy, the decrease of compression strength is in the order of T-300/Epoxy > AS-4/PPS > AS-4/PEEK. This order can be explained by the fracture mechanism and the damage area as presented in Figure 6. AS-4/PEEK has smallest damage area, therefore, it has smallest decrease of compression strength. Figure 6 shows that the damage area of AS-4/PPS is somewhat larger than that of T-300/Epoxy. However, the decrease of compression strength of AS-4/PPS is less than that of T-300/Epoxy since the major fracture is delamination for AS-4/PPS while the T-300/Epoxy composite has deminiation, severe resin crack and fiber breakage.

3.4 Compression Strength After Repair

The impact damaged thermoplastic specimens were repaired with thermoreforming or patch-thermo-reforming. The repaired specimens have good consolidation without C-Scan detectable defects. The strength recovery of the repair of the penetrated AS-4/PEEK is 83.5% and 88.5% for thermo-reforming and patch-thermoreforming respectively as shown in Figures 11 and 12. In addition, at low damage area and impact energy, the thermo-reformed specimen has lower compression strength than that of un-repaired specimen. This might due to resin loss or annealing effect. But at high damage area and impact energy, the recovery of strength is apparent.

For the patch-thermo-reforming method, the damaged specimen is patched on one side with four layers of 0°, 4"x4" prepreg and reformed and consolidated. As compared with thermoreforming method, the repair with patch should be 25% stronger. However, only about 5% increasement is tested, owing to the unsymmetric one-side patch that may cause buckling. In addition, the stress concentration along the edge of the patch is also harmful to the material.

4.   CONCLUSION

About the characterization of impact damage and repair of the three materials, AS-4/PEEK, AS-4/PPS, and T-300/Epoxy, the following conclusion can be made.

(1) At the same impact energy, the damage area detected by C-Scan is in the order of AS-4/PPS > T-300/Epoxy > AS-4/PEEK.

(2) With the same damage area, the retention of compression strength is in the order of AS-4/PPS > AS-4/PEEK > T-300/Epoxy.

(3) Impacting with the same energy, the retention of compression strength is in the order of AS-4/PEEK > AS-4/PPS > T-300/Epoxy.

(4) The thermo-reforming and patch-thermo-reforming repair can increase the compression strength of the damaged composites.

5. REFERENCES

1. J.P. Jog and V.M. Nadkarni, "Crystallization Kinetics of Polyaryl Ether Ketones, " J. Appl. Polym. Sci. 32, 3317, 1986.

2. C.N. Velisaris and J.C. Seferis, "Crystallization Kinetics of Polyetherether Ketone(PEEK)," Polym. Eng. Sci. 26 (22), 1574, 1986.

3. Ching-Long Ong, Ming-Fa Sheu, Wen-Long Chung and Jan-Han Lin, "The Measurement of Crystallinity of Advanced Thermoplastic's," 33rd International SAMPE Symposium and Exhibition, Anaheim, CA, March, 7-10, 1988.

4. Wen-Liang Lin, Jiann-Tsun Hu, Chen-Chi M. Ma and Lin-Tee Hsiue, "Rheological Properties of High Performance Engineering Thermoplastic Resins," MRL bull. res. dev., 2, 9-15, 1987.

5. A.A. Ogale and R.L. McCullough, "Influence of Microstructure on Elastic and Viscoelastic Properties of Polyether Ether Ketone," Composites Science and Technology, 30, 185, 1987.

6. J.A. Nixon and M.G. Phillips, "A Study of the Development of Impact Damage in Cross-Ply Carbon Fiber/PEEK Laminates Using Acoustic Emission," Composite Science and technology, 31, 1, 1988.

7. C.T. Spamer and N.D. Brink, "Investigation of the Compression Strength after Impact Properties of Carbon/PPS and Carbon/APC-2 Thermoplastic Materials," 33rd International SMAPE Symposium and Exhibition, Anaheim, CA, March, 7-10, 1988.

8. D.R. Moore and R.S. Prediger, "A Study of Low-Energy Impact of Continuous Carbon-Fiber-Reinforced Composites," Polymer Composites, 9, 330, 1988.

9. David C. Leach, Don C. Curtis, and David R. Tamblim, "Delamination Behavior of Carbon Fiber/ Poly (etherether ketone) (PEEK) Composites," in Toughened Composites, ASTM STP 937, Norman J. Johnston, editor, NASA-Langley Research Center, 1987, pp. 358-380.

10. Peggy, Cebe, Su-Don Hong, Shirley Chung and Amitava Cupta, "Mechanical Properties and Morphology of Poly (etherether ketone)" ibid, ASTM, STP 937, pp. 342-357.

11. Charles F. Griffin, "Damage Tolerance of Toughened Resin Graphite Composite," ASTM STP 937,

pp. 23-33.

6. BIOGRAPHIES

Dr. Ching-Long Ong is an Associate Researcher in Material Research and Developing Center and Aeronautical Research Lab. He is in charge of material and process for an aircraft development program. He is specialized in non-metallic materials applications and developments, especially in the fields of composites and adhesive bonding technology. Dr. Ong received his B.S. in chemical engineering from Chung Cheng Institute of Science and Technology, Taiwan at 1970, and M.S. in Chemical Engineering from University of Washington at 1975. During the period from June 1978 to June 1988, he received an M.S. in computer science and the Ph.D. in the field of polymer material application and computer simulation at University of Washington.

Ming-Fa Sheu is a group leader of composites at CSIST, Taiwan, R.O.C. since 1986. He received his M.S. degree in organic chemistry from National Tsing Hua University in Hsin-Chu, Taiwan, R.O.C. in 1974. In the past he worked at United Industrial Research Laboratory (UIRL) of Industrial Technology Research Institute (ITRI) as a research engineer (1976-1983), and China Carbon Fiber Company (1983-1985) as a section head of R&D in Hsin-Chu, Taiwan, R.O.C. His research interests are in the field of synthesis of polymer and the application of thermoplastic composites.

Yie-Yih Liou is a research engineer at CSIST, Taiwan, R.O.C. since 1987. He received his B.S. degree in civil engineering from National Cheng Kung University in Tainan, Taiwan, R.O.C. at 1985 and M.S. degree in civil engineering from National Chiao Tung University in Hsin-Chu, Taiwan, R.O.C. at 1987. His research interests are in the field of structural analysis and mechanical tests of composite materials.

Table 1.The Physical Properties of Raw Materials

Product Designation	Product Supplier	Nominal Fiber Areal Weight	Ply Thickness
PPS Matrix AS-4/PPS	Phillips Petroleum Company	145±5 g/m²	0.008"
PEEK Matrix AS-4/PEEK	Fiberite ICI	145±5 g/m²	0.0055"
EPOXY Matrix T-300/976	Fiberite ICI	145±5 g/m²	0.005"

Table 2. Laminate Processing Parameters

Material UD-Prepreg	Processing	Fiber Content (% Volume)	Resin Content (% Weight)
AS-4/PPS	316°C/200 psi/20 min 600 psi/15 min 200°C/600 psi/30 min	56	38
AS-4/PEEK	380°C/200 psi/20 min 600 psi/15 min 300°C/600 psi/30 min	62	32
T-300/976	Standard 177°C Autoclave Cure	62	35

Table 3. The Mechanical Properties of Composites

Material \ Property	AS-4/PEEK	AS-4/PPS	T-300/976
Tensile (0°) Strength, ksi Modulus, msi	333.0 22.6	245.0 16.2	230.0 21.0
Compressive (0°) Strength, ksi Modulus, msi	195.3 16.4	95.5 13.4	190.8 19.0
In-Plane Shear Strength, ksi	19.83	3.17	14.70

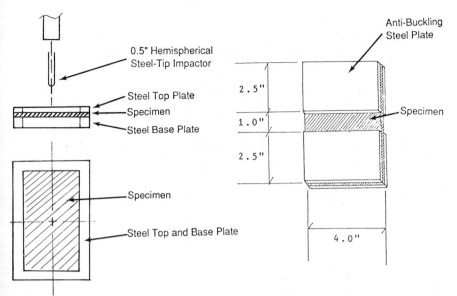

0.5" Hemispherical
Steel-Tip Impactor

Steel Top Plate
Specimen
Steel Base Plate

Specimen

Steel Top and Base Plate

2.5"

1.0"

2.5"

Anti-Buckling
Steel Plate

Specimen

4.0"

Figure 1. The Impactor and Specimen Assembly

Figure 2. Compression Test Specimen and
Anti-Buckling Steel Plate

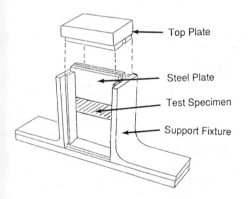

Top Plate

Steel Plate

Test Specimen

Support Fixture

Figure 3. Compression After Impact Test
Fixture with Specimen

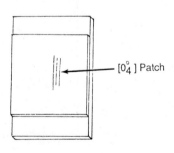

$[0_4^\circ]$ Patch

Figure 4. The Repaired Composite Specimen
with a Patch on One Side

AS-4/PEEK   AS-4/PPS   T-300/EPOXY

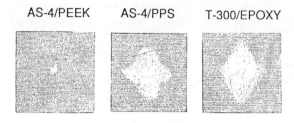

Figure 5. Ultrasonic Detected Impact Damage Area
of Different Composites at 40 in-lb
Impact Energy

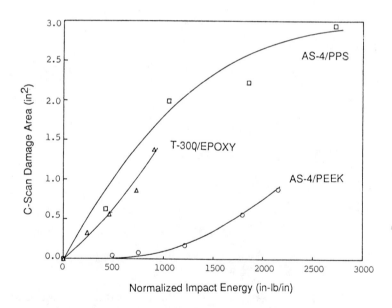

Figure 6. The Relationship of Normalized Impact Energy and
C-Scan Damage Area of Different Composites

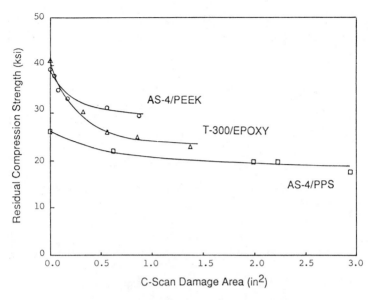

Figure 7. The Relationship of C-Scan Damage Area and
Residual Compression Strength of Different
Composites

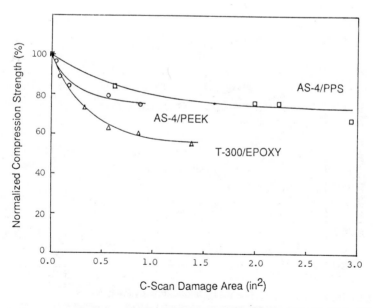

Figure 8. The Relationship of C-Scan Damage Area and
Normalized Compression Strength of
Different Composites

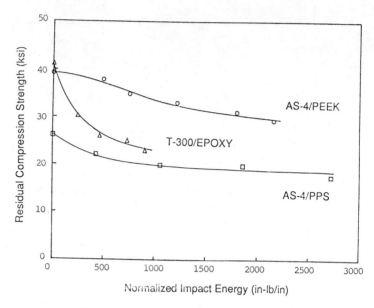

Figure 9. The Relationship of Normalized Impact Energy
and Residual Compression Strength of
Different Composites

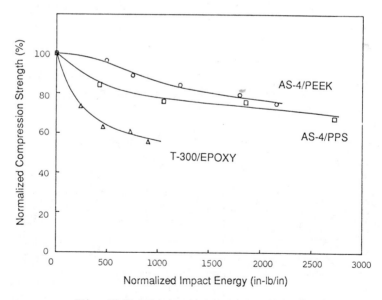

Figure 10. The Relationship of Normalized Impact Energy
and Normalized Compression Strength of
Different Composites

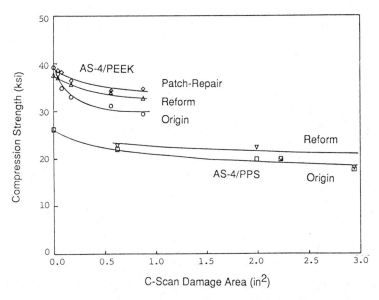

Figure 11. The Compression Strength of Repaired Specimens
with Originally Different Impact Damage Areas

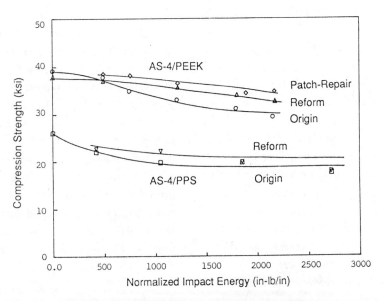

Figure 12. The Compression Strength of Repaired Specimens
with Originally Different Normalized Impact Energies

Use Of The Four Point Flex Test for Examining The Compression Stress-Strain Behavior Of Unidirectional Composites

Perry R. Wagner
Air Force Materials Laboratory / MLBC
Wright-Patterson Air Force Base, Ohio

Abstract

The objective of this paper is to investigate the advantages that the four point flex test offers in acquiring insight into the compression behavior of low compression strength unidirectional composite systems. Several conclusions can be drawn from the ASTM D790 flexural test. First, the strength and modulus values for flex are not equivalent to similar figures of merit derived from tension and compression tests. Secondly, a comparison of the flexural and tensile strength values qualitatively indicates the value of the compression strength. And finally, an analysis for bimodular, anisotropic materials combined with strain gage data from the top and bottom surfaces of the flex coupon is used to reasonably measure a material's tensile and compressive moduli. In addition to these points being enumerated, test coupon preparation techniques as well as nondestructive characterization methods are described.

1. Introduction

It has been standard practice in the composites industry to perform flexural tests (per ASTM D790) as a means of screening materials, establishing quality control, evaluating on-line manufacturing process changes and investigating research concepts. The flex test is popular for many reasons: (1) it is an inexpensive and simple test to perform, (2) the data reduction methods are straightforward and (3) there is general industry-wide acceptance of the test as a material qualifier. In lieu of these advantages, however, the flex test does possess various shortcomings. First off, it is a general practice in the composites arena to tacitly assume an inherent relationship between flexural, tensile and compressive data. But for many advanced composite systems, this is not the case. Many systems tend to be bimodular and have a compression strength lower than their tensile strength. The state of stress across the thickness of a flex coupon is non-uniform[1], thus creating an averaging of the tensile and compressive stresses into the somewhat vague term known as the flexural strength. This flexural averaging or "smearing" may apply to the modulus term as well.

Another issue worth mentioning, but which will not be specifically addressed in this paper, is that different advanced composite systems may (and often do) exhibit widely different flexural failure modes[2]. For this case, the meaningfulness in quantitatively comparing flex strengths becomes nebulous. With these limitations having been enumerated, this paper will focus on the merits of the flex test -- what can be learned and how it can be used.

In order to elucidate the benefits of the flex test, two unidirectional composite materials are compared: Hercules AS-4/3501-6 and IM-6/3501-6. These material systems were chosen for the following reasons. Both systems possess well documented manufacturer's data.[3] Also, AS-4 and IM-6 fibers have similar tensile strengths, but different compressive strengths (IM-6 has a much lower compression strength than AS-4). This fact is ascertained not from single fiber tests, but from the manufacturer's compression data for the different fibers in the same matrix. A final reason for choosing these materials is that both systems exhibit a bimodular nature. The objectives of this study are (1) to show the discrepancies between flex and tensile strengths for both materials, realizing that this difference is wider for IM-6/3501-6 because its compression strength is lower,

and (2) to show that the bimodular nature of these two systems can be accurately quantified by applying strain gages to the top and bottom surfaces of the flex coupon in addition to performing a mechanics analysis which offers a slightly modified formula to the standard beam theory modulus equation.

2. Experimental Procedures

A brief description of the methods used to fabricate, characterize and test the previously mentioned material systems is in order.

2.1 Panel Fabrication

One panel from each of the materials was manually fabricated from 12" prepreg tape, bagged and autoclave cured. Neither system required postcuring. Both panels are 12 ply, 12" x 12" unidirectional laminates. The prepreg for both materials was manufactured in early 1987, and was placed in appropriate cold storage for the interim period. A Thermal Equipment autoclave (Model 8397) was used to cure both panels. The cure cycles for both systems were provided by the manufacturer.

2.2 NDE and Physical Properties Check

Both composite laminates were subjected to ultrasonic testing by a Testech Ultrasonic Immersion system. C-scans of the panels were created to check for delaminations and/or voids. Photomicrographs, density and percent fiber volume content measurements were taken from three sections chosen randomly from both of the panels. The photomicrographs were taken at 300x magnification, normal to the fiber axis, so as to inspect for voids. The density and percent fiber volume content measurements were performed to check for the resin and fiber content in the panel.

2.3 Mechanical Testing

The two materials were subjected to the test matrix shown in Table 1 below. The number of specimens tested is in brackets. All tests were performed at room temperature.

	Four Point Flex	Tension
AS-4/3501-6	[5]	[5]
IM-6/3501-6	[5]	[5]

Table 1. Material Test Matrix

The four point flex test was performed according to procedures outlined in ASTM D790. The span-to-depth ratio was nominally set at 32:1. The flex coupon dimensions were nominally 3" x 0.5" x thickness. Strain gages (BLH type FAE-18-12-S6HL) were used to record strain on the top and bottom surfaces of the flex coupon. The flex coupons were tested on an Instron testing machine (Model # 1115).

The tension tests were performed per ASTM D3039. The tension coupon dimensions were 9" x 1" x thickness. The gage length for these coupons were 6". Fiberglass cloth/epoxy end tabs were affixed to the tension coupons with fast curing epoxy. These tabs were 1.5" long with a machined 20° bevel to reduce possible stress concentrations. An extensometer was used to record strain on the tension coupons. The tension tests were performed on an Instron (Model #1123).

All of the mechanical test coupons and physical characterization samples were machined from two laminates according to a schematic which staggered their positions so as to create a random sampling from the panel.

2.4 Data Reduction

For the flex test, standard beam theory equations were used to calculate the ultimate flexural strength and the modulus. The modulus was calculated at four different strain levels so as to examine the relationship between modulus and strain. In addition to the beam theory equation, an analysis was performed which resulted in a slightly modified modulus equation, taking into account the bimodular nature of these composites. For a given material, the modified modulus values were calculated at the same strain levels as were the beam theory modulus values.

The tensile data was reduced according to ASTM D3039. The ultimate strength was calculated. In addition, four moduli were measured at varying strain levels. The strain levels for tension were different from those for flex, but were nominally chosen at (1) initial strain, (2) intermediate strain, (3) near-ultimate strain and (4) ultimate strain.

2.5 Failure Analysis

A fractographic analysis was performed on two (2) flex coupons (one from each material) on a Jeol scanning electron microscope. The flex failure surfaces were contrasted to one another and differences in the mode of failure were noted. In addition, these photographs were compared to failure surfaces of known origin in order that a correlation might be made[4].

3. Experimental Results

From the procedures described previously, a sufficient amount of data was collected to fulfill the mechanical test matrix and to verify that the coupons were well characterized.

3.1 NDE and Physical Characterization Results

A visual inspection of the panels showed no signs of improper curing, no discolorations or radical thickness variations. The ultrasonic C-scan of the two panels displayed no delaminations or voids. All of the photomicrographs taken exhibited good fiber packing, no voids and few resin-rich areas. A listing of the density and

percent fiber volume data is shown in Table 2.

AS-4/3501-6

Specimen Number	Specific Gravity	Percent Fiber Volume
SP-1	1.57	58
SP-2	1.60	62
SP-3	1.58	60
Average	1.58	60
Std. Dev.	0.02	2.0

IM-6/3501-6

Specimen Number	Specific Gravity	Percent Fiber Volume
MP-1	1.56	62
MP-2	1.57	62
MP-3	1.56	60
Average	1.56	61
Std. Dev.	0.01	1.2

Table 2. AS-4/3501-6 and IM-6/3501-6 Density and Percent Fiber Volume Data.

AS-4/3501-6

	Four Point Flex	Tension
Strength (Ksi)	225	276
Std. Dev.	10.3	22.9
Failure Mode	Complex	Tensile

IM-6/3501-6

	Four Point Flex	Tension
Strength (Ksi)	190	299
Std. Dev.	15.6	16.1
Failure Mode	Complex	Tensile

Table 3. Comparison of Strength Values for AS-4/3501-6 and IM-6/3501-6

AS-4/3501-6
(Vf=60%)

Test	Data Reduction Method	Initial Modulus (Msi)	Intermediate Modulus (Msi)	Near Ultimate Modulus (Msi)	Ultimate Modulus (Msi)
0°-4 Pt. Flex	ASTM D790 (Top Gage)	16.1	17.2	17.6	17.8
0°-4 Pt. Flex	Modified Analysis (Tension Modulus)	16.3	17.7	18.4	18.8
0°-Tension	ASTM D3039	18.6	18.8	19.4	19.7
0°-4 Pt. Flex	ASTM D790 (Bottom Gage)	16.0	16.2	16.1	15.9
0°-4 Pt. Flex	Modified Analysis (Comp. Modulus)	15.9	15.7	15.4	15.0

IM-6/3501-6
(Vf=61%)

Test	Data Reduction Method	Initial Modulus (Msi)	Intermediate Modulus (Msi)	Near Ultimate Modulus (Msi)	Ultimate Modulus (Msi)
0°-4 Pt. Flex	ASTM D790 (Top Gage)	18.4	18.6	19.4	20.0
0°-4 Pt. Flex	Modified Analysis (Tension Modulus)	18.5	18.9	20.0	21.0
0°-Tension	ASTM D3039	20.4	20.6	21.6	22.3
0°-4 Pt. Flex	ASTM D790 (Bottom Gage)	18.2	18.2	18.3	18.3
0°-4 Pt. Flex	Modified Analysis (Comp. Modulus)	18.2	18.1	17.9	17.5

Table 4. Comparison of Various Moduli for AS-4/3501-6 and IM-6/3501-6

3.2 Mechanical Test Results

The raw data produced from the test matrix was reduced according to the aforementioned equations. The calculated strength data are shown in Table 3. The modulus values are tabulated in Table 4.

3.3 Failure Analysis Results

Photographs of the fractured flex surfaces were compared to pictures of composite failures whose origin is well characterized. For both materials, the flex coupons showed the typical features associated with flexural failure. There is a distinct separation in appearance between the tension side and the compression side of the coupon. The line of demarcation is the neutral axis. The tension area appears rough due to the variations in failed fiber lengths. The compression region, on the other hand, appears smooth because the fibers have been smeared to the approximately the same length. For the most part, both materials' fracture surfaces were similar in appearance. The IM-6/3501-6 flex coupon, however, showed more cracks in the failure surface quite possibly due to resin depletion[5].

4. Discussion of Experimental Results

Several key topics require discussion to elucidate the impact of the data presented.

4.1 Discrepancy between flex and tensile strength

Whitney and Knight suggest that "data generated from a unidirectional flexure test usually yield higher strength than data obtained from a standard tensile coupon". This is so hypothesized because the non-uniform stress distribution in the flex coupon statistically exposes fewer flaws to a critical stress than does the uniform tensile stress distribution[6]. However, an opposite trend is noted for both the AS-4/3501-6 and the IM-6/3501-6 systems examined here; the flex strength is lower than the tensile strength. For AS-4/3501-6, this difference is 51 Ksi; for IM-6/3501-6, this difference is 109 Ksi. Because of the non-uniform state of stress in a flex coupon, the flex test tends to incorporate (average) the material's tension and compression strength together into its flex strength value. In light of this information, the compression strength is predicted to be lower than the tensile strength for both systems, but much lower for the IM-6/3501-6 system. This qualitative estimation is supported by Hercules' product data.

4.2 Modified Beam Analysis

The standard beam theory equation used to calculate the modulus of a flex coupon as a function of its strain assumes the tested material to be unimodular (tension modulus equals compression modulus). However, as mentioned previously, many advanced composite systems exhibit a bimodular characteristic; these systems may require a modified flexural analysis which takes into account a shift in the coupon's neutral axis.

AS-4/3501-6 and IM-6/3501-6 are material systems which fall into this category. Strain data from flex tests performed on these materials was entered into the modified modulus equation. Values for tensile and compressive moduli were calculated at the various strain levels.

The tensile modulus calculated using the modified beam analysis is very close to the modulus from the tensile test. The modified beam analysis predicts the material's modulus slightly better than does standard beam theory. As an example, for the AS-4/3501-6 material at the intermediate modulus range (approximately 0.7% strain), the difference between the standard beam analysis and the modulus from the tensile test is 9%. The difference between the modified beam analysis modulus and the tensile test is 6%. The ability of the modified analysis to properly measure the material's tensile modulus improves slightly as the strain increases. In this manner, IM-6/3501-6 behaves similarly to AS-4/3501-6.

Other important observations can be drawn from this data. Note that for both materials the ASTM (bottom gage) modulus stays constant as strain increases, whereas the ASTM (top gage) modulus increases with increasing strain. Note also how the disparity in the modified moduli calculations increases as a function of strain. At the ultimate modulus, this difference is 20% for AS-4/3501-6 and 17% for IM-6/3501-6. Much of this disparity is due to the reverse stress-strain tensile nature of both of the graphite fibers. This characteristic is present in the flex curves as well as the tensile curves. In light of these observations, the modulus characteristics of the AS-4/3501-6 system are similar to those of the IM-6/3501-6 system except that the modulus values for IM-6/3501-6 are approximately 10% higher in both tension and compression.

5. Conclusion

It has not been determined experimentally just how applicable the modified beam analysis is to other advanced composite systems. It should be noted that both the tensile and compression stress-strain behaviors are assumed to be Hookean. If a material is non-Hookean, the modified analysis may not be applicable. For those materials that are linear, the data recorded from the flex and tensile tests can give insight into the material's compression stress-strain behavior. This can be very helpful in screening applications which require many batches of materials to be characterized as efficiently and cheaply as possible.

6. Acknowledgements

Special thanks is given to the technicians at the Materials Lab for their excellent support on this project; they are Chuck Fowler, Bill Ragland and Jim Tarkany.

7. Appendix

The derivation which follows is a modification of standard beam theory for the four point flex test. In this analysis, the neutral axis is allowed to shift as a result of the bimodular nature of the tested material. The four point flex test coupon is shown in Figure A.1. The corresponding moment diagram is displayed in Figure A.2.

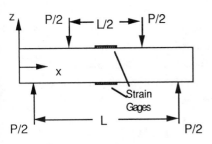

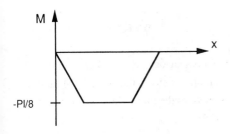

Figure A.1 Four point flex coupon with reference frame

Figure A.2 Four point flex moment diagram

Strain gages are attached to the top and bottom surfaces of the coupon. Load readings are recorded and plotted as a function of these strain readings. From the moment diagram, we conclude that the moment M applied to the midsection of the beam equals $(-PL)/8$. The neutral axis shifts an amount delta as seen in Figure A.3.

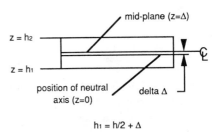

$$h_1 = h/2 + \Delta$$
$$h_2 = -h/2 + \Delta$$

Figure A.3 Four point flex coupon showing the neutral axis shift

In accordance with standard beam theory, the strain throughout the middle section of the beam (where the moment is constant) is assumed to be a linear function of z. Mathematically, this is

$$\varepsilon = \varepsilon_0 + (K_x) z \qquad (1)$$

But, the strain at the neutral axis (z=0) is equal to zero. Therefore,

$$\varepsilon = (K_x) z \qquad (2)$$

It is at this point in the analysis that the derivation takes a different route from standard beam theory. Here, we assume no prior knowledge of the neutral axis' position. We refer to laminated analysis[7] which presents the constitutive relations for symmetric beams. The normalized moment term M_x is given as a function of the strain curvatures. M_x is the applied moment M normalized by the width b. Assuming only curvatures in the x-direction, we have

$$M_x = D_{11} K_x \quad , \text{where}$$

$$D_{11} = \int_{h1}^{h2} Q_{11}^{(k)} z^2 \, dz \tag{3}$$

For the unidirectional composite laminates under consideration, $Q_{11}^{(k)}$ is approximately equal to the longitudinal modulus E_L. Thus, (3) becomes

$$M = (b)(K_x) \int_{h1}^{h2} E_L z^2 \, dz \tag{4}$$

Now, the integral of equation (4) can be expanded so as to sum the tensile and compressive portions of the coupon separately. Thus,

$$M = (b)(K_x) \left[\int_{h1}^{0} E_T z^2 \, dz + \int_{0}^{h2} E_C z^2 \, dz \right] \tag{5}$$

Integrating (5) gives

$$M = \frac{(b)(K_x)}{3} \left[E_C h_2^3 - E_T h_1^3 \right] \tag{6}$$

The second equation to be used states simply that the summation of stresses in the beam's midsection must equal zero. Splitting this equation into its tensile and compressive parts gives

$$\int_{h1}^{0} \sigma_T \, dz + \int_{0}^{h2} \sigma_C \, dz = 0 \tag{7}$$

Substitution of Hooke's Law in conjunction with equation (1) into equation (7) let's us write

$$\int_{h1}^{0} E_T z \, dz + \int_{0}^{h2} E_C z \, dz = 0 \tag{8}$$

When integrated, (8) becomes

$$E_C h_2^2 - E_T h_1^2 = 0 \tag{9}$$

We now have two equations: (6) and (9); and we have two unknowns: E_T and E_C. Terms K_x, h_1 and h_2 can be written as functions of the upper strain (ε_U), the lower strain (ε_L) and the thickness (h) as shown below.

$$K_x = \frac{\varepsilon_U - \varepsilon_L}{h} \tag{10}$$

$$h_1 = \frac{\varepsilon_L \, h}{\varepsilon_U - \varepsilon_L} \tag{11}$$

$$h_2 = \frac{\varepsilon_U \, h}{\varepsilon_U - \varepsilon_L} \tag{12}$$

Substitution of (10)-(12) into the simultaneous solution of (6) and (9) provides the following formulas for E_T and E_C.

$$E_T = \left(\frac{3 \, P \, L}{8 \, b \, h^2} \right) \left(\frac{\varepsilon_L - \varepsilon_U}{\varepsilon_L^2} \right) \tag{13}$$

$$E_C = \left(\frac{3 \, P \, L}{8 \, b \, h^2} \right) \left(\frac{\varepsilon_L - \varepsilon_U}{\varepsilon_U^2} \right) \tag{14}$$

8. References

1. Timoshenko, S., Strength of Materials, vol. II, (Van Nostrand Co., 1962), p. 368.

2. Whitney, J. M. and Husman, G. E., Use of the Flexure Test for Determining Environmental Behavior of Fibrous Composites, (Experimental Mechanics: May, 1978, vol. 18, No. 5), pp. 185-190.

3. AS-4/3501-6 and IM-6/3501-6 Material Datasheet, Hercules, 1985.

4. Grove, R. and Smith, B., Compendium Of Post-Failure Analysis Techniques For Composite Materials, AFWAL-TR-86-4137, January 1987 Interim Report, p. 6-103.

5. Private meeting with Patricia Stumpff (expert in failure analysis), Wright-Patterson AFB Materials Laboratory, January, 1989.

6. Whitney, J. M. and Knight, M., The Relationship Between Tensile Strength and Flexure Strength in Fiber-reinforced Composites, (Experimental Mechanics: June, 1980, vol. 20, No. 6).

7. Whitney, J. M., Structural Analysis Of Laminated Anisotropic Plates, Technomic Publishing Company, 1987, p. 24.

9. Biography

Perry Wagner received his B.S. in Mechanical Engineering at the University of Dayton in December, 1986. He is presently working in the Materials Laboratory at Wright-Patterson Air Force Base, Ohio. His areas of interest include high-temperature structural materials and mechanical testing.

34th International SAMPE Symposium
May 8-11, 1989

IMPACT FATIGUE TESTING: A TECHNIQUE FOR THE ASSESSMENT OF
DAMAGE TOLERANCE IN POLYMER COMPOSITES

B. P. Jang, C. Christiansen, L. R. Hwang, W. K. Shih, R. C. Wilcox
Materials Engineering Program
Composites Research Labs, 201 Ross Hall
Auburn University, AL 36849

ABSTRACT

A new method for evaluating the damage tolerance is herein proposed. This technique involves repeated instrumented impact testing of the same specimen using the same tester. An instrumented impact testing machine capable of giving load-deflection traces is required in the present technique. A load-deflection curve obtained for a specimen in response to the 1st impact is recorded, which includes the numerical data of the maximum load (P_m^1). This impacted specimen is then loaded for a second time with its load-deflection curve traced and P_m^2. Alternatively, several curves can be overlayed together in the same diagram after n repeated impacts. The normalized values, $\log (P_m^n/P_m^1)$, if plotted versus $\log n$, usually demonstrates a good straight line. This indicates the existence of an exponential decay relationship, $P_m^n = P_m^1 (n^{-b})$. A smaller value of the slope b would indicate a more damage tolerant composite. Various loading modes and sample geometries can be selected for the present test.

INTRODUCTION

Fiber reinforced polymer composites are becoming more widely used for structural applications because of their high strength to weight and stiffness to weight ratios. This has resulted in an increasing need to develop and improve the analytical and experimental methods to characterize and predict the mechanical behavior of these materials. A major concern in using brittle matrix composites for aerospace applications is the poor impact damage tolerance commonly found with these materials. A low energy impact on these materials may cause a dramatic reduction in the material integrity even though the damage is invisible from the surface. The development of reliable techniques for assessing the damage tolerance of fiber composites is the main objective of this research. The most popular technique has been the compression-after-impact test [1-5]. This technique usually involves a tedious sample fabrication process and requires a special specimen holding fixture. The presently proposed impact fatigue technique involves repeated instrumented impact testing of the same specimen using the same tester. The reduction in maximum load (an indication of strength) and curve slope (an indication of stiffness) on the load-deflection traces, as well as the total absorbed energy can be regarded as a measure for damage tolerance.

EXPERIMENTAL

Materials and Sample Preparation

Two groups of fiber composites were made. The first group was made out of either graphite, glass, or Kevlar-49 unidirectional Cofab[R] fabrics (Composite Reinforcements, Inc., Tuscaloosa, AL) impregnated with Epon 828 epoxy resin mixed with Z-curing agent (Shell Chemicals). These samples were cured in a compression molding machine at 80°C for two hours and then post-cured at 150°C in a vacuum oven for 2.5 hours. The other group was prepared from either graphite, glass, or Kevlar-49 prepreg tapes (3M Company). The Kevlar and graphite prepreg samples were cured at 121°C for 65 minutes and post-cured at 138°C for one hour. All of these samples were cut into 5.1 cm x 1.27 cm specimens for impact fatigue test.

Equipment and Test Procedure

The set-up for this research was a Dynatup model 730-I instrumented impact tester manufactured by the General Research Corporation. A load transducer (accelerometer) was mounted to the impactor tip of which the output signals were transferred to a data acquisition board built in an IBM PC-AT computer. The energy calculations performed by the 730-I require the data on the tup velocity just before impact. This can be obtained by measuring the time necessary for a flag to pass through a photodiode detector. The incident or impact energy is based on the conservation of kinematic and potential energies of the falling dart. Plots of impact load as a function of time (or force-deflection curve) and energy absorbed by the specimen as a function of time (or absorbed energy-deflection curve) were displayed on the computer monitor instantaneously after each test. The total absorbed energy was determined by the area under each force-deflection curve. Different impact energies or velocities were achieved by varying the height and/or the weight of the falling tower.

RESULTS AND DISCUSSION

Load-Deflection Traces

The load-deflection curve obtained for a specimen in response to the first impact was recorded, which included the numerical data of the maximum load (P_m^1), the energy absorbed by the specimen up to maximum load (E_m^1), the slope of the curve before reaching its elastic limit (S^1). This impacted specimen was then loaded for a second time to obtain a second load-deflection trace and P_m^2 and E_m^2 as well. The ratios P_m^2/P_m^1, E_m^2/E_m^1, and S^2/S^1 can be used as a measure for the damage assessment. However, we have found it more informative to overlay many load-deflection curves together in a same diagram after several repeated impacts. Figure 1 shows such a diagram for a glass-fiber fabric-epoxy laminate. As the number of repeated impacts increases, the maximum load (an indication of the material strength) decreases. Also found to be decreased is the slope of the load-time curve before reaching its elastic limit, which is proportional to the stiffness of the sample. As a result of the stiffness reduction, the maximum deflection also increases. In general, the total absorbed energy is also reduced as the degree of damage increases.

Decay Diagrams

A wide scope of incident energies can be exerted on a sample by adjusting the drop weight and/or height of the falling tower. A large number of fiber composites, subjected to impact fatigue testing with various incident energies, have been examined. For a given material, there usually exists a critical incident energy (E_c) above which cracks will be initiated in response to just a few impacts. The maximum load of nth impact is normalized with respect to that of 1st one, (P_m^n/P_m^1), then plotted versus the number of impacts, n, as shown in Figs.2-7. A linear decrease in these log-log plots suggests an exponential decay relationship such as $P^{mn} = P_m^1(n^{-b})$. A smaller value of the slope b would imply a more damage tolerant composite. Here, the slope in the log P vs. log n diagram is a good indication of the impact fatigue durability or the damage tolerance of the material.

When the incident energy is less than E_c, the number of cycles to develop appreciable damage, N_c, (when delamination is first observed) is an indicator of the damage tolerance of a given composite. Prior to this incipient damage point, the log P vs. log n curve is essentially a horizontal line. After the damage occurs, the curve for the most part exhibits one or more discontinuous linear segments of different slopes, corresponding to different failure modes.

The critical incident energy, E_c, for the graphite, Kevlar, and glass fabric reinforced epoxy composites are approximately 2.3 J, 2.5 J, and 5.0 J, respectively. However, for the prepreg-based graphite, Kevlar, and glass composites, the values of E_c are 3.25 J, 5.0 J and 7.5 J, respectively. Under comparable conditions, the glass fiber composites are observed to have the smallest slope (b), while the graphite ones have the largest slope. Therefore, the order of damage tolerance from high to low will be glass, Kevlar and graphite composites.

Failure Modes

The results of visual observation and SEM examination of the failure modes and damage mechanisms in fiber composites in relation to the repeated impacts will be presented and discussed at the conference.

CONCLUSIONS

1. Repeated impacts or impact fatigue tests represent a convenient method for assessing the damage tolerance of fiber composites.

2. For a given composite laminate, there exists a critical incident energy (E_c) above which significant damage will occur to the composite in response to just a few impacts. In this case, the slope (b) of the log P_m vs. log N curve can be used as a damage tolerance index; a smaller b means a better damage resistant material.

3. Below the critical incident energy, the number of cycles to develop appreciable damage (N_c) is also a useful index for damage tolerance.

4. Based on the values of E_c, b, and N_c, the glass fiber composites possess the greatest damage tolerance, followed by Kevlar and then graphite fiber composites.

ACKNOWLEDGE

We gratefully acknowledge the financial support of the U.S. Army Research Office. Also authors L.R.H and R.C.W. would like to thank NSF EPSCoR for their support for this project.

REFERENCES

1. C.F. Griffin, "Damage Tolerance of Toughened Resin Graphite Composites," ASTM STP 937, ASTM, Philadelphia, PA, 1987. pp. 23-33.
2. M.M. Sohi, H.T. Hahn, and J.G. Williams, "The Effects of Resin Toughness and Modulus on Compressive Failure Modes of Quasi-Isotropic Graphite/Epoxy Laminates," Ref. 1, pp. 37-60.
3. J.G. Williams, "Effects of Impact Damage and Open Holes on the Compressive Strength of Tough Resin/High Strain Fiber Toughness", NASA TM-85756, National Aeronautics and Space Administration, 1984.

4. K.R. Hirschbuehler, "A Comparison of Several Mechanical Tests Used To Evaluate the Toughness of Composites," Ref. 1, pp. 61-73.
5. B.A. Byers, "Behavior of Damaged Graphite/Epoxy Laminates Under Compressive Loading," NASA Contractor Report 159293, NASA, August 1980.

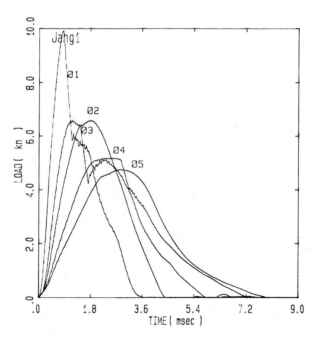

Fig. 1 Load-time traces of a glass Cofab laminate subjected to various times of impacts.

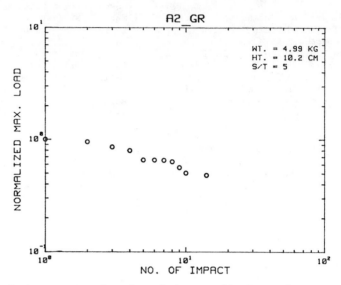

Fig. 2   A representative plot of the normalized max. load
(P_m^n/P_m^1) vs. the no. of impact (N) of a graphite
Cofab composite.

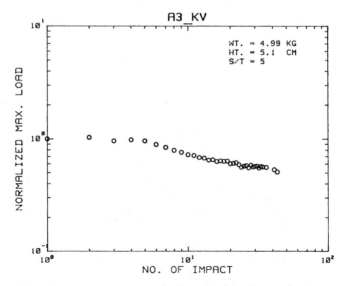

Fig. 3   A representative plot of the normalized max. load
(P_m^n/P_m^1) vs. the no. of impact (N) of a Kevlar Cofab
composite.

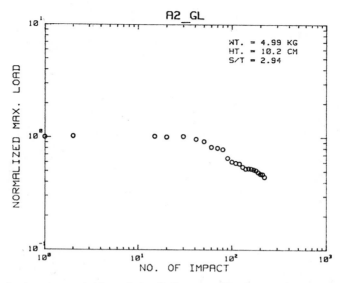

Fig. 4 A representative plot of the normalized max. load
(P_m^n/P_m^1) vs. the no. of impact (N) of a glass Cofab
composite.

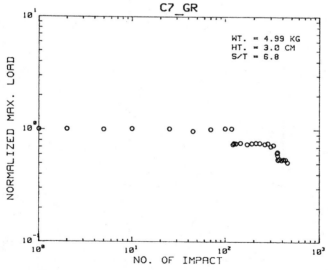

Fig. 5 A representative plot of the normalized max. load
(P_m^n/P_m^1) vs. the no. of impact (N) of a graphite
prepreg composite.

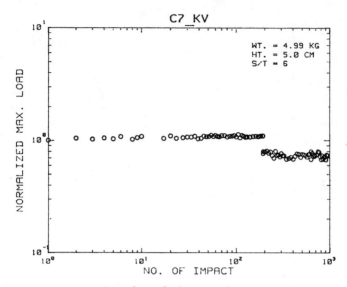

Fig. 6   A representative plot of the normalized max. load
(P_m^n/P_m^1) vs. the no. of impact (N) of a Kevlar
prepreg composite.

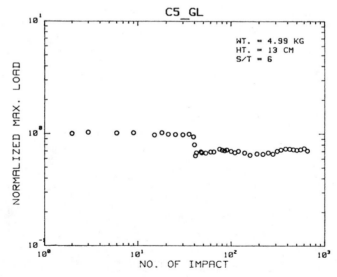

Fig. 7   A representative plot of the normalized max. load
(P_m^n/P_m^1) vs. the no. of impact (N) of a glass
prepreg composite.

A SIMPLIFIED ACCURATE STRAIN ENERGY RELEASE RATE ANALYSIS OF THE END NOTCH FLEXURE SPECIMEN FOR COMPOSITE MATERIALS

James M. Whitney

Materials Laboratory

Air Force Wright Aeronautical Laboratories

Wright-Patterson Air Force Base, Ohio

ABSTRACT

State-of-the-art calculation of interlaminar Mode II critical strain energy release rate in conjunction with the end notch flexure (ENF) specimen for composite materials is based on classical beam theory. Recently a data-reduction scheme has been developed for the ENF specimen based on a more accurate higher order beam theory. Although in closed form, the strain energy release rate is in terms of hyperbolic functions which are not convenient for routine data reduction. In the present paper it is shown that for a large range of unidirectional composite material properties and for beam dimensions of practical value the higher order beam theory solution can be accurately reduced to a simple three term polynomial involving the ratio of the interlaminar shear modulus to the inplane tensile modulus, and the ratio of the crack length to the span length of the beam. The accuracy of the approximation is ascertained by comparing numerical results for three different material properties to the original solution and to finite element results currently available in the open literature. Excellent agreement is obtained. Thus, the simplified relationship for determining critical strain energy release rate provides a very useful and accurate data reduction tool for the ENF test.

1.   INTRODUCTION

An end notch flexure (ENF) specimen is illustrated in Fig. 1. This test method is based on a 3-point bend specimen containing a mid-plane starter crack of desired length. A Mode II (sliding shear mode) critical strain energy release rate, G_{IIC}, can be determined by measuring the load and center deflection at the time the starter crack propagates. From classical beam theory

$$\delta = \frac{(2L^3 + 3a^3)\,P}{8E_x\,b^2h^3} \qquad (1)$$

where δ is the beam deflection under the load nose and E_x is the effective bending modulus of the beam parallel to the x axis. Using the definition of strain energy release rate for fixed load in conjunction with eq. (1), we obtain the result

$$G_{IIC} = \frac{P_C}{2b} \frac{d\delta_C}{da} = \frac{9a^2 P_C{}^2}{16E_x\, b^2 h^3} \qquad (2)$$

where the subscript C denotes critical values associatied with the onset of crack propagation.

Although the ENF test has been utilized in conjunction with a number of laminate stacking geometries, current emphasis is on unidirectional composites. This is due to non-self-similar crack propagation (crack not remaining in the midplane) which is usually encountered with multidirectional laminates[1].

A finite element analysis of the ENF specimen has been performed by a number of investigators[2-5]. In each of these studies significant departure from beam theory, eq. (2), was observed for a range of values of a/L. A higher order beam theory has been applied to an analysis of the ENF specimen[6]. The beam theory was derived from Reissner's variational principle[7] and is applicable to homogeneous, orthotropic materials. Excellent agreement for Mode II strain energy release rate was obtained between the higher order beam theory and the finite element results presented by Salepekar, Raju, and O'Brien[5]. Although the higher order beam theory solution is in closed form, the resulting expression for strain energy release rate is in terms of hyperbolic functions.

In the present paper it will be shown that for a large range of values of material properties and for beam dimensions of practical value the solution in Ref. 6 can be accurately reduced to a simple three term polynomial involving the ratio of the interlaminar shear modulus to the inplane tensile modulus and the ratio of the crack length to the span length of the beam. The accuracy of the approximation is ascertained by comparing numerical results for three different material properties to the original closed form solution and to the finite element results presented in Ref. 5. For continuity purposes the model presented in Ref. 6 is briefly reviewed here.

2. HIGHER ORDER BEAM ANALYSIS

Consider a homogeneous beam of width b and thickness h with the coordinate system in the middle surface. The x and z coordinates denote the axial and thickness directions of the beam, respectively. A surface traction $q = \tau_{xz}(x, -h/2)$ is applied to the bottom surface of the beam. The displacements are assumed to be of the form

$$u = u^0(x) + z\psi(x) + \frac{z^2}{2}\phi(x)$$
$$w = w(x) \qquad (3)$$

where u is the inplane displacement (x direction) and w is the transverse deflection (z direction). The inplane normal stress,

σ_x, is assumed to have the following through-the-thickness distribution:

$$\sigma_x = \frac{3}{4bh} [3 - 20 \left(\frac{z}{h}\right)^2] N$$
$$+ 12\frac{z}{bh^3} M - \frac{30}{bh^3} [1 - 12\left(\frac{z}{h}\right)^2] S \qquad (4)$$

where

$$N, M, S = b \int_{-h/2}^{h/2} \sigma_x (1, z, \frac{z^2}{2}) \, dz$$

Equilibrium considerations in conjunction with eq. (4) lead to the distribution of τ_{xz}, the interlaminar shear stress relative to the x-z plane.

$$\tau_{xz} = \frac{3}{bh} [1 - 4 \left(\frac{z}{h}\right)^2] Q$$
$$\frac{30z}{bh^2} [1 - 4 \left(\frac{z}{h}\right)^2] R - [1 - 6 \left(\frac{z}{h}\right)$$
$$-12 \left(\frac{z}{h}\right)^2 + 40 \left(\frac{z}{h}\right)^3] \frac{q}{4} \qquad (5)$$

where

$$Q, R = b \int_{-h/2}^{h/2} \tau_{xz} (1, z) \, dz$$

In addition, it is assumed that the other inplane stresses σ_y and τ_{xy} along with the interlaminar shear stress τ_{yz} vanish. The effect of the transverse normal stress, σ_z, is neglected in the formulation of the field equations.

The constitutive relations are developed from Reissner's variational principle with the result

$$N = E_1 \, bh \, (\frac{du^0}{dx} + \frac{h^2}{24} \frac{d\phi}{dx})$$

$$M = E_1 \frac{bh^3}{12} \frac{d\psi}{dx}$$

$$S = E_1 \frac{bh^3}{24} (\frac{du^0}{dx} + \frac{3h^2}{40} \frac{d\phi}{dx}) \qquad (6)$$

$$Q = \frac{bh}{6} [5G_{13} (\psi + \frac{dw}{dx}) + \frac{q}{2}]$$

$$R = \frac{7bh^2}{120} (G_{13}h\phi - \frac{3q}{2})$$

where E_1 is the inplane modulus parallel to the x axis and G_{13} is the shear modulus relative to the x-z plane. The equilibrium equations as obtained from Reissner's principle are of the form

$$\frac{dN}{dx} - bq = 0$$

$$\frac{dM}{dx} - Q + \frac{bh}{2} q = 0$$
$$\qquad (7)$$
$$\frac{dQ}{dx} = 0$$

$$\frac{dS}{dx} - R - \frac{bh^2}{8} q = 0$$

Substituting eqs. (6) into eqs. (7), we obtain four equations in the kinematic variables u^0, ψ, ϕ, and w.

3. ANALYSIS OF THE ENF SPECIMEN

For purposes of the analysis it is only necessary to consider the upper half of the ENF specimen as shown in Fig. 2. Over the crack interval, $- a \leq x \geq 0$, the surface traction vanishes, $q = 0$, while in the cracked region, $0 \leq x \geq (2l - a)$, $q \neq 0$. In addition, pure bending deformation is assumed in the uncracked region, i. e. $u(x, -h/2) = 0$. Thus

$$u^0 = \frac{h}{2} \psi - \frac{h^2}{8} \phi, \quad 0 \le x \ge (2L - a) \quad (8)$$

and the surface traction q now becomes a dependent variable. In the interval $-a \le x \ge 0$, $q = 0$, and the four kinematic functions in eqs. (3) are the dependent variables.

In the analysis a solution is obtained separately for both the cracked and uncracked regions. Continuity of u^0, ψ, ϕ, w, N, M, N, and Q are enforced across the boundary $(x = 0)$ between the two regions. The resulting solutions for the deflection under the load nose, denoted by δ, and the Mode II strain energy release rate are of the form[6]

$$\delta = \frac{P}{8E_1 b} \{2\bar{L}^3 + 3\bar{a}^3$$

$$+ \frac{56 (704\bar{L} + 51\bar{a})}{425 \lambda^2} + \frac{9\bar{a}}{\lambda^2} [1$$

$$+ \frac{1}{\sinh \lambda(2\bar{L} - \bar{a})} (\lambda\bar{a} \cosh \lambda(2\bar{L} - \bar{a})$$

$$- \sinh \lambda\bar{L})]$$

$$+ \frac{56 \sinh \lambda\bar{L}}{55 \lambda^3 \sinh \lambda(2\bar{L} - \bar{a})} [\lambda\bar{a}$$

$$+ 2 \sinh \lambda(\bar{L} - \bar{a})] \} \quad (9)$$

$$G_{II} = \frac{9P^2 \bar{a}^2}{16E_1 b^2 h} \{1 + \frac{131}{75\lambda^2 \bar{a}^2}$$

$$+ \frac{1}{\sinh^2 \lambda(2\bar{L} - \bar{a})} [1$$

$$+ \frac{2}{\lambda\bar{a}} (\sinh \lambda(2\bar{L} - \bar{a})$$

$$- \sinh \lambda\bar{L}) \cosh \lambda(2\bar{L} - \bar{a})$$

$$- \frac{2}{\lambda^2 \bar{a}^2} \sinh \lambda(2\bar{L} - \bar{a}) \sinh \lambda\bar{L}]$$

$$+ \frac{56 \sinh \lambda\bar{L}}{495 \bar{a}^2} [\sinh \lambda(2\bar{L} - \bar{a})$$

$$+ \lambda\bar{a} \cosh \lambda(2\bar{L} - \bar{a})$$

$$- 2 \sinh \lambda\bar{L}] \} \quad (10)$$

where

$$\lambda = 4\sqrt{\frac{14}{5} (\frac{G_{13}}{E_1})},$$

$$\bar{L} = L/h, \quad \bar{a} = a/h$$

It should be noted that this solution is perfectly compatible with deformations that occur in the bottom half of the beam. In particular, a solution can be obtained in the lower half of the beam which will produce the same distribution of $q(x)$ in the uncracked region as the current solution. Since $u = 0$ along the centerline of the uncracked region and w is independent of z, complete compatibility of the upper and lower halves of the beam will be assured.

4. SIMPLIFICATION OF SOLUTION

In actual application of the ENF test, the crack is arrested under the load nose. Thus

$$2\bar{L} \le (2\bar{L} - \bar{a}) \ge \bar{L} \quad (11)$$

Considering eq. (11) in conjunction with the fact that L/h ≥ 20 for most applications of the ENF test, we can make the following approximation:

$$\sinh \lambda(2\overline{L} - \overline{a}) = \cosh \lambda(2\overline{L} - \overline{a}) \quad (12)$$

Taking eq. (12) into account, we now consider the following approximation for the deflection under the load nose:

$$\delta = \frac{P}{8E_1 b} [2\overline{L}^3 + 3\overline{a}^3$$

$$+ \frac{(704\overline{L} + 51\overline{a})}{340} (\frac{E_1}{G_{13}})$$

$$+ \frac{9\overline{a}}{\lambda^2} (1 + \lambda\overline{a})] \quad (13)$$

Combining eq. (13) with the definition of strain energy release rate, we find

$$G_{II} = \frac{P}{2b} \frac{d\delta}{da} = \frac{9a^2 P^2}{16E_1 b^2 h^3} (1$$

$$+ \frac{2}{\lambda\overline{a}} + \frac{131}{75\lambda^2 \overline{a}^2}) \quad (14)$$

It should be noted that the first term in eq. (14) represents the classical beam solution as given by eq. (2).

5. RESULTS AND DISCUSSION

Numerical examples are based on the unidirectional composite properties shown in Table 1. Here E_3 and v_{13} denote Young's modulus in the z-direction and Poisson's ratio as measured from contraction in the z-direction during a uniaxial tensile test in the x-direction, respectively.

Ratios of $G_{II}/G_{II}{}^{BT}$, where the superscript BT denotes the beam theory solution as given by eq. (2), are shown in Table 2 as a function of a/L for the three materials listed in Table 1. Results from eq. (14) are compared to eq. (10) and the finite element results obtained by Salpekar, Raju, and O'Brien[5]. Results in the last column are obtained from the relationship

$$G_{II} = \frac{9P^2\overline{a}^2}{16E_1 b^2 h^3} [1 + \frac{0.2}{\overline{a}^2} (\frac{E_1}{G_{13}})] \quad (15)$$

This expression was developed by Carlsson, Gillespie, and Pipes[8] and is based on shear deformation theory in the uncracked region ($0 \leq x \geq 2L - a$) and on an approximate elasticity solution for an end loaded cantilever beam[9]. Continuity of displacement at the crack tip, x = 0, is not attained, however, with this formulation.

The numerical results in Table 2 show excellent agreement between the approximate expression for G_{II}, eq. (14), and the exact solution to the higher order beam theory analysis, eq. (10). Furthermore, good correlation is obtained between both of these solutions and the finite element results presented by Salepekar, Raju, and O'Brien[5]. Although reasonable agreement is shown between the finite element results and the approximation developed by Carlsson, Gillespie, and Pipes[8], better agreement is obtained with the higher order beam theory, either eqs. (10) or (14). Thus, it appears that the simplified approximation given by eq. (14) for determining G_{IIC} provides a very useful and accurate data reduction tool for the ENF specimen.

As a final comment it should be noted that, unlike G_{II}, the center deflection, δ, is accurately described by classical beam theory, eq. (1). Since G_{II} is proportional to the derivative of δ, one would not anticipate this result. Such behavior has also been noted by other authors[2-5].

6. REFERENCES

1. Russell, A. J. and Street, K. N., "Factors Affecting the Interlaminar Fracture Energy of Graphite/Epoxy Laminates," *Proceedings of the Fourth International Conference on Composite Materials,* Elsevier, North Holland, 1984, pp. 279-286.

2. Mall, S and Kochhar, N. K., "Finite-Element Analysis of End-Notch Flexure Specimens," *Journal of Composite Materials Technology and Research,* **8**, 54 (1986).

3. Barrett, J. D. and Foschi, R. O., Mode II Stress Intensity Factors for Cracked Wood Beams," *Engineering Fracture Mechanics,* **9**, 371 (1977).

4. Gillespie, J. W., Jr., Carlsson, L. A., and Pipes, R. B., "Finite Element Analysis of the End Notched Flexure Specimen for Measuring Mode II Fracture Toughness," *Composite Science and Technology,* **27**, 177 (1986).

5. Salepekar, S. A., Raju, I. S., and O'Brien, T. K., "Strain-Energy Release Rate Analysis of the End Notch Flexure Specimen Using the Finite Element Method," *Journal of Composite Technology and Research,* **10**, 133 (1988).

6. Whitney, J. M., "Analysis of the End Notch Flexure Specimen Using a Higher Order Beam Theory Based on Reissner's Principle," *Proceedings of the American Society for Composites, Third Technical Conference,* Technomic Publishing Co., Lancaster, PA, 1988, pp. 103-112.

7. Reissner, E., "On a Variational Theorem in Elasticity," *Journal of Mathematics and Physics,* **29**, 90 (1950).

8. Carlsson, L. A., Gillespie, J. W., Jr., and Pipes, R. B., "On the Analysis and Design of the End Notch Flexure (ENF) Specimen for Mode II Testing," *Journal of Composite Materials,* **20**, 594 (1986).

9. Timoshenko, S. P. and Goodier, J. N., *Theory of Elasticity,* Second Edition, McGraw-Hill, New York, 1951, pp. 35-39.

7. BIOGRAPHY

Dr. J. M. Whitney is a Materials Research Engineer in the AFWAL Materials Laboratory at Wright-Patterson Air Force Base, Ohio, where he has been involved in research in the area of mechanics of composite materials for over twenty-five years. He is currently technical leader of an inhouse research program in advanced composites. He received his Ph.D. in Engineering Mechanics from the Ohio State University. Dr. Whitney is also an adjunct professor of Materials Engineering at the University of Dayton, Dayton, Ohio.

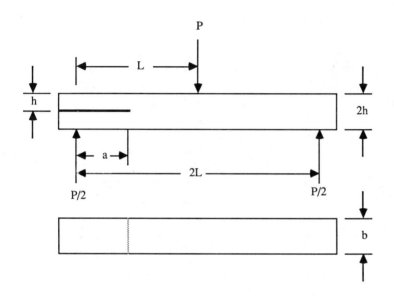

Figure 1. End Notch Flexure Specimen

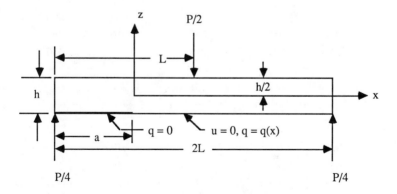

Figure 2. Nomenclature for Stress Analysis Model

TABLE 1 - MATERIAL PROPERTIES

Mat #	E_1/E_3	E_1/G_{13}	ν_{13}
1	2.5	10.5	0.25
2	11.9	25.7	0.30
3	14.2	31.7	0.37

TABLE 2 - MODE II STRAIN ENERGY RELEASE RATE

G_{II}/G_{II}^{BT} (L/h = 22.4)			
a/L	EQ. 14	EQ. 10	EQ. 15	REF. 5
---	---	---	---	---
MATERIAL #1				
0.2	1.237	1.237	1.105	1.168
0.4	1.113	1.113	1.026	1.069
0.6	1.074	1.074	1.012	1.037
0.8	1.055	1.055	1.007	1.021
0.9	1.049	1.049	1.005	1.014
MATERIAL #2				
0.2	1.388	1.388	1.256	1.305
0.4	1.181	1.181	1.064	1.142
0.6	1.118	1.118	1.028	1.090
0.8	1.088	1.087	1.016	1.064
0.9	1.079	1.074	1.013	1.050
MATERIAL #3				
0.2	1.437	1.437	1.315	1.337
0.4	1.203	1.203	1.079	1.156
0.6	1.132	1.132	1.035	1.098
0.8	1.098	1.097	1.020	1.068
0.9	1.086	1.081	1.016	1.051

HIGH TEMPERATURE BMI MATRIX SYSTEM FOR SANDWICH STRUCTURES

J. Meissonnier
Rhône-Poulenc Chimie, Lyon, France
P.R. Lopez
Rhône-Poulenc Inc., Seattle, USA

Abstract

This paper details the use of a high temperature KERIMID bismaleimide matrix system for lightweight sandwich structures. This system can be used for the skins with a honeycomb core. It can also be used as the matrix for a syntactic foam core as well as the matrix for the skins. The two solutions offer different advantages in terms of processability and performances. The effect of processing pressure on the final structure is investigated. The system presented here exhibits very high property retention up to and over 300°C due to its exceptional Tg of 370°C. The target applications for this system range from structural casings for carbon reinforced structures to low dielectric constant electro-magnetic windows submitted to temperatures up to 400°C for a few minutes when used with glass or quartz reinforcements. It has been qualified by Electronique Serge Dassault for use in radomes of supersonic equipments due to its good balance of mechanical, thermal and electrical properties.

1. Introduction

The resin system Kerimid 70006 is part of the solvent free non-MDA resin systems developed by Rhône-Poulenc for composite applications. Throughout these developments the emphasis has been on reaching epoxy-like processing. It is a siloxane-modified bismaleimide of first generation of which the main characteristics are a very high glass transition temperature for a BMI system and high property retention at elevated temperature. Therefore, it is the system of choice when high temperature properties retention rather than room temperature properties are the dominant design factor.

2. Uncured Resin Properties

The resin is designed for hot melt processing and allows manufacturing of flexible prepregs with the main fibers used for advanced composites including glass, graphite, Kevlar and quartz.

It offers the possibility of curing under standard autoclave pressure of 7 bar at 200°C.

Parts obtained exhibit outstanding capability of aging over 250°C for continuous use and up to 350°C for short term exposure.

It contains no diamine and emits no volatiles at cure, which means no odor and good safety during processing and no toxicological risk involved.

Appearance: amber-colored wax, tacky at 40°C.

Density: 1.25 kg/dm3
Viscosity at 80°C: about 3.0 Pa.s
Viscosity at 90°C: about 1.2 Pa.s

Viscosity at 80°C as a function of the time:
- about 3.0 Pa.s (initial)
- about 4.0 Pa.s (1 hour)

Gel-time at 150°C: about 30 min
Gel-time at 170°C: about 12 min

Solubility: Solutions of 50 % in weight can be obtained with methylene chloride or methylethyl ketone.

Shelf-life: At least 3 months at room temperature in metallic can.

3. Characteristics Of The Molded Resin

Cure of 1 hour at 150°C + 1 hour at 200°C and postcure 15 hours at 250°C.

Density: 1.25 kg/dm3

Coefficient of thermal
expansion (CTE):

    $35 \times 10_{-6}$ cm/cm/°C

Thermogravimetric analysis
(10°C/minute): beginning of
decomposition at 425°C in
air.

Glass transition temperature
(DMA):
    360°C dry
    350°C wet
Water absorption (100 hours –
boiling water): 2.0 %

Elongation at break by
tensile testing: 1.9%

Mechanical properties initial
and after 1000 hours at 250°C
are shown in Table I.

K1c (MPa. m): 0.365

G1c (J/m^2): 65

4. Processing

Impregnation

It is easily carried out with
all the classical
reinforcements fibers or
fabrics of glass,
graphite ...

Coating by scraper or by
transfer is possible with the
melted resin for instance at

about 90°C. Impregnation can
also be achieved in a
classical treater from
solution in methylene
chloride or
methylethylketone.

Prepregs obtained are
flexible at room temperature.
Provided that prepregs are
packed in sealed bags, the
storage at +5°C does not
impair their processing
properties.

When removing prepreg from
+5°C or lower temperature,
the sealed bag should not be
opened until the product has
reached room temperature
(prevention of atmospheric
condensation on the product).

5. Composite Curing

Composite curing is achieved
through standard vacuum bag
process.

For laminates the following
conditions can be used:
- heat up to 150 °C at
1°C/min
- maintain for 1 hour at
150°C
- raise the temperature to
200°C at 1°C/min and maintain
for 1 hour to obtain
consolidation.
- pressure (7 bar) is applied

from the beginning of the cycle on.
- vacuum (30 torr) is applied at the beginning of the cycle and removed when temperature reaches 180°C.
- postcure 12 to 24 hours at 250°C.

Characteristics on composites (graphite fiber reinforcement)

Unidirectional (T300 fiber)

A 2.5 mm thick laminate with 65% reinforcement by weight showed a GIc of 220 J/M2

Fabrics

A laminate (4 mm in thickness) was prepared with 28 plies of prepreg (hot melt transfer coating) graphite fiber AS4H/FE 70006 (42% of resin content in weight on the prepreg).

Standard vacuum bag cure and free standing postcure were used. For this laminate: GIc = 200 J/M2.

The flexural characteristics and interlaminar shear strength are the following at room temperature and 250°C (Table II).

6. Syntactic Foam

Syntactic foams can be made from Kerimid 70006 and hollow glass spheres either through solution mixing or through powder processing. Microspheres from several suppliers were used for this purpose. Since the apparent specific weight of the spheres is of the order of 100 to 300 Kg/m3 it was possible by varying the ratio of spheres to resin to obtain foam specific weights between 150 and 500 Kg/m3 for the properties of interest (specific weight of the resin alone is 1250 Kg/m3). Relative permittivity was evaluated between 1.3 and 1.5. Glass transition temperature was around 350°C. Moisture untake after 24 hours at 40°C and 90% relative humidity was between 0.5 and 1% (these fairly mild testing conditions were chosen because the target application was short term). Very low coefficients of thermal expansion were obtained (between 2 and 10 ppm). Other properties are under evaluation.

7. Honeycomb Structure

For an application under

development honeycomb samples were fabricated. The chosen honeycomb was 8 mm thick Oxcore. The resin was hot melt impregnated onto a quartz fiber cloth (type 5465) of areal weight of 140 g/m2. The resin content of the prepreg was 45%.

The first part of the work consisted in defining a proper cure cycle (Figure 1) for cocuring a honeycomb structure, the resin flowing from the prepreg being used to create the interface between the honeycomb and the cured skins. The pressure during the cure schedule was then optimized for this application (Figure 2). The best results were obtained for a curing pressure of 3 bar. The sandwich structures obtained under these conditions were then evaluated in temperature (Figure 3). The results showed a 90% retention in flexural modulus and an 80% retention in flexural strength at 300°C as shown in Table III. Further testing to 400°C is underway.

Fire testing showed the good properties that one would expect from a bismaleimide system not modified by less fire resistant materials. The sandwich structure passed the ATS 1000.01 par. 4.1 test 7.1.4 norm (equivalent FAR 25853a, the best rating) for sandwich structure for aircraft interiors. This is a vertical test, bunsen flamme 38 mm (1.5'), 850°C, for 60 seconds. No combustion, dripping, or destroyed area was observed after the flame removal. Only the local heat degradation in the flame area was apparent.

Under a test for foams the sandwich material received the highest rating UL 94 HF1. Horizontal test, same flame for 60 seconds: no dripping, no combustion. Electrical testing on the sandwich structure showed the following results:
    Permittivity   = 2.7
    Loss factor tan = 6.1 x
    10E-3
For a thickness of 8.6 mm the maximum voltage before rupture of the dielectric was 25 KV.

8. Biographies:

Julien Meissonnier is a development engineer for structural composites at Rhône-Poulenc's Center for technical plastics (CLYPT) in Lyon, France. He holds an engineering degree from INSA Lyon (1986) and obtained a Master's degree in Chemical Engineering at the University of Washington in 1987.

Patrick Lopez is a 1984 Chemical Engineer from ENS Chimie Paris, France. He also holds a Master's degree in Materials Science from the University of Washington (1985). He joined Rhone-Poulenc in 1986 and presently heads the Technical Center for Materials in Seattle, Washington.

9. Acknowledgements:

The authors would like to thank Mr. Foucault and Mr. Pacreau from Electronique Serge Dassault for their collaboration in the development of the sandwich structures and Mr. Dessinges and Mr. Koler from Cotton Frères for collaborating on the prepregging trials, as well as Mr. Peyrat for his work in the laboratory.

10. References:

1. Corden, J.L., and Bitzer, T.N., SAMPE Series Vol. 32. pp. 68-79 (1987)

2. French Patent n° 8317128 (1983).

3. Pouzols, G., and Rakoutz M., SAMPE Series Vol. 30. pp. 606-609.

4. Mc. Garry, N.A., Pouzols, G., and Lopez, P.R., SAMPE Series Vol. 32, pp. 13-23.

5. Camberlin, Y., Giraud Y., and Lopez, P.R. SAMPE Series Vol. 33, 1593-1603.

6. Lopez, P.R. Characterization and processing of polyimide matrix composites, Master of Science Thesis, Univ. of Washington, 1986.

7. Meissonnier, J., Processing optimization of bismaleimide matrix composites, Master of Science Thesis, Univ. of Washington, 1988.

Note :
FE 70006 is a development product and is not yet fully evaluated. When fully developed it may be re-designated as a standard product in the KERIMID range.

Table I:

Time	20°C		250°C	
(hours)	Flexural Strength (MPa)	Flexural Modulus (MPa)	Flexural Strength (MPa)	Flexural Modulus (MPa)
0	74	1690	42	1100
1000	81	2150	46	1400

Table II:

Temperature of test	23°C	250°C
Flexural strength (MPa)	860	540
Flexural modulus (GPa)	84	79.7
Interlaminar shear strength (MPa)	55	28
Interlaminar shear strength (MPa) (after 1000 hours at 250°C)	40	30

Table III:

OPTIMIZATION OF PRESSURE
****

Pressure	Modulus	Failure Stress	Failure Stress (Skins)
(Bar)	(MPa)	(MPa)	(MPa)

****

2,2	4370	49	220
3	4540	54	240
5	4510	47	203
7	4420	43	187

(Mean on 4 samples per pressure value)
****

temperature properties
****

Test Temp.	Modulus	Failure Stress	Failure Stress (Skins)
(°C)	(MPa)	(MPa)	(MPa)

****

23	4860	44	193
170	4510	46	203
250	4490	39	170
300	4320	35	154

(Mean on 4 samples per temperature value)
****

Sandwich structure FE 70006/Quartz

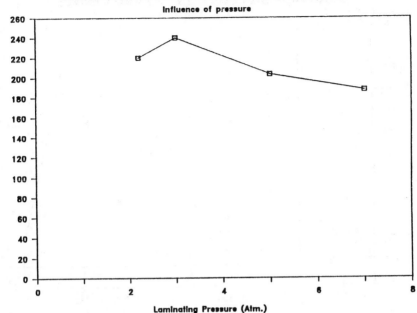

Sandwich Structure FE 70006/Quartz

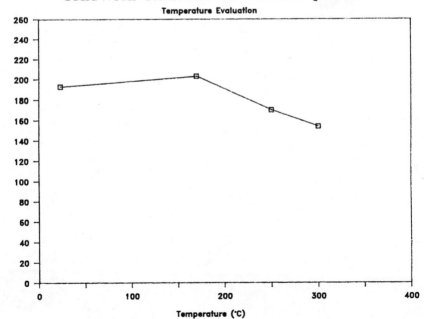

Sandwich Structure FE 70006/Quartz

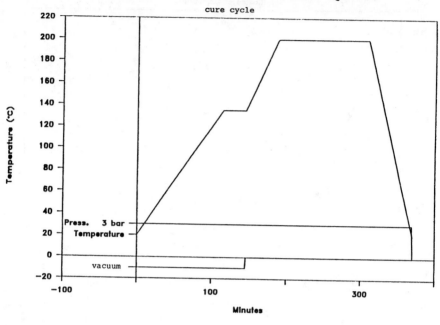

V-391
A NOVEL COMPOSITE MATRIX WITH THE TEMPERATURE
PERFORMANCE OF BMI'S AND THE TOUGHNESS OF THERMOPLASTICS

Mark M. Konarski
U.S. Polymeric
Santa Ana, Ca.
(714) 549-1101

ABSTRACT

New technology developed at U.S. Polymeric has led to a novel modified BMI, V-391, exhibiting a substantial increase in toughness not previously available with high temp matrices. When combined with intermediate modulus fibers such as Hitex 46-8B, the system yields a post-impact compression value of 35 ksi (after 1500 in-lb/in). Mechanical properties on the system are excellent, with good hot-wet retention up to 350F. The system combines outstanding process-ability with good tack,drape and flow control.The resin is curable with true epoxy-like cycles and variable free-standing postcures from 350-475F. Demanding cross-plied laminates with intermediate modulus fibers remain micro-crack-free, even after thermal cycling from -108 to 350F. The effect of cure and post-cure variations on composite toughness and mechanical properties is also discussed.

1. INTRODUCTION

BMI's have long been the material of choice for intermediate temperature composite engineering due to their excellent hot and hot-wet performance. One of the inherent drawbacks to these materials has been their lack of toughness. The highly crosslinked nature of BMI's which yields a high glass transition temperature, also creates a brittle matrix with relatively low damage tolerance.

Thermoplastics have found increasing popularity as composite matrices in recent years. They have been hampered by difficulties in prepregging, relatively poor thermo/mechanical performance and they tend to have high solvent sensitivity. Still, the high toughness and damage tolerance of these materials makes them attractive for many applications.

Recently,innovative technology

at U.S.P. has led to V-391, a new composite matrix that combines the toughness of thermoplastics with the temperature performance of BMI's. Proprietary semi-IPN technology has allowed the formulation of an extremely tough resin that combines good tack, drape and flow control in the prepreg form with a wide window of autoclave cure and postcure processability.

2. RESIN PROPERTIES

V-391 is modified BMI resin developed and tailored for the production of prepregs suitable for the advanced composite marketplace. The system exhibits excellent composite toughness and mechanical properties while retaining the ability to be prepregged, handled and cured with existing industry equipment designed for "350F" epoxies. The resin cures to a homogeneous single phase and retains good tack and prepreg drapeability for a minimum of 2 weeks. RDS measurements indicate glass transitions of 263C (505F) in the dry state and 209C (408F) after 48 hours in boiling water. The weight-gain was 2.0% after immersion. Resin density is 1.25 g/cc.

One potential problem area for BMI's is their flow behavior. These materials are traditionally high flow materials which often leads to difficulties in fabrication. V-391 is a controlled flow system. The RDS viscosity profile is depicted in Figure 1. Heatups at typical autoclave rates yield viscosity minima of 790 to 2000

centipoise in the region of 88C (190F) to 101C (214F).

3. MECHANICAL PROPERTIES

V-391 yields impressive mechanical properties on intermediate modulus fibers as shown in Table 1. Composites fabricated from V391 deliver compression after impact numbers rivaling those of high temperature thermoplastics. Strength and modulus translation is excellent on these fibers and property retention is good to 350F.

An attractive feature of of V-391 is its ability to form high quality, low void and microcrack-free laminates under a variety of different cure and postcure cycles. Table 2 shows 5 cycles that were evaluated. The layup is a demanding cross-plied sequence involving stacked zero degree plies that tend to maximize thermal microcrack formation. All cycles produce high quality, low-void laminates that were microcrack-free as examined under high resolution C-scan as well as traditional miscroscopy following sectioning and polishing. Limited mechanical property testing shows excellent correlation from one cycle to the next.

Laminates were also examined after rapid thermal cycling from -78C (-108F) to 177C (350F). Examination after 20 cycles showed all panels to be microcrack free. No microcracking was found with other fibers such as IM-7 and T-300 indicating that the resin is not "fiber sensitive" in this regard. Overall, the system exhibits excellent processability and seems to be very "forgiving" to perturbations during cures. Postcures are always a concern for BMI's and were extensively examined for V-391. High temperature postcures often cause problems since most other composite materials such as cores and adhesives degrade upon exposure to these extremes. Tables 3 and 4 show the short beam shear and flexure performance V-391/Hitex 46-8B unitape with varying postcures from 177C (350F) to 243C (470F) Although higher temperature postcures deliver the best hot wet numbers, acceptable performance can be achieved with extended postcures at temperatures as low as 177C (350F).

Damage tolerance was also measured as a function of postcure as shown in Figure 2. Small differences are seen for the varying postcure conditions with the best performance being achieved following a postcure of 24 hours at 177C (350F). Post impact compression is still excellent even under the worst condition of 24 hours at 277C (440F) and as a whole, the excellent toughness of the material is maintained regardless of the postcure time and temperature. Furthermore, the material does not signigicantly embrittle upon extended aging as shown by the value after 100 hours at 177C (350F).

4. SUMMARY

V-391 offers superior toughness in a high temperature composite matrix. The resin has controlled flow and prepreg retains tack and drape for a minimum of two weeks. The system is not cure cycle or fiber sensitive and delivers outstanding tolerance and mechanical perform-

ance with postcures from 177C (350F) to 243C (470F).

5. ACKNOWLEDGMENTS

Many thanks to all those at U.S. Polymeric who played a part in the generation of the materials and data that went into this paper.

6. BIOGRAPHY

Dr. M. Konarski is a Senior Chemist with over 8 year experience in matrix develops ment, ranging from adhesives-to high temperature composites. In the last four years he has been heavily involved with polyimides including PMR-15, high temperature BMI's, toughened BMI's and resin transfer molding.

TABLE 1

UNITAPE PROPERTIES OF V-391

ON INTERMEDIATE MODULUS FIBERS

		HITEX 46-8B	IM-7
OPEN HOLE TEN. RT	MPa(Ksi)	579(84)	614(89)
OPEN HOLE T.MOD	GPa(Msi)	86(12.5)	79(11.4)
FLEX MOD.RT	GPa(Msi)	169(24.5)	158(22.9)
F MOD 121C WET	GPa(Msi)	166(24.1)	163(23.6)
F MOD 177C WET	GPa(Msi)	159(23.0)	148(21.4)
F MOD 191C WET	GPa(Msi)	132(19.2)	139(20.1)
FLEX STR RT	MPa(Ksi)	1765(256)	1544(224)
FLEX 121C WET	MPa(Ksi)	1213(176)	1262(183)
FLEX 177C WET	MPa(Ksi)	841(122)	855(124)
FLEX 191C WET	MPa(Ksi)	738(107)	724(105)
SBS RT	MPa(Ksi)	124(18.0)	121(17.6)
SBS 121C WET	MPa(Ksi)	84(12.2)	78(11.3)
SBS 177C WET	MPa(Ksi)	55(8.0)	62(9.0)
SBS 191C WET	MPa(Ksi)	37(5.4)	53(7.7)
OHC RT *	MPa(Ksi)	400(58)	434(63)
OHC 121C WET *	MPa(Ksi)	352(51)	372(54)
OHC 177C WET *	MPa(Ksi)	338(49)	359(52)
OHC 191C WET *	MPa(Ksi)	324(47)	338(49)
CAI **	MPa(Ksi)	238(34.5)	233(33.8)
CAI ***	MPa(Ksi)	317(46.0)	296(43.0)

TENSILE, FLEX AND COMPRESSIVES NORMALIZED TO 5.2 MILS/PLY
WET = 96 HOUR BOIL
LAMINATES WERE CURED FOR 2 HOURS AT 350F.
POSTCURE = 6 HOURS AT 470F.

* OPEN HOLE COMPRESSION (+/-45,90,0,0,+/-45,0,0,+/-45,0)sym.
** BOEING COMPRESSION AFTER IMPACT AT 265 J/M2 (1500 in-lbs/in)
*** NORTHROP COMPRESSION AFTER IMPACT
    AT 265J/M2 (1500 in-lbs/in)

TABLE 2

V-391/HITEX 46-8B CURE CYCLE SENSITIVITY EVALUATION

	CYCLE				
PROPERTY	1	2	3	4	5
MICROCRACKING (58% ZERO)	NO	NO	NO	NO	NO
OHC, RT, MPa(Ksi)	503(73)	510(74)	462(67)	510(74)	496(72)
OHC, 177C WET, MPa(Ksi)	317(46)	310(45)	283(41)	276(40)	303(44)
OHC, 191C WET, MPa(Ksi)	276(40)	269(39)	262(38)	276(40)	276(40)

OHC = OPEN HOLE COMPRESSION (+/-45,90,0,0,0,0,+/-45/0,0,0)sym.
WET = 96 HOUR WATER BOIL.

CYCLE #	INITIAL PRESS.	HEATING RATE	INTERMED TEMP	DWELL TIME	CURE PRESSURE	CURE TEMP/TIME	POSTCURE TEMP/TIME
1	VAC/85PSI	3-5F	NONE	NONE	85PSI*	350F/2HRS	425F/6HRS
2	VAC/85PSI	3-5F	NONE	NONE	85PSI*	350F/2HRS	475F/4HRS
3	VAC/85PSI	3-5F	NONE	NONE	85PSI**	350F/2HRS	425F/6HRS
4	VAC/85PSI	0.5-1F	NONE	NONE	85PSI*	350F/2HRS	425F/6HRS
5	VAC ONLY	3-5F	250F	45'	85PSI***	350F/2HRS	425F/6HRS

* VENT VACUUM AFTER 300F.
** HOLD VACUUM THROUGHOUT THE CYCLE.
*** APPLY PRESSURE AFTER THE HOLD AND VENT THE VACUUM

TABLE 3

V-391/HITEX 46-8B UNITAPE

SHORT BEAM SHEAR VERSUS POSTCURE

TEST TEMPERATURE:	RT DRY	121C (250F) WET *	149C (300F) WET *	177C (350F) WET *	191C (375F) WET *
POSTCURE	RESULTS, MPa(KSI)				
NO POSTCURE	142(20.6)	66(9.6)	**	**	**
6 HRS @ 177C (350F)	146(21.2)	76(11.0)	**	**	**
24 HRS @ 177C (350F)	147(21.3)	80(11.6)	63(9.1)	46(6.7)	**
6 HRS @ 204C (400F)	141(20.4)	79(11.5)	67(9.7)	46(6.6)	26(3.8)
24 HRS @ 204C (400F)	143(20.8)	81(11.8)	68(9.8)	54(7.8)	52(7.6)
6 HRS @ 218C (425F)	139(20.2)	81(11.8)	71(10.3)	51(7.4)	29(4.2)
24 HRS @ 218C (425F)	137(19.8)	82(11.9)	76(11.0)	57(8.2)	54(7.8)
6 HRS @ 227C (440F)	137(19.8)	81(11.8)	69(10.0)	52(7.6)	30(4.3)
24 HRS @ 227C (440F)	141(20.4)	82(11.9)	72(10.5)	57(8.3)	54(7.9)
6 HRS @ 243C (470F)	139(20.1)	81(11.7)	72(10.4)	55(8.0)	42(6.1)
24 HRS @ 243C (470F)	139(20.2)	82(11.9)	74(10.8)	64(9.3)	54(7.8)

* WET = 48 HOUR WATER BOIL
** COMPRESSION JAMMING

TABLE 4

V-391/HITEX 46-8B UNITAPE

**FLEXURE VERSUS POSTCURE

TEST TEMPERATURE:		RT DRY	121C (250F) WET *	177C (350F) WET *	191C (375F) WET *
POSTCURE		FLEX STRENGTH/FLEX MODULUS			
NO POSTCURE	MPa(Ksi) GPa(Msi)	1910(277) 163(23.7)	1117(162) 169(24.5)	372(54) 11.7	241(45) 58(8.4)
6 HRS @ 177C (350F)	MPa(Ksi) GPa(Msi)	1937(281) 171(24.8)	1262(183) 170(24.6)	558(81) 131(19.0)	303(44) 58(8.4)
24 HRS @ 177C (350F)	MPa(Ksi) GPa(Msi)	2013(292) 173(25.1)	1324(192) 180(26.1)	752(109) 162(23.5)	462(67) 103(14.9)
6 HRS @ 204C (400F)	MPa(Ksi) GPa(Msi)	1696(246) 181(26.2)	1296(188) 172(25.0)	958(139) 175(25.4)	696(101) 151(21.9)
24 HRS @ 204C (400F)	MPa(Ksi) GPa(Msi)	1868(271) 170(24.7)	1269(184) 168(24.4)	1034(150) 177(25.6)	786(114) 159(23.1)
6 HRS @ 218C (425F)	MPa(Ksi) GPa(Msi)	1827(265) 171(24.8)	1282(186) 170(24.6)	951(138) 172(25.0)	724(105) 153(22.2)
24 HRS @ 218C (425F)	MPa(Ksi) GPa(Msi)	1786(259) 169(24.5)	1331(193) 174(25.2)	1062(154) 176(25.5)	951(138) 177(25.7)
6 HRS @ 227C (440F)	MPa(Ksi) GPa(Msi)	2006(291) 179(25.9)	1241(180) 166(24.1)	924(134) 168(24.3)	703(102) 157(22.7)
24 HRS @ 227C (440F)	MPa(Ksi) GPa(Msi)	1855(269) 166(24.1)	1331(193) 169(24.5)	1082(157) 171(24.8)	986(143) 172(25.0)
6 HRS @ 243C (470F)	MPa(Ksi) GPa(Msi)	1979(287) 169(24.5)	1289(187) 170(24.7)	945(137) 173(25.1)	752(109) 158(22.9)
24 HRS @ 243C (470F)	MPa(Ksi) GPa(Msi)	2117(307) 173(25.1)	1317(191) 176(25.5)	1145(166) 180(26.1)	979(142) 173(25.1)

* WET = 48 HOUR WATER BOIL
** ALL RESULTS ARE NORMALIZED TO .0052"/PLY

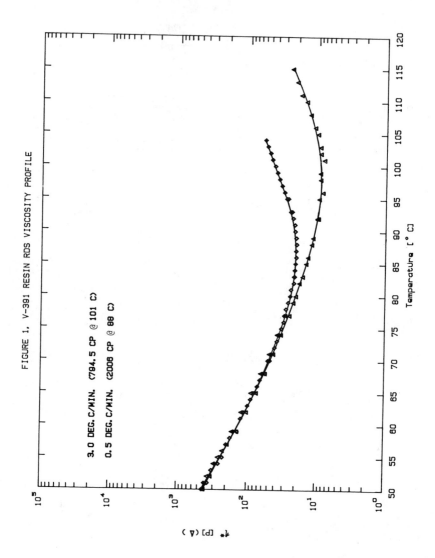

FIGURE 1. V-391 RESIN RDS VISCOSITY PROFILE

3.0 DEG. C/MIN. (794.5 CP @ 101 C)

0.5 DEG. C/MIN. (2006 CP @ 88 C)

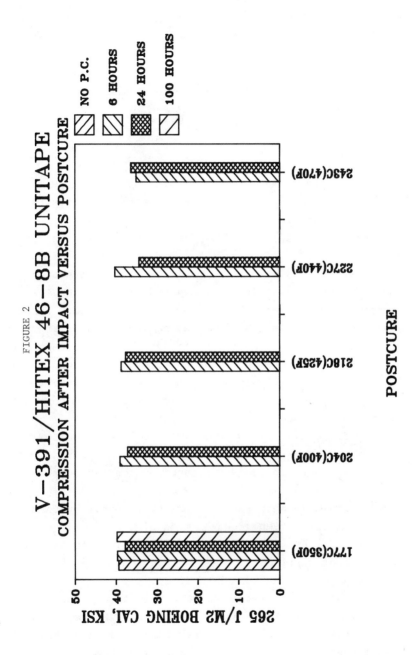

FIGURE 2

V-391/HITEX 46-8B UNITAPE
COMPRESSION AFTER IMPACT VERSUS POSTCURE

NO P.C.
6 HOURS
24 HOURS
100 HOURS

265 J/M2 BOEING CAI, KSI

177C(350F)   204C(400F)   218C(425F)   227C(440F)   243C(470F)

POSTCURE

513

34th International SAMPE Symposium
May 8-11, 1989

A BMI SYSTEM WITH HIGH IMPACT STRENGTH
Victor Ho
CIBA-GEIGY Composites

Abstract

In recent years, bismaleimide resin has been studied extensively for potential application in primary aircraft structure. However, its inherent brittleness has hindered its wide acceptance by composite design engineers. Lately, much effort has been spent to improve the resin toughness, but the improvement was usually a trade off for high temperature properties. This paper is to discuss a bismaleimide resin system and its composite that provide high impact resistance and good mechanical strength retention at elevated temperature. The neat resin was characterized for its chemical reaction and polymerization kinetics by differential scanning calorimetry and for glass transition temperature by thermomechanical analysis. Mechanical properties and toughness of resin matrix and its carbon fiber composite were tested and results are reported. Techniques used to measure the toughness include compression after impact, GIC by double torsion and GIIC by end notch flexural are briefly discussed. Conclusions are drawn on the relationship between resin matrix and composite toughness and the fiber/resin interface effect related to composite toughness.

1. INTRODUCTION

BMI resin was initially applied for fabrication of P.C. board having higher temperature capability than that made of epoxy. It has been used for aircraft and space structures since the late 1970's and early 1980's. The advantage of using BMI in composites is its higher temperature resistance than epoxy and easier processibility than other high temperature resins. The aircraft industry now also requires

514

highly improved toughness in addition to higher temperature properties of the BMI resin. Because resin matrix composites are non-homogeneous material in contrast to metals, the methods and techniques used to measure and interpret the composite toughness greatly effect the resulting conclusions. For instance, to use neat resin toughness data to predict composite toughness can be misleading due to the non-linear relationship between them.

This paper discusses a BMI resin system, RX130-9, which has been greatly improved for its toughness in terms of impact strength, emphasizing on description of various test methods and corresponding test results in order to demonstrate the true toughness properties of this resin system. Different fibers were selected in combination of the various test methods to examine the effect of resin fiber interface on the composite toughness.

2. RESIN CHARACTERIZATION

2.1 DSC, DMA and TGA.

RX130-9 neat resin samples were examined by three thermal analysis instruments. They are Differential Scanning Calorimetry (DSC), Dynamic Mechanical Analysis (DMA) and Thermogrametric Analysis (TGA). DSC was used to characterize resin chemical reaction and polymerization kinetics. DSC curve was obtained using the Mettler TA-3000 system. Table 1 shows that at various heating rates, the onset and peak exotherm temperature increased as the heating rate was increased, while the ΔH varies with the heating rates. This provides a clue that higher thermal stress may build up in the cured resin system. Figure 1 is a graphic presentation for Table 1 that also indicates a smooth one-step chemical reaction. Table 2 reveals the reaction kinnetics of this resin system. It lists the time-temperature relation for curing of this resin on which the cure cycle for the laminate was based. DMA scan is shown in Figure 2. The instrument used is a Dupont 990 system. The operating conditions are included in the graph. The glass transition temperature is taken as the peak of the loss modulus curve or Tg=278°C. The TGA was also measured on the same Dupont instrument. It was tested under N2 atmosphere. The TGA curve is shown in Figure 3. The weight loss became rapid above 350°C and is due to the thermal decomposition of the resin.

Leaving a 45% residue at final testing temperature 550°C.

2.2 Mechanical Properties and Toughness.

Table 3 illustrates the mechanical properties of the neat resin system. The flexural strength at 450°F retain 48% of its R.T. strength and its modulus remain 63% of its R.T. strength. 450°F tensile strength retention is about 50% of its R.T. strength. G_{IC} value measured by compact tension method illustrated in Figure 4. It shows 3.1 in-lb/in^2 which is 100% improvement over the R6452 toughen BMI system.

2.3 Moisture Absorption

Resin specimens were conditions at 165°F and 95% relative humidity for 22 days until no weight gain could be detected. This is taken as a total saturation state and the moisture absorption data are plotted and shown in Figure 5. The moisture curve levels out at 3.71% weight gain which is normal for BMI resin system.

3. PREPREG AND LAMINATE PREPARATION.

3.1 Prepreg

Resin mixture was prepared under moderate temperature and no solvent was added. It was then coated into thin film of predetermined film weight using a blade and hot plate coater under moderate heating temperature. The coated film was then consolidated with graphite fibers under pressure and temperature. The finished prepreg product contains 36±2% resin and 145±5 grams per meter square of fiber.

3.2 Laminates.

Laminates were made with the above-mentioned prepreg, with various lay-up sequences to meet different test requirements. The various laminate sizes and lay-up sequences are listed below:

Flexural, Compression and Short Beam Shear Strength: 12"x12" and $[0°]_{16}$;

G_{IC}: 12"x12" and $[0°]_8$;

G_{IIC}: 6"x6" and $[0°]_{24}$;

Open Hole Compresion: 12"x12" and $[\pm45/90/0_2/\pm45/0_2/\pm45/0]_s$;

Compression After Impact: Type 1 12"x12" and $[+45/90/-45/0]_{2s}$;

Type 2 8"x14" and $[+45/90/-45/0]_{4s}$;

Type 3 13"x24" and $[+45/90/-45/0]_{6s}$.

They were cured with vacuum bag in an autoclave under 85 PSI and 2 hrs. at 175°F plus 4 hrs. at 350°F, then post-cured in an air circulated oven for 4 hrs. at 475°F.

4. LAMINATE PROPERTIES

4.1 Mechanical.

Table 4 shows the test data of

laminates made with T-300 and AS-6 fiber prepregs. The flexural, compression and short beam shear specimens were prepared from 16-ply 0° laminates and tested according to ASTM standard methods. The open hole compression specimens were made using a lay-up sequence of [±45/90/02/±45/02/±45/0]s. The specimen size is 3"x1" with 0° fiber direction parallel to the 3" dimension. A 0.25 inch diameter hole in the center of each specimen was machined. The specimen was tested under compressive load at 0.05 inch per minute. Test results indicate that the 350°F flexural strength for both fibers hold above 80% of their R.T. strength. 350°F wet data also show high retention in comparison with 350°F dry strength. Flexural modulus has no indication of any decrease at 350°F dry and wet test conditions. Compression strength tested at 350°F dry remains 84% for T-300 fiber and 89% for AS-6 fiber of their R.T. strength. The 350°F wet compression strength are both above 80% of their dry value. Short beam shear strength shows a larger drop for 350°F test data in comparison with the R.T. test results. However, their 350°F wet strength has good retention of the 350°F dry strength.

The open hole compression test was selected for the reason that composite material strength can be more clearly characterized by its compressive failure around the highly stressed open hole. The results for 375°F wet strength retains 90% of its R.T. strength for T-300 fiber laminate. This indicates that even though the laminate was totally saturated with moisture, it still showed excellent strength at temperatures up to 375°F.

4.2 Toughness.

GIC of the resin laminate was measured by double torsion test method. This is illustrated in Figure 6. It is a technique to characterize the transverse cracking in unidirectional fiber composites. In this test, a number of specimens were tested for their compliance value with respect to the predetermined crack lengths. A linear relationship can be drawn from the plot using compliance value vs. crack length, then GIC values can be calculated with the formula listed in Figure 6.

The GIC value of RX130-9

laminate is listed in Table 5 and compared with a toughened BMI system and a toughened epoxy system. RX130-9 system shows great improvement over R6452 and very close to R6376 toughened epoxy system.

G_{IIC} of the laminate was measured by end-notched flexural test method. This test is designed to measure the composite toughness more related to the interply shear strength. Specimens were tested in the 3-point bend test fixture as illustrated in Figure 7. The compliance of the laminate was calculated to insert into formula as shown in Figure 7 for G_{IIC} determination.

Test data are listed in Table 5 that indicates a 43% improvement over the R6452 system and slightly better than the R6376 system.

4.3 Impact Resistance.

Impact resistance of RX130-9 laminate was measured using the compression after impact test. It is a two-step test and illustrated in Figure 8 and 9. The specimen was first to be impacted by a drop weight and then the resulting specimen was tested under compression load until failure according to various test methods which includes CIBA-GEIGY in-house test method,

NASA 1092 and Boeing BSS 7260 test methods. Two impact energy levels were used for the above-mentioned impact test. They are 1000 in-lb/in. and 1500 in-lb/in.

Table 6 listed all the test data obtained from various laminates testings. The 16-ply specimens were tested using CIBA-GEIGY in-house test method. a 3"x6" specimen was first impacted with a 12-lb. drop weight having a 0.5" diameter tup. After the impact test, the specimen was trimmed to 2.7"x5.9" for compression test at 0.05 inch per minute loading speed. The 32-ply specimen was tested according to Boeing test method BSS 7260. The 48-ply specimen was examined with NASA 1092 specification.

Test results indicate that the compression after impact strength varies with the laminate thickness and lay-up sequence for AS-6 fiber specimens tested at 1000 in-lb/in. impact level. It does not show much difference within the other fiber groups, such as T-300, T-650 and IM-7 fiber. However, at 1500 in-lb/in. impact level, strength differences in each fiber group become less pronounced. This can be understood that as the impact level increases, more damage is registered and the laminate thickness tends to be less important to the impact resistance. Table 7 lists only the 16-ply laminate made with four different fibers. It shows the effect of fiber-resin interface to the compression after impact strength. Again, at 1000 in-lb/in. impact level, fiber-resin interface seems to influence more than that tested at 1500 in-lb/in. on the compression strength. It can be explained with the same rational described for the effect of laminate thickness. As the impact level increases, the resulting damage increases that overshadows the effect of fiber-resin interface. Among the four fibers selected, IM-7 fiber gives the best results.

5. CONCLUSIONS

A highly impact resistant resin system, RX130-9, has been developed. It has been characterized not only for its neat resin properties, but its laminate strength by means of various toughness and impact resistant testings. It has also shown that this resin system has high temperature capability up to 375°F. The compression after impact strength obtained from various testings provide enough evidence that this resin system has high impact resistance. This resin system is very comparable to the toughened epoxy system R6376 which is widely accepted by the composites user industry for its excellent toughness and mechanical properties.

Continued efforts have been devoted to further improve the toughness of RX130-9 resin system, and several new BMI systems with even higher compression after impact strength have been obtained, primarily test data are shown in Table 8. These newer resin systems are under full characterization. It is anticipated that they will compete with thermoplastic in toughness and be capable of using existing cure processes and equipment.

6. ACKNOWLEDGEMENTS

The author would like to acknowledge the contributions of Marie Liu and Jessy Gonzalez for specimen preparation and testing, and Dr. Shaw Lee for his helpful discussions in mechanical test data.

7. REFERENCES

1. Ho, V. "Development of a New Modified Bismaleimide Prepreg--R6451" National SAMPE Symposium Exhibition, vol. 29, pp 409-421.

2. Ho, V., "The Development of a Modified Bismaleimide Resin System with Improved Toughness for Composites," proceedings of 31st International SAMPE Symposium and Exhibition, 1986, pp 1362-1373.

3. Lee, S. M., "Double Torsion Fracture Toughness Test for Evaluating Transverse Cracking in Composites," Journal of Material Science, Letter 1, 1982, pp 511-515.

4. Rhodes, M.D., Williams, J. G. and Starnes, jr., J. H. "Low Velocity Impact Damage in Graphite Fiber Reinforced Epoxy Laminates," Polymer Composites, Jan. 1981, vol. 2, No. 1, pp 36-44.

8. BIOGRAPHY

V. Ho is a Group Leader of Prepreg Development at Composite Materials of CIBA-GEIGY Corporation. His current responsibility is to supervise the group in developing resin-fiber prepreg material for various industrial applications. He has been with CIBA-GEIGY for 10 years. He has 20 years of experience in nonmetallics and for the last 17 years has been actively involved in material and process activities on advance organic composites, adhesives and electrical insulations.

TABLE 1

DSC STUDY ON RX130-9 RESIN MATRIX

Heat Rate	On-Set Temp.	Peak Temp.	H (Joule/g)
5°F/ Min.	122°F	235°F	245.6
10°F/Min.	135°F	255°F	249.3
20°F/Min.	155°F	275°F	236.9

Note: Data obtained using Mettler TA3000 System.

TABLE 2

REACTION KINETICS ON RX130-9 RESIN MATRIX

| Temp. °C | Time (Min.) to Reach Cure at | | | |
	50%	75%	85%	95%
150	421.7	896.5	1216.6	2243.0
170	120.4	256.0	349.9	640.6
190	38.3	81.5	112.0	203.8
210	13.4	28.5	39.4	71.3

Note: Data Obtained Using Mettler TA-3000 System

TABLE 3

NEAT RESIN MECHANICAL PROPERTIES
AND TOUGHNESS

	R6452	RX130-9
Flexural STR (KSI)		
RT	19.2	24.8
350°F	11.1	13.7
450°F		12.0
Flexural MOD (MSI)		
RT	0.56	0.67
350°F	0.40	0.58
450°F		0.42
Tensile STR (KSI)		
RT	10.3	12.3
350°F	7.5	8.4
450°F		6.4
G_{IC} (in-lb/in^2)		
Compact Tension	1.5	3.1

TABLE 4

LAMINATE MECHANICAL PROPERTIES

RX130-9

	T-300	AS-6
Flexural STR (KSI) / MOD (MSI)		
RT	261/17.5	258/17.2
350°F	210/17.4	200/17.1
350°F Wet[1]	193/17.2	173/17.1
Compressive STR (KSI) / MOD (MSI)		
RT	198/17.7	210/18.2
350°F	167/17.6	186/18.0
350°F Wet[1]	144/17.6	158/19.1
Short Beam Shear (KSI)		
RT	17.9	15.8
350°F	12.5	9.7
350°F Wet[1]	9.9	7.2
Open Hole Compression (KSI)		
RT	59.9	--
375°F	55.7	--
375°F Wet[2]	53.7	--

[1]Water boil 24 hrs.
[2]Water boil 96 hrs.

TABLE 5

LAMINATE TOUGHNESS

	R6452 T-300	RX130-9 AS-6	R6376 T-500
G_{IC} (in-lb/in^2)			
Double Torsion	1.05	2.24	2.12
G_{IIC} (in-lb/in^2)			
End Notch Flex	3.02	4.31	4.0

TABLE 6

COMPRESSION AFTER IMPACT TEST RESULTS
OF RX130-9 SYSTEM

| Fiber | No. of Ply | CAI Strength (KSI) | |
		Impacted at 1000 in-lb/in.	Impacted at 1500 in-lb/in.
AS-6	16	42	30
	32	--	28
	48	32	--
T-300	16	31	27
	32	--	25
	48	31	26
T-650	16	34	28
	32	--	--
	48	--	--
IM-7	16	39	33
	32	32	27
	48	--	29

TABLE 7

FIBER EFFECT ON COMPRESSION AFTER IMPACT
STRENGTH OF RX130-9

| Fiber | No. of Ply | CAI Strength (KSI) | |
		Impacted at 1000 in-lb/in.	Impacted at 1500 in-lb/in.
AS-6	16	42	30
T-300	16	31	27
T-650	16	34	28
IM-7	16	39	33

523

TABLE 8

PRELIMINARY TEST DATA OF

RX116-67 AND RX116-67-1/IM8 SYSTEMS

	RX116-67	RX116-67-1
Compression After Impact (KSI)		
1000 in-lb/in	44.6	--
1500 in-lb/in	38.6	44.7
Open Hole Compression (KSI)*		
R.T. Dry	83.8	--
375°F Wet**	63.5	53.2

* Lay up: $(+45/0/-45/90)_{2s}$
** 96 hrs. water boil

DSC CURVE OF RX130-9 RESIN MATRIX

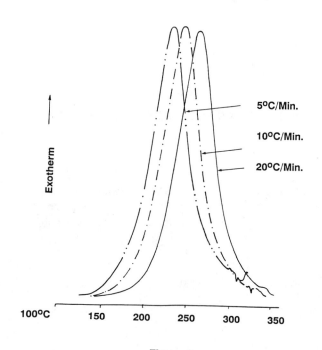

5°C/Min.

10°C/Min.

20°C/Min.

Exotherm

100°C   150   200   250   300   350

Figure 1

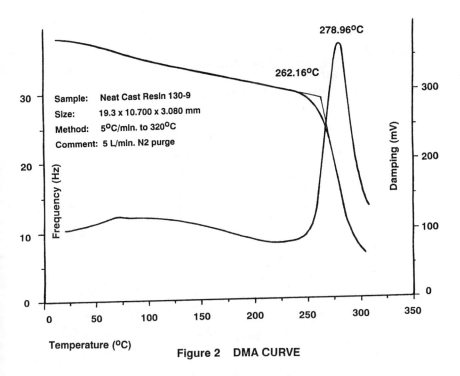

Figure 2   DMA CURVE

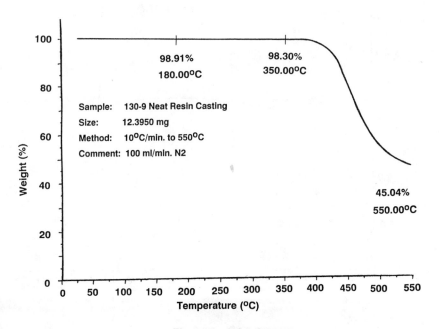

Figure 3   TGA CURVE

525

COMPACT TENSION SPECIMEN

FOR G$_{IC}$ (RESIN) MEASUREMENT

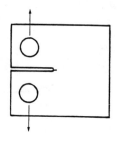

Figure 4

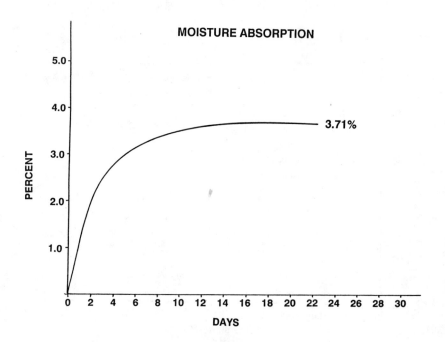

Figure 5

TRANSVERSE CRACKING FRACTURE TOUGHNESS TEST

DOUBLE TORSION METHOD

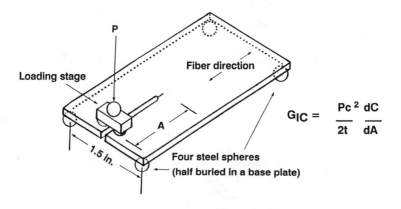

$$G_{IC} = \frac{Pc^2}{2t} \frac{dC}{dA}$$

Figure 6

END NOTCHED FLEXURE (ENF) TEST FOR G_{IIC}

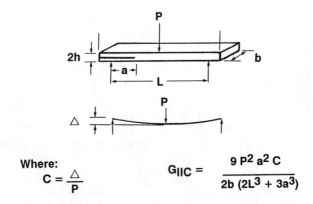

Where:
$$C = \frac{\triangle}{P}$$

$$G_{IIC} = \frac{9 P^2 a^2 C}{2b (2L^3 + 3a^3)}$$

Figure 7

INSTRUMENTED DROP-WEIGHT IMPACT TESTER

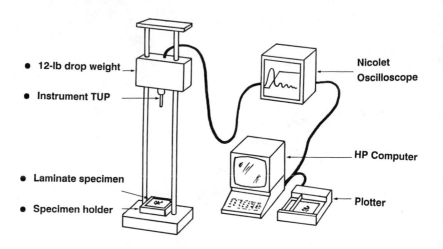

- 12-lb drop weight
- Instrument TUP
- Laminate specimen
- Specimen holder

Nicolet
Oscilloscope

HP Computer

Plotter

Figure 8

COMPRESSION AFTER IMPACT TEST

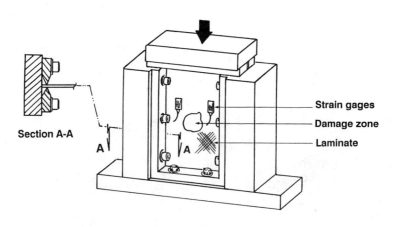

Section A-A

Strain gages

Damage zone

Laminate

Figure 9

Design of Composite Laminates With Ply Failure

Y. M. Han and H. T. Hahn
Department of Engineering Science and Mechanics
The Pennsylvania State University
University Park, PA 16802

Abstract

When composite laminates are loaded, degradation of mechanical properties may take place long before catastrophic final failure. One of the causes for the degradation is subcritical ply cracking which is found to appear in most multidirectional laminates.

To avoid ply cracking in service, the design load must be kept within the first ply failure envelope. This design philosophy can be overly conservative, especially if ply cracking is not allowed even in long term service. Therefore, the design limit may have to be maintained above the first ply failure load. Such design is possible only if we know how to handle progressive ply failure.

In this paper, the behavior of symmetric balanced laminates after first ply failure is analyzed under static and cyclic loadings. Specifically, the stress-strain relations are predicted as functions of applied load in quasi-static tension and of applied cycle in fatigue. The method is based on the concept of the through-the-thickness inherent flaw, the Paris law, and the resistance curve which has been proposed by the authors. A simple equation has been found to predict the crack density as a function of fatigue cycles.

1. INTRODUCTION

When composite laminates are loaded, degradation of mechanical properties may take place long before catastrophic final failure. One of the causes for the degradation is subcritical ply cracking which is found to appear in most multidirectional laminates. The resulting cracks increase in number with the applied load in quasi-static tension and the applied cycles in fatigue. Although these ply cracks do not lead immediately to catastrophic failure, their presence can be deleterious.

To avoid ply cracking in service, the design load must be kept within the first ply failure envelope. However, this design philosophy can be overly conservative, especially if ply cracking is not allowed even in long term service. It is impractical to keep all the ply stresses low enough to prevent ply cracking load in fatigue. Therefore, a design limit may have to be maintained above the first ply cracking load in fatigue. Such design is possible only if we know how to handle progressive ply failure. We need to know the property changes as functions of the applied load and the applied cycle under quasi-static and fatigue loads, respectively.

Since the early 1970's, extensive research in both theory and experiment has been done in the area of transverse ply cracking in an effort to understand the behavior of the laminates after first ply failure (for a detailed literature survey, see Ref.[1]). The main focus of these investigations may be categorized as: 1) analysis of property degradation due to crack formation, 2) failure analysis for transverse crack initiation and multiplication.

Most effort has been directed toward predicting the first ply cracking load and corresponding property degradation while the crack density is known. However, only a few analytical models have been proposed to explore the crack multiplication under static tension [2-7]. Statistical strength distribution [2] and energy balance principle [3-7] have been used to evaluate the crack formation. Once the crack density is known under a certain applied load, one can obtain the corresponding property degradation[9-16]. Then, the behavior of the laminate after first ply cracking can be predicted.

Meanwhile, to explore the crack multiplication under fatigue loading, only one model has been proposed by Chou and Wang [3]. They proposed a model based on the assumption that 1) the growth of a through-the-width type inherent flaw was the mechanism of ply cracking, 2) a power law between the crack growth rate and energy release rate could delineate the formation of ply cracking, 3) new cracks form when an effective flaw grows to a critical length. Parameters were adjusted from a statistical flaw distribution via computer simulation. Comprehensive experimental data on ply

cracking under static and fatigue loadings could be found in Ref. [3].

As long as the crack density is known as a function of the number of fatigue cycles, the stiffness of the laminate can be predicted in the same manner as was done previously [9].

Recently, Boniface and Ogin [17] showed that the fatigue crack growth of transverse ply cracks can be represented by the Paris law. They used transparent glass/epoxy cross-ply laminates for ease of crack detection. Cracks were noted to start not only from the specimen edges but also from the inside of the specimen. They also observed that the crack growth rate depended not on the crack length but on the crack density. This can be explained by the through-the-thickness-flaw concept [18] since the energy release rate of the flaw depends only on crack density which is not true for the through-the-width inherent flaws. The applicability of Paris' law means the energy release rate is a critical parameter under fatigue loading.

In Refs. [7-9], the authors presented a simple method of analyzing progressive ply cracking and corresponding property degradation in symmetric balanced laminates under general in-plane loading. The method was based on the through-the-thickness-flaw concept and energy balance principle. The resistance curve which represents the inhomogeneity of fracture energy had been proposed as a means of characterizing the ply cracking. The curves were found to be independent of the type of lay-up as long as the thickness of the transverse ply remained the same.

In this paper, the behavior of cross-ply laminates after first ply failure under static loading is analyzed first. The model is then extended to the fatigue loading case.

Specifically, the stress-strain relations are predicted as functions of applied load in quasi-static tension and applied cycle in fatigue. The method is based on the through-the-thickness inherent flaw, the resistance curve, and Paris' law. The goal is to establish constitutive relations for cracked composite laminates under quasi-static and fatigue loadings.

2. BEHAVIOR OF COMPOSITE LAMINATES AFTER FIRST PLY FAILURE

2.1 Static loading

Suppose a $[0_i/90_j]_s$ laminate is subjected to a biaxial loading (Fig. 1) and it is desired to find the stress-strain relation even after first ply cracking. This relation can be found using previous analytical results [8-9] as follows.

Assuming the effect of N_y on the transverse cracking in sublaminate 2 is negligible and vice versa, the crack resistance curves $G_I^R(N)$, where N is the crack density, for sublaminate 1 and 2 can be found from $[0/90_j]_s$ laminates [8]. Since the resistance curves have a dominant linear region in typical composites, one may assume the resistance curve is linear with respect to the crack density [8].

Then, the failure criterion of each sublaminate for progressive transverse cracking is

$$G_I(N_2, N_x) = G_I^R(N_2, h_2)$$
$$G_I(N_1, N_y) = G_I^R(N_1, h_1)$$
(1)

Where the equations for G_I are given in the Appendix. Here, N_1 and N_2 are the crack densities in sublaminates 1 and 2, respectively. Once the crack density is known, one can evaluate the degraded compliance matrix since the relations between engineering constants and crack density can be found in Ref. [9].

Then, the constitutive relation of the cracked laminate is

$$\varepsilon_i = a_{ij} N_j$$
(2)

where

$$a_{11} = \left[2(h_1 + h_2)(E_x)_N\right]^{-1}$$

$$a_{22} = \left[2(h_1 + h_2)(E_y)_N\right]^{-1}$$
(3)

$$a_{12} = -\left[2(h_1 + h_2)\frac{(E_x)_N}{(v_{xy})_N}\right]^{-1}$$

$$a_{66} = \left[2(h_1 + h_2)(G_{xy})_N\right]^{-1}$$

Here a_{ij} is the in-plane compliance matrix of the laminate in the laminate coordinate system and subscript N denotes N crack density. $(E_x)_N$, $(E_y)_N$, $(v_{xy})_N$, and $(G_{xy})_N$ are the degraded engineering constants of the cracked laminates of which equations can be found in Ref. 9 The thickness of the sublaminate i is denoted by h_i. Note that $(E_x)_N$ and $(E_y)_N$ are a function of N_x and N_y, respectively, whereas $(v_{xy})_N$ and $(G_{xy})_N$ are a function of not only N_x but also N_y due to the longitudinal cracks in sublaminate 1. For the case of general in-plane loading, one needs to change failure criterion (Eq. 1) as the mixed-mode fracture criterion [9].

It should be noted that the stiffness of cracked laminate would not show the symmetry since the moduli under compression and tension are different, i.e.,

$$E_i v_{ji} \neq E_j v_{ij} \quad i, j = x, y, z$$
(4)

It is obvious that the existence of ply cracks will make the laminate deform more in tension than compression. However, Eq. (3) was derived with the assumption that the cracked laminate was keeping its symmetry.

Suppose a $[0_2/90_3]_s$ AS/3501-6 laminate was subjected to a uniaxial tension 520 MPa and it is desired to find the crack density and the degraded engineering constants. The resistance curve $G_I^R(N)$ can be obtained from Eq. (A-11). Then the resulting crack density can be calculated by equating Eq. (A.1) to the resistance $G_I^R(N)$ as,

$$G_I(N_2, N_x) = 189 + 3.28\, N_2 \qquad (5)$$

From the above equation, the resulting crack density turns out 5.2 cracks/cm. The degraded engineering constants can then be predicted from Eqs. (A-6)-(A-8) as follows.

	value	reduction %
$(E_x)_N$	60.2 GPa	3.7
$(G_{xy})_N$	3.95 GPa	17.6
$(v_{xy})_N$	2.7 E-2	-

Figure 2 shows the stress-strain curves of AS/3501-6 cross-ply laminates which were obtained by the same method in the above case. Curve number 1, 2, and 3 represent $[0/90]_s$, $[0/90_2]_s$, and $[0/90_3]_s$ laminates, respectively. Curve number 4 is the σ-ε curve of $[0/90]_s$ laminate under bi-axial loading when N_x/N_y equal to one. The experimental data for $[0/90]_s$ laminate are also shown for the comparison. The deviations were observed at the final stage i.e., close to the laminate failure in ε_y and v_{xy}. It is believed that this deviation is due to the other extraneous failures such as crack branching. This corresponds to region 3 of the typical resistance curve [8] and it is not included in the analysis. As shown for curve number 4, the biaxiality (when N_x/N_y equal to one) did not affect the longitudinal strain response. The curve is just a little stiffer than curve number 1(uniaxial loading). However, the effective laminate Poisson's ratio degrades faster than that under uniaxial loading. This is due to the ply cracking in sublaminate 1. As shown in curve 1, 2, and 3, the effect of ply cracking to the σ-ε relation becomes larger as the thickness of sublaminate 2 (90° plies) increases.

2.2 Fatigue loading

Suppose a symmetric balanced laminate such as $[(\pm\theta)_i/90_j]_s$ or $[90_i/(\pm\theta)_j]_s$ is subjected to a constant-stress fatigue loading and it is desired to find the behavior of the laminate as the applied cycles increases. This relation can be found in two steps: 1) develop a methodology for the prediction of transverse crack multiplication under fatigue loading; 2) calculate the in-plane compliance matrix of the cracked laminate. The first step will give the resulting crack density as a function of the applied cycles and the second, the stiffnesses as a function of the applied cycles. The second step is the same as in static loading case.

As shown in Ref. [17], we may assume the energy release rate is a critical parameter for the growth of inherent flaws and a power law is applicable:

$$\frac{d\,a}{d\,n} = A_1 (\Delta G)^{\alpha_1} \qquad (6)$$

Here n is the applied cycles, a is the flaw length, and ΔG is the range of the energy release rate in the cyclic loading. A_1 and α_1 are parameters to be determined.

Assuming that an inherent flaw becomes visible only when it reaches the width of the specimen, we may use the crack density N in leu of a on the left-hand side of Eq. (6). Furthermore, since the resistance to crack multiplication increases with crack density, we normalize the range of energy release rate with respect to G_I^R. Then Eq. (6) becomes

$$\frac{dN}{dn} = \frac{1}{A}\left(\frac{\Delta G}{G_I^R}\right)^\alpha \tag{7}$$

This can be integrated to predict the number of cycles required to reach the crack density N:

$$n = A \int_0^N \frac{dN}{\left(\dfrac{\Delta G}{G_I^R}\right)^\alpha} \tag{8}$$

Note that ΔG depends on both fatigue stresses and crack density N while G_I^R depends on N only.

The usefulness of this equation will depend on how universally parameters A and α can be used. If these parameters turn out to be material constants, Eq. (8) will be extremely useful.

To check the validity of Eq. (8) and the nature of A and α, the equation was used to fit the experimental results of AS-4/3501-6 $[0_2/90_i]_s$ laminates [3]. The comparison appears very good as shown in Figs. 3 and 4. It turns out that α is a shape parameter and A is a scaling factor.

Figure 3 shows the correlation between the predictions and the experimental results of $[0_2/90_2]_s$ laminates under 3 different loading levels. Only one value of α (α=20.0) is needed to predict 3 curves. Values of A increase as the load level increase. It is interesting to note that Chou and Wang [3] found the same value for the shape parameter (α) even though the concept and the equation of their model is different from Eq. (8). Figure 4 shows the correlations of $[0_2/90_3]_s$ laminates under 2 different loading levels. Again, the same value of α (α=20.0) can predict the test data even though the laminate stacking sequence is different. Thus, it is conjectured that α may be a material property. The value of A also increased

as the load level increased. Figures 3 and 4 show that the incubation time for the first ply cracking can also be estimated by extrapolating the prediction curve.

To analyze the tendency of the scaling factor 'A', it can be assumed that the energy release rate is again a critical parameter. As a matter of fact, the energy release rate includes all the important parameters such as laminate stacking sequence, thickness of the sublaminate 2, stiffness of the adjacent sublaminate, load level, crack density, and so on. Figure 5 shows the correlation of 'A' with the energy release rate ratio ($\Delta G/G_I^R$). It is interesting to note that 'A' varies linearly with the energy release rate in semi-log scale. For this specific material, the correlation is

$$\log(A) = 20 * \left|\frac{\Delta G}{G_I^R}\right|_{N=0} - 15 \tag{9}$$

It is also interesting to note that the slope of the curve is same as the value of α. However, it can not be concluded at this time whether this is always true.

Apparently, Eq. (8) can predict the crack density N as a function of the applied cycles. Once the crack density is known, the stress-strain relation as a function of the applied cycles can be calculated from Eq. (2) as same as the static loading case.

3. CONCLUSION

The behavior of composite laminates after first ply failure is analyzed under static and fatigue loading. Specifically, the stress-strain relations are predicted as functions of applied load in quasi-static tension and applied cycle in fatigue. The method is based on the through-the-thickness inherent flaw, Paris' law, and the resistance curve which has been proposed by

the authors. A simple equation has been found
to predict the crack density as a function of
fatigue cycle.

4. ACKNOWLEDGMENTS

This paper is based on work supported in part
by E. I. du Pont de Nemours Co. under a grant.
The authors wish to thank Dr. Robert Croman for
his interest and encouragement.

5. REFERENCE

1) Han, Y.M. and Hahn, H.T., "Ply Cracking in
   Composite Laminates: Phenomenon and
   Modeling," Proc. of 34th International
   SAMPE Symposium, May. 1989.

2) Fukunaga, H., Chou, T.W., Peters, P.W.M.,
   and Schulte, K., "Probabilistic Failure
   Strength Analysis of Graphite/Epoxy Cross-
   Ply Laminates," J. of Composite Materials,
   18 (1984), pp339-356.

3) Chou, P.C. and Wang, A.S.D., "Cumulative
   Damage Model for Advanced Composite
   Materials Phase II," AFWAL-TR-84-4004
   1984.

4) Tan, S.C. and Nuismer, R.J., "A Theory For
   Progressive Matrix Cracking In Composite
   Laminates," to be published in the J. of
   Composite Materials.

5) Nairn, J.A., "The Strain Energy Release Rate
   of Composite Microcracking: A Variational
   Approach," to be published in the J. of
   Composite Materials.

6) Laws, N. and Dvorak, G.J., "Progressive
   Transverse Cracking in Composite
   Laminates," J. of Composite Materials, Vol.
   22, 1988, pp900-916.

7) Han, Y.M., Hahn, H.T., and Croman, R.B., "A
   Simplified Analysis of Transverse Ply
   Cracking in Cross-Ply Laminates,"

Composite Science and Technology 31
(1988), pp165-177.

8) Hahn, H.T., Han, Y.M., and Kim, R.Y.,
   "Resistance Curves for Ply Cracking in
   Composite Laminates," Proc. of 33rd
   International SAMPE Symposium, Mar.
   1988, pp1101-1108.

9) Han, Y.M. and Hahn, H.T., "Ply Cracking and
   Property Degradation of Symmetric
   Balanced Laminates Under General In-Plane
   Loading," to be published in Composite
   Science and Technology.

10) Highsmith, A. L. and Reifsnider, K. L.,
    "Stiffness-Reduction Mechanisms in
    Composite Laminates," ASTM STP 775
    (1982), pp103-117.

11) Laws, N. and Dvorak, G. J., "The Loss of
    Stiffness of Cracked Laminates," Proc.
    IUTAM Eshelby Memorial Symp., Cambridge
    University Press (1985) pp119-127.

12) Talreja, R., "Transverse Cracking and
    Stiffness Reduction in Composite
    Laminates," J. of Composite Materials,
    Vol. 19 (1985), pp355-375.

13) Allen, D. H., Groves, S. E., and Harris, C. E.,
    "A Thermomechanical Constitutive Theory
    for Elastic Composites with Distributed
    Damage, Part II. Application to Matrix
    Cracking in Laminated Composites,"
    Mechanics and Materials Center Texas A &
    M University, MM-5023-85-15, Oct. 1985.

14) Hashin, Z., "Analysis of Stiffness Reduction
    of Cracked Cross-Ply Laminates,"
    Engineering Fracture Mechanics Vol. 25,
    Nos 5/6, pp771-778, 1986.

15) Aboudi, J., "Stiffness Reduction of Cracked
    Solids," Engineering Fracture Mechanics
    Vol. 26, No. 5, pp637-650, 1987.

16) Nuismer, R. J. and Tan, S. C., "Constitutive
    Relations of a Cracked Composite Lamina,"

J. Composite Materials, Vol. 22 No. 4
(1988), pp306-321.

17) Boniface, L. and Ogin, S.L., "Application of the Paris Equation to The Fatigue Growth of Transverse Ply Cracks," to be published in the J. of Composite Materials.

18) Hahn, H.T. and Johannesson, "Fracture of Unidirectional Composites: Theory and Applications," Mechanics of Composite Materials, AMD-Vol. 58 (1983), ASME, pp135-142.

6. BIOGRAPHY

Young-M. Han is a Ph.D. student in the department of Engineering Science and Mechanics, The Pennsylvania State University. He is currently working on ply cracking of thermoplastic as well as thermoset matrix composites. He holds a Master of Science degree in Mechanical Engineering from Korea Advanced Institute of Science and Technology.

7. APPENDIX

7.1 Energy release rate and engineering constants

When a symmetric balanced laminate is under biaxial loading (Fig. 1), the energy release rate due to the formation of ply crack can be calculated as follows [7-9].

$$G_1(N_2,N_x)=2h_2\left\{\left(\frac{E_x^{(2)}(h_1+h_2)}{h_1E_x^{(1)}+h_2E_x^{(2)}}\frac{N_x}{2}+\sigma_x^{T(2)}\right)^2\left(\frac{h_1E_x^{(1)}+h_2E_x^{(2)}}{12h_1E_x^{(1)}E_x^{(2)}G_T}\right)^{\frac{1}{2}}\left(\tanh\left(\frac{\phi_x}{2N_2}\right)-\frac{\phi_x}{2N_2}\mathrm{sech}^2\left(\frac{\phi_x}{2N_2}\right)\right)\right\}$$
(A.1)

$$G_1(N_1,N_y)=2h_1\left\{\left(\frac{E_y^{(1)}(h_1+h_2)}{h_1E_y^{(1)}+h_2E_y^{(2)}}\frac{N_y}{2}+\sigma_y^{T(1)}\right)^2\left(\frac{h_1E_y^{(1)}+h_2E_y^{(2)}}{12h_2E_y^{(1)}E_y^{(2)}G_T}\right)^{\frac{1}{2}}\left(\tanh\left(\frac{\phi_y}{2N_1}\right)-\frac{\phi_y}{2N_1}\mathrm{sech}^2\left(\frac{\phi_y}{2N_1}\right)\right)\right\}$$
(A.2)

where

$$\phi_x=\left(\frac{3G_T\left(h_1E_x^{(1)}+h_2E_x^{(2)}\right)}{h_1E_x^{(1)}E_x^{(2)}}\right)^{\frac{1}{2}},\qquad \phi_y=\left(\frac{3G_T\left(h_1E_y^{(1)}+h_2E_y^{(2)}\right)}{h_2E_y^{(1)}E_y^{(2)}}\right)^{\frac{1}{2}}$$
(A.3)

$$\bar{N}_1=N_1h_1,\qquad \bar{N}_2=N_2h_2$$

Here N_i is the crack density in sublaminate i and G_T is transverse shear modulus of sublaminate 2. $E_x^{(i)}$ and $E_y^{(i)}$ are effective longitudinal and transverse moduli, which take into account the biaxial stress state in each sublaminate. These are defined as follows [8].

$$\frac{1}{E_{x,y}^{(i)}}=\frac{2h_i}{\alpha^{(i)}}\left[A_{22,11}^{(i)}-A_{12}^{(i)}\left(\frac{A_{12}^{(i)}\left(A_{22,11}^{(1)}+A_{22,11}^{(2)}\right)-A_{22,11}^{(i)}\left(A_{12}^{(1)}+A_{12}^{(2)}\right)}{A_{11,22}^{(i)}\left(A_{22,11}^{(1)}+A_{22,11}^{(2)}\right)-A_{12}^{(i)}\left(A_{12}^{(1)}+A_{12}^{(2)}\right)}\right)\right]$$
(A.4)

where,

$$\alpha^{(i)}=A_{11}^{(i)}A_{22}^{(i)}-\left(A_{12}^{(i)}\right)^2$$
(A.5)

Here $A_{kl}^{(i)}$ is stiffness matrix of sublaminate i.

The degraded engineering constants also can be obtained as follows (residual stress are ignored in this analysis).

$$\frac{(E_x)_N}{E_x^o} = \left[1 + \frac{h_2}{h_1} \frac{2\bar{N}_2}{\phi_x} \frac{E_x^{(2)}}{E_x^{(1)}} \tanh\left(\frac{\phi_x}{2\bar{N}_2}\right) \right]^{-1} \tag{A.6}$$

$$\frac{(E_y)_N}{E_y^o} = \left[1 + \frac{h_1}{h_2} \frac{2\bar{N}_1}{\phi_y} \frac{E_y^{(1)}}{E_y^{(2)}} \tanh\left(\frac{\phi_y}{2\bar{N}_1}\right) \right]^{-1} \tag{A.7}$$

$$\frac{(G_{xy})_N}{G_{xy}^o} = \left\{ 1 + \frac{h_2}{h_1} \frac{2\bar{N}_x}{\mu_2} \frac{G_{xy}^{(2)}}{G_{xy}^{(1)}} \tanh\left(\frac{\mu_2}{2\bar{N}_2}\right) + \frac{h_1}{h_2} \frac{2\bar{N}_1}{\mu_1} \frac{G_{xy}^{(1)}}{G_{xy}^{(2)}} \tanh\left(\frac{\mu_1}{2\bar{N}_1}\right) \right\}^{-1} \tag{A.8}$$

$$(\nu_{xy})_N = \frac{1}{A_{22}^{(1)} + A_{22}^{(2)}} \left[A_{12}^{(1)} + A_{12}^{(2)} \frac{\delta x^{(2)}}{\delta x^{(1)}} - \left\{ A_{12}^{(1)} A_{22}^{(2)} - A_{12}^{(2)} A_{22}^{(1)} \frac{\delta x^{(2)}}{\delta x^{(1)}} \right\} \frac{\bar{N}_1 \tanh\left(\frac{\phi_y}{2\bar{N}_1}\right)}{h_2 E_y^{(2)} \phi_y} \right] \tag{A.9}$$

where,

$$\mu_1 = \sqrt{3\left(\frac{G_{xy}^{(1)} h_1 + G_{xy}^{(2)} h_2}{G_{xy}^{(2)} h_2}\right)} \quad , \quad \mu_2 = \sqrt{3\left(\frac{G_{xy}^{(1)} h_1 + G_{xy}^{(2)} h_2}{G_{xy}^{(1)} h_1}\right)} \tag{A.10}$$

$$\frac{\delta x^{(2)}}{\delta x^{(1)}} = \frac{E_x^{(1)} \left\{ 1 - \frac{2\bar{N}_2}{\phi_x} \tanh\left(\frac{\phi_x}{2\bar{N}_2}\right) \right\}}{E_x^{(2)} \left\{ \frac{E_x^{(1)}}{E_x^{(2)}} + \frac{h_2}{h_1} \frac{2\bar{N}_2}{\phi_x} \tanh\left(\frac{\phi_x}{2\bar{N}_2}\right) \right\}}$$

Here, superscript o denotes the laminate without crack.

7.2 Resistance curves

As shown in Ref. [8], the resistance curves have a dominant linear region in typical composites. Thus, we assumed the curve was linear with respect to the crack density. The equations obtained from the curve fitting with the experimental data shown in Ref. [8] is follows.

$$G_I^R(N) = 2\left(\gamma_I + A N\right) \tag{A.11}$$

where,

$$\frac{\gamma_I}{\gamma_o} = 0.36\frac{h_2}{t} + 0.29 \qquad \frac{A}{A_o} = 0.64\frac{h_2}{t} - 0.28 \tag{A.12}$$

Here A_o and γ_o are the slope and interception for the best fit curve of the reference laminate $[0/90_2]_s$ and the values for the typical graphite/epoxy are as follows.

	A_o	γ_o
AS/3501-6	4.45	68.98
T300/934	10.75	110.94

Now, one can calculate the resistance of $[(\pm\theta)_i/90_j]_s$ or $[90_i/(\pm\theta)_j]_s$ laminate as a function of crack density.

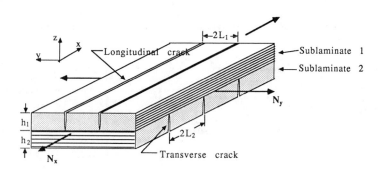

Figure 1 Cross-ply laminate under biaxial loading.

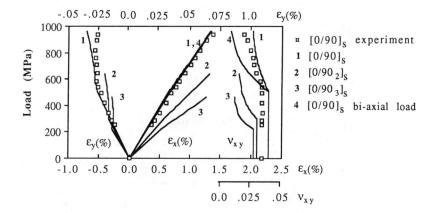

Figure 2 Stress-strain relations of AS-4/3501-6 cross-ply laminates

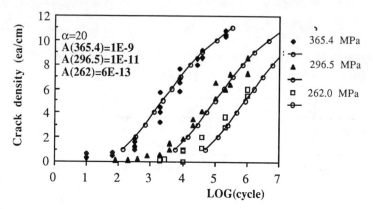

Figures 3. Crack density vs. fatigue cycles for $[0_2/90_2]s$ laminates

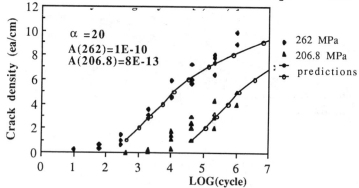

Figure 4.   Crack density vs. fatigue cycles for $[0_2/90_3]s$ laminates

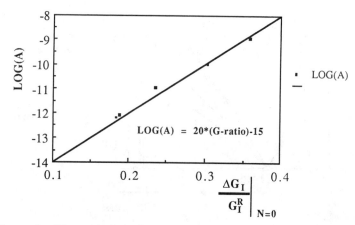

Figure 5.   The variation of the scaling factor 'A' to energy release rate

A SIMPLE APPROACH FOR THE BUCKLING OF UNIDIRECTIONAL COMPOSITES WITH CIRCULAR AND NON-CIRCULAR FIBERS

Seng C. Tan
AdTech Systems Research Inc.
US Air Force Materials Laboratory
AFWAL/MLBM, Wright Patterson AFB, OH 45433

Abstract

A simple model is presented for the buckling of unidirectional composite laminates containing continuous fibers with circular and non-circular cross-sectional shapes. The non-circular shapes include elliptical, rectangular, triangular and c-shell. The analysis is based on a beam column theory. It is shown that a unidirectional laminate with non-circular fibers could have either a higher or a lower buckling stress than that with circular fibers. The ratio of the buckling stresses, laminate with non-circular fibers versus that with circular fibers, depends on the orientation of the non-circular fibers and the fiber volume fraction. In addition, the fibers of a laminate with non-circular fibers may not align in one direction. Therefore, a distribution function for the orientation of the non-circular fibers is also introduced to study this problem.

1. INTRODUCTION

Non-circular cross-sectional fibers can be found in natural composites. For advanced composite materials, such as graphite/epoxy, non-circular fibers are still in developing stage. They are not available commercially.

Based on a single filament test, Edie, Fox and Barnett[1] showed that trilobal carbon fibers have both a higher tensile strength and modulus than circular carbon fibers. The mechanical properties of composite laminates with non-circular fibers have not been reported in the literature. Therefore, whether the design of a structure, such as weight, can be improved using non-circular fibers is not known.

If a stability analysis is based on minimechanics, it would not be able to show the difference of the critical buckling stresses of composite laminates with circular and non-circular fibers. This is because minimechanics assume that a material is homogeneous on the lamina basis. Stability analyses can be found for unidirectional composite laminates with circular fibers, for instance, Hahn and Williams[2]. However, no analytical analysis has been done in the area of buckling of composite laminates with non-circular fibers. The purpose of this study is to show if the critical buckling stress of unidirectional composite laminates can be improved using non-circular fibers.

2. A ROW OF FIBERS EMBEDDED IN A MATRIX

The stability analysis of a unidirectional composite is performed under a simply supported condition and subject to a longitudinal compression load, P, Figure 1.

2.1 Critical Buckling Stress

Let t, h and L denote the thickness, width and length of the laminate, respectively. The moment deflection relation of a laminate with multiple fibers has been derived in References 3-4 by the present author as

$$w'' = \frac{-M}{E_f \sum I_f + E_m \sum I_m} \qquad (1)$$

where w'' is the second derivative of the displacement in the z axis with respect to x; M is the bending moment caused by load P; E_f and E_m denote the modulus of fibers and matrix, respectively, and I_f and I_m designate the respective moment of inertia, with respect to the y-axis, due to the fibers and matrix. Solving Equation (1) with zero displacement boundary conditions, $w = 0$, at $x = 0$ and $x = L$ and substituting the moment of inertia of the matrix and a row of elliptical fibers which are all slanted at the same angle ψ from the thickness direction, Figure 2, we obtain the critical buckling stress, P_{cr}. The critical buckling stress, σ_{cr}, is obtained by dividing σ_{cr} by the cross-sectional area of the laminate:

$$\sigma_{cr}^{(e)} = \frac{\pi^2 E_f}{4L^2} \left\{ V_f^{(e)} \left(a^2 \cos^2\psi + b^2 \sin^2\psi \right)(1 - E_R) \right.$$

$$\left. + \frac{t^2}{3} E_R \right\} \tag{2}$$

where

$$V_f^{(e)} = \frac{m\pi ab}{th} \tag{3}$$

$$E_R = \frac{E_m}{E_f}$$

The parameters $V_f^{(e)}$ is the fiber volume fraction of a laminate with elliptical fibers, E_R is the ratio of matrix modulus to fiber modulus, and a and b denote the semi-major and semi-minor diameters of the elliptical fibers, respectively. For circular fibers, $b = a = R$, Equation (2) reduces to

$$\sigma_{cr}^{(c)} = \frac{\pi^2 E_f}{4L^2} \left\{ V_f^{(c)} (1 - E_R) R^2 + \frac{t^2}{3} E_R \right\} \tag{4}$$

where $V_f^{(c)}$ is the fiber volume fraction and R represents the radius of the fibers. Note that this derivation is based on the assumptions: (1) the dimensions of the laminates with circular fibers and non-circular fibers are the same and; (2) the cross-sectional areas of the circular fibers and non-circular fibers are the same. The solutions for laminates with other shape of fibers such as rectangular, triangular and c-shell are given in References 3-4.

2.2 Ratio of Critical Buckling Stresses

The ratio of critical buckling stresses, σ_R, is defined as the critical buckling stress of a laminate with non-circular fibers divided by

that with circular fibers. In the case of laminates with elliptical fibers, the solution of σ_R is

$$\sigma_R = \frac{\sigma_{cr}^{(e)}}{\sigma_{cr}^{(c)}}$$

$$= \frac{\left(\frac{a}{b}\cos^2\psi + \frac{b}{a}\sin^2\psi\right)(1 - E_R)V_r + SE_R}{1 - E_R + SE_R} \tag{5}$$

where

$$V_r = V_f^{(e)} / V_f^{(c)} \tag{6}$$

$$S = \frac{t^2}{3ab V_f^{(e)}}$$

The parameter V_r is the ratio of fiber volume fraction of a laminate with elliptical fibers and that with circular fibers. If σ_R is greater than one, the two digits after the decimal point give the percentage of improvement for the critical buckling stress.

2.3 Distribution of Fiber Slanted Angle

The slanted angle, ψ, of a laminate with non-circular fibers, Figure 1, does not necessary to be all align in the same direction. In the case that the chance is equal for ψ to occur in any direction between $0°$ and $90°$ or a condition of random distribution, the solution of the $\overline{\sigma}_{cr}^{(e)}$ and $\overline{\sigma}_R$ of a laminate can be acquired by integrating Equations (2) and (5) with respect to ψ. The result is

$$\overline{\sigma}_{cr}^{(e)} = \frac{\pi^2 E_f}{4L^2} \left\{ V_f^{(e)} \frac{(a^2 + b^2)}{2}(1 - E_R) + \frac{t^2}{3} E_R \right\} \tag{7}$$

$$\overline{\sigma}_R = \frac{\frac{1}{2}\left(\frac{a}{b} + \frac{b}{a}\right)(1 - E_R)V_r + SE_R}{1 - E_R + SE_R} \tag{8}$$

where a bar on top of a variable defines the average of that variable.

Next we consider non-uniform distributions. From the construction of the fibers in Figure 1, one can see that it is more stable for the fibers to occur at $\psi = 90°$ than $\psi = 0°$. Therefore, it is logical to assume that the slanted angles of the elliptical fibers will distribute in the following probability function:

$$P(\psi) = \sin^n \psi \qquad (9)$$

The critical buckling stress and the ratio of critical buckling stresses of a laminate with elliptical fibers distributed with the probability function given in Equation (9) are

$$\bar{\sigma}_{cr}^{(e)} = \frac{\int_0^{\pi/2} \sigma_{cr}^{(e)} P(\psi) \, d\psi}{\int_0^{\pi/2} P(\psi) \, d\psi} \qquad (10)$$

and

$$\bar{\sigma}_R = \frac{\int_0^{\pi/2} \sigma_R P(\psi) \, d\psi}{\int_0^{\pi/2} P(\psi) \, d\psi} \qquad (11)$$

Substituting Equations (2), (5) and (9) into (10) and (11) we arrive at

$$\bar{\sigma}_{cr}^{(e)} = \frac{\pi^2 E_f}{4L^2} \left\{ \frac{V_f^{(e)}}{n+2} \left[a^2 + (n+1)b^2 \right] (1 - E_R) + \frac{t^2}{3} E_R \right\} \qquad (12)$$

$$\bar{\sigma}_R = \frac{1}{1 - E_R + SE_R} \left\{ \frac{V_r}{n+2} \left[\frac{a}{b} + (n+1)\frac{b}{a} \right] \right.$$
$$\left. \times (1 - E_R) + SE_R \right\} \qquad (13)$$

When $b = a$, Equation (12) reduces to Equation (4) and σ_R recovers to unity.

3. MULTIPLE ROWS OF FIBERS

An advanced composite material normally contains multiple rows of fibers. The ratio of critical buckling stresses of composite laminates with multiple rows of fibers is not proportional to that with a single row of fibers. The shape and the locations of the fibers as well as the fiber volume fraction all contribute to the solution. In order to solve the problem using a simple model yet still able to capture the first order effect, we make the following assumptions: (1) the central portion of the laminate is homogeneous and; (2) the outer rows of fibers touch the outer surface, as shown in Figure 3. As the previous case, a single row of fibers embedded in a matrix, the dimensions of the laminates and the cross-sectional areas of the fibers are again assumed the same for laminates with circular and non-circular fibers. Under these conditions, the $\sigma_{cr}^{(c)}$ and $\sigma_{cr}^{(e)}$ are obtained as

$$\sigma_{cr}^{(c)} = \frac{\pi^2 E_f}{L^2} \left\{ \left[V_f^{(c)} + \left(1 - V_f^{(c)} \right) E_R \right] \frac{(t - 4R)^3}{12t} \right.$$

$$+ \frac{V_f^{(c)} R^3}{t}(1 - E_R) + \frac{4R^3}{3}\frac{}{t}E_R + V_f^{(c)}\frac{R}{t}(t - 2R)^2$$

$$\left. \times (1 - E_R) + \frac{R}{t}(t - 2R)^2 E_R \right\} \qquad (14)$$

where

$$V_f^{(c)} = \frac{2n\pi R^2}{4Rh} \qquad (15)$$

and

$$\sigma_{cr}^{(e)} = \frac{\pi^2 E_f}{L^2} \left\{ \left[V_f^{(e)} + \left(1 - V_f^{(e)} \right) E_R \right] \frac{(t - 4R)^3}{12t} \right.$$

$$+ \frac{V_f^{(e)} b^2 R}{t}(1 - E_R) + \frac{4R^3}{3}\frac{}{t}E_R + V_f^{(e)}\frac{R}{t}(t - 2b)^2$$

$$\left. + \frac{R}{t}\left(1 - V_f^{(e)}\right)(t - 2R)^2 E_R \right\} \qquad (16)$$

where

$$V_f^{(e)} = \frac{2m\pi ab}{4Rh} \qquad (17)$$

The ratio of critical buckling stresses, σ_R, is obtained by dividing $\sigma_{cr}^{(e)}$ by $\sigma_{cr}^{(c)}$, i.e. Equation (14) by Equation (16).

4. PARAMETRIC STUDIES

The result of this analysis is illustrated graphically using the assumed material properties and geometry of the laminate given in the following:

$$E_m/E_f = 1/20, \qquad t = 2a$$

The solutions of laminates with triangular and c-shell fibers are given in References 3-4. Figure 4 shows the σ_R, Equation (5), and $\bar{\sigma}_R$, Equation (8), for laminates with a single row of: (a) elliptical fibers; (b) triangular fibers and; (c) c-shell fibers. In this figure, we assume that $V_f^{(e)} = V_f^{(t)} = V_f^{(s)} = V_f^{(c)} = 60\%$ where $V_f^{(t)}$ and $V_f^{(s)}$ are the fiber volume fraction of the laminates with triangular and c-shell fibers, respectively. When the major diameter, 2a, is parallel to the thickness direction of the laminate, $\psi = 0$, the critical buckling stress of the laminate could be significantly higher than that with circular

541

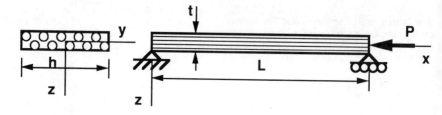

Figure 1. A unidirectional composite subject to compressive loading.

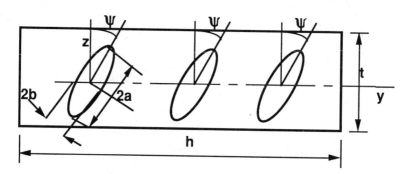

Figure 2. A unidirectional composite containing a row of elliptical fibers, all slanted at an angle ψ from the z-axis.

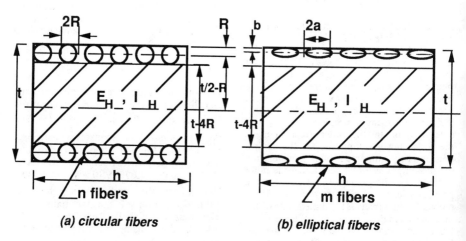

(a) circular fibers　　　　　**(b) elliptical fibers**

Figure 3. Unidirectional composites with multiple rows of (a) circular fibers and (b) elliptical fibers.

fibers. However, σ_R drops below unity for higher degree of fiber slanted angle. The buckling curves for laminates with rectangular fibers is similar to that with elliptical fibers.

When the distribution function of the fiber slanted angle is taken into account, Equations (9-13), the critical buckling stresses are plotted as a function of the power n in Figures 5 and 6 for laminates with elliptical fibers and triangular fibers, respectively. An increasing value of n means that more fibers appear for higher slanted angles, ψ, and less fibers occur for lower slanted angles. For n>0, the probability of $\psi = 0$ is zero because it is unstable for elliptical fibers to exist at this angle. The ratio of critical buckling stresses decreases when the distribution of the fiber slanted angle is taken into account.

For laminates with multiple rows of fibers, Figures 7-11, σ_R decreases rapidly as the thickness of the laminate increases. When the thickness, t, increases to more than thirty times of the minor elliptical diameter or height of the triangular fibers, σ_R reduces to unity for same amount of fiber volume fraction. When the fiber volume fraction of a laminate with elliptical fibers changes from 60% to 50% and 40% while the fiber volume fraction of a laminate with circular fiber remains 60%, Figure 8, σ_R could be significantly less than unity. A similar result is observed for laminates with multiple rows of triangular or rectangular fibers, Figures 9-10. For laminates with c-shell fibers, $\sigma_R = 1$ is the upper bound for same fiber volume fractions, $V_f^{(s)} = V_f^{(c)}$. Similarly, σ_R is significantly less than unity if the fiber volume fraction is less than that for laminates with circular fibers.

5.   CONCLUSIONS

A simple approach is presented for the study of buckling of unidirectional composites with circular and non-circular fibers. This analysis assumes that the cross-sectional areas of a non-circular fiber and a circular fiber are the same; and the dimensions of the laminates with circular and non-circular fibers are the same. The following conclusions can be drawn from this study:

1. A laminate containing a row or a few rows of non-circular fibers could have

significantly higher critical buckling stress than that with circular fibers.

2. For laminates with multiple rows of non-circular fibers, the critical buckling stress is approximately the same or lower than that with circular fibers, for same amount of fiber volume fraction.

3. The slanted angle of the non-circular fibers and the distribution of the fiber slanted angle are taken into account in this analysis.

4. Due to packing's problem, a laminate with non-circular fibers has less fiber volume fraction than that with circular fibers, which further reduces the critical buckling stress.

6.   REFERENCES

1.   Edie, D. D., N. K. Fox and B. C. Barnett, "Melt-Spun Non-Circular Carbon Fibers," *Carbon*, Vol. 24, pp.477-482 (1986).

2.   Hahn, H. T., and J. G. Williams, "Compression Failure Mechanisms in Unidirectional Composites," NASA Technical Memorandum 85834 (1984).

3.   Tan, S. C., "Buckling of Unidirectional Composites with Circular and Non-Circular Fibers Part I: Derivation," will submit to J. Composite Materials soon.

4.   Tan, S. C., "Buckling of Unidirectional Composites with Circular and Non-Circular Fibers Part II: Application," will submit to J. Composite Materials soon.

7.   BIOGRAPHY

Dr. Tan obtained his B.S. degree from the National Taiwan University, Mechanical Engineering Department, and a Ph.D degree from the University of Utah, Mechanical Engineering Department in 1983. He was awarded the Resident Research Associateship by the National Research Council to conduct research in mechanics, failure and design of composite materials at the Materials Laboratory, Wright Patterson AFB. After that he continued to work at the Mechanics and Surface Interactions Branch of the Materials Laboratory as an on-site contractor. Officially he is senior research scientist of the AdTech Systems Research Inc. Dr Tan has published nearly thirty papers in technical journals in the area of composite materials. He has been working and publishing papers in the areas of: progressive failure, notched strength, micro-mechanics, fabrication and repair, optimization design, mechanics of ordered polymers, delamination and testing design, etc.

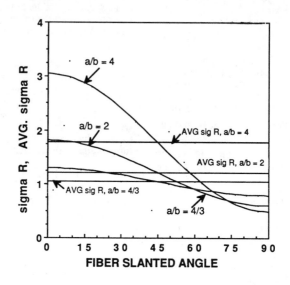

(a) Elliptical fibers

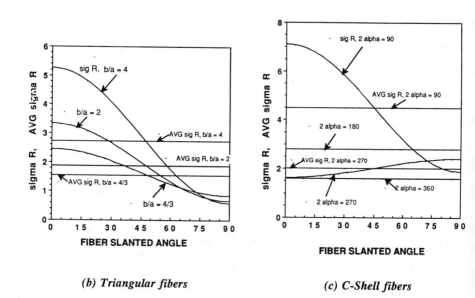

(b) Triangular fibers　　　　　*(c) C-Shell fibers*

Figure 4.　The ratio of critical buckling stresses, σ_R, and the σ_R of unidirectional composites with a row of non-circular fibers.

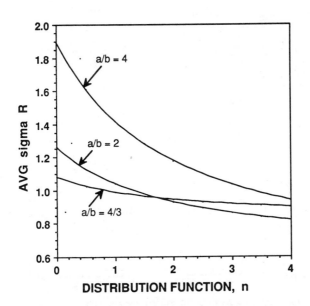

Figure 5. Ratio of effective critical buckling stresses, σ_R, for unidirectional composites with a row of elliptical fibers distributed in a $\sin^n \psi$ function.

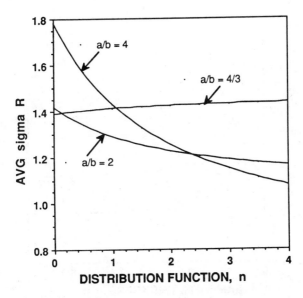

Figure 6. Ratio of effective critical buckling stresses, σ_R, for unidirectional composites with a row of triangular fibers distributed in a $\sin^n \psi$ function.

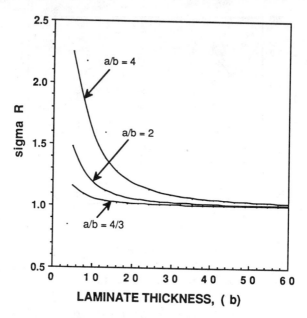

Figure 7. Ratio of critical buckling stresses, σ_R, of composite laminates with multiple rows of elliptical fibers, $V_f^{(e)} = V_f^{(c)}$.

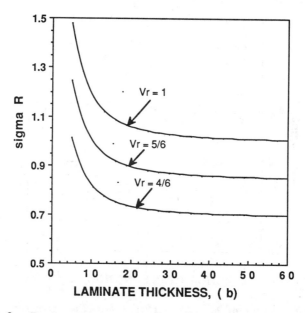

Figure 8. Ratio of critical buckling stresses, σ_R, of composite laminates with multiple rows of elliptical fibers, $a/b = 2$.

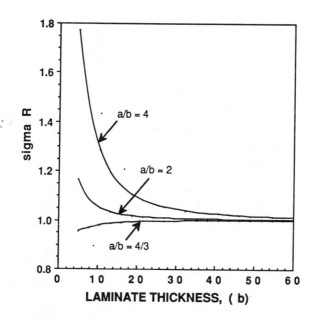

Figure 9. Ratio of critical buckling stresses, σ_R, of composite laminates with multiple rows of triangular fibers, $V_f^{(t)} = V_f^{(c)}$.

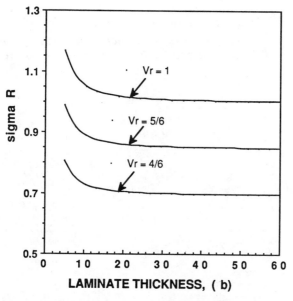

Figure 10. Ratio of critical buckling stresses, σ_R, of composite laminates with multiple rows of elliptical fibers, $a/b = 2$.

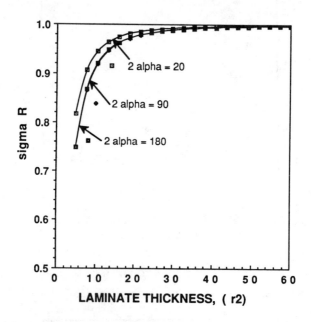

Figure 11. Ratio of critical buckling stresses, σ_R, of composite laminates with multiple rows of c-shell fibers, inner radius/ outer radius = 1/2 and 2 alpha is the angle between the two ends.

34th International SAMPE Symposium
May 8-11, 1989

RESPONSE OF THICK LAMINATED COMPOSITE RINGS DUE TO THERMAL STRESSES

Ajit K. Roy
University of Dayton Research Institute
300 College Park
Dayton, OH 45469–0001

ABSTRACT

Thermal stress analysis of thick laminated rings due to curing is presented. The layers of the ring are assumed cylindrically orthotropic. The analysis is based on treating the rings in plane stress in (r–θ) plane. If the ring is cut through radially at a point, the ring may open or close depending on the values of the stress resultants due to the thermal stresses. The analysis predicts such opening or closing displacements which are then compared with the measured values. It is found that the moment stress resultant mostly determines the opening or closing displacements, and moment stress resultant is strongly dependent of the stacking sequence wound layers.

1. INTRODUCTION

Recently there is a growing interest in developing fiber reinforced cylindrical composite structures for use as deep submersible structures to carry high external pressure[1]. In order for these structures to perform under high external pressure, the thickness of these cylinders are to be thick.

Processing and curing such thick laminated cylinders to date are challenging. Moreover, due to anisotropy of the fiber reinforced composites, curing of these structural components at a temperature much higher than its operating temperature induces complex thermal residual stresses at its operating conditions. The objective of this work is to correctly predict the thermal residual stresses in these structures, and then to identify the controlling parameters behind the residual stresses.

For multilayered composite cylinders the state of the thermal residual stresses are complex. If thin rings (thin in the axial direction of the cylinder) are cut out of the cured cylinder, then the axial stress which was present in the cylinder, is essentially released in the ring, then the ring can be modeled as stress free in the axial direction of the cylinder, and thus can be considered as in the state of plane stress in (r–θ) plane. This axial stress release in the ring simplifies the problem somewhat, thus the residual stress analysis of composite laminated rings

549

is done in this paper as a first step to understand the mechanics of the more complex thermal stress field in composite cylindrical structures.

2. STRESS ANALYSIS

Filament wound composite cylinders are manufactured by winding wet filament tows around a mandrel. The mandrel can be of any material, normally of Aluminum, Stainless Steel, Salt. Filament wound cylinders are made with adjacent ($\pm\phi$) angle lay-ups. An adjacent ($\pm\phi$) angle lay-up is assumed here to behave as an orthotropic unit. An orthotropic unit of ($\pm\phi$) angle lay-up is referred in this paper as an orthotropic layer of angle ϕ.

The scope of this paper, as discussed in the introduction, is to perform thermal stress analysis of laminated composite rings cut from filament wound cylinders. The linear theory of elasticity is used to make the analysis applicable for thick rings (radius to thickness ratio can be less than 10). The ring is assumed in state of plane stress in (r–θ) plane, Figure 1(a). Since each layer of the ring is assumed to be orthotropic and circumferentially symmetric, $\tau_{r\theta}$ is zero everywhere, and then the constitutive relations (strain–stress) in cylindrical coordinates including thermal strains are:

$$\sigma_r^{(i)} = \frac{1}{S_{rr}^{(i)}\left(1-v_{\theta r}^{(i)}v_{r\theta}^{(i)}\right)}\left[\varepsilon_r^{(i)}+v_{r\theta}^{(i)}\varepsilon_\theta^{(i)}\right.$$
$$\left.-\left(\alpha_r^{(i)}+v_{r\theta}^{(i)}\alpha_\theta^{(i)}\right)\Delta T\right] \tag{1}$$

$$\sigma_\theta^{(i)} = \frac{1}{S_{\theta\theta}^{(i)}\left(1-v_{\theta r}^{(i)}v_{r\theta}^{(i)}\right)}\left[\varepsilon_\theta^{(i)}+v_{\theta r}^{(i)}\varepsilon_r^{(i)}\right.$$
$$\left.-\left(\alpha_\theta^{(i)}+v_{\theta r}^{(i)}\alpha_r^{(i)}\right)\Delta T\right] \tag{2}$$

where

$$v_{r\theta}^{(i)} = -\frac{S_{r\theta}^{(i)}}{S_{\theta\theta}^{(i)}} \ , \ v_{\theta r}^{(i)} = -\frac{S_{\theta r}^{(i)}}{S_{rr}^{(i)}} \ , \ \text{and} \ \Delta T = T_o\text{-}T_c$$

T_o : operating temperature, T_c : cure temperature, and $S_{ij}^{(i)}$'s are the elements of the compliance matrix of the i–th layer.

The equation of equilibrium with circular symmetry:

$$\frac{d\sigma_r^{(i)}}{dr} + \frac{\sigma_r^{(i)}\text{-}\sigma_\theta^{(i)}}{r} = 0 \tag{3}$$

Substituting equations (1) and (2) in (3) and using the kinematic relations for circular symmetry, we get:

$$\frac{d^2u^{(i)}}{dr^2} + \frac{1}{r}\frac{du^{(i)}}{dr} - \frac{k_i^2}{r^2}u^{(i)}$$
$$= \frac{1}{r}\left[\alpha_r^{(i)}\left(1-v_{r\theta}^{(i)}\right)-\alpha_\theta^{(i)}\left(k_i^2-v_{r\theta}^{(i)}\right)\right]\Delta T \tag{4}$$

where

$$k_i = \sqrt{\frac{S_{rr}^{(i)}}{S_{\theta\theta}^{(i)}}}$$

The solution for equation (4) can be obtained by following a solution procedure for solving a linear second order nonhomogeneous ordinary differential equation. Then the displacement, $u^{(i)}$, and the stresses, $\sigma_r^{(i)}$ and $\sigma_\theta^{(i)}$, for each layer can be expressed in terms of interfacial normal tractions, q_i's, acting at the interfaces of the layers, Figure 1(b). If the ring consists of n number of such layers, then the number of q_i's, are n+1.

The interfacial normal tractions, q_i's are to be determined from the boundary conditions and the contact condition at each interface of the layers. The rings being analyzed here are obtained from filament wound cylinders by cutting thin slices perpendicular to the axis of the cylinders. For filament wound cylinders, wet filament tows are normally wound around the mandrel with some tension on the fibers at about room temperature. Then the wound composite cylinder with the mandrel is cured at the curing temperature. Consolidation of the cylinder normally takes place at the curing temperature. At the curing temperature and just before the consolidation of the cylinder, the resin of the matrix is essentially fluid which makes the fibers of the cylinder readjust in the matrix in such a way to allow almost free expansion of the mandrel. The displacement at the inner radius of the cylinder at the curing temperature is due to pushing of the mandrel and thus is modeled as that of the mandrel at the curing temperature due to its free expansion.

Thus the boundary condition at the inner radius of the ring is:

$$u_0^{(1)} = -\alpha_r^{(d)} a_0 \Delta T \qquad \text{at } r=a$$

$$(5)$$

where $u_0^{(1)}$ is the displacement of the ring at its inner radius because of the expansion of the mandrel and $\alpha_r^{(d)}$ is the mandrel thermal expansion coefficient in the radial direction. After substituting the expression for $u_0^{(1)}$ in equation (5) we get,

$$q_0 S_{\theta\theta}^{(1)} \left(k_1 \frac{1+c_1^{2k_1}}{1-c_1^{2k_1}} + v_{r\theta}^{(1)} \right) - q_1 S_{\theta\theta}^{(1)} \frac{2k_1 c_1^{k_1-1}}{1-c_1^{2k_1}}$$

$$= -\alpha_r^{(d)} \Delta T$$

$$(6)$$

The contact condition at each interface is,

$$u^{(i)} = u^{(i+1)} \qquad \text{at } r = a_i$$

which gives a set of simultaneous equations to determine q_i's:

$$q_{i+1} \beta_{i+1} a_{i+1} + q_i \gamma_i a_i + q_{i-1} \beta_i a_{i-1}$$
$$= (X_{i+1} - Y_i + Z_{i+1} - Z_i) a_i \Delta T$$
$$\text{for } i = 1, 2, \ldots, (n-1)$$

$$(7)$$

where

$$\beta_i = S_{\theta\theta}^{(i)} \frac{2k_i c_i^k}{1-c_i^{2k}}$$

$$\gamma_i = S_{\theta\theta}^{(i)} \left(v_{r\theta}^{(i)} - k_i \frac{1+c_i^{2k_i}}{1-c_i^{2k_i}} \right)$$
$$- S_{\theta\theta}^{(i+1)} \left(v_{r\theta}^{(i+1)} + k_{i+1} \frac{1+c_{i+1}^{2k_{i+1}}}{1-c_{i+1}^{2k_{i+1}}} \right)$$

and if $k_i \neq 1$,

$$X_i = \frac{\alpha_r^{(i)} - \alpha_\theta^{(i)}}{1-k_i^2} \left[v_{r\theta}^{(i)} + k_i \frac{1+c_i^{2k_i} - 2c_i^{k_i-1}}{1-c_i^{2k_i}} \right]$$

$$Y_i = \frac{\alpha_r^{(i)} - \alpha_\theta^{(i)}}{1-k_i^2} \left[v_{r\theta}^{(i)} - k_i \frac{1+c_i^{2k_i} - 2c_i^{k_i+1}}{1-c_i^{2k_i}} \right]$$

$$Z_i = \frac{\alpha_r^{(i)}(1-v_{r\theta}^{(i)}) - \alpha_\theta^{(i)}(k_i^2 - v_{r\theta}^{(i)})}{1-k_i^2},$$

for $k_i = 1$

$$X_i = Y_i = 0, \text{ and } Z_i = \alpha_r^{(i)}$$

The equations (6) and (7) give a set of n number of equations to determine n number of q_i's for a ring consisting of n number of layers. Once the q_i's are known the stresses and displacement are thus determined from the solution of equation (4).

3. RING RESIDUAL STRESS RESULTANTS

When the rings are cut from the cured cylinder there are induced residual stresses in the ring due to curing the cylinder at a higher temperature. At room temperature, the stress resultants due to these residual stresses can be determined by cutting the ring radially at a circumferential point as shown in Figure 2. When the ring is cut radially, the radial cut surface is made stress free due to release of the stresses at the cut surface. In other words, one can apply an equal and opposite stress resultants (Figure 2) on the cut surface to make the surface stress free. In this analysis, the stress being released is the hoop stress, which induces the two stress resultants acting on the cut surface as defined below:

In–plane stress resultant

$$P = - \frac{1}{(b-a)} \sum_{i=1}^{n} \int_{a_{i-1}}^{a_i} \sigma_\theta^{(i)} dr \tag{8}$$

and the bending stress resultant

$$M = - \sum_{i=1}^{n} \int_{a_{i-1}}^{a_i} (\sigma_\theta^{(i)} + P) r \, dr \tag{9}$$

These two stress resultants try to open or close the ring depending on their respective values. The cut opening displacement of the ring due to the stress resultant, P, is:

$$\Delta V_P = - \pi \bar{S}_{\theta\theta} P (a+b) \tag{10}$$

and that due to M, derived by using the expressions for stresses[2] due to applied moment, M, is:

$$\Delta V_M = \frac{\pi M}{b^2 g} (\bar{S}_{\theta\theta} - \bar{S}_{rr}) (a+b) \tag{11}$$

where

$$g = \frac{1-c^2}{2} - \frac{k}{k+1} \frac{(1-c^{k+1})^2}{1-c^{2k}} + \frac{kc^2(1-c^{k-1})^2}{k-1} \frac{}{1-c^{2k}}$$

$$c = \frac{a}{b} \quad \text{and} \quad k = \sqrt{\frac{S_{rr}}{S_{\theta\theta}}}$$

The total cut displacement of the ring is:

$$\Delta V = \Delta V_P + \Delta V_M \tag{12}$$

Here $\bar{S}_{rr}$ and $\bar{S}_{\theta\theta}$ are effective compliances respectively in radial and hoop direction for the laminate of the ring. The value of $\bar{S}_{\theta\theta}$ is readily available from laminated plate theory. For a multidirectional laminate, either in bending or in–plane mode of deformation, the value of $\bar{S}_{rr}$ is not the same as that of the transverse compliance of an unidirectional ply[3]. The authors of reference[3] have observed that for a typical laminate in bending mode of deformation the variation on the value of $\bar{S}_{rr}$ is within ± 20% of that of the transverse compliance of an unidirectional ply of same material. The above observation is for flat laminates. If one assumes the above observation is to be true for moderately curved laminates (for rings), and takes the value of $\bar{S}_{rr}$ same as that of the transverse compliance of an unidirectional ply, then the error translates in calculating ΔV_M is about 14%. Because of the unavailability, to the authors knowledge to date, of the exact value of $\bar{S}_{rr}$ for curved laminates, the value of $\bar{S}_{rr}$ for this analysis is taken as that of the unidirectional ply, consequently in some cases an error in ΔV_M of magnitude discussed above may be expected to be present.

The positive sign of ΔV implies the opening of the ring, otherwise the ring is going to close. By measuring the cut displacement one can measure the residual stress resultants and thus the residual stresses. Figure 3 shows that a hoop wound S2–Glass/Epoxy ring closed after the radial cut. The cut displacement of two such rings of different aspect ratios (a/(b–a)) were then compared with the calculated results as shown in Figure 4. The cut rings were supplied by the Oak Ridge National Laboratory, and were cured at 300°F (149°C). The rings were cut and the cut displacements were measured at room temperature, at 75°F (24°C). Thus ΔT used for the calculation was -125°C. The calculated results are within 15% of the measured data which seems to be a reasonable agreement.

4. DISCUSSION OF RESULTS

The above comparison between the measured and predicted values of the cut displacements indicates that the present modeling for predicting residual stresses in a ring due to curing is reasonably acceptable. Next, a set of parametric studies is done to identify important parameters controlling these residual stresses. The material data used for the parametric study, if not otherwise mentioned, is for T300/5208. The material data is taken from reference[4].

In Figure 5 the cut displacement, ΔV, of angle–ply laminates, $[\pm\phi]$, is plotted for different radius to thickness ratios, a/(b–a). For all winding angle, except for winding angle near zero, the value of ΔV is negative, and its magnitude increases with increasing winding angle and with increasing radius to thickness ratio, a/(b–a). With the increasing winding angle the transverse orthotropy of the ring increases. Thus, in other words, for a

single layer, the ring tries to close more and more as the transverse orthotropy increases. However, for more than one winding angle, i.e. for a multilayered ring the closing or opening of the ring is not as obvious as that for rings of one layer, as in Figure 5.

In Figure 6 the values of the cut displacement for two–layered rings are plotted for three types of winding angle combinations. As is seen in this figure, for some angle combinations, the value of the cut displacement is positive, i.e., the ring opens up after the cut. However, the curves in Figure 6 do not reveal a simple relationship between the cut displacement and the winding angle combinations. In the analysis it is shown, however, that the opening or closing of the ring is because of two stress resultants. The value of these two stress resultants are again dependant on the through–the–thickness distribution of the hoop stress, σ_θ. So, to look for the opening and closing of the ring more closely, we need to see the contribution of the in–plane and moment stress resultants on the total cut displacement, ΔV. Thus in Figure 7 the components of the cut displacements due to the in–plane and moment stress resultants are plotted along with the total cut displacement for a representative two layered ring of winding angle combination $[30/\phi]_T$. Here layers are of equal thickness, i.e., each layer is of 50% of the ring thickness. All the laminates studied later are also of layers of equal thickness. It is seen from this figure that the moment stress resultant component of the displacement mostly controls the total displacement. This particular laminate is chosen to show that the in–plane stress resultant component of the displacement is somewhat comparable to that of the moment component for $\phi<40°$, however, the contribution of the in–plane component to the total displacement is almost negligible for most of the other two layered laminates studied.

Even if two rings of different lamination scheme have same value of average hoop stress, i.e. in–plane stress resultant, P, they will have different values of moment stress resultant, M, because the value of M depends on the through–the–thickness distribution of hoop stress, and the hoop stress distribution depends on the lamination scheme. We thus then look into the through–the–thickness hoop stress distribution of two representative laminates in Figure 8. The hoop stress for both of these two laminates, $[90/0]_T$ and $[60/90]_T$, are tensile, thus the value of the in–plane stress resultant, P, for both the rings are of same sign. However, the distributions of the stress , $(\sigma_\theta+P)$, yield moment resultants of opposite sign for these two laminates, see Figure 9. Because the sign of these two moment stress resultants are opposite in sign, the cut displacements for these two laminates are opposite in sign, as seen in Figure 10. Figure 10 is also shown to emphasize the point, as stated earlier, that the moment stress resultant is the dominant force in deciding cut displacement, and is directly related to the cut displacement as is shown for four two layered rings of equal layer thickness in this figure. Thus to predict whether a laminated ring going to close or open after a radial cut, one needs mainly to calculate the moment stress resultant.

5. CONCLUSIONS

A method of calculating the thermal residual stresses due to curing in a thick laminated orthotropic ring is presented. The ring is considered in plane–stress in (r–θ) plane and linear theory of elasticity theory is used in calculating the residual stresses. It is shown that if a cured ring is cut through radially at a circumferential point then the ring is open or closed depending on the distribution of the residual hoop stress. The method presented here can predict the cut displacement due to the residual stresses. By measuring the cut displacement in the hoop direction one can compare the predicted result with measured one, and thus can determine the state of the residual stresses. The opening or closing displacement of the ring is highly dependent on stacking sequence of the layers.

The analysis presented here is considered as a first step to understand the mechanics of more complex state of thermal stresses in thick composite cylindrical structures. The technology that is being developed for the thick composite cylinders is mainly for the cylinders to operate under high hydrostatic external pressure. The hydrostatic pressure imposes compressive stresses in the cylinder. If a cylinder (a ring in this case) opens up after the radial cut, that means the cylinder as a unit internally in tensile action due to the thermal stresses. Such a tensile action may improve the performance of the cylinder under external hydrostatic pressure which is however needs to be investigated.

ACKNOWLEDMENT
The financial support for this work was obtained from the Air Force Materials Laboratory under the contract F33615–87–C–5239. The financial support is gratefully acknowledged. The author greatly benefited

from Dr. Stephen W. Tsai of Air Force Materials Laboratory for many technical discussions for this work.

REFERENCES
1. Thick Composites in Compression workshop, Oak Ridge, TN, July 12–13, 1988, Sponsored by DARPA, Office of Naval Technology, and Oak Ridge National Laboratory.
2. Lekhnitskii, S.G., Anisotropic Plates, translated by S.W. Tsai and T. Cheron, Gordon and Breach Science Publishers, 1968, pp 95–98.
3. Roy, A.K. and S.W. Tsai, "3–D Effective Moduli of Laminated Orthotropic Plates", to be published.
4. Tsai, S.W., Composites Design, 4th Edition, Think Composites, Dayton, 1988, Appendix B.

BIOGRAPHY
Dr. Ajit K. Roy is currently an Associate Research Engineer at the University of Dayton Research Institute. During 1985–87 he was a recipient of the National Research Coucil's Research Fellowship affiliated with the Air Force Materials Laboratory. His research interest is in structural analysis and simplified design of structures with composite materials. Dr. Roy received both of his M.S. and PhD degrees in Mechanics from the University of Minnesota. He is a member of ASME and American Society for Composites.

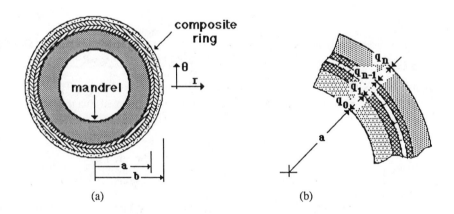

Figure 1. (a) Wound Composite Ring with the Mandrel. (b) Enlarged view of the cross section of the ring with interfacial normal tractions.

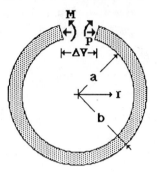

Figure 2.   Cured composite ring with a radial cut. **P** and **M** are the stress Resultants for opening or closing of the ring.

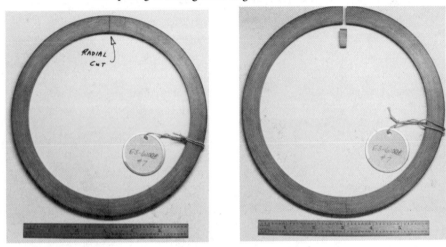

Figure 3.   A hoop wound S2–Glass/Epoxy ring before and after radial cuts. The dimension of the piece removed from the ring reveals that the ring closed after the radial cuts.

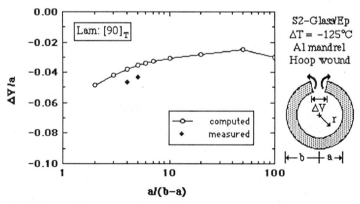

Figure 4.   Comparison of computed cut displacement, ΔV, with that of the measured values for S2–Glass/Epoxy hoop wound rings.

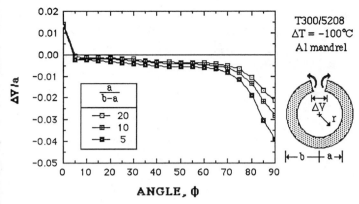

Figure 5.   Cut displacement, ΔV, versus winding angle, φ, for angle ply laminated rings of different aspect ratios, a/(b–a).

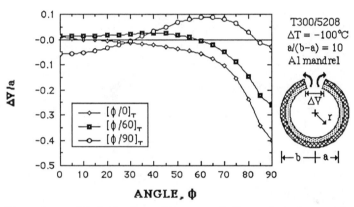

Figure 6.   Cut displacement, ΔV, versus winding angle, φ, for several two layer laminated rings.

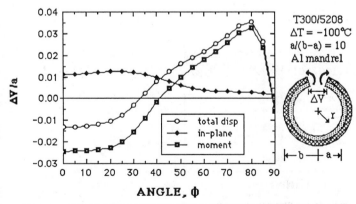

Figure 7.   The cut displacement, ΔV, and its components due to in–plane and moment stress resultants for [30/φ]$_T$ laminated rings.

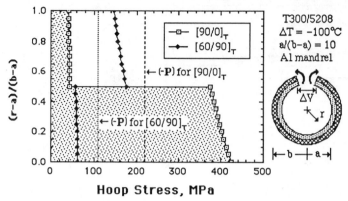

Figure 8.   Through–the–thickness hoop stress distribution for [90/0]$_T$ and [60/90]$_T$ rings.

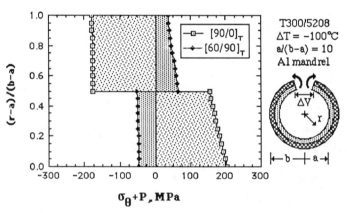

Figure 9.   Through–the–thickness distribution of the part of the hoop stress that causes moment resultant for opening or closing of the rings.

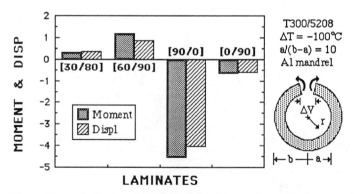

Figure 10.   Influence of the moment resultant on the cut displacement for several laminates.

DAMAGE TOLERANCE OF LAMINATED COMPOSITES CONTAINING
A HOLE AND SUBJECTED TO TENSION OR COMPRESSION

*Fu-Kuo Chang, **Larry Lessard, Kuo-Yen Chang and Sheng Liu

Abstract

Recently, two computer codes, PDHOLE and PDHOLEC, were developed for predicting failure and strength of laminated composite plates containing a hole and subjected to tension or compression, respectively. In this investigation, a parametric study was conducted using the computer codes to evaluate the effect of loading direction on the strength and failure mode of laminated composite plates containing a hole. T300/976 Graphite/Epoxy composites were used in the calculations, and four different ply orientations, $[(0/\pm45/90)_3]_s$, $[(\pm45)_6]_s$, $[(0/90)_6]_s$, and $[(\pm30)_6]_s$, were selected for the study. Based on the study, it was found that the loading direction can significantly affect the strength of laminated composite plates containing holes. Tension and compression on the laminates could produce completely different failure modes and failure loads. The change in failure loads can be attributed to the change of failure mechanisms which are strongly dependent upon the ply orientation and the loading direction. Therefore, not only the strength but also the information on failure modes and failure mechanisms is critically important for the design of optimal composite structures containing holes or cutouts.

* Assistant Professor, member of SAMPE
** Ph.D. Students

1. INTRODUCTION

A progressive damage model was proposed recently by the authors [1-4] for analyzing the response and damage of laminated composites containing a hole. Based on the model, two computer codes, PDHOLE and PDHOLEC, were developed for predicting failure load and failure mode of laminated composites containing a hole and subjected to tension or compression, respectively [3,4]. An extensive experiment was performed to verify the model and the computer codes. Excellent agreements were found between the computer simulations and the test data [1-4].

In this investigation, the objective was to evaluate how sensitive the strength of laminated composites with a hole is to the direction of the applied load. It was of particular interest to find the effect of tension and compression on the strength and failure modes of the composites. Using the computer codes, PDHOLE and PDHOLEC, a parametric study was performed. Specimens with the same configurations and ply orientations were numerically evaluated by the codes to determine the strength and failure mode.

2. COMPUTER CODES

The computer codes, PDHOLE and PDHOLEC, [3,4] were used to evaluate the strength and failure mode of laminated composites containing a hole and subjected to tension or compression, respectively. The basic configurations of the specimens that can be handled by the codes are given in Figure 1. Basically, the plates were made of fiber-reinforced laminated composites. The ply orientations can be arbitrary, but must be symmetric with respect to the middle plane. Uniformly distributed loads are applied on the both ends of the specimens by tension or compression as shown in Figure 1. For compressive loading, the dimensions of the specimens are chosen so that the plates would not deform out-of-plane until the plates collapsed due to material failure. Hence, no buckling or out-of-plane related deformation such as delamination- buckling was considered.

Extensive comparisons were made between the test data and the numerical calculations from the codes to verify the model and the computer codes. In general, the predictions agreed with the data very well with less than a 20 percent difference. Details of the verifications of the codes can be found in [1-4]. The codes are available and can be obtained form Prof. Fu-Kuo Chang at the address given on the first page.

3. PARAMETRIC STUDY

In this section, the calculated tensile and compressive strengths of T300/976 Graphite/Epoxy laminated composites containing a hole are compared with each other as a function of the specimens' width-to-diameter ratio. The material properties of the composites used in the calculations are listed in Table 1. Four different ply orientations were considered in the comparison.

The strength distributions of $[(0/90)_6]_s$ specimens subjected to either tension or compression were calculated by the codes. The laminates finally failed by fiber breakage of 0 degree plies in tension, and fiber buckling of 0 degree plies in compression. Computer simulations of the internal damage growth of a specimen as a function of the applied load are illustrated in Figures 2 and 3 for tension and compression, respectively. Interestingly, the compressive strengths of the $[(0/90)_6]_s$ specimens were substantially higher than the tensile strengths by as much as 50 percent, as shown in Figure 4. However, the difference between the ply longitudinal tensile strength and the ply longitudinal compressive strength was less than 5 percent (see Table 1).

By carefully examining the failure modes predicted from the codes, it was found that the lower tensile strength of the laminates can be attributed to weak matrix tensile strength in 90 degree plies and the higher compressive strength is due to the increase of local fiber buckling strength near stress concentration [4,6]. It was demonstrated in [6] that stress concentration could enhance the local fiber buckling strength by reinforcing the neighboring fibers to use as supports to prevent the fibers from buckling. A schematic of the fiber buckling diagram is shown in Figure 5. The local fiber buckling strength could be substantially higher than the average ply compressive strength which was commonly measured from unidirectional composites subjected to uniform loading.

A comparison between tensile and compressive strengths of $[(\pm 45)_6]_s$ specimens is shown in Figure 6. The tensile and compressive strengths of $[(\pm 45)_6]_s$ specimens were very close, although, the compressive strengths were slightly higher than the tensile strengths by a difference of less than 5 percent. The consistancy in both strength distributions can be attributed to the failure mode of the specimens, which failed predominantly by fiber-matrix shearing under tension or compression. Computer simulations of the damage growth in the composites are presented in Figures 7 and 8 for tension and compression, respectively.

Figure 9 presents the calculations of the tensile and compressive strengths of $[(0/\pm45/90)_3]_s$ specimens. Based on the predictions, the compressive strengths of $[(0/\pm45/90)_3]_s$ laminates are considerably higher than the tensile strengths by as much as 30 percent. Again, the difference in tensile and compressive strengths was due to a weaker matrix tensile strength of 90 degree plies than to higher local fiber buckling strength in 0 degree plies.

The tensile and compressive strength distributions of $[(\pm30)_6]_s$ laminates are presented in Figure 10. Unlike the other ply orientations, $[(\pm30)_6]_s$ laminates have higher tensile strengths than compressive strengths. An estimated 20 to 30 percent increase of tensile strengths over compressive strength was predicted. By examining the predicted failure modes, it was found that for tensile loading, the specimens failed by matrix compression, but for compressive loading, the specimens failed by tensile matrix cracking. The computer simulations of the internal damage growth of a $[(\pm30)_6]_s$ laminate are given in Figures 11 and 12.

4. CONCLUDING REMARKS

A parametric study, using the computer codes PDHOLE and PDHOLEC, was performed to evaluate the effect of loading direction on the strength and failure mode of laminated composites containing a hole. Four different ply orientations were considered in the study. They were $[(0/90)_6]_s$, $[(\pm45)_6]_s$, $[(0/\pm45/90)_3]_s$, and $[(\pm30)_6]_s$. Based on the study, the following remarks can be made for laminated composites containing holes:

1) the strength of notched laminated composites strongly depends on the loading direction,

2) the tensile strength can be substantially different from compressive strength,

3) the different failure modes will result in totally different failure loads,

4) the laminates, except $[(\pm30)_6]_s$, have higher compressive strengths than tensile strengths;

5) both strength and failure mode provide important information for the design of composite structures containing holes.

6. ACKNOWLEDGEMENTS

The support of the Charles Lee Powell Foundation Award for this investigation is greatly appreciated. Dr. Larry Lessard would also like to acknowledge the support of a scholarship from F.C.A.R. (Fonds pour la Formation de Chercheurs et L'aide à la Recherche) of Québec.

7. REFERENCES

1. Chang, F. K. and Chang, K. Y., "A Progressive Damage Model for Laminated Composites Containing Stress Concentrations," J. of Composite Materials, 21, 834–855, (1987).

2. Chang, F. K. and Chang, K. Y., "Post-Failure Analysis of Bolted Composite Joints in Tension or Shear-Out Failure Mode," J. of Composite Materials, 21, 809–833, (1987).

3. Chang, F. K. and Chang, K. Y., "Damage Tolerance of Laminated Composites Containing an Open Hole and Subjected to Tension," J. of Composite Materials, (Submitted).

4. Chang, F. K. and Lessard, L. B., "Damage Tolerance of Laminated Composites Containing an Open Hole and Subjected to Compressive Loadings: Part I—Analysis," J. of Composite Materials, (Submitted).

5. Lessard, L. B. and Chang, F. K., "Damage Tolerance of Laminated Compostes Containing an Open Hole and Subjected to Compressive Loadings: Part II—Experiment," J. of Composite Materials, (Submitted).

6. Chang, F. K. and Lessard, L. B., "The Effect of Stress Distribution on the Fiber Buckling Strength of Unidirectional Composites," J. of Composite Materials, (Submitted).

TABLE 1. Material properties of T300/976 Graphite/Epoxy prepreg tape:

Ply Longitudinal Modulus	E_{xx} = 27700000 psi
Ply Transverse Modulus	E_{yy} = 1320000 psi
Out-of-Plane Modulus	E_{zz} = 1320000 psi
In-Plane Shear Modulus	G_{xy} = 1010000 psi
Out-of-Plane Shear Modulus	G_{xz} = 1010000 psi
Out-of-Plane Shear Modulus	G_{yz} = 537459 psi
Posson's Ratio	$v_{xy} = v_{xz} = v_{yz} = 0.228$
Ply Longitudinal Tensile Strength	X_t = 220000 psi
Ply Longitudinal Compressive Strength	X_c = 231000 psi
Ply Transverse Tensile Strength	Y_t = 7110 psi
Ply Transverse Compressive Strength	Y_c = 36700 psi
Ply Shear Strength	S = 16300 psi

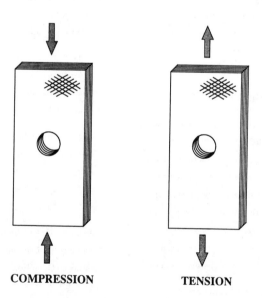

COMPRESSION   **TENSION**

Figure 1. Basic Geometry of the Problem.

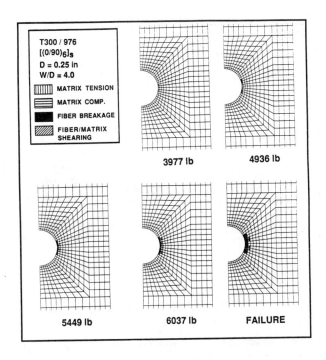

Figure 2. Illustration of the predicted damage growth in $[(0/90)_6]_s$ composites under tension as a function of applied load.

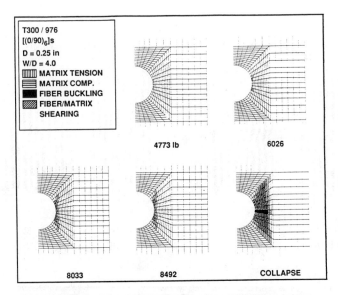

Figure 3. Illustration of the predicted damage growth in $[(0/90)_6]_s$ composites under compression as a function of applied load.

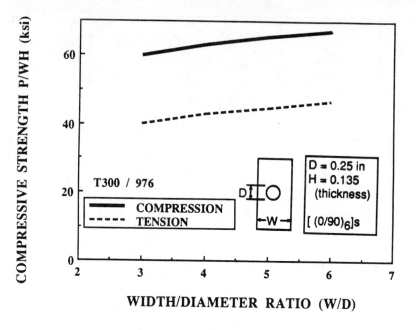

Figure 4. Strength distributions of $[(0/90)_6]_s$ composites containing a hole and subjected to tension or compression.

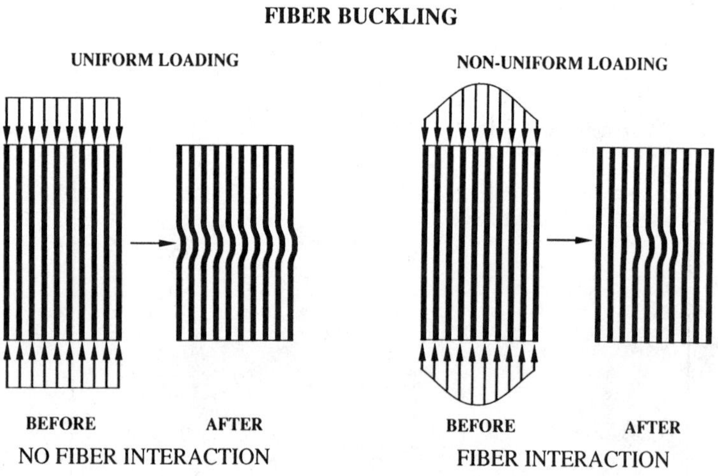

FIBER BUCKLING

UNIFORM LOADING   NON-UNIFORM LOADING

BEFORE   AFTER   BEFORE   AFTER

NO FIBER INTERACTION   FIBER INTERACTION

Figure 5. A schematic of fiber buckling diagram. Left: unidirectional composites subjected to uniform distributed load. Right: unidirectional composites subjected to nonuniform distributed load.

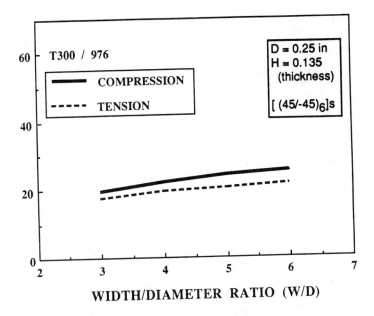

Figure 6. Strength distributions of $[(\pm 45)_6]_s$ composites containing a hole and subjected to tension or compression.

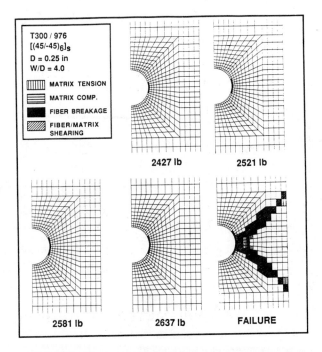

Figure 7. Illustration of the predicted damage growth in $[(\pm 45)_6]_s$ composites under tension as a function of applied load.

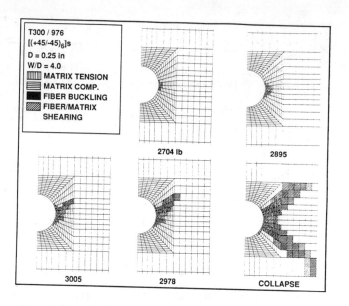

Figure 8. Illustration of the predicted damage growth in $[(\pm45)_6]_s$ composites under compression as a function of applied load.

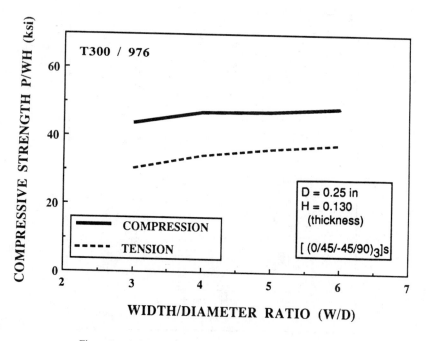

Figure 9. Strength distributions of $[(0/\pm45/90)_3]_s$ composites containing a hole and subjected to tension or compression.

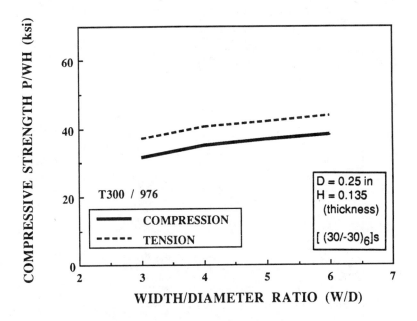

Figure 10. Strength distributions of $[(\pm 30)_6]_s$ composites containing a hole and subjected to tension or compression.

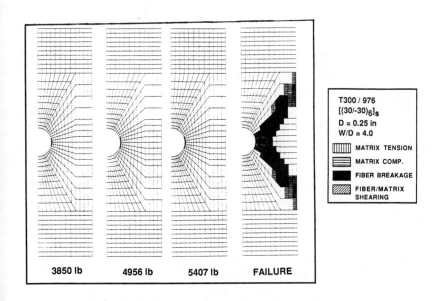

Figure 11. Illustration of the predicted damage growth in $[(\pm 30)_6]_s$ composites under tension as a function of applied load.

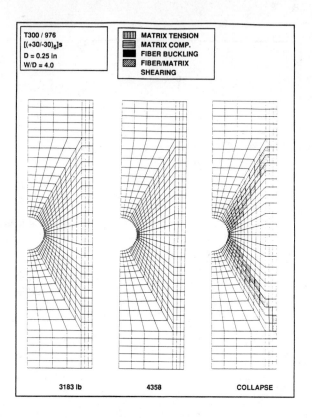

Figure 12. Illustration of the predicted damage growth in $[(\pm30)_6]_s$ composites under compression as a function of applied load.

568

THE EFFECT OF UNBONDED INCLUSIONS ON THE FAILURE
OF ADVANCED COMPOSITE COUPONS WITH CIRCULAR HOLES

Marvin Knight

Materials Laboratory

Air force Wright Aeronautical Laboratories

Wright-Patterson Air Force Base, Ohio

ABSTRACT

Mechanical fasteners are still used extensively in assembling aerospace structures. Advanced composite components are assembled with mechanical fasteners when they are used on aerospace system. This subjects them to operations involving putting holes through the thickness. The operations can cause damage to the material such as delamination around the holes. This damage can influence the failure process of the material. The influence of holes on the failure of advanced composite materials has been studied before. However, the present paper reports on a program that combined two parameters. The laminates contained no 0 degree plies and the holes were drilled thru unbonded inclusions placed in the laminates. The coupons were loaded in tension to failure. The data were compared with data from coupons with no inclusions and a failure model. For the laminate orientation and the coupon parameters tested, there was no significant effect of the inclusion on the tensile strength.

1. INTRODUCTION

There will always be holes in aerospace structures as long as mechanical fasteners are used to join components. Therefore advanced composites components will have holes in them. There have been many programs to study the effect of holes on the failure of advanced composite materials. In most of these programs the laminate contained 0 degree plies. The 0 degree plies usually result in creating a fiber dominated failure mode. Usually, care was taken to avoid creating damage in the area of the hole. Therefore, little information was developed on laminates without 0 degree plies containing holes with delaminations around the holes.

The present paper reports on a program that developed data on a graphite/epoxy laminate which contained no 0 degree plies and therefore no strong fiber domination in the failure mode. Also, circular disks of a nonbonding material were placed in the center of the gage section of the coupons to create a delamination. Holes were drilled thru the center of the disks to form a delamination around the edge of the holes. The coupons were tested in tension to study the effect of the combination of holes and delaminations on the tensile strength and failure mode.

2. EXPERIMENTAL PROGRAM

Data reported in this paper were generated from tests on coupons taken from one 35.6 cm (14 inches) x 35.6 cm (14 inches) twelve ply laminate. AS4/3502 graphite/epoxy prepreg was fabricated into a laminate with a [+30/ -30/ -30/ +30/ 90/90]$_S$ stacking sequence. Circular 12.7mm (0.5 inch) diameter teflon coated glass fabric disks (approx. 0.07 mm thick) were placed at the midplane of the panel. The disks were located in the panel in such a way that when the coupons were cut from the panel half of them would contain a disk in the center of the gage section. The layup was vacuum bag-autoclave cured with a final cure temperature of 177o C (350o F).

The panel was inspected with; x-ray, c-scan, and visual techniques to determine quality and to confirm the location of the inclusions before cutting the coupons. Diiodomethane (DIM) was used as an x-ray enhancer. All coupons were x-rayed after cutting and at various stages during the loading process to check for cracks.

Two coupon configurations were cut from the panel. One type contained the included disk and the other type contained no disk. As shown in Figure 1, the coupons were

177.8 mm (7 inches) x 34.9 mm (1.37 inches). Each end was covered with 25.4 mm (1 inch) long fiberglass tabs. Three sizes of holes were used in the program. They were nominally 3.12 mm (0.123 in), 6.35 mm (0.25 in) and 9.47 mm (0.373 in) in diameter. Also, tests were conducted on coupons with no holes to establish a baseline value.

All specimens were tested in a closed-loop hydraulic testing system under stroke control with a stroke rate of 0.0025 mm/sec. The tests were interrupted and the coupon removed several times to allow for radiographic inspection. X-ray radiographs were made to monitor damage progression. The failure loads were recorded. Foil type strain gages were used on some of the coupons to indicate strain.

3. RESULTS AND DISCUSSION

The tensile strength data are summarized in Table 1. Each strength value is an average of two data points. The trend in the data is as expected. The values for strength decrease with increasing hole diameter. The no-hole, no- inclusion strength value of 366 MPa (53.2 Ksi) is within 10% of the calculated theoretical value 405 MPa (58.7 Ksi.) for the laminate. The decrease in tensile strength for the coupons with inclusions ranges from 1% for the smallest size hole, 3.12 mm (0.125 in.) to 5% for the largest size hole, (0.373 in.). A comparison of the two sets of data is shown in Figure 2.

The x-ray radiographs taken during the loading process were examined for changes in the failure process. There were no indications of significant changes observed. The cracks and delaminations appear the same for coupons with the inclusions as those in the coupons without inclusions.

S.C. Tan [1-3] proposed a point strength model for the prediction of the ultimate strength of multidirectional unnotched and notched composite laminates. The equation for a circular hole is shown in Eq. (1).

$$\frac{\sigma_p}{\overline{\sigma}_\chi} = \frac{\left\{2+\xi_1^2+3\xi_1^4-(K_T^\infty-3)(5\xi_1^6-7\xi_1^8)\right\}}{2} \quad (1)$$

where

$$\xi_1 = \frac{a}{a+b_1} \quad (2)$$

Eq. (2) defines the term ξ_1 which relates the hole radius, a, with b_1, an empirically determined constant for a characteristic distance on the axis normal to the applied load. The applied stress is represented by $\overline{\sigma}_\chi$ and the normal stress at point $(0,b_1)$ across the y-plane by σ_p. The Tsai-Wu criteria is used along with Eq.(1) to determine the first-ply failure stresses required for the theoretical calculations of the notched strength.

In this model the first-ply-failure (FPF) stress ratio is assumed to be the same as the ultimate strength reduction factor (SRF).

$$SRF = \frac{\sigma_N^\infty}{\sigma_0}$$

$$= \frac{FPF \text{ Notched Strength at } (0,b_1)}{FPF \text{ Unnotched Strength}} \quad (3)$$

SRF is defined as the strength reduction factor and σ_N^∞ and σ_0 denote the ultimate notched strength and the ultimate unnotched strength respectively.

Figure (3) shows good agreement between the theoretical curve for the reduction in strength as determined by Tan's point strength model and the data from this test program.

4. CONCLUSIONS

A comparison of the data from coupons with hole but no inclusions with data from coupons with holes and inclusions does not indicate that the unbonded inclusion had a significant effect on the tensile strength of the laminate. Also, the data from both types of coupons agree very good with the theoretical values indicated by Tan's point strength model for holes in multidirectional laminates. It is concluded that for the coupons tested unbonded material around the circumference of a hole does not influence the value of tensile strength.

5. ACKNOWLEDGEMENT

The author wishes to acknowledge the assistance of R. Cornwell and R. Esterline of UDRI for fabricating the panel and coupons and conducting the tensile tests under Air Force contract F33615-87-C-5239. Also, Dr. S.C. Tan of AdTech Systems Research Inc. for help with his model.

6. REFERENCES

1. Tan, S. C., "Effective Stress Fracture Models for Unnotched and Notched Multidirectional Laminates", Journal of Composite Materials, **22**, pp. 322-324, (1988)
2. Tan, S. C., "Mixed-Mode Fracture of Notched Composite Laminates Under Uniaxial and Multiaxial Loading", Journal of Engineering Fracture Mechanics, **31**, pp. 733-746, (1988)
3. Tan, S. C., "Fracture Strength of Composite Laminates with an Elliptical Opening", Composite Science and Technology, **29**, pp. 133-152, (1987)

7. BIOGRAPHY

Marvin Knight is a Materials Research Engineer in the Air Force Wright Aeronautical Laboratories at Wright-Patterson Air Force Base, Ohio. His activities include research in the determination of the mechanical properties and failure mechanisms of advanced composites. He has been involved with advanced composite materials for over twenty-five years. He received his B.S. in Chemical Engineering from the Kansas University in 1958.

Table 1. Tensile Strength

| hole dia. mm | Tensile Strength | |
	without inclusion MPa	with inclusion MPa
9.47	258	246
6.35	312	302
3.12	343	340
no hole	366	352

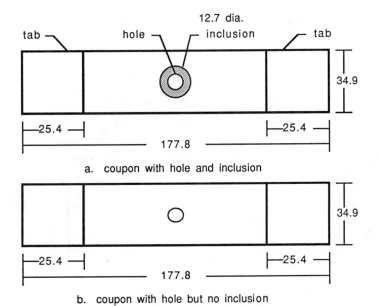

a. coupon with hole and inclusion

b. coupon with hole but no inclusion

all dimensions are millimeters

Figure 1. Test Coupon

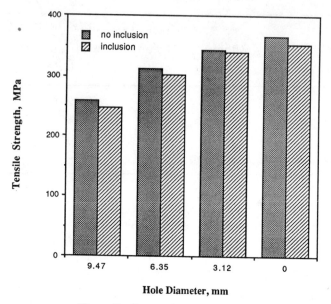

Figure 2. Comparison Of Tensile Strengths

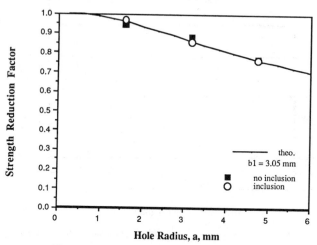

Figure 3. Comparison of Data With Point Strength Model

ANALYSIS OF THERMAL STRESSES IN POLYMER MATRIX COMPOSITES

David E. Bowles
NASA Langley Research Center
Hampton, Virginia
and
O. H. Griffin, Jr.
Virginia Polytechnic Institute and State University
Blacksburg, Virginia

ABSTRACT

A micromechanics approach was utilized to investigate the thermally induced stress fields developed in the fiber and matrix of continuous fiber reinforced polymer matrix composites at very cold temperatures. Results from a finite element stress analysis, developed specifically for this problem, were compared to an analytical solution of the composite cylinder model for several fiber/matrix materials. The influence of microstructural geometry and constituent properties were investigated. A global-local formulation, combining laminated plate theory and FE analysis, was used to determine the influence of fiber orientation on thermally induced stresses in multidirectional laminates. Damage initiation predictions were also made using simple failure criteria and available matrix strength data. The results of this investiation showed that the assumed microstructural geometry of the composite (i.e. composite cylinder, square or hexagonal array) did affect the distributions and magnitudes of thermally induced stresses. The matrix stresses were shown not to be strong functions of the fiber properties. However, the temperature dependence of the matrix properties was shown to significantly affect the magnitudes of thermally induced matrix stresses. Damage initiation was predicted in unidirectional and cross-ply P75/934 and T300/934 laminates at use temperatures of -150 °F . These predictions were in agreement with experimental data only for the P75/934 cross-ply laminates. Possible reasons for the discrepancies included interfacial effects and a lack of data on the temperature dependent stress-strain behavior of the matrix.

1.0 INTRODUCTION

Continuous graphite fiber reinforced composites are candidate materials for many space structures because of their high stiffness, low coefficient of thermal expansion, and light weight. One application currently under consideration is the large truss structure of NASA's Space Station Freedom. Materials in the space environment are subjected to large cyclic changes in temperature. For example, materials on the Space Station Freedom truss structure will experience approximately 175,000 thermal cycles over a temperature range as high as ±150 °F during the projected 30 year life[1]. Previous research has shown that large temperature changes and/or repeated thermal cycling can cause damage in composite materials and adversely affect their performance[2].

In order to design and fabricate structures with composite materials the effects of this thermal environment must be well understood and predictable. The majority of past research in this area has focused on analysis and testing of laminate response[3-5]. The effects of constituent properties and microstructural characteristics (i.e. micromechanics) have not been thoroughly investigated for composites exposed to the thermal environment of space. The objective of this research, therefore, was to analyze the deformations and stresses induced by thermal loading, in continuous fiber reinforced composites, using the properties and behavior of the constituents (i.e. fiber and matrix). The material parameters that control the behavior were identified and material modifications to improve the behavior were suggested. Predicted damage initiation locations were compared with experimental data in selected cases.

Reference to specific commercial materials in this paper is provided to adequately describe the materials and does not constitute official endorsement, expressed or implied, of such products or manufacturers by NASA.

2.0 THEORETICAL DEVELOPMENT

Two approaches have normally been taken to predict the stress-strain behavior of unidirectional composites. The first approach involves modeling of the actual microstructure (i.e. fiber geometry and placement) in some idealized fashion so as to account for continuous variations in the stress-strain behavior of both constituents. In the second approach the microstructural details are neglected and average values of stress and strain are assumed for each constituent. Analyses that follow the second approach are best suited for problems in which only the global response is desired. However, problems that require details of the local stress fields in each constituent, such as attempts to predict damage initiation, need analyses that follow the first approach. Two such analyses were selected for the current study. A brief description of the problem geometry and analytical formulations follows.

2.1 Problem Description

The problem under consideration was the determination of the local stress fields in a body, consisting of continuous (infinite length) fibers embedded in a matrix material, exposed to a change in temperature. The geometry and material coordinates are shown in figure 1. There are several basic assumptions that are common to both analyses and can be stated as follows:

1. The fibers are circular in cross-section and infinitely long in the 1-direction.

2. The fibers are elastic and transversly isotropic.

3. The matrix is elastic and isotropic.

4. The displacements are continuous at the fiber/matrix interface (i.e. no interfacial slip).

5. The temperature change is uniform throughout the body.

2.2 Composite Cylinder Formulation

One of the analyses used for predicting the local stress fields in the constituents was the solution to the composite cylinder (CC) boundary-value problem. The CC model, which consists of a circular fiber embedded in a cylindrical region of matrix, is shown in figure 2, along with the coordinate system and boundary conditions. The use of the CC model for providing the solution to a composite consisting of many fibers (figure 1) is based on the composite cylinder assemblage (CCA) formulation[6]. This formulation assumes that a composite can be modeled as a collection

of composite cylinders of varying size, all of which have the same ratio of fiber radius to matrix radius (i.e fiber volume fraction). A single composite cylinder becomes representative of the entire composite by requiring that, for a given load state, the stored strain energy in this single composite cylinder is equal to the strain energy in a cylinder of homogeneous material with the same "effective" thermoelastic properties. Consequently, the stresses and strains in a single composite cylinder represent only the average stresses and strains in the "real" composite.

The CC model is axisymmetric, and when combined with the assumption of generalized plane strain, the elasticity solution yields displacements, strains, and stresses that depend only upon the radial coordinate. The solution for pure thermal loading results in only nonzero normal stress and strain components (i.e. no shear components). Details of the solution procedure for this boundary value problem can be found in the literature[7].

2.3 Finite Element Formulation

The other analysis used in this study was a finite element (FE) analysis. The FE analysis of the geometry shown in figure 1 was greatly simplified by assuming that the fibers are arranged in a regular and periodic array. This allows the analysis to be performed on a representative unit cell rather than the entire composite. Further simplifications to this unit cell were obtained by applying symmetry of the geometry and load. The two array geometries assumed for this investigation(square and hexagonal) and their simplified representative cells and boundary conditions for thermal loading only are shown in figure 3.

The FE formulataion used in this study assumes that a condition of generalized plane strain exists in the composite. The displacement field for generalized plane strain may be written as

$$
\begin{aligned}
u &= U(y, z) + \epsilon_x \cdot x \\
v &= V(y, z) \\
w &= W(y, z)
\end{aligned}
\tag{1}
$$

where U, V, and W are unknown functions of y and z, and ϵ_x is a uniform strain in the x direction. The term ϵ_x may be a known applied strain or treated as an unknown for a uniformly applied force in the x direction. For thermal loading only, this uniform axial applied force is set equal to zero. A linear elastic displacement formulation was used to solve for the above unknowns, using eight node isoparametric quadratic elements. The FE mesh used in this study is shown in figure 4. Details of this type of FE formulation may be found in the literature[8]. The above formulation was implemented in a computer program called FECAP, developed and written at NASA-Langley Research Center to run interactively on a desktop microcomputer[9].

2.4 Temperature Dependent Properties

Both analyses described above were formulated to allow for temperature dependent constituent material properties. The formulation, refered to in the literature as a "total strain theory"[10], requires the elastic moduli and Poisson's ratios be known only at the temperature of interest. Their path dependence with temperature from the reference or stress-free-temperature (SFT) is not required. However, the path dependence of the coefficients of thermal expansion (CTE's) are required. This may be written mathamatically in a simplified form as

$$\sigma(T) = H(T) \int_{T^{SFT}}^{T} J(\tau)d\tau \qquad (2)$$

where $\sigma(T)$ is the stress at some temperature T, $H(T)$ represents some function of the moduli and Poisson's ratios evaluated at T, and $J(\tau)$ is some function of the CTE's, which is integrated from T^{SFT} to T.

The above formulation is only valid for elastic constituent material properties (i.e. properties not a function of stress). When the properties are inelastic, an incremental approach must be used.

3.0 RESULTS AND DISCUSSION

Thermally induced stresses were computed from the two analyses described above. The constituent properties used in these analyses are discussed below. Results are presented for unidirectional and multidirectional laminates. Failure predictions are also discussed.

3.1 Constituent Properties

The majority of results were generated for two fiber/matrix composite systems; pitch-based 75 Msi modulus carbon fibers (Amoco P75) in a 350 °F cure epoxy resin (Fiberite 934), and PAN-based 30 Msi modulus carbon fibers (Amoco T300) in the same epoxy resin. As stated earlier, the fibers and matrix were assumed to be transversely isotropic and isotropic, respectively. This reduces the number of independent elastic constants to five for the fiber, written as

$$E_1^f, \ E_2^f = E_3^f, \ \nu_{12}^f = \nu_{13}^f, \ \nu_{23}^f, \ G_{12}^f = G_{13}^f \quad (3)$$

and two for the matrix written as

$$E^m, \ \nu^m \qquad (4)$$

E, ν, and G represent the Young's moduli, Poisson's ratios, and shear moduli, respectively. The subscripts refer to the material coordinates of figure 1, and the superscripts f and m refer to fiber

and matrix, respectively. There are two additional relations for the shear moduli written as

$$G_{23}^f = E_2^f/2(1 + \nu_{23}^f) \qquad (5)$$

and

$$G^m = E^m/2(1 + \nu^m) \qquad (6)$$

In addition to the elastic constants, there are two independent CTE's for a transversely isotropic fiber, α_1^f and α_2^f, and one for an isotropic matrix, α^m.

Constituent property data, especially as a function of temperature, are very difficult to find. The fiber properties for T300 and P75 were assumed to be temperature independent. The five elastic constants and two CTE's are given in Table 1. These data were taken from various literature sources, including both research papers and manufacturers product data sheets[11-13]. Experimentally measured values were used when available. However, the transverse fiber properties represent values that were back-calculated from composite properties using available micromechanics theories for predicting "effective" properties.

The 934 matrix properties were assumed to be temperature dependent. The values of E^m and ν^m, at room temperature (RT) and +250 °F , were taken from reference[14]. The properties at -250 °F were back-calculated for this study, from T300/934 unidirectional lamina properties[15] at -250 °F using the CCA formulation for predicting "effective" properties[16]. The temperature dependent values of α^m for 934 CTE were back-calculated at - 250 °F , RT, and +250 °F from T300/934 unidirectional lamina CTE data, obtained at LaRC, using the same "effective" property formulation discussed above.

A summary of the 934 matrix properties at -250 °F , RT, and +250 °F is given in Table 2. Values at intermediate temperatures were approximated by fitting second order interpolating polynomials to the data in Table 2.

3.2 Unidirectional Laminates

Stress components are presented in terms of the cylindrical coordinate system shown in figure 2 (i.e. σ_x, σ_r, σ_θ, and $\tau_{r\theta}$, the only nonzero shear stress component). The thermal load used, unless otherwise noted, was a uniform ΔT of -500 °F . This ΔT corresponds to a SFT of +350 °F , which is the cure temperature for 934 epoxy , and a use temperature of -150 °F , typical of many space structural applications.

3.2.1 Comparison of analyses. Thermal stress results from both analyses are presented for unidirectional P75/934, with a fiber volume fraction (V_f) of 0.6, in figures 5-8. The matrix stresses at

the fiber/matrix interface as a function of the circumferential position around the fiber (θ is measured from the y axis of figure 3) are shown in figures 5 and 6. The maximum values of σ_x (16.2 Ksi) and σ_θ (15.2 Ksi) occurred on this interface at the circumferential locations shown in the figures. Both the CC and FE analyses predict approximately the same magnitude and distribution for σ_x. The FE results for σ_θ do exhibit a small dependence on θ, and differ in magnitude from the CC results. For all cases, the FE results using the hexagonal fiber array geometry were in closer agreement with the CC results than those using the square array. This was expected, due to the fact that the hexagonal array more closely resembles an axisymmetric geometry.

The largest differences between the analyses are exhibited in the σ_r and $\tau_{r\theta}$ components at the interface. As shown in figure 5, the σ_r component varied from approximately -7 Ksi at $\theta = 0°$, to 0 Ksi at $\theta = 45°$ for the square array FE results. The CC results predicted a constant value of -3.3 Ksi. A tensile value of σ_r was never predicted at the interface with either analysis. There was also a significant $\tau_{r\theta}$ component (figure 6) in the square array FE results that was nonexsistent in the CC results. The maximum value of $\tau_{r\theta}$ was 5 Ksi (not shown on figure 6), which occurred at $\theta = 22.5°$, not on the interface but at $r/r_f = 1.2$, where r_f is the fiber radius.

Figures 7 and 8 show the stresses along a radial line of maximum distance between fibers ($\theta = 30°$ or $45°$). The radial coordinate was normalized with respect to the fiber radius. The CC results are the same for all radial lines. There is no $\tau_{r\theta}$ predicted along this radial line with the FE analysis because it is a line of symmetry. Both the CC and FE analyses predict similar magnitudes and distributions for the fiber stresses. All three components are compressive, with a maximum value of approximately -11 Ksi for σ_x. Both analyses also predict approximately the same magnitude and dit ribution for the σ_x matrix stress.

There are significant differences between the predicted values of σ_r and σ_θ in the matrix from the two analyses. The σ_θ component predicted from the FE analysis is significantly smaller than σ_θ from the CC analysis (figure 7). The other major difference between the two analyses is exhibited in the σ_r component along this radial line (figure 8). The CC analysis predicts a σ_r stress that is compressive at the interface and decreases to zero at the outer boundary of the CC model, as required by the free surface boundary conditions. The FE analysis also predicts a compressive σ_r at the interface, but this component reaches a tensile value of 5.3 Ksi at the boundary of the FE model (i.e the midpoint of maximum fiber spacing). This is because the FE model does not treat the fiber and surrounding matrix as an isolated problem with

stress free boundaries, but rather takes into account the influence of adjacent fibers.

The effects of V_f on the stress distributions in unidirectional P75/934 were also determined for each analysis. Both analyses predicted positive increases (i.e. in the tensile direction) in all of the stress components with increasing V_f. The array geometries used in the FE analysis have upper bounds on V_f for contiguous fibers. These maximum values are $V_f = .785$ and $V_f = .907$ for the square and hexagonal arrays, respectively. The upper bound on V_f for the CC analysis is 1.0, or no matrix phase. However, the stresses predicted for that case are zero. The maximum tensile matrix stresses for V_f's of .75, .85, and .99, corresponding to the FE square array, FE hexagonal array, and CC analyses, respectively, are compared to the maximum stresses at $V_f = .60$ in Table 3. The values of .75 and .85 were used as upper limits on V_f for the square and hexagonal array FE analyses, respectively, due to difficulties in modeling a contiguous fiber array with the type of elements used in the analysis. These maximum stresses may be thought of as upper bounds on the stresses in localized regions of high V_f which are often present in real composite materials.

3.2.2 Effect of constituent properties.

A comparison of the stress distributions for P75/934 and T300/934 are shown in figure 9. The normal stresses at the interface are compared for the FE square array analysis at a $V_f = .60$. The differences in the stresses are relatively small compared to the large differences in fiber moduli and CTE (Table 1). This may be explained by examining a simple one-dimensional strength of materials formulation for predicting axial thermally induced stresses. Assuming temperature independent properties, the axial stress in the fiber and matrix may be written as[17]

$$\sigma_x^f = V_m E^m E_1^f \left(\frac{\alpha^m - \alpha_1^f}{V_f E_1^f + V_m E^m} \right) \Delta T \quad (7)$$

$$\sigma_x^m = -V_f E^m E_1^f \left(\frac{\alpha^m - \alpha_1^f}{V_f E_1^f + V_m E^m} \right) \Delta T \quad (8)$$

where $V_m = (1 - V_f)$. In polymer matrix composites reinforced with graphite fibers, where $E_1^f \gg E^m$, $V_f E_1^f + V_m E^m$ may be approximated by $V_f E_1^f$. This approximation results in less than a 2% error for V_f's greater than .5. The term $(\alpha^m - \alpha_1^f)$ may also be approximated by α^m without introducing greater than a 3% error. This is because $\alpha^m \gg \alpha_1^f$.

These two approximations result in simplified forms of equations (7) and (8) written as

$$\sigma_x^f = (V_m/V_f) E^m \alpha^m \Delta T \quad (9)$$

578

$$\sigma_x^m = -E^m \alpha^m \Delta T \qquad (10)$$

The fiber properties do not appear at all in equations (9) and (10). Although the above simplified analysis is only valid for the axial stress component, the same trend is exhibited by the other components. It is also interesting to note that V_f does not appear in equation (10), implying that the axial matrix stresses are not a strong function of V_f for V_f's greater than .5.

In order to significantly reduce the magnitudes of thermal stresses for a fixed ΔT, the term $E^m \alpha^m$ must be reduced. Unfortunately, there exsists an inverse proportionality between E^m and α^m for a wide range of polymer systems[18], as shown in figure 10. The product, $E^m \alpha^m$, ranges from a high of 17.7 to a low of 12 psi/°F for the polymers shown in the figure. The 934 epoxy has a value of 15.4 psi/°F . Therefore, for a given ΔT, the matrix stresses in a 934 system could be reduced approximately 22% by using one of the other polymers shown in the figure (i.e. polyphenylene) as the matrix. It is not known whether all of these other polymers would make suitable matrix materials for graphite reinforced composites. Further reductions in the level of residual stress must be obtained by lowering the SFT of the material, thereby reducing the ΔT during use.

The discussion above demonstrated the importance of matrix properties on thermally induced stresses. Figure 11 shows the importance of properly accounting for the temperature dependence of these properties. Stresses at the fiber/matrix interface, at a circumferential location of $\theta = 45°$, were compared for the cases of temperature independent matrix properties and temperature dependent matrix properties. The RT values shown in Table 2 were used for the temperature independent case. As shown in the figure, the temperature independent property results exhibit stresses that are significantly smaller than the temperature dependent property results for σ_x and σ_θ. This is because the stiffening of the matrix at lower temperatures is neglected when constant properties are assumed.

3.3 Multidirectional Laminates

A global/local formulation was used to determine the thermally induced matrix stresses in multidirectional laminates. The thermally induced strains in each individual lamina, ϵ_x, ϵ_y, and γ_{xy}, were determined from classical laminated plate theory (LPT)[17] for a given ΔT. These strains were then used as displacement boundary conditions on the FE model of a single fiber and surrounding matrix exposed to the same ΔT. The FE model shown in figure 3 could not be used for this formulation because of a difference in symmetry conditions. Instead, the "quarter-symmetry"

model (i.e. modeling of a quarter of a fiber) shown in figure 12 was used.

Lamina strains were determined for a $[0/90]_s$ P75/934 laminate exposed to a uniform ΔT of -500 °F . The $[0/90]_s$ laminate is a "worst case" layup for thermally induced stresses because it maximizes the mismatch in CTE's between plies. A comparison of unidirectional and $[0/90]_s$ matrix stresses at the fiber/matrix interface is shown in figure 13. The stress levels in the $[0/90]_s$ laminate are significantly higher than those in the unidirectional laminate. Also, the stress distributions in the $[0/90]_s$ laminate are not symmetric about $\theta = 45°$.

Table 4 shows a comparison of the stresses predicted from LPT with those predicted from the micromechanics FE analysis. Laminated plate theory assumes that a state of plane stress exists in the laminate, with σ_x, σ_y, and τ_{xy} as the only nonzero stress components. These stresses are computed for individual lamina, which are modeled as homogeneous orthotropic layers. The micromechanics FE analysis models the fiber and matrix as distinct individual phases, and the stresses predicted from this analysis refer to these individual phases. As shown in Table 4, the micromechanics FE analysis predicts a three-dimensional state of stress in the matrix, with stress levels much larger than the matrix dominated lamina component, σ_y, predicted from LPT. Such differences should have a significant influence on the prediction of thermally induced damage.

3.4 Failure Predictions

The ultimate goal of a stress analysis is to predict the loading conditions, in the present case temperature, that initiate failure. Thermally induced failures, in the form of matrix cracks, are well documented for polymer matrix composites[3,5]. In order to successfully predict damage initiation the temperature dependent stress-strain behavior of the material, up through failure, must be well understood. This type of information for epoxy in the neat resin form is very limited. Elevated and room temperature tensile data on 934 epoxy were found in the literature[14], but no data for temperatures below RT could be found. The RT 934 ultimate strength ($\sigma_{ult} = 8.53$ Ksi) was used in the failure predictions presented below.

A simple maximum stress failure criterion, using the square array FE results, predicted failure in the unidirectional P75/934 material at approximately +50 °F . This failure was due to the σ_x component, and is shown graphically in figure 14. This maximum stress occurred on the fiber/matrix interface at a point of maximum distance between adjacent fibers (i.e $\theta = 45°$).

The von Mises yield theory was used as a combined stress failure criterion for predicting damage initiation. This criterion predicts failure when

579

$$\tau_{oct} = \sqrt{2}\sigma_{ult}/3 \qquad (11)$$

where

$$\tau_{oct} = \frac{\sqrt{(\sigma_1 - \sigma_2)^2 + (\sigma_2 - \sigma_3)^2 + (\sigma_3 - \sigma_1)^2}}{3}$$
$$(12)$$

The components σ_1, σ_2, and σ_3 are the principal stresses. This criterion predicted failure in the unidirectional P75/934 at approximately $+110\,°F$, using the square FE results. The maximum value again occurred on the fiber/matrix interface, but at the minimum distance between adjacent fibers (i.e. $\theta = 0°$). This result is also shown in figure 14. For comparison purposes, the maximum stress and von Mises criterion, using the CC analysis results, predicted damage initiation at $70\,°F$ and $65\,°F$, respectively. Based on the insensitivity of fiber properties on matrix stresses, as discussed earlier, damage was also predicted to occur in unidirectional T300/934 laminates at approximately the same temperature.

Experimental evidence sugests that unidirectional P75/934 does not experience damage even when exposed to cyclic temperature excursions between $\pm250\,°F$ [14]. This finding was based on no observed changes in stiffness and CTE, and examination of polished specimen edges using an optical microscope at 200x magnification. There are two possible explanations for the apparent discrepancies between the predicted and experimental results. First, changes in the properties measured might have been too small to detect, and optical microscopy of only the specimen edges may not have provided enough magnification to detect damage. Secondly, matrix yielding may have occurred, thus lowering the thermally induced stresses. More information on the temperature dependent stress-strain behavior of the neat resin is required to address the second possibility. No data on microscopic examinations of unidirectional T300/934 exposed to use temperatures of $-150\,°F$ could be found.

The same two failure criteria described above were used to predict damage initiation in the $[0/90]_s$ P75/934 laminate, using stress results from the square array FE analysis, and are shown in figure 15. The maximum stress failure criteria predicted damage initiation at approximately $+100\,°F$ due to either the σ_x or σ_θ, both of which were approximately equal in magnitude at this temperature. The maximum σ_x occurred on the interface at a circumferential location of $\theta = 34°$. The maximum σ_θ occurred a short distance away from the interface at $\theta = 90°$. The von Mises criterion predicted damage initiation at $+150\,°F$ a short distance away from the interface at $\theta = 83°$. Again, damage was also predicted to occur in $[0/90]_s$

T300/934 laminates at approximately the same temperatures.

Experimental data does show matrix cracking in $[0/90]_s$ P75/934 laminates occuring above $+75\,°F$ [3]. However, experimental data shows that T300/5208 laminates (5208 is very similar to 934) do not exhibit matrix cracking until temperatures of $-200\,°F$ and below[5]. A possible explanation for this discrepancy is a difference in the interfacial properties of the two material systems. The analysis assumes a perfect bond between the fiber and the matrix. T300 and P75 graphite fibers are processed differently, which could lead to differences in interfacial bond characteristics.

4.0 CONCLUSIONS

The results of an analytical investigation presenting thermally induced stresses in continuous graphite fiber reinforced epoxy composites were presented. There were several major conclusions that were made from these results. They may be summarized as follows:

1. The assumed microstructural geometry of the composite (i.e. composite cylinder, square or hexagonal array) affected the distributions and magnitudes of thermally induced stresses.

2. Thermally induced matrix stresses were not a strong function of fiber moduli or coefficients of thermal expansion.

3. The temperature dependence of epoxy properties did significantly affect the magnitudes of thermally induced matrix stresses.

4. Damage initiation was predicted in unidirectional and cross-ply P75/934 and T300/934 laminates at temperatures well above the assumed use temperature of $-150\,°F$.

5. Damage initiation predictions were in qualitative agreement with available experimental data for P75/934 cross-ply laminates.

6. There was insufficient data on the temperature dependent stress-strain behavior of polymer matrices to accurately predict damage initiation.

5.0 REFERENCES

1. Bowles, D. E.; and Tenney, D. R.:Composite Tubes for the Space Station Truss Structure. Proceedings 18th National SAMPE Technical Conference, 1986, pp. 414-428.

2. Tenney, D. R,; Sykes, G. F.; and Bowles, D. E.:Composite Materials for Space Structures. Proceedings 3rd European Symposium on Spacecraft Materials in Space Environment, Noordwijk, Netherlands, 1985.

3. Bowles, D. E.; and Shen, J.:Thermal Cycling Effects on the Dimensional Stability of P75 and P75-T300(Fabric) Hybrid Graphite/Epoxy Laminates. Proceedings 33'rd International SAMPE Symposium and Exhibition, 1988, pp. 1659-1671.

4. Bowles, D. E.:Effects of Microcracks on the Thermal Expansion of Composite Laminates. Journal Composite Materials, Vol. 18, No. 2, March 1984, pp. 173-187.

5. Adams, D. S.; Bowles, D. E.; and Herakovich, C. T.:Thermally Induced Transverse Cracking in Graphite/Epoxy Cross-Ply Laminates. Journal of Reinforced Plastics and Composites, Vol. 5, July 1986, pp. 152-169:

6. Hashin, Z:Theory of Fiber Reinforced Materials. NASA CR-1974, March 1972.

7. Avery, W. B.; and Herakovich, C. T.:Effect of Fiber Anisotropy on Thermal Stresses in Fibrous Composites. Journal of Applied Mechanics, 1986.

8. Zienkiewicz, O. C.:The Finite Element Method. McGraw-Hill Book Company, New York, NY, 1977.

9. Bowles, D. E.:Finite Element Composite Analysis Program (FECAP) for a Microcomputer. NASA Technical Memorandum 100670, July 1988.

10. Hahn, H. T.; and Pagano, N. J.:Curing Stresses in Composite Laminates. J. Composite Materials, Vol. 9, January 1975, pp. 91-106.

11. Kowalski, I. M.:Determining the Transverse Modulus of Carbon Fibers. SAMPE Journal, July-August 1986, pp. 38-42.

12. Helmer, J. F.; and Diefendorf, R. J.: Transverse Thermal Expansion of Carbon Fiber/Epoxy Matrix Composites. Proc. 5'th International Symposium on Composite Metallic Materials, 1983, pp. 15-20.

13. Amoco Performance Products Material Data Sheets, 1987.

14. Fox, D. J.; Sykes, G. F.; and Herakovich, C. T.:Space Environmental Effects on Graphite-Epoxy Compressive Properties and Epoxy Tensile Properties. CCMS-87-11, Virginia Tech, July 1987.

15. Milkovich, S. M.; Sykes, G. F.; and Herakovich, C. T.: Space Radiation Effects on the Thermo-Mechanical Behavior of Graphite-Epoxy Composites. J. Composite Materials, Vol. 20, No. 6, Nov. 1986, pp. 579-593.

16. Hashin, Z.:Analysis of Properties of Fiber Composites with Anisotropic Constituents. J. Applied Mechanics, Vol. 46, Sept. 1979, pp. 543-550.

17. Tsai, S. W.; and Hahn, H. T.:Introduction to Composite Materials. Technomic Publishing Co., 1980.

18. Margolis, J. M.:Engineering Thermoplastics, Properties and Applications. Marcel Decker Inc., 1985.

Table 1. T300 and P75 graphite fiber properties.

	T300	P75
E_1^f (Msi)	33.8	79.8
E_2^f (Msi)	3.35	1.38
G_{12}^f (Msi)	1.3	1.0
ν_{12}	0.2	0.2
ν_{23}	0.4	0.4
α_1^f (10^{-6}/°F)	-0.3	-0.75
α_2^f (10^{-6}/°F)	5.6	3.8

Table 2. Temperature dependent 934 epoxy properties.

	-250°F	75°F	250°F
E^m (Msi)	1.20	.674	.489
ν^m	.363	.363	.341
α^m (10^{-6}/°F)	7.40	23.0	29.9

Table 3. Maximum tensile matrix stresses in unidirectional P75/934 for $\Delta T = -500$°F

	FE-Square		FE-Hex.		CC[1]	
V_f =	.60	.75	.60	.85	.60	.99
σ_x (Ksi)	16.2	17.6	15.8	18.0	16.0	18.6
σ_r (Ksi)	5.3	7.1	5.0	7.8	—	—
σ_θ (Ksi)	15.2	17.3	13.7	17.0	13.3	16.9
$\tau_{r\theta}$ (Ksi)	5.0	6.5	3.1	4.7	—	—

[1] There are no tensile σ_r or $\tau_{r\theta}$ stresses predicted in the matrix for the CC analysis.

Table 4. Maximum stresses in $[0/90]_s$ P75/934 for $\Delta T = -500\,°\text{F}$

	LPT		FE
Lamina Strains (10^{-6})	Lamina Stresses (Ksi)		Matrix Stresses (Ksi)
$\epsilon_x = -2.87$	$\sigma_x = -9.95$		$\sigma_x = 19.9$
$\epsilon_y = -2.87$	$\sigma_y = 9.95$		$\sigma_r = 12.1$
$\gamma_{xy} = 0.00$	$\tau_{xy} = 0.00$		$\sigma_\theta = 23.4$
			$\tau_{r\theta} = 2.6$

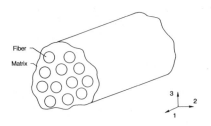

Figure 1. Problem geometry and material coordinates.

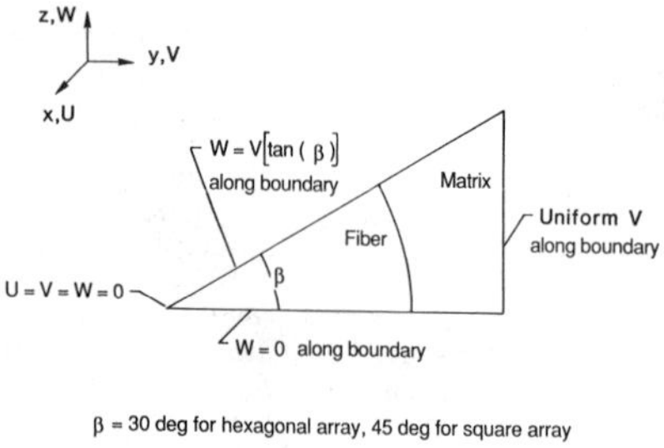

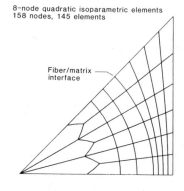

β = 30 deg for hexagonal array, 45 deg for square array

Figure 3. Finite element (FE) model geometry and boundary conditions.

8-node quadratic isoparametric elements
158 nodes, 145 elements

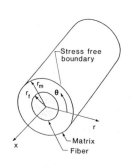

Figure 2. Composite cylinder (CC) model geometry and boundary conditions.

Figure 4. Finite element mesh.

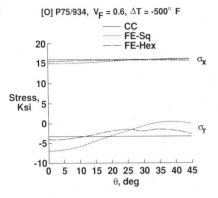

Figure 5. Axial and radial matrix stresses at the fiber/matrix interface.

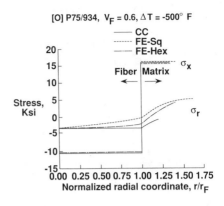

Figure 8. Axial and radial stresses along the radial line of maximum distance between fibers.

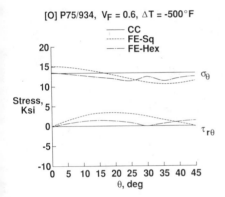

Figure 6. Tangential and shear matrix stresses at the fiber/matrix interface.

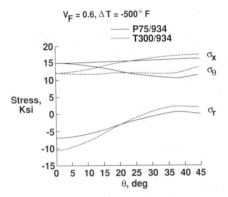

Figure 9. Comparison of matrix stresses at the fiber/matrix interface in [0] P75/934 and T300/934.

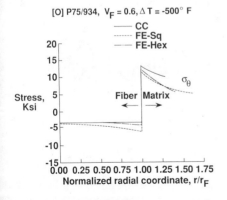

Figure 7. Tangential stresses along the radial line of maximum distance between fibers.

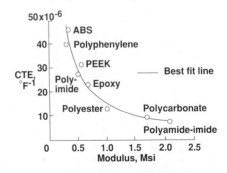

Figure 10. Relationship between CTE and modulus for various polymers.

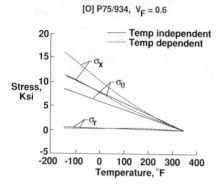

Figure 11. Effects of temperature dependent properties on matrix stresses at the fiber/matrix interface ($\theta = 45°$).

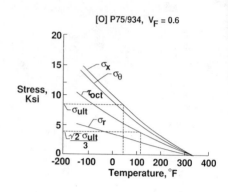

Figure 14. Maximum tensile matrix stresses in [0] P75/934.

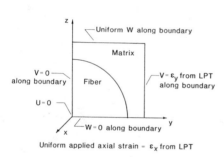

Figure 12. Finite element model geometry for global/local analysis of $[0/90]_s$ laminates.

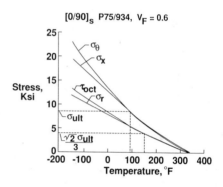

Figure 15. Maximum tensile matrix stresses in $[0/90]_s$ P75/934.

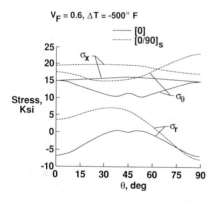

Figure 13. Comparison of matrix stresses at the fiber/matrix interface in [0] and $[0/90]_s$ laminates.

34th International SAMPE Symposium
May 8-11, 1989

The Application of the Weibull Strength Theory to Advanced Composite Materials

Tsay-Hsin G. Hu
Lockheed Engineering & Sciences Company
2400 NASA Road 1,B14
Houston, TX 77058

Daniel B. Goetschel
Hughes Aircraft Company
El Segundo, CA 90245

Abstract

The experimental data generated from a large-scale test program[1] are used to justify the application of the Weibull Strength Theory to advanced composite materials.

The failure stresses from the test program are used to determine the shape parameter by using the Maximum Likelihood estimate. The scale parameter is calculated from the failure stresses of unnotched laminates. A master Weibull curve can then be constructed for Graphite/Epoxy used in this study.

There are two ways to predict the failure stress. It can be calculated from the proposed Weibull model with use of shape parameter and scale parameter. It can also be obtained from the failure stress ratio (FSR) and the mean failure stress of referenced specimen. The FSR is from the proposed Weibull model with use of shape parameter. The predicted strength from the latter one matched better with test data.

The conclusions of this study and the recommendations for improvement of the proposed Weibull model are presented and discussed.

1 INTRODUCTION

The Weibull theory assumes a distribution of "weak place" in the form of crack or "dislocation" in the atomic grid. These discontinuities eventually propagate to cause final failure.

In essence, this failure theory is based on "weakest link hypothesis", which states that a component will fail when the stress intensity at any flaw (or weak place) reaches a critical value for crack propagation. Thus, the structure is represented as a chain model with components being small parts of the structure. Failure strength depends on the strength of the weakest link.

The cumulative failure probability of the brittle material under uniaxial loading can be approximated by a Weibull distribution defined by: (see Figure 1).

$$F(\sigma) = 1 - \frac{1}{V} \int_{v} \mathrm{EXP}(-B)\mathrm{d}v \quad \text{for} \quad \sigma > \sigma_u$$

$$F(\sigma) = 0. \quad \text{for} \quad \sigma < \sigma_u$$

Where

$$B = \left(\frac{\sigma - \sigma_u}{\beta}\right)^{\alpha}$$

F : cumulative failure probability

σ : applied stress

σ_u : the threshold stress
($\sigma_u = 0$. for practical use)

α : the Weibull modulus or shape parameter

β : location parameter

$\overline{V}$: volume unit

V : stressed volume.

The mean failure stress and variance are obtained by following equations:

$$\sigma_m = \sigma_u + \int_{\sigma_u}^{\infty} \text{EXP}(-B)d\sigma$$

and

$$a^2 = \int_{\sigma_u}^{\infty} d\sigma^2 + \sigma_u^2 - \sigma_m^2$$

Where,

σ_m : Mean Failure Stress

a : Variance

In 1964, Wail, N. A. & Daniel, I. M. [2] applied this theory for nonuniformly stressed brittle homogeneous objects. They experimentally verified the implicit concept of Weibull statistic theory. This implicit concept is that the failure probability is governed only by tensile normal stresses ignoring shear stress and stress gradient effects.

For brittle homogeneous material under multiaxial stresses, the Weibull strength model is used in conjunction with the Principle of Independent Action. This principle states that the survival probability of a given specimen under multiaxial stresses is equal to the product of survival probability of the specimen for the principal stresses applied independently, i.e.

$$F(\sigma_1, \sigma_2, \sigma_6) = 1 - \int_v \text{EXP}(-B^*)dv \text{ for } \sigma > \sigma_u$$

and

$$B^* = \sum_{i=1}^{n} \left(\frac{\sigma - \sigma_u}{\beta} \right)_i^{\alpha}$$

Where

$\sigma_1, \sigma_2, \sigma_6$ are principal stress for homogeneous body.

This is a very convenient formulation because of its simplicity, but it leads to non-conservative estimate of the failure probability due to the fact that interactions among the principal stresses are ignored.

In 1974, Bullock, R. E. [3] experimentally found that the ratio of flexural strength to tensile strength for composite material agrees well (5% error) with 2-parameter Weibull strength theory for Thornel 300/5208 and Modmor II/5208 system.

Two conclusions are drawn by Sendeckyi, G. P., Stalnaker, H. D., Bates, L. G., Kleisnit, R. A. and Smith, J. V. [4] from their testing of AS/3501-6 Graphite Epoxy composite: the first is that the thickness variation in the specimens does not affect the scatter of the static strength data, hence, the value of thickness is not important; the second is that the specimens exhibit a width effect that is consistent with Weibull theory for laminated materials.

In 1978, Hitchon, J. W. and Phillip, D. C. [5] suggested that under some circumstances, a Weibull treatment could be used to calculate the effect of size on component strength, i.e. the Weibull treatment could be successful in predicting the difference in strength when volume was a result of length changes in the fiber direction but not of cross-section area changes. This conclusion was confirmed by Weber, C. Z. [6]. A simple statistical model is proposed for internal failure mechanisms of composite materials under uniform stress.

$$F(\sigma) = 1 - \text{EXP}\left[-L\left(\frac{\sigma}{\beta}\right)^{\alpha}\right]$$

Where:

F : the probability of failure at a stress level

L : fiber length

α, β : Parameters of distribution

In 1980, Whitney, J. M. and Knight, M. [7] observed a larger variation in tensile strength from tensile coupons than from flexural specimens for unidirectional Graphite/Epoxy composite. They suggested this lack of correlation might be a result of test methodology or may simply be an indication that Weibull distribution is an inadequate model for describing failure in the fiber direction for a unidirectional fiber reinforced composite. Whitney, J. M. and Kim, R. Y. [8] also found that notched and unnotched tensile strength for the same laminate did not necessarily yield the same 2-parameter Weibull distribution curve.

In 1981, Wetherhold, R. C. and Whitney, J. M. [9] applied a 2-parameter Weibull model to predict the notched strength of a fiber-reinforced composite laminate under uniaxial loading. The composite is assumed to be homogeneous. The notched strength is evaluated by using numerical integral of a reduced, one-dimensional high-risk-to-failure volume for the specimens with a circular hole. In 1982, Wetherhold, R. C. [10] extended this model for notched composites under biaxial loading. Conservative strength predictions are obtained from this model.

2 PROPOSED MODEL

2.1 ASSUMPTIONS

Three assumptions are made ;

1. The volumetric flaw govern the fracture strength of composite laminates.

2. Fibers dominate the failure behavior for laminated composites.

3. For practical use, the location parameter of the Weibull theory is assumed to be zero. The shape parameter and scale parameter are assumed to be material constants.

2.2 LAMINA

When uniaxial load is applied in fiber direction, the density function for 2-parameter Weibull strength theory is readily written as:

$$B = \left[\frac{\sigma}{\beta}\right]^{\alpha} \qquad EQ(1)$$

In the multiaxial in-plane loading case, a straightforward application of the Principle of Independent Action yield the density function:

$$B = \sum_{i=1,2,6} D_i$$

where,

$$D_i = \left(\frac{\sigma_i}{\beta_i}\right)^{\alpha}_i$$

i=1,2,6 are the stress components in the material axis direction.

However, with the assumption that the fiber dominate the failure behavior, the density function can be simplified as EQ (1).

2.3 LAMINATE

Since composite material is not homogeneous, the Weakest Link Theory should be extended to ply (group) level. The survival probability of a laminate is the product of the survival probability of each individual ply (group), i.e. :

$$S = \Pi_{i=1}^{n} S_i$$

Where,

$$S_i = \mathrm{EXP}\left[-(\frac{\sigma_{1i}}{\beta})^{\alpha}\right]$$

2.4 STRENGTH PREDICTION

There are two ways for strength prediction:

1. With known shape parameter and scale parameter, the mean failure stress can be calculated with the assumption that the specimen fails at cumulative failure probability of 50%. i.e. :

$$F = 0.50 \ = 1 - \frac{1}{\overline{V}}\int_{v} \mathrm{EXP}(-B)\mathrm{d}v$$

Where

$$B = \left(\frac{\sigma(x,y,z)}{\beta}\right)^{\alpha}$$

F : cumulative failure probability
$\sigma(x,y,z)$: applied stress
α : shape parameter
β : scale parameter
$\overline{V}$: volume unit

2. With known shape parameter and referenced failure stress (σ_{n2}) , the failure stress ratio (FSR) and the mean failure stress (σ_{n1}) can be obtained by equating the failure probability for these two testing configurations, i.e. :

$$FSR = \frac{\sigma_{n1}}{\sigma_{n2}} = \left[\frac{\sum_{i=1}^{N_2} \mathrm{K}_{2i}^{\alpha} \int \mathrm{G}_2^{\alpha}\left(x,y\right)\mathrm{d}x\mathrm{d}y}{\sum_{i=1}^{N_1} \mathrm{K}_{1i}^{\alpha} \int \mathrm{G}_1^{\alpha}\left(x,y\right)\mathrm{d}x\mathrm{d}y}\right]^{\frac{1}{\alpha}}$$

Where,
$\quad G_j(x,y) * \sigma_{nj}$: the stress distribution.
$\quad \sigma_{nj}$: the far-field stress.
$\quad N_j$: the number of plies.
$\quad K_{ji}$: the ratio of the fiber stress to the average through-thickness stress. (see Appendix)

If these two specimens are made of the same lay-up, the FSR can be expressed as follows :

$$FSR = \frac{\sigma_{n1}}{\sigma_{n2}} = \left[\frac{\int \mathrm{G}_2^{\alpha}\left(x,y\right)\mathrm{d}x\mathrm{d}y}{\int \mathrm{G}_1^{\alpha}\left(x,y\right)\mathrm{d}x\mathrm{d}y}\right]^{\frac{1}{\alpha}}$$

3   TEST PROGRAM

Experimental data with a high level of confidence is the best tool to assess the validity and accuracy of the proposed model. A large scale experimental program was designed and conducted for composites with general stress concentration problems.

It is obvious that the increase of the replicates will reduce data scatter but increase the cost. With the assumption that test data can fit the Weibull distribution, 5 replicates for each test configuration seems to be an optimum compromise between accuracy and cost. It corresponds to 95% confidence and 5% error with shape parameter of 24, or 90% confidence and 10% error for shape parameter of 10.

The test matrix are presented in Table 1 Through Table 3. The specimen configuration and notch type are shown in Figure 2. The specimens are made of Fiberite Hy-E 3048 AIK unidirection prepreg tape consisting of Union Carbide T-300 Graphite fibers and Fiberite's low temperature 948 A1 epoxy resin.

According to the specification from manufacturer, the epoxy content is about 60% in

588

volume, the remaining 40% is graphite and a small amount of volatile substances. The material properties are characterized as follows:

. Lamina Material Property
   E1 = 19.420 Msi
   E2 = 1.338 Msi
   E6 = 0.725 Msi
   V = 0.294
   t = 0.0058 in.

. Lamina Strength Data
   X = 194.10 Ksi
   Y =   3.408 Ksi
   S =   8.624 Ksi

4 COMPUTER SIMULATION

4.1 SHAPE PARAMETER

The shape parameter is determined by using the Maximum Likelihood estimate. The detailed procedures and FORTRAN subroutine are shown in MIL-HDBK-17B(11).

Test data are pooled to estimate the shape parameter after the raw data are normalized by their mean for each testing configuration. This work scheme is repeated for different data subgroup. The shape parameter estimated from each data subgroup are summarized in Table 4.

The shape parameter can be assumed to be a material constant because deviations in the shape parameter do not significantly affect the results. In the following study, the shape parameter of 11.18 (from group with all available data except those from lay-up of $[\pm 45]_{2s}$ and $[90/\pm 30]_s$) is used.

The master Weibull distribution curve for composites is presented in Figure 3. Its plot on probability paper is shown in Figure 4.

4.2 SCALE PARAMETER

The scale parameter for each type of lay-up is determined by assuming that the cumulative failure probability of unnotched specimen with the mean failure stress is 50%. Table 5 lists the scale parameters estimated from each type of lay-up.

Scale parameter of 171.75 Ksi from $[0/\pm 45/90]_s$ is selected for further study based on the following justifications. The smaller value of scale parameter will yield more conservative strength prediction. The data from $[0/\pm 15]_s$ and $[0/\pm 30]_s$ are screened out because their failure mechanism may not fit the assumptions made for this study.

4.3 FINITE ELEMENT ANALYSIS

NASTRAN/MSC. is used to obtained the stress distribution at the laminate level and at the ply level. A 4 noded CQUAD element type is selected and there are approximately 650 nodes, 1300 DOF(degree of freedom) for each finite element model.

4.4 POST-PROCESSOR

A post-processor is written to perform the required data reduction. numerical integration and result calculation.

1. Retrieving the stresses for the points along the failure path. This failure path starts at the point with peak stress and extends along the direction perpendicular to the loaded direction.

2. Calculating the value for the stress to (α) power order for each point in step 1.

3. Performing the curve-fitting technique. The stress to (α) power order can be expressed as a function of location. A six order polynomial equation is selected to assure the error in the location with peak stress to be less than 2%.

4. Conducting the numerical integration along the failure path and calculating the integrated value to $1/(\alpha)$ power order.

5 SIMULATION RESULTS

For the current work, only the cases for specimens with a circular hole is studied. The circular hole is a symmetric notch, i.e., the notch is symmetric with respect to a line parallel to the loading axis.

The failure path of notched specimens starts at the point with peak stress and extends along the direction perpendicular to the loading direction. Because the failure path of notched specimens in this study can be fully predicted, the volume integral can be substituted by the area integral. This area is prescribed by the failure path and thickness.

The scale parameter obtained from the unnotched specimens is modified by a factor of $[length]^{\frac{1}{\alpha}}$.

The Error is defined as,

$$\left(\frac{V_{exp.} - V_{pred.}}{V_{exp.}}\right) * 100\%$$

Where,
$V_{exp.}$ and $V_{pred.}$ are data from tests and computer simulation respectively.

The test data, the simulation results and their deviation are presented as follows.

5.1 CALCULATING THE MEAN FAILURE STRESS WITH KNOWN SHAPE PARAMETER AND SCALE PARAMETER

The comparisons of the mean failure stress between predictions and test are shown in Table 6 through Table 8.

The results for unnotched specimens with different width are presented in Table 6. There are two different lay-ups ($[0/\pm45/90]_s$ and $[0/\pm90]_{2s}$) and three different widths (0.90 in., 1.80 in. and 2.70 in.).

Table 7 is for notched specimens with different width but constant notch-to-width ratio (0.25/0.90, 0.50/1.80 & 0.75/2.70). Only the lay-up of $[0/\pm45/90]_s$ is used.

The results for constant-width specimens are listed in Table 8. Three types of lay-ups ($[0/\pm45/90]_s$, $[0/\pm45]_s$ & $[0/\pm75]_s$ and five different notch sizes (0.0 in., 0.125 in., 0.250 in., 0.375 in. and 0.500 in.) are studied.

Some observations are noticed:

1. It is difficult to determine the width effect from test data due to data scatter. However, the width effect appears in the predictions from the Weibull Model.

2. The predicted strength matches quite well with test data for unnotched specimens. This can be attributed to the fact that the scale parameter is determined by using test data from unnotched specimens. This is also the reason why the same unnotched strength of $[0/\pm45/90]_s$ is obtained from test and prediction.

3. For notched specimens of the same lay-up, the discrepancy between test data and prediction decreases as the notch size increases.

4. The Errors for notched specimens of dif-

590

ferent lay-up are approximately in the same level.

5.2 CALCULATING THE FAILURE STRESS RATIO WITH A KNOWN SHAPE PARAMETER

For specimens made from the same lay-up, the unnotched specimens are designated as the referenced ones. There are two relationships between notch size and width; constant notch-to-width ratio and constant width.

Table 9 is for the cases of constant notch-to-width ratio. The lay-up of $[0/\pm45/90]_s$ is selected. The prediction of FSR agrees very well with test data. The error decreases as the notch size increases.

The results for cases of constant width are shown in Table 10. The lay-up of $[0/\pm45/90]_s$, $[0/\pm45]_s$ and $[0/\pm75]_s$ are used for this study. The errors are found to be approximately in the same level.

The failure stress ratio can be calculated for laminates with the same notch size form two different lay-ups. The $[0/\pm45/90]_s$ lay-up is selected as the referenced one. The results are shown in Table 11. The discrepancy between test and prediction decreases as the notch size increases.

6 CONCLUSIONS

The following conclusions can be drawn from this study.

1. The stress concentration factor is not the only parameter to determine notched strength. Stress gradient is also important.

2. From the plot of Master Weibull Distribution Curve on the probability paper,

it is believed that the location parameter should not be zero. However, its effect on the results can be ignored.

3. The shape parameter of the Weibull Strength Model for composites can be treated as a material constant. The notch type, notch size and lay-up may have little effect on the shape parameter. The scale parameter can also be assumed to be a material constant.

4. For the Graphite/Epoxy used in this investigation, the shape parameter is about 11.13. The scale parameter is 171.75 Ksi.

5. There are some limitations for the applicability of the current Weibull model. The failure mechanism may be an important criterion for the success of this model. In this study, the current Weibull model appears to be useful for laminates with combination of 0 ply(plies) and other ply (plies) with orientation angle greater than 30°.

6. The strength predictions for FSR with a known shape parameter comparatively match better with test data. This may be attributed to two factors. The error due to scale parameter is eliminated and the errors in both the denominator and dividend tend to cancel out.

7. The Weibull theory yields a conservative prediction for notched strength from the unnotched strength. The discrepancy between prediction and test data tends to decrease with the increase of notch size.

7 RECOMMENDATIONS

Some suggestions are presented for further investigation and model inprovement.

1. In this study, only the cases of circular holes are presented. This type of notch

generates a uniaxial stress along the failure path. It should be extended to cover the cases with unsymmetrical notches.

2. The current model of the Weibull strength Theory can not predict the stacking sequence effect on the strength. The inclusion of interlaminar stresses in the model is unavoidable even though it will complicate the model.

3. The area integral instead of the line integral is another possible evolution. In the practical structure, it is difficult to define the failure path for integral calculation. The critical volume instead of the failure path for integral calculation can resolve this predicament.

REFERENCE :

1. Hu, T. H., "Improving the Strength Prediction for Advanced Composite Material with Stress Concentration", Ph.D. Thesis, Rensselaer Polytechnic Institute.

2. Wail, N. A. & Daniel, I. M. "Analysis of Fracture Probabilities in Nonuniformly Stressed Brittle Materials", J. American Ceramic Society, Vol. 47 (1964), P 268.

3. Bullock, R. E. "Strength Ratio of Composite Materials in Flexure and in Tension", J. Composite Material, Vol. 18 , April 1974, P200

4. Sendeckyi, G. P., Stalnaker, H. D., Bates, L. G., Kleisnit, R. A. and Smith, J. V. "Within-Panel Variability and Scaling Effect in Composite Materials", Composite Tech. Review, Vol. 4, No 4, Winter 1982.

5. Hitchon, J. W. and Philip, D. C. "The Effect of Specimen Size on the Strength of CFRP", Composites, April 1978, P119.

6. Weber, C. Z. "The Effect of Stress Nonuniformity and Size on the Strength of Composite Materials", Composite Tech. Review, winter 1980.

7. Whitney, J. M. & Knight, M. "The Relationship Between Tensile Strength and Flexural Strength in Fiber-Reinforced Composites", Experimental Mechanics, June 1980, P212.

8. Whitney, J. M. & Kim, R. Y. "Effect of Stacking Sequence on the Notched Strength of Laminated Composites", ASTM STP617 (1977) P229.

9. Wetherhold, R. T. & Whitney, J. M. "Tensile Failure of Notched Fiber-Reinforced Composite Materials", Polymer Composites, Vol. 12, No 3 (July, 1981) P112.

10. Wetherhold, R. T. "A Weibull Brittle Failure Model for Biaxial Loading of a Notched Composite Materials", J. Material Science and Engineering, Vol 47(1981), P271.

11. MILITARY HANDBOOK 17B : Polymer Matrix Composites, P8-32. Feb. 29, 1988.

APPENDIX

The strain-stress relationship for the balanced laminates can be written as:

$$
\left\{ \begin{array}{c} \epsilon_x \\ \epsilon_y \\ \epsilon_s \end{array} \right\} = \left[\begin{array}{ccc} C_{xx} & C_{xy} & 0. \\ C_{yx} & C_{yy} & 0. \\ 0. & 0. & C_{ss} \end{array} \right] \left\{ \begin{array}{c} \sigma_x \\ \sigma_y \\ \sigma_s \end{array} \right\}
$$

For specimens with a symmetric type of notch. ($\epsilon_y = 0., \epsilon_s = 0.$)

$$ \epsilon_x = C_{xx}\sigma_x $$

$$ \epsilon_y = C_{xy}\sigma_x $$

Where :

$\sigma_x, \sigma_y, \sigma_s$ are the through-thickness
stress

$\epsilon_x, \epsilon_y, \epsilon_s$ are the average
through- thickness stress

$C_{ij}, i, j = x, y, s$ is the compliance
matrix of the laminate.

The strain field in the ply with orientation angle θ can be found in terms of laminate strain as follows :

$$\begin{Bmatrix} \epsilon_1 \\ \epsilon_2 \\ \epsilon_6 \end{Bmatrix} = \begin{bmatrix} \cos^2\theta & \sin^2\theta & \sin\theta\cos\theta \\ \sin^2\theta & \cos^2\theta & -\sin\theta\cos\theta \\ -2\sin\theta\cos\theta & 2\sin\theta\cos\theta & \cos^2\theta - \sin^2\theta \end{bmatrix} \begin{Bmatrix} \epsilon_x \\ \epsilon_y \\ \epsilon_s \end{Bmatrix}$$

The stress field is this ply is :

$$\begin{Bmatrix} \sigma_1 \\ \sigma_2 \\ \sigma_6 \end{Bmatrix} = \begin{bmatrix} Q_{11} & Q_{12} & 0. \\ Q_{21} & Q_{22} & 0. \\ 0. & 0. & Q_{66} \end{bmatrix} \begin{Bmatrix} \epsilon_1 \\ \epsilon_2 \\ \epsilon_6 \end{Bmatrix}$$

Where :

θ is the orientation angle

$\sigma_1, \sigma_2, \sigma_6$ are the stress in material
coordinate

$\epsilon_x, \epsilon_y, \epsilon_s$ are the strain in global
coordinate

$Q_{ij}, i, j = 1, 2, 6$ is the compliance
matrix of the laminate.

The fiber stress in each ply with orientation angle of θ can now be written in the following form:

$$\sigma_1 = [(Q_{11}\cos^2\theta + Q_{12}\sin^2\theta)C_{xx} + (Q_{11}\sin^2\theta + Q_{12}\cos^2\theta)C_{xy}]\sigma_x$$

The ratio of hte fiber stress to the average through-thickness stress can be written as :

$$K = \left(\frac{\sigma_\perp}{\sigma_x}\right)$$
$$= [(Q_{11}\cos^2\theta + Q_{12}\sin^2\theta)C_{xx} + (Q_{11}\sin^2\theta + Q_{12}\cos^2\theta)C_{xy}]$$

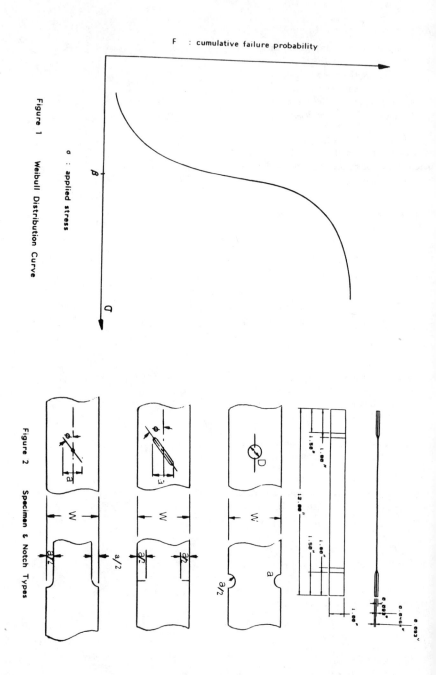

F : cumulative failure probability

σ : applied stress

Figure 1   Weibull Distribution Curve

Figure 2   Specimen & Notch Types

Figure 3 Master Weibull Distribution Curve for Composites

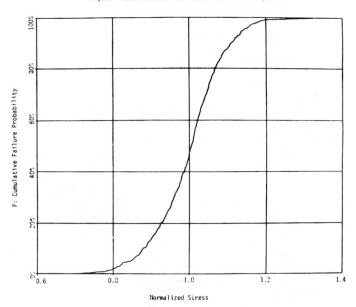

Figure 4 Master Weibull Distribution Curve for Composites

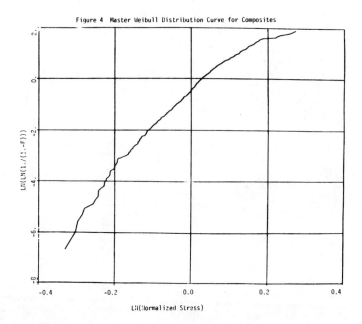

595

Table 1 Test Matrix for Specimens with Circular Hole

Lay-up/ Dia.(in)	0.00	0.035	0.065	0.125	0.250	0.375	0.500	0.750"
$[90/\pm 45/0]_s$	•		•	•	•	•	•	
$[\pm 45/0/90]_s$	•		•	•	•	•	•	
$[0/\pm 45/90]_s$	•	•	•	•	•	•	•	•
$[0/\pm 45]_s$	•		•	•	•	•	•	
$[0_2/\pm 45]_s$	•	•	•	•	•	•	•	•
$[0_4/\pm 45]_s$	•		•	•	•	•	•	
$[0/\pm 15]_s$	•		•	•	•	•	•	
$[0/\pm 30]_s$	•		•	•	•	•	•	
$[0/\pm 60]_s$	•		•	•	•	•	•	
$[0/\pm 75]_s$	•		•	•	•	•	•	
$[0/90]_{2s}$	•		•	•	•	•	•	
$[90/\pm 30]_s$	•		•	•	•	•	•	
$[\pm 45]_{2s}$	•		•	•	•	•	•	
$[90/\pm 45/0]_s^1$			•	•	•		•	

Note : 1. The notch is implanted by using carbide tip twist drill bit.

Table 2 Test Matrix for Lay-up of $[0/\pm 45/90]_s$ and $[0/\pm 45]_{2s}$

Notch Type/ Notch Size(in)	0.065	0.250	0.500	0.750
30° Slant Slot	•	•	•	•
45° Slant Slot	•	•	•	•
60° Slant Slot	•	•	•	•
90° Slant Slot	•	•	•	•
30° Slant Fine Slot		•	•	•
45° Slant Fine Slot		•	•	•
60° Slant Fine Slot		•	•	•
90° Slant Fine Slot		•	•	•
Double Edge Semi-Hole		•	•	•
Double Edge Fine Slot		•	•	•
Shoulder		•	•	•

Table 3 Test Matrix for Width effect for Lay-up of $[0/\pm 45/90]_s$ and $[0/90]_{2s}$

Specimen Width(in)/ Notch Size(in)	Unnotch	a = 0.25	a = 0.50	a = 0.75
W = 0.9	•	•		
W = 1.8	•		•	
W = 2.7	•			•

Table 4 The Estimated Shape Parameters

Data Group	Number of Datapoint	Estimated Shape Parameter	Normalized Scale parameter
All Specimens	800	11.34	1.0406
Unnotched Specimens	60	13.73	1.0353
Notched Specimens	740	11.04	1.0418
Notch Size of 0.25"	180	9.47	1.0473
Notch Size of 0.50"	180	12.70	1.0394
Specimen Group 1[1]	760	11.18	1.0414
Specimen Group 2[2]	700	10.93	1.0420

Note :
1. All specimens except layups of $[90/\pm 30]_s$ & $[\pm 45]_{2s}$
2. All specimens except layups of $[90/\pm 30]_s$, $[\pm 45]_{2s}$, $[0/\pm 15]_s$ & $[0/\pm 30]_s$.

Table 5 The Estimated Scale Parameters

Data Group	Estimated Scale Parameter (ksi)
$[90/\pm 45/0]_s$	186.78
$[\pm 45/0/90]_s$	154.20
$[0/\pm 45/90]_s$	171.75
$[0/\pm 45]_s$	196.49
$[0_2/\pm 45]_s$	222.90
$[0_4/\pm 45]_s$	236.74
$[0/\pm 15]_s$	137.25
$[0/\pm 30]_s$	163.41
$[0/\pm 60]_s$	206.73
$[0/\pm 75]_s$	181.39
$[0/90]_{2s}$	213.21

Table 6 Comparison of Unnotched Strength

For Lay-up of $[0/\pm 45/90]_s$

Width(in)	W = 0.90	W = 1.80	W = 2.70
Prediction (Ksi)	79.03	74.28	71.63
Test Data (Ksi)	78.53	81.17	76.71
Error (%)	-0.64	-8.49	-6.62

For Lay-up of $[0/90]_{2s}$

Width(in)	W = 0.90	W = 1.80	W = 2.70
Prediction (Ksi)	102.70	96.53	93.08
Test Data (Ksi)	120.97	120.00	115.56
Error (%)	15.10	19.56	19.45

Table 7 Comparison of Notched Strength for Specimens of $[0/\pm 45/90]_s$ with Constant Ratio of Notch size to Width (0.25/0.90)

Width(in)	W = 0.90	W = 1.80	W = 2.70
Prediction (Ksi)	35.58	33.10	31.82
Test Data (Ksi)	38.42	37.74	34.16
Error (%)	7.91	12.29	6.85

Table 8 Comparison of Strength for Specimens with Constant Width (1") but Various Notch Size

Predicted Strength (Unit : Ksi)

Lay-up/ Dia.(in)	D = 0.000	D = 0.125	D = 0.250	D = 0.375	D = 0.500
$[0/\pm 45]_s$	87.50	38.39	36.29	32.92	28.13
$[0/\pm 75]_s$	76.49	35.90	33.18	28.99	24.01
$[0/\pm 45/90]_s$	78.29	41.53	36.26	31.25	25.69

Strength (Unit : Ksi) from Test

Lay-up/ Dia.(in)	D = 0.000	D = 0.125	D = 0.250	D = 0.375	D = 0.500
$[0/\pm 45]_s$	100.11	67.76	49.60	41.92	32.57
$[0/\pm 75]_s$	80.99	63.05	50.71	39.97	33.51
$[0/\pm 45/90]_s$	78.29	54.06	43.32	37.06	29.92

Error (%)

Lay-up/ Dia.(in)	D = 0.000	D = 0.125	D = 0.250	D = 0.375	D = 0.500
$[0/\pm 45]_s$	12.60	43.34	26.83	21.47	13.63
$[0/\pm 75]_s$	5.56	43.06	34.57	27.47	28.35
$[0/\pm 45/90]_s$	0.	23.18	16.30	15.67	14.14

Table 9 Comparison of the Failure Stress Ratio for Specimens of $[0/\pm 45/90]_s$ with Constant Ratio of Notch size to Width (0.25/0.90)

Lay-up/ Width(in)	W = 0.90	W = 1.80	W = 2.70
Prediction	0.4503	0.4456	0.4442
Test Data	0.4890	0.4650	0.4453
Error(%)	7.91	4.17	0.25

Table 10 Comparison of the Failure Stress Ratio (Notched Strength/Unnotched Strength) for Specimens of Same Lay-up with Constant Width (1 in.)

Predicted Failure Stress Ratio

Lay-up/ Dia.(in)	D = 0.125	D = 0.250	D = 0.375	D = 0.500
$[0/\pm 45]_s$	0.4387	0.4147	0.3762	0.3215
$[0/\pm 75]_s$	0.4694	0.4337	0.3790	0.3138
$[0/\pm 45/90]_s$	0.5304	0.4632	0.3992	0.3282

Failure Stress Ratio from Test

Lay-up/ Dia.(in)	D = 0.125	D = 0.250	D = 0.375	D = 0.500
$[0/\pm 45]_s$	0.6769	0.4955	0.4187	0.3253
$[0/\pm 75]_s$	0.7785	0.6261	0.4935	0.4138
$[0/\pm 45/90]_s$	0.6905	0.5533	0.4734	0.3822

Error (%)

Lay-up/ Width(in)	D = 0.125	D = 0.250	D = 0.375	D = 0.500
$[0/\pm 45]_s$	35.19	16.31	10.15	1.17
$[0/\pm 75]_s$	39.70	30.73	23.21	24.17
$[0/\pm 45/90]_s$	23.19	16.28	15.67	14.13

Table 11 Comparison of Failure Stress Ratio between Specimens with Same Notch Size (Specimens with Lay-up of $[0/\pm 45/90]_s$ are referenced).

For Lay-up $[0/\pm 45]_s$

Lay-up/ Dia.(in)	D = 0.000	D = 0.125	D = 0.250	D = 0.375	D = 0.500
Prediction	1.1176	0.9245	1.000	1.0534	1.0948
Test Data	1.2787	1.2530	1.1449	1.1310	1.0880
Error(%)	12.60	26.22	12.66	6.86	-0.06

For Lay-up $[0/\pm 75]_s$

Lay-up/ Width(in)	D = 0.000	D = 0.125	D = 0.250	D = 0.375	D = 0.500
Prediction	0.9771	0.8645	0.9149	0.9278	0.9343
Test Data	1.0345	1.1611	1.1706	1.0785	1.120
Error (%)	5.55	25.54	21.84	13.97	16.58

THE EFFECTS OF THREE-DIMENSIONAL STATES OF
STRESS ON DAMPING OF LAMINATED COMPOSITES

S. J. Hwang and R. F. Gibson
Mechanical Engineering Department
University of Idaho
Moscow, Idaho

Abstract

A three-dimensional finite element technique is developed for the characterization of the effects of three-dimensional states of stress on damping of laminated composites. The calculation of laminate damping is performed with the use of a strain energy method and the damping properties of the individual laminae. Particular attention is paid to the effects of interlaminar stresses on the laminate damping. These effects are studied by varying fiber orientation and by varying laminate width-to-thickness ratio. The work described in this paper also involves experimental measurements of damping of composite specimens using the impulse-frequency response vibration technique. The measured damping data are in reasonably good agreement with those predicted by the three-dimensional finite element method. This correlation indicates that the three-dimensional finite element method is a powerful technique for the determination of damping of laminated composites, and that it provides considerable potential for full three-dimensional characterization in more complex structures and loading situations.

1. INTRODUCTION

The increasing need for high performance structures has stimulated considerable research in the characterization of dynamic properties of advanced composite materials. In recent years, these materials have been extensively used in many aerospace applications because of their light weight, stiffness and excellent damping qualities.

"Damping" is a measure of the energy dissipation in any vibrating structure. There are a number of mechanisms involved in damping. One of the primary sources of damping in undamaged and properly bonded composites is the linear visco-elastic behavior of matrix and fiber materials. Nonlinear damping mechanisms, such as the friction between fiber and matrix materials, are only present in damaged or poorly bonded composites, and are not important otherwise.

Significant progress has been achieved in analysis and measurement of dynamic properties of composite materials. For example, closed form solutions for dynamic stiffness and damping properties of laminated plates and laminated beams have been derived, and finite element methods have been used in both macro-mechanical and micromechanical modeling[1-3]. Recently, experimental techniques for the characterization of dynamic properties of composite materials have been developed and improved[1,4].

Although previous research has produced valuable insight, it has generally been limited by the usual assumptions of classical lamination theory, and the effects of three-dimensional states of stress have not been fully investigated. It is well known that three-dimensional stress states arise at free edges and at geometric discontinuities in many composite materials and structures[5]. This is the so called "free edge effect." The existence of such states of stress means that part of the energy dissipation is contributed by the interlaminar stresses.

Since part of the difficulty of analyzing the dynamic properties of laminated composites stems from complex geometries and loading situations, versatile numerical methods such as finite element methods are well suited to this analysis[2,3]. While some work has been done on finite element modeling of damping in composite materials, none of this work has fully included the effect of interlaminar stresses. A systematic investigation into the effect of the interlaminar stresses would further the understanding of the damping properties of composite laminates. The objective of this research was therefore to develop a full three-dimensional finite element method for investigating the contribution of interlaminar damping in laminated composites.

Applications of the strain energy method have been previously demonstrated in several papers[2,3]. It appears that the strain energy method is an efficient and flexible technique for predicting damping of composite materials. The concept of damping in terms of energy was apparently first introduced by Ungar and Kerwin[6] and was later implemented in finite element analysis[2,3]. In the current research, this method was used in a three-dimensional finite element formulation for determining damping of laminated composites.

The work described in this paper also involves the fabrication of graphite/epoxy composite specimens and experimental measurements of the composite damping for comparison with the analytical results. The composite specimens were fabricated using an autoclave-style curing process[7]. Experimental verification of the composite damping was carried out using the impulse-frequency response vibration technique. This technique was recently developed by Gibson et al[4], and it has been extensively used for the characterization of dynamic properties of composite materials at the University of Idaho.

2. 3-D FINITE ELEMENT METHOD

In order to account for three-dimensional states of stress, a three-dimensional finite element method was developed for macro-mechanical modeling of damping in laminated composites. The finite element code used in this work is the SAP IV finite element program[8]. Since this program does not have the capability of calculating strain energy, a modification to the program was required for the purpose of applying the strain energy method in the finite element formulation. The basis of the strain energy method is that the laminate damping can be obtained by the use of lamina damping properties and by calculating strain energy stored in each lamina. As shown in Eqn. (1), the dimensionless loss factor (a measure of damping) is calculated by summing the energy dissipation in each lamina and dividing by the total strain energy stored in the laminate. The strain energy stored in each lamina is based on the resulting stresses and strains in the lamina, and it can be divided into six strain energy terms that correspond to each of the six independent stress components.

$$\eta = \sum_{k=1}^{n} \left[\frac{\eta_x^{(k)} W_x^{(k)} + \eta_y^{(k)} W_y^{(k)}}{W_t} \right.$$

$$+ \frac{\eta_{xy}^{(k)} W_{xy}^{(k)} + \eta_z^{(k)} W_z^{(k)} + \eta_{yz}^{(k)} W_{yz}^{(k)}}{W_t}$$

$$\left. + \frac{\eta_{xz}^{(k)} W_{xz}^{(k)}}{W_t} \right] \qquad (1)$$

where

η = laminate loss factor (a measure of damping)

k = lamina number

n = total number of laminae

W_t = total strain energy stored in a laminate

x, y, z = global laminate coordinates

$\eta_x^{(k)}$, $\eta_y^{(k)}$, $\eta_{xy}^{(k)}$ = in-plane loss factors of the kth lamina

$\eta_z^{(k)}$, $\eta_{yz}^{(k)}$, $\eta_{xz}^{(k)}$ = interlaminar loss factors of the kth lamina

and the strain energy terms are

$$W_x^{(k)} = \frac{1}{2} \int_v \sigma_x^{(k)} \epsilon_x^{(k)} \, dv$$

$$W_y^{(k)} = \frac{1}{2} \int_v \sigma_y^{(k)} \epsilon_y^{(k)} \, dv$$

$$W_{xy}^{(k)} = \frac{1}{2} \int_v \tau_{xy}^{(k)} \gamma_{xy}^{(k)} \, dv$$

$$W_z^{(k)} = \frac{1}{2} \int_v \sigma_z^{(k)} \epsilon_z^{(k)} \, dv$$

$$W_{yz}^{(k)} = \frac{1}{2} \int_v \tau_{yz}^{(k)} \gamma_{yz}^{(k)} \, dv$$

$$W_{xz}^{(k)} = \frac{1}{2} \int_v \tau_{xz}^{(k)} \gamma_{xz}^{(k)} \, dv$$

where

$\sigma_x^{(k)}$, $\sigma_y^{(k)}$, $\tau_{xy}^{(k)}$ = in-plane stresses of the kth lamina

$\sigma_z^{(k)}$, $\tau_{yz}^{(k)}$, $\tau_{xz}^{(k)}$ = interlaminar stresses of the kth lamina

$\epsilon_x^{(k)}$, $\epsilon_y^{(k)}$, $\gamma_{xy}^{(k)}$ = in-plane strains of the kth lamina

$\epsilon_z^{(k)}$, $\gamma_{yz}^{(k)}$, $\gamma_{xz}^{(k)}$ = interlaminar strains of the kth lamina

v = volume of the kth lamina

As illustrated in Eqn. (1), the application of the strain energy method requires the use of lamina loss factors. In this work, the lamina in-plane loss factors were determined by the use of a micromechanical approach[9]. Since the matrix material is the bonding agent between laminae, it is believed that most of the energy dissipation near the interlaminar interfaces is dominated by the matrix material. For this reason, and because no reliable micromechanical theory is available for the determination of lamina interlaminar loss factors, the matrix loss factors were used as interlaminar loss factors of the composite lamina to simplify the calculation of the laminate loss factor. This assumption would overestimate the energy dissipation in the lamina, because the actual interlaminar loss factors of the composite lamina should be less than those of the matrix material.

One of the advantages of the current three-dimensional finite element technique is that, with the use of the strain energy method, the effect of interlaminar stresses on damping can be studied. As shown in Eqn. (2), the contribution of inter-laminar damping due to each of the interlaminar stress components is calculated by summing the energy dissipation due to the corresponding interlaminar stress and dividing by the total energy dissipation in the laminate.

$$F_z = \frac{D_z}{D_t} \ , \quad F_{yz} = \frac{D_{yz}}{D_t} \ , \quad F_{xz} = \frac{D_{xz}}{D_t} \quad (2)$$

where

D_z, D_{yz}, D_{xz} = energy dissipation due to σ_z, τ_{yz} and τ_{xz}, respectively

D_t = total energy dissipation in the laminate = ηW_t

F_z, F_{yz}, F_{xz} = fraction of inter-laminar damping due to σ_z, τ_{yz} and τ_{xz}, respectively

The technique can be applied by either using static loads to stimulate the maximum deformations in a vibrating laminate, or by using the theoretical modal deformations from a dynamic analysis. In order to study the effects of laminate width-to-thickness ratio (i.e. w/t) and fiber orientation on the composite damping, a static finite element analysis was carried out under uniaxial extensions. The strain energy calculation is performed with the use of the associated maximum deformation of a vibrating laminate.

For the case of dynamic analysis, the three-dimensional finite element technique was designed to execute modal analysis in composite structures. Of particular interest are the resulting modal parameters such as frequencies, mode shapes and damping. While frequencies and mode shapes can be obtained from the original SAP IV program, damping was calculated using the strain energy method. The procedure for calculating damping is similar to that used in the static analysis. However, instead of using actual displacement amplitudes for the calculation of strain energy and damping, normalized displacement data obtained from the associated mode shape was used. This is the so called "Modal Strain Energy" method[2].

In order to make the finite element modeling more tractable, the boundary conditions are formulated based on symmetry considerations. A typical finite element gridwork of a four-ply symmetric composite laminate is shown in Figure 1. In the case of extensional vibrations, the boundary conditions along the X-Y plane, which is a plane of symmetry, prevent displacements in the Z direction. Similarly, boundary conditions along the Y-Z plane prevent displacements in the X direction. Poisson contractions in the Y direction are allowed, however.

As with any finite element model, the accuracy of the results is measured by how well the model can represent the actual stress distributions. Therefore, care must be exercised in the selection and modeling of the elements. In this work, three-dimensional eight-node thick shell elements were used. The model was started with a network of large elements, and the element size was reduced to determine the required element size for convergence. Specifically, in order to account for the high stress gradients at laminate free edges and interfaces between two adjacent

603

laminae, refined smaller elements were used in such regions. Resulting stress distributions were compared with previous "benchmark" solutions[5] as an additional check. It should be mentioned that, for comparison with the experimental results, finite element models used here were based on twelve-ply graphite/epoxy composite laminates. The finite element models that were finally selected are shown in Figures 2 and 3. For details of the three-dimensional finite element models, the reader is referred to Reference (10).

3. DESCRIPTION OF EXPERIMENTAL PROCEDURES

All specimens tested were fabricated from twelve plies of Fiberite Hy-E1034C (T300 graphite fibers/934 epoxy resin) prepreg tape. An autoclave-style press cure[7] was employed to produce laminated plates with a thickness of 0.057" (0.145 mm). Symmetric angle-ply laminated beams with a fiber orientation ranging from 0° to 90° were machined from the laminated plates. In order to maintain approximately the same resonant frequency under extensional vibration tests, the specimen length and the attached end masses were adjusted as described in Reference (4). For the case of flexural vibration tests, the specimen length was varied to investigate the effect of frequency on damping.

In the impulse-frequency response vibration technique, the loss factor of the composite specimens is obtained with the half-power bandwidth relationship.

$$\eta = \frac{\Delta f}{f_n} \qquad (3)$$

where

Δf = half-power bandwidth of resonant peak in frequency response curve at resonant frequency f_n.

In this technique, the vibration was induced by using an electromagnetic impulse hammer which has a piezo-electric force transducer in its tip. The specimen response was measured by a piezoelectric accelerometer in the extensional vibration test and by a non-contacting eddy current proximity transducer in the flexural vibration test. For details of the impulse vibration technique, the reader is referred to Reference (4).

The use of extensional vibrations for off-axis specimens eliminates the coupling effect between bending and twisting that would have resulted in flexural vibrations. The flexural vibration technique was only used for unidirectional specimens in order to avoid the coupling effect. In this work, four unidirectional graphite/epoxy laminated beams having dimensions of 8.125" (20.638 mm) long x 0.742" (1.885 mm) wide x 0.057" (0.145 mm) thick, were tested under flexural vibrations. All experimental data was taken from the first mode of vibration and was then compared with the results obtained from the three-dimensional finite element method.

4. RESULTS AND DISCUSSION

Figure 4 shows the predicted contribution of interlaminar damping as a function of fiber orientation for $[\pm\theta]_s$ graphite/epoxy laminates under extensional vibrations. These laminates were modeled with a width-to-thickness ratio of four and a length-to-thickness ratio of six (i.e. w/t=4 and ℓ/t=6) as shown in Figure 1. It appears that the contribution of interlaminar damping increases up to a maximum (i.e. 11%) around 15°, and then decreases with increasing fiber orientation. The effect of off-axis fibers on interlaminar damping is only significant at fiber orientations between approximately 5° and 50° for such laminates. Outside this region, the total energy dissipation of the laminate is dominated by the in-plane energy dissipation.

According to the results shown in Figure 4, the maximum contribution of interlaminar damping was found at a fiber orientation around 15°. For this reason, $[\pm 13/\pm 13/\pm 13]_s$ laminates with various width-to-thickness ratios ranging from 1 to 13 were selected to investigate the effect of w/t on damping in off-axis composite laminates. Due to the difficulty of machining off-axis specimens having low w/t (i.e. delamination and damage occurred during the machining process), only the finite element results are presented.

Figure 5 shows the predicted contribution of interlaminar damping as a function of w/t for $[\pm 13/\pm 13/\pm 13]_s$ graphite/epoxy laminates with a length-to-thickness ratio of 140 as given in Figure 2. The contribution of interlaminar damping increases with decreasing width-to-thickness ratio, and the total amount of this contribution is less than 2%. Recall that for $\ell/t=6$ in Figure 4, the interlaminar contribution to damping was much greater, however. This is due to the fact that the effect of interlaminar stresses on damping is proportional to the relative size of the "boundary layer" near the free edges. The volume of this boundary layer was too small in comparison with the total specimen volume to provide any significant interlaminar damping for the case of $\ell/t=140$. On the whole, it can be concluded that the contribution of interlaminar damping is trivial for long laminates subjected to extensional vibrations, and that short laminates would have greater damping due to a higher contribution of interlaminar damping.

Figure 6 shows the variation of the total loss factor with w/t. Over the range of width-to-thickness ratios investigated here, damping increased with increasing w/t, and a drastic change in damping was found in the low w/t region between 1 and 3.5. This is because the in-plane shear deformation is significantly increased in this region, which in turn resulted in a rapid increase of energy dissipation.

Figure 7 shows the variation of the total loss factor with fiber orientation for $[\pm\theta/\pm\theta/\pm\theta]_s$ laminates under uniaxial extensions. The angle-ply laminates tested were based on w/t = 13 and ℓ/t = 140. Therefore, the contribution of interlaminar damping is negligible as discussed in Figure 5. Generally, there is good agreement between the predicted and measured data. The resulting damping data increases up to a maximum for an optimum fiber orientation at approximately 45°, and then decreases slowly with increasing fiber orientation. This is because the maximum in-plane shear strain energy occurs at this angle.

A partial modal analysis was also carried out with the use of the impulse vibration technique. Only the first flexural mode of unidirectional laminated cantilever beams was analyzed for the purpose of demonstrating the general application of the three-dimensional finite element method in modal analysis. As shown in Figure 8, there is good agreement between the experimental and analytical frequency data, with both results showing that frequency decreases with increasing specimen length.

Figure 9 shows the predicted and measured damping data as functions of frequency for unidirectional laminated cantilever beams. On the whole, not much variation of damping was observed within the frequency range tested (30-130 Hz). This observation confirms previous experimental results on damping over the frequency range 30-1400 Hz[4]. It should be noted that the measured damping is generally higher than the predicted damping. This is probably due to the effects of air damping and delamination produced in the machining process. The air damping increases with increasing vibration amplitude, and larger amplitudes are generated as the beam length increases (at lower frequencies). The effect of air damping could also be the major cause for the large scatter in the experimental measurements.

According to the analysis of the finite element stress results for the cantilever beam, only the through-the-thickness shear stress and the extensional stress (i.e. τ_{xz} and σ_x, respectively) were produced. This was expected, since the unidirectional laminated cantilever beam had no coupling effect. Therefore, only the through-the-thickness shear stress and the extensional stress contributed to the laminate damping.

Subsequent calculations of energy dissipation were carried out to investigate the effect of τ_{xz} on damping. It was found that the energy dissipation due to both τ_{xz} and σ_x increased with increasing frequency. This observation agrees with the expectation from the Timoshenko Beam Theory[11] that the shear effect becomes significant at high frequency.

The contribution of through-the-thickness shear stress to the overall laminate damping property is calculated according to Eqn. (2). As indicated before, the energy dissipation due to both τ_{xz} and σ_x increased with increasing frequency. However, since the rate of increase of energy dissipation due to σ_x was much higher than that due to τ_{xz}, the contribution of τ_{xz} to damping was reduced with increasing frequency. As shown in Figure 10, within the frequency range tested, the contribution of τ_{xz} to damping decreases with increasing frequency.

5. CONCLUDING REMARKS

A three-dimensional finite element technique has been developed for the characterization of damping in composite laminates. Subsequent comparisons between experimental results and predictions from the three-dimensional finite element method showed reasonable agreement.

A rapid increase in damping was found in the low w/t region (i.e. transition between rectangular cross sections and square cross sections) for off-axis laminates under extensional vibrations. In addition, an optimal fiber orientation at approximately 45° for maximum damping in off-axis graphite/epoxy composite laminates was found.

The contribution of interlaminar damping is negligible in long angle-ply laminates under extensional vibrations, and such contribution is only important in short angle-ply laminates. However, for the case of unidirectional graphite/epoxy laminates under flexural vibrations, the interlaminar damping contributed significantly to the overall laminate damping (i.e. up to 22% for the cases investigated).

According to the finite element modal analysis, the through-the-thickness shear energy dissipation increased with increasing frequency. In contrast, the ratio of through-the-thickness shear damping to total damping decreased with increasing frequency.

Throughout this research, the three-dimensional finite element implementation of the strain energy method has proven to be a powerful technique for full three-dimensional characterization of composites which can be applied to complex damped structures and loading situations. The impulse vibration technique appears to be a fast, reliable and accurate tool for non-destructive determination of damping of composite materials.

6. ACKNOWLEDGEMENTS

The authors gratefully acknowledge the donations of computers and instrumentation by the Hewlett-Packard Company. We are also indebted to Raju Mantena and Darrel Brown for their assistance in the experiments, and to Valerie Smith for careful typing of the manuscript.

7. REFERENCES

1. Gibson, R.F., The Shock and Vibration Digest 19 (7), pp 13-22 (July 1987).

2. Johnson, C.D. and Kienholz, D.A, AIAA Journal 20 (9), pp 954-957 (Sept. 1982).

3. Hwang, S.J. and Gibson, R.F., J. Engineering Materials and Tech. 109, pp 47-52 (Jan. 1987).

4. Suarez, S.A. and Gibson, R.F., J. Testing and Evaluation 15 (2), pp 114-121 (March 1987).

5. Pipes, R.B. and Pagano, N.J., J. Composite Materials 4, pp 538-548 (Oct. 1970).

6. Ungar, E.E. and Kerwin Jr., E.M., J. Acoustical Soc. of America 34 (7), pp 954-958 (July 1962).

7. Gibson, R.F., et al, J. Composites Tech. and Research 7 (2), pp 49-54 (Summer 1985).

8. Bathe, K.J., et al, SAP IV a Structural Analysis Program for Static and Dynamic Response of Linear Systems, College of Engineering, University of California, Berkeley, CA (April 1974).

9. Suarez, S.A., et al, Experimental Mechanics 26 (2), pp 175-184 (June 1986).

10. Hwang, S.J., Characterization of The Effects of Three-Dimensional States of Stress on Damping of Laminated Composites, Ph.D. Dissertation, University of Idaho (July 1988).

11. Thomson, W.T., Theory of Vibration with Application, Second Ed., Prentice-Hall, Inc. (1981).

8. BIOGRAPHIES

Ronald F. Gibson received a BSME from the University of Florida in 1965, a MSME from the University of Tennessee in 1971, and a PhD in Mechanics from the University of Minnesota in 1975. He has experience with the Nuclear Division of Union Carbide, NASA Langley Research Center, Iowa State University, University of Florida, University of Idaho and Michigan State University. He is currently a Professor of Mechanical Engineering at the University of Idaho, where he teaches courses in applied mechanics and materials, and conducts research on the dynamic behavior of composite materials.

Shwilong J. Hwang received a BS in Aeronautical Engineering from Tamkang University, Taiwan, in 1980. He received a MSME in 1985 and a PhD in 1988 from the University of Idaho. He is currently a Post-Doctoral Research Assistant in Mechanical Engineering at the University of Idaho, where he is doing research in the areas of analytical and experimental characterization of dynamic mechanical behavior of composite materials.

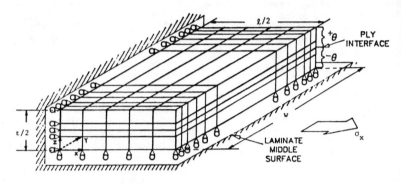

Note: w/t = 4
ℓ/t = 6

Figure 1.   Finite element model for four-ply symmetric composite laminates under uniaxial loading (quarter domain only).

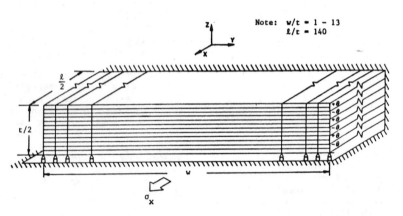

Note: w/t = 1 – 13
ℓ/t = 140

Figure 2.   Finite element gridwork for a typical cross section of twelve-ply symmetric composite laminates under uniaxial loading.

Note: w/t = 13

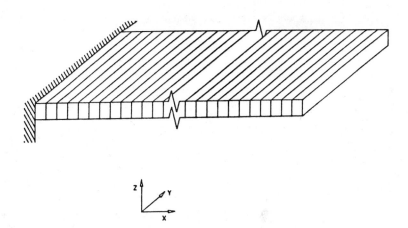

Figure 3. Finite element model for the first mode of unidirectional composite laminated cantilever beam.

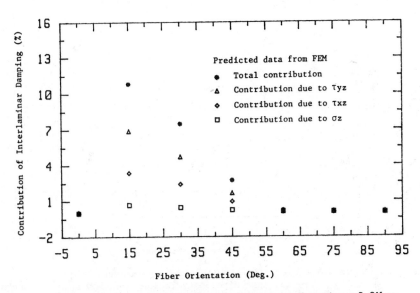

Figure 4. Contribution of interlaminar damping as a function of fiber orientation for $[\pm \theta]_s$ graphite/epoxy laminates (with w = 4t) under uniaxial loading.

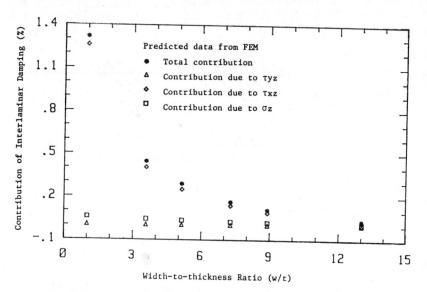

Figure 5. Contribution of interlaminar damping as a function of width-to-thickness ratio for $[\pm\,13/\pm\,13/\pm\,13]_s$ graphite/epoxy laminates under uniaxial loading.

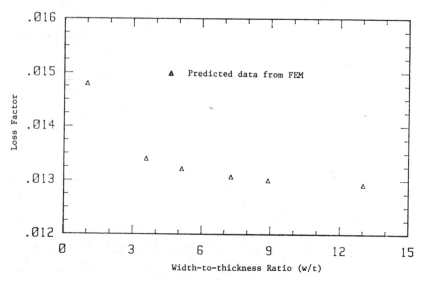

Figure 6. Variation of loss factor with width-to-thickness ratio for $[\pm\,13/\pm\,13/\pm\,13]_s$ graphite/epoxy laminates under uniaxial loading.

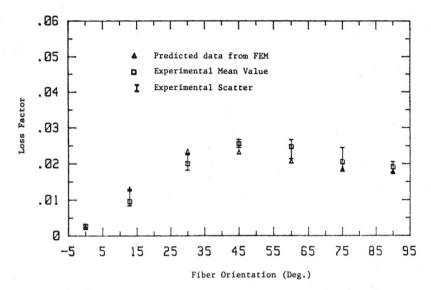

Figure 7. Variation of loss factor with fiber orientation for $[\pm\ \theta/\pm\ \theta/\pm\ \theta]_s$ graphite/epoxy laminates under uniaxial loading.

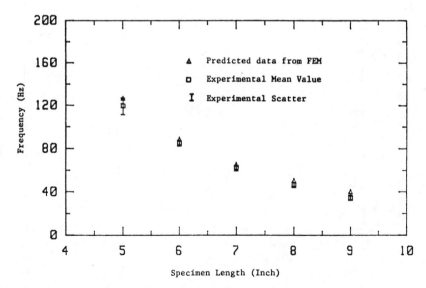

Figure 8. Variation of resonant frequency of the first mode with specimen length for unidirectional graphite/epoxy laminated cantilever beams.

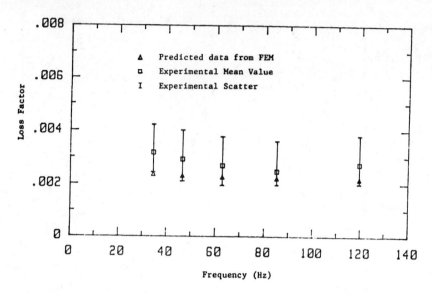

Figure 9.   Variation of loss factor with frequency for unidirectional
graphite/epoxy laminated cantilever beams.

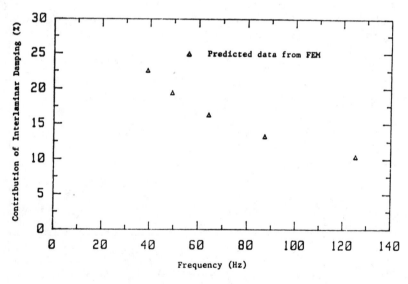

Figure 10.   Variation of damping contribution of τ_{xz} with frequency for
unidirectional graphite/epoxy laminated cantilever beams.

ADHESIVE BOND STRENGTH AND DURABILITY STUDIES
USING THREE DIFFERENT ENGINEERING PLASTICS
AND VARIOUS SURFACE PREPARATIONS
John Osterndorf
Roberta Rosty
Michael J. Bodnar

Abstract

Studies of adhesive bonding strength and durability were conducted on three types of engineering plastics. The three substances used were a modified polyethylene oxide (NORYL) , an aromatic polyester liquid crystal polymer (VECTRA) , and a poly(amide-imide) polymer (TORLON) . Specimens of these materials were surface treated using physical, chemical and gas plasma methods prior to adhesive bonding. The adhesives used were two high-temperature curing epoxy adhesives as well as a one-part room temperature setting amide-imide adhesive. The bonded specimens were tested for lap-shear tensile strength after bonding and after increasing periods of exposure to a high temperature and humidity environment. Test results indicate that strong durable bonds are obtained with the proper combination of substrate, surface preparation and adhesive. The surfaces of these substrate materials were examined with the scanning electron microscope to establish how the surface morphology was affected by the various treatments.

aromatic polyester liquid crystal plastic; and Torlon, a poly (amide-imide) plastic are used, or being considered for use, in military items. A preliminary study (ref. 1) was made of various methods of adhesive bonding the Noryl and Vectra plastics. The study consisted of the testing of various surface preparations and adhesive types on two different grades of Noryl plastic and various surface preparations on eight different grades of Vectra.

The surface treatments which yielded the best results in the preliminary studies of the adhesive bonding of Vectra and Noryl were then tested for their durability to high temperature and high humidity conditions. Since the Torlon plastic was admitted late into this program, the preliminary testing portion of this plastic was omitted and five different surface treatments with one adhesive type were subjected directly to the durability testing portion.

1. INTRODUCTION

Noryl, a modified polyethylene oxide plastic; Vectra, an

2. DISCUSSION

2.1 Durability Studies

Vectra

The A230 grade of Vectra studied was a composite containing 30% carbon fiber reinforcements. Abrasion and chemical etching are known to enhance Vectra's adhesive bonding strength (ref. 2). Two surface treatments were analyzed for durability in a hot, humid environment. The first surface treatment was an abrasion procedure and the second treatment used the same abrasion procedure followed by a chemical etching procedure.

A two-part epoxy adhesive (Fusor 310 A/B) was tested with two different surface preparations because reference 2 showed that a two-part epoxy resulted in the best lap-shear strength results on a treated Vectra surface at room temperature.

The specimens treated with the same surface treatment number (1 or 2) were bonded on the same day. Surface treatment 1 was a solvent wipe/abrasion/ solvent wipe procedure, and surface treatment 2 was a solvent wipe/abrasion/etch/ rinse/oven dry procedure; the details on these surface preparation procedures can be found in reference 3. Three of the specimens for each surface treatment were lap-shear tested at room temperature, without any adverse environmental exposure, as controls. The remaining specimens were placed into a 145+5 degrees F environmental chamber with 100% relative humidity. Three specimens from each surface preparation batch were taken out of the environmental chamber after 672; 1,007; and 1,512 hours of exposure time, and then conditioned prior to lap-shear testing at room temperature.

A curve showing the results has been drawn in figure 1. As indicated in this figure, both surface treatments resulted in similar lap-shear strengths versus time in the environmental chamber. With both surface treatments, the primary mode of failure of the control specimens was cohesive within the Vectra material itself. After humidity exposure, the primary mode of failure changed to adhesive failure, which indicated a general weakening of the adhesive bond.

Torlon

Torlon is a poly(amide-imide) polymer manufactured by Amoco Chemical Company. The A4203, an extrusion grade of this polymer containing 3% titanium dioxide, was used in this study because it was a high strength grade and did not contain any fluorocarbon (all other grades did). Fluorocarbons greatly hinder adhesion and would complicate the primary objective of studying the bondability of the poly(amide-imide) material itself (ref 4).

One of the adverse properties of Torlon is its tendency to absorb moisture, therefore it must be dried prior to bonding. It absorbs as much as 2.5% of its weight in water at room temperature and 50% relative humidity. As much as 4% of its weight can be absorbed at higher temperatures and relative humidities. According to Amoco Chemical Company's recommendations, Torlon parts under 1/4-inch thick should be dried for at least 24 hours at 300 degrees F in a dessicating oven.

The surface preparations recommended by Amoco Chemical Company for the adhesive bonding of Torlon involved either an abrasion procedure with a solvent wipe or a gas plasma treatment. Based on its testing program on bonding, Torlon (which included seven general types of adhesives and 36 commercial adhesives) (ref 5), Amoco recommends its amide-imide-based adhesive (AI335) with 40% supercured fines of Amoco 4000TF polyamide-imide resin (ref 4).

One of the two surface treatments investigated in the durability testing in this study was a solvent wipe/abrasion/solvent wipe procedure. The other surface treatment involved abrasion followed by chemical etching. (The adhesive bond strength results from a plasma treatment of the Torlon plastic will be covered separately in the gas plasma section.)

The specimens treated with the same surface treatment number (6 or 7) were bonded on the same day. Surface treatment 6 was an oven dry/solvent wipe/abrasion/solvent wipe procedure and surface treatment 7 was an oven dry/solvent wipe/abrasion/dry/etch/rinse/scrub/rinse/oven dry procedure. Four or five of the specimens for each surface treatment were lap-shear tested at room temperature as controls. The remaining specimens were placed into a 145+5 degrees F environmental chamber with 98% relative humidity. Five specimens from each surface preparation batch were removed from the chamber after 690; 1,672; 2,993; and 3,497 hours of exposure time and lap-shear tested at room temperature after 4 hours of conditioning.

Figure 2 shows that both surface treatments 6 and 7 yield similar initial average lap-shear strengths, as well as similar lap-shear strengths after 3,500 hours in the high temperature/humidity cabinet.

The mode of adhesive joint failure was primarily cohesive failure of the Torlon substrate (when using either surface treatments 6 or 7) from 0 to 3,500 hours of exposure in the high temperature/humidity cabinet. In most cases, the amide-imide adhesive was tougher than the Torlon material itself.

The two surface treatments could not be distinguished from this testing, because both sets of specimens exceeded normal testing times. The AI335 adhesive is exceptionally durable because of its chemical makeup and the high temperature cure cycle used, which included 24 hours at 106 degrees F, 24 hours at 300 degrees F, and 2 hours at 400 degrees F.

The differences in the curves in figure 2 are due to variances in the way the Torlon failed cohesively, i.e., cohesive failure through the thickness of the Torlon or failure of the top layer of Torlon in the bond area, as opposed to differences in adhesive bond strength from different surface treatments. The cohesive strength of the Torlon substrate was definitely the limiting strength factor with the surface treatment/ adhesive variations tested.

Noryl

Noryl is a polyphenylene oxide polymer. An extrudable black grade of Noryl (EN265-701) was studied and two surface treatments were examined. Solvent cementing, as a method of bonding Noryl, was also evaluated. These systems were evaluated for durability in a hot, humid environment.

The first surface treatment evaluated was merely a surface wipe using a solvent. The second was a solvent wipe/ abrasion/rinse/oven dry procedure. The epoxy adhesive used with each was Scotchweld 2216 B/A.

The specimens treated with the same surface treatment designation (11-solvent wipe or 12-solvent wipe/abrasion/ rinse/oven dry) were bonded on the same day. Four to six specimens, surface treated and bonded exactly the same way, were lap-shear tested at room temperature as controls for each test. The remaining specimens were placed in a 145+5 degrees F environmental chamber with 98% relative humidity. For each test, six specimens surface treated and bonded exactly the same way were taken out of the humidity chamber after 94; 508; 1,540; 2,524; and 4,348 hours of exposure time, and lap-shear tested at room temperature after conditioning (fig. 3).

Some Noryl specimens were solvent cemented after a surface preparation procedure of solvent degreasing/hand abrading/solvent degreasing. The solvent-cementing was achieved with the use of cyclohexanone. Caution should be observed with the use of this solvent due to its harmful vapor (ref 6).

Six of the specimens were lap-shear tested at room temperature as controls. The remaining specimens were placed into a 145+5 degrees F environmental chamber with 98% relative humidity. Six specimens were removed from the chamber after 94; 508; 1,540; 2,524; and 4,348 hours of exposure time and lap-shear tested at room temperature after conditioning. Results of this durability study are also drawn in figure 3.

Surface treatment 12/Scotchweld 2216 B/A adhesive combination had the best initial average lap-shear strengths (fig. 3). After 4,348 hours of high temperature/humidity exposure, the surface treatment 11/Scotchweld 2216 B/A adhesive combination was by far the better system, with a 410 psi (residual lap-shear strength as opposed to residual strengths of 240 to 270 psi) with the systems tested.

This result is surprising since surface treatment 11 was merely a solvent-wipe treatment as opposed to surface treatment 12, which involved abrasion.

The grade of Noryl used for this testing was EN265-701 which was black in color and flame retardant. This grade of Noryl probably contains carbon as a filler, which accounts for the color, and a fluoride compound, which accounts for its flame retardancy. Abrasion was probably a worse surface treatment than solvent-wiping due to the exposure of more fluoride or carbon from the bulk of the material. Both carbon and fluoride are detrimental to good adhesive bonds. Normally, abrasion results in higher bond strengths than solvent-wiping due to a better mechanical interlocking of the adhesive with the roughened surface, but the above explanation would account for the poorer results from abrasion as opposed to solvent-wiping.

The surface treatment 13 (solvent wipe/abrasion/solvent wipe)/solvent cement system had a failure graph line which paralleled that of the surface treatment 12/Scotchweld adhesive failure graph line after about 500 hours in the humidity chamber (fig. 3). The curves declined in lap-shear strength at about the same rate versus time in the humidity chamber, with the solvent cemented system always having slightly lower lap-shear strengths.

The solvent cemented system had the worst lap-shear strength results from durability testing in a hot, humid environment. It also had the worst results in the initial control tests. This might have been caused by the type of solvent used, which was cyclohexanone. The cyclohexanone did not completely dissolve the plastic Noryl or evaporate from the bond area after the Noryl pieces were solvent cemented together. A slight amount of solvent remained in the middle of the bond and was slow to diffuse out of the bonded area. The outer edges of the cemented area dried first and trapped a small quantity of the solvent within the joint.

This was evidenced by a cyclohexanone aroma when conducting lap-shear testing on the solvent cemented joint. During the solvent cementing procedure, only one drop of cyclohexanone had been placed on each bonding surface, so the amount of solvent in the bond was not really excessive. The solvent in the center of the bond could not evaporate because the edges of the bond had cemented shut when the solvent at the edges had evaporated. Therefore, the solvent in the center of the bond remained there, causing an inherent weakness in the bond. This problem must be addressed when considering solvent cementing as opposed to the adhesive bonding of plastics in actual applications, especially where large bond areas are concerned.

The solvent cemented bonds were slightly worse than the surface treatment 12/Scotchweld 2216 B/A adhesive combination after 4,000 hours of adverse environmental exposure. In both tests the surfaces had been abraded prior to bonding.

2.2 Gas Plasma Treatment

A gas plasma surface treatment was described (refs. 2 and 5) as a possible way to prepare Vectra and Torlon for adhesive bonding. This treatment was, therefore, attempted on all three plastics being studied (Vectra, Torlon, and Noryl).

Gas plasma is a good surface preparation for the adhesive bonding of plastics because it involves no solvents, chemical fumes, disposal problems, or heat, which could harm the plastic surface. The plasma reacts to a depth of 100 to 1,000 angstroms (ref 7).

Five sets of specimens of Vectra, Torlon, and Noryl were acetone-degreased, gas plasma treated, and adhesive bonded as quickly as possible after they reached ARDEC. The remaining specimens were saved for future scanning electron microscopic (SEM) work.

The room temperature lap-shear strengths resulting from the various gas plasma treatments for Vectra, Torlon, and Noryl are charted in figure 4. One type of gas did not have overall superior results with all three plastics. It was found that the argon treatment was best on Vectra; the oxygen treatment on Torlon; and the ammonia treatment on Noryl.

2.3 Scanning Electron Microscope
   (SEM) Studies

Vectra

Vectra A230 is a liquid crystal polymer (LCP) with 30% carbon reinforcement. Liquid crystal polymers have highly ordered fibrous structures. During flow, before solidification, the LCP molecules align in a highly ordered parallel fashion analogous to a stack of pencils (ref 8).

A SEM photo of the control (acetone-degreased) Vectra A230 surface magnified 260 times (fig. 5) is compared to a photo of an acetone-degreased Vectra A230 surface magnified 210 times that was subsequently gas plasma etched using argon gas for 7 minutes at 200 watts (fig. 6). The molecular structure in figure 6 is not aligned parallel as in figure 5 and also shows deeper pitting of the surface. The nonpitted areas on the specimen surface appear to be smoother after gas plasma treatment.

An explanation of the different topography in figures 5 and 6 may be that gas plasma etching is taking the top layer off the surface to reveal random carbon fibers amid the highly oriented LCP.

If gas plasma etching exposed carbon fibers, the process would be detrimental to adhesive bonding. Carbon has a smooth, slippery surface that is difficult to bond. The adverse effect on adhesive bond strengths due to carbon fiber exposure would greatly outweigh the beneficial effect of surface cleaning and pitting from the gas plasma treatment.

A 260 times magnified SEM photo of the Vectra A230 control surface that was acetone degreased (fig. 7), is compared to a 260 times magnified photo of the same surface after it was acetone degreased and gas plasma-treated using oxygen gas for 7 minutes at 200 watts (fig. 8). The gas plasma treatment again appears to etch away part of the surface. The evidence for this is the smooth area between pits in figure 8 as compared to figure 7. Also, the surface in figure 8 shows more fibers and more extensive and deeper pitting than figure 7 at the same magnification.

The gas plasma-treated Vectra specimens resulted in lap-shear strengths from 970 to 1,120 psi, whereas Vectra, treated with surface treatment numbers 1 (solvent wipe/abrasion/solvent wipe) and 2 (solvent wipe/abrasion/etch/rinse/oven dry) were much higher before high temperature/humidity testing (1,950 to 2,040 psi).

3. CONCLUSIONS

1. Test results indicate that strong, durable bonds are obtainable with the proper combination of substrate (Noryl, Vectra, or Torlon) surface preparation and adhesive.

2. The type of gas used when gas plasma treating plastic surfaces for adhesive bonding purposes affects lap-shear strength results. Ammonia was best with Noryl plastic; Argon gas was best with Vectra plastic; and Oxygen gas was best with Torlon plastic.

3. From scanning electron microscopic analysis, the argon and oxygen gas plasma treatments appear to etch away the top surface layers of the Vectra plastic.

4. REFERENCES

1. Rosty, R., Devine, A.T., Bodnar, M.J., "Preliminary Adhesive Bonding Studies of Vectra and Noryl Plastics," Technical Report ARAED-TR-87008, ARDEC, Picatinny Arsenal, NJ, March 1987.

2. "Adhesive Bonding of Vectra Liquid Crystal Polymers," Letter number RCH-36-49, Celanese Corp., October 7, 1986.

3. Rosty, R., Devine, A.T., Bodnar, M.J., "Durability Testing of Various Surface Preparations and Adhesives for Bonding Vectra®, Torlon®, and Noryl® Plastics," Technical Report ARAED-TR-88004, ARDEC, Picatinny Arsenal, NJ, May 1988.

4. "Torlon Engineering Polymers/ Design Manual," Bulletin TAT-35A, Amoco Chemicals Co., Chicago, IL.

5. "Adhesive Bonding of Torlon Parts," Bulletin TAT-36A, Amoco Chemicals Co., Chicago IL.

6. Windholz, Martha (editor), "The Merck Index, " 9th Edition, Merck & Co., Inc., Rahway, NJ, 1976.

7. Rose, P.W., Liston, E.M., "Treating Plastic Surfaces with Cold Gas Plasmas," Plastics Engineering, pp 41-45, October 1985.

8. Jaarsma, F.C., "Status of Fasteners of Vectra Liquid Crystal Polymer for Carbon Fiber Reinforced Panels," Proceedings of the 32nd International SAMPE Symposium, Vol. 32, pp 185-194, April 1987.

BIOGRAPHIES

John F. Osterndorf is a materials engineer with the Adhesives Section of the Organic Materials Branch at ARDEC. He is active in a number of adhesive bonding programs involving munitions items at ARDEC. Mr. Osterndorf has served on the AED Environmental Committee for over two years. He has been employed at ARDEC for the past 10 years. He holds a Chemical Engineering Degree from Manhattan College. Mr. Osterndorf is a Past Chairman of the New Jersey Chapter of SAMPE and is a member of the AIChE and ASM.

Roberta Rosty has been a materials engineer in the Adhesives Section of the Organic Materials Branch at ARDEC for eight and a half years. During those years she has worked on the durability of surface preparations for various metallic, plastic, elastomeric, and composite materials. She received her BS and MS degrees in chemical engineering at New Jersey Institute of Technology and is a member of SAMPE.

Michael J. Bodnar is Chief of the Adhesives Section, Organic Materials Branch, at ARDEC. He is a graduate of Carnegie Tech and has been in materials engineering on adhesives since 1951 when he first joined Douglas Aircraft Company. He has published widely in the field and is editor of four books on structural adhesives bonding.

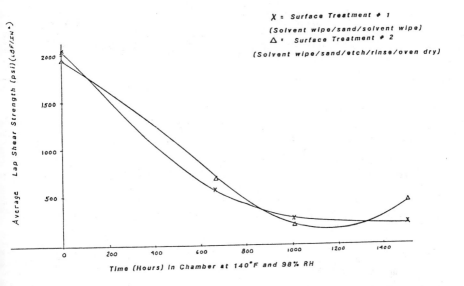

Figure 1   Room temperature lap-shear strengths of bonded Vectra specimens (surface treated and exposed to adverse conditions)

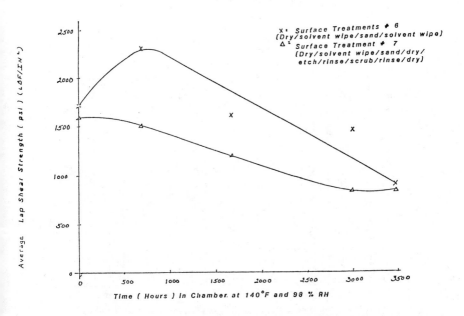

Figure 2   Room temperature lap-shear strengths of bonded Torlon specimens exposed to high temperature and humidity.

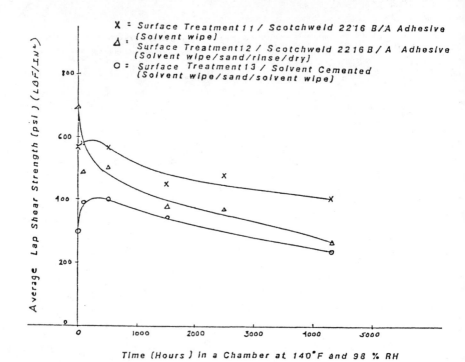

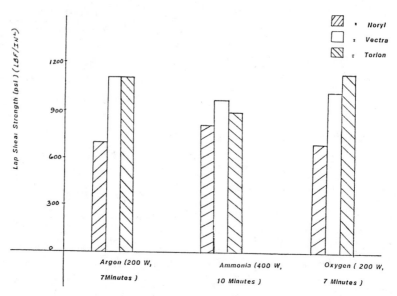

Figure 3   Room temperature lap-shear strengths of bonded Noryl specimens
(exposed to high temperature and humidity)

Figure 4   Room temperature lap-shear strengths of adhesive bonded Vectra,
Torlon, and Noryl specimens, gas plasma-treated prior to bonding.

Figure 5   A SEM photo of an acetone degreased Vectra A230 control surface
(mag 260x)

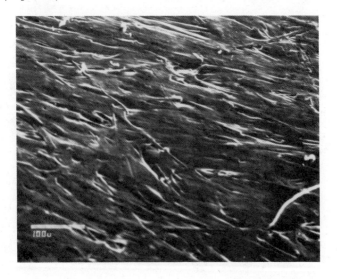

Figure 6   A SEM photo of an acetone degreased, gas plasma treated (with
argon) Vectra A230 surface (mag. 210x)

Figure 7   A SEM photo of an acetone degreased Vectra A230 control surface (mag. 260x)

Figure 8   A SEM photo of an acetone degreased, gas plasma treated (with oxygen) Vectra A230 surface (mag. 260x)

HIGH PERFORMANCE EPOXY ADHESIVES

Dean T. Behm

CIBA-GEIGY Corporation
Madison Heights, Michigan

Ed Clark

CIBA-GEIGY Corporation
Furane Aerospace Products
Los Angeles, California

Abstract

The Aerospace Industry has for many years, relied on room temperature curing epoxy adhesives as a primary construction material in the assembly of aircraft. These adhesives are used in metal to metal bonding, core splicing, and liquid shim applications. Traditionally, these adhesives have suffered from poor shelf life, low peel strengths, and have required special safety handling procedures. After a review of industry needs and an analysis of current product deficiencies, it was decided that a research program would be initiated to develop epoxy chemistries suitable to meet current and future Aerospace requirements. The initial results of this work have been the development of two epoxy adhesives based on a new family of epoxy resins and hardeners.

1. INTRODUCTION

Assembly techniques and repair procedures require that a significant portion of the adhesives used in manufacturing aircraft, be room temperature curing. These adhesives are generally based on epoxy resin chemistry due to their excellent environmental resistance and ability to achieve high temperature performance without a heat cure. In order to achieve high levels of performance without heating, it has traditionally been accepted that these adhesives have poor shelf life, low peel strength and require special safety handling procedures. Additionally, due to limited focus, these materials have never benefitted from packaging and application design. Because of these deficiencies and the ever continuing demand for better products, a new class of epoxy adhesives have been developed.

2. EXPERIMENTAL

Either bare or clad (0.063") aluminum 2024-T3 alloy was used as substrate for mechanical tests, other than T-peels. All aluminum was etched as per ASTM D2651, method A (chromic acid). All samples were cured at 77°F for 7 days prior to testing, and lap shear specimens were tested according to ASTM D1002. Bondline thickness was maintained at 0.004-0.005". In most exposure tests, Federal Specification MMM-A-132A procedures were followed. Testing temperatures for lap shears were also done in accordance with the above specification.

3. RESULTS AND DISCUSSION

Our goals for this project were the following:

1) To develop a flexible, yet thermally resistant adhesive with high peel strength and ability to bond a variety of substrates.

2) A toughened room temperature curing system with convenient mix ratios, which maintains good mechanical strength over a wide temperature range.

In addition, the resins and hardeners should possess a shelf life of 1 year at room temperature.

Up until the present, epoxy adhesive formulators have relied heavily on epoxy resins based upon bisphenol A chemistry. While adhesives of this resin class demonstrate good mechanical strengths after a heat cure, their performance after an ambient cure is limited. However, because of the development of new chemistries in both resins and hardeners, we have been able to minimize this problem. Ambient temperature curing of adhesives with excellent mechanical strengths are now obtainable. In addition, the stability of the resin systems has been greatly increased.

The first product developed from this new

TABLE 1

PHYSICAL PROPERTIES —— LMH 263-29

Color	Resin	White
	Hardener	Grey
	Mixed	Grey
Mix Ratio		100/230 pbw
		100/275 pbv
Viscosity (Brookfield RVF; 75°F)		
	Resin, Spindle #5 at 2RPM	107,000 cps
	Hardener	Paste
	Mixed, Spindle #7 at 4RPM	310,000 cps
Gel Time (100g Mass, 75°F)		75 min.
Tensile Strength (ASTM D638); 7 Days/ 77°F		2650 psi
Elongation at Break		Approx. 50%
Cure Schedule		7 Days/ 77°F or 1.5 hr/ 190°F

chemistry is a highly toughened epoxy adhesive, L M H 2 6 3 - 2 9. The physical properties of this adhesive are listed in Table 1. The flexibility of this adhesive is apparent from both the elongation and T-peel strength listed in Table 2. The exceptionally high lap shear strength at -67°F makes this adhesive well suited for applications with subambient temperatures. This adhesive, as well as the following adhesive, can be effectively cured either at room temperature or at 190°F for 1.5 hours.

L M H 2 6 3 - 2 9 is designed to bond substrates where significantly different thermal expansion coefficients exist or where flexible materials are to be bonded. Because of its high level of toughness, L M H 2 6 3 - 2 9 would be an excellent adhesive for high vibrational areas or where thermal cycling is encountered. With a mix ratio of 100/230 (pbw), it has a high level of mix ratio insensitivity (100/200 to 100/250).

L M H 2 6 2 - 4 8 is a toughened, epoxy adhesive suitable for a variety of aero-space applications. Physical properties for L M H 2 6 2 - 4 8 are listed in Table 3. Perhaps the most important and useful handling property of this adhesive is its 1:1 mix ratio, by volume. This allows for the adhesive to be easily dispensed from Accumix® or Supermix® cartridges.

The resin component shows no increase in viscosity after aging 4 weeks at 54°C, and the hardener viscosity increased slightly to 162,500 cps after this same aging period. The high elongation of this adhesive (11%) is significant, because typical epoxy adhesives only possess elongations of 1-2%.

While maintaining this high degree of elongation, L M H 2 6 2 - 4 8 demonstrates excellent mechanical properties as shown in Table 4. One of the most attractive properties of this adhesive is its excellent retention of lap shear strength over a wide temperature range. The lap shear strengths on aluminum are not dependent on either the clad or bare alloys. The elongation of this adhesive is also reflected in the T-peel strength.

TABLE 2

MECHANICAL PROPERTIES——L M H 2 6 3- 2 9

Temperature	Lap Shear Strength
-67°F	6210 psi
77°F	3340 psi
180°F	1140 psi

Bare 2024-T3 aluminum alloy; Chromic acid etch (ASTM D2651, Method A. Lap shears tested as per ASTM D1002.

    T-Peel (77°F; ASTM D1876, 0.010" bondline)   26 pli

Bare 2024-T3 aluminum (0.032") alloy; Chromic acid etch (ASTM D2651, Method A.

TABLE 3

PHYSICAL PROPERTIES —— L M H 2 6 2 - 4 8

Color	Resin	Grey
	Hardener	Clear Yellow
	Mixed	Grey

| Mix Ratio | | 100/70 pbw |
| | | 100/100 pbv |

Viscosity (Brookfield RVF; 75°F)

	Resin, Spindle #6 at 4RPM	91,250 cps
	Hardener, "	102,500 cps
	Mixed, "	53,750 cps

Gel Time (100g Mass, 75°F)	55 min.
Tensile Strength (ASTM D638); 7 Days/ 77°F	4634 psi
Elongation at Break	11%
Tensile Modulus	212,000 psi
Cure Schedule	7 Days/ 77°F or 1.5 hr/ 190°F

Besides bonding aluminum, epoxies are also being used to bond high performance thermoplastics. Ryton R-5 and Ultem 1000 are examples presented in Table 4, and in both cases, the substrate breaks prior to adhesive failure. Fatigue, environmental exposures, and thermal aging are shown in Table 5. Good

TABLE 4

MECHANICAL PROPERTIES—— L M H 2 6 2 - 4 8

| Aluminum Bonding Temperature | Lap Shear Strength | |
	Bare	Clad
-67°F	3520 psi	3330 psi
77°F	4310 psi	4340 psi
180°F	2570 psi	2580 psi

ASTM D1002; Aluminum etched per ASTM D2651, Method A.

T-Peel (77°F; ASTM D1876, 0.010" bondline)   7 pli

Thermoplastic Bonding Substrate	Lap Shear Strength
Ultem 1000	1370 psi (SF)
Ryton R-5	522 psi (SF)

Cured 190°F/ 1.5 hr. Ultem-Dry wipe only before applying adhesive. Ryton R-5-Chromic acid etched before applying adhesive. 0.020" bondline, 1.0" overlap. SF= Substrate Failure.

TABLE 5

DURABILITY TESTING OF L M H 2 6 2 - 4 8

Fatigue (ASTM D3166)
    750 psi at 1×10^6 cycles, 3600 cpm   Pass

Fluid Immersion	Lap Shear Strength
JP-4 (7 Days/ 75°F)	4946 psi
Hydraulic Oil (7 Days/ 75°F)	4742 psi
Humidity Exposure	
7 Days/ 100°F at >96% RH	4000 psi
Thermal Aging	
7 Days/ 180°F	4750 psi
7 Days/ 250°F	4110 psi

Bare 2024-T3 aluminum alloy, etched as per ASTM D2651, Method A. Testing at 75°F.

resistance to fluid immersions and humidity has been demonstrated. After thermal aging, little or no drop off in properties are seen.

L M H 2 6 2 - 4 8 was formulated to achieve higher temperature performance than L M H 2 6 3 - 2 9. This adhesive can be used in metal to metal bonding such as ribs to aircraft skins, liquid shim applications where large adhesive bondline thicknesses are common, and in core splicing situations. With improved peel strength and toughness, this material can be considered for applications where current materials fail due to embrittlement and inflexibility. Along with improvements in mechanical properties, this adhesive has been designed to take advantage of new packaging capabilities.

With a 1:1 mix ratio, by volume, L M H 2 6 2 - 48 has been designed for meter mixing applications and convenient hand held mix and dispense units. The hand held mix and dispense unit, a double barrel syringe with a static mix head is ideal for use both in OEM and field applications. This type of dispensing unit has several advantages over traditional packaging as shown in the following:

- Always dispenses the correct mix ratio.
- Mixes and dispenses only what is needed, minimizes waste.
- No contamination from reuse of same container.
- Safe to handle, no direct contact with materials.
- Safe disposal, only disposable material is catalyzed.
- Labor saving, package premeasures and mixes adhesive.
- Material and package storable at 77°F for 1 year.

4. CONCLUSIONS

While we are continuing to study the durability of L M H 2 6 3 - 2 9 and

LMH 262-48, their applicability as room temperature curing, high performance adhesives has been well demonstrated. They combine to provide the first in a series of high performance adhesives that have superior shelf stability, improved toughness, ease of handling, and require no special safety handling procedures. Through the use of current packaging technology, adhesives such as LMH 262-48 can be used in a safe, repeatable, and economical fashion. By thorough evaluation of customer needs and a commitment to technical advancement, LMH 262-29 and LMH 262-48 evolved to meet today's Aerospace adhesive needs.

5. ACKNOWLEDGEMENTS

The authors wish to thank the efforts of a number of people, among them Tom LaBelle, Greg Ferguson, Al Rademaker, and Jose Salazar.

6. BIOGRAPHY

Dean T. Behm; B.S. in Chemistry (1980), University of Michigan; Ph.D. (1985), University of Massachusetts. He joined CIBA-GEIGY in 1987 and has been involved in developing adhesives for General Industrial and Aerospace applications. Prior to joining CIBA-GEIGY as a Senior Chemist, he held the same position with Union Carbide involved in silicone chemistry research.

Edwin C. Clark; B.S. Chemistry (1979), MBA-Marketing (1985), University of Akron. Work experience has been in the areas of adhesive, coatings and composite research and development. He joined Furane Products Company in 1986 as a Technical Service Supervisor-Aerospace Products. Current responsibilities inclu research, development, and customer relations for Aerospace adhesives, synta tics, and laminating products.

DEVELOPMENT OF A 180°F HOT/WET SERVICE TEMPERATURE PASTE ADHESIVE FOR COMPOSITE FABRICATION

Bill Nickolson
Dexter Adhesives & Structural Materials Division
The Dexter Corporation
Pittsburg, California

ABSTRACT

Many 250°F curing adhesives initially give excellent properties at temperatures ranging from -67°F to 250°F. Very few maintain performance properties at 180°F after exposure to a hot/wet environment. The increased use of composite materials in the aerospace industry has created a need for toughened adhesives that can adequately perform under hot/wet conditions. In many instances, adhesives formulated for metal bonding have been used for composite assembly with poor results due to rheology and moisture absorption in the composite substrate.

This paper discusses the effects of moisture in a bonded joint and the research effort that led to the development of a high strength adhesive with excellent hot/wet characteristics. Mechanical properties will be reviewed along with possible applications.

1. INTRODUCTION

The increased use of composite structures to achieve weight savings in the aircraft industry has prompted formulators to take a closer look at factors that influence durability. Composite structures pose additional challenges due to the high moisture content at equilibrium. It has been shown that aluminum substrates may be stabilized against moisture by the FPL etch followed by phosphoric acid anodizing and the use of corrosion inhibiting primers [1]. Factors that affect the long-term durability of the adhesive are: 1) absorbed moisture in the composite and adhesive, 2) rheology of the adhesive during the cure cycle, requiring a low minimum viscosity to wet the bonding surface, 3) surface preparation of the composite prior to bonding, 4) contamination from the mold release agents applied to the peel ply surface, 5) bonding substrates with a different coefficient of thermal expansion.

The adhesive of choice for a 250°F curing system would have the following properties:

1. One component paste adhesive.
2. Low minimum viscosity.
3. Toughness at temperatures ranging from -67°F to 250°F.
4. Cure under minimal vacuum bag pressure.
5. Retain performance after a 180°F hot/wet exposure.

The objective of this paper is to discuss the effects of moisture in a bonded composite laminate and its effect on the bond joint. An overview of the raw materials available for adhesive formulating and a review of the mechanical properties of a new one component paste adhesive will be presented.

2. MECHANISM OF MOISTURE ATTACK

There are many pathways for moisture to enter a composite or a bonded joint. The more common pathways are:

1) Diffusion through the adhesive from exposed edges. Bond joints generally have many exposed sides. The edges are areas of the most stress so small amounts of moisture can lead to greatly reduced bond strengths.

2) Transport along the adhesive/adherend interfaces. Moisture migrates into the bonded joint by breaking hydrogen bonds and displacing the adhesive.

3) Capillary action through cracks and voids in the adhesive. This is very typical of film adhesives which contain a supportive scrim.

4) Diffusion through porous adherends such as carbon fiber, fiberglass, and Kevlar.

5) Freeze-thaw cycling of water in the bond line accelerates the breakdown of the adhesive bond [2].

Figure 1 shows that the moisture absorbed at equilibrium is a function of the level of humidity, not temperature in 250°F curing epoxies. An increase in temperature only accelerates the absorption process. An adhesive or composite laminate at 75°F/100% relative humidity will eventually become moisture saturated over a 2-year period whereas in boiling water it might take as little as 48 hours. Moisture saturated adhesives evaluated at ambient temperatures show similar properties to adhesives not subjected to harsh environments. As the test temperature is increased the properties drop off drastically in the conditioned adhesive due to the increase in free volume and the depression of the glass transition temperature.

Figure 2 is a comparison of the moisture absorption in a carbon/epoxy tensile lap shear specimen and an aluminum tensile lap shear specimen in a 160°F/99% relative humidity environment. The aluminum specimen absorbs a negligible amount of moisture while the carbon/epoxy sample may absorb many times that amount.

The service life and/or temperature of an adhesive system may be tailored to suit the end use by compromising the mechanical properties. An adhesive with a high wet Tg will have increased hot/wet durability at the expense of peel strength. This relationship shows that peel strength is inversely proportional to durability. Durability is also a function of cure temperature where 350°F cures are more durable than 250°F and 250°F cures are more durable than room temperature cures.

3. PROJECT OBJECTIVES

• Formulate a one component paste adhesive that cures at 250°F and has excellent mechanical properties from -67°F to 250°F.

• Develop an adhesive that bonds carbon/epoxy substrates with good durability in hot/wet environments.

• Develop an adhesive that can be cured after a long open time assembly.

4. MAJOR ADHESIVE COMPONENTS

4.1 Epoxide Resins

Epoxide resins are the most versatile because their properties may be modified in so many ways [3]. They are also compatible with a wide variety of substrates. The first commercially available epoxy resins were the reaction products of epichlorodhydrin and bisphenol A. These reaction products are low molecular weight liquids when n is less than one and brittle solids when n is greater than one. The "n" value is the number of repeating units in the epoxy chain. Difunctional epoxies are the most widely used liquid epoxy resins due to their low cost, handleability and performance properties. Multifunctional resins provide increased performance where elevated temperature (>300°F) properties are called for, but are significantly more expensive and in most cases are solid or semi-solid at room temperature. This renders them less useful as a component for a one part adhesive with good handleability.

4.2 Curing Agents

Curing agents and catalysts for one component adhesives must be latent to allow for room temperature fabrication of parts without the fear of gelling or clogging the dispensing equipment before completing the bonding operation.

The best known latent curing agent is dicyandiamide. Dicyandiamide is a crystalline solid that is soluble in water and has a latency of over one year at room temperature when blended into a bisphenol A type resin [4]. Dicyandiamide may be cured at 350°F or may be cured at 250°F when properly catalyzed, but this usually diminishes the adhesive latency. Good bond strengths with high peel and shear are characteristics of dicyandiamide cured adhesives. The main drawback of dicyandiamide cured adhesives are generally poor hot/wet properties and their tendency to exotherm in thick masses without proper precautions. Other common curing agents and catalysts are listed in Table 1. All of these have advantages and disadvantages when used in one component adhesives.

4.3 Tougheners

Early adhesive formulations consisted of resins, curing agents and fillers. These provided good tensile lap shear properties at elevated temperatures beyond 300°F, but provided little toughness as measured by a T-peel test. First generation adhesives incorporated flexibilizers resulting in a "single phase" toughening by being soluble in the resin matrix. These systems were soft adhesives with excellent low temperature properties and peel strength, but provided very little in elevated temperature performance.

"Two phase" toughening was developed by introducing a rubber that was insoluble in the resin and would precipitate as a dispersed phase during cure into particles 1000 → 2000A° in diameter [5]. Peel strengths were comparable to "single phase" toughening without sacrificing the high temperature performance. Figure 3 shows the performance properties of various toughening methods over a wide temperature range.

4.4 Fillers

A large selection of fillers are

available to the formulator. Fillers may be used to lower the cost or improve adhesive properties. Fillers can range from calcium carbonate to silver. Adhesive properties that can be altered by filler selection are flow and sag control, shrinkage, exotherm during cure, the coefficient of thermal expansion, reduced permeability and swelling by water and oxygen. Fillers may also enhance electrical conductivity, dielectric properties and provide pigmentation [6]. Table 2 lists filler selections, end use applications and loading levels.

4.5 Silanes

Silane coupling agents are used in very small amounts to increase the wetting capability of the adhesive on the substrate by decreasing the contact angle. Silanes are known to form stable bonds between dissimilar surfaces such as fillers, resins and substrates. Silane primers are commonly used on metal with little surface preparation and form a good barrier to moisture [6].

4.6 Diluents

Diluents are often used to lower viscosity and ultimately increase filler loading to lower the cost. Diluents are used at levels of 5-20 PHR for improving handling properties. Most diluents used in epoxy systems are either monofunctional epoxides or difunctional epoxides. Monofunctional epoxide diluents tend to lower the elevated temperature properties but may increase peel strength. Difunctional epoxide diluents are preferred for lowering viscosity and maintaining elevated temperature properties. Caution must be used with many epoxy diluents due to the possibility of skin and eye irritation [8].

5. FORMULATING CONSIDERATIONS

Whenever developing a new adhesive product the main concerns are safety and performance properties. Ultimately we are trying to achieve a balance of properties. High glass transition temperature for good hot/wet properties, toughness for good peel strength, and a chemistry that has latency and low moisture absorption are the main goals. The end product must also be user friendly.

Screening combinations of raw materials was performed by evaluating tensile lap shear properties from -67°F to 300°F and T-peel strength from -67°F to 180°F. The initial work was performed on aluminum adherends for ease of fabricating and testing specimens. Adhesives that showed promise were subjected to hot/wet evaluation on both carbon/epoxy and aluminum substrates. Hot/wet testing was accomplished by subjecting specimens to a 48 hour water boil, 14 days at 180°F/95% RH and 30 days at 160°F/ 95% RH. There was a very close correlation in properties between the environmental soaks when testing tensile lap shear, measuring moisture absorption, and testing DMTA specimens [9].

The final evaluation was performed using laminates made from four commercially available carbon/epoxy prepregs. These included Hysol/ Grafil Apollo 43-600, US Polymeric E7K8, Hercules 3501-IM6 and Fiberite 934.

Sensitivity to pre-bond humidity was evaluated by applying adhesive to carbon/epoxy and aluminum adherends and storing them at 75°F/60% RH for 30, 60 and 90 days before mating the surfaces together. Tensile lap shear and bell peel panels were then cured for 1 hour at 250°F and tested. Test values showed no loss in properties from the initial tests after ninety days open time. This would make bonding parts in the shop environment much easier and more forgiving. Table 3 shows mechanical properties after a sixty-two day open time assembly.

Figure 4 shows the moisture absorption of DMTA specimens subjected to 30 days/160°F/99% RH before analytical testing.

Figure 5 shows a comparison of our first generation one component adhesive EA 9304.1 and our second generation adhesive EA 9346 tested by DMTA. Specimen dimensions are .40" x .050" x 2.2". These were tested before environmental conditioning. Both adhesives start at 75°F with a tensile modulus of about 380,000 psi. As the temperature is increased to 180°F, the tensile modulus of both adhesives is approximately 300,000 psi. Beyond this temperature to 250°F, the EA 9304.1 tensile modulus has dropped to 6500 psi with a dry Tg of 217°F. EA 9346 at 250°F has a tensile modulus of 13,000 psi and dry Tg of 250°F. The same trend applies after environmental conditioning at 30 days/160°F/ 99% RH. Both adhesives at 75°F have a tensile modulus of 345,000 psi. At 180°F the EA 9304.1 has dropped to a tensile modulus of 5,900 psi and a wet Tg of 167°F, 13°F lower than our target test temperature. At 180°F the EA 9346 has a tensile modulus of 200,000 psi and a wet Tg of 207°F, 27°F higher than the 180°F test temperature shown in Figure 6.

Table 4 shows a comparison of mechanical properties when tested on aluminum, Hercules 3501-IM6 composite and Fiberite 934 composite. Most of the values are very close at each test temperature before and after environmental soak. Values on the composite are lower in some instances due to interlaminar failure and fiber tear at the surface.

EA 9346 one component paste adhesive has been qualified to Lockheed-Georgia Specification STM 30-107 Revision B and to Beech Aircraft Specification 23726.

6. CONCLUSION

The objectives of our program to develop a new one component paste adhesive have been met. This adhesive offers excellent mechanical properties over a wide temperature range with good durability when bonded to either aluminum or carbon/epoxy substrates. The latency at room temperature and the long open time assembly enable the user greater latitude in production scheduling without any loss in adhesive performance.

7. REFERENCES

1. FPL Etch Process Developed by Forrest Products Laboratory.
2. Kinloch, A.J., Durability of Structural Adhesives, 1983, pp. 86-88.
3. Lee, H. and Neville, K., Handbook of Epoxy Adhesives, McGraw-Hill, New York, 1982 (Re-issue).
4. Schneberger, C.L., Adhesives in Manufacturing, 1983, pp. 176-181.
5. Wake, W.C., Developments in Adhesives, pp. 88-92.
6. Wright, C.D., and Muggee, J.M., Epoxy Structural Adhesives, 1986, pp. 113-131.
7. Marsden, J.G., Function, Applications and Advantages of Silane Coupling Agents. Plastics Compounding, July/August 1978 (Reprint).
8. Specialty Epoxy Resins and reactive Diluents, Wilmington Chemical Corporation.
9. DMTA, Dynamic Mechanical Thermal Analyzer, Polymer Laboratories.

8. BIOGRAPHY

Bill Nickolson is a Technical Specialist in Dexter's Adhesives and Structural Materials Division and holds a Bachelor of Science Degree from the University of California, Davis. He has ten years experience formulating both aerospace film and paste structural adhesives. Recent work has focused on the development of 350°F service temperature film adhesives and both latent and ambient curing paste adhesives.

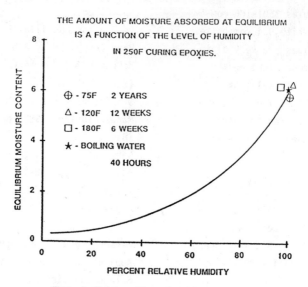

Figure I. Moisture Absorption With Respect To Time.

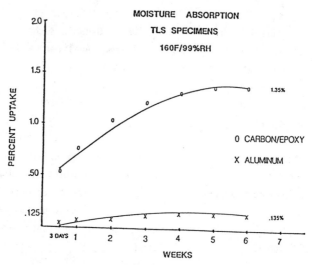

Figure 2. Moisture Absorption Of Carbon/Epoxy And Aluminum
Tensile Lap Shear Specimens.

TYPICAL CURING AGENTS

TYPE	CURE TEMP. CENTIGRADE	PROPERTIES
DIAMINODIPHENYL SULFONE	150-200	HIGH TEMP LOW MOISTURE
DICYANDIAMIDE	100-175	HIGH TEMP HIGH MOISTURE
BF$_3$ AMINE COMPLEX	40-150	HIGH TEMP LOW MOISTURE
NADIC METHYL ANHYDRIDE	150-180	HIGH TEMP LOW MOISTURE
IMIDAZOLES	75-150	HIGH TEMP LOW MOISTURE
UREA DERIVATIVES CATALYST	90-120	MID TEMP RANGE

Table I. Latent Curing Agents.

FILLERS

END USE	FILLER SELECTION	LOADING (PHR)
LOW DENSITY	GLASS MICROBALLOONS	5-30
MACHINEABILITY	POWDERED ALUMINUM	25-100
IMPACT RESISTANCE	GLASS FIBER	2-20
ELECTRICAL	SILVER FLAKES	25-100
THERMAL CONDUCTIVITY	COATED GLASS FIBER	50-200
ABRASION RESISTANCE	ALUMINA	25-100
THIXOTROPE (NON-SAG)	COLLOIDAL SILICAS	2-25

* SOME OF THE HEAVIER FILLERS SUCH AS COURSE SAND OR HEAVY METALS ARE USED AT 500-1000 PHR.

Table II. Typical Fillers Used With Epoxy Adhesives.

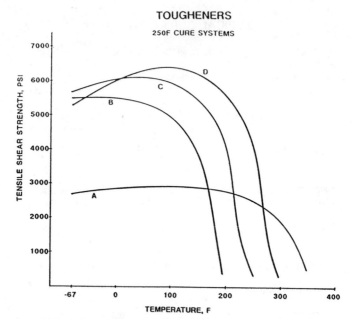

TOUGHENERS

250F CURE SYSTEMS

A) RESIN, CURING AGENT, FILLER   C) RESIN, LIQUID RUBBER

B) RESIN, FLEXIBLIZER   D) RESIN, POWDERED OR SOLID RUBBER

Figure 3. Performance Of 250F Cured Adhesives.

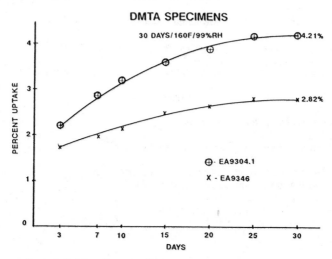

DMTA SPECIMENS

30 DAYS/160F/99%RH

4.21%

2.82%

⊕ - EA9304.1

X - EA9346

Figure 4. Moisture Absorption Of EA9304.1 And EA9346 DMTA Specimens.

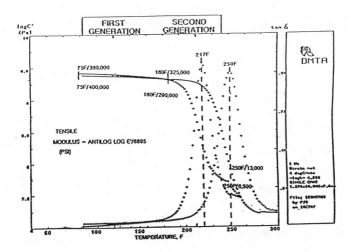

Figure 5. DMTA Scan Of EA9304.1 and EA9346 Before Environmental Conditioning.

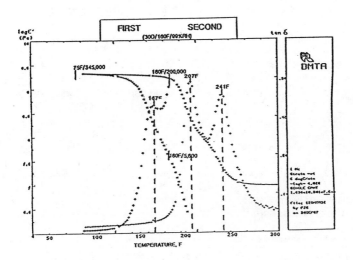

Figure 6. DMTA Scan Of EA9304.1 And EA9346 After Environmental Conditioning

62 DAY OPEN TIME ASSEMBLY

TEST VALUES

TLS/75F	8045 PSI
TLS/180F	6345
TLS/250F	3060
TLS/300F	1075
BELL PEEL/75F	54 PIW

OVEN CURE: 1 HR/250F

METAL: 7075 T6 BARE

Table III. EA9346 Mechanical Properties After
A Long Open Time Assembly.

EA9346 MECHANICAL PROPERTIES

SUBSTRATES	ALUMINUM	HERCULES 3501/IM6	FIBERITE 934★
TENSILE LAP SHEAR			
-67F	4800 PSI	4000* PSI	4500 PSI
75F	7000	4400*	6700
180F	5800	4800*	4900
250F	2800	2300	2300
180F HOT/WET 6 WKS/160F/99%RH	4500	4200	4300

* INTERLAMINAR FAILURE

★ DATA GENERATED BY AN OUTSIDE SOURCE.

Table IV. Comparison of EA9346 On Various Substrates
Over A Wide Temperature Range.

A TOUGHENED BISMALEIMIDE FILM ADHESIVE
FOR AEROSPACE APPLICATIONS

Manette M. Gebhardt
Dexter Adhesives & Structural Materials Division
The Dexter Corporation
Pittsburg, California

ABSTRACT

The usefulness of current bismaleimide adhesives is limited in
aerospace bonding applications
because of their lack of toughness. Formulating solutions were
therefore undertaken at Dexter
Adhesives & Structural Materials
Division to address toughness
improvement in these adhesives
without sacrificing their elevated
temperature performance capabilities. The goal of this work was
to develop an adhesive system with
substantial gains in toughness
properties concomitant with good
175°C hot/wet performance. This
paper describes the results of
this work. Several adhesive formulations afforded significant
levels of toughness as measured by
Bell metal-to-metal peel testing.
One system, LF 8707-2, provided
the best balance of toughness
(66N/25mm, 15 pli peel strength)
with good hot/wet shear strength.
Adhesive performance data over a
wide temperature range (-55°C to
230°C) are summarized.

1. INTRODUCTION

Future aircraft are demanding
adhesives withstand wider service
envelopes than ever before.
Performance environments from -55°C
to 230°C are typical. Moreover,
these adhesives must perform well
under hot/wet conditions to endure
in humid environments of up to
175°C.

At present, several commercialized
bismaleimide (BMI) adhesive systems
provide for good performance in the
service envelope of 230°C dry -
175°C wet. Hysol Aerospace Product
EA 9673 is an example of such an
adhesive.[1] This product is
currently used on several production
aircraft. The limitation of EA 9673
and of other BMI adhesives is their

lack of toughness in lower temperature environments. Tough adhesives are desirable in that they afford good impact and fatigue resistance. Although epoxy adhesives provide for significant levels of toughness, accepted temperature limits of 175°C dry - 135°C wet for the epoxy adhesives do not approach hot/dry and hot/wet requirements for next generation aircraft.

Dexter Adhesives & Structural Materials Division initiated a program to develop formulating solutions to increase toughness of a bismaleimide matrix for adhesive applications. The goals of the program are:

1) Identify effective toughening approaches for BMI adhesive applications;
2) Evaluate trade-offs and limitations of effective toughening on thermal performance;
3) Characterize adhesive stress-strain behavior of promising formulations; and
4) Develop adhesive data base on a wide variety of adherends.

The following presents the status of this development effort. Several toughening approaches were effective in providing adhesives with good peel performance at ambient temperature. One system,

LF 8707-2, afforded good peel concomitant with good hot/wet performance at 175°C. This adhesive was further characterized via thick adherend testing to gain shear stress-strain information. Neat resin properties were also evaluated, and are presented herein.

2. EXPERIMENTAL DETAILS

2.1 Adhesive Formulations

All of the toughened adhesive formulations studied contain a bismaleimide base matrix. This system cures at 175°C and requires an elevated temperature post cure. Toughening approaches were selected on the basis of compatible cure chemistry and required formulating materials with low volatile components. The approaches investigated include chain extension to reduce crosslink density, and modification of the matrix with thermoplastic and elastomeric modifiers. All resin systems were filmed onto 104 style fiberglass cloth to a 490 g/m^2 (0.10 lb/ft^2) areal weight. EA 9673 was selected as the untoughened control formulation, and LF 8707-1, 2 and 3 represent toughened formulations.

2.2 Mechanical Testing of Bonded Specimens

2.2.1 Specimen Fabrication

Floating roller or Bell peel specimens were prepared using 2024 T3 bare aluminum. The adherends were treated to Phosphoric Acid Anodize (PAA) surface preparation prior to bonding. No adhesive primer was used. Adherend thicknesses were 0.5 mm/1.6 mm (0.020 in/0.063 in). Specimen widths were 2.5 cm (1 in). Honeycomb climbing drum peel specimens were fabricated with 2024 T3 bare aluminum (PAA) facesheets and degreased 5052 aluminum alloy core. Facesheets were 0.5 mm (0.020 in) thick, and the core was 1.3 cm (0.5 in) thick with 0.64 cm (0.25 in) cells. Specimens were fabricated in 7.6 cm (3 in) widths.

Single overlap tensile shear specimens were fabricated using 2024 T81 bare aluminum alloy (PAA treated). Overlap dimensions were 1.3 cm x 2.5 cm (0.50 in x 1.0 in).

Thick adherend test specimens were prepared using 0.95 cm (0.375 in) thick 2024 T3 bare aluminum panels (PAA). Specimens were fabricated to 2.5 cm (1 in) widths and notched to a 0.95 cm (0.375 in) overlap.

Tensile shear and peel assemblies were cured in an autoclave according to following:

a) Pressurize to 0.24 MPa (35 psi) under vacuum. Release vacuum after 0.10 MPa (14.5 psi).

b) Heat-up at 2.5°C/minute to 175°C.

c) Hold at 175°C for one hour.

d) Cool down at 2.5°C/minute to 32°C before releasing pressure.

Thick adherend panels were cured in a press under 0.24 MPa pressure with the temperature schedule described above.

Cured assemblies were post cured freestanding in an air circulating oven for 6 hours at 230°C.

2.2.2 Mechanical Testing

Bell Peel measurements were performed per ASTM method D3167. Honeycomb climbing drum peel (HCCD) tests were performed using a 2.5 cm/minute (1 in/minute) rate per ASTM method D1781.

Single overlap tensile shear specimens were tested per ASTM method D1002. Dry specimens were soaked 10 minutes at the test temperature before testing. Wet specimens were conditioned for 30 days at 77°C/99% RH, and tested after a 2 minute soak at the test temperature. Heat aged specimens were conditioned in a 205°C air circulating oven for 500 hours, then were tested in accordance with dry specimen procedures.

Thick adherend specimens were tested on a Model 60 United test instrument with a KGR-1 extensometer. The specimens were tested in accordance with Rohr test specification

RETS 1280-9013 and other publications[2]. Soak times used were the same as those for the tensile shear specimens.

2.3 Neat Resin Properties

2.3.1 Uncured Properties

Viscoelastic behavior of the uncured resins were evaluated using a Rheometrics RVE parallel plate viscometer. Complex viscosity vs. temperature were monitored using the following test parameters:

Gap setting - 0.600 mm
Frequency - 6.3 radians/second
Strain - 15%
Heat rise - 2°C/minute

Thermogravimetric Analyses (TGA) in air were performed with a Cahn Model 113 test instrument using a 10°C/minute heat-up rate and an air flow rate of 50 cc/minute. Temperature at 10% weight loss was recorded for each resin.

2.3.2 Cured Properties

Neat resin castings were fabricated in aluminum molds and autoclave cured under 1.4 MPa (200 psi) pressure per the temperature schedule described earlier. After post cure, the castings were machined to 6.0 cm x 1.2 cm x 0.16 cm dimensions. From these specimens, shear moduli (G') and glass transition temperatures (Tg) were measured using a Rheometrics RDS-7700 Series II test instrument. Testing was performed at 5°C steps from ambient temperature to 350°C, using a nominal strain level of

0.05% and a frequency of 10 radians/second. Additional specimens were exposed to a 48 hour water boil, weighed for moisture content, then tested as above.

Fractured surfaces of the cured resins were analyzed via Scanning Electron Microscopy (SEM) for morphological characterization. Analyses were performed using a ISI-SS40 Scanning electron microscope at 1500-5000X magnifications.

3. RESULTS AND DISCUSSION

3.1 Peel Performance

Table 1 provides peel performance for EA 9673 and the toughened systems LF 8707-1, 2 and 3. All of the LF 8707 adhesives afford substantial increases in Bell peel strength over that of EA 9673 (57-79 N/25mm, 13-18 pli, vs. 4 N/25mm, 1 pli, respectively). The failure mode for the toughened adhesives is cohesive, whereas for EA 9673, failure occurs at the adhesive-metal interface. Superior honeycomb peel strengths are also provided with the toughened adhesives. Honeycomb peel values range from 27-38 cm-N/cm (18-26 in-lb/3 in) for the LF 8707 systems, compared to 18 cm-N/cm (12 in-lb/3 in) for EA 9673.

3.2 Tensile Shear Performance

Table 2 lists tensile shear properties for EA 9673 and the toughened LF 8707 systems. Figure 1 is a graphical presentation of the data contained in Table 1 for LF 8707-2 and EA 9673. All of the toughened systems afford higher lap shear strengths compared to the control EA 9673 adhesive in the temperature regime from -55°C to 175°C. Above 175°C, the toughened systems begin a decline in performance; however, the best of these, LF 8707-2, provides equivalent lap shear performance to EA 9673 at 205°C. Beyond 205°C, all of the toughened systems provide strengths below that of the control adhesive.

Lap shear data for moisturized specimens are provided in Table 3. At ambient temperature, all of the adhesives produce wet strengths equal to their dry performance levels. Tested at 175°C, LF 8707-2 and EA 9673 afford comparable strengths (15 MPa, 2200 psi), whereas the LF 8707-1 and 3 adhesives each provide approximately 11 MPa (1600 psi).

The above data show that the LF 8707-2 adhesive affords substantial toughness improvement over EA 9673 while providing comparable elevated temperature shear strengths in 205°C dry and 175°C wet environments. To see if the toughening modifiers compromise long-term thermal stability of the LF 8707-2 adhesive matrix, bonded lap shear specimens were heat aged in a 205°C air circulating oven for 500 hours prior to testing. Results are provided in Table 4. The data show both LF 8707-2 and EA 9673 lose some ambient temperature shear strength performance after thermal aging (82% retention and 91% retention, respectively), but retain essentially 100% of their initial 205°C performance.

3.3 Adhesive Stress-Strain Behavior

Although peel performance reflects the degree of toughness in an adhesive, a better description of toughness can be developed from shear stress-strain profiles on the adhesive in the bond line. Figures 2 and 3 provide these data for LF 8707-2 and EA 9673 from thick adherend testing. Table 5 provides a tabular listing of the data.

In Figure 2 are plots of shear stress-strain measurements for LF 8707-2 at room temperature and -55°C, and of EA 9673 at room temperature. The limited extensibility of EA 9673 adhesive at ambient temperature is clearly seen, as adhesive failure occurs at a very low strain level (0.034 mm/mm), with no yield phenomenon apparent. Stress-strain profiles for LF 8707-2 show distinct linear and yield regions at both test temperatures, and significant elongation afforded beyond the yield region at ambient temperature (0.34 mm/mm). In the simplest sense, toughness can be considered as the area under a stress-strain curve from zero to the ultimate stress.[3] Thus, from this consideration the curves clearly illustrate that the LF 8707-2 adhesive is much tougher than EA 9673 in low temperature environments. Figure 3 plots represent stress-strain measurements performed at 175°C. Again, the EA 9673 adhesive has limited extensibility relative to LF 8707-2 in the dry state (0.12 mm/mm ultimate strain vs. 0.62 mm/mm, respectively). Moisturized specimens afford much higher levels of strain comcomitant with reduced levels of stress: EA 9673 retains 51% of its dry shear strength performance at 175°C compared to 56% strength retention for LF 8707-2.

3.4 Neat Resin Properties

Table 5 provides neat resin data for LF 8707-2 and EA 9673, and includes minimum viscosity, TGA weight loss, shear modulus and glass transition temperature measurements. Uncured rheometrics data show that the LF 8707-2 resin has significantly higher minimum viscosity compared to that for EA 9673 (1020 poise vs. 70 poise). EA 9673 exhibits excessive flow during cure, thus the data suggest that increased minimum viscosity for LF 8707-2 may afford better adhesive flow properties during cure. TGA weight loss measurements on the uncured resins indicate both adhesives have reasonable thermo-oxidative stability (10% weight loss temperatures of 378°C and 352°C for LF 8707-2 and EA 9673, respectively). Shear moduli and glass transition temperatures (Tg) are also listed in Table 5. Modulus data obtained from RDS measurements on the bulk resin are higher than those derived from thick adherend testing on the adhesives in the bond line. Bulk resin data show that EA 9673 has higher shear moduli than LF 8707-2 at both ambient temperature and 175°C, which is confirmed from thick adherend test data. Generally, a higher shear modulus is indicative of lower ductility in a resin. Dry and wet glass transition temperatures (Tg) provided are determined from the temperatures at which shear moduli begin to sharply decline: the dry Tg for EA 9673 is significantly higher than that for LF 8707-2 (298°C vs. 227°C); however, wet Tg data are more comparable (210°C vs. 199°C), thus indicating similar performance in hot/wet environments. Moisture pickup in the EA 9673 resin is significant (5.9% vs. 3.6% for LF 8707-2). Neat resin specimens fabricated from EA 9673 swelled profusely after the 48-hour water boil, making modulus determinations from the bulk resin impractical. SEM photomicrographs of fractured resin surfaces are provided in Figures 4-6. Figures 4 and 5 are of EA 9673 and LF8707-2 at 1500X magnification, and Figure 6 details LF 8707-2 at 5000X magnification. EA 9673 has an irregular morphology consisting of smooth and rough surfaces. The LF 8707-2 resin exhibits a second phase morphology throughout the viewed surface. At 5000X magnification, discreet second phase particles are clearly seen, which appear to be nominally 1 micron in diameter. This type of morphology is consistent with a toughened resin system.[4]

4. CONCLUSIONS

Several toughening approaches were effective in providing BMI adhesives with significant levels of peel strength relative to an untoughened control (EA 9673). Of these, the LF 8707-2 formulation provided the best balance of toughness and hot/wet performance as measured by both peel and adhesive stress-strain measurements. The stress-strain characteristics of LF 8707-2 are illustrative of a toughened resin system. Although the toughened resin has a lower dry Tg relative to EA 9673, moisturized specimens give comparable wet Tg measurements, indicating that similar hot/wet performance is available from both adhesives at 175°C. SEM analyses show a distinct second phase morphology exists in LF 8707-2, which is consistent with a toughened resin system.

Excellent mechanical property performance of LF 8707-2 on aluminum adherends has been demonstrated in the service envelope of -55°C to 205°C dry, and at 175°C wet. Future work will focus on bond performance of the adhesive on alternative substrates, most notably composite adherends.

5. ACKNOWLEDGEMENTS

I wish to thank Paul R. Schreiner for his invaluable contributions to this project, to Sue Taylor and Diane Wood for their assistance in testing the adhesive specimens, and to Will Gebhardt and Jim Jarvis for sharing their expertise in thick adherend test procedures.

6. REFERENCES

1. Hysol EA 9673, Film Adhesive Product from Dexter Adhesive & Structural Materials Division, The Dexter Corporation, Pittsburg, California.

2. a. Specification RETS-1280-9013, Rohr Industries, Riverside, California.

   b. KGR-1 Extensometer, Product of American Cyanamid Company, Polymer Products Division, Wayne, New Jersey.

3. Faupel, J.H. and Fisher, F.E., Engineering Design, Wiley-

Interscience, 2nd Edition, pp.
13-14 (1981).

4. Rowe, E.H., Siebert, A.R., and
Drake, R.S., Modern Plastics,
<u>47</u>, Vol. 8, pp. 110-117
(1970).

7. BIOGRAPHY

Manette Gebhardt is a Senior
Chemist in the Aerospace Film
Adhesive Research and Development
group at the Dexter Adhesives &
Structural Materials Division of
Dexter Corporation. She joined
Dexter in 1984, and has worked in
the area of high temperature
adhesives. She received a B.S.
degree from California State
University in Sacramento in 1978,
and worked at Aerojet Strategic
Propulsion Company prior to
joining Dexter.

Adhesive	Bell Peel Strength, N/25mm (pli)	Honeycomb Climbing Drum Peel, cm-N/cm (in-lb/3 in)
LF 8707-1	57 (13)	27 (18)
LF 8707-2	66 (15)	36 (24)
LF 8707-3	79 (18)	38 (26)
EA 9673	4 (1)	18 (12)

Table 2. Dry Tensile Shear properties of BMI Adhesive Films

Temperature, °C (°F)	LF 8707-1 MPa (psi)	LF 8707-2 MPa (psi)	LF 8707-3 MPa (psi)	EA 9673 MPa (psi)
-55 (-67)	28.1 (4080)	31.0 (4490)	30.9 (4480)	17.9 (2600)
25 (77)	23.2 (3370)	31.7 (4590)	31.4 (4560)	17.2 (2500)
175 (350)	22.2 (3220)	29.9 (4330)	24.8 (3590)	20.7 (3000)
205 (400)	17.7 (2570)	23.8 (3450)	18.2 (2640)	22.8 (3300)
230 (450)	10.1 (1460)	14.8 (2150)	12.8 (1850)	24.5 (3550)

Adherends: 2024 T81 bare aluminum (PAA)
Cure: 1 hr. @ 350°F/35 psi + 6 hrs. @ 450°F

FIGURE 1. TENSILE SHEAR PROPERTIES OF LF8707-2 AND EA9673 ADHESIVES

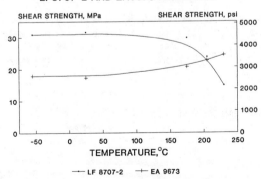

Table 3. Moisture Effects on BMI films

Tensile Lap Shear Strength
after 30 Days at 77°C/99% RH

System	Tensile Lap Shear Strength at RT				Tensile Lap Shear Strength at 175°C			
	Initial		Post Exposure		Initial		Post Exposure	
	MPa	psi	MPa	psi	MPa	psi	MPa	psi
LF 8707-1	23.2	(3370)	27.0	(3920)	22.2	(3220)	11.1	(1610)
LF 8707-2	31.7	(4590)	32.6	(4720)	29.9	(4330)	15.2	(2200)
LF 8707-3	31.4	(4560)	30.5	(4420)	24.8	(3590)	11.4	(1650)
EA 9673	19.0	(2760)	19.0	(2760)	20.6	(2980)	14.9	(2160)

Table 4. 205°C Heat Aging Data for BMI Films

Lap Shear Strength Effects

System	Initial Strength				Post 500 Hr. @ 205°C			
	RT		205°C		RT		205°C	
	MPa	psi	MPa	psi	MPa	psi	MPa	psi
LF 8707-2	31.7	(4590)	23.8	(3450)	26.1	(3780)	24.5	(3550)
EA 9673	17.2	(2500)	22.1	(3200)	15.6	(2260)	21.2	(3080)

Adherends: 2024 T81 Aluminum (PAA)

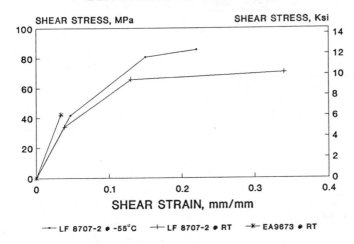

FIGURE 2. ADHESIVE STRESS-STRAIN
BEHAVIOR AT RT AND -55°C

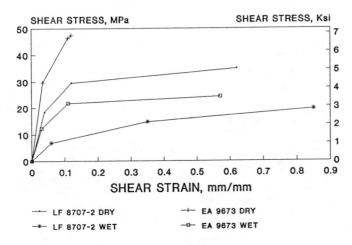

FIGURE 3. ADHESIVE STRESS-STRAIN
BEHAVIOR AT 175°C

Table 5. Thick Adherend Stress-Strain Behavior for
BMI Adhesives LF 8707-2 and EA 9673

Adhesive	Test Temp, °C	Ultimate Stress, MPa (Ksi)	Ultimate Strain, mm/mm	Stress at Knee, MPa (Ksi)	Strain at Knee, mm/mm	Linear Limit Stress, Mpa MPa (Ksi)	Linear Limit Strain, mm/mm	Shear Modulus, MPa (Ksi)
LF 8707-2	-55	85.4 (12.4)	0.22	80.6 (11.7)	0.15	41.8 (6.06)	0.047	923 (134.0)
	RT	70.1 (10.2)	0.34	65.7 (9.52)	0.13	33.9 (4.92)	0.039	877 (127.0)
	175	35.0 (5.07)	0.62	29.6 (4.29)	0.12	18.5 (2.68)	0.039	491 (71.2)
	175 wet	19.7 (2.86)	0.85	14.8 (2.14)	0.35	6.8 (0.99)	0.059	120 (17.4)
EA 9673	RT	42.2 (6.12)	0.034	-	-	-	-	1280 (185.0)
	175	47.4 (6.88)	0.12	46.4 (6.73)	0.11	29.7 (4.31)	0.034	903 (131.0)
	175 wet	24.3 (3.53)	0.57	21.8 (3.16)	0.11	12.2 (1.77)	0.030	425 (61.7)

Table 6. Neat Resin Properties

Uncured Properties	LF 8707-2	EA 9673
Minimum Viscosity, poise[1]	1020	70
Temperature at Minimum Viscosity, °C	131	136
10% Weight Loss Temperature in Air, °C[2]	378	352

Cured Properties[3]	LF 8707-2	EA 9673
Shear Modulus (G') at RT, MPa (Ksi)		
Dry	1430 (208)	1630 (237)
Wet	1260 (183)	-
Shear Modulus at 175°C, MPa (Ksi)		
Dry	1070 (155)	1250 (181)
Wet	740 (108)	-
Glass Transition Temperature, °C[4]		
Dry	227	298
Wet	199	210
% Moisture Pickup (48 hour water boil)	3.6	5.9

1) Rheometrics RVE complex viscosity
2) TGA analyses
3) RDS-7700 analyses
4) Glass transition temperature (Tg) taken as temperature at which
   shear modulus begins sharp decline

654

Figure 4.   SEM Photomicrograph of EA 9673 (1500X)

Figure 5.   SEM Photomicrograph of LF 8707-2 (1500X)

Figure 6.   LF 8707-2 at 5000X

34th International SAMPE Symposium
May 8-11, 1989

DESIGN AND ANALYSIS OF

AEROSPACE STRUCTURES AT ELEVATED TEMPERATURES

C. I. Chang

System Assessment Division
National Aeronautics and Space Administration
Washington, D. C.

Abstract

The design and analysis of aerospace structures (aircraft, missiles and space platforms) are undergoing major changes. Instead of being a secondary consideration, proper incorporation of thermal loads into the design process has become necessary and essential. Also, because of their unique high stiffness/strength-to-weight ratio, composite materials have been used extensively for aerospace structures. Since the response of composite materials to thermal environment is far more complicated than that of the metal structures, design and analysis of advanced aerospace composite structures is a technical challenge. It is not the intent of this paper to provide answers to all of the design problems. Instead, this paper focuses on issues that are useful to advanced aerospace structural design and analysis, and discusses the latest technical advancements in these areas. The airframe and engine of aircraft and missiles are addressed. The dynamics and control of large, flexible space structures also are examined.

1. INTRODUCTION

Performance and survivability are two major considerations in the design and analysis of aerospace structures. This paper addresses two of the structural subsystems that comprise an aerospace system: airframe and propulsion. For performance, advanced aircraft and missile skin temperatures as well as engine temperatures are expected to increase due to faster air speed and higher thrust-to-weight ratio requirements, respectively. For survivability, ballistics is no longer the only threat that an aerospace structure should be designed against. Intense thermal heating generated from thermal weapons (Direct Energy Weapons) also must be considered.

When thermal threats (High Energy Lasers) are considered, airframe structures made of an epoxy matrix will have serious survivability problems. Therefore, major programs

656

have been developed to address hardening techniques. Elevated temperature materials and counter-measure techniques also are being developed. Vulnerability and survivability analysis of composite structures is much more complicated than similar analysis of metallic structures. Evaluation methodology and material properties are major issues. Since several articles have been written on the subject of survivability evaluation methodology (Refs. 1-5), only elevated material properties are discussed here.

2. AIRCRAFT, MISSILES AND SPACE PLATFORM

Epoxy composites are used for major aerodynamic lifting surfaces construction and will continue to be used for construction of the next generation of aerospace structures. Because epoxy composites lose their strength at a temperature less than epoxy curing temperatures, airframe structures made of these materials typically are designed to operate at a skin temperature of approximately 200°F. In this case, the differential temperature between ambient and the skin is only about 120°F. The relatively small thermal load can be handled easily by using conventional design and analysis tools. Technically, temperature distributions are computed from heat conduction equations. Structural analysis is performed by considering thermally induced strain as an additive to the stress and strain law. To cover the increased temperature ranges that an advanced structure is expected to experience, composites having elevated temperature capability, such as metal matrix composites (MMC), have been investigated. However, it is very difficult to achieve controlled MMC processing and the cost is prohibitive. Therefore, MMC has not proven to be a viable material for aircraft or missile applications, except where cost is less of an issue (such as for space systems).

One of the most important factors in aerospace system design and analysis is the consideration of elevated temperature material properties (thermophysical and thermomechanical). To measure the properties directly, bulk material must be heated to a uniformed temperature, and the measurements taken represent properties at this temperature. It is very difficult to achieve thermal equilibrium of extremely low thermally and electrically conductive material such as epoxy matrix composites. This is especially true when conventional heating methods (such as resistance heating, convection and surface heating) are employed. Therefore, the task of measuring the bulk material properties of epoxy matrix composites at elevated temperatures is a challenge.

Initially, surface heating methods were used to measure transient temperature maps using thermo couples. Then, heat conduction and thermal ablation equations were invoked to "back out" or deduce the much needed thermophysical properties of these materials. The problem with this method is that the COMPUTED properties are only good within the test parameter space; hence, there is not much confidence in data extrapolation. Typical curves generated are illustrated in Figures 1 through 3. To correct the main limitation of the data generation method, a new device that is capable of achieving instantaneous bulk material heating is being used by the Naval Research Laboratory in Washington, D.C.

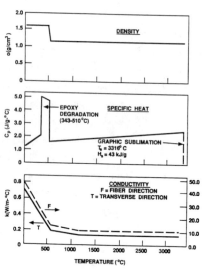

Figure 1

Material temperature can be raised uniformly and instantaneously by an electron beam. When an electron beam passes through a material, some electrons are stopped by the material. The amount of temperature raise is proportional to the number of electrons trapped by the mate-

rial. Every material has its own characteristics to stop these electrons from passing through. The parameter to characterize this phenomenon is called "stopping power." The higher the stopping power of a material, the larger the percentage of electrons that are stopped by the material and the higher the material temperature that is raised. To adjust the voltage and current of the electron beam, one can control the total number of electrons stopped by the material and the bulk material temperature raise. Because electrons travel relativistically, instantaneous heating of a bulk material is achieved.

Figure 4 is a schematic of the test set-up. Ultimate tensile strength at different temperatures of two types of epoxy composites are illustrated in Figure 5. Because of the spatial distribution of the electron beam (Figure 4), temperatures at failure recorded at front face are different from those at the back face (Figure 5). However, for the purpose of engineering design, the solid lines are acceptable. Figure 6 is an illustration of failure from surface heating (High Energy Laser) and from uniform bulk heating (Electron Beam). As shown, surface heating produces temperature gradient within the material, and the test can be considered a direct material property measurement. However, uniform localized bulk heating has been achieved by using electron beam.

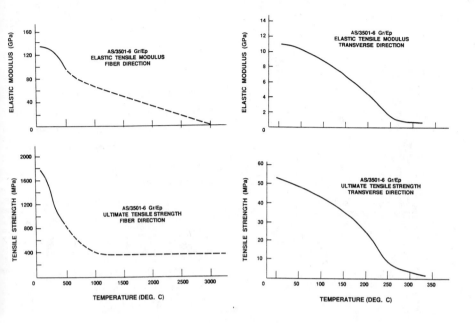

Figure 2

Figure 3

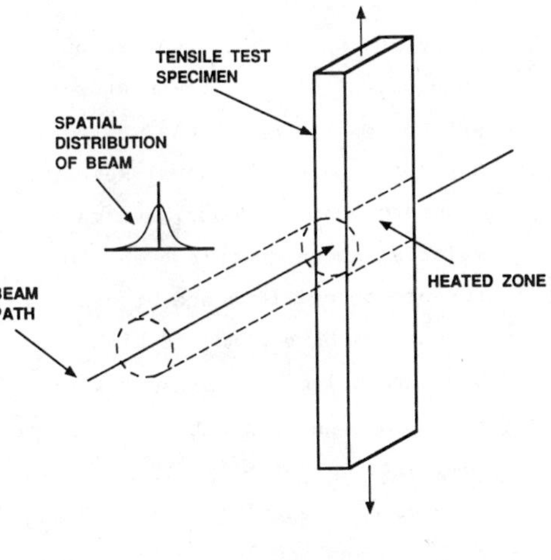

Figure 4

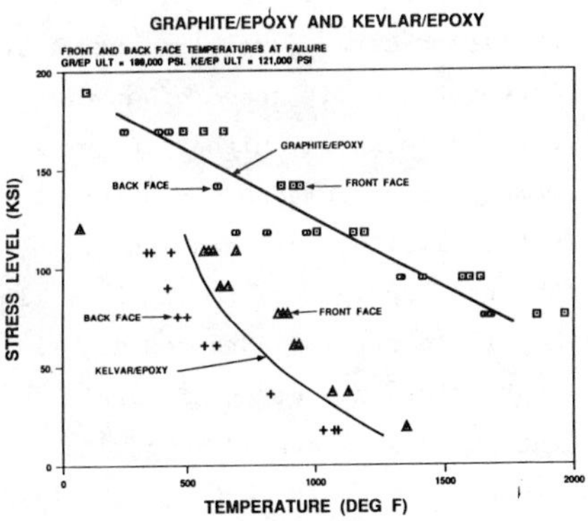

Figure 5

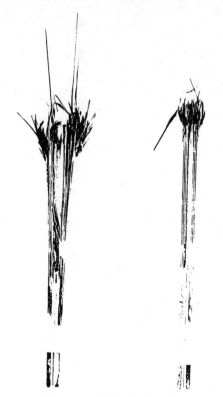

Figure 6

Since aircraft, missiles and space platform operate in different environments, they are designed to different sets of requirements. To increase the air speed of an aircraft or missile, higher temperature materials are needed for aerodynamics lifting surfaces and higher thrust-to-weight ratio engines. The key is to develop advanced materials that maintain their structural integrity at elevated temperatures. Since an aircraft performs multiple missions while a missile functions one time only, analysis techniques and material requirements differ considerably. Existing structural analysis methodology and techniques are adequate to handle the design of

both aircraft and missiles. However, thermal performance requirements place severe demands on materials. For this reason, intensive research and development effort has gone into material development.

In designing the space platform, outgasing, thermal stability (which is structural and material stability from thermal cycling), and material stability in the presence of atomic oxygen are equally as important as maintaining structural integrity at elevated temperatures. Therefore, different sets of material requirements are imposed on space-based platforms. It has been noted that material is not the only issue; analysis and testing techniques of the space platform also are major challenges.

In the material community, one of the major efforts is focused on development of high temperature polymer matrix materials. Organizations such as the Naval Research Laboratory and DuPont, have made major advances in this area. Different compositions and processing techniques have produced high temperature polymer matrix materials and also high temperature polymeric composites. Typically, these composites are capable of maintaining strength and modulus at temperature levels that are above glass transition temperatures and below the expected skin temperatures of advanced aircraft and missiles. It should be noted that such advancement is still at the laboratory stage. Technology transition to full-scale fabrication and processing is needed.

For the engine, advanced materials such as Carbon/Carbon (C/C) composites and ceramic composites are promising candidates. However, both materials require major technology breakthrough before their potential can be fully realized. C/C is very sensitive to oxidation. Efforts to coat C/C with thermally stable materials, such as Si_3N_4, have been the subject of many investigations (Refs. 6&7). Unfortunately, success has been limited. The major technical problem has been the cracking of protection coating. The structural integrity of a C/C can be degraded from oxidation as oxygen enters through the cracked coating systems and carbon migrates out of the C/C composites. For a one-time, short-duration application (such as for a missile engine), C/C may function adequately with a cracked coating system before its structural integrity is completely lost (Figs. 7-9). For ceramic composites, processing represents the major technical challenge. Fundamental understanding of the interactions among the constituents as a function of processing parameters is not understood.

A ceramic composite is composed of two or more "brittle" phases. For the purpose of illustrating the "toughened" effects, a schematic stress-strain curve of a idealized two-phase ceramic composite (Figure 10) is used. The linear limit of the curve is sometimes labeled as composite yield strength. As the stress level exceeds σy, matrix cracking follows and secant modulus decrease. When maximum matrix crack density is reached (σu), ultimate strength of the composite is achieved. After σu, extensive fiber debonding is initiated and the final failure results from fiber pullout and fracture. The locations of σy and σu, and the slope of the stress-strain curve depend on properties of the constituents and composite processing parameters.

Three major observations are illustrated in Figure 10: (1) yield strength of the composite is always greater than that of the matrix, but less than that of the fibers; (2) interphase (bond, no-bond and partially bond) is the key that shapes the curve; and (3) there are always more than two phases present after processing. This processing-induced phenomenon is very difficult to control or understand. Consequently, research and development is needed before the potential of ceramic composites can be realized.

The space platform is in a singular category, because of the unique environment it experiences and its special performance requirements. Similar to aircraft and missiles,

GENERIC COATING CONCEPT

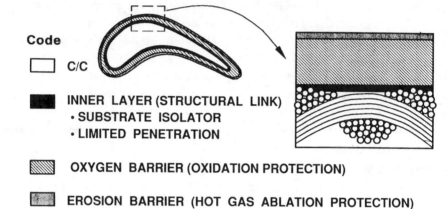

Code

☐ C/C

■ INNER LAYER (STRUCTURAL LINK)
   • SUBSTRATE ISOLATOR
   • LIMITED PENETRATION

▨ OXYGEN BARRIER (OXIDATION PROTECTION)

▧ EROSION BARRIER (HOT GAS ABLATION PROTECTION)

Figure 7

UTRC Si_3N_4 BASED COATING

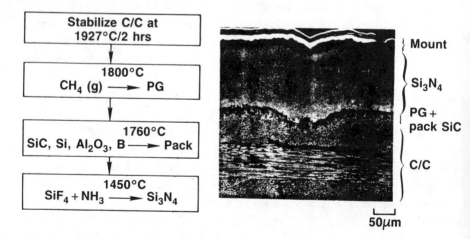

Stabilize C/C at
1927°C/2 hrs

$CH_4 (g) \xrightarrow{1800°C} PG$

$SiC, Si, Al_2O_3, B \xrightarrow{1760°C} Pack$

$SiF_4 + NH_3 \xrightarrow{1450°C} Si_3N_4$

} Mount

Si₃N₄

PG +
pack SiC

C/C

|—| 50μm

Figure 8

662

Si₃N₄ COATED STATOR VANE

2.5 mm

Figure 9

CERAMIC MATRIX BEHAVIOR

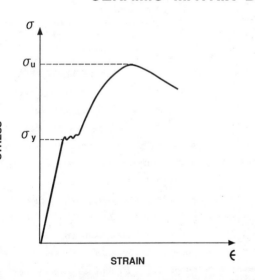

STRESS

STRAIN

- $\sigma_{ym} < \sigma_y < \sigma_{yf}$
  σ_{ym} – MATRIX FRACTURE
  σ_{yf} – FIBER FRACTURE
- INTERPHASE CONTROLLED
  BEHAVIOR
  – NO SLIPPAGE
  – PARTIAL SLIPPAGE
  – NO BONDING
- MULTIPLE INTERPHASE FROM
  PROCESSING

Figure 10

materials that have high strength/
stiffness-to-mass ratios are good
candidates. However, dimensional
stability to thermal cycling, minimum outgasing and chemical stability
in the space environment are equally
important considerations for material selection. For all of these
reasons, MMC, C/C composites, and
ceramics composites are potential
materials for advanced space platform constructions.

MMC has the attribute of being
stable in the space environment and,
if "properly processed," MMC is also
dimensionally stable to cyclic thermal loadings. During the processing
stage, metal is heated to the molten
state followed by the introduction
of fibers. During the cool down
stage of the process, large tensile
residual stresses are developed in
the matrix due to differential thermal expansion between the matrix
and the fibers. When this highly
stressed matrix is subjected to
thermal cyclic loadings, permanent
deformation results at only a fraction of the yield strength of the
virgin metal. Therefore, this type
of MMC is not dimensionally stable
(Figure 11). However, when "properly processed," this problem can
be resolved with success. An UTRC
study sponsored by the Air Force has
discovered that one of the means to
control this histersis is to use
high-yield-strength matrix materials, and to heat treated composites
properly to reduce fabrication-

induced residual stress in the metal
matrix (Figure 12).

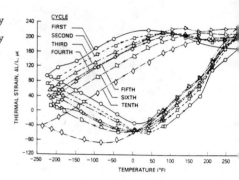

Figure 11

[± 14]$_s$ P100/6061-T6

$V_f = 37.7\%$ $\sigma_{ys}{}^m = 40$ ksi

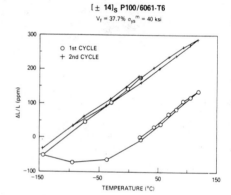

Figure 12

Generally, space structural components are thin and lightweight. The
major technical issues of using C/C
composites for space platform construction are processing and methods
to join them. Under a joint Navy
and DARPA program, both issues are
being addressed. Figure 13 depicts
a C/C tube that is being fabricated
under this program. For the ceramic
composites, technical issues of
understanding the fundamentals
between the processing and composite

properties remains a major challenge to material scientists.

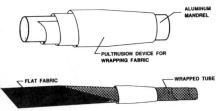

ALUMINUM MANDREL

PULTRUSION DEVICE FOR WRAPPING FABRIC

FLAT FABRIC

WRAPPED TUBE

Figure 13

For space platform design and analysis, it is this author's opinion that the sets of new requirements imposed on the advanced space platform can be met only by adopting a new interdisciplinary approach. Figure 14 is a schematic of the Space Station Freedom. The sheer size of this system makes the issue of dynamics and control a major technical challenge. Materials, whether currently available or to be developed, will not be the only answer. Structural design tools must be much more sophisticated so that system dynamics can be properly evaluated without extensive experimental data to "twig" the analysis. New active and passive control techniques, including new sensors, must be developed to measure system response as well as to provide feedback to activate configuration control mechanisms. Smart computers must be used when real-time solutions to the system dynamics and control can be computed, and commands can be initiated to activate active or passive system control.

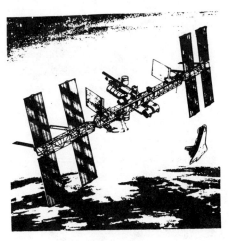

Figure 14

3. CONCLUSION

This paper provides a general overview of design, analysis and materials related to advanced aerospace systems. The operational environment of these advanced systems dictates that effects of elevated temperature must be an considered in the design and analysis process. The unique performance requirements of the advanced aircraft, missiles, and space platforms also require that material development be integrated with the structural design and analysis.

References

1. Nemes, J.A., Chang. C.I.; J. of Thermophysics and Heat Transfer, Vol. 1. No. 3, 1987.

2. Griffis, C.A., Chang. C.I., Stonesfer, F.R.; Theoretical and Appl. Fracture Mech., Vol. 3., 1985.

3. Griffis, C.A., et al; J. of
   Composite Mat., Vol. 20, 1986.
4. Chang. C.I., et al; J. of Thermophysics and Heat Transfer,
   Vol. 1, No. 2, 1987.
5. Griffis, C.A., Masumura, R.A.,
   Chang., C.I.; J. of Composite
   Mat., Vol. 15, 1981.
6. United Technology Research
   Center, "Development of High Temperature Oxidation Protection for
   Carbon/Carbon Composites,"
   sponsored by DARPA.
7. Vought, Co.; "Elite," sponsored
   by DARPA.

SPEC-CHECK:
A BASIC PROGRAM FOR CHECKING THE INTERNAL
CONSISTENCY OF COMPOSITE MATERIALS
SPECIFICATIONS

Stephen C. Darfler and Robert A. Buyny
Hexcel Corporation
Dublin, California

Abstract

Composite materials specifications typically require that fabricated laminate properties such as fiber volume, resin content, density, and per ply thickness fall into a certain range. Often, however, these specifications are not internally consistent. For example, void content has a strong effect on laminate per ply thickness. Similarly, for a given void content, laminate dry resin content has a strong effect on laminate fiber volume. SPEC-CHECK uses basic composite materials calculations to obtain fundamental laminate properties from constituent materials properties. This paper outlines these calculations and presents a listing of a BASIC program which will be useful to most composites workers who are concerned with materials specifications. An example material specification is analyzed for illustrative purposes.

1.   INTRODUCTION

Composite materials specifications are often internally inconsistent. Specification-required fabricated laminate properties such as fiber volume, resin content, cured ply thickness, void volume, and resin flow during processing are frequently defined without properly considering the interrelationships between these properties. The result is a specification which cannot be complied with. This paper will show how simple composite materials calculations can be used to eliminate specification inconsistencies.

2.   BACKGROUND

It is intuitively obvious that the laminate cured ply thickness, resin content, and void volume are related. For a given laminate resin content the cured ply thickness will increase as the void volume increases. Similarly, cured ply thickness will decrease as resin flow during processing increases. The same resin flow will also affect the laminate density. What is needed is a simple method for relating these quantities to one another in terms of the properties of the materials which comprise the composite material.

Model Equations

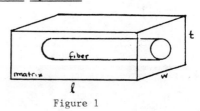

Figure 1

The composite mass, M_c, is a summation of the fiber, resin, and filler masses.

$$M_c = M_f + M_r + M_{filler} \qquad (1)$$

By definition, the component density, P_i, is the mass per unit volume. Thus, for a given laminate volume the composite density is

$$P_c = P_f \, V_f + P_r \, V_r + P_{filler} \, V_{filler} \qquad (2)$$

Where V_i are the component volume fractions and P_i are the component densities. Volume fractions and mass fractions sum to unity

$$V_f + V_r + V_{filler} + V_v = 1 \qquad (3)$$

$$M_f + M_r + M_{filler} = 1 \qquad (4)$$

where V_v is the composite void volume. These equations can be used to show that

$$V_v = 1 - P_c \left\{ \frac{m_f}{P_f} + \frac{m_r}{P_r} + \frac{m_{filler}}{P_{filler}} \right\} \qquad (5)$$

which can be used to define the void volume. Additional equations can be obtained from these five. Most of these are simplified by defining

$$R \equiv \frac{M_r}{M_r + M_{filler}}$$

which results in

$$M_f + M_r + M_{filler} = 1$$

becoming

$$M_f + M_r \left(\frac{1}{R} \right) = 1$$

The laminate cured ply thickness, t,

is deduced from Figure 1:

$$t = \frac{M_c}{P_c \ WL} = \frac{1}{P_c} (P_c V_c) \frac{1}{WL}$$

Since $V_f = \dfrac{\bar{V}_f}{\bar{V}_c}$ and $P_f = \dfrac{M_f}{\bar{V}_f}$ and

defining $Aw \equiv M_f/WL$

$$t = \frac{Aw}{V_f \ P_f} \qquad \text{where } Aw$$

is the reinforcement areal weight, V_f is the fiber volume fraction, and P_f is the fiber density.

The effect of resin flow during processing is accounted for by defining flow as the percent weight change in the prepreg stack during processing, taking appropriate care to consider volatiles in the definition. If the initial weight of the devolatilized prepreg stack was 100 grams and after processing it was 90 grams, then the flow was 10 percent.

3. SPECCHECK

SPECCHECK is a BASIC program which uses the equations in the previous section to calculate expected laminate physical properties. It is written to run on most personal computers. SPECCHECK is listed at the end of this paper.

Specification Analysis: Example

We've chosen to look at the sixth draft of the U.S. Army Materials Lab Specification MIL-U-46187, the unidirectional graphite tape PMR-15 specification proposed in June 1987.

Table VIII of this specification lists the required prepreg physical properties:

Resin Solid Content, wt% 38 ± 3
Fiber Areal Weight, g/m² 145 ± 5

Table IX gives the required laminate properties:

Density, g/cm³   1.57 ± 0.03
Void Content, %   2.0 max
Fiber volume, %   60 ± 4
Resin Content,   32 ± 3
Ply Thickness, in   0.005 ± 0.0005

4. RESULTS

SPECCHECK was used to generate Table 1. Since the prepreg is required to be 38 ± 3 percent resin solids and the laminate must be 32 ± 3 percent resin to meet the specification requirements, we assumed flow values of 0, 5, and 10 percent in the analysis. Calculated quantities in the table which are out of the specification-allowed ranges are noted with an asterisk. Figures 2 through 6 are various plots of the data in Table 1. Figures 2, 3, and 4 show a "window" bounded vertically by the required laminate resin contents and horizontally by the required fiber volumes. As Figure 2 shows, with no resin flow during processing only the 35 percent resin solids prepreg is in the specification window. As flow increases to 5 percent, 38 percent resin solids prepreg will result in laminates which fall within the window. Figure 4 shows properties sticking out of the upper left corner of the window. Figure 5 shows that a "flow window" of roughly 7 to 8 percent is required for all the prepregs to fall into the specification window at a zero percent void content level. Figure 6 shows the effect of resin flow on the cured ply thickness of the 41 percent resin solids prepreg. Notice that even though the prepreg could be forced into the fiber volume-resin content window at 5 percent flow, the laminate cured ply thickness would be out of tolerance.

5. CONCLUSIONS

The interrelationships of a number of quantities must be considered in the complete definition of a specification. A very important consideration is how the material will process and whether it has a chance of meeting the specification requirements. Much insight into processing requirements can be gained by a simple analysis using SPECCHECK. Similarly, specification requirements can be written broadly enough to allow for the "personality" of the material system being processed. In this manner internal inconsistencies in materials specifications can be eliminated.

6. BIOGRAPHIES

Steve Darfler is a Product Manager in the Advanced Composites Business Unit at Hexcel. His current areas of responsibility include materials for jet engine applications, as well as thermoplastic development activities. He was formerly a Research Specialist at Hexcel in Composite Materials Development. He holds a bachelors degree in Chemistry from California State University and a Master of Science in Chemical Engineering from the University of California. His past publications have been in the areas of polyimide prepreg processing technology and the prediction of multicomponent distillation efficiencies.

Robert Buyny is a Group Leader for Composite Materials Development at Hexcel. He directs several bismaleimide matrix development programs and manages other new matrix development activities. Prior to joining Hexcel in 1981, he was employed by TRW in Redondo Beach, Ca. and served as Program Manager and Principal Investigator on materials development programs sponsored by various government agencies. He received a B.S. in Chemistry in 1971 from U.C. Berkeley.

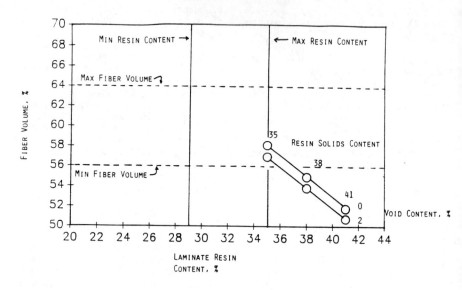

FIGURE ___2___

WITH NO RESIN FLOW
DURING LAMINATE PROCESSING
IT IS DIFFICULT TO MEET
FIBER VOLUME AND RESIN
CONTENT SPECIFICATION REQUIREMENTS

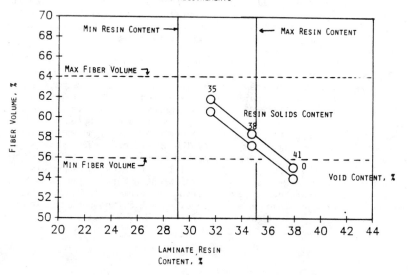

FIGURE ___3___

FIVE PERCENT RESIN FLOW
DURING LAMINATE PROCESSING
RESULTS IN 35 AND 38
PERCENT RESIN SOLIDS CONTENT
PREPREG MEETING V_F AND
DRC REQUIREMENTS

FIGURE ___4___   TEN PERCENT RESIN FLOW
DURING LAMINATE PROCESSING
CAUSES DIFFICULTY IN
MEETING V_F AND DRC
REQUIREMENTS.

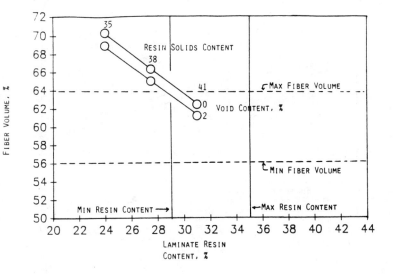

FIGURE ___5___   THERE APPEARS TO BE A
FLOW WINDOW TO KEEP
LAMINATES WITHIN SPEC
IN TERMS OF DRY RESIN
CONTENT.

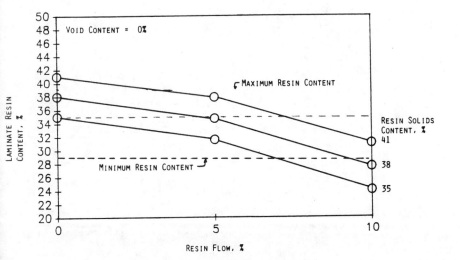

FORTY ONE PERCENT RESIN
SOLIDS CONTENT PREPREG
WILL REQUIRE CARE TO
MEET PLY THICKNESS REQUIREMENTS

FIGURE ___6___

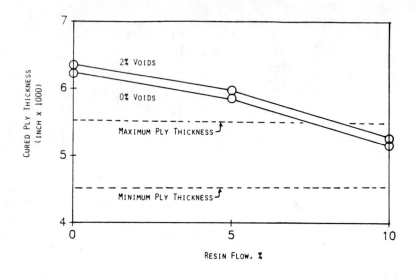

Table 1

Assuming the graphite density is 1.77 g/cm^3 and the PMR-15 density is 1.323 g/cm^3 then SPECCHECK gives the following table:

Aw	RSC	V_v	Flow	V_f	P_c	PPT	RC
g/m^2	%	%	%	%	g/cm^3	mils	%
145	35	0	0	58.13	1.5828	*5.5487	35.00
		0	5	61.82	1.5994	5.2167	31.58
		0	10	*70.33	*1.6374	4.5861	*23.98
		2	0	56.96	1.5512	*5.6619	35.00
		2	5	60.59	1.5674	5.3232	31.58
		2	10	*68.92	*1.6046	4.6797	*23.98
	38	0	0	*54.95	1.5686	*5.8699	*38.00
		0	5	58.41	1.5841	*5.5219	34.74
		0	10	*66.35	*1.6196	4.8607	*27.49
		2	0	*53.85	*1.5372	*5.9897	*38.00
		2	5	57.24	1.5524	*5.6346	34.74
		2	10	*65.03	1.5872	4.9599	*27.49
	41	0	0	*51.82	1.5546	*6.2237	*41.00
		0	5	*55.06	1.5691	*5.8581	*37.89
		0	10	62.46	*1.6022	5.1633	30.99
		0	0	*50.78	1.5235	*6.3508	*41.00
		2	5	*53.96	*1.5377	*5.9776	*37.89
		2	10	61.22	1.5702	5.2687	30.99
Specification Requirements				56-64	1.54-1.60	4.5-5.5	29-35

*out of complicance with specification

```
10 CLS
20 KEY OFF
30 LOCATE 6,35
40 PRINT "SPEC-CHECK"
50 LOCATE 7,35
60 PRINT "**********"
70 LOCATE 16,10
80 PRINT "Specification-supplied prepreg physical properties are input"
90 LOCATE 17,10
100 PRINT "by the program user.  This program calculates expected cured"
110 LOCATE 18,10
120 PRINT "laminate properties and additional prepreg physical properties."
130 LOCATE 23,25
140 GOSUB 1420
150 CLS
160 LOCATE 12,10
170 PRINT "Enter numbers as prompted.  If you make a mistake don't"
180 LOCATE 13,10
190 PRINT "worry, you'll get a chance to fix it."
200 LOCATE 23,23
210 GOSUB 1420
220 CLS
230 LOCATE 12,25
240 INPUT "Enter fiber density (g/cc) = ", PF
250 CLS
260 LOCATE 12,20
270 INPUT "Enter cured resin density (g/cc) = ",PR
280 CLS
290 LOCATE 12,9
300 INPUT "Does this prepreg have a filler <iron, silica, etc.>  Y/N ? ", F$
310 IF F$ = "N" THEN PFL = 9999999!
320 IF F$ = "Y" THEN GOTO 340
330 GOTO 370
340 CLS
350 LOCATE 12,25
360 INPUT "Enter filler density (g/cc) = ", PFL
370 CLS:LOCATE 12,25:INPUT "Enter void content, % = ", VV
380 CLS:LOCATE 20,20:PRINT "For most prepregs this value is 1"
390 LOCATE 21,13:PRINT "For all prepregs it is less than or equal to 1"
400 LOCATE 22,8 :PRINT "Think of this number in terms of off line film casting.'
410 LOCATE 23,8:PRINT "If a film (minus the fibers) is 25 % resin and 75 %"
420 LOCATE 24,8:PRINT "filler, then enter 0.25 at the command of the prompt."
430 LOCATE 17,25:PRINT "********* NOTE **********"
440 LOCATE 12,25:INPUT "Enter wt resin/wt film = ", R
450 CLS:LOCATE 12,20:INPUT "Enter Prepreg Dry Resin Content, % ",WR
460 WRSAVE = WR/100
470 WR=WR/100
480 GOSUB 1280
490 CLS:LOCATE 18,15:PRINT "***** Conversion Factors *****"
500 LOCATE 20,15:PRINT "1 oz/sq yd    =    33.9063 g/sq meter    "
510 LOCATE 21,15:PRINT "1 lb/sq ft    =    4882.510 g/sq meter"
520 LOCATE 12,15:INPUT "Enter fiber areal weight (g/sq meter) = ", AW
530 GOSUB 1460
540 GOTO 670
550 CLS
560 PRINT "Wt. resin/wt film      = ";R
570 PRINT "Fiber Density (g/cc)   = ";PF
580 PRINT "Resin Density (g/cc)   = ";PR;"         Initial Properties    "
590 IF PFL = 9999999! THEN GOTO 620
600 PRINT "Fillr Density (g/cc)   = ";PFL
610 GOTO 630
620 PRINT "Fillr Density (g/cc)   =     0"
630 PRINT "Prepreg Resin Content  = ";WRSAVE*100
640 PRINT "Void Content, % v/v    = ";VV
```

```
1820 LOCATE 5,15:PRINT "A.   Fiber Density (g/cc)              =      ", PF
1830 LOCATE 6,15:PRINT "B.   Resin Density (g/cc)              =      ", PR
1840 IF PFL = 9999999! THEN GOTO 1870
1850 LOCATE 7,15:PRINT "C.   Filler Density (g/cc)             =      ", PFL
1860 GOTO 1880
1870 LOCATE 7,15:PRINT "C.   Filler Density Not Applicable"
1880 LOCATE 8,15:PRINT "D.   Void Content, %                   =      ", VV
1890 LOCATE 9,15:PRINT "E.   Wt Resin/Wt Film                  =      ", R
1900 LOCATE 10,15:PRINT "F.   Prepreg Resin Content,%    =      ", WRSAVE*100
1910 LOCATE 11,15:PRINT "G.   Flow During Processing, %   =      ", F
1915 LOCATE 12,15:PRINT "H.   Fiber areal weight g/sq.meter. =    ",AW
1920 RETURN
1930 PRINT:PRINT "Prepreg Properties"
1940 PRINT "--------------------------------------------------------"
1950 PRINT "Prepreg Areal Weight (g/sq.meter)   =  "; MC
1960 PRINT "Film Areal Weight    (g/sq.meter)   =  "; (MFL+MR)
1970 PRINT "Film thickness, cm                  =  "; FILMT
1980 PRINT:PRINT "Laminate Properties"
1990 PRINT "--------------------------------------------------------"
2000 PRINT "Wt. Fraction Fiber  = ";WF;"  Volume Fraction Fiber  =  ";VF
2010 PRINT "Wt. Fraction Resin  = ";DRC;"   Volume Fraction Resin  ";VR
2020 PRINT "Wt. Fraction Fillr  = ";WFL;"   Volume Fraction Fillr  ";VFL
2030 PRINT "Composite Density (g/cc)  = ";PC
2040 PRINT "Cured Ply Thickness, mils =   ";PPTMIL
2050 PRINT
2060 GOSUB 1420
2070 RETURN
2080 REM
2090 CLS:LOCATE 12,30:PRINT "PREPARE THE PRINTER"
2100 LOCATE 20,30
2110 GOSUB 1420
2120 LPRINT "Initially Input Data"
2130 LPRINT "-------------------------------------------------------"
2140 LPRINT
2150 LPRINT "Prepreg Resin Content, % = "; WRSAVE*100
2160 LPRINT "Fiber Areal Weight, g/sq.meter = ";AW
2170 LPRINT "Laminate Void Content, %      = ";VV
2180 LPRINT "Percent Resin Flow            = ";F
2190 LPRINT "Fiber Density   (g/cc)        = ";PF
2200 LPRINT "Resin Density   (g/cc)        = ";PR
2210 IF PFL = 9999999! THEN 2240
2220 LPRINT "Fillr Density   (g/cc)        = ";PFL
2230 GOTO 2250
2240 LPRINT "Fillr Density   (g/cc)        =      0"
2250 LPRINT "Wt. Resin/Wt. Film            = ";R
2260 LPRINT
2270 LPRINT "Calculated Prepreg Properties"
2280 LPRINT "-----------------------------------------------------------"
2290 LPRINT
2300 LPRINT "Prepreg Areal Weight,g/sq.meter  = ";MC
2310 LPRINT "Film Areal Weight, g/sq.meter    = ";(MFL+MR)
2320 LPRINT "Film Thickness, cm               = "; FILMT
2330 LPRINT
2340 LPRINT "Calculated Laminate Properties"
2350 LPRINT "-----------------------------------------------------------"
2360 LPRINT
2370 LPRINT "Weight Fraction Fiber            = ";WF
2380 LPRINT "Weight Fraction Resin            = ";DRC
2390 LPRINT "Weight Fraction Filler           = ";WFL
2400 LPRINT
2410 LPRINT "Volume Fraction Fiber            = ";VF
2420 LPRINT "Volume Fraction Resin            = ";VR
2430 LPRINT "Volume Fraction Filler           = ";VFL
2440 LPRINT
2450 LPRINT "Composite Density (g/cc)         = ";PC
2460 LPRINT "Cured Ply Thickness, mils        = ";PPTMIL
```

```
1210 LPRINT "VOLUME FRACTION RESIN ", VR
1220 LPRINT "VOLUME FRACTION FILLER ", VFL
1230 LPRINT
1240 LPRINT "----------------------------------------------------------"
1250 INPUT "ANOTHER TRY (Y,N)?",T$
1260 IF T$="Y" THEN GOTO 380
1270 END
1280 CLS:LOCATE 20,20:PRINT "In this program resin flow is the percent weigh
1290 LOCATE 21,20:PRINT "change in the prepreg stack during processing. If t
1300 LOCATE 22,20:PRINT "initial weight of the prepreg stack was 100 grams a
1310 LOCATE 23,20:PRINT "after processing it was 90 grams, the flow was 10 %
1320 LOCATE 12,23:INPUT "Enter percent resin flow during processing  = ", F
1330 X1 = 1- (F/100)
1340 VX=WR
1350 X2 = WR/(1-WR)
1360 X3 = 1+X2
1370 X4 = X1*X3
1380 X5 = X4-1
1390 DRC = X5/X4
1400 WR2 = DRC
1410 RETURN
1420 PRINT "(Press any key to continue)"
1430 A$=INKEY$
1440 IF A$ = "" THEN 1430
1450 RETURN
1460 CLS
1470 GOSUB 1820
1480 LOCATE 20,15:INPUT "Are these numbers correct (Y/N) ?  ", C$
1490 IF C$ = "Y" THEN 670
1500 CLS
1510 GOSUB 1820
1520 LOCATE 20,15:INPUT "Enter CAPITAL letter of incorrect number =  ",L$
1530 IF L$ = "A" THEN 1610
1540 IF L$ = "B" THEN 1630
1550 IF L$ = "C" THEN 1650
1560 IF L$ = "D" THEN 1670
1570 IF L$ = "E" THEN 1690
1580 IF L$ = "F" THEN 1710
1590 IF L$ = "G" THEN 1760
1600 IF L$ = "H" THEN 1740
1610 CLS:LOCATE 12,20:INPUT "Enter fiber density (g/cc)  = ", PF
1620 GOTO 1460
1630 CLS:LOCATE 12,20:INPUT "Enter resin density  (g/cc)  = ",PR
1640 GOTO 1460
1650 CLS:LOCATE 12,20:INPUT "Enter filler density  (g/cc)  = ", PFL
1655 IF PFL = 0 THEN PFL = 9999999!
1660 GOTO 1460
1670 CLS:LOCATE 12,20:INPUT "Enter void content, %  =   ", VV
1680 GOTO 1460
1690 CLS:LOCATE 12,20:INPUT "Enter wt resin/wt film   =  ", R
1700 GOTO 1460
1710 CLS:LOCATE 12,20:INPUT "Enter laminate resin content, %  =  ",WR
1715 WRSAVE = WR/100
1720 WR=WR/100
1722 GOSUB 1330
1730 GOTO 1460
1740 CLS:LOCATE 12,20:INPUT "Enter fiber areal weight (g/sq.meter) = ";AW
1750 GOTO 1460
1760 CLS:LOCATE 20,15:PRINT "Percent flow is the change in weight of prepreg'
1770 LOCATE 21,15:PRINT "stack during laminate processing."
1780 LOCATE 12,20:INPUT "Enter % flow during processing  = ", F
1785 GOSUB 1330
1790 GOTO 1460
1800 WR = SAVT/100
1810 RETURN
1820 LOCATE 5,15:PRINT "A.  Fiber Density (g/cc)                =    ", PF
```

```basic
650 PRINT "Resin Flow, %              =  ";F
660 GOTO 870
670 MF=AW
680 IF F > Ø THEN WR = DRC
685 IF F = Ø THEN WR = WRSAVE
687 IF F=Ø THEN GOSUB 1330
690 MR= (WR*AW)/(1-WR*(1+ ((1-R)/R)))
700 MFL = ((1-R)/R)*MR
710 MC=MFL+MF+MR
720 WR=MR/MC
730 WF=MF/MC:WFL=MFL/MC
740 VV=VV/100
750 PC=(1-VV)/((WFL/PFL)+(WF/PF)+(WR/PR))
760 VR=PC*WR/PR:VF=PC*WF/PF:VFL=PC*WFL/PFL
770 PPTCM= (AW*(1/100)^2)/(VF*PF)
780 PPTMIL= (PPTCM/2.54)*1000
790 REM    VOLUME QUANTITIES
800 VOLFIB=WF/PF:VOLRES=WR/PR:VOLFL=WFL/PFL
810 VRSTAR=(1/PR)/(((1-R)/(PFL*R))+(1/PR))
820 VFLSTAR=1-VRSTAR
830 PFILM=PR*VRSTAR + PFL*VFLSTAR
840 FILMT= (MFL+MR)*(1/100)^2/PFILM
850 FILMAW= MFL+MR
855 VV = VV*100
860 GOTO 550
870 GOSUB 1930
880 CLS:LOCATE 12,20:INPUT "Would you like hardcopy (Y/N)   ";H$
890 IF H$ = "Y" THEN 910
900 IF H$ = "N" THEN 920
910 GOSUB 2080   'HARDCOPY SUBROUTINE
920 CLS:LOCATE 12,20:INPUT "Another Calculation     (Y/N)   ";A$
930 IF A$ = "Y" THEN 940
935 GOTO 950
940 CLS:GOTO 1470
950 IF A$ = "N" THEN 960
960 CLS:LOCATE 12,30:PRINT "Vaya con Dios"
970 KEY ON
980 END
990 LPRINT
1000 LPRINT "VOID CONTENT = ", VV*100
1010 LPRINT "RESIN CONTENT =",WR
1020 LPRINT "AREAL WEIGHT   =",AW
1030 LPRINT "FLOW = ", F
1040 LPRINT "R-RATIO        =",R
1050 LPRINT "FLOW CORRECTED RESIN CONTENT ", DRC
1060 LPRINT:PRINT
1070 LPRINT "PREPREG PROPERTIES"
1080 LPRINT
1090 LPRINT "PREPREG AREAL WEIGHT = ", MC
1100 LPRINT "FILM AREAL WEIGHT    = ", (MFL+MR)
1110 LPRINT "FILM THICKNESS, CM   = ", FILMT
1120 LPRINT :PRINT
1130 LPRINT "CURED LAMINATE PROPERTIES"
1140 LPRINT
1150 LPRINT "WEIGHT FRACTION FIBER ", WF
1160 LPRINT "WEIGHT FRACTION RESIN ", WR
1170 LPRINT "WEIGHT FRACTION FILLER ", WFL
1180 LPRINT "COMPOSITE DENSITY ", PC
1190 LPRINT "CURED PLY THICKNESS, MILS ", PPTMIL
1200 LPRINT "VOLUME FRACTION FIBER ", VF
```

677

COMPOSITE DESIGN FOR STRUCTURAL APPLICATIONS

H. B. Chin, D. C. Prevorsek and H. L. Li

Allied-Signal Inc.
Corporate Technology
P.O. Box 1021R
Morristown, NJ 07960

Abstract

The increasing use of composites in structural applications calls for reliable design analysis methods of composite structures that include long term performance, safety margin and part manufacturing reproducibility.

A methodology of composite structure design is presented. Micromechanics is used in predicting the properties of composites to develop an initial design. Fabrication and testing of prototype are used to establish realistic design parameters and safety margins. Optimal design and maximum part performance are achieved using an iterative process of feedback and improvement. A complex filament wound structure is used to demonstrate the design analysis, manufacturing, testing procedures and failure analysis that are required to develop the final design.

1. INTRODUCTION

Polymer composites are gaining more recognition as efficient load bearing structural materials. Thus the growing acceptance of polymer composites in aerospace and underwater applications has brought about a need for reliable design methods of composite parts and structures.

The design methodology for composite structures or parts is more complex than for metals or metallic alloys because their properties are anisotropic and depend on the composition, reinforcing fiber length and distribution, fiber orientation, microstructure and properties of each component. In the past, composite part designs were often directly substituted by metal part designs. As a result, the full potential of composites was not realized. Therefore, composite parts should be designed considering the characteristics of composite materials.

The composite part design is an iterative process, beginning with the development of design concepts in which the configuration for the part is defined by taking into account the given overall envelope, loading and environmental conditions. The feasibility of the design concept is then verified analytically and experimentally using full or part of the conceptual structure. Once the design concept is verified, the detailed design is carried out followed by the fabrication of prototype.

Performance of the prototype is then tested and the results are analyzed in comparison with the predicted performance. The findings and observations of the prototype evaluations are used for the improvements of the design in the next iteration until the design goal is achieved.

The methodology of composite structure design is discussed using the design of an underwater hull structure as an example. The method of design analysis is demonstrated using various analytical techniques.

2. MICROMECHANICS OF COMPOSITES

Composite materials are heterogeneous from a microscopic point of view. It is therefore assumed that the effective properties can be defined by utilizing an averaging process over a characteristic volume element which is small enough to serve as the microstructure of the material yet large enough to represent overall behavior of the material.

Micromechanics predicts the effective properties that include elastic, thermal, transport and physical properties. The main properties of concern in structural design are the elastic properties. Several approaches have been used in micromechanical modeling of unidirectional composites; mechanics of materials method, self-consistent field method, bounding method and numerical method. Among these, the mechanics of materials models, in spite of lack of rigor, provide useful guidelines for composite design with a minimum effort. The rule of mixtures is derived from the mechanics of materials approach.

It has been demonstrated that for longitudinal properties of continuous fiber composites, the rule of mixtures gives excellent agreement between predicted and observed properties. However, the transverse and shear properties are seriously under estimated by this model because these properties are more sensitive to the geometry of fiber, fiber spacing and arrangement. To compensate for the

geometrical features neglected in the rule of mixtures, Halpin and Tsai have proposed a semi-empirical model which is simple but widely applicable:

$$P_c = \frac{P_m (1 + \xi \chi v_f)}{1 - \chi v_f} \quad (1)$$

$$\chi = \frac{P_f - P_m}{P_f + \xi P_m} \quad (2)$$

where P represents an appropriate property of the composite; the subscripts c, m and f denote the composite, matrix and fiber, respectively; ξ is the reinforcing factor which can be estimated from the geometrical structure or determined empirically. Note that the Halpin-Tsai equation reduces to the longitudinal rule of mixtures (Voigt form) as $\xi \to \infty$, and the equation reduces to the transverse rule of mixtures (Reuss form) as ξ approaches zero. Also note that the upper bound of the effective properties of a unidirectional composite is the Voigt form and the lower bound is the Reuss form.

In the preliminary design stage, it is often desired to estimate the composite properties. The Halpin-Tsai model is quite adequate for this purpose. For most cases, the predicted properties by this model are quite accurate with $\mu = \infty$ for longitudinal properties and $\mu = 2$ for transverse properties for circular fibers packed in a square array. In Table 1, the predicted properties by this model are compared with experimentally measured properties. As seen, the predictions are in good agreement with observed values.

More rigorous approaches mentioned above, such as self-consistent field, or numerical method, may provide improved results but require a more laborious effort due to computational complexities. The bounding approach will provide the upper and lower bounds of the effective properties thus can serve as guides to the material behavior. A more detailed discussion of these approaches can be found in the literature [1 - 3].

For short fiber composites, the models of unidirectional composites have been modified to account for discontinuity of fibers and the degree of randomness in fiber orientation [4].

The predicted properties can be used in the preliminary design for the feasibility study of design concepts, but they have to be verified by experimental measurements in the detailed design stage.

3. LAMINATION THEORY

The lamination theory is of importance in composite designs because in most engineering applications, composites are used in laminate forms. The lamination theory is based on the classical theory of homogenous plates [5]. In lamination theory, effective homogeneous properties are used and the stress strain relationship for nth layer is given by

$$\sigma_i = Q_{ij} \epsilon_j + Q_{ij} z k_j \qquad (3)$$

where Q_{ij} are the stiffness moduli, ϵ_j denote the mid-plane strains and k_j denote the curvatures of the plate. For a multidirectional laminate, the stress resultants are defined, by averaging the stress of each ply across the laminate, as

$$N_i = \int_{-h/2}^{h/2} \sigma_i \, dz \qquad (4)$$

where h is the thickness and z is the coordinate in the thickness direction. The moment resultants can be defined in the same manner. From the above equations, the constitutive relationship of a laminate can be expressed as

$$N_i = A_{ij} \epsilon_j + B_{ij} k_j \qquad (5)$$

and

$$A_{ij} = \int_{-h/2}^{h/2} Q_{ij} \, dz \qquad (6)$$

$$B_{ij} = \int_{-h/2}^{h/2} Q_{ij} z \, dz \qquad (7)$$

where A_{ij} are the effective extensional moduli of a multidirectional laminate and B_{ij} are called coupling stiffnesses. For symmetric laminates, B_{ij} vanish, resulting in uncoupling of bending and stretching.

4. TRANSFORMATION OF STIFFNESS

Stresses and strains can be expressed in different orientation of coordinate axes. The transformation of stress and strain components is given by

$$\sigma_i' = T_{ij} \sigma_j \qquad (8)$$

$$\epsilon_i' = T_{ij}^* \epsilon_j \qquad (9)$$

where T_{ij} and T_{ij}^* are coordinate transformation matrices. The expression of these transformation matrices can be found in the text books.

The transformation of stiffness moduli from the fiber direction (unprimed coordinates) to a rotated off axis direction (primed coordinates) can be expressed as

$$Q_{ij}' = T_{im}^{-1} Q_{mk} T_{kj}^* \qquad (10)$$

where the matrix T_{ij}^{-1} is the inverse matrix of T_{ij}.

5. ENGINEERING MODULI

From the above constitutive relationships and stiffness transformation, the effective engineering moduli and Poisson's ratios of a multidirectional laminate can be obtained, i.e.,

$$E_{11} = 1/a_{11}, \quad E_{22} = 1/a_{22}$$

$$E_{33} = 1/a_{33}, \quad G_{12} = 1/a_{66}$$

$$G_{23} = 1/a_{44}, \quad G_{13} = 1/a_{55} \qquad (11)$$

$$\nu_{12} = -a_{12}/a_{11}, \quad \nu_{23} = -a_{23}/a_{22}$$

$$\nu_{13} = -a_{13}/a_{11}$$

where a_{ij} are the inverse matrix of A_{ij}.

These engineering moduli are used in the finite element analysis of the structure. The predicted properties of a multidirectional laminate $[0/65.5/-65.5]_{3S}$ were compared with experimentally measured values in Table 3. The predictions are in good agreement with observed values.

6. HULL STRUCTURE DESIGN

The stability of cylindrical hull structures subjected to external pressure is one of the most important problems in designing underwater applications such as ships and submarines. The elastic instability will cause buckling and eventually lead to catastrophic failure of the structure. In the past, both theoretical and experimental investigations have been made by numerous researchers [6 - 9] to understand the stability of such structures for the purpose of stable structure designs. However, most of these investigations were confined to the buckling behavior of simple cylindrical shells subjected to various loadings.

The elastic stability of a structure is greatly influenced by the geometrical configuration of the structure. For many applications, stiffening ribs are widely used to enhance the buckling load. The conventional analytical techniques can handle only limited geometrical configurations. Thus the buckling behavior of such structures as beams, plates and shells under simple loadings is well understood. However, the structures with stiffening ribs do not conform to these configurations.

Thus the design analysis focused on the buckling behavior of composite hull structures, e.g., circular shell stiffened by circumferential ribs. The main emphasis was placed on the effects of geometrical configuration of the structure such as rib thickness, rib height, and rib spacing. The finite element analysis technique was employed to analyze the response of the hull structure, to design the most

weight efficient structure with the highest buckling load.

6.1 Buckling Analysis

In order to determine the maximum allowable buckling load, the effects of geometrical configurations were investigated using the finite element analysis. The finite element code used was MARC developed by Marc Analysis Research Company. The theoretical basis for the finite element buckling analysis is discussed in detail by Zienkiewicz [10]. The governing equation to be solved is essentially an eigenvalue problem which takes the following form:

$$\{ [K] + \lambda_i [K_G] \} \{\phi_i\} = \{0\} \quad (12)$$

where K represents the elastic stiffness matrix, K_G is known as the geometric stiffness matrix which depends on the stress level. λ_i is ith eigenvalue and ϕ_i being the corresponding eigenvector of displacement.

It is assumed that the bifurcation point exists, and an improvement over the classical linear buckling analysis can be achieved through a non-linear analysis by performing an eigenvalue analysis after each increment of load. Since the primary interest is in the determination of an optimum geometrical configuration, the post buckling analysis was not emphasized.

In addition to the geometrical aspects, the effects of material properties on buckling behavior were analyzed to optimize the composite properties such that the potential of composite materials can be fully utilized.

6.2 Material and Fabrication Process

The material used in the design was the carbon fiber and interpenetrating network (IPN) matrix composite, developed by Allied Signal, derived from dicyanate ester of bisphenol A with polysulfone. The properties of the IPN composite are shown in Table 2. As can be seen, the IPN composite has high degree of damage tolerance after impact and high temperature characteristics, while exhibiting superior or comparable mechanical strength to high performance epoxy composites. In addition, the IPN matrix has advantages of good processability and unlimited shelf life at ambient temperature, thus there is no need for low temperature storage.

The fabrication process employed was a filament winding process. A cylindrical shell stiffened with ribs can be fabricated in several ways. When the stiffening ribs are fabricated separately and bonded onto the shell, extreme caution must be exercised to prevent delamination during the service.

In order to ensure perfect bonding and proper stress transmission from the shell to the ribs, an integrated fabrication process was used in which the shell and ribs were fabricated in an one-step filament winding process. The fabrication process is shown in Fig. 1.

The fabrication process is essentially an inline dry winding process. The fiber is passed through the IPN solution bath to impregnate the fiber with the IPN matrix then the impregnated fiber is dried to make a narrow prepreg tape. The prepreg tape is wound on to the hot mandrel which is maintained at a proper temperature to provide tackiness and good flow of the matrix resin. This process provides good control of resin content and processing parameters. During winding, a compacting device is used to ensure straightness of the fiber and eliminate entrapped air. Manufacturing defects such as wrinkling, waviness of fiber and voids are detrimental to the performance of the final parts. The filament wound structure is then cured in an autoclave at about 235^{0}C for one to two hours depending on the part thickness. The IPN matrix has much longer gel time than epoxies thus the fabrication of thick or complex parts does not pose a problem.

6.3 Properties of IPN Composite

The elastic properties of the unidirectional IPN composite was predicted using micromechanics of composite materials discussed earlier. However, theoretical predictions cannot completely substitute experimental data. Thus the predicted values were then verified by experimental measurements. Table 1 shows experimentally measured properties of a typical unidirectional IPN composite together with predicted values. The lamination theory was applied to predict the elastic properties of multidirectional laminate of IPN composite required for the finite element analysis.

6.4 Factors Considered in the Design

The major geometrical design variables considered in this study were rib height, rib thickness, shell thickness and rib spacing. The effects of material properties on buckling behavior were then analyzed. Studies on these variables were made using a three dimensional model. The type of element used was determined through a preliminary screening analysis. The number of elements and the geometry of the model were determined such that computation time can be minimized without sacrificing the accuracy.

The basic approach was to study first the effects of the construction variables using a simplified but sufficiently accurate analysis to conduct preliminary process optimization. A more accurate and detailed analysis was made in the final design stage using more refined geometry and increased number of elements to improve the accuracy of the results.

The design concepts of the hull structure having internal and external stiffening ribs are shown in Fig. 2. The structure has dimensions of 0.508 m (20 in.) in diameter and 0.69 m (27 in.) in length. Optimization was carried out using a quarter model of 0.508

m in diameter and 0.505 m in length. A uniform pressure load and axial load due to hydraulic pressure were applied and the boundary conditions were imposed using the symmetry of axis with one end of the shell constrained in axial direction.

In the optimization process, a series of computational runs was made with various geometrical configurations of hulls at different conditions. First, the results of this analysis were compared with the known buckling behavior of isotropic material to verify the accuracy of the analysis.

The highlights of the results on the geometrical configurations are shown in Figs. 3 through 5. Figs. 3 and 4 depict buckling modal shapes of a quarter section model of composite hull with internal ribs and composite cylinder without ribs, respectively. It is seen from these figures that multilobe modal shapes were observed. Fig. 5 shows the effect of geometrical configurations of the ribs on the critical buckling pressure. In evaluating the effects of rib dimensions and rib spacing, the shell thickness was kept constant, i.e., 0.0127 m (0.5 in.). The shell thickness effect was evaluated keeping the overall envelope constant, i.e., the total height of shell and rib was 0.0381 m (1.5 in.). The rib thickness was 0.0127 m unless specified otherwise.

As can be seen from Fig. 5, the rib height plays the most important role whereas the shell thickness has less profound effect on the buckling load if the overall envelope is kept constant. The analysis results also showed that the internal ribs are more effective than the external ribs.

In addition to the above geometrical variables, incorporation of rounded fillets at the base of the ribs increased the buckling pressure by about 10%.

6.5 Fiber Orientation

The strength and elastic properties of composite material depend on the fiber orientation. Thus the strength and elastic modulus can be tailored as required. Various fiber orientations of the shell were investigated to optimize fiber orientation with respect to buckling load. The fiber orientation of the ribs is always in the hoop direction. Table 4 shows the critical buckling pressure of various fiber orientations.

The first mode gives the lowest buckling pressure (critical buckling load). The construction $[0_2/75/-75/0]_{ns}$ gives the highest critical buckling load, while $[0_2/60/-60/0]_{ns}$ shows only a slightly lower critical buckling load but higher buckling pressure in all other modes. The latter construction was selected for experimental work.

Based on these results, the hull structure was designed using $[0_2/60/-60/0]_{ns}$ construction with the shell thickness 0.0127 m and rib dimensions of 0.0127 m thick and 0.0254 m high. This composite hull structure offered approximately 50% weight saving and 80% performance of the aluminum structure having 0.0165 m (0.65 in.) shell thickness.

6.6 Failure Analysis

Two types of failure modes should be considered in composite structure designs, i.e., failure due to instability such as buckling, and failure due to yield or strength limit of the material. Therefore, in addition to the buckling failure discussed above, the strength failure should be analyzed.

The composite strength may be predicted from the strength of an individual ply and the layup construction. Various strength models have been proposed in the literature based on various criteria [11] and the following failure criteria are most widely used:

- Maximum stress and strain criteria

$$\sigma_i < X_i \qquad (13)$$
$$\epsilon_i^i < X_i^i/E_i \qquad i = x,y,s \qquad (14)$$

- Quadratic interaction criterion (Tsai-Wu failure criterion)

$$F_{ij}\ \sigma_i\ \sigma_j + F_i\ \sigma_i = 1 \qquad (15)$$
$$G_{ij}\ \epsilon_i\ \epsilon_j + G_i\ \epsilon_i = 1 \qquad (16)$$

$$i,j = 1,2,3,4,5,6$$

where

σ_i = stress components
ϵ_i^i = strain components
X_i^i = ultimate strength
F_{ij}, F_i = strength parameters in stress space
G_{ij}, G_i = strength parameters in strain space

The maximum stress criterion states that failure results if one of the stress or strain components exceeds the corresponding intrinsic strength property. The quadratic interaction criterion accounts for the interaction of stress or strain components in determining strength in a general stress or strain field, e.g., a biaxial stress field. Fig. 6 illustrates a typical failure envelope of the IPN composite laminate with a layup construction of $[0/65.5/-65.5]_{ns}$, in the $\sigma_x - \sigma_y$ plane, based on the quadratic interaction criterion, and experimental results are shown together. The solid line indicates the failure envelope of 65.5° plies and the dotted line is that of 0° plies. The predicted tensile strength is in good agreement with the experimental value whereas the prediction of compressive strength is higher than experimental values. This may be attributed to fabrication defects such as fiber waviness and wrinkles which have a detrimental effect on compressive strength.

The strength envelope for other constructions can be established in the same manner. These failure criteria are used to determine whether the structure will fail or not under the operating load.

6.7 Design Criteria and Safety Factor

The design analysis provides the basis to optimize design of the hull structure and to establish the safety factor. The performance of fabricated composite hulls should be evaluated to verify the validity of assumptions used in the design. Experimental evaluation of performance is an essential step in the design of composite structures. It is not unusual to see that the performance of the fabricated hull is inferior to that predicted. This discrepancy can be attributable to the voids, flaws, fiber misalignment and imperfections introduced during the fabrication process.

After fabricating 5 experimental shells as part of the process development program, the weakest strength of fabricated structure was approximately 65% to 75% of the theoretical strength. For a satisfactory safety margin we must, therefore, without additional process optimization, consider an overdesign factor of ~30 - 50%. This safety margin can, of course, be reduced by a systematic fabrication optimization.

7. CONCLUSIONS

The stiffening ribs enhance the buckling load of hull structures under external pressure and the effectiveness of the ribs varies depending on the geometrical configuration of the ribs. The height of stiffening ribs greatly influences the buckling pressure whereas the shell thickness plays less important role. By optimizing the fiber orientation and using an efficient composite hull design, we achieved significant weight saving with minimum sacrifice of performance. The use of IPN's and filament winding resulted in, after a short process optimization, structures whose weakest sections were ~70% of predicted values.

REFERENCES

1. Jones, R. M., "Mechanics of Composite Materials," Hemisphere Publishing Company, New York, 1975, pp. 85.

2. Whiteney, J. M., and McCullough, R. L., "Composite Design Guide," Vol. 2, Center for Composite Materials, University of Delaware, September, 1982, Section 2.3.

3. Chamis, C. C., and Sendeckyj, G. P., "Critique on Theories Predicting Thermoelasitc Properties of Fibrous Composites," J. Composite Materials, Vol. 2, No. 3, pp. 332, 1968.

4. Lavengood, R. F., and Goettler, L. A., Contract Report, ONR/ARPA, Contract No. N00014-67-C-0218, 1987.

5. Halpin, J. C., "Primer on Composite Materials: Analysis," Revised edition, Technomic Publishing Co., Inc., 1984, pp. 35.

6. Benoit, J. M., and Bellamy, G. P. J., "Elasto-Plastic Buckling Stability Under Hydrostatic Pressure," Offshore Technol. Conf. 10th Annu. Proc., Houston, Tex., May 8-10, 1978. Available from Offshore Technol. Conf., Dallas, Tex., 1978, Vol. 1, Pap OTC 3084, pp. 303-316.

7. Greszczuk, L. B., and Miller, R. J., "Advanced Design Concepts for Buckling-Critical Composite Shell Structures," Journal of Aircraft, Vol. 8, No. 5, 1971, pp. 367-373.

8. Sun, G., "Optimizations of Laminated Cylinders for Buckling," University of Toronto Institute of Aerospace Studies Report No. 317, 1987.

9. Ouellette, p., Hoa, S. V., and Sankar, T. S., "Buckling of Composite Cylinders Under External Pressure," Polymer Composites, Vol. 7, No. 5, 1986, pp. 363-374.

10. Zienkiewicz, O. C., "The Finite Element Method," 3rd edition, McGraw-Hill Book Company (UK), 1977, pp. 504.

11. Tsai, S. W., and Wu, E. M., "A Theory of Strength for Anisotropic Materials," J. Composite Materials, Vol. 5, Jan. 1971, pp. 58-80.

TABLE 1 - PROPERTIES OF UNIDIRECTIONAL IPN COMPOSITE

	Measured	Predicted
Fiber		
Modulus (GPa)	231	
Strength (MPa)	3013	
IPN Unidirectional Composite (Fiber 60% by vol.)		
Modulus (GPa)		
E_x	143	139
$-E_x$	138	
E_y	8.3	13
$-E_y$	8.8	
E_{xy}	5.5	4.5
Poisson's Ratio	0.23-0.3	
Strength (MPa)		
S_x	1241	
$-S_x$	1207	
S_y	61	
$-S_y$	203	
S_{xy}	72	

x is fiber direction, "-" denotes compressive property

TABLE 2 - COMPARISON OF CARBON FIBER COMPOSITE PROPERTIES

	IPN	High Performance Epoxy*
Flex Strength (MPa)	1965	1979
Flex Modulus (GPa)	152	133
Compressive Strength (MPa)	1207	1220
@71°C/Wet	1034	931
Compressive Modulus (GPa)	138	138
Transverse Tensile Strength (MPa)	62	48
Transverse Tensile Modulus (GPa)	8.3	9.7
In-Plain Shear Strength (MPa)	72	72
In-plain Shear Modulus (GPa)	5.5	4.8
Short Beam Shear Strength (MPa)	97	97
Compressive after Impact		
@1500 in-lb/in (MPa)	290	172
Tg (°C)	1241 - 1786	1220

* MY-720/DDS Commercial System

TABLE 3 - PROPERTIES OF MULTIDIRECTIONAL IPN COMPOSITE
$[0/65.5/-65.5]_{3S}$

	Measured	Predicted
Modulus (GPa)		
Tensile	61	68
Compressive	53	
Strength (MPa)		
Tensile	547	566
Compressive	345	643
Poisson's ratio	0.29	0.25

686

TABLE 4 - EFFECT OF FIBER ORIENTATION ON BUCKLING PRESSURE

Unit: MPa

ORIENTATION	1st MODE	2nd MODE	3rd MODE	4th MODE
$[0_2/45/-45/0]_{ns}$	50.58	61.63	102.37	153.53
$[0/45/-45]_{ns}$	45.99	63.80	103.04	142.09
$[0_2/60/-60/0]_{ns}$	55.65	62.26	102.12	116.17
$[0/60/-60]_{ns}$	47.52	69.16	100.00	126.21
$[0_2/75/-75/0]_{ns}$	57.05	61.39	96.57	94.69
$[0/75/-75]_{ns}$	47.89	64.82	96.14	93.05

Hoop is 0°; Ribs are orientated 0°; Shell diameter : 0.508 m
Rib dimensions: 0.0127 m thick and 0.0254 m

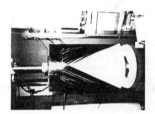

Fig. 1. Fabrication Process of Hull Structure

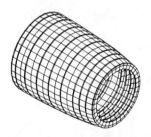
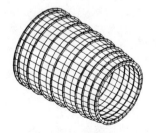

Shell with Internal Ribs   Shell with External Ribs

Fig. 2. Design concepts of hull structure

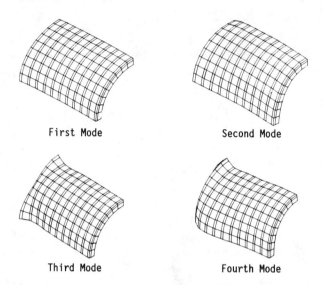

First Mode   Second Mode

Third Mode   Fourth Mode

Fig. 3.   Buckling Modal Shapes of Quarter Model with Ribs

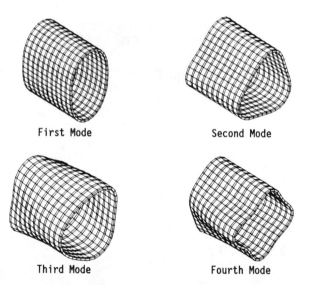

First Mode   Second Mode

Third Mode   Fourth Mode

Fig. 4.   Buckling Modal Shapes of Composite Cylinder

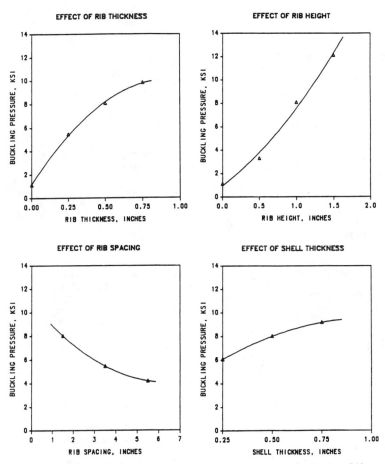

Fig. 5. Effect of Geometrical Configuration of Stiffening Ribs on Buckling Pressure

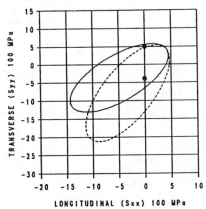

Fig. 6. Strength envelop of typical IPN laminate of $[0/65.5/-65.5]_{ns}$, $0°$ is X direction

Hong B. Chin

Education and Experience:

Seoul National University
B. S. Chemical Engineering   1963

Polytechnic Institute of New York
Ph. D. Chemical Engineering   1978

1978-Present Allied-Signal Inc.
    Research Associate

Major Professional Activities:

Present activities include theoretical analysis of composite materials, strength and failure analysis, composite structure design and development of composite materials and manufacturing processes.

Previous activities include polymer rheology, mathematical modeling of polymer processing, polymerization kinetics, and flow behavior of non-Newtonian fluids. Author or co-author of ten scientific papers in the area of polymer composites, polymer processing and polymer rheology. Inventor or co-inventor of several U.S. patents.

Dusan C. Prevorsek

Education and Experience:

University of Ljubljana
Diploma Chemical Engineering 1949
Ph. D. Chemistry   1956

University of Paris
Postdoctoral Fellow   1956-1958

Textile Research Institute Princeton
Postdoctoral Fellow   1961-1962

1958-1961 Goodyear Tire & Rubber
          Research Chemist
1962-1965 Textile Research
          Institute Princeton
          Principal Scientist 1962
1965-Present Allied-Signal Inc.
          Mgr Polymer Science 1980

Major Professional Activities:

Prior to 1957, study of structure of complex organic molecules. Since 1958 theoretical and experi-

mental aspects of fiber fracture, time to break under complex loading histories, laws of accumulative damage. Theoretical and experimental aspects of viscoelasticity and diffusion in uniaxially oriented semicrystalline polymers. Fiber morphology and quantitative interpretations of fiber properties. New fiber processes, textile processed. Polymer stabilization, synthesis and properties of ordered copolymers. Adhesion and adhesives nonlinear viscoelasticity. Molecular conformation and mechanical properties of amorphous polymers. Tire and tire cord mechanics. Over 90 publications and 40 patents in the above fields.

Honors:

ASTM - Harold Dewitt Smith 1975
Fellow American Physical Society
Fiber Society Lecturer

Distinguished Lectures:

11 Gordon Conference Lectures and 8 others.

H. L. Li

Education and Experience:

University of Michigan
B. S. Mechanical Engineer   1954

University of Illinois
M. S. Mechanical Engineer   1955
Ph. D. Mechanical Engineer   1959

1957-1960 University of Illinois
          Research Assistant Prof.
1960-1964 E.I. duPont
          Research Engineer

1964-Present Allied-Signal Inc.
          Sr. Research Associate

Professional Accomplishments:

Yarn deformation and properties, texturing of yarns, formed yarns and composites. 12 papers published 31 patents received.

Honors:

Co-recipient of the "Best paper award" from the Society of the Plastic Ind. (Composite Division) 1970

INFLUENCE OF THE FIBER-MATRIX INTERFACE ON THE MOISTURE ABSORPTION CHARACTERISTICS OF ARAMID-EPOXY COMPOSITES

Willem Janssens, Lawrence E. Doxsee, Jr., and Ignaas Verpoest
Department of Metallurgy and Materials Engineering
Katholieke Universiteit Leuven, Belgium

Abstract

Tests were performed to evaluate the ability of a fiber surface treatment to improve the moisture absorption properties of Twaron aramid-epoxy composites. Specimens with untreated aramid fibers and specimens with treated aramid fibers were moisturized in one of four different environmental test chambers for a period of ten months. The specimens were periodically weighed in order to determine the maximum moisture content and the diffusivities of the composites. These tests showed that the fiber surface treatment has little influence on the maximum moisture content and the diffusivity in the directions perpendicular to the fibers. However, the surface treatment reduces the diffusivity in the direction parallel to the fibers by as much as 50%. In addition, a numerical procedure was developed to obtain the maximum moisture content and the diffusivities of composite materials from experimental gravimetric data.

1. INTRODUCTION

Fiber reinforced organic matrix composites absorb moisture when subjected to humid environments. The presence of moisture in a composite causes the composite to expand and to lose some of its strength. It is commonly accepted that the absorption of moisture into a composite is fairly accurately described by Fickian diffusion.[1] This model states that the rate at which moisture is absorbed is determined by two material properties: the diffusivity in the fiber direction D_l, and the diffusivity in the directions transverse to the fibers D_t. The model also states that in a given environment, a compos-

ite can absorb only a certain maximum amount of moisture: the maximum moisture content M_m.

In composites made with glass or carbon fibers, the moisture is absorbed by the epoxy matrix alone. In aramid-epoxy composites, the moisture is absorbed by both the matrix and the fibers. Thus the moisture absorption characteristics of aramid-epoxy composites are significantly different from those of other types of composites. It has been proposed that a recently developed surface treatment of the fiber, which affects the fiber-matrix interface, may improve the hygromechanical properties of aramid-epoxy composites. Therefore, the objective of the present research is to determine how the fiber treatment affects the maximum moisture concentration, the moisture diffusivities, the interlaminar shear strengths, and the transverse tensile strengths of aramid-epoxy composites. This paper presents results concerning the maximum moisture concentration and the diffusivities; results concerning the strengths are presented elsewhere.[2] In a previous paper,[3] the moisture absorption properties of aramid-epoxy composites subjected to five different environmental conditions were examined. The present research extends the previous work by examining four additional environmental conditions to create a more complete and accurate data base. Also, to better interpret the experimental moisture absorption data, a numerical procedure was developed to obtain the maximum moisture content and the diffusivities of composite materials from experimental gravimetric data.

2. EXPERIMENTAL PROCEDURE

The maximum moisture content and the diffusivities of the aramid-epoxy specimens were determined by subjecting them to warm and humid environments for a period of ten months, making numerous weight measurements during this time, and then comparing the experimental data with the Fickian model of the diffusion process.

The materials used in the moisture absorption experiments were Twaron HM aramid fibers, manufactured by Akzo, imbedded in an epoxy system manufactured by Ciba-Geigy. For some composite specimens, the surfaces of the fibers were chemically treated in order to improve the interface bonding between the fibers and the epoxy matrix. For the other specimens, the aramid fibers were untreated. The material properties of the fibers and the epoxy were supplied by Akzo and Ciba-Geigy and are given in Table 1. The fibers and treatment were described by Willemsen et al. in a U.S. patent.[4]

Composite rods, 300 mm long, 12.7 mm wide and 2 mm thick, were manufactured by wet winding resin coated fibers onto a hexagonal mandrel and then curing according to Table 2. The fibers were in the length direction and the finished composites had a fiber volume fraction of 60%. Specimens of lengths 10, 30 and 90 mm were cut from the rods with a water cooled diamond saw.

One half of the specimens were dried in an oven at 60°C for $1\frac{1}{2}$ months, until no further weight loss was measured. Then they were weighed in order to determine the initial mass m_o of each. Half of these specimens were placed into an environmental chamber at 76°C and 70% relative humidity; the other half were placed into an environmental chamber at 76°C and 85% relative humidity. The other specimens were dried in an oven at 60°C for 3 months while two other environmental chambers were being built. It was assumed that the additional drying would have no effect on the specimens. After three months of drying, these specimens were also weighed and placed into environmental chambers. Half of these specimens were placed into an environmental chamber at 50°C and 95% relative humidity; the other half were placed into an environmental chamber at 76°C and 95% relative humidity.

Thus, two different temperatures (50°C and 76°C) and three different relative humidities (70%, 85% and 95% r.h.) were employed. The temperatures and humidities were chosen in order to complement the experimental work performed by this research group in a previous

---

Table 1

Properties of Akzo Twaron HM aramid fiber and Ciba-Geigy Epoxy LY556/HY917/DY070.

Material Property	Aramid fiber	Epoxy Matrix
Fiber diameter (μm)	12	
Density (g/cm^3)	1.44	1.17
Longitudinal Modulus (GPa)	125	3.44
Transverse Modulus (GPa)	4	3.44
Longitudinal Shear Modulus (GPa)	2.9	1.27
Transverse Shear Modulus (GPa)	1.5	1.27
Longitudinal Poisson Coefficient	0.35	0.35
Transverse Poisson Coefficient	0.35	0.35
Longitudinal Heat Conductivity (W/mK)	0.05	0.18
Transverse Heat Conductivity (W/mK)	0.04	0.18
Longitudinal Coefficient of Thermal Expansion (1/K $\times 10^{-6}$)	-2	69
Transverse Coefficient of Thermal Expansion (1/K $\times 10^{-6}$)	54	69
Tensile Strength (GPa)	2.9	0.085
Failure Strain (%)	2.7	4

Table 2
Cure cycle for specimens.

- Wet winding. Resin and mandrel at 80°C.
- Mechanical pressure applied by closing mandrel. No vacuum.
- Place in oven preheated to 80°C.
- Four hours at 80°C.
- Increase temperature to 140°C and cure for six hours.
- Cool with air.

Table 3
Environmental test conditions.

	Relative Humidity				
Temperature	50%	70%	85%	95%	100%
50°C				●	o
62°C					o
76°C	o	●o	●	●	o

● present study   o previous study[3]

---

investigation.[3] Table 3 shows the environmental conditions employed in the present investigation (filled circles) and those employed in the previous investigation (empty circles).

Two Hereaus environmental test chambers, type VLK 04/150, were used for the 70% and 85% relative humidity conditions. The other two chambers were built in-house and controlled by two Hereaus heating elements and an external Rotronic Hygroskop DV-2 hygro-thermometer. The specimens were weighed using a Mettler AE 240 analytical balance with an accuracy of ±0.02 mg.

For both the untreated and treated aramid composites, there were three specimens for each length (10 mm, 30 mm, 90 mm) at each of the four environmental conditions. Thus a total of 72 specimens were employed. Periodically, the specimens were temporarily removed from the chambers, weighed and their masses m recorded. The tests spanned a period of ten months. Near the beginning of the tests, the specimens were weighed several times per day, later they were weighed once per week, and towards the end of the testing once every other

week. More than 3000 weight measurements were made during the course of the investigation.

3. RESULTS
3.1 Moisture absorption curves

The moisture content M of each of the specimens was determined from the weight measurements and employing

$$M = \frac{m - m_o}{m_o}. \qquad (1)$$

These experimental values are plotted versus the square root of time $t^{1/2}$ in Figures 1 and 2. Each of the data points in these figures represents the average moisture content of three specimens. In nearly every case, the moisture content of the specimens increased rapidly at the beginning of the absorption process and then slowly approached a saturation level or maximum moisture content M_m.

The one case that did not conform to the norm was that of the specimens subjected to 76°C temperature and 95% relative humidity, the harshest environmental condition. The wide scatter near the end of those tests was probably due to a build up of rust on the specimens from their holder which could not be cleaned off consistently. However, even the early portion of the absorption curve is qualitatively different from those for the other, less harsh environments: the moisture absorption is more erratic and no clear maximum moisture content is evident.

Qualitatively, the moisture absorption curves show that the specimens with treated aramid fibers absorbed moisture less quickly than the specimens with untreated fibers. Note that in the specimens with untreated fibers, the moisture content increases most rapidly for the shortest specimens. This fact implies that moisture quickly diffuses in the fiber direction. The fiber surface treatment seems to minimize this rapid longitudinal diffusion. These same conclusions are reached below in the quantitative analysis of the absorption data.

3.2 Data reduction scheme

As discussed above, it is generally accepted that the absorption of moisture into a composite is fairly accurately described by Fickian diffusion, and that three material properties, namely the

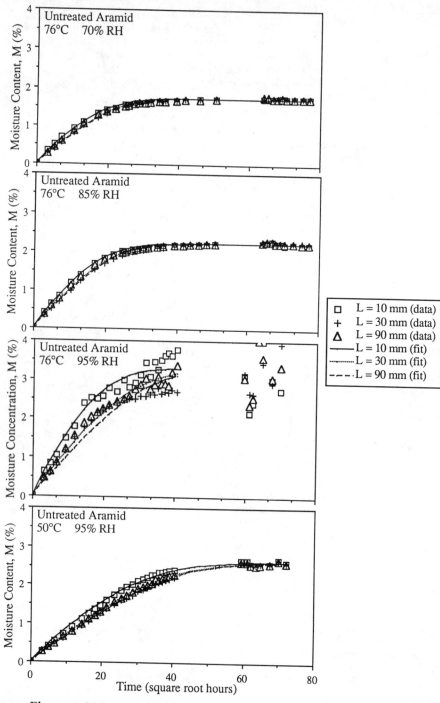

Figure 1 Moisture absorption curves for untreated aramid-epoxy composites subjected to the four environmental conditions listed in Table 3. Each data point represents the average moisture content of 3 specimens.

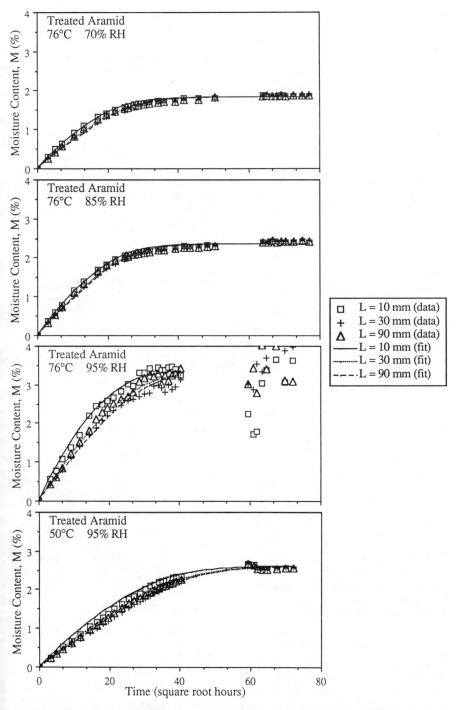

Figure 2 Moisture absorption curves for treated aramid-epoxy composites subjected to the four environmental conditions listed in Table 3. Each data point represents the average moisture content of 3 specimens.

maximum moisture content and the two diffusivities, govern this process. The goal of the data reduction scheme is to determine these material properties from the experimental data.

For an initially dry, rectilinear specimen subjected to a humid environment at time $t = 0$, the Fickian model predicts that at a later time t, the moisture content of the specimen will be

$$\frac{M}{M_m} =$$
$$1 - \frac{512}{\pi^6} \sum_{i=0}^{\infty} \sum_{j=0}^{\infty} \sum_{k=0}^{\infty} \frac{1}{\alpha_i \alpha_j \alpha_k} \exp \left\{ \right.$$
$$\left. - \pi^2 t \left[D_l \frac{\alpha_i}{l^2} + D_t \frac{\alpha_j}{w^2} + D_t \frac{\alpha_k}{h^2} \right] \right\}, \quad (2)$$

where $\alpha_i = (2i + 1)^2$, $\alpha_j = (2j + 1)^2$, $\alpha_k = (2k+1)^2$; M_m is the maximum moisture content; and l, w, h are the length, width, and thickness of the composite, respectively. During the initial stages of the absorption process, the simplified formula obtained by Aronhime, et al. is valid[5]:

$$\frac{M}{M_m} =$$
$$4t^{1/2} \left[\left(\frac{1}{w} + \frac{1}{h} \right) \left(\frac{D_t}{\pi} \right)^{1/2} \right.$$
$$\left. + \frac{1}{l} \left(\frac{D_l}{\pi} \right)^{1/2} \right]$$
$$- 16t \left[\left(\frac{1}{w} + \frac{1}{h} \right) \frac{(D_l D_t)^{1/2}}{l\pi} + \frac{D_t}{hl\pi} \right]$$
$$+ 64t^{3/2} \frac{D_t D_l^{1/2}}{lwh\pi^{3/2}}. \quad (3)$$

The first term of the sum on the right hand side of Eq. (3) (which is linear in $t^{1/2}$) was obtained by Shen and Springer.[1] Equations (2) and (3) are displayed graphically in Figure 3.

The goal of the present data reduction scheme is to choose the material properties M_m, D_l, and D_t, such that the moisture absorption curves given by Eqs. (2) and (3) are as close to the actual experimental data as possible. This method is similar to previous methods. A common method, developed by Shen and Springer,[1] is to pick M_m from a visual inspection of the moisture absorp-

tion curves. Then D_l and D_t are chosen so that the first term of the right hand side of Eq. (3), the term linear in $t^{1/2}$, fits the experimental data as closely as possible. A limitation of this method is that only those experimental data that are nearly linear in $t^{1/2}$, those at the very beginning of the tests, can be used in the data reduction scheme. Sighting this limitation, Rothwell and Marshall[6] and Grayson[7] developed methods for isotropic materials which allowed them to use additional experimental data points (in addition to those that were nearly linear in $t^{1/2}$) to find the diffusivity. Aronhime et al. did the same for anisotropic materials; they employed equation Eq. (3) to choose both diffusivities D_l and D_t.

In the present investigation, two slightly different methods were used. Both methods employed either Eq. (2) or (3) to calculate M. The value given by Eq. (2) was used except for short times, when Eq. (2) converged slowly from above and Eq. (3) gave a lower value of M; then the lower value given by Eq. (3) was used. In both methods, the damped Gauss-Newton method was employed to determine the material properties such that the calculated values of M matched the experimental data as closely as possible.[8] This procedure was automated with a FORTRAN computer program.

The two methods differed in the number of experimental data points they each employed and in the way each determined M_m. In the first method, all of the moisture data shown in Figures 1 and 2 were employed (except for the specimens at 76°C and 95% relative humidity, for which only the data before 40 square root hours were employed). With these data, the values of D_l, D_t, and M_m were determined with the computer code and are given in Table 4. The curves defined by Eq. (2) with these values of D_l, D_t, and M_m are shown as the lines in Figures 1 and 2.

In the second method, only the first 5 to 12 data points of each of these curves were employed. The maximum moisture contents M_m were chosen by visual inspection and then D_l and D_t were determined by the computer code. This method is similar to that described by Aronhime, et al.[5] Table 5 gives the value of M_m selected, the number of data points included in the analysis and the values of D_l and D_t thus obtained.

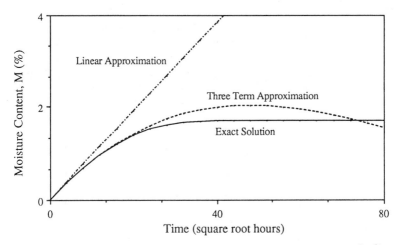

Figure 3 Typical moisture absorption curve. The curves shown are the linear approximation (the first term of Eq. 3), the three term approximation (all of Eq. 3), and the exact solution (Eq. 2).

3.3 Data reduction evaluation

By comparing Tables 4 and 5, it is noted that when only the first few moisture absorption data points are employed, a lower value of D_l and a higher value D_t are obtained than are obtained when all of the data points are employed in the analysis. From this result two important conclusions can be drawn. First, in order to determine the diffusivities which are most valid during the *entire* moisture absorption process, the maximum number of data points must be included in the curve fitting analysis. Second, because the values obtained for D_l and D_t depend on the number of data points included in the curve fitting analysis and because these values depend on the number of data points in a consistent way (i.e. the value obtained for D_l is always lower when only the first few data points are employed than the value of D_l when all the data points are employed), it follows that Eq. (2) is not perfectly valid. (If Eq. (2) were perfectly valid, then the values obtained for D_l and D_t would be independent of the data points employed in the analysis.) However, the fact that the calculated curves in Figures 1 and 2 pass near the experimental data suggests that the values of D_l and D_t obtained with the present method are accurate enough for most engineering purposes.

The method outlined above for determining D_l, D_t, and M_m from the experimental data has several advantages over previous methods. i) All of the experimental data points are included in the data reduction scheme, reducing the effects of individual errors in the mass measurements. ii) The maximum moisture content is determined numerically along with the diffusivities. iii) The diffusivities and maximum moisture content which best fit the experimental data are obtained through an automated procedure and may be determined to any desired accuracy.

3.4 Maximum moisture content

A summary of the maximum moisture content and diffusivity data is presented in Figures 4 through 6. The data for these figures were taken from Table 4, except for the data corresponding to 76°C and 95% relative humidity. For this harsh condition, the data from Table 5 was employed because the data of the absorption curves (Figures 1 and 2) suggest that, in this environment, the moisture absorption was nearly Fickian only during the initial stages of the test. The values of M_m obtained for the specimens subjected to a temperature of 76°C are shown in Figure 4 as a function of relative humidity. The data points in this figure corresponding to relative humidities of 50% and 100% were obtained in a previous study.[3] The new data are consistent with the previous data and indicate that the maximum moisture content increases with relative humidity and that the aramid fiber treatment has negligible effect on the maximum moisture content.

Table 4
Summary of Maximum Moisture Content and Diffusivities
Determined by Employing All of the Absorption Data.

Material	Environment	M_m (%)	D_l (mm^2/s) $\times 10^{-6}$	D_t (mm^2/s) $\times 10^{-6}$
Untreated	76°C 70% r.h.	1.7	1.5	0.31
Untreated	76°C 85% r.h.	2.2	1.6	0.31
Untreated	76°C 95% r.h.	3.3	5.0	0.16
Untreated	50°C 95% r.h.	2.6	0.68	0.10
Treated	76°C 70% r.h.	1.8	1.4	0.25
Treated	76°C 85% r.h.	2.3	0.91	0.27
Treated	76°C 95% r.h.	3.4	3.0	0.19
Treated	50°C 95% r.h.	2.6	0.33	0.10

Table 5
Summary of Maximum Moisture Content and Diffusivities
Determined by Employing the First Few Data Points
of the Absorption Data Curves.

Material	Environment	No. Data Points Employed	M_m (%)	D_l (mm^2/s) $\times 10^{-6}$	D_t (mm^2/s) $\times 10^{-6}$
Untreated	76°C 70% r.h.	7	1.7	1.3	0.34
Untreated	76°C 85% r.h.	6	2.2	1.4	0.35
Untreated	76°C 95% r.h.	5	2.7	2.9	0.38
Untreated	50°C 95% r.h.	12	2.6	0.46	0.11
Treated	76°C 70% r.h.	7	1.8	1.1	0.30
Treated	76°C 85% r.h.	6	2.3	0.52	0.31
Treated	76°C 95% r.h.	5	3.0	1.8	0.28
Treated	50°C 95% r.h.	12	2.6	0.23	0.10

The solid lines in Figure 4 are curves generated by fitting the following equation to the data:

$$M_m = a(\% \text{ r.h.})^b, \qquad (4)$$

where the values of a and b are given in Table 6. Equation 4 and the values of a and b given in Table 6 can be used to estimate the maximum moisture content for other values of relative humidity.

3.5 Diffusivities

The diffusivities D_l and D_t for specimens subjected to a temperature of 76°C and relative humidities of 70%, 85% and 95% are presented in Figure 5. This figure indicates that the diffusivities in the directions transverse to the fibers D_t are much less than the diffusivities in the direction parallel to the fibers D_l. The figure also demonstrates that the fiber surface treatment greatly reduces the longitudinal diffusivity, at least for the specimens subjected to the higher relative humidities. The transverse diffusivity does not appear to be affected by the fiber surface treatment. These conclusions are also sup-

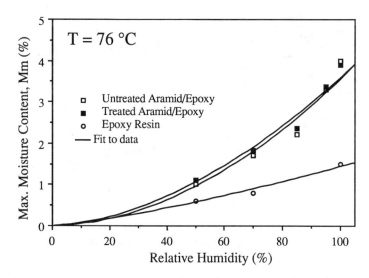

Figure 4 Maximum moisture content of treated aramid-epoxy and untreated aramid-epoxy, exposed to 76°C and relative humidities 50%, 70%, 85%, 95% and 100%.

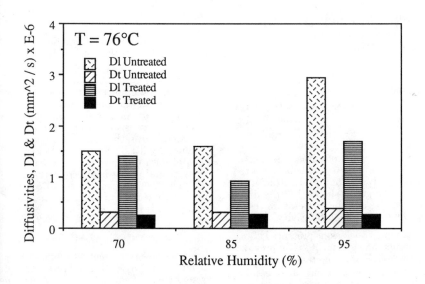

Figure 5 Diffusivities of untreated and treated aramid-epoxy in the longitudinal (D_l) and transverse (D_t) directions for 76°C and relative humidities 70%, 85%, and 95%.

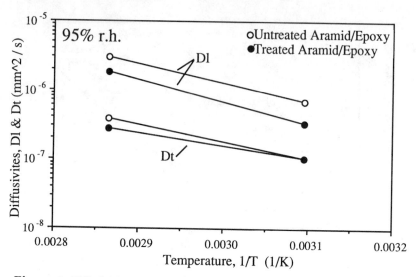

Figure 6 Diffusivities of untreated and treated aramid-epoxy, in the longitudinal (D_l) and transverse (D_t) directions for temperatures 50°C and 76°C and for relative humidity 95%.

Table 6
Coefficients for Equation (4) which Describes the Variation of M_m with Relative Humidity at 76°.

Material	a	b
Untreated aramid-epoxy	0.0032	1.3
Treated aramid-epoxy	0.0010	1.8
Epoxy resin	0.00054	1.9

ported by the graph of diffusivities versus temperature for the specimens subjected to 95% relative humidity (Figure 6). In addition, the graph shows that the diffusivities increase with temperature, especially the longitudinal diffusivity.

The data and conclusions presented above are in general agreement with previous work,[3] but there do seem to be a few questions remaining concerning these results. Recall that the analysis of the experimental data is based upon the assumption that the moisture absorption process can be modeled by Fickian diffusion. However, some of the data indicate that this assumption is not completely justified. First, if the diffusivities (material properties) are truly independent of the moisture concentration, as is assumed in the Fickian model, then they should also be independent of the relative humidity. The data in Figure 5 show that this is not

the case. Second, in analyzing the data, D_l, D_t and M_m were chosen such that Eq. (2) best represents the experimental data. Figures 1 and 2 indicate that Eq. (2) represents the data fairly well but not exactly, i.e., the data fit curves do not pass through all of the data points. This discrepancy can not be attributed to random errors in the weight measurements since the data fit curves miss the data points in a consistent way. Finally, as discussed above, the values of D_l and D_t obtained by fitting Eq. (2) to the experimental data depends on the number of experimental points included in the analysis. This fact also implies that Eq. (2) is not exactly correct and that the moisture absorption is not exactly Fickian.

4. CONCLUSION

A new surface treatment on aramid fibers to improve the hygrothermal properties of aramid-epoxy composites was evaluated. To do so, experiments were performed and a numerical procedure implemented to determine the maximum moisture content and the diffusivities of aramid-epoxy composites.

Although the experimental data suggest that moisture absorption in aramid-epoxy composites is not precisely governed by the diffusion equation, the data do imply that the diffusion equation is accurate enough for most engineering applications. Therefore, important conclusions relevant to the use of aramid-epoxy composites may still be drawn.

i) The maximum moisture content M_m is not affected much by the fiber treatment.

ii) In many applications, where the thicknesses of composite parts and structures are much less than the other dimensions, the rate of moisture absorption is determined primarily by the transverse diffusivity D_t. Tables 4 and 5 and Figure 5 show that this quantity is not affected much by the fiber surface treatment.

iii) Near edges, holes, and cracks in protective coatings, where the aramid fibers might be exposed to the environment, the fiber treatment would reduce moisture uptake since it reduces the diffusivity in the fiber direction.

REFERENCES

[1] Shen, C.-H. and Springer, G.S., *J. Compos. Mater.*, **10**, 2 (1976).

[2] Janssens, W., Doxsee, L.E., and Verpoest, I., to be published in *Proc. ECCM*, Bordeaux, (1989).

[3] Verpoest, I., and Springer, G.S., *Journal of Reinforced Plastics and Composites*, **7**, 2 (1988).

[4] Willemsen, S., Weening, W.E., and Steenbergen, A., US Patent 4,557,967, Adhesive-coated multifilament yarn of an aromatic polyamide, a yarn package, a cord, a fabric, a reinforced object and a process for making said yarn, December, 1985.

[5] Aronhime, M.T., Neumann, S., and Marom, G., *Journal of Materials Science*, **22**, 2435 (1987).

[6] Rothwell, W.S., and Marshall, H.P., LMSC-D566642, (1977).

[7] Grayson, M.A., *Journal of Polymer Science: Part B: Polymer Physics*, **24**, 1747 (1986).

[8] Dahlquist, G., and Björck, Å., *Numerical Methods*, Prentice-Hall, Englewood Cliffs, New Jersey, 1974, p 444.

Acknowledgement

The Akzo Co. (Arnhem, The Netherlands), the European Space Agency (through Fulmer Research Ltd.) and the Research Council of the K.U. Leuven are kindly acknowledged for supporting this research project. We especially thank B. Naughton (Akzo), D. Bashford (Fulmer), D. Eaton (ESA) and Prof. Springer (Stanford University, USA) for fruitful discussions.

Biographies

Ignaas Verpoest is a Research Associate of the Belgian National Fund for Scientific Research (NFWO) and associate professor in the Department of Metallurgy and Materials Engineering of the Katholieke Universiteit Leuven. He Lectures on material science and composite materials, and coordinates the research of the interdisciplinary Composite Materials group at K.U. Leuven. He graduated in 1982 with a Ph.D. thesis on "Fatigue of Steel Wires". Current research concentrates on damage development in polymeric matrix composites, interfaces, thermoplastic composites and new fabrics for composites.

Lawrence E. Doxsee, Jr. is a research fellow of the Department of Metallurgy and Materials Engineering of the K.U. Leuven. He received his Ph.D. in 1988 from the Department of Aeronautics and Astronautics at Stanford University. His thesis was entitled "Hygrothermal Deformations of Laminated Composite Shells".

Willem Janssens received his Engineer degree from the Department of Metallurgy and Materials Engineering of the K.U. Leuven in 1988. He is currently pursuing a Masters degree in nuclear engineering at K.U. Leuven.

CHARACTERIZATION OF IMPACT DAMAGE
IN LAMINATED COMPOSITES

*Fu-Kuo Chang, **Hyung Yun Choi and ***Syh-Tsang Jeng

Department of Aeronautics and Astronautics

Stanford University, Stanford CA 94305

Abstract

An investigation was performed to study impact damage of laminated composites caused by a line-nose impactor. The major objective of the study was to fundamentally understand the failure mechanisms in composites caused by impact, and to identify the essential parameters causing the damage in composites. The primary concern of the failure modes were matrix crackings and delaminations. An unique and special impact test facility was designed and built for the investigation. The major characteristic of the facility was the use of a rectangular barrel so that a line-nose impactor could be adopted to produce uniformly distributed, transient dynamic loadings across the specimen's width and substantially simplify impact damage patterns. T300/976 Graphite/Epoxy prepregs were selected to fabricate specimens. All specimens were X-rayed and C-scanned before and after impact to examine damage caused by impact. An analytical model was also developed for simulating the impact response of the specimens and to determine the important parameters dominating the impact damage in composites. An excellent agreement was found between the data and the predictions. Based on the experiments and the numerical calculations, it can be concluded that 1). matrix cracks were the initial impact damage mode, (2). delamination was initiated by the matrix cracks during impact, 3). laminates with inherent cracks, resulting from manufacturing, are much more susceptible to impact than laminates without, 4). residual thermal stresses are crucial for impact damage in composites, and 5). the interlaminar shear stresses and in-plane tensile stresses are the dominating stresses causing the initial matrix cracking.

1. INTRODUCTION

Low velocity impact could cause internal damage in laminated composites, such as matrix crackings and delaminations. These types of damage are hard to detect without the use of X-ray or C-scan machines, and could potentially cause significant reduction of mechanical properties of the materials [1-11]. Therefore, considerable work has been performed in the literature to study

---

* Assistant Professor, member of SAMPE
** Ph.D. Student
*** Visiting Scholar from the Institute of Aeronautics and Astronautics, National Cheng-Kong University, Taiwan, ROC

damage in fiber-reinforced laminated composites caused by low-velocity impact [12–20]. Numerous experiments were conducted by researchers using either drop weight tests or air guns with point-nose impactors. Several analytical models were also proposed to estimate impact damage.

However, the impact damage results produced by a point-nose impactor are three-dimensional and very complex, involving the dynamic interaction between matrix crack propagation and delamination growth. As a consequence, although a considerable amount of test data has been produced, the current understanding of impact damage is still very limited. The knowledge of impact damage on damage mechanisms and mechanics is very premature. Hence, the analyses proposed on the basis of the previous experiments are very preliminary.

Therefore, the objective of this investigation is to design a new impact tester to simplify impact damage so that impact damage mechanisms can be fundamentally understood and the essential parameters governing the impact damage event in composites can be identified. During the investigation, a new impact tester was designed and built. Tests were performed to generate impact damage in composites. An analytical model was also developed to simulate the impact test and to evaluate the impact damage.

2. A NEW IMPACT TESTER

A new impact testing facility was designed and built during this investigation. The major apparatus of the facility consists of a pressure tank, a precision-made barrel, a high precision timer, optical fiber photoelectric sensors, and supporting fixtures as shown in Figure 1. The essential characteristic of the design which is different from any others is the use of a rectangular barrel and the impactors. Because of the use of the rectangular barrel, the impactors were designed

into two parts, a rectangular base and the noses which can be changed (see Figure 2). Different types of noses can be mounted to the base to produce different types of damage patterns.

The impactor is driven by compressed air from the air tank through the rectangular barrel. The velocity of the impactor can be controlled by selecting the proper weights of the base and the nose of the impactor and adjusting the air pressure from the air tank. The impactor will hit on the target and rebound back into the barrel without leaving the barrel. Therefore, this facility can be used to evaluate the impact damage in composites as a function of the weight and velocity of the impactor and nose shape of the impactor. The range of the velocity of the impactor is between 2 and 30 m/sec, depending upon the weight of the impactor.

In this investigation, a line-nose impactor was chosen for the study as shown in Figure 2. The use of the line-nose impactor will result in an uniformly distributed transient dynamic loading across the specimen, which is clamped on two parallel free edges. It was expected that such uniform loading would produce a consistent and uniform damage pattern through the specimen width; hence, substantially simplifying impact damage mechanisms from a three-dimensional to a two-dimensional event.

3. EXPERIMENTS AND RESULTS

Extensive impact tests were performed to study impact damage in laminated composites subjected to a line-nose impact. Different ply orientations and various thicknesses of the specimens were selected for the tests. During impact, different weights and velocities of the impactor were also used as test parameters.

T300/976 Graphite/Epoxy prepregs were selected to fabricate specimen panels. An autoclave was used to cure the panels. Panels were then sliced into specimens by a diamond-coated saw. All the specimens were X-rayed before testing to evaluate internal pre-existing damage caused by curing or cutting. Initially, a standard cure cycle was selected to cure the panels. However, for some ply orientations, such as $[0_6/\pm 45_4/90_5]_s$, the cured panels under the standard cure cycle contained significant internal matrix cracks as shown in Figure 3. As a consequence, an altered cure cycle with a slower heat-up rate and longer curing time was chosen for most of the panels to minimize the matrix cracks due to the residual stresses. No matrix cracks were found in these panels.

Overall, more than one hundred tests were performed during this investigation. Significant results have been produced. Due to a limited space available, details of the test results are presented elsewhere [21], hence, only some typical results are presented in this paper.

3.1 Matrix Cracks and Delaminations

Figure 4 shows a typical schematic of the impact damage pattern in $[0_n/90_m]_s$ laminated composites impacted by a line-nose impactor. A few matrix cracks were generated in 90 degree plies and could be clearly seen from the sides of the specimen in two possible positions; one was near the center but away from the impacted area and the other was located near the ends of the clamped areas. An enlarged view of the impact damage near the center region is drawn in Figure 4. It strongly indicated that matrix cracking was the initial failure mode of impact damage in laminated composites. A photograph of a life-size specimen of $[0_6/90_2]_s$ after impact is shown in Figure 5. Apparently, delaminations were initiated from these matrix cracks (refered to as "critical" matrix cracks) and propagated along the interfaces between 0 degree plies and 90 degree plies. Figure 6 shows the X-radiograph of a

$[0_6/90_2]_s$ specimen before and after impact. No pre-matrix cracks were found in the specimen before impact. However, extensive micro-matrix cracks were detected in the X-radiograph made after impact. These cracks could not be seen by the naked eyes and were most likely generated during delamination growth. the cracks were confined to the extent of the size of delaminations. Similar results were also found for specimens with other ply orientations.

3.2 Thermal Residual Stresses

Due to the thermal expansion coefficient mismatch, manufacturing produces significant thermal residual stresses in laminated composites [22]. The amount of residual stresses depends strongly on the degree of the thermal coefficient mismatch, the ply orientation, and the cure cycle. For some ply orientations, residual stresses could well exceed the transverse tensile strength of each individual ply in the laminate and result in premature matrix cracks as shown in Figure 3 for a $[0_6/\pm 45_4/90_5]_s$ specimen under a standard cure cycle.

Figure 3 also shows the X-radiograph of a $[0_6/45_4/90_5]_s$ specimen with premature matrix cracks after impact. No additional matrix cracks were found after the impact, but delaminations were initiated from one of the existing matrix cracks and propagated into the interfaces with a similar pattern as shown in Figure 4. It was also found that for the specimens with pre-matrix cracks, the impact energy required to initiate damage was substantially lower than for those without pre-matrix cracks. However, for laminates without premature matrix cracks, the residual stresses still exist in the materials and could also have significantly affected impact damage as will be verified in the analysis in Section IV.

3.3 Impact Energy Threshold

By examining impacted specimens, it was found

that the impact energy, the mass and the velocity of the impactor, significantly affect the impact damage. There apparently exists an impact energy threshold beyond which damage occurs. Figure 7 presents the measured delamination sizes in $[0_6/90_2]_s$ and $[0_3/\pm 45_4/90_3]_s$ specimens as a function of impact energy. For $[0_6/90_2]_s$ laminates, the energy threshold is about 9 Joules beyond which significant delaminations were produced in the laminate. No damage (neither matrix cracks nor delaminations) was found in these specimens tested below that energy. The impact energy threshold for $[0_3/\pm 45_4/90_3]_s$ laminates is about 17 Joules. Similar phenomena was also found for the specimens with other ply orientations.

4. ANALYSIS AND NUMERICAL SIMULATIONS

During the investigation, an analytical model was also developed for modeling the impact damage in laminated composites. A two-dimensional transient dynamic finite element analysis was developed which can be used to calculate transient stresses, strains, and deformations inside the laminate during impact. The analysis was based on plane strain condition. Owing to the importance of the residual stresses to impact damage, the residual stresses resulting from manufacturing can also be calculated in the finite element analysis. Details of the finite element analysis is very lengthy, hence it will not be given here but can be found in [21]. The material properties used for the calculations are listed in Table 1.

In order to analyze the impact damage mechanisms, failure criteria were adopted in the model for predicting initial damage, especially the matrix cracking. Physically, there are three major stress components contributing to initial matrix cracking under the given loading condition considered in this investigation, as shown schematically in Figure 8. These are the interlaminar shear stress σ_{13}, in-plane tensile stress σ_{11}, and out-of-plane normal stress σ_{33}. In this investigation, three-dimensional Hashin matrix tensile failure criterion was selected for predicting initial failure [23]. The criterion can be expressed as follows:

$$\frac{1}{Y_T^2}(\sigma_{yy} + \sigma_{zz})^2 + \frac{1}{S^2}(\sigma_{yz}^2 - \sigma_{yy}\sigma_{zz}) + \frac{1}{S^2}(\sigma_{xy}^2 + \sigma_{xz}^2) \geq e_M \tag{1}$$

$$e_M \geq 1 \quad \text{failure}$$

$$e_M < 1 \quad \text{no failure}$$

where Y_T is the in situ ply transverse tensile strength [24,25] and S is the in situ ply shear strength [24–27]. The subscripts x and y indicate the directions parallel and normal to the fiber direction, respectively. The subscript z denotes the direction normal to the ply $(x - y)$ surface.

Table 2 shows, for a given mass, the predicted velocities, with and without inclusion of thermal residual stresses, required to cause initial matrix cracking for T300/ 976 Graphite/epoxy composites as compared with the test data. The predictions with consideration of thermal residual stresses agreed with data very well. However, for the calculations without thermal residual stresses, the predictions over estimated the results by as much as 200 percent. Clearly, the introduction of the thermal residual stresses in the analysis is crucial for prediction of impact damage in laminated composites.

Figure 9 shows the predicted strength ratio (e_M) of $[0_6/90_2]_s$ and $[0_3/\pm 45_4/90_3]_s$ specimens based on the Hashin criterion as a function of position. It indicated that the peak strength ratio occurs at two possible positions; one is close to the impacted area and the other is near the ends of the specimens. These predicted locations are also consistant with the experimental findings (see

Figure 10). Similar results were also found for other specimens. It is worth pointing out that the predicted matrix cracking near the center did not occur directly under the impacted area but a distance away from the area. By carefully examining the stress distributions near the center impacted area as shown in Figure 11, the interlaminar shear stress and the in-plane tensile stress were comparably higher than the out-of-plane normal stress. The out-of-plane normal stress σ_{33} decreased rapidly once it was away from the impacted area (see Figure 11). Apparently, the interlaminar shear stress and the in-plane tensile stress are the dominating stresses which cause matrix cracking during impact. Accordingly, the contribution of the out-of-plane normal stress to the initiation of impact damage is negligible.

To understand how the initial "critical" matrix cracks can initiate delaminations, material properties within the elements where matrix crack failure has been predicted were reduced according to the property degradation models developed previously [24,28]. The stresses and strains were recalculated in the finite element analysis at the same instant time again. Figures 12–14 show the stress distributions along the specimen length before and after material reduction. Peak out-of-plane normal tensile stresses along the interfaces were found comparably higher than the others immediately adjacent to the damaged elements. This clearly indicated that delamination would be initiated by the highly concentrated normal tensile stress due to mode I fracture. Two peak stresses along the upper and lower interfaces of 0 degree and 90 degree plies were found as shown in the Figure 12, which could initiate upper and lower interface delaminations propagating in two opposite directions. The results coincided with the physical findings of the delamination propagation as shown in Figures 4 and 5.

5. CONCLUDING REMARKS

An investigation was performed to study impact damage in laminated composites. Both experiments and analysis were involved in the study. Based on the test data and the numerical calculations, the following remarks can be made:

1) matrix crack was the initial failure mode,

2) delamination was initiated by the initial "critical" matrix cracks,

3) residual thermal stresses could substantially reduce impact resistance of composites,

4) there apparently exists an impact energy threshold above which impact damage occurs,

5) interlaminar shear stresses and in-plane tensile stresses are the dominating factors causing initial matrix cracks;

6) delamination growth was dominated by suddenly increased out-of-plane normal stress (Mode I fracture) as a result of matrix cracking.

6. ACKNOWLEDGEMENTS

The support of Army Research Office Contract No. DAAL 03-87-K-0115 and the National Science Foundation grant MSM 87-02892 is gratefully appreciated. The authors would also like to thank Mr. R. J. Downs for helping design and build the impact test facility.

7. REFERENCES

1. Talreja, R., "Transverse Cracking and Stiffness Reduction in Composite Laminates," J. of Composite Materials, 19, 355, (1985).

2. Sun, C. T. and Jen, K. C., "On the Effect of Matrix Cracks on Lamiante Strength," J. of Reiforced Plastics and Composites, 16, 208–222, (1987).

3. Peters, P. W. M., "The Strength Distribution of 90° Plies in 0/90/0 Graphite-Epoxy Laminates," J. of Composite Materials, 18, 545–556, (1984).

4. Garg, A. G., "Delamination—A Damage Mode in Composite Structures," Engineering Fracture Mechanics, 29, 557–584, (1988).

5. Bowles, D. E., "Effect of Microcracks on the Thermal Expansion of Composite Laminates," J. of Composite Materials, 17, 173–187, (1984).

6. Aronsson, C. and Bäcklund, J., "Tensile Fracture of Laminates with Cracks," J. of Composite Materials, 20, 287–307, (1986).

7. Dvorak, G. J., Laws, N. and Hejazi, M., "Analysis of Progressive Matrix Cracking in Composite Laminates, I. Thermoelastic Properties of a Ply with Cracks," J. of Composite Materials, 19, 216–234, (1985).

8. Manders, P. W., Chou, T., Jones, F. R. and Rock, J. W., "Statistical Analysis of Multiple Fracture in 0°/90°/0° Glass Fiber/Epoxy Resin Laminates," J. Material Science, 18, 2876–2889, (1983).

9. Garrett, K. W. and Bailey, J. E., "Multiple Transverse Fracture in 90° Cross-Ply Laminates of a Glass Fibre-Reinforced Polyester," J. of Material Science, 12, 157–168, (1977).

10. Parvizi, A. and Bailey, J. E., "On Multiple Transverse Cracking in Glass Fibre Epoxy Cross-Ply Laminates," J. of Material Science, 13, 2131–2136, (1978).

11. Parvizi, A., Garrett, K. W. and Bailey, J. E., "Constrained Cracking in Glass Fibre-Reinforced Epoxy Cross-Ply Laminates," J. of Material Science, 13, 195–2015, (1978).

12. Wu, H. T. and Chang, F. K., "Transient Dynamic Analysis of Laminated Composite Plates Subjected to Transverse Impact," J. of Computers and Structures, (To appear in March 1989 issue).

13. Wu, H. T. and Springer, G. S., "Measurements of Matrix Cracking and Delamination Caused by Impact on Composite Plates," J. of Composite Materials, 22:6, 518–532, 1988.

14. Wu, H. T. and Springer, G. S., "Impact Induced Stresses, Strains and Delaminations in Composite Plates," J. of Composite Materials, 22:6, 533–560, 1988.

15. Joshi, S. P. and Sun, C. T., "Impact-Induced Fracture in Quasi-Isotropic Laminate," J. Composite Technology and Research, 19:2, 40–46, (1986).

16. Glosse, J. H. and Mori, P. B. Y., "Impact Damage Characterization of Graphite/ Epoxy Laminates," Proceedings of the Third Technical Conference of the American Society for Compostes, Seattle, WA, 334–353, (1988).

17. Joshi, S. P., "Impact-Induced Damage Initiation Analysis: An Experimental Study," Proceedings of the Third Technical Conference of the American Society for Compostes, Seattle, WA, 325–333, (1988).

18. Ross, C. A. and Malvern, L. E., Sierakowski, R. L. and Taketa, N., "Finite-Element Analysis of Interlaminar Shear Stress Due to Local Impact," Recent Advnaces in Comp. in the United States and Japan, ASTM STP 864,(J. P. Vinson and M. Taya, Eds.) American Society for Testing and Materials, Philadelphia, PA, 335–367, (1985).

19. Aggour, H. and Sun, C. T., "Finite Element Analysis of a Laminated Composite Plate Subjected to Circularly Distributed Central

Impact Loading," J. Computers and Structures, 28:6, 729–736, (1988).

20. Sun, C. T. and Rechak,S., "Effect of Adhesive Layers on Impact Damage in Composite Laminates," Composite Materials: Testing and Design (Eighth Conf.), ASTM STP 972 (J. D. Whitcomb, Ed.), American Society for Testing and Materials, Philadelphia, PA, 97–123, (1988).

21. Chang, F. K. and Choi, H. Y., "Impact Damage Mechanics of Laminated Composites by a Line-Nose Impactor," J. of Composite Materials, (Submitted).

22. Flaggs, D. L. and Kural, M. H., "Experimental Determination of the In Situ Transverse Lamina Strength in Graphite/Epoxy Laminate," J. of Composite Materials, 16, 103–116, (1982).

23. Hashin, Z., "Failure Criteria for Unidirectional Fiber Composites," J. Applied Mechanics, 47, 329–334, (1980).

24. Chang, F. K. and Lessard, L. B., "Damage Tolerance of Laminated Compostes Containing an Open Hole and Subjected to Compressive Loadings: Part I—Analysis," J. of Composite Materials, (Submitted).

25. Lessard, L. B. and Chang, F. K., "Damage Tolerance of Laminated Compostes Containing an Open Hole and Subjected to Compressive Loadings: Part II—Experiment," J. of Composite Materials, (Submitted).

26. Chang, F. K. and Chen, M., "the In Situ Ply Shear Strength Distributions in Graphite/ Epoxy Laminated Composites," J. of Composite Materials, 21, 708–732, (1987).

27. Chang, F. K., Tang, J. M. and Peterson, D. G., "The Effect of Testing Methods on the Shear Strength Distribution in Laminated Composites," J. of Reinforced Plastics and Composites, 6, 304–318, (1987).

28. Chang, F. K. and Chang, K. Y., "A Progressive Damage Model for Laminated Composites Containing Stress Concentrations," J. of Composite Materials, 21, 834–855, (1987).

Table 1. Material properties of T300/976 used in the calculations.

Moduli	Symbol (unit)	
In-plane longitudinal modulus	E_{xx} (Gpa)	156
In-plane transverse modulus	E_{yy} (Gpa)	9.09
In-plane shear modulus	G_{xy} (Gpa)	6.96
Out-of-plane shear modulus	G_{yz} (Gpa)	3.24
In-plane poisson's ratio	v_{xy}	0.228
Out-of-plane poisson's ratio	v_{yz}	0.400
Density	ρ (Kg/m^3)	1540
Thermal expansion coefficient	α_x((μm/m)/K)	0.33
	α_y((μm/m)/K)	7.78

Strength	Symbol (unit)	
Longitudinal tension	X_T (Mpa)	1520
Longitudinal compression	X_C (Mpa)	1590
Transverse tension	Y_T (Mpa)	49
Transverse compression	Y_C (Mpa)	252
Ply longitudinal shear *	S_C (Mpa)	105

Impactor	Symbol (unit)	
Modulus	E (Gpa)	207
Poisson's ratio	v	0.3
Nose radius	r (mm)	1.5

* Shear strength measured from a cross-ply [0/90]s composites

Table 2. The velocities of an impactor required to initiate "critical" matrix cracks in T300/976 composites. Comparison between the data and the predictions.

Ply orientation	mass (Kg)	length (cm)	Predicted Velocity (m/s)		Test Velocity (m/s)
			Without residual stress	With residual stress	
[07/901]s	0.08	10	40	25	22±2.0
[06/902]s	0.08	10	45	20	16.5±1.0
[03/±454/903]s	0.12	10	50	21	17±0.2

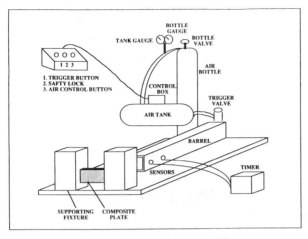

Figure 1. A schematic of the impact test facility.

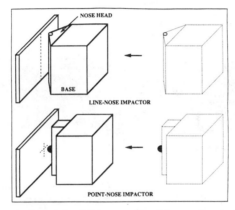

Figure 2. A Description of the impactor. (Above): line-nose impactor. (Below): point-nose impactor.

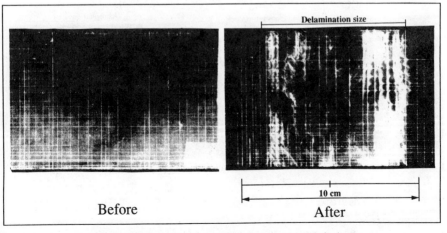

Figure 3. X-Radiographs of $[0_6/\pm45_4/90_5]_s$ specimen before and after impact.

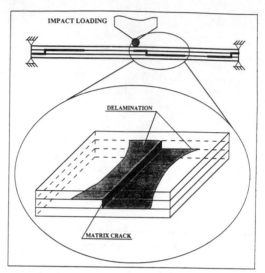

Figure 4. A schematic of the typical impact damage pattern in $[0_n/90_m]_s$ composites impacted by a line-nose impactor.

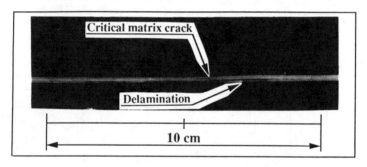

Figure 5. A photograph of a sideview of a life size specimen of $[0_6/90_2]_s$ after impact.

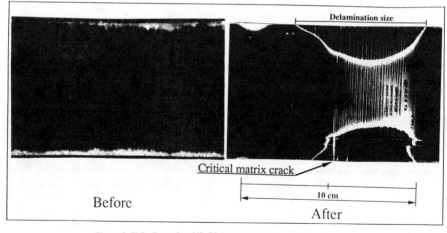

Figure 6. X-Radiographs of $[0_6/90_2]_s$ specimen before and after impact.

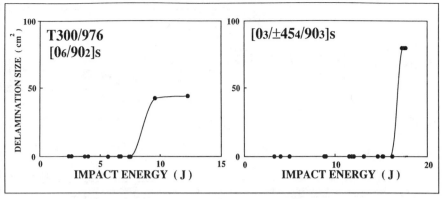

Figure 7. The measured delamination sizes in $[0_6/90_2]_s$ and $[0_3/\pm45_4/90_3]_s$ impacted specimens as a function of impact energy.

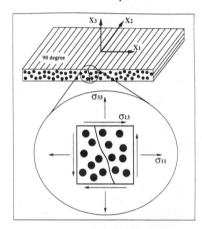

Figure 8. A schematic of the major stress components contributing the matrix cracking in 90 degree layers.

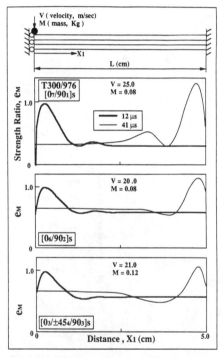

Figure 9. The predicted strength ratio (e_M: Hashin criterion) of $[0_6/90_2]_s$ and $[0_3/\pm45_4/90_3]_s$ specimens as a function of position.

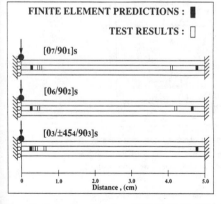

Figure 10. Comparison of locations of initial "critical" matrix cracks between the data and the predictions.

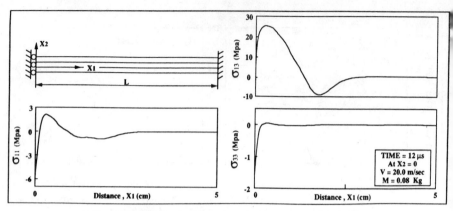

Figure 11. Instant stress distributions near the center impacted area of a $[0_6/90_2]_s$
specimen (No thermal residual stresses were included).

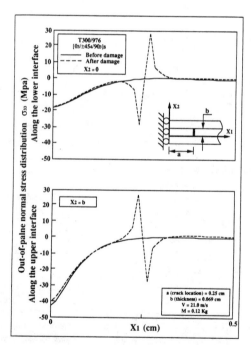

Figure 12. Comparison of instant out-of-plane normal stress distributions along the upper
and lower interface of 90 degree plies before and after material degradation
within the damaged area (No thermal residual stresses were included).

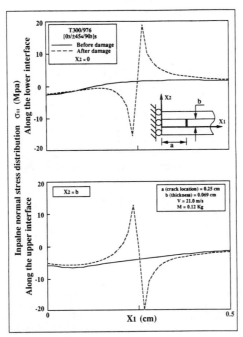

Figure 13. Comparison of instant in-plane normal stress distributions along the upper and lower interface of 90 degree plies before and after material degradation within the damaged area (No thermal residual stresses were included).

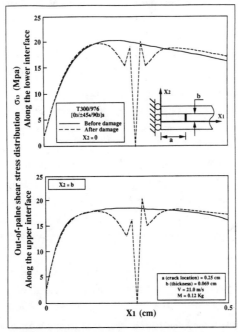

Figure 14. Comparison of instant interlaminar shear stress distributions along the upper and lower interface of 90 degree plies before and after material degradation within the damaged area (No thermal residual stresses were included).

NEW CONCEPTS IN DAMAGE TOLERANT COMPOSITES - LIGHTLY CROSSLINKED THERMOSETS

L. D. Bravenec, A. G. Filippov, and K. C. Dewhirst

Shell Development Company

P. O. Box 1380

Houston, Texas 77251

Abstract

Single phase, "lightly crosslinked thermosets" have been developed which have a tailored range of toughness properties. The dependence of composite material impact (delamination) resistance and damage tolerance (post impact compression) on resin and composite properties has been studied. Relationships between resin elongation and compact tension toughness, G_{Ic} and G_{IIc} delamination toughness, and compression after impact (CAI) are examined. These relationships, in addition to other processing and performance properties, are useful for design and selection of materials for applications.

1. INTRODUCTION

In order to provide products for the advanced composites industry, we have developed a resin materials technology termed lightly crosslinked thermosets (LXT's). The objective is to provide candidate materials which possess the required balance of processing and mechanical performance properties.

St Clair, et al.[1] at NASA-Langley have identified general requirements for resin matrix systems including:

(a) monomer or oligomer (permits low T and viscosity processing),

(b) simple stable formulation (provides product consistency),

(c) liquid or low melting solid ,

(d) polymerizes without evolution of volatiles, and

(e) forms solvent resistant, tough polymer.

More specifically, our goal has been to develop resins which are processable at maximum temperatures of 177 °C (350 °F), and result in a composite with unidrectional hot (82 °C)/wet compression strengths of 1-1.3 GPa (150-200 ksi) and compression after impact (CAI) strengths of 0.28-0.34 GPa (40-50 ksi). In a previous paper we described processing and property data for two research materials, RSS-982 and RSS-1474[2].

RSS-982 and RSS-1474 are the first two examples of lightly crosslinked thermosetting (LXT) resins, a materials technology Shell is pursuing. New backbone components are incorporated into tailored polymer chain structures. In general, LXT's are single phase polymers, which are formed from monomeric species and use both stiff and flexible backbone moieties to provide temperature and toughness properties.

The following is a description of some of the structure-property relationships for these polymers, and also, the techniques used to form the desired structures. Subsequently, we discuss the translation of resin properties to required composite performance properties.

2. DESIGNING LXT POLYMERS

A traditional way of toughening epoxy thermosets is to add an excess of tetrafunctional amine curing agent (increased M_c for toughenability) and a CTBN rubber modifier. The general result of this approach is that modulus is reduced with CTBN rubber addition and Tg is reduced for corresponding gains in toughness. Example data are shown in Figure 1 for EPON HPT® Resin 1079 cured with EPON HPT Curing Agent 1062, and this approach is discussed in a companion paper[3].

As noted previously, our approach is to build a lightly crosslinked thermoset architecture that provides temperature performance and toughness properties. The crosslink density is reduced by incorporating predominantly difunctional constituents, not by a stoichiometric imbalance. Additionally, "stiffened" polymer chain backbone components are used to provide required Tg's at reduced crosslink densities. A schematic of this thermomechanical-toughness improvement strategy is presented in Figure 2 for Shell's EPON HPT Resin and Curing Agent technology and the lightly crosslinked thermosets (LXT's).

Stiffened backbone components are moieties which enhance Tg of the polymer by containing segments which require more thermal energy for mobility. Aromatic or fused aromatic rings are examples. In flexible segments, such as aliphatic linkages, a number of bond rotations can be activated at lower temperatures. Examples of resins that have been used as stiff and flexible components are DGBPFL (diglycidyl ether of bisphenol 9-fluorenone) and DGBPA (diglycidyl ether of bisphenol acetone), respectively, as shown in Figure 3. Given a description of the polymer structure, the polymer Tg can be approximated as presented in Figure 4.

One method of producing lightly crosslinked structures is to react a di-epoxide with a bisphenol for linear chain extension, as shown in Figure 5a. A slight excess (5 to 10% equivalents) of epoxy is incorporated, which reacts with formed hydroxyl groups to provide a lightly crosslinked structure, illustrated in Figure 5b. These crosslinking branched points have been identified by NMR spectrocopy, as shown in Figure 6, and correspond to resin stoichiometry. For example, when the ratio of phenolic to epoxy end groups was 0.96, 4 percent crosslinking was expected and 5 percent was observed by NMR spectroscopy.

The relationships between chain stiffness, crosslinking, and resulting Tg and toughness have been determined for compositions of BPFL and BPA moieties as shown in Figures 7 and 8. In Figure 7 the effects of changing crosslink density on properties is illustrated. The basic material was a 50/50 ratio of stiff BPFL and more flexible BPA moieties. The crosslink density was varied from 0 (essentially linear polymer) to 60 percent (which means that 3 out of every 5 repeat units incorporate branched tie points). The Tg of the linear polymer was 170 ^{o}C, and the Tg increased linearly with increasing crosslinking, as predicted. The concurrent decrease in fracture energy was observed as the high toughness of the linear polymer of 1030 J/m^2 was reduced to 280 J/m^2 at 60 percent crosslink density. Note that the fracture energy of a standard aerospace prepreg resin based on TGMDA/DDS is approximately 70-100 J/m^2.[4] For the fixed composition of chain groups the modulus also increased with increasing crosslink density. One conjecture is that the degree of chain packing was constant and thus chain-chain forces which contribute to glassy modulus of the polymer remained relatively constant. These forces were bolstered by increasing bonds between chains (crosslinks) for the studied range of crosslink densities.

The effects on properties of changing the ratio of stiff BPFL linkages to flexible BPA linkages is shown in Figure 8. The all-BPA, linear polymer backbone is represented on the Y-axis as 0 percent stiff component. The Tg and fracture energy were 115 ^{o}C and 5690 J/m^2, respectively. The 100 percent stiff polymer is the 100 percent BPFL backbone, linear polymer. The Tg increases to 212 ^{o}C, however, the toughness is reduced to 176 J/m^2. A relative maximum in toughness and a minimum in modulus is observed at 40-50 percent ratio of BPA/BPFL moiety. Poorer chain packing resulting from most heterogeneous group content may have resulted in lower modulus, but allowed greater local chain mobility and toughness.

As shown by the previous discussion, we have developed predictive calculations, analytically confirmed selected polymer structures, and developed resin structures which provide designed properties.

3. COMPOSITE TOUGHNESS RELATIONSHIPS

As resin/fiber composites are being considered for primary aircraft structures, a challenge for the materials developer is to correlate resin properties with key performance properties of composite laminates including unidirectional compression (RT and hot/wet) strength, delamination resistance, and compression after impact (CAI) strength. Results by Johnston[5] and analytical predictions by Hahn[6] indicate that compression properties are primarily dependent on matrix shear modulus. Hunston[4] and others[7] have surveyed the relationship between Mode I fracture toughness of the neat resin and Mode I delamination toughness of the composite.

The CAI test, however, includes an impact event and subsequent compression strength evaluation. Delamination toughness alone, especially in Mode I, does not seem sufficient to provide CAI strength[8,9]. A useful clarification is to separate the CAI evaluation into tests of (1) impact (delamination) resistance and (2) (resulting) damage tolerance. Dost, et al.[10] have demonstrated that residual compression strength properties of the CAI panel are primarily dependent on the size of the damage produced during impact. Thus, CAI damage tolerance for a variety of resin systems seems more dependent on delamination geometry than on resin matrix properties. The issue then centers on providing matrix properties which result in laminate impact resistance, i.e. a small delamination zone. Literature results indicate that if the delamination area is less than 5 cm^2, resulting from a 67 J/cm (1500 in-lbs/in) impact, residual compression strengths are obtained which are on the order of 0.31-0.34 GPa (45-50 ksi)[8,11,12] and 0.006 strain[10].

In Table 1, neat resin and composite data is presented for two systems, RSS-982 and RSS-1474. These two materials were significantly different in toughness properties. RSS-982 had a moderate toughness of 460 J/m^2 as measured by the mini-compact tension test (modified ASTM E399), but a high flexural elongation of greater than 8 percent. Conversely, RSS-1474 had a high resin toughness of 1870 J/m^2, but had a relatively low elongation of 3 percent. For both of these materials the neat resin G_{Ic} toughness was translated well to the composite delamination toughness as measured by the double cantilever beam test (Boeing XBMS 8-276). Therefore, RSS-982 was tougher by measurement of area under the stress strain curve, whereas, RSS-1474 had significantly higher mode I toughness both in the neat resin and composite.

The mode II delamination toughness further distinguishes the toughness properties of these two materials. For RSS-982 this value, determined by the end notch flex method[13], was 1310 J/m^2, a factor of 1.7 times the mode I delamination toughness. However, for RSS-1474 the mode II toughness was 960 J/m^2, which was approximately 60 percent of the mode I delamination toughness.

The comparison of mode I delamination fracture toughness with compression strength after impact (Figure 9) for these two resins and others reported in the literature[8,9,11,12,14,15] shows that there is no correlation between GIc and CAI. On the other hand, Figure 10 shows that mode II fracture toughness[8,9,15] is a more preferred parameter to predict damage tolerance of composite laminates.

4. CONCLUSIONS

The results indicate that mode II toughness is key in delamination resistance of composites during impact, and thus higher residual strengths are retained after impact, as mode II toughness is increased. Single phase, lightly crosslinked thermosetting resins such as RSS-982 and RSS-1474 provide a variety of toughness properties. LXT resin structure-property relationships have been described, as well as the methodolgy to produce selected polymer structures. Thus, as the understanding of the relationships between composite performance properties and resin property requirements increases, improved materials can be developed.

5. REFERENCES

[1]St. Clair, T. L., N. J. Johnston, and R. M. Baucom, "High Performance Composites Research at NASA-Langley," Report No. 880110.

[2]Bravenec, L. D., K. C. Dewhirst, and A. G. Fillipov, 33rd International SAMPE Symposium, 1377-84, March 7-9, 1988.

[3]Schlaudt, L. M., R. S. Bauer, and C. A. Blackburn, 34th International SAMPE Symposium, May 8-11, 1989.

[4]Hunston, D. L., Composites Technology Review, 6 (4) 176 (1984).

[5]Johnston, N. L., "Synthesis and Toughness Properties of Resins and Composites," NASA CP-2321, 75-95 (1984).

[6]Hahn, H. T. and J. G. Williams, "Compression Failure Mechanisms in Unidirectional Composites," NASA TM-85834 (1984).

[7]Toughened Composites, N. L. Johnston, ed., ASTM STP 937 (1987).

[8]Odagiri, N., T. Muraki, and K. Tobukuro, 33rd International SAMPE Symposium, 272-83, March 7-9, 1988.

[9]Maikuma, H., J. W. Gillespie, and D. J. Wilkins, "Analysis and Experimental Evaluation of the Center Notch Flexural Test Specimen for Mode II Interlaminar Fracture," J. Comp. Mat., (accepted for publication).

[10]Dost, E. F., L. B. Ilcewicz, and J. H. Gosse, Proceedings of the American Society for Composites 3rd Technical Conference, 354-63, September 25-29, 1988.

[11]Gawin, I., 31st International SAMPE Symposium, 1204-13, April 7-10, 1986.

[12]Almen, G., et al., 33rd International SAMPE Symposium, 979-89, March 7-10, 1988.

[13]Carlsson, L. W., J. W. Gillespie, and R. B. Pipes, J. Comp. Mat., 20, 594-604 (1986).

[14]Chang, I. Y., 33rd International SAMPE Symposium, 194-205, March 7-10, 1988.

[15]Becht, G. J. and J. W. Gillespie, "Numerical and Experimental Evaluation of Mode III Interlaminar Toughness of Composite Materials, 'Polym. Comp. (accepted for publication).

5. BIOGRAPHIES

LARRY BRAVENEC obtained his Ph.D. in Chemical Engineering in 1983 from the University of Delaware. He joined Shell Development Company in the Resins Department, Advanced Composites Applications and has worked on development of wet filament winding and resin transfer molding systems for composite fabrication. Current activities include development of new damage tolerant resin systems for commercial aircraft composites and other applications.

KEN DEWHIRST joined Shell Development Company in 1959 at Emeryville, California as a research chemist. He has served in a variety of management positions including Manager-Corporate Chemistry and Manager-Technical Support/Resins. His research interests include organic synthesis, homogeneous organometallic catalysis, and structure-property relationships of polymeric systems. He is currently Research Associate in the Resins Department developing new resins for advanced composite applications.

ANDREI FILIPPOV joined Shell Development Company after obtaining a Ph.D. in Materials Science from the University of Massachusetts in 1981. Currently, he is a Staff Research Engineer in Engineering R&D at the Westhollow Research Center. His background is in structure-mechanical properties of polymeric materials. His work since joining Shell has been the study of deformation and fracture behavior of homopolymers, polymeric blends, and composite materials. Other interests include thermodynamics of deformation, stability and fracture of polymeric solids.

Table 1: Mechanical Properties

PROPERTY	RSS-982		RSS-1474	
Tg (tan delta)	177 $^{\circ}$C	350 $^{\circ}$F	170 $^{\circ}$C	338 $^{\circ}$F
Flexural Strength	138 MPa	20 ksi	101 MPa	14.7 ksi
Flexural Elongation	> 8%		3%	
Flexural Modulus	2.62 GPa	380 ksi	3.72 GPa	540 ksi
Flex Modulus (82 $^{\circ}$C/wet)	2.41 GPa	350 ksi	3.38 GPa	460 ksi
G_{Ic} (mini compact tension)	460 J/m^2	2.6 in-lbs/in^2	1870 J/m^2	10.7 in-lbs/in^2
G_{Ic} (double torsion)	400 J/m^2	2.3 in-lbs/in^2	-	-
COMPOSITE	with AS4-unsized		with IM6-G	
(64 % volume fiber)				
Short Beam Shear	69 MPa	10 ksi	8.3 MPa	12 ksi
RT/Dry Compression	1.17 GPa	170 ksi	1.38 GPa	200 ksi
82 $^{\circ}$C/Wet Compression	1.05 GPa	152 ksi	1.17 GPa	170 ksi
G_{Ic} (DCB)	780 J/m^2	4.5 in-lbs/in^2	1540 J/m^2	8.8 in-lbs/in^2
G_{IIc} (ENF)	1310 J/m^2	7.5 in-lbs/in^2	960 J/m^2	5.5 in-lbs/in^2
CAI	290 MPa	42 ksi	214 MPa	31 ksi

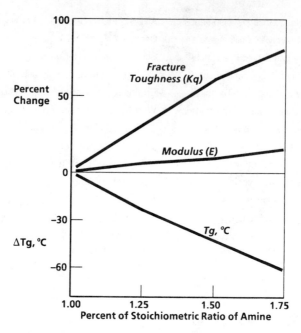

Figure 1: Influence of Curing Agent Stoichiometry on Fracture Toughness, Modulus, and Tg of EPON HPT Resin 1079/EPON HPT Curing Agent 1062 with 10 phr CTBN. Reference material Kq = 0.75 MPa-m$^{1/2}$ (0.68 ksi-in$^{1/2}$), E = 2.9 GPa (423 ksi), and Tg (tan delta) = 240 °C.

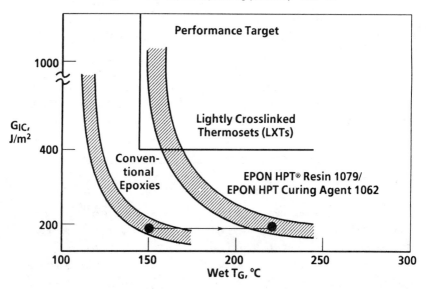

Figure 2: Toughness-Temperature Performance Improvement Strategy for Shell Products Incorporating "Stiffened" Backbone Components.

720

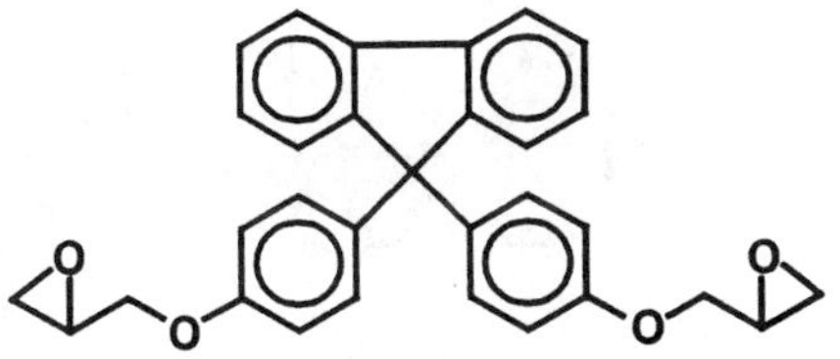

	Linear Polymers
	Tg, °C
DGBPA/BPA	115
DGBPFL/BPA	175
DGBPFL/BPFL	220

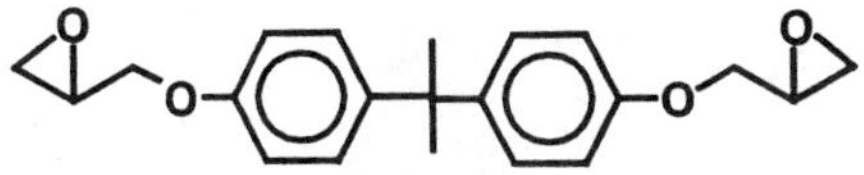

Figure 3: Examples of "Stiff" and "Flexible" Chain Resin Constituents, DGBPFL (diglycidyl ether of bisphenol fluorenone) and DGBPA.

Thermoplastics

$$\log Tg \sim \frac{\text{mol Rings}}{\text{mol Total}}$$

Thermosets

$$\Delta Tg \sim 1/M_C$$

Example

Resin	Type	Tg, °C	
		Calc.	Obs.
Polystyrene	TP	99	107
Peek	TP	152	145
BPA/DGBPA	LXT	112	115
RSS-982	LXT	176	175
MDA/DGBPA	TS	176	180
1062/1079*	TS	241	246

* *EPON HPT CURING AGENT 1062 / EPON HPT Resin 1079*

Figure 4: Tg Calculations Based on Chain Structure and Observation.

721

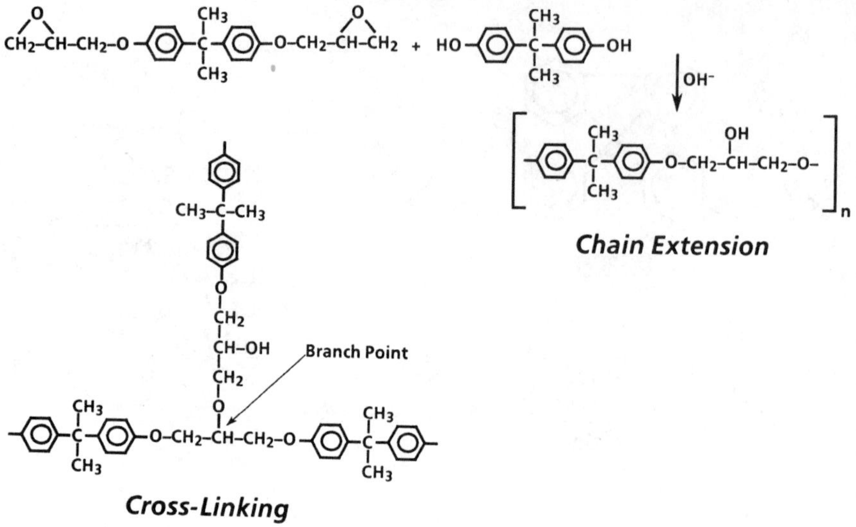

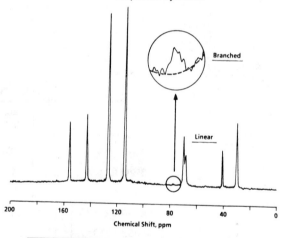

Chain Extension

Cross-Linking

Branch Point

Figure 5: Chain Extension (a) and Crosslinking (b) Reactions for Epoxy-Bisphenol Systems.

P/E	NMR, % Branch	Gel, %	Tg, °C	Kq, psi $\sqrt{in.}$
1.00	–	75	112	3600
0.96	5	100	115	3600
0.90	9	100	118	3700

Figure 6: Control of Crosslink Density; Verification by NMR Spectroscopy for the DGBPA/BPA System.

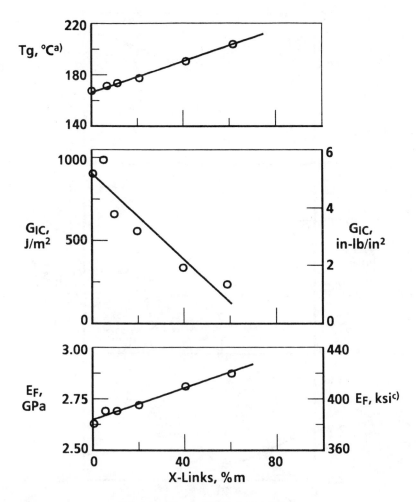

Properties vs. X-Link Density

a) DSC
b) Mini Compact Tension
c) 3 Point Bending

Figure 7: Properties Versus Crosslink Density. Base System is 50/50 Ratio of BPFL/BPA Chain Moieties.

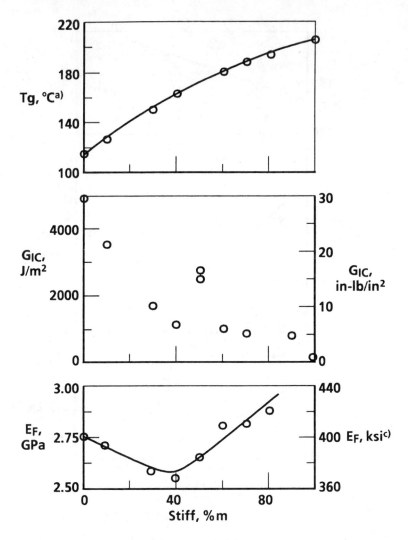

Properties vs. Stiff Content

a) DSC
b) Mini Compact Tension
c) 3 Point Bending

Figure 8: Properties Versus BPFL Content. Base System is 100 Percent BPA
Chain Moiety at 4 Percent Crosslinking.

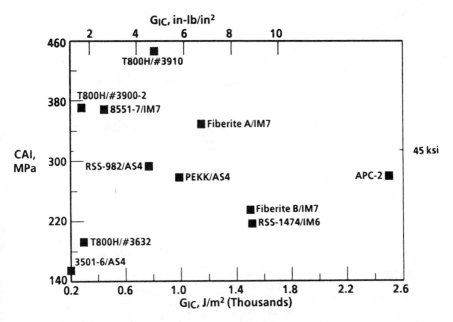

Figure 9: Compression After Impact (CAI) strength versus
Mode I delamination toughness[8,9,11,12,14,15].

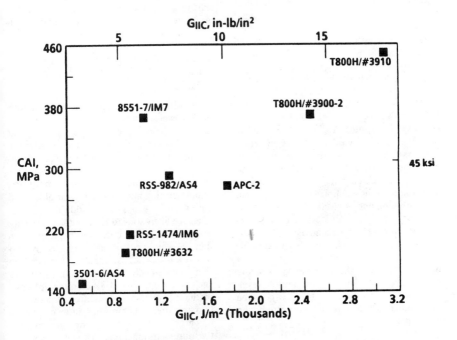

Figure 10: Compression After Impact (CAI) strength versus
Mode II delamination toughness[8,9,15].

DETERMINATION OF MULTIVARIABLE GI AND GIIc FRACTURE TOUGHNESS
RESPONSE FUNCTIONS FOR FIBER/RESIN COMPOSITES

Todd K. Saczalski
GENERAL DYNAMICS, SPACE SYSTEMS
P. O. Box 85990, San Diego, CA 92138 • MZ C1-8440

Abstract

This paper examines a factorial-based design strategy which provides an efficient and statistically reliable means for accurately assessing the influence of multivariable effects on the fracture toughness of laminated fiber/resin composites. The experimental results obtained from the above test strategy is utilized to form an empirical response function or polynomial which relates fracture toughness for values of the variables which were not tested. In addition, the response function assists in the identification of key variables and interactions of key variables which may influence synergistic effects not easily ascertained by the traditional single variable test strategies. The experimental methodology is demonstrated by testing for multivariable GI and GIIc fracture toughness of laminated graphite/epoxy composites. Variables examined in the GI example included: fiber/resin ratios; stiffness/flexibility (i.e., thickness and span lengths of end-notch flexure (ENF) test articles); and "crack-start" length variations. The results of the example study showed that fiber bridging and edge conditions could significantly alter the GI mode of fracture toughness by at least 350 percent. The GII results showed that the "crack-start" length variable was the most significant factor likely to alter the interlaminar shear mode of fracture toughness. The polynomial form of the resultant test data has potential for incorporation into numerical/ analytical failure prediction techniques

1. INTRODUCTION

This paper focuses on a multivariable experimental/empirical methodology for efficiently analyzing and evaluating fracture toughness and damage tolerance of fiber/resin composites. Lightweight composites offer beneficial performance advantages, relative to metallic structures, for use in high-performance aircraft, ballistic missiles, and earth orbiting space structures. In all of the above composite structure applications, extreme variations in temperature can lead to subtle forms of damage such as interlaminar shear delamination. For instance, recent studies have found that graphite/epoxy composites subjected to certain thermal cycling environments such as those associated with near earth orbiting structures, would experience extensive interlaminar ply failure and loss of structural integrity [1].

In addition to the thermal problem, various subtle levels of surface impact damage associated with normal handling conditions prior to mission use could also lead to reduction in fracture toughness, residual strength, and general degradation of mission performance capabilities. Furthermore, resin impurities, manufacturing and processing variables, and void sites formed by resin additives or volatiles, are likely to lead to sites for stress concentrations and micro-mechanical resin damage which are not easily modeled by analytical approaches. Morgan[2, 3, 4] points out that commercially available pre-preg epoxies such as tetraglycidyl –4, 4' –diaminodiph enylmethane (TGDDM), which are currently used in many aircraft composites, often contain as much as 15–20% fewer epoxide groups than the pure tetrafunctional TGDDM molecule and these show large variations in cure reaction rates of samples taken from the same prepreg unit. These inhomogeneities and materials processing irregularities are often not within the control of the fabricator and can result in stress concentration sites and regions for enhanced micro-cracking and resin crazing when the composite is thermally or mechanically cycled or shock loaded.

Improved fracture toughness and resistance to ply delamination in filament wound composites can be obtained through several means, such as: 1) crack deflection mechanisms in the resin matrix and along the fiber/matrix interface; 2) fiber splitting along the fiber length (i.e., occurs in Kevlar 49 aramid fibers); and 3) fiber bridging resulting from nested fiber groups of adjacent lamina. In carbon fibers the mechanism of lengthwise fiber splitting, with subsequent crack-energy absorption, is not likely to occur. Similarly, the energy-absorbing crack-deflection mechanism along the fiber/matrix interface is not likely to occur due to the brittle nature of the carbon fiber. On the other hand, the improved fracture toughness effect of fiber bridging in graphite/epoxy and S-glass/epoxy was noted by Saczalski[5] for the modes I, II, and III interlaminar toughness on wet-wound composites. Subsequent studies by W. S. Johnson of NASA Langley[6] and Scott Beckwith of Hercules[7] also noted improved mode I fracture toughness with the fiber bridging effect showing increases as high as approximately 350 percent in the mode I strain energy release rate values. Studies on the effects of addition of elastomers and plasticizers to epoxy resin systems for enhanced fracture toughness have also been conducted and show some increase in fracture toughness, although not as great an increase as obtained from fiber bridging[8, 9, 10]. Other factors such as moisture absorption, fiber/resin densities, laminate geometry, edge effects, and size of crack initiation mechanisms also cause significant variations and possibly synergistic effects in the fracture toughness and damage tolerance of fiber/resin composite.

One important point that can be inferred from the above is that "pure" laboratory-controlled test articles are not likely to be representative of the response associated with "real world" manufactured structural component subjected to materials processing irregularities and a range of thermal/mechanical load conditions. Along these lines, Bau and Beckwith from Hercules have investigated the influences of certain "real-world" variables related to fracture mechanics of filament wound case materials[11]. This paper attempts to provide another approach for obtaining an efficient understanding of multivariable damage tolerance and fracture toughness of composites manufactured in realistic environments that includes processing variables as part of the matrix of parameters. The approach utilized in this paper to study multivariable effects is based on the factorial method which has been widely used in the chemical processing industry. Details and examples of the experimental/analytical approach are covered in the following sections.

2. MULTIVARIABLE EXPERIMENTAL DESIGN STRATEGIES

The use of multivariable experimental design strategies based on the factorial response polynonial approach enables easy identification of key variables and interactions, as well as inexpensive prediction of system response for combinations of variable parameters not tested. Obviously, if an adequate theory is available for prediction of the multivariable response of interest, the theory should be employed to derive a compatible experimental strategy to "fill-in" the missing pieces of the puzzle. However, in most "real-world" situations the theories are somewhat limited in reliable predictive capability for multivariable interactions and associated failure mechanics of composite structures. For such situations the development of an experimentally-based empirical model offers certain advantages of confidence and statistical reliability. A careful initial experimental screening study can be conducted through methods such as the Plackett-Burman method[12] to help "weed-out" unimportant variables. Dimensionless analysis can also be used to help reduce the number of unknowns, and hence experiments, required for development of accurate predictive polynomial response functions.

The basis for most multivariable experimental design strategies is the factorial method. The two-level factorial method utilizes maximum and minimum levels (High and Low) for each variable being examined. The above method requires that all independent variables (p) and dependent variables be carefully identified. The minimum number of tests (n) required for statistical reliability is given as:

$$n = 2x(2^p) \quad (1)$$

where all tests are run in a random order with at least 1 repeat test run for each test condition. The test results are combined into polynomial form (response surfaces) and pooled standard deviations along with the student "t" test are used to evaluate significant variables and interaction factors of the polynomial coefficients. Equation 2, shown below, illustrates the general form of the multivariable response surface polynomial for a two-level (high ($+$) and low ($-$)) factorial situation.

$$Y_{out} = a_0 + a_1x_1 + a_2x_2 + \ldots a_ix_i + \ldots \quad (2)$$
$$a_{12}x_1x_2 + \ldots a_{ij}x_ix_j + \ldots$$
$$a_{123}x_1x_2x_3 + \ldots \text{etc}$$

The term Y_{out} represents the dependent variable response. The polynomial coefficients are obtained from certain combinations of the test results and are also known as the regression coefficients. The tests are run in a random order, but the combination of test parameters (x_i) have a unique configuration which will be explained through an example which follows. The "x_i" terms represent a dimensionless scaled version of the actual independent variables (X_i) with maximum and minimum values being scaled to $+1$ and -1 respectively. Equation 3 relates the actual values of the independent variables (X_i) to the scaled values (x_i).

$$X_i(scaled) = \frac{X_i(Actual) - (X_i(Highest) + X_i(Lowest))/2}{(X_i(Highest) - X_i(Lowest))/2}$$
$$(3)$$

Statistically significant factor effects (SFE) can be evaluated by equation 4 where the term $\bar{S}$ represents the pooled standard deviation (given in equation 5) and "t" represents the approximate student "t" values for a desired level of statistical confidence. The value of "p"

$$SFE = \bar{S}t(2/(pr))^{1/2} \quad (4)$$

represents the number of variables being examined and "r" represents the number of replicates of each test condition. The value of S_i

$$\bar{S}^2 pooled = \frac{\sum_{i=1}^{N}(r_i - 1)S_i^2}{\sum_{i=1}^{N}(r_i - 1)} \quad (5)$$

the above equation denotes the variation associated with each parameter being tested. The "N" term designates the number of basic test combinations of the independent variables. Tests for the validity of utilizing a linear polynomial approximation as opposed to higher order polynomial forms are determined by equation 6 which checks for significant curvature effects (SFCE) by testing at only average levels of the independent variables. The value

$$SFCE = \bar{S}t(1/(pr) + 1/C)^{1/2} \quad (6)$$

of "C" represents the total number of tests conducted with all variables at the mid-points or average levels.

The following example of a "two-level" factorial design problem is taken from an earlier study[13] and is used to demonstrate the experimental strategy associated with the development of response surface polynomials. In this example, a continuous wave CO_2 laser beam is irradiated normal to the surface of graphite/epoxy tensile bar targets which were mechanically preloaded to various levels of ultimate load-carrying capacity. The objective of the test series was to develop a response function which related time to failure for a given composite configuration to variations in two independent parameters, laser flux level (X_1) and amount of mechanical preload (X_2). Table I illustrates the range of high ($+$) and low ($-$) values associated with the two independent variables X_1 and X_2 of this example. Table II illustrates the actual test results with repeat values for each test configuration shown in Table I. Table III shows the standard scheme for calculating the two-level factor effects or polynomial coefficients for the resultant empirical function which describes the dependent variable of failure time "t" for any combination of laser flux (X_1) and amount of preload (X_2). The resulting response polynomial function is given in Table III and is shown schematically in Figure 1. It should be pointed out that the computation matrix for the two level (high ($+$) and low ($-$)) factorial method can be easily formed by noting that the column of plus ($+$) and minus signs ($-$) follow a very ordered pattern. For instance, if there are two variables (i.e., $p = 2$), then there will be 2^p trials or test configurations N (i.e., N = 4 trials in this example). The first column of the computation matrix deals with the average value or A_0 polynomial coefficient and only plus ($+$) values are associated with each trial condition. The second column deals with the X_1 variable and the $\pm$ signs alternate down the column (i.e., –, +, –, +, etc). For the second independent variable X_2, the $\pm$ signs alternate in pairs down the column (i.e., –, –, +, +, etc.). If another variable X_3 had been of interest the $\pm$ signs would alternate in groups of four down the column (i.e., –, –, –, –, +, +, +, +, etc.). The corresponding + or – sign for each trial of the interaction coefficient $X_1 X_j$ is found by multiplying the corresponding signs of the individual terms of interest for a given interaction coefficient. For example, the trial 1 coefficient for the $X_1 X_2$ term is a plus (+) value which is obtained by multiplying the corresponding trial 1 coefficient for X_1 (i.e., a minus (–) value) times the corresponding trial 1 coefficient for X_2 (i.e., another minus (–) value) to give a plus (+) coefficient. The coefficient values are found by multiplying the nominal value obtained from the test results of each trial by the corresponding sign under the column of interest. These values are then added or subtracted as indicated by the sign term and the sum is then divided by the number of trials N to obtain the regression coefficient or polynomial factor.

Table I. Factorial Method Example Max./Min. Independent Variables.

	CODE		ACTUAL VALUES	
TRIAL	X_1	X_2	X_1 (W/CM²)	X_c (% ULT.)
1	–	–	800	50
2	+	–	1500	50
3	–	+	800	75
4	+	+	1500	75

Figure 1. Schematic of the resulting response polynominal function.

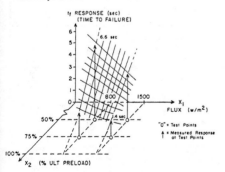

Table II. Measured Dependent Variable Response of Time to Failure for Test Configurations (Trials) of Table II.

TRIAL	MEASURED FAILURE TIME (EXPERIMENTAL) w/REPEATS		MEAN RESPONSE
	FIRST TEST	REPEAT TEST	
1	7.0 SEC	6.2 SEC	6.6 SEC
2	4.3 SEC	3.9 SEC	4.1 SEC
3	2.4 SEC	2.8 SEC	2.6 SEC
4	1.4 SEC	N/A	1.4 SEC

Table III. Computation Table and Results for Factorial Example.

Trial	Weight Factor For Polynomial Coefficient				Measured Mean Response (Sec)
	A_0	X_1	X_2	X_1X_2	
1	+	–	–	+	X 6.6
2	+	+	–	–	X 4.1
3	+	–	+	–	X 2.6
4	+	+	+	+	X 1.4
Σ (+/–)	+ 14.7	–3.7	–6.7	+ 1.3	
$\Sigma \div$ by 4	+ 3.68	–0.93	–1.68	+ 0.33	
FACTOR	A_0	A_1	A_2	A_{12}	

$$t_f = 3.675 - 0.925 X_1 - 1.675 X_2 + 0.325 X_1 X_2$$

where: $Xi = \dfrac{\text{Desired Factor Amount} - \text{(High + Low Values)} / 2}{\text{(High – Low Values)} / 2}$

The Box-Behnken Method[14] is a more accurate and efficient experimental design methodology which is based on a subset of the the three-level factorial approach and enables examining the nonlinear functional relationship between a certain dependent response (such as fracture toughness) and high and low levels of various independent quantitative experimental variables (such as fiber/resin ratios, stiffness, etc.). The response variable functional relationship can be expressed in the form of an incomplete, second-degree graduating polynomial of independent variables, fitted by the method of least squares, and either meeting or approximately meeting certain criteria for rotatability and orthogonal blocking of factors or test parameters. The above polynomial results in what is termed a response surface which, if desired, could be used to identify maximum and minimum levels of variable and combinations of variables. The notion of rotatability stems from the fact that only random replicates of nominal or central values of independent test parameters are run to determine variation (or precision) with respect to the high and low values of each of the independent test parameters. It can be shown that this variation will remain essentially uniform from parameter to parameter (the term "test parameter" is used synonymously with the term "independent variable" throughout the text of this paper).

Equation 7, shown below, illustrate the general form of the Box-Behnken response surface polynominal.

$$\hat{Y} = b_0 + \sum_{i=1}^{k} b_i X_i + \sum_{i=1}^{k} \sum_{j=i}^{k} b_{ij} X_i X_j \qquad (7)$$

The $\hat{Y}$ term in equation 7 represents the dependent response function term (i.e., fracture toughness in this study) and the X_i values, as described earlier, are the values of independent parameters (such as fiber/resin ratio, etc.) scaled non-dimensionally such that $+1$ represents the highest level of the parameter and -1 represents the lowest level value of the parameter (a value of zero indicates an average value for the parameter). The coefficients b_0, b_i and b_{ij} are also termed regression coefficients and are obtained from the results of experimental tests conducted in a specific manner. For example, a three-variable Box-Behnken experimental design would require 15 tests to be run with the specific combinations of independent parameter levels shown in Table IV.

The above test configuration would be run in a random order and the results of the tests would be used to compute the polynomial coefficients. Table V illustrates the Box-Behnken test configurations for four independent parameters or variables. The complete test matrix for four variables requires 27 tests and five variables requires 46 tests. Screening of variables by methods such as Plackett-Burman[12], to determine the most important variables, will assist in reducing the number of tests required to generate a response surface polynomial of the form shown in equation 7. The method for developing appropriate test configurations for more than four variables or test parameters is contained in reference 14.

Table V. Four variable Box-Behnken design.

X_1	X_2	X_3	X_4	
+1	+1	0	0	
+1	-1	0	0	
-1	+1	0	0	
-1	-1	0	0	
0	0	+1	+1	Block 1
0	0	+1	-1	
0	0	-1	+1	
0	0	-1	-1	
0	0	0	0	
+1	0	0	+1	
+1	0	0	-1	
-1	0	0	+1	
-1	0	0	-1	
0	+1	+1	0	Block 2
0	+1	-1	0	
0	-1	+1	0	
0	-1	-1	0	
0	0	0	0	
+1	0	+1	0	
+1	0	-1	0	
-1	0	+1	0	
-1	0	-1	0	
0	+1	0	+1	Block 3
0	+1	0	-1	
0	-1	0	+1	
0	-1	0	-1	
0	0	0	0	

As noted, the regression coefficients and respective variances are computed from the experimental results of tests conducted with

Table IV. A three-variable Box-Behnken test configuration.

Test Configuration	Independent Variable Combinations		
	X1	X2	X3
1	1	1	0
2	1	-1	0
3	-1	1	0
4	-1	-1	0
5	1	0	1
6	1	0	-1
7	-1	0	1
8	-1	0	-1
9	0	1	1
10	0	1	-1
11	0	-1	1
12	0	-1	-1
13	0	0	0
14	0	0	0
15	0	0	0

*Center points are denoted when all variables are tested simultaneously at their average levels (0).

specific combinations of the parameter levels, depending upon the number of independent parameters or test variables. Equations 8 through 11 and Table VI provide information necessary to calculate the regression coefficients for response surface polynomial functions with up to five variables or test parameters. The test configurations which employ only average values for each parameter are termed "center points" and it is only these center points which are tested for repeatability. The results of the center point tests can be used to estimate the experimental error variance (σ^2). For the constant and linear polynomial terms the regression coefficients are:

$$b_0 = \overline{Y}_0 \text{ (mean value of center point} \quad (8)$$
$$\text{test results)}$$

$$b_i = A \sum_{(u=1)}^{N} X_{iu}\, Y_u \qquad (9)$$

In equation 9, N is the total number of tests for a particular design (i.e., N = 15 for a three-variable test series), Y_u is the test result for a test configuration "U", X_{iu} is the nondimensional coefficient (i.e., + 1, –1, or zero) taken from the design matrix (i.e., Table V is the design matrix for a four-variable test series), and the coefficient "A" is given in Table VI as a function of the number of variables in the test series. The second-order nonlinear regression terms are given as:

$$b_{ij} = B \sum_{(u=1)}^{N} X_{iu}\, X_{ju}\, Y_u \qquad (10)$$

$$b_{ii} = C \sum_{(u=1)}^{N} X_{iu}^2\, Y_u + D \sum_{j}^{N_i} \sum_{(u=1)}^{N} X_{ju}^2\, Y_u - b_{0/s}\,(11)$$

where the coefficients B, C, D and S are also given in Table VI and the N_i value represents the number of independent variables in the test design (i.e., $N_i = 5$ for a five-variable design).

Table VI. Constants for calculation of Box-Behnken regression coefficients and error data.

a.

Number of	Constants for Regression Coefficients					
Variables	A	B	C	D	S	n_0
3	1/8	1/4	1/4	-1/16	2	3
4	1/12	1/4	1/8	-1/48	2	3
5	1/16	1/4	1/12	-1/96	2	6

b. Standard error data for regression coefficient

$$V(b_0) = (\sigma^2/n_0)^{1/2} \qquad V(b_{ij}) = ((C + 1/(s^2 n_0))\sigma^2))^{1/2}$$
$$V(b_i) = (A\sigma^2)^{1/2} \qquad V(b_{ii}) = (B\sigma^2)^{1/2}$$

Several examples of an earlier study[15] demonstrate the Box-Behnken method applied to the evaluation of multivariable effects on fracture toughness of certain types of graphite/epoxy composites.

3. FRACTURE TOUGHNESS EXAMPLES

In reference 15, the major focus was on the generation of the multivariable response surfaces and the interpretation of results for fracture toughness parameters G_I (peel mode) and G_{IIc} (interlaminar shear mode). Hinged double cantilever beam (HDCB) test articles were used for the G_I study. Variables examined in the G_I study included: fiber/resin ratios; beam stiffness (thickness); and width effects. ENF test articles were used with three-point bending to examine the G_{IIc} interlaminar shear mode of fracture toughness. Variables examined in the G_{IIc} study included: fiber/resin ratios; stiffness/flexibility (i.e., thickness and span length of test articles); and "crack-start" length variations. All test articles were made of wet-wound IM-6 graphite fibers with an amine-curved epoxy resin system. Table VII shown below provides information on the materials and cure cycles used in the study. Details of the test article geometries and ranges of parameters are given below.

3.1. G_I Fracture Toughness Test Results

A uniaxial, wet-wound, graphite/epoxy material, characterized by the data shown in Table VII, was used to demonstrate multivariable effects on the G_I mode of fracture toughness. As noted, a HDCB configuration was used for the test article. Table VIII illustrates the independent variable and sizes used for the G_I study. Fiber/resin weight ratios were adjusted by through 11 as:

$$G_I = 1450 - 34.3X_1 - 74.3X_2 - 120.1X_3$$
$$- 203.2X_1^2 + 145.4X_2^2 - 147.6X_3^2 \qquad (12)$$
$$+ 50.4X_1X_2 - 19.4X_2X_3 + 9.63X_1X_3$$

where, as noted previously, the X_1, X_2 and X_3 parameter values are nondimensionalized terms (i.e., $+1$ indicates a maximum value, -1 indicates a minimum value, 0 indicates an average of the maximum and minimum values for each variable, and values other than the maximum or minimum would be represented by appropriate scaling from the maximums or minimums).

Examination of the regression coefficients of the polynomial response function of equation 12 indicates that X_3 (the fiber/resin ratio) is the strongest linear parameter and that increasing fiber/resin ratios (i.e., tighter packing of fibers and possible lower void content) tends to reduce the G_I fracture toughness parameter due to the negative sign on the b_3 regression coefficient ($b_3 = 120.14$). The next strongest linear parameter is the X_2 variable (width). The weakest linear parameter is associated with the stiffness effect (X_1 variable). In an opposite sense, the stiffness variable plays a strong role in the higher order terms (i.e., X_1^2) and due to the negative sign of the b_{11} regression coefficient this term indicates that a stiffer structure tends to have a lower fracture toughness or vice versa a more flexible structure is likely to exhibit greater fracture toughness than a stiff structure. The positive sign on the b_{22} regression coefficient indicates that the width factor has a nonlinear effect on the G_I mode fracture toughness such that very narrow or very wide samples are likely to see an increased fracture toughness above that associated with a nominal width test article. The higher-order X_3 term (i.e. $b_{33} = -147.63$) plays a similar but opposite role to that of the X_2 higher-order term. Finally, the cross-coupling or interaction terms indicate that the X_1 and X_2 effects (stiffness and width) are the most strongly coupled factors and the X_1 and X_3 effects (stiffness and fiber/resin ratio) have the least interaction and influence on the G_1 fracture toughness mode. Overall the interaction terms are weak in comparison to the first and second-order terms.

Because equation 12 represents an incomplete second-order polynomial, back substitution of the appropriate $+1$, -1, and zero values for a given test configuration will only give approximations to the corresponding experimentally derived G_I fracture toughness values shown in the last column of Table IX. Overall, however, equation 12 shows reasonably good agreement between predictions and the corresponding experimentally derived values for G_I. More important, however, is the fact that reasonable estimates can be made for levels of the parameters (i.e., X_1, X_2, and X_3) not tested. For instance, a fiber/resin weight ratio of 62 percent would correspond to a nondimensional X_3 value of $+0.5$ which was not tested. If the G_I fracture toughness of such a fiber/resin ratio ($X_3 = +0.5$) were of interest with, as an example, a thickness of 1 cm ($X_2 = +1$) and a width of 2.54 cm ($X_1 = -1$) then equation 12 could be used and would predict a G_I fracture toughness value of approximately 1191 Joules per meter squared. Thus, the response surface polynomial of equation 12 can be used to predict the response of variable levels or parameter levels not actually tested, provided that the new variable levels are not extrapolated significantly beyond the ± 1 extremes. In some instances it may be possible to successfully extrapolate to variable levels of ± 2 with reasonable accuracy (i.e., $\pm 35\%$). As an example, a fiber/resin weight ratio of 74 percent would correspond to a X_3 nondimensional value of $+2$ in this study. Assuming all other parameters to have average values (i.e., $X_1 = 0$, and $X_2 = 0$) the resulting G_I value predicted by equation 12 for the condition of 74 percent fiber/resin weight ratio ($X_3 = +2$), with $X_2 = 0$ (i.e., a width of 6.54 cm) and $X_1 = 0$ (i.e., a thickness of 0.75 cm) would be 620 Joules per meter.

The relatively high fracture toughness values measured in this study appear to be a consequence of a large amount of fiber bridging. As noted previously, the uniaxial fiber bridging effect tends to raise the fracture toughness levels by as much as 500 percent over values likely to be obtained in cross-plied or pre-preg laminates with lower levels of fiber nesting between adjacent plies.

3.2. G_{IIc} Fracture Toughness Test Results

An ENF sample was used, with three-point bending, as the basic test article for the G_{II} fracture toughness study. Figure 3, shown below, illustrates the configuration of the ENF test article. Four primary variables were initially selected for examination in the G_{II} study; these were: 1) percent weight fiber/resin ratio; 2) crack-start length ("a"); 3) span length of the test article ("2L"); and 4) the thickness ("2h") of the test article (related to stiffness). By using dimensionless parameters the above four variables were reduced to the following three variables: 1) percent fiber/resin weight ratio; 2) a nondimensional crack-start length ("a/L"); and 3) a nondimensional stiffness factor ("h/L").

In this phase of the study the mylar peel ply was used as the crack start mechanism. Two layers of mylar were inserted into the test article during the wet-winding fabrication process. No attempt was made to induce a micro-crack at the end of the peel ply through wedging actions or other means. Steel rollers were used for the reaction lines (i.e., "R_1", "R_2") and the load "P" application line. The ENF sample was linearly loaded in a stroke control mode using the Instron servo-hydraulic materials test machine. Sudden load drop-off indicated the critical interlaminar fracture load level.

The graphite/epoxy material used in this phase of the study was identical to that used in the G_I fracture toughness test articles. Table X illustrates the dimensionless parameters and corresponding range of values used in this phase of the study. The total span length of 2L was fixed at 3.8 cm (1.5 inches). The sample width was fixed at 2.54 cm. The load at failure was used to calculate the G_{II} fracture toughness according to the method used by Murri and O'Brien [16]. Equation 13 for G_{II} is given as:

$$G_{II} = \frac{9p^2a^2}{16b^2E_{11}h^3} \qquad (13)$$

where the p value is the measured load at failure; the "a" value is the crack-start length; the "b" value is the width of the sample; the "h" value is the 1/2 thickness of the sample; and the E_{11} value is the Young's tensile modules measured for each of the three different fiber/resin ratio values. The tensile modulus values used in this study were: 1) 110 x 10^9 N/m^2 for the 50 percent fiber/resin weight ratio; 2) 150 x 10^9 N/m^2 for the 58 percent fiber/resin weight ratio; and 3) 190 x 10^9 N/m^2 for the 66 percent fiber/resin weight ratio.

Table XI lists the Box-Behnken test configurations for the dimensionless parameters used in this study. The last column in Table XI also lists the G_{II} fracture toughness data computed from the experimental results corresponding to each of the 15 test configurations.

Table XI. G_{II} results for Box-Behnken test series.

TEST CONFIGU-RATION	CODED TEST VARIABLES LEVELS			EXPERIMEN-TALLY DERIVED G_{II} VALUES (J/M^2)
	X_1 (FIBER/RESIN %)	X_2 (a/1)	X_3 (h/L)	
1	+1	+1	0	3192
2	+1	-1	0	114
3	-1	+1	0	3448
4	-1	-1	0	150
5	+1	0	+1	958
6	+1	0	-1	725
7	-1	0	+1	1595
8	-1	0	-1	2802
9	0	+1	+1	2641
10	0	+1	-1	1235
11	0	-1	+1	107
12	0	-1	-1	82
13	0	0	0	1487
14	0	0	0	981
15	0	0	0	1270

The Box-Behnken response surface polynomial corresponding to the results tabulated in Table XI is calculated to be:

Table X. Variables and ranges for G_{II} study.

VARIABLE	VALUES
X_1 = FIBER/RESIN RATIO	+1 = 66% (HIGH) 0 = 58% (AVERAGE) -0 = 50% (LOW)
X_2 = a/l	+1 = 0.666 (HIGH) 0 = 0.400 (AVERAGE) -1 = 0.133 (LOW)
X_3 = h/l	+1 = 0.533 (HIGH) 0 = 0.400 (AVERAGE) -1 = 0.266 (LOW)

Figure 3. ENF test article configuration for G_{II} study.

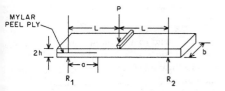

733

Table VII. Graphite/epoxy material specifications.

FIBER: HERCULES IM-6 (12 K)
RESIN: SHELL EPON 828
HARDENER: TONOX 60-40
MIX: 100 PARTS RESIN WITH 25 PARTS
       HARDENER
CURE CYCLE: 2 HOURS AT 93°C (200°F),
              1 1/2 HOURS AT 121°C (250°F),
              AND 2 HOURS AT 149°C (300°F)
PLY THICKNESS: 0.032 cm (0.0125"/PLY)
FIBER/RESIN RATIO: VARIED BY THE NUMBER
                     OF FIBERS PER PLY

maintaining a constant ply thickness with variation only of the fiber count per ply.

Figure 2 provides a schematic of the HDCB test article configuration. It should be noted that a 1 cm-thick steel bar was bonded to each side of the HDCB test article to act as a stiffening mechanism for the piano-hinge load application line along the width of the test article. All HDCB test articles were 20.3 cm long. The appropriate three-variable test configuration design matrix is shown in Table IX along with the average G_I fracture toughness data computed from the experimental results of each test configuration.

Table VIII. Independent variables and levels for G_I study.

Independent Variables	Variable Levels		
	Low (-1)	Average (0)	High (+1)
X_1 – Thickness (Stiffness)	0.50 cm	0.75 cm	1.00 cm
X2 – Width	2.54 cm	6.45 cm	10.16 cm
X3 – Fiber/resin Ratio (by wt)	50%	58%	66%

Figure 2. HDCB test article for G_I (peel mode) fracture toughness.

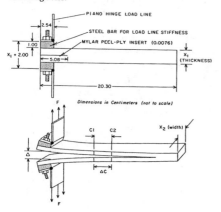

All test articles were tested on an Instron servo-hydraulic controlled materials test machine. The crack opening load "F" and the crack opening size "Δ" were measured and recorded as a function of crack opening length "ΔC". Measurements were made by loading the test articles and observing the propagation of the crack along each side of the test article up to a given location (usually one inch increments of crack growth). When a predetermined crack length was reached, the crack opening "Δ" was held constant while accurate measurements and checks were performed. This phase of the process took about 45 seconds at each crack length position. Load versus deflection plots were made for each sample tested and the "energy-area" integration method was then used to calculate the G_I fracture toughness along the length of the crack for a given test article configuration. All tests were run in random order and not the test configuration order shown in Table IX.

Table IX. Test configurations and results for G_I fracture toughness study.

Test Configuration	Coded Test Variable Level			Experimentally Derived G_i
	X_i (Thickness)	X_2 (Width)	X_3 (Fiber/Resin)	Values (J/M^2)
1	+1	+1	0	1210
2	+1	-1	0	1294
3	-1	+1	0	1389
4	-1	-1	0	1674
5	+1	0	+1	1207
6	+1	0	-1	1133
7	-1	0	+1	1046
8	-1	0	-1	1010
9	0	+1	+1	1105
10	0	+1	-1	1679
11	0	-1	+1	1256
12	0	-1	-1	1751
13	0	0	0	1571
14	0	0	0	1378
15	0	0	0	1461

The values of +1, -1, and 0 correspond to the high, low, and average values cited in Table IX.

The experimentally derived G_I data shown in Table IX lead to a second-order, incomplete, response surface polynomial representation of opening mode fracture toughness as a function of the three variables identified in Table VIII. The resulting G_I fracture toughness polynomial is calculated from equations 7

A check of the equation 14 polynomial shows

$$G_{IIc} = 1246 - 376\ X_1 + 1258\ X_2 + 57\ X_3$$

$$+ 622X_1^2 + 118\ X_2^2 - 607\ X_3^2 \qquad (14)$$

$$+ 360X_1\ X_3 - 1106\ X_1\ X_2 + 345\ X_2\ X_3$$

that for most cases a reasonable prediction or interpolation can be made to obtain an estimate of fracture toughness for parameters either tested or untested. The one exception to the above deals with the cases of very small crack-start lengths (i.e., see test configurations 2, 4, 11 and 12 of Table XI). In the case of the small crack-start lengths the predicted fracture toughness values from equation 14 yield negative values which indicates that interpolation or extrapolation around the low values of X_2 (i.e., $X_2 = -1$) would not be meaningful. In part, the above problem is due to the large deviation associated with the center points of this test series. The above deviation is indicative of the influence of other noncontrollable subtle factors such as void content. The above is also due in part to the strong linear effect of the X_2 term on the equation 14 polynomial. This indicates that the linear X_2 variable (crack-start length) is the most significant term in effect on the G_{II} fracture toughness of the material configurations studied in this research effort. The negative sign on the X_1 linear term regression coefficient indicates that as the fiber/resin ratio becomes greater the G_{II} fracture toughness value should diminish due to the lower likelihood of fiber bridging. This affect is consistent with the results found in the G_I study. The linear term for the X_3 variable (thickness or flexibility) has the least influence on the G_{II} fracture toughness. In contrast the nonlinear terms corresponding to the X_1 and X_3 parameters show a stronger influence on the G_{II} fracture toughness than does the X_2 nonlinear term. The greatest interaction appears to be between the fiber/resin ratio (X_1) and the crack-start length effect (X_2). In all cases the interaction terms play a strong role in resultant G_{II} output. Figure 4 shown below illustrates a graphical representation of the G_{IIc} polynomial response surface for the case of X_3 (stiffness) equal to the nominal value (i.e., $X_3 = 0$).

3.3. Damage Tolerance Applications

The above methodology for evaluation of multivariable effects can also be applied to the

Figure 4. Polynomial response surface for the G_{IIc} case with $X_3 = 0$.

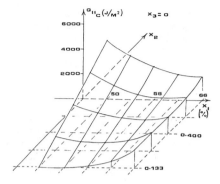

assessment of damage tolerance of fiber/resin composite structures. For instance, some independent variables of interest in assessment of damage tolerance might be the geometric size, energy and velocity of an impactor shock loaded into the surface of a laminated fiber/resin composite. Measurements of the residual strength of the damaged composites would provide one measure of a dependent variable. These results could be correlated with visible surface damage or nondestructive evaluations of internal changes in microstructure by using techniques such as acoustic emission analysis.

4. CONCLUSIONS

An experimental method has been demonstrated for efficiently examining multivariable effects on composite fracture toughness damage tolerance. The G_{II} multivariable study has indicated that the amount of energy required for mode II interlaminar crack propagation in a uniaxial wound graphite/epoxy composite is strongly affected by variations in the crack-start length. The results of the G_I multivariable study indicate that mode I ply delamination is more likely to occur at cross-plied interfaces or regions of high fiber/resin ratios due to the diminished fiber nesting and fiber bridging effects. The experimental designs demonstrated in this paper could be utilized for the study of greater numbers of variables; however, it is recommended that dimensionless analysis and preliminary screening of variables (by methods such as Plackett-Burman) be used to reduce the total number of variables and tests to a minimum.

5. REFERENCES

1. Personal communication between Dr. K. Saczalski and Dr. R.J. Morgan, 1987.

2. Morgan, R.J., "Structure-Property Relations of Epoxies Used as Composite Matrices" In Advances in Polymer Science, 72, "Epoxy Resins and Composites I" ed. K. Dusek, Springer-Verlag, Ch. 1, 1985.

3. Morgan, R.J., Walkup, C.M., Fung-Ming Kong, Mones, E.T., "Development of Epoxy Matrices for Filament-Wound Graphite Structures, "Proceedings of the 30th National Society for the Advancement of Material and Process Engineering (SAMPE) Symposium, 1985, pgs. 1209-1220.

4. Morgan, R.J., Walkup, C.M., Hoheisel, T., "Characterization of the Cure of Carbon Fiber/Epoxy Composite Prepregs by Differential Scanning Calorimetry", Journal of Composites Technology and Research, Vol. 7, No. 1, Spring 1985, pgs 17-19.

5. Saczalski, K.J., "Effects of fiber bridging on fracture toughness of fiber/resin composites," presentation made to NASA Langley Materials and Structures Groups, November 5, 1985.

6. Johnson, W.S. and Mongalgiri, P.D., "Investigation of fiber bridging in double cantilever beam specimens," NASA Technical Memorandum 87716, April 1986.

7. Personal communications between Dr. K. Saczalski and Dr. Scott W. Beckwith of Hercules Inc. (Magma, Utah), November, 1986.

8. Bascom, W.D., Ting, R.Y., Moulton, R.J., Riew, C.K., and Siebert, A.R. "The fracture of an epoxy polymer containing elastromeric modifiers," Journal of Materials Science, No. 16, 1981, pgs. 2657-2664.

9. Bascom, W.D., Bullman, G.W., Hanston, D.L., and Jensen, R.M. "The width tapered double cantilever beam for interlaminar fracture testing," paper presented at the 29th National Society for the Advancement of Material and Process engineering (SAMPE) Symposium, 1984.

10. Bascom, W.D. and Hanston, D.L. "The fracture of epoxy and elstomer-modified epoxy polymers," ADHESION-6 (Chapter 14) ed. K.W. Allen, paper presented at the 19th Annual Conference on Adhesion and Adhesives (held at The City University, London), 1981, Applied Science Publishers. 185-220.

11. Bau, H. and Beckwith S.W. "Fracture mechanics evaluation of filament wound case materials subjected to operational environments," paper No. AIAA-82-1070, presented at the 18th AIAA/SAE/ASME Joint Propulsion Conference, Cleveland, Ohio, June 21-23, 1982.

12. Plackett, R.L. and Burman, J.P. "The Design of Optimum Multifactorial Experiments," Biometrika 33, pgs. 305-325, 1946.

13. Saczalski, K.J., "Hybrid composites for laser hardening of ballistic missile motorcase structures: Phase II," Northern Arizona University Report 36-CO prepared for the Naval Research Laboratory under contract N00014-83-K-2002, December 15, 1985.

14. Box, E.E.P. and Behnken, D.W., "Some new three level designs for the study of quantitative variables," Technometrics 2, pgs. 455-475, 1960.

15. Saczalski, K.J., King, W.F., Saczalski, T.K., and Peterson, E.J., "Evaluation of Multivariable Effects on G_I and G_{IIc} Fracture Toughness of Graphite/Epoxy," presented at the 1987 JANNAF Propulsion Meeting, San Diego, Ca. 15-17 December, 1987.

16. Murri, G.B. and O'Brien, T.K. "Interlaminar G_{IIc} evaluation of toughened resin matrix composites using the end notched flexure test," AIAA Paper No. 85-0647, April 15, 1985.

BIOGRAPHY

TODD K. SACZALSKI, Engineer

Degree of Mechanical Engineering Technology, Nothern Arizona University, 1987.

Mr. Saczalski has been with General Dynamics one and a half years in the Advanced Structures Design department following five years of experience in the area of composite materials at Northern Arizona University. Past assignments include: Trade Study Leader for Tank Configuration Selection for the Liquid Rocket Booster Program, Principle Investigator of Lightweight High Pressure Tanks IRAD program and Principal Investigator of Lightweight Cryogenic Composite Tanks Marketing Assist program.

Mr. Saczalski presented a paper on "Evaluation of Multivariable Effects on G_I and G_{IIc} Fracture Toughness of Graphite/Epoxy" to the JANNAF Conference, December 1987.

34th International SAMPE Symposium
May 8-11, 1989

FRACTURE BEHAVIOR OF PITCH-BASED CARBON FIBER COMPOSITES WITH TOUGHENED EPOXY RESIN SYSTEMS

Osamu Watanabe, Shinkichi Murakami, Hiroshi Inoue
Toa Nenryo Kogyo K.K., Corporate Research & Development
Laboratory,Carbon Fiber Project Group, Ohimachi, Irumagun,
Saitamaken,Japan

Atsushi Murakami, Tadatsugu Yoshiki
Department of Chemical Engineering,
Himeji University, Himejishi, Hyougoken, Japan

ABSTRACT

A series of toughened epoxy resin systems with different molecular weights of Bisphenol A epoxy resin oligomers has recently been proved highly effective for use in carbon fiber reinforced plastics (CFRP). The epoxy resin systems and their pitch based carbon fiber composites underwent rigorous testing to determine tensile, dynamic visco-elastic, and impact properties. Fracture surfaces were also observed under a scanning electron microscope (SEM) and optical microscope. This study also examined CTBN rubber-toughened epoxy formulations. The superior toughness of the rubber modified epoxy resin was demonstrated. It has been demonstrated that the toughness of these cured resins depends upon network density, which is directly related to molecular relaxation. Consequently, the results of this study suggest that the toughness of the matrix resin has a distinct effect on the mechanical properties of the CFRP.

1. INTRODUCTION

Applications of carbon fiber composites in aircraft, ships, vehicles and sporting goods have increased markedly over the past several years. Thermoset polymers, in particular epoxy resins, are popular matrices for these applications. However, their characteristic brittleness promotes microcracking and the debonding of composites under mechanical and thermal loading. Therefore, recent efforts have focused on the improvement of toughness and understanding of the fracture mechanism for epoxy resins and composites. Many useful and attractive results have been reported[1-4].

The addition of a rubbery phase to the matrix resin is one of the most successful methods for improving its toughness. Much attention has been paid to the addition of a CTBN to the epoxy resin.

Another approach, controlling network density, was also successful in improving toughness [5,6]. Network density depends upon the molecular weight of the epoxy resin oligomer.

This paper is particularly concerned with the influence of network density on the fracture toughness of matrix resins and CFRP composites.

2. EXPERIMENTAL PROCEDURE

Four epoxy formulations, based on bisphenol A epoxy resin, but with differing molecular weights, were used in this study.

Dynamic visco-elasticities were measured at 110 Hz by a Rheo-vibron DDV-III-EA (Orientec Corp.)

The compact tension (CT) method was applied in the measurement of fracture toughness. Dimensions of specimens for the CT test and the equations for calculating fracture toughness, K1c, are shown in Fig. 1. The CT test was conducted at 0.5 mm/min. according to ASTM E-399-72 using an Autograph IS-500 (Shimazu

Corp.).

Izod impact tests and tensile property tests were conducted according to JIS(Japan Industrial Standard) K-6911. Puncture tests were also conducted at testing speeds of 0.6, 3, and 9 m/sec using a Hydroshot HTM-1(Shimazu Corp.). Dimensions of the specimens used in the puncture tests were 100mm x 100mm x 3mm.

Fracture behavior was characterized for the composites with a mono-filament of pitch based carbon fiber or PAN based carbon fiber embedded in the epoxy resins. The characteristics of these carbon fibers are listed in Table 2. A schematic diagram of the composite specimen with a mono-filament is shown in Fig. 2.

3. RESULTS AND DISCUSSION

3.1 Dynamic Visco-elasticities

The spectra of dynamic visco-elasticities of cured resins are shown in Fig. 3. The tan δ(max) temperature corresponded to the Tg, which dropped slightly as the molecular weight of the oligomer rose. Dynamic modulus E' curves showed a rubbery plateau at high temperatures. E' in the rubbery state is known to relate to the network density of the cured resin based of the following equation(1)[7,8].

$$E = 3\nu RT \qquad (1)$$

where E is the elastic modulus in

the rubbery state, ν is the network density, R is the universal gas constant and T is the absolute temperature. The network densities of the cured resins are listed in Table 3. Network density decreased as the molecular weight of the oligomers increased, as shown in Fig. 4. It is assumed that the high molecular weight of the oligomers contributed to the increase in the chain length between crosslinked points. Tan δ (max) increased with the molecular weight of the oligomers.

3.2 Impact Properties

Izod impact strength is plotted versus oligomer molecular weight in Fig. 5. Izod impact strength increased as a function of the molecular weight of the oligomers. Fracture surfaces of Izod specimens were observed under a SEM. Cured resins with high molecular weight oligomers (No. 3 and No. 4) showed rough fracture surfaces. It was noted that the surfaces were highly strained before catastrophic fracture. The plastic deformation at the crack tip was probably induced by the long chain between linkages, which resulted in a high impact energy.

The plots of puncture impact energy as a function of oligomer molecular weight are shown in Fig. 6. Puncture impact energy also tended to increase with oligomer molecular weight.

3.3 Fracture Toughness (K1c)

Fracture toughness is plotted versus oligomer molecular weight in Fig. 7. K1c also depends upon the molecular weight of the oligomers. The fracture surface of sample No. 4 revealed a high K1c and showed an unstable stick-slip crack propagation. On the other hand, fracture surfaces of the other samples showed brittle stable crack propagation with no clear stick-slip tendencies.

Rubber modified epoxy resin showed much higher K1c than non-rubber modified epoxy resin. K1c was plotted versus oligomer molecular weight in Fig. 8. K1c of rubber modified epoxy resin also depends upon the molecular weight of the oligomers.

3.4 Fracture Behavior of Composites

The fracture behavior of composites with mono-filament carbon fiber was thoroughly tested. The crack length in the composites with No. 1 resin was much greater than in those with No. 4. It became apparent that cracks which started at the point of the fractured fibers were subsequently arrested in the toughened matrix resin (No. 4). The toughened resins developed in this study are considered to be suitable for use as a CFRP matrix.

4. CONCLUSIONS

As a result of the detailed studies of the toughening and fracture mechanisms of epoxy resins and their composites, the following conclusions have been drawn:

(1) A series of toughened epoxy resin systems can be produced with minimal sacrifice in heat resistance and modulus.

(2) Izod impact strength, puncture impact energy, and K1c of epoxy resins increase as the oligomer molecular weight increases. The high toughness and high impact strength are thought to be due to low network density, which is directly related to molecular relaxation.

(3) Addition of CTBN to epoxy resin was able to improve fracture toughness, which is related to oligomer molecular weight.

(4) The toughened resins developed in this study are highly effective in preventing crack propagation and are suitable for use as CFRP matrices.

REFERENCES

1. S. K. Doulass, P. W. R. Beaumont and M. F. Asjby, J. Mater. Sci., $\underline{15}$, 1109 (1980).

2. W. D. Bascom, R. Y. Ting, R. J. Moulton, C. K. Riew and A. R. Siebert, J. Mater. Sci., $\underline{16}$, 2657 (1981)

3. J. M. Scott and D. C. Phillips, J. Mater. Sci,. $\underline{10}$, 551 (1975)

4. Alan C. Meeks, Polymer, $\underline{15}$, 675 (1974)

5. A. Murakami, H. Matsushita, T. Yoshiki and M. Shimbo, J. Adhes. Sci., $\underline{19}$, 529 (1985)

6. J. Diamant and R. J. Moulton, Proceedings of the 29th National SAMPE Symposium, April 3-5 (1984)

7. D. Katz and A. V. Tobolsky, J. Polym. Sci, $\underline{A-2}$, 1595 (1964)

8. L. R. G. Trelore, The Physics of Rubber Elasticity. Oxford, London, (1958)

BIOGRAPHIES

O. Watanabe graduated from Waseda University (Master of Engineering) in 1987. He then joined Toa Nenryo Kogyo K.K., Corporate Research and Development Laboratory as a member of the Carbon Fiber Project Group, and has been involved with research and development of thermosetting resins for CFRP matrices. He has authored several papers on toughened epoxy resins and curing reactions.

S. Murakami graduated from Osaka University (Master of Engineering) in 1982. He then joined Toa Nenryo Kogyo K.K., Corporate Research and Development Laboratory and was initially engaged in research and development of thermoplastic resins. From 1984, he has been involved with research and development of thermosetting resins for CFRP matrices as a member of the Carbon Fiber Project Group. He has authored several papers on toughened epoxy resins and curing reactions.

H. Inoue graduated from Nagoya University (Master of Engineering)

in 1972. He then joined Toa Nenryo
Kogyo K.K., Corporate Research and
Development Laboratory and was
initially engaged in research and
development of thermoplastic resins.
From 1984, he has been involved
with research and development of
thermosetting resins for CFRP as a
group leader of the Carbon Fiber
Project Group. He has authored
several papers on epoxy resins.

Dr. T. Yoshiki obtained his Ph. D.
in Metallurgy from Tohoku
University. He is a professor in
Chemical Engineering Department at
Himeji Institute of Technology. His
background is plastic deformation of
metal and polymeric solids.

Dr. A. Murakami obtained his Ph. D.
in chemistry from Kansai University.
He is an associate professor of the
Chemical Engineering Department at
Himeji Institute of Technology. His
work has been the study of fracture
and fatigue properties of
crosslinked polymers. His
responsibilities have included the
development of toughened epoxy.

Table 1   Resin Composition

Sample No	Mn	Hardner	Acceler-ator	Cure Condition
1	337	DICY	DCMU	
2	489	DICY	DCMU	130°C
3	565	DICY	DCMU	x2hr
4	633	DICY	DCMU	

M n - Number Average Molecular Weight of the oligomers

Table 2   Characteristics of Carbon Fibers

Quality		Pitch-Based CF (TONEN)		Pan-Based CF (TORAY)	
		HM	UHM	T-300	M-40
Tensile Strength	(MPa)	3000	3300	3500	2700
Tensile Modulus	(GPa)	500	700	230	390
Tensile Elongation at Break	(%)	0.6	0.4	1.5	0.6
Density	(g/cm^3)	2.1	2.2	1.76	1.81
Filament diameter	(micron)	10	10	7	6.5
Filament Number	(x1000)	6	3	6	6

Table 3   Cured Resin Properties

Sample No	Mn[1]	Network[2] (mol/cm^3)	Modulus[3] (GPa)
1	377	2.65×10^{-3}	3.4
2	489	2.38×10^{-3}	3.3
3	565	2.30×10^{-3}	3.2
4	633	1.77×10^{-3}	3.3

1) Number Average Molecular Weight of
   the oligomers
2) Density of Molecular Network Structure
3) Tensile Modulus

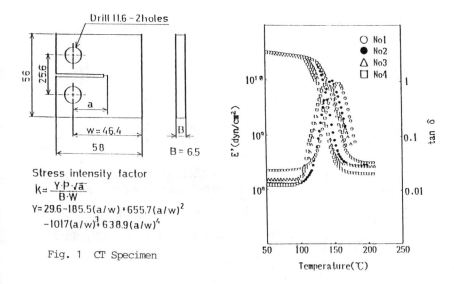

Drill 11.6 - 2 holes

$w = 46.4$

58

256

56

a

B

$B = 6.5$

Stress intensity factor

$$k = \frac{Y \cdot P \cdot \sqrt{a}}{B \cdot W}$$

$Y = 29.6 - 185.5(a/w) + 655.7(a/w)^2$
$\quad -1017(a/w)^3 + 638.9(a/w)^4$

Fig. 1   CT Specimen

○ No1
● No2
△ No3
□ No4

E' (dyn/cm^2)

10^{10}

10^9

10^9

1

0.1

0.01

tan δ

50   100   150   200   250

Temperature (℃)

Fig. 3   Dynamic Mechanical Data

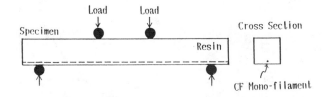

Load   Load

Specimen

Resin

Cross Section

CF Mono-filament

Fig. 2   Schematic Diagram of 4 Points Bending,
mono-filament Tensile Test

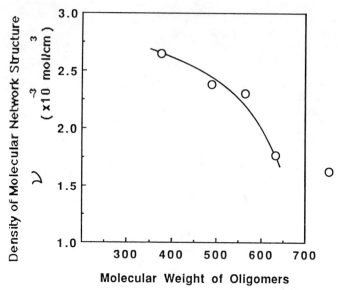

Fig. 4   Density of Molecular Network Structure
          vs. Molecular Weight of Oligowers

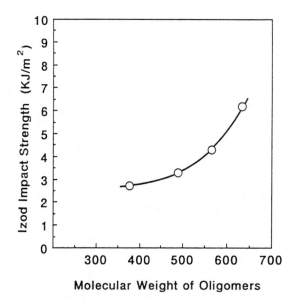

Fig. 5 Izod Impact Strength vs. Molecular
        Weight of Oligomers

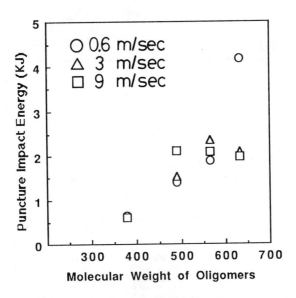

Fig. 6   Puncture Impact Energy vs.
Molecular Weight of Oligomers

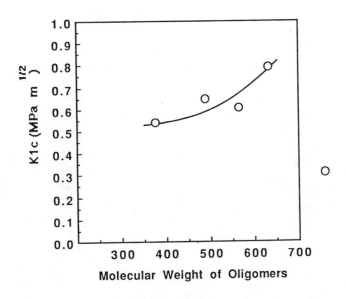

Fig. 7   K1c vs. Molecular Weight of
Oligomers

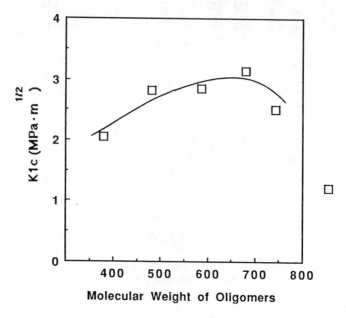

Fig. 8   K1c vs. Molecular Weight of
Oligomers with CTBN

34th International SAMPE Symposium
May 8-11, 1989

HIGHLY DAMAGE TOLERANT CARBON FIBER EPOXY COMPOSITES FOR PRIMARY AIRCRAFT STRUCTURAL APPLICATIONS

H. G. Recker

BASF Structural Materials Inc., Narmco Materials

1440 N. Kraemer Blvd., Anaheim, CA 92806

T. Allspach, V. Altstädt, T.Folda, W. Heckmann, P. Ittemann, H.Tesch, T. Weber

Polymer Research Laboratory, BASF AG, D-6700 Ludwigshafen, Federal Republic of Germany

Abstract

Based on fundamental studies on thermoplastic modified epoxy neat resins, prepreg resin systems with a significant improvement in fracture toughness and damage tolerance have been achieved. Key investigations focused on understanding and control of morphology within phase separated resin systems. A special morphology was observed that correlates to a distinct maximum in neat resin fracture toughness. Further understanding of structure-property-relationships within laminates was used to optimize mechanical properties. Highly damage tolerant systems with excellent hot/wet properties and solvent resistance were obtained.

1. INTRODUCTION

Low impact resistance of carbon fiber reinforced thermoset composites is one of the major restrictions for designing load-bearing primary aircraft structures from those materials. To obtain the utmost weight sav-

ing potential of advanced composites in aircraft structures, new high-strain carbon fibers and improved toughened polymer matrices for a better delamination resistance of the composites have to be used.

For commercial aircraft applications the service temperature requirements usually do not exceed 120 °C, so that 180 °C- curable epoxy resin systems are prime candidates.

New epoxy prepreg resins for commercial aircraft applications have to be significantly improved in toughness, with sufficiently high values in modulus and glass transition temperature, as well as little sensitivity of these values to moisture.

Numerous attempts have been made to increase the toughness of epoxy matrices for composites. Two frequently used approaches are modification with liquid rubber or reduction of the crosslink density of the thermoset network. In both cases the increase in toughness can often only be achieved at the expense of high temperature performance of the material.

Recently excellent results were obtained by modifying epoxies with engineering thermoplastics (1-5). However this approach seems to imply various shortcomings such as solvent sensitivity and handling characteristics.

The goal of the present study was to understand the fundamental structure-property-relationships within thermoplastic modified epoxy resin systems.

This understanding was successfully used for developing matrix systems with improved property profiles. The overall performance of these modified thermoset resins meets the requirements for primary aircraft structural applications.

2. STATUS ON THERMOPLASTIC MODIFICATION OF EPOXY PREPREG RESINS

The incorporation of thermoplastics into epoxy resins has already been described in the late 1960s / early 1970s (6). Various thermoplastics like polyethersulfone and polyetherimide have been suggested, and in most cases no, in other cases some improvements in toughness by addition of a thermoplastic modifier were reported (7-9). But until recently there have been no studies showing that a synergistic combination of the advantageous processing characteristics of thermosets and the toughness of thermoplastics can be achieved.

The modification of epoxy resins with specially synthesized thermoplastic compounds is reported to create significant improved toughness without high temperature performance being sacrificed. Mc Grath et al. found functionally terminated low molecular weight thermoplastics, e.g. polysulfones to be most effective for increasing toughness (1).

Those thermoplastic modifiers, chemically linked to the epoxy network, are superior to those simply physically blended. The toughening effect is reported to be strongly dependent on the molecular weight of the thermoplastic. The morphologies are phase-separated with polysulfone inclusions dispersed in the continuous epoxy matrix. At higher polysulfone loading phase inversion was observed, and the thermoplastic becomes a continuous matrix with dispersed spheres of epoxy (2).

Phase-inversion at high concentrations of a thermoplastic oligomer in an epoxy resin is also reported by Kim and Brown (10).

Sefton et al. (3,4) describe a thermoplastic modified epoxy system which shows optimum toughness properties because of its spinodal, a two-continuous phased morphology. It is shown that the excellent resin toughness translates into a composite exceeding the goal of 0.6 % residual strain-to-failure for primary aircraft applications considerably without compromising hot/wet properties.

In a most recent report Odagiri et al. (5) also described highly damage tolerant composites, which have been achieved by a not exactly defined thermoplastic modification of epoxy resins.

3. EXPERIMENTAL

3.1. Materials

Resin chemistry

The resin systems selected for this study were based on various epoxies including di-, tri- and tetrafunctional epoxies with different backbones. The thermoplastic modifiers with functional endgroups of different molecular weight (Mn), determined by titration of the functional endgroups, and backbone structure were synthesized according to proprietary procedures. In all cases the epoxy was prereacted quantitatively with the thermoplastic modifier. After this procedure the curing agent diaminodiphenylsulfone (DDS) was added.

For basic neat resin mechanical investigations different formulations were prepared by systematically varying the molecular weight of the thermoplastic, and by varying the thermoplastic/epoxy ratio. Neat resin plaques of 4 mm thickness were prepared by casting degassed resin mixtures between parallel polished steel plates. The mixtures were heated to and held at 180 °C for 2 hours for curing and then post cured for another 2 hours at 200 °C.

In the case of prepreg resin systems, resin viscosities were adjusted to guarantee sufficient tack and drape at room temperature even under normal out-time conditions.

Fibers

Two intermediate modulus carbon fibers, Celion G 40-800-12K (BASF Structural Materials, Inc., USA) and Hercules IM7-12K (Hercules Corp., USA) were selected for prepreg fabrication.

Prepreg and laminate fabrication

UD-prepregs were produced by a hot melt process. The fiber areal weight was 145 ± 5 g/m^2, the resin content 33 ± 2 %. Laminates were laid up and cured in an autoclave for 3 h at 180 °C with a heating and cooling rate of 2.5 °C/min. The fiber volume content in the cured panels was $60 \pm 3\%$.

3.2. Test methods

All mechanical testing of neat resins and laminates was done as outlined in Table 1. For further detailed information see references (11), (12) and (15).

Optical and scanning electron microscopy
For morphological investigations thin epoxy films were made by curing the neat resin between two glass carriers.

Hot/wet performance
To evaluate the hot / wet performance, laminate specimens of 1 mm thickness were stored in hot water at a temperature of 70 °C for 14 days. The moisture uptake was monitored gravimetrically. Softening temperatures T_S associated with the onset of the glass transition region of the resin were determined with a DuPont Thermal Analyzer. A test frequency of 1 Hz and a heat-up rate of 4 K/min was applied. The softening temperatures were determined in accordance to DAN 432.

Solvent resistance
Solvent uptake of neat resin systems was determined gravimetri-

Test method	Lay-up sequence	Test procedure
Neat resin	—	Ref. 11
Compression 0°	$[0]_8$	SACMA SRS 1-88
Fract. Toughn. G_{IC}	$[0]_{24}$	Ref. 13
Fract. Toughn. G_{IIC}	$[0]_{24}$	Ref. 14
CAI	$[+45/0/-45/90]_{4s}$	SACMA SRS 2-88
ILSS	$[0]_8$	SACMA SRS 8-88
DMA	$[0]_8$	DAN 432

Table 1: Mechanical test methods for neat resins and laminates, lay-up sequences, and applied test procedures.

cally by immersing samples for 30 days in methylethylketone (MEK). The solvent resistance of laminates was tested by inter-laminar shear strength after soaking of specimens for 21 days in MEK, acetone or methylene chloride at room temperature.

4. RESULTS AND DISCUSSION

4.1. Neat resin fracture energy and morphological investigations

It has been shown for 180 °C-curable single phase as well as for 125 °C-curable single phase and phase-separated CTBN rubber modified systems that there is a strong correlation between composite interlaminar fracture energies under Mode I and the fracture energies of corresponding neat resins (11,12).

Consequently neat resin toughness of thermoplastic modified systems was evaluated by fracture energy measurements under

Mode I loading condition, although it is not yet fully understood what the controlling neat resin parameters for interlaminar crack resistance and composite damage tolerance in multiphase epoxy / thermoplastic blends are.

4.1.1 Influence of molecular weight of the thermoplastic on neat resin properties

An epoxy resin system containing 30 wt% functionalized thermoplastic material of different molecular weight was used for initial neat resin studies. Figure 1 shows a linear 4-fold increase in neat resin fracture energy G_{IC} in the molecular weight (Mn) range between 2000 and 10000, remaining almost constant for higher Mn values.

Softening temperatures Ts and shear moduli G' of the systems are not influenced by molecular weight of the thermoplastic modifier; T_S is at about 180 °C and G' at 23 °C is at about 1100 MPa.

For testing solvent resistance on neat resins MEK was used because of the thermoplastic being swellable in MEK.

The plot of the MEK uptake versus thermoplastic molecular weight (Figure 2) shows a drastic increase in solvent uptake for Mn > 8000. Since all of the investigated systems are of the same phase-inverted morphology (see 4.1.2), this increase in solvent sensitivity is not represented by a change in morphological structure of the system.

Thus, the optimum thermoplastic must represent a compromise between improved toughness and acceptable solvent resistance. Therefore a thermoplastic in the molecular weight range from 5000 to 7000, which would give a significant improvement in toughness, and at the same time would exhibit the required solvent resistance, was selected for further systematic studies.

4.1.2. Influence of thermoplastic loading on neat resin properties

The influence of the thermoplastic content on neat resin fracture energy is shown in Figure 3.

Surprisingly, a pronounced reproducible G_{IC} maximum at a thermoplastic concentration of about 25 % is observed. This maximum in G_{IC} corresponds to a special morphology, in which epoxy domains from below 1 to about 100 µm are dispersed throughout a thermoplastic continuous phase (Figure 4). The large epoxy domains themselves are of discontinuous structure with thermoplastic inclusions from about 0.1 to 3 µm in diameter. This distinct reproducible

morphology is clearly shown in a scanning electron microscope photograph of the fracture surface of a K_{IC} test specimen (Figure 5).

The morphologies beside the distinct G_{IC} maximum are characterized by a continuous epoxy phase with discontinuous thermoplastic inclusions for formulations with low loadings of thermoplastic, and by phase-inverted structures with the thermoplastic being the continuous phase and small dispersed epoxy domains for formulations containing higher loadings of thermoplastic (Figure 4).

4.2. Evaluation of laminate properties

Based on previous neat resin investigations and additional understanding of structure-property-relationships and morphologies several optimized toughened epoxy prepreg resin systems were developed. The following data outline the basic features of two developmental prepreg systems.

4.2.1. Fracture toughness and damage tolerance

Interlaminar fracture toughness of developmental systems, designated A and B, on IM7 carbon fiber are shown in Figure 6. Clear advantages in toughness for the new experimental systems over Rigidite 5245C / IM7 are reflected in improved Mode I as well as Mode II crack growth resistance. For example the system A shows a nearly 50 % improvement in both G_{IC} and G_{IIC} over Rigidite 5245C.

Of special importance for damage tolerant applications is the increase in compression after impact (CAI) which is in good agreement with improved G_{IC} and G_{IIC} fracture toughness. Fig. 7 shows the comparison of CAI-data for first and second generation prepreg systems with newly developed systems A and B on the same IM-fiber. The new developmental system A shows a CAI of 310 MPa (45 ksi) at an impact energy of 6.7 kJ/m (1500 in lb/in) versus 200 MPa (29 ksi) for Rigidite 5245C and 150 MPa (22 ksi) for Rigidite 5208. This increase in damage tolerance is also reflected in a substantial damage area reduction for our new system. System B developed for improved hot/wet performance (see 4.2.3.) also turns out to be significantly improved in damage tolerance over Rigidite 5245C.

4.2.2. Comparison of intermediate modulus carbon fibers

In Table 2 interlaminar fracture toughness and damage tolerance performance of system A on two different intermediate modulus carbon fibers (Hercules IM7 and Celion G40-800) are compared. The G40-800 laminate shows a lower G_{IC} fracture toughness than the IM7 laminate, while G_{IIC} and CAI data are comparable in the range of accuracy of measurement.

4.2.3. Hot/wet performance

While developing highly damage tolerant prepreg systems one frequently faces the problem of generating toughness at the expense of hot/wet performance. Sufficiently high softening temperatures Ts of dry and water immersed specimens of developmental system A in Table 3 indicate that a system with superior fracture tough-

ness and damage tolerance without sacrificing hot/wet properties has been obtained. In the case of system B it was possible to achieve even higher softening temperatures with only a slight decrease in damage tolerance.

The fundamental understanding of the applied toughening concept allows to mutually adjust damage tolerance and hot/wet performance in a certain range.

For overall judgment of high temperature performance of materials hot/wet compression strength data are still to be performed.

4.2.4 Solvent resistance

Solvent resistance is frequently considered to be a major drawback of thermoplastic modified thermoset resin. With systems A and B the problem of solvent sensitivity has been minimized by optimizing the properties of the thermoplastic modifiers, which was already discussed in 4.1.1.

Table 4 shows the excellent solvent resistance profile of system A. In solvents like MEK and acetone there is almost no solvent absorption even after three weeks soaking, and therefore ILSS is almost not effected. In the case of methylene chloride the solvent absorption is 2.4 % after three weeks with a 90 % retention in ILSS.

5. CONCLUSIONS

The main goal of this study was the development of a basic understanding of toughening epoxy thermosets with thermoplastics. In order to achieve this goal major contributions were made by detailed fracture toughness and morphological investigations. Key parameters were epoxy backbone structures and functionalities, thermoplastic backbone structure, molecular weight and concentration, as well as the epoxy/curing agent ratio.

Based on these investigations and further understanding of structure-property-relationships a series of new toughened prepreg resin systems was developed. From fracture toughness, damage tolerance, softening temperature and solvent resistance properties of two experimental systems it can be concluded that these new thermoset resins meet the requirements for primary aircraft structural applications.

6. REFERENCES

(1) J. L. Hedrick, I. Yilgör, G.L. Wilkes, J. E. Mc Grath, Pol. Bull. 13, 201 (1985).

(2) J. A. Cecere, J. E. Mc Grath, Polym., Prepr. 27, 299 (1986).

(3) M.S. Sefton et al. , 19rd Int. SAMPE Techn. Conf., 700 (1987).

(4) G. R. Almen et al., 33rd Int. SAMPE Symp. 33, 272 (1988).

(5) N. Odagiri et al, 33rd Int. SAMPE Symp. 33, 272 (1988).

(6) E.W. Garnish et al., British Patent 1 299 177, Reinforced Composites, January 1969.

(7) R.S. Raghava, 28th Nat. SAMPE Symp. 28, 367 (1983).

(8) C.B. Bucknall, I.K. Partridge, Polymer 24, 639 (1983).

(9) J. Diamant, R.J Moulton, 29th Nat. SAMPE Symp. 29, 422 (1984).

(10) S.C. Kim, H. R. Brown, J. Mat. Sci. 22, 2589 (1987).

(11) R. W. Lang et al., in "High Tech - the Way into the Nineties", Elsevier Sci. Publ. B.V., Amsterdam, 261 (1986).

(12) R.W. Lang et al., in "Looking ahead for Materials and Processes", Elsevier Sci. Publ. B.V., Amsterdam, 109 (1987).

(13) Standard Tests for Toughened Resin Composites, NASA RP 1092, Revised Edition (1983).

(14) J.D. Barret and R.O. Foschi, Eng. Fract. Mechanics 9, 371 (1977).

(15) SACMA RECOMMENDED STANDARDS, SRS 2-87, Suppliers of Advanced Composite Materials Association.

7. BIOGRAPHY

Dr. Hans G. Recker joined BASF AG Central Research Laboratory in 1984 after obtaining his PhD in organic chemistry from the Univ. of Hannover/FRG and a post-doctoral experience in Vancouver/Canada. He joined BSM Narmco Research and Development in 1988 and got responsible for development of new toughened epoxy prepreg systems.

Dr. Thomas Allspach joined the Polymer Research Laboratory of BASF AG in 1987. As an organic chemist he is responsible for developing new epoxy prepreg resin formulations.

Dr. Volker Altstädt studied physics and received his PhD as a mechanical engineer from the Institut für Werkstofftechnik in Kassel. He joined the Polymer Research Laboratory of BASF AG in 1987. He is now involved in material science aspects of the composite research specialized in the field of fracture mechanics and fatigue.

Dr. Thomas Folda, a PhD in polymer chemistry, joined BSM Narmco 1985 after working for one and a half year as a visiting scientist at DuPont. In 1988 he became group leader in the Polymer Research Laboratory of BASF AG. He is now responsible for the development of high performance reinforced composites and structural adhesives.

Dr. Walter Heckmann studied physics at TH Darmstadt and received his PhD from the Deutsche Kunstoffinstitut in Darmstadt. He joined BASF AG in 1977. He previously worked on X-Ray analysis of polymers. As a group leader he is now involved in the characterization of polymeric materials with electron microscopy and thermal methods.

Dr. Peter Ittemann is responsible for synthesis and characterization of high performance thermoplastic materials. He joined the Polymer Research Laboratory of BASF AG in 1985 after earning his PhD in organic chemistry.

Dr. Helmut Tesch is a group leader in the Polymer Research Laboratory of BASF AG responsible for composite materials. He has a PhD in polymer chemistry from Univ. of Mainz. Dr. Tesch joined BASF in 1982. He has a total of seven years experience in working in the field of thermoset polymer systems for advanced structural composite applications.

Dr. Thomas Weber joined BASF AG Polymer Research Laboratory in 1988 after obtaining a PhD in solid state chemistry from Univ. of Osnabrück. He is involved in fundamental studies and morphological investigations in the field of toughened epoxies.

	Resin system / fiber	
	A / IM7	A / G40-800
G_{IC} [J/m²]	600	450
G_{IIC} [J/m²]	920	940
CAI [MPa]	310	300

Table 2: Fracture toughness and damage tolerance of system A on two different IM carbon fibers.

	Resin system / fiber	
	A / IM7	B / IM7
T_S dry [°C]	217	237
T_S wet [°C]	179	185

Table 3 : Softening temperatures under dry and wet conditions of systems A and B.

	ILSS [MPa]	Solvent absorption [%]
dry (reference)	112	---
MEK	112	0,3
Acetone	105	0,1
CH_2Cl_2	101	2,4

Table 4: Solvent resistance of resin system A/IM7 after three weeks soaking in MEK, acetone and methylene chloride.

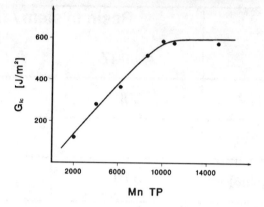

Figure 1:   Neat resin G_{IC} of epoxy systems with thermoplastic modifier of different molecular weight (Mn).

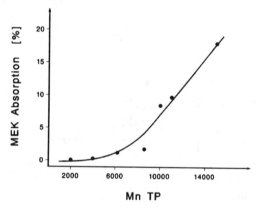

Figure 2:   MEK absorption (30 d) of epoxy systems with thermoplastic modifier of different molecular weight (Mn).

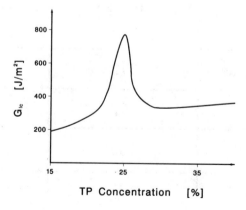

Figure 3:   Neat resin G_{IC} of epoxy systems with different concentrations of thermoplastic modifier.

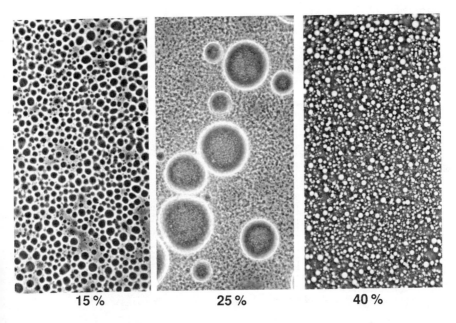

15 %   **25 %**   **40 %**

Figure 4:   Morphology of thermoplastic modified (15 %, 25 %, 40 %) epoxy resins
(Phase contrast light microscopy).   [50 μm   ⊢————⊣]

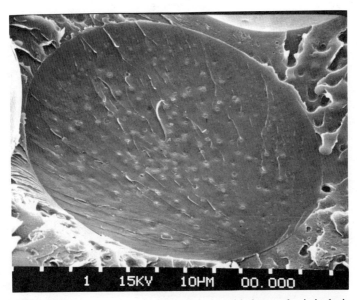

Figure 5:   Epoxy domain of about 100 μm in diameter with thermoplastic inclusions of
below 3 μm, dispersed in a continuous thermoplastic phase.
(Crack surface of a thermoplastic modified (25 %) epoxy system by SEM)

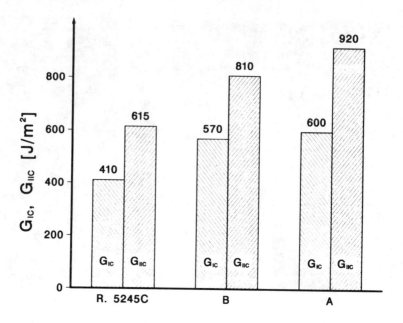

Figure 6: Comparison of interlaminar fracture toughness data G_{IC} and G_{IIC} of developmental systems A and B with Rigidite 5245C on IM7 carbon fiber.

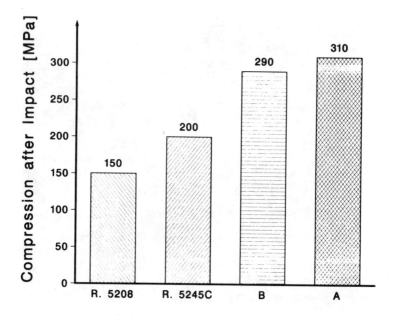

Figure 7: Comparison of compression after impact data of developmental systems A and B with Rigidite 5208 and Rigidite 5245C on IM7 fiber.

MATERIAL APPLICATIONS ON THE SPACE STATION
KEY ISSUES AND THE APPROACH TO THEIR SOLUTION

D. F. Thompson and H. W. Babel
McDonnell Douglas Space Systems Company
5301 Bolsa Avenue
Huntington Beach, CA 92647

Abstract

The Space Station represents a new dimension for materials in space because of the 30 year service life requirement. This paper presents an overview of the low Earth orbit environments that are degrading to materials and the approaches chosen by McDonnell Douglas Space Systems Company to counter these environments. Key material issues are identified for various hardware elements with particular emphasis on the composite truss structure planned for the Space Station. A summary of the future materials development work to be performed in support of the Space Station as well as company funded work applicable to generic large space structures is also presented.

1. INTRODUCTION

The Space Station (SS) provides a challenge to the Materials Engineering community to provide materials which will last for the 30 year design life in low Earth orbit (LEO) at an altitude of 278 to 500 kilometers. Knowledge of the long term behavior of materials in space has been based on the results of flight experiments and ground simulation tests. Because of the limited amount of data from space, the validation of ground simulation tests needs to be further verified. The success of our satellites for shorter duration flights provides a good indication of the adequacy of the ground simulation tests even though these tests may not perfectly reproduce space conditions.

Data from space is basically limited to performance measurements on satellites, material experiments on the Space Shuttle and retrieval by the Space Shuttle of a portion of the satellite known as Solar Max and subsequent evaluation of its materials. The satellite and Solar Max data are not conclusive and the Space Shuttle data are for limited time exposures. For the satellites, e.g., when a change in temperature is indicated due to a change in surface optical properties, it is not known whether the change was produced by atomic oxygen, UV, radiation induced changes, contamination deposited on the surface, or combinations of these effects. Solar Max was the first major piece of structure retrieved intact from space and consequently was extensively analyzed. It was not designed as a materials experiment so the data derived was obtained by examination of the materials on the structure. Considerable insight into the the environmental effects in LEO was derived from this analysis.[1] However, degradation of the silverized Teflon coating used on one of the returned modules was indefinite because the thermal, UV and ionizing radiation exposure due to the vehicle altitude history were not completely definable. Local areas of oxidation, or blackening of the silver was evident on a number of areas and was attributable to atomic oxygen (AO). A number of excellent material experiments have been conducted on the Space

Shuttle, particularly relative to the effects of atomic oxygen.[2-4] These experiments have provided us a comparison of the relative resistance of various materials and their relative reaction rates to AO.

The objective of this paper is to review the key materials issues and the approach to their resolution associated with selecting and ensuring the 30 years of life in LEO of materials for the SS. This review is restricted to the environmental degrading effects on the materials for the hardware elements associated with MDSSC's Work Package-2 effort as indicated in Figure 1.

2. MATERIAL DEGRADING ENVIRONMENTS IN LEO - NATURAL AND INDUCED

The Space Station Program has defined the natural environment as the environment that would exist if the SS were not present. Therefore, the debris created by breakup of such hardware as booster bodies and satellites is included in this definition, even though it is man made. The induced environment refers to the contamination produced from many sources, but for the degradation of thermal control coatings, it is primarily related to thruster firings and the outgassing of materials from all over the SS which may condense on and degrade the thermal control coatings. The natural environments that can degrade material performance are micrometeoroids and debris, UV, atomic oxygen, energetic radiation, i.e the electrons and protons in the trapped radiation belt, galactic/cosmic rays coming from outer space, and the diurnal temperature cycles produced by movement in and out of the Earth's shadow. The difference in material degrading environments between LEO and geosynchronous orbits are shown in Table 1.

A detailed discussion of each of the environments is beyond the scope of this paper. It was therefore decided to provide an overview of the effects that each of these environments has on materials and the key issues associated in the selection and life verification for each environment or synergisms between them. The debris environment is discussed in more detail as it is a dynamic environment. Changes have increased the severity of the environment and for certain hardware elements debris impact could represent a major safety hazard that must be carefully ac-

counted for in the design and operation of the SS. Also, UV and AO and their possible synergisms are important to the survival for 30 years of any organic material, dry-film lubricant, or thermal control coating.

2.1 Charged Particle Radiation

Such radiation is of primary concern relative to the degradation of exposed organic coatings and electronics. For exposed organic coatings the trapped radiation belt often called Van Allen radiation provides the largest dosages, particularly of electrons. Our analysis shows that the total accumulated dosage say of 100 Rads is about 98 parts from trapped electrons, 2 parts from trapped protons and a negligible amount from charged particles in space. Since most of the electrons are absorbed within the first few mils of a materials, their effects are primarily associated with introducing changes in the optical properties of thermal control coatings. The total accumulated dosage of radiation can approach the thresholds which can cause embrittlement of materials. One of our concerns for the thermal radiators is that the 0.1 mm thick coating of Teflon would crack and allow atomic oxygen to attack and oxidize (blacken) the silver backing. How far this oxidation would extend is not known. Radiation can also influence other optical surfaces such as anodized surfaces contributing to increases in solar absorptivity. However, the main concern with radiation is selecting and qualifying electronic components and assemblies when exposed to galactic radiation. For the low 28.5° orbit inclinations of the SS, the earth's magnetic field deflects most of the radiation from sun flares. Only the high energy galactic particles penetrate into LEO where the SS will be located. The penetrating power of these particles allows them to penetrate the electronic blackboxes and cause single event upsets and latchups. These subjects are being addressed in great detail elsewhere for the Space Station Program[5] so this paper will concentrate on environmental effects on structural materials.

2.2 Temperature Cycles

The orbital cycle depends on the altitude of the spacecraft. For analysis purposes we have used 90 minutes for one cycle around the Earth. A number of systems have been analyzed to determine the temperature cycle that can be expected. The truss tubes coated with anodized aluminum foil, absorptance of 0.35 and an emissivity of 0.65, results in a temperature variation from around -57° C to +38° C as the truss moves in and out of the Earth's shadow. The range is extended or decreased depending on the type of foil used, the heat treat or work hardened condition and the associated optical properties obtained by anodizing the foil. When a truss tube is constantly shaded, the temperature is depressed but the temperature variation is considerably reduced, to within the neighborhood of 17° C. The truss tubes for the SS have been extensively analyzed to assess the thermal distortion of the entire truss structure and whether the pointing and tracking requirement of ±0.25 degrees can be achieved. Currently we have baselined graphite epoxy composite tubes with an aluminum foil coating. The foil provides AO resistance and the ability to tailor optical properties. In addition to thermal distortion, the diurnal temperature variation of the truss tubes could also result in microcracking of the resin system. This subject has been extensively analyzed, tested and reported and is described in more detail later in this paper. Initial analysis has shown that all metal tubes have too high a coefficient of expansion to meet the pointing and tracking requirement and consequently cannot be used as the load bearing structure for the Space Station.

2.3 Space Debris

Space debris is a new dimension that has been added to the design of spacecraft for LEO because it is now considerably more severe than micrometeoroids in the larger size ranges. When attention was directed towards this subject in the 1950's, only a micrometeoroid environment existed. Since that time, many spacecraft and satellites have either intentionally or unintentionally exploded in orbit, leaving debris in space for decades. On the average there has been a breakup of 6 structures per year. Like so many other natural resources, space is not limitless and we are quickly creating a very hazardous environment. The U.S. recognizing the seriousness of uncontrolled debris growth in space and its serious threat to future missions, particularly manned missions, has established a policy to ensure the rapid re-entry of any vehicle launched into space after its service mission has been completed. This policy is

followed for both military and civilian applications. For many spacecraft and boosters, this means that residual fuel and attitude control rockets must be available to bring the structure into a low enough orbit that the residual atmosphere present in LEO and the drag that it exerts will in the matter of months or weeks cause the structure to re-enter the atmosphere in such a way that it will burn up.

The probability of being struck by debris depends on the duration of the mission, the exposed area and the particle sizes of interest. For most nonredundant structures, designs are developed for the largest single particle that can be expected in a specified time period. Unlike the typical 1 mm particle for meteoroids, there are many large particles in space of sufficient size to seriously damage a structure. An analogy has been made that a solid aluminum sphere 1.6 cm in diameter traveling at a typical relative velocity of between 10 and 12 km/sec has the force upon impact of a hand grenade exploding. Table 2 shows the weight growths required if one were to design for 30 years with the new debris environment model developed by Don Kessler of JSC[6] which contains a modest 5% debris growth. These weights show that in 30 years man could make low Earth orbit so inhospitable that manned flight would be seriously restricted. Furthermore, this table shows that the shielding weights become so heavy that the equivalent of almost a full shuttle flight would have to be dedicated for launching shielding just for the propulsion pallets. There are a number of ways to circumvent this serious problem. North American Aerospace Defense Command, identifies, tracks and catalogs large debris particles approximately 10 cm and larger. If such a particle were ever headed for a collision with the SS and a minimum of a 2 hour warning were provided, the SS could be boosted to a higher altitude at a velocity up to 1.5 m/sec to avoid collision. However, a portion of the technical community disagrees with this concept because of the large number of uncatalogued particles. The range between 1.6 cm and 10 cm is viewed as the most significant problem area. Since the probability of impact on the SS is smaller than specified for design, shielding is not required to account for such a particle in the design. Others have taken steps to make measurements in this size range to establish whether Kessler's new model is conservative or not.[7] Other suggestions have been made to remove some of the debris from space which could be applied to a specific altitude range such as the SS will fly.[8-9] Most of the concepts impart a change in trajectory such that the debris will enter higher atmospheric density regions so that the friction will cause them to reenter quickly. For the Space Station altitudes, high solar activity such as is now occurring will help reduce the debris in LEO because the residual air density is raised to higher altitudes as the atmosphere expands due to heat input from the sun.

Finally, Materials Engineers can help by providing materials for the shields which are lighter in weight and more efficient in transferring the particle energy into a liquid/vapor cloud which does not create harmful ejecta from the shield. The different design concepts that have been and are being studied are shown in Figure 2. Because of the uncertainty of the increase in the debris environment, these concepts only have to be designed for 10 year service life with the ability to retrofit additional shielding later. Shield concepts have been developed which have demonstrated the ability to stop the equivalent of an approximately 2 cm diameter aluminum sphere. The energy was dissipated by multiple layers of Kevlar cloth similar to that used for bullet proof vests after the first shield layer disrupted the particle. This concept had an areal density of about 10 gm/cm^2. Such weights are manageable, but weight reductions for the same stopping power are viewed as appropriate efforts. Since most of the concepts studied to date are an extension of the Whipple concept for micrometeoroid shields,[10] there is plenty of room for new, novel concepts and materials to help reduce the shielding weights required for the larger size debris particles.

2.4 UV and AO

Ultraviolet radiation (UV) and atomic oxygen (AO) are of primary concern relative to the degradation of exposed organic and inorganic materials, particularly solar array substrates and thermal control coatings. UV dosage is the same at geosynchronous orbit as in LEO. The much higher radiation dosage that occurs from solar flares and galactic radiation and can degrade thermal coatings at geosynchronous orbit is not present in LEO as mentioned earlier. Therefore, the performance data obtained at geoaltitudes is only of limited value for the evaluation of coatings be-

cause of the possible synergistic effect of these environments. Atomic oxygen is only significant in LEO and is very altitude dependent.[11] Therefore in LEO, one is concerned whether there is a synergistic effect between AO and UV which would increase either the erosion of forward facing surfaces or changes in optical properties of a thermal control coating. Almost all ground test data to date is with either one environment or the other, but not for both.

3. ENVIRONMENTAL SIMULATION

As already mentioned, there is a very limited database to draw on with regard to selecting and certifying materials for a 30 year service life in LEO. Many of the degrading environments found in LEO can be simulated to an acceptable degree in terrestrial test facilities, often with a significant level of intensification to reduce the required test duration. There are however, some environments for which there are only limited simulation facilities or for which there is no effective way to speed up the testing. One of the most significant degrading environments for which high fidelity simulation is lacking is atomic oxygen exposure. Atomic oxygen has only been recognized as a problem for about a decade. Simulation facilities are being developed here on Earth but the quality of the simulation requires further refinement. The facility being developed at Los Alamos is perhaps the most advanced and is a useful tool for evaluating materials behavior when exposed to high fluence levels of atomic oxygen.[12] Ultraviolet radiation is also recognized as a potentially serious degrading environment. Terrestrial simulation of the UV environment can be accomplished but there is some question about the degree of intensification that can be employed without causing unacceptable heating of the test specimens. In addition, most of the UV exposure testing that has been done to date has been done in the "near" UV region, that is, above wavelengths of around 2000 angstroms. We know that the shorter "far" UV wavelengths, also degrade materials, but testing requires more elaborate facilities using special window materials capable of passing the wavelengths of interest. It has been shown that materials like anodized aluminum suffer most of their degradation from UV in the "near" region[13] but the "far" UV radiation has a significant high energy component that can introduce bond scission in polymers such as Teflon which will be used in the construction of the thermal radiator coatings for Space Station.

Effects such as sustained loads on composite pressure vessels are not amenable to accelerated testing. Our planned approach is to start testing sufficiently in advance of actual flight service so we will later have several years headstart for realtime testing of these effects. The test program will continue during the service life of the space station with the goal of identifying any degradation in advance of failure to permit retrofit or changeout of the pressure vessels in service onboard the station. Vessels that are struck by debris if a shield is penetrated but which do not suffer penetration will be taken out of service so this condition will not be considered in the test program.

Hardware elements that have periodic duty cycles such as motors, compressors, rotary joints etc. will have their service capability evaluated through accelerated testing. As discussed later, the composite truss tubes that may be sensitive to the thermal cycling caused by the 90 minute orbit around the Earth will be subjected to accelerated thermal cycling to verify their service capability.

Our ability to terrestrially simulate degrading environments encountered in LEO is summarized in Table 3. The table also shows whether the simulation can be accelerated or intensified to reduce the test duration needed to demonstrate adequate life capability.

4. DESIGN CONSIDERATIONS

It is acknowledged from cost considerations alone that some of the materials planned for use in the construction of the space station will not have the 30 year service life planned for the station as a whole. With this realization, the space station is being designed with the provision that all hardware elements are either repairable insitu or are part of what is referred to as an Orbital Replaceable Unit (ORU). An example of an ORU is an electronic blackbox which would not be repaired on orbit but rather, simply exchanged for a replacement unit in the event of failure. Materials such as elastomers fall into this category while lubricants for rotary

joints will be replenished by the astronauts. NASA has imposed a requirement that detailed records for all elastomeric materials and other life limited materials be kept indicating the date the part was fabricated and its utilization on the space station to assist in future repair or replacement.

Most of the nonmetallic materials planned for use on the space station are subject to environmental degradation in LEO. Most of these issues pertain to the AO, and UV environments, or to thermal cycling. Nonmetallic materials planned for use on the space station include graphite epoxy composites, elastomeric seals, lubricants, thermal control materials, solar array substrates, and flexible fluid lines. Concern also exists relative to the contamination from the baseline flexible fluid lines. These lines are made of Teflon which may have an unacceptably high permeability to ammonia (used for the active thermal control system) resulting in a contamination problem. Fluid line fittings with very low initial leak rates have been demonstrated which can be assembled on orbit by astronauts performing EVA activity.[14] Large amounts of high performance multilayer thermal insulation (MLI) will be required for the Space Station. These materials are usually made from metallized Kapton or mylar to minimize weight. Both of these organic materials are very rapidly degraded by atomic oxygen. Alternative designs such as all metal MLI will be required or design solutions will be needed to protect the sensitive Kapton and mylar from the AO. Rubber "O" rings and seals are also considered to be problem areas. The causes of time dependent failure for rubber seals is not well understood. The common practice on Earth is to simply replace the seals when they fail, so careful study of the reasons for failure has not been made. We plan to investigate this area in some detail. Our current thinking is that failure is related to flaws and inclusions introduced into the parts during fabrication. It may be possible to screen these parts out by careful inspection of all seals and "O" rings used on the Space Station.

The foregoing has been a very brief outline of material issues related to some of the hardware elements of the Space Station. The key materials issues and our approach to their resolution for the composite truss tubes has been selected for detailed discussion in this paper. Restrictions on the length of the paper prevent detailed discussion of the other hardware elements.

5. TRUSS TUBES

The key material issues associated with the composite truss tubes are resin microcracking due to thermal cycling and impact damage tolerance. The Space Station will experience approximately 175,000 thermal cycles over a temperature range of about -57° C to 38°C during its 30 year service life. If resin microcracking occurs, the coefficient of thermal expansion (CTE) of the tubes will change as the crack density increases, possibly resulting in a failure to meet the ±0.25 degree pointing accuracy requirement imposed on the Space Station. Microcracking is not viewed as a major problem with regard to changes in the mechanical properties of the tubes such as strength or stiffness.

Another issue is the impact damage that can occur either from crew activities or from hypervelocity impact from debris or micrometeoroids. Impact damage is of concern for impacts that damage or remove the protective foil coating of the tubes as well as impacts that result in damage to the composite tube itself. Removal of the foil renders the tube susceptible to attack from UV and AO and can cause tube failure even if the impact event causes no structural damage. Crew activities pose a significant risk of damaging the tubes or their foil coating. Each of the tubes is handled during assembly on-orbit and the truss structure is planned to be used as a mobility aid for crewmembers during extravehicular activity (EVA).

The problem of resin microcracking has been extensively studied.[15-17] The use of a tough resin system coupled with low ply angles (less than 30°) is expected to minimize or eliminate any problems with microcracking. Our life certification test program will include an accelerated thermal cycling test which will cycle production tube segments for 175,000 (one lifetime) cycles using the predicted service temperature range. This test program is expected to take approximately 2.5 years of continuous testing to complete based on a 5-6 minute cycle time. Tube segments for this test will have the protective foil coating applied to verify that there are no problems with the foil debonding or fatigue

cracking. In addition, a mechanical fatigue test program will be conducted to expose test samples to as many as 700,000 load cycles. This test program will use mechanical load to simulate the thermally induced stress the tubes will experience in service. It is recognized that the actual inservice stress states cannot be completely duplicated using only uniaxial mechanical load, however the test will provide additional confidence that NASA's requirement for a 4X fatigue life can be satisfied.

Low velocity impact and crew induced damage will be evaluated to verify that the tubes can survive the worst case predicted events of these types. NASA specifications require that the tubes be capable of sustaining a 131.5 N load applied at the strut center and also that they can support a 42 N local crippling load applied over a 0.81 cm^2 area without failure. Production tube samples will be tested using a low velocity impact test device such as a Dynatup tester to evaluate the tube's capability to withstand the specified loads. Impacted tubes will be examined using NDT methods to detect any damage, followed by measurement of any changes to mechanical properties and CTE. The use of a relatively thick (0.08-0.13 mm) hard foil coating on the tubes is also expected to improve their resistance to low velocity impact and crew induced damage. Visual examination will be relied upon to detect damage to the foil.

We plan to conduct hypervelocity impact testing on tube segments using the impact facility at NASA JSC. Particle size and velocity will be determined by analysis based on the number and severity of impacts predicted for the truss structure using the debris environment models being developed by NASA as described earlier in this paper. After subjecting the tube samples to impact, they will be evaluated for extent of damage and changes in mechanical properties and CTE. Impact damaged tubes will also be thermal cycled using a test facility at NASA LaRC to study the effects of thermal cycling. Analysis will also be done to establish a threshold level above which damage would be viewed as unacceptable and below which, damage would not result in significant loss of performance. Damaged tubes will also be subjected to AO and UV exposure. One of the concerns is for the case of a penetration through one wall of the tube where the penetration causes a hole small enough for the structural damage to be below the tolerance threshold. In cases like this, the hole would allow AO to reach the interior volume of the tube, with the potential for degradation away from the actual impact site due to reflection and scattering of the AO from the inside surface of the tube. We plan to study this problem by partially coating the inner surface of damaged tubes with silver and then exposing them to AO. The silver will oxidize and turn black upon exposure to the AO allowing a mapping of the reflection and scattering of the AO from the tube inner wall surfaces. While this test is expected to be qualitative in nature it will provide data useful in assessing the severity of the problem.

6. FUTURE WORK

There is a considerable amount of work in progress or planned at McDonnell Douglas Space Systems Company to verify the suitability of existing materials for use on large space structures and on the Space Station in particular. This presents a significant engineering challenge because previous satellite programs were not intended to remain operational for 30 years or longer during their design lifetimes. The development work to accomplish these objectives specifically for Space Station is funded under contract to NASA while the more generic work is being planned and accomplished under company IRAD funding. Efforts planned or in progress under NASA funding include ensuring reliable composite pressure vessels, long life truss tubes, low permeability flexible fluid lines, and stable radiator coatings. Company funded work includes atomic oxygen effects, molecular contaminant deposition and subsequent reevaporation, welding in space, advanced orbital debris shields, and on-orbit damage detection and impact assessment for composite structures.

7. SUMMARY AND CONCLUSION

In conclusion, we think we have viable approaches to demonstrating adequate service lives for most material applications on the Space Station. For those materials without adequate service life capability, the provision for on-orbit repair or replacement is built into the design. The Space Station does not depend on the invention of any new materials, although the possibility of optimization exists in a number of cases. While we think that successful strategies

have been identified for resolution of all of the known material issues, additional work will ensure a successful program.

8. References

1. Proceedings of the SMRM (Solar Maximum Repair Mission) , Degradation Study Workshop, Goddard Space Flight Center Report 408. SMRM-79-0001, May 9-10, 1985.

2. "Atomic Oxygen Effects Measurements for Shuttle Missions STS-8 and 41-G," NASA Technical Memorandum 100459. Volumes I, II & III, compiled by Jim Visentine, NASA JSC, September 1988.

3. Leger, L. J., Spiker, I. K., Kuminecz, J. F., Ballentine, T. J., and Visentine, J. T., "STS-5 LEO Effects Experiment: Background Description and Thin Film Results, " AIAA Paper No. 83-2631-CP, Nov. 1983.

4. Leger, L. J., Visentine, J. T., and Kuminecz, J. F., "Low Earth Orbit Atomic Oxygen Effects on Surfaces," AIAA Paper No 84-0548, Jan. 1984.

5. Srour, J. R., Long, D. M., Fitzwilson, R. L., Millsward, D.G., & Chadsey, W.L., Radiation Effects and Dose Enhancement of Electronic Materials, Noyes Publications, Park Ridge, New Jersey, 1984.

6. Pending Revision of Space Station Program Specification JSC30425.

7. Dr. Faith Vilas, presented at the, In-Space Technology Experiments Program 88, 1988 Workshop, Atlanta, Georgia, Dec 6-9, 1988. Publication pending.

8. Metger, J. D./, LeClaire Jr., R. J., Howe, S. D., & Burgin, K. C., "Nuclear-Powered Space Debris Sweeper," Los Alamos National Laboratory Preprint LA-UR-87-3816, Scheduled for Publication.

9. Johnson, L. N. and McKnight, D. S., Artificial Space Debris, Orbit Book Co. Inc., Malabar, Florida, 1987.

10. Whipple, F. L., Chapter X entitled, Meteoritic Phenomena and Meteorites, PP 137-170, Physics and Medicine of the Upper Atmosphere, White, C. S. & Benson, O. O. Jr.,ed. Symposium Proceedings, University of New Mexico Press, Albuquerque 1952.

11. Cross, J. B., Spangler, L. H., Hoffbauer, M. A & Archuleta, F. A., "High Intensity 5 eV CW Laser Sustained O-Atom Exposure Facility for Material Degradation Studies," pp. 740-751, 18th International SAMPE Technical Conference, Vol. 18, Oct 7-9, 1986.

12. Vaughan, W. W., "Natural Environment Design Criteria for the Space Station Definition and Preliminary Design," 1st Rev., NASA TM-86460j, Sept. 1984.

13. Donohoe, M. J. , McIntosh, R. Jr & Henniger, J. H., ":The Degradation of Alzak by Short Wavelength Ultraviolet Radiation," ASTM/IES/AIAA Space Simulation Conference, Sept. 14-16, 1970, Paper No. 26.

14. Anderson, R. H., and Pearson, S. J., "On Orbit Tube Joint Preparation and Repair," ASME/ASTM Pressure Vessels and Fluid Piping Conference, Honolulu, Hawaii, July 23-24, 1989. Publication pending.

15. Babel, H. W., Thompson, D. F., and Shumate, T. P., "Microcrack Resistant Structural Composite Tubes For Space Station," 18th International SAMPE Symposium, October 7-9, 1986.

16. Tompkins, S. S., Sykes, G. F., and Bowles, D. E., "The Thermal And Mechanical Stability Of Composite Materials For Space Structures," IEEE/ASM/ASME/SME Space Tech Conference, September 23-25, 1985, Anaheim, California.

17. Wolff, E. G., "Dimensional Stability Of Carbon Fiber Reinforced Plastic Tubes," SAMPE Quarterly, October 1984.

9. BIOGRAPHIES

Daniel F. Thompson is a Lead Technology Engineer in Materials &Processes at McDonnell Douglas Space Systems Company. He has been with McDonnell Douglas since 1977 with assignments in the areas of adhesive bonding, development of X-ray shielding materials, and design support roles in a variety of aerospace and missile programs. He holds a BS degree in Chemical Engineering from California State University, Long Beach and is completing a MS degree in Materials Engineering at the University of California, Irvine.

Henry W. Babel is currently the manager for Materials and Processes on the Space Station Program at McDonnell Douglas Space Systems Company. He formerly was manager of all M&P laboratories. He has held a variety of managerial and technical assignments in M&P in his 29 years with McDonnell Douglas. He received his PhD from Ohio State University and his BS and MS from the University of Illinois. He has presented and published more than 25 technical papers. He is frequently a TV moderator on world trade issues.

TABLE 1. A COMPARISON OF GEOSYNCHRONOUS AND
LEO ENVIRONMENTS THAT CAN INFLUENCE DESIGN

Material Degrading Environments	Orbital Environments	
	Geosynchronous	Low Earth
Galactic Radiation	Yes	Yes - primarily electronics
Solar Flare Radiation	Yes	No
Trapped Radiation	No	Yes - primarily thermal control coatings
UV Radiation	Yes - Same - Yes	
Atomic Oxygen	No	Yes
Micrometeoroids/Debris	Minor	Major
Diurnal Temperature Cycle	24 hours	90 minutes

TABLE 2 - ESTIMATED SHIELDING WEIGHTS FOR KESSLER'S NEW MODEL
FOR
3 SPACE STATION PROPULSION PALLETS

Design Life (Years)	Critical Particle Diameter cm (inches)	Weight Kg (Lb)
10	2.60 (1.023)	2,317 (5,097)
30	27.00* (10.63)	15,557 (34,226)

*NORAD Tracks/Catalogs Particles from 10 cm and larger

Table 3. Accelerated Environmental Simulation Testing

Examples of Accelerated Testing Scheduled	Simulation
175,000 accelerated thermal cycles of the composite truss tubes to verify resin microcracking resistance	Good
Equivalent of 30 years of high intensity UV exposure of thermal control coatings in the near and far UV range	Permissible degree of intensification needs to be verified
Full life cycle testing of intermittent duty cycle mechanisms, motors, compressors, etc.	Good
Load and temperature effects - used successfully for the Kevlar yarn on metal-lined pressure bottles for the Space Shuttle	Good
Vessels cycled the required number of lives to verify liner ability to meet the cyclic life	Good

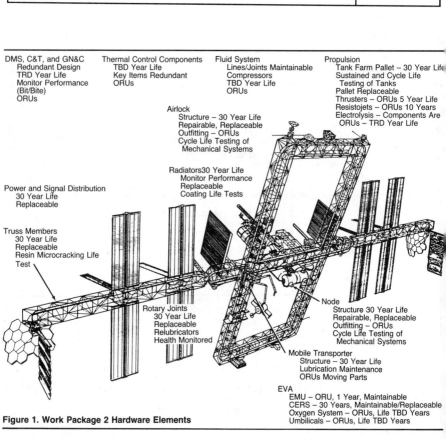

DMS, C&T, and GN&C
  Redundant Design
  TRD Year Life
  Monitor Performance
  (Bit/Bite)
  ORUs

Thermal Control Components
  TBD Year Life
  Key Items Redundant
  ORUs

Fluid System
  Lines/Joints Maintainable
  Compressors
  TBD Year Life
  ORUs

Propulsion
  Tank Farm Pallet – 30 Year Life
  Sustained and Cycle Life
    Testing of Tanks
  Pallet Replaceable
  Thrusters – ORUs 5 Year Life
  Resistojets – ORUs 10 Years
  Electrolysis – Components Are
    ORUs – TRD Year Life

Airlock
  Structure – 30 Year Life
  Repairable, Replaceable
  Outfitting – ORUs
  Cycle Life Testing of
    Mechanical Systems

Radiators 30 Year Life
  Monitor Performance
  Replaceable
  Coating Life Tests

Power and Signal Distribution
  30 Year Life
  Replaceable

Truss Members
  30 Year Life
  Replaceable
  Resin Microcracking Life
  Test

Rotary Joints
  30 Year Life
  Replaceable
  Relubricators
  Health Monitored

Node
  Structure 30 Year Life
  Repairable, Replaceable
  Outfitting – ORUs
  Cycle Life Testing of
    Mechanical Systems

Mobile Transporter
  Structure – 30 Year Life
  Lubrication Maintenance
  ORUs Moving Parts

EVA
  EMU – ORU, 1 Year, Maintainable
  CERS – 30 Years, Maintainable/Replaceable
  Oxygen System – ORUs, Life TBD Years
  Umbilicals – ORUs, Life TBD Years

Figure 1. Work Package 2 Hardware Elements

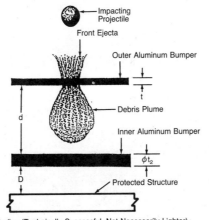

Impacting
Projectile

Front Ejecta

Outer Aluminum Bumper

t

Debris Plume

d

Inner Aluminum Bumper

ϕt_2

D

Protected Structure

Alternatives Studies (Technically Successful, Not Necessarily Lighter)

■ Initial Bumpter – Ideal: Convert Particle K. E. to Vaporized Cloud
  ● High Temperature Ceramics
  ● Divide Into Multiple Metal Layers – Optimize Spacing/No. of Layers
  ● Used Higher Density Metals
  ● Put Energy Absorbers Between 1st and 2nd Plate – Foams

■ Secondary Bumper – Ideal: Stop the Particle Remnants, no Back Surface Spall
  ● Multiple Layers of Kevlar 29 as Energy Absorber

Figure 2. Some Typical Shield Design Concepts Studied by the Technical Community

GRAPHITE AND KEVLAR THERMOPLASTIC COMPOSITES
FOR SPACECRAFT APPLICATIONS

EDWARD M. SILVERMAN, RICHARD A. GRIESE, and WARD F. WRIGHT

TRW SPACE & TECHNOLOGY GROUP
ONE SPACE PARK
REDONDO BEACH, CA 90278

Abstract

Graphite/polyetherether-ketone (PEEK) composites were evaluated for spacecraft application requirements. Composite characterization of the AS-4/PEEK composite included design-oriented mechanical properties, coefficient of thermal expansion, outgassing/condensable volatiles and equilibrium moisture absorption at 120 °F (49 °C) and 95% R.H. Characterization was also performed on a typical baseline epoxy composite system for comparison. Results indicated that AS-4/PEEK composites exhibited equivalent mechanical pro-perties and lower moisture uptake and outgassing compared to T300/934 epoxy composite.

Water absorption tests were performed on a variety of thermoplastic resins reinforced with Kevlar 49 and Kevlar 149 fibers and the results were compared to a Kevlar 49 reinforced epoxy composite. Results indi-cated that Kevlar reinforced thermoplastics absorbed less water and exhibited superior dimensional stability compared to Kevlar reinforced epoxy composite.

Several joining concepts for bonding advanced thermo-plastic matrix composites were investigated. Tensile lap shear coupons made from AS-4/PEEK thermoplastic prepreg tapes were bonded using a commercially available epoxy system, mechanical fasteners plus adhesive bonding, resistance heating, focused infrared heating, ultrasonics welding, and a novel technique employing an amorphous thermoplastic film. FM300 adhesive with plasma etched AS-4/PEEK substrates produced the best bond with a lap shear strength over 6000 psi (41.4 MPa). Amorphous bonding of the AS-4/PEEK substrates with Ultem film produced lap shear strengths in excess of 5000 psi (34.5 MPa).

1. INTRODUCTION

During the past 10 to 15 years graphite fiber- and Kevlar fiber-reinforced epoxies have been the principle composite materials used on spacecraft. For most of the early applications, reduced weight was the principal impetus for composite usage. However, the trend towards development of high-performance communication satellites (e.g., INTELSAT 6) and precision space-science instruments (e.g., the Space Telescope) have brought about changes in spacecraft materials requirements. Along with decreased weight, new levels of environmental resistance, dimensional stability, structural capability, and intrinsic hardening are now essential. Epoxy composites may not be able to meet the future requirements of dimensional stability because of moisture absorption prior to launch and microcracking of the epoxy resin during thermal cycling.

Thermoplastic composites, however, possess a combination of properties that appear to match the requirements of several spacecraft applications. A recent investigation by one of the authors [1] points to emerging new graphite fiber reinforced thermoplastic PEEK composite materials as offering performance improvements over current graphite/epxoy composites in the areas of lower moisture absorption, no evidence of thermally induced microcracking, and minimum outgassing. Enhanced microcrack resistance is attributed to the tough nature of thermoplastic resins. The fracture toughness of unreinforced PEEK is 23 in.-lb/in^2 (4.03 KJ/m^2) which is much higher than that for the second generation of toughened epoxies now available, which range from 1.1 (.2 KJ/m^2) to 2.9 in.-lb/in.^{2} (.5 KJ/m^2).

Compared to the current thermoset matrix composites, thermoplastic matrix composites have the potential for significantly reducing acquisition and life-cycle costs for a composite assembly. The acquisition cost-reduction is obtained through innovative and rapid forming processes in contrast to the long processing cycles typical of thermoset materials. Thermoplastics have no requirements for refrigeration of prepreg and minimal requirements for ancillary tooling materials. Also, the reprocessibility of thermoplastics enables the co-consolidation of sub-assemblies, and offers the potential to eliminate the producibility issues associated with adhesively bonded structures. Previous work [2-4] has shown that thermoplastic composites can be joined by locally consolidating the joint interface using a variety of techniques, such as resistance bonding, ultrasonic welding, and focused infrared heating.

The intent of this paper is to expand on the potential performance benefits of thermoplastic matrix composites highlighted in earlier studies [1,5] and to generate the information required to increase the level of confidence in joining technology such that designers and engineers can implement these assembly techniques in the construction of spacecraft structures.

2.0 EXPERIMENTAL DESCRIPTION

Conventional unidirectional PEEK prepreg tapes reinforced with AS-4 graphite fibers and unidirectional commingled woven G30 graphite/PEEK fabrics were investigated. The commingled fabrics consist of hybrid yarns of intimate blends of continuous thermoplastic PEEK filaments with G30 graphite filaments. The Kevlar reinforced thermoplastic matrices investigated were polyethersulfone (PES), polyphenylene sulfide (PPS), and polyetherimide (PEI Ultem). Table 1 summarizes the materials of this study.

All laminates for the physical and mechanical characterization study were fabricated by compression molding techniques. Several plies of prepreg tape or fabrics were placed into matched metal die and then placed into a press preheated to the manufacturer's recommended melt temperature. The lay-up was heated to 50°F (28°C) below the melt temperature at which point a pressure of 200 psi (1.38 MPa) was applied for subsequent heating to the final melt temperature. The part was held at 200 psi (1.38 MPa) and the specified temperature for a time period of 30 to 60 minutes before being removed to a cold press for quenching. The press platens were cooled by circulating ambient water through the platens.

All mechanical properties were determined using ASTM procedures with an Instron universal machine using a sample size of five. Coefficients of thermal expansion were measured over the temperature range of -300°F (-184 °C) and 212°F (100 °C) using a dilato-

meter. Equilibrium moisture absorption of test specimens consisted of exposure to 95 percent relative humidity and 120°F (49 °C). All samples were dried prior to testing at 216 °F (102°C) for 8 days. Moisture absorption and transverse hygroscopic strain were monitored by periodically removing the specimens for weighing and thickness measurements.

Several bonding techniques were evaluated by preparing tensile lap shear specimens and measuring bond strengths. AS-4/APC-2 PEEK prepreg tapes were used to fabricate 16-ply cross-ply laminates. FM-300 film adhesive, a 350°F (177 °C) curing epoxy, was used to establish a baseline bond strength. FM-300 represents the state of the art in epoxy film adhesives, and offers moisture and corrosion resistance in humid environments. Several surface preparation methods, including chromic acid etch, 50 mesh Al_2O_3 grit blasting, and a cold (CF_2+O_2) plasma treatment, were employed to enhance adhesion by removing unbound organic contamination and to micro-etch the surface.

Ultrasonic welding requires the application of static pressure plus superimposed dynamic vibration. For this work, a Branson Model 1300P ultrasonic welder was used. Bonding is accomplished by applying low amplitude (.013 mm - 0.25 mm, 0.0005 inch- 0.010 inch) high frequency (20-40 KHz) mechanical vibration to parts.

Infrared heating utilizing a "focused, single lamp, infrared reflector" was performed by the Entwistle Company, Hudson, MASS. In this method, the interfaces to be bonded are sufficiently heated through exposure to an intense narrow beam line of infrared heat without thermally damaging the adherends. Once the thermoplastic matrix is molten, the parts are pressed together until the thermoplastic has cooled.

Resistance heating is a method for quickly heating and melting composites at the bond surface with an electric current. One resistive bonding technique places high resistance wires in the joint which act as heating elements when connected to a power supply. However, once the joint has consolidated, the wires remain trapped. The resistance heating technique used in this study involved the flow of electric current directly through the composite panels, taking advantage of the high electrical conductivity of the graphite fibers. Rapid joining of thermoplastic components is possible using resistive heating. Joints can be consolidated in minutes at room temperature, compared to hours at 350°F for many epoxy adhesives.

Thermoplastic bonding was evaluated by utilizing amorphous polyetherimide (PEI Ultem) film. The film was co-consolidated with the AS-4/PEEK prepreg tapes to prepare the substrate adherend, and subsequently bonded together in an secondary operation for 5 minutes at a lower temperature 600°F (316 °C)) than the PEEK resin melt temperature of 680°F (360 °C). Ultem's melt temperature is 540°F (282 °C).

3. RESULTS AND DISCUSSION

3.1 Physical and Mechanical Characterization

The physical and mechanical properties of graphite/PEEK laminates fabricated from uni-directional AS-4/PEEK prepreg tapes and G30-500/PEEK commingled woven fabrics are summarized in Table 2, and the results are compared to a typical T300/934 epoxy composite. The tensile properties of the specimens fabricated from the uni-directional prepreg tapes were observed to be higher than that of the specimens fabricated from the uni-directional commingled woven fabrics. For example, the tensile modulus for the unidirectional prepreg tape specimen was 19.4 Msi (133.7 GPa) versus 17.2 Msi (118.6 GPa) for the unidirectional fabric specimen. This can be attributed to fiber breakage during the commingling and weaving or fiber misalignment during laminate consolidation. Compared to T300/934 epoxy, the mechanical properties measured for the unidirectional AS-4/PEEK prepreg tape composites are equivalent.

The outgassing/volatiles testing indicated that the graphite/thermoplastics had total mass loss (TML) values in the range of 0.035 to 0.070% and collected volatile condensable materials (CVCM) of 0.005%. In contrast, TML and CVCM values for the T300/934 epoxy were determined to be 0.0145% and 0.007%, respectively. The low values of TML and CVCM for the PEEK composites indicate that thermoplastic composites can meet the low outgassing requirements needed to avoid contamination of infrared sensors and sensitive optics.

3.2 Moisture Absorption

The effect of absorbed moisture on graphite composites was examined. Figure 1 shows the moisture absorption behavior of cross-ply AS-4/PEEK and T-300/934 laminates at 120°F (49 °C) and 95% relative humidity. Both materials approached saturation after approximately 100 hours of exposure to the humid environment. The PEEK composite exhibited a very low saturation value of 0.20%, whereas the epoxy composite absorbed over 0.5% water. This behavior is consistent with the Fickian diffusion model, and the low saturation moisture content for the PEEK matrix composite is characteristic of crystalline polymers.

Aramid Kevlar 49 fiber-reinforced epoxy matrix composites are used in satellite components due to its radio frequency (RF) transparency. However, the performance of such composites suffers during exposure to moist environments because of moisture absorption by both the resin and the fiber (see References 6-8).

Moisture absorption curves for Kevlar 49/epoxy, Kevlar 49/PES, Kevlar 49/PEI, Kevlar 49/PPS, and Kevlar 149/PEI are illustrated in Figure 2. The equilibrium moisture levels, summarized in Table 3 for the various Kevlar/thermoplastic composites, were lower in comparison with the Kevlar epoxy composite. The Kevlar 49 Ultem composite exhibited less than one-half the moisture gain of the Kevlar 49/epoxy composite, 2.28 versus 4.61 percent. Additional reduction in equilibrium moisture gain was observed for the Kevlar 149/Ultem composite which absorbed only 1.38 percent.

Transverse hygroscopic strains for the Kevlar composites are also summarized in Table 3. The low moisture pick-up for the Kevlar/thermoplastic composites resulted in lower strains compared to that of the Kevlar 49 epoxy composite.

The diffusivity values listed in Table 3 are higher for the amorphous thermoplastic composites than for the epoxy composite, indicating equilibrium moisture contents will be reached more quickly in the thermoplastic composites. The diffusivities of the PES and Ultem matrix composites were identical, at 1.15×10^{-5} mm^2/s. The Kevlar 49/PPS diffusivity was much lower due to PPS crystallinity, at 1.56×10^{-6} mm^2/s.

Hence, Kevlar 49/thermoplastic composites absorb far less moisture compared to Kevlar 49/epoxy composites, which means that dimensional changes are sharply reduced. Further reduction in moisture pick-up and transverse hygroscopic strains can be achieved with thermo-plastic composites reinforced with Kevlar 149 fibers.

3.3 Thermoplastic Bonding Study

Joints produced either by welding or based on inherently tough thermoplastic adhesives such as PEEK, offer significant advantages over the conventional thermoset adhesives in that they are not brittle and do not suffer from moisture susceptibility. In this study, several fusion bonding techniques were compared to adhesive bonding using a traditional epoxy film adhesive and a novel technique employing an amorphous thermoplastic film.

Table 4 compares the effects of the different preparation techniques on the lap shear strengths of the AS-4/PEEK substrate with the FM300 film adhesive as well as the lap shear results of the various fusion bonding methods and amorphous bonding method. Of the various surface preparation methods investigated, FM300 adhesive with plasma etched AS-4/PEEK substrates produced the best bond with lap shear strength over 6000 psi (41.4 MPa). Amorphous bonding of the AS-4/PEEK substrates with PEI film produced lap shear strengths in excess of 5000 psi (34.5 MPa).

Of the three fusion bonding/welding investigated; focused IR heating, resistance heating, and ultrasonic welding, using AS-4/PEEK lap shear coupons; the best results were obtained with the focus infrared heating method. The ultrasonic welding method proved much less successful since the conductive graphite fibers directed heat away from the interface, even when an unreinforced PEEK film was placed at the interface.

These results indicate that thermoplastic composites are amenable to joining techniques that utilize heat to melt either the matrix resin material or an unreinforced PEI film placed at the interface. When this heat can be concentrated at the bondline through selection of appropriate methods and equipment, efficient subassembly will be achieved. The main advantage of this focus infrared heating and the amorphous bonding methods is the rapid joining time (5 minutes) compared to that of the FM-300 epoxy film adhesive (1 hour) while retaining most of the epoxy adhesive bond strength.

4.0 CONCLUSIONS

Several thermoplastic polymers offer increased per-performance over epoxies for use as matrix resins in composites for spacecraft applications. AS-4/ PEEK composites exhibited lower moisture pick-up, reduced out- gassing and equivalent mechanical properties compared with a T-300/934 epoxy material. The combination of Kevlar 49 fibers with thermoplastic resins PES, PEI, and PPS results in composites with lower moisture absorption and hygroscopic strain compared to a Kevlar 49/epoxy. The use of Kevlar 149 fibers with a PEI matrix resulted in in-creased moisture resistance and decreased strain compared to the use of Kevlar 49 fibers.

Results given here also indicate that graphite thermoplastic composites are amenable to joining techniques that utilize heat to melt either the matrix resin or an unreinforced PEI film placed at the interface. When this heat can be concentrated at the bondline through selection of appropriate methods and equipment, efficient subassembly will be achieved. The main advantage of the focused infrared heating and the amorphous bonding methods is the rapid joining time (5 minutes) compared to that of the FM-300 epoxy film adhesive (1 hour) while retaining most of the epoxy adhesive bond strength.

ACKNOWLEDGMENTS

The authors would like to thank W.C. Forbes, K.K. Ueda, Dr. P.G. Cheng and C. R. Wiacek who contributed to the research described in this paper. The authors would also like to thank Dr. T.T. Serafini and Dr. R.J. Jones for their technical input, comments, and suggestions regarding this work.

BIOGRAPHIES

Dr. E.M. Silverman is the Section Manager for Composites Development in the Materials Technology Department at TRW. Dr. Silverman has extensive experience in the processing of thermosetting and thermoplastic resins with graphite, Kevlar, and glass fibers, in structure-property-performance correlations, as well as in failure mechanisms of fiber-reinforced plastics. Current research interests include the development of specialized materials and components for spacecraft and missile applications with emphasis on composites, adhesives, coatings, and elastomers. Prior to joining TRW in 1986, Dr. Silverman performed product development research with polymeric composites at B.F. Goodrich and with the Bendix Corporation. Dr. Silverman received his Ph.D. in chemical engineering at Stanford University in 1980.

R.A. Griese is currently a member of the technical staff in the Materials Technology Department of TRW's Applied Technology Division. He is responsible for the charac-terization of advanced thermoplastic composites for spacecraft applications, and is currently involved with determining the effect of thermal cycling on the physical properties of thermoplastic composites. He is also experienced in polymer rheological measure-ments and non-destructive structural composites analysis. Mr. Griese

received his M.S. in polymer science at the University of Illinois in 1987.

W.F. Wright is currently a member of the technical staff in the Materials Technology Department of TRW's Applied Technology Division. He is responsible for environmental testing/analysis of coatings, adhesives, and elastomers. Mr. Wright has been involved in a range of projects for TRW including the Lunar Module Descent Engines and the Viking Program.

REFERENCES

(1) E.M. Silverman and R.J. Jones, Technical Proceedings, 33rd International SAMPE Symposium (March 7 1988) 1418.

(2) A. Benatar and T.G. Gutowski, Technical Proceedings, 33rd International SAMPE (March 1988) 1787.

(3) J.R. Krone, T.P. Murtha, and J.A. Stirling, Technical Proceedings, 33rd Inter-national SAMPE Symposium (March 1988) 829.

(4) A. Benatar and T.G. Gutowski, SAMPE Quarterly, 18 (October 1986) 34.

(5) E.M. Silverman and R.J. Jones, SAMPE Journal, 24 (July/August 1988) 33.

(6) A.C. Loos and G.S. Springer, Environmental Effects on Composite Materials, Techhnomic Press, Vol. 1 (1981) 34.

(7) S.W. Beckwith and B.D. Wallace, Technical Proceedings, SAMPE International Symposium, 28 (1983) 287.

(8) I. Verpoest and G.S. Springer, J. of Reinforced Plastics and Composites, 7 (January 1988) 2.

Table 1: Product Information

Fiber/Resin	Manufacturer	Product Form
AS4/PEEK	ICI	Unidirectional prepreg tap
T300/934 epoxy	Fiberite	Unidirectional prepreg tape
Kevlar 49/5208 epoxy	Narmco	Unidirectional prepreg tape
Kevlar 49/PES	FERRO	Prepreg fabric
Kevlar 49/Ultem	FERRO	Prepreg fabric
Kevlar 49/PPS	Quadrax	Interlaced unidirectional prepreg tape
Kevlar 149/Ultem	Textile Products	Commingled fabric

Table 2: Comparative Mechanical Properties of Low Modulus Graphite PEEK and Epoxy [0°] Laminates[1]

	AS-4/PEEK Tape	G30-500/PEEK Commingled	T-300/934 Epoxy
Ply thickness, mils	5	8	5
Longitudinal tension			
• Strength, ksi (MPa)	>170.0 (1172)	>113.5 (782)	230.3 (1588)
• Modulus, Msi (GPa)	19.1 (131.7)	18.4 (126.9)	21.9 (151.0)
Transverse tension			
• Strength, ksi (MPa)	13.2 (91.0)	9.3 (64.1)	6.8 (46.9)
• Modulus, Msi (GPa)	1.29 (8.9)	1.29 (8.9)	1.37 (9.5)
• Elongation at failure, %	1.00	0.28	0.52
Longitudinal compression			
• Strength ksi, (MPa)	170.6 (1176)	125.4 (865)	88.3 (608)
• Modulus Msi, (GPa)	16.4 (113.1)	16.7 (115.1)	17.6 (121.3)
Coefficient of thermal expansion, 10^{-6} in/in·°F (10^{-6} in/in·°C)			
• Axial (x)	0.16 (0.29)	0.21 (0.38)	−0.06 (−0.11)
• Transverse (z)	13.6 (24.5)	15.9 (28.6)	13.7 (24.7)
Outgassing			
• % TML	0.035	0.070	0.145
• % CVCM	0.005	0.005	0.007

(1) Normalized to 60% fiber volume

Table 3: Moisture Absorption Results for Exposure to 160°F (71°C) and 95% R.H.

Material	Weight Change (%)	Transverse Hygroscopic Strain (%)	Diffusivity (mm^2/s)
Kevlar 49/508 epoxy	4.61	2.15	1.76×10^{-6}
Kevlar 49/PES	2.41	1.06	1.2×10^{-5}
Kevlar 49/Ultem	2.28	0.87	1.2×10^{-5}
Kevlar 49/PPS	1.18	0.39	1.6×10^{-6}
Kevlar 149/Ultem	1.38	0.46	2.5×10^{-5}

Table 4: Thermoplastic Composites Bonding Results

Bonding Method	Cure Temp/Time	Surface Treatment	AS-4/PEEK Adherends Lap Shear Strength, PSI (MPa) (Failure Mode)
Film adhesive (FM 300)	350°F/1 hour	Chromic acid etch (30 min)	2778 (19.2) s.d. = 150 (1.0) (adhesive)
Film adhesive (FM 300)	350°F/1 hour	Grit blast	3028 (20.9) s.d. = 240 (1.7) (adhesive)
Film adhesive (FM 300)	350°F/1 hour	Plasma etch ($CF_4 + O_2$) (5 min)	6037 (41.6) s.d. = 671 (4.6) (50% cohesive)
Amorphous bonding	600°F/5 min	PEI Ultem film	5156 (35.6) s.d. = 773 (5.3) (adherend)
Focus IR heating	—	PEEK film	4640 (32.0) s.d. = 1088 (7.5) (adhesive)
Resistance heating	—	—	3704 (25.5) s.d. = 579 (4.0) (adherend)
Ultrasonics	—	—	2188 (15.1) s.d. = 419 (2.9) (adherend)

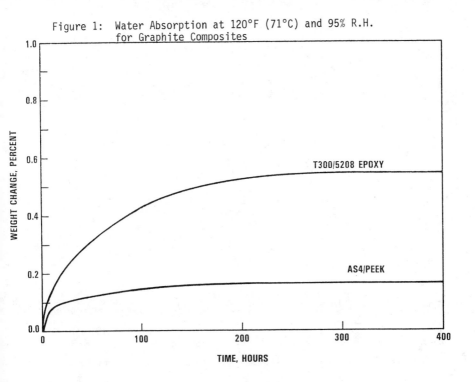

Figure 1: Water Absorption at 120°F (71°C) and 95% R.H. for Graphite Composites

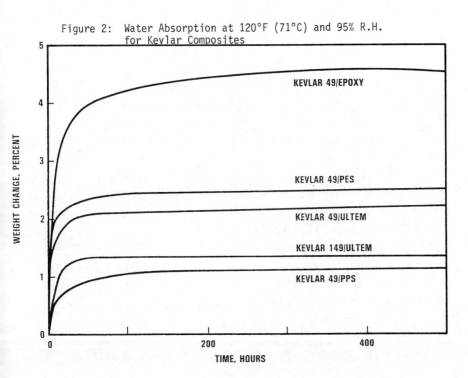

Figure 2: Water Absorption at 120°F (71°C) and 95% R.H. for Kevlar Composites

MEASUREMENTS OF PRINT-THROUGH
IN GRAPHITE FIBER EPOXY COMPOSITES
Donald A. Jaworske
National Aeronautics and Space Administration
Lewis Research Center
Cleveland, OH 44135
Timothy T. Jeunnette and Judith M. Anzic
Cleveland State University
Cleveland, OH 44114

Abstract

High-reflectance accurate-contour mirrors are needed for solar dynamic space power systems. Graphite fiber epoxy composites are attractive candidates for such applications owing to their high modulus, near-zero coefficient of thermal expansion, and low mass. However, mirrors prepared from graphite fiber epoxy composite substrates often exhibit print-through, a distortion of the surface, which causes a loss in solar specular reflectance. Efforts to develop mirror substrates without print-through distortion require a means of quantifying print-through. Methods have been developed to quantify the degree of print-through in graphite fiber epoxy composite specimens using surface profilometry.

1.   INTRODUCTION

Lightweight, highly accurate mirrors are needed for advanced solar dynamic space power systems. In a solar dynamic power system, sunlight is reflected by a parabolic mirror which focuses the light into the aperature of a heat receiver. The performance requirements for the mirror imply certain specularity characteristics and a suitable construction appropriate to achieve these characteristics.

One threat to the ability of a mirror to accurately focus

reflected sunlight is thermal expansion due to the cyclic temperature variation encountered in low Earth orbit. The temperature of a concentrator will vary over several tens of degrees Celcius while in orbit. One way to minimize the thermal expansion of the concentrator structure, and hence maintain high accuracy in the mirror, is to fabricate a composite mirror using an epoxy having a positive coefficient of thermal expansion and a graphite fiber woven mat having a negative coefficient of thermal expansion. By selecting the appropriate ratio of epoxy to graphite, a composite structure with a near-zero thermal expansion can be made.

Graphite fiber epoxy composites are attractive candidates for solar dynamic concentrators based on their low mass and the ability to tailor their thermal expansion. However, the goal of high specularity is hindered by a phenomenon called print-through. Print-through may be defined as a quilting of the surface where the weave of the underlying graphite fabric is transmitted to the surface.

Graphite fiber epoxy composites for mirror applications are prepared using a glass mold to obtain the smooth surface for the mirror finish. Ideally, the surface of the composite released from the glass mold should be as smooth as the surface of the glass template. However, experience has shown that when the composite is released from the glass mold, the epoxy surface often exhibits print-through.

A likely mechanism to account for print-through is the shrinkage of the epoxy that occurs during curing. It has long been known that almost all polymers shrink upon polymerization, with conventional epoxies shrinking about 4-5%[1-3]. Between the graphite fabric and the glass mold, there are epoxy rich regions and epoxy poor regions, as shown schematically in figure 1. Epoxy rich regions of the composite mirror may shrink more than epoxy poor (high graphite fiber content) regions, resulting in surface distortion or print-through.

Print-through is not limited to graphite fiber epoxy composites. A thin aluminum or microsheet-glass face sheet attached to a honeycomb substrate with epoxy also suffers from print-through. In this case, the print-through can be traced to the shrinkage of the epoxy filets holding the face sheet to the honeycomb substrate.

To develop graphite fiber epoxy composites for high performance solar dynamic concentrators, the degree of print-through must be both quantified and minimized. This paper presents a method to quantify print-through in composite specimens by using a profilometer to measure the surface roughness and a statistical method to analyze the profilometer data. In this way, print-through in specimens prepared under different conditions can be compared numerically. In addition, an attempt was made to minimize print-through by curing selected specimens in a temperature gradient.

Minimizing print-through by physical means, such as curing the specimen in a temperature gradient, has the advantage of processing simplicity. In the proposed physical technique, the graphite fiber epoxy composite specimen is cured

in a temperature gradient such that the face of the composite mirror is held at a higher temperature than the back. Establishing such a temperature gradient across the specimen should cause the front face to cure first. As polymerization procedes, additional uncured resin is available from the back face (next to the top platen) to compensate for the shrinkage occuring at the front. This replenishing process should continue until the entire cross section of the composite has cured. Ideally, the front face should be as smooth as the glass template while the back face should exhibit the surface roughness associated with shrinkage.

2.   MATERIALS AND METHODS

All specimens were prepared on glass slides. Each glass slide was pretreated with a mold release agent (Frekote 33) by applying it to a cloth, wiping the glass surface with the cloth, and curing the thin layer of release agent above 100°C for two hours. The pretreated glass slide was then placed on a thin piece of acetate. A thin layer of premixed EA956 resin and hardener (58%

hardener by weight) was spread on the pretreated glass slide, followed by a piece of pitch-based P-75 graphite fabric. A second layer of resin and hardener was spread on top of the graphite fabric and an alumina slide was placed on top of the final layer of resin and hardener. The alumina served as a backing material for subsequent handling. A second piece of acetate was placed on top of the alumina slide, and the entire stack was placed between two preheated aluminum platens. The acetate film prevented any of the resin from flowing onto the aluminum platens. The temperature of each aluminum platen was controlled separately by circulating ethylene glycol through its center.

The EA956 epoxy cures in 24 hours at 20°C, and it cures in 2 hours at 60°C. For the isothermal print-through studies, specimens were prepared at 10°C increments between 20°C and 60°C. For the temperature gradient print-through studies, specimens were prepared using the temperature gradient established between platens held at 30°C and 60°C. The

distance between the platens was approximately 2 mm.

The pressure limits were established by the mass of the top platen in combination with any additional mass placed on the top platen. Using the area occupied by a glass slide, the nominal pressure on the specimens ranged from 5 kPa (0.7 psi) to 17 kPa (2.4 psi).

Pitch-based P-75 graphite fibers were chosen as the filler material because of their negative coefficient of thermal expansion. The pitch-based fibers have the added advantage of high modulus (stiffness).

After curing, the specimen was removed from the glass mold by prying the glass slide from the composite. Care was taken not to damage the surface that was to be subsequently analyzed by profilometry.

The surface profile of each specimen was obtained with a Dektak IIA profilometer. Several scans were obtained on each specimen, and the profilometer data were merged into a computer file to give a 3-dimensional map of the surface roughness. Each 1 cm scan of the profilometer yielded 500 data points (a point-to-point resolution of 20 μm), and each specimen was scanned 10 times. Hence, the surface profile of the specimen was described by 5000 different points taken in a 1 cm^2 area. Regions with obvious defects, such as bubbles or holes, were removed from the data file so as not to interfere with the subsequent standard deviation calculations.

Standard deviation calculated by the conventional method is sensitive to both linear tilt and curvature. Fitting a straight line to the data and computing the root mean square difference from that line compensates for the linear tilt, but does not correct for any subtle curvature. Since the actual mirror surfaces fabricated for solar dynamic applications will have some degree of parabolic curvature, the technique of standard deviation by successive differences (SDSD) was chosen to interpret the profilometer data[4]. This method offers a way to characterize surface roughness superimposed on top of gradually curving surfaces. In standard

deviation by successive differences, the difference between every pair of adjacent points is pooled according to equation (1).

$$SDSD = \left[\frac{\sum_{i=1}^{n-1} (X_{i+1} - X_i)^2}{2(n-1)} \right]^{1/2} \quad (1)$$

The value calculated serves as an estimate of the surface roughness, yet it is immune to any variation in the surface that occurs relatively slowly compared with the distance between the individual points. (The reader should notice that although there are 5000 data points per specimen, there are only 4990 pairs of adjacent points because a point at the end of one 500-point scan is not considered adjacent to another point at the beginning of the next 500-point scan.)

3. RESULTS AND DISCUSSION

Before addressing the differential curing results, it is appropriate to first discuss the use of profilometry and standard deviation by successive differences to quantify the degree of print-through in specimens prepared isothermally, as well as specimens observed over time. After these two results are presented the results of the differential curing experiments will be discussed.

3.1 Using Profilometry to Quantify Print-through

Figure 2 shows a 3-dimensional plot of the surface profile of a composite specimen. The plot is composed of 5000 data points covering an area of 1 cm^2. It is interesting to note the gentle sloping contour of the diagram. This indicates that the glass slide was not parallel to the alumina backing material during curing. As a result, the surface of the composite specimen was not parallel to the stage of the profilometer during the measurement. This observation was quite common, as it was difficult to position the alumina backing material exactly. Fortunately, the gentle sloping of the specimen did not interfere with the SDSD calculation.

Figure 3 is a histogram showing the successive difference values obtained from the same specimen shown in figure 2. The width of this curve offers a visual measure of the surface roughness of the specimen. The wider the curve, the rougher the surface. The SDSD value for this specimen was 190 Å. For comparison, figure 4 is a histogram showing the successive difference values obtained from a glass slide coated with the release agent of choice. The SDSD value for the Frekote-coated glass slide was 71 Å.

To measure reproducibility, duplicate composite specimens were prepared under identical conditions. The duplicate specimens had SDSD values of 130.3 and 133.4 Å.

To establish the functionality of the SDSD value with respect to spatial resolution, several SDSD values were determined from a single glass slide specimen data set, using 20 to 500 evenly spaced points along a 1 cm scan . A similar set of SDSD values were determined for one of the epoxy composite test specimens. In both cases, one calculates a larger SDSD value with wider spaced data points, however, the epoxy to glass SDSD ratio was the same over the entire range of evenly spaced data points, suggesting that it is safe to compare SDSD values derived from data sets having the same spatial resolution (i.e the same number of data points).

The smoothest surface that we can expect from the composite specimens is defined by the glass slide treated with Frekote 33. Hence, the SDSD value of this specimen will serve as the baseline value for the rest of the study.

3.2 Print-through in Specimens Made Isothermally

The following matrix of curing conditions was used to prepare a number of specimens for print-through analysis: pressures of 5, 11, 13, and 17 kPa, each at temperatures of 20, 30, 40, 50, and 60°C. Figure 5 shows the SDSD values obtained for each specimen. The overall trend appears to be that curing the specimens at higher temperatures increases print-through, as quantified by SDSD. Likewise, curing the specimens at higher pressures increases print-through, although to a lesser degree.

One explanation is offered to account for the increased print-through at elevated curing temperatures. The kinetics of polymerization are faster for specimens cured at elevated temperatures. The resin becomes viscous more quickly, and reaches the gel point faster, thus restricting uncured material from migrating to the mirror surface to compensate for any shrinkage. At lower curing temperatures, the resin is free to migrate in the specimen for a longer period of time.

Another explanation is offered to account for the print-through dependance on pressure. At higher pressures, the graphite fabric may be pressed closer to the glass template so that the differences in shrinkage between epoxy rich and epoxy poor regions are accentuated.

Graphite fiber epoxy composites are known to age, that is, their mechanical properties tend to vary over time. To see if print-through varies over time, another isothermally prepared specimen was observed for over a month. The same region of the specimen was measured with the profilometer each time. As shown in figure 6, there was little change in the observed degree of print-through over the time frame of the observations.

3.3 Print-through in Specimens Prepared in a Temperature Gradient

To demonstrate the concept that curing a composite specimen in a temperature gradient can diminish print-through, specimens were prepared at four different pressures, each with the bottom platen at a temperature of 60°C and the top platen at a temperature of 30°C. The profilometry results from these specimens (also shown on figure 5) revealed SDSD values between the SDSD values obtained isothermally at 30°C and 60°C. None of the specimens prepared in a temperature gradient approached the SDSD value of glass (83 Å).

From these results, it is difficult to specify the exact impact of curing a specimen in a temperature gradient. Clearly, the conditions chosen for this demonstration did not yield the best possible results.

Further work is needed to optimize the effect of differential curing. Perhaps a model based on polymerization kinetics could be used to aid in finding the optimum temperature conditions.

4. CONCLUSIONS

Graphite fiber epoxy composites may be useful as solar dynamic concentrators owing to their low mass and high modulus. The ability to tailor the thermal expansion of these composites also makes them attractive for solar dynamic applications. However, to use graphite fiber epoxy composites as a substrate for concentrator mirrors, the degree of print-through, or quilting of the composite surface, must be quantified and minimized.

Profilometry was chosen to measure the surface roughness of the composite specimens prepared for this study, and standard deviation by successive differences was chosen to quantify the degree of print-through numerically. Using several different curing conditions, it was found that print-through decreased with decreasing curing temperature and to a lesser extent with decreasing curing pressure. The idea of reducing print-through by curing the specimens in a temperature gradient was demonstrated. However, additional work is needed to optimize the temperature gradient conditions.

5. REFERENCES

1. Parry, H.L. and Mackay, H.A., SPE Journal, 14(2), 22 (1958).
2. Shimbo, M., Ochi, M., and Shigeta, Y., J. of Appl. Poly. Sci., 26, 2265, (1981).
3. Bailey, W.J., et al., Polym. Mater. Sci. Eng., 54, 23, (1986).
4. Mark, H. and Workman Jr., J., Spectroscopy, 2(11), 38, (1987).

Dr. Donald A. Jaworske is a research scientist in the Electro-Physics Branch of NASA Lewis Research Center. His research interests are in advance materials for space power systems, with emphasis on graphite fiber and diamond film technologies. Jaworske is a graduate of the University of Maryland at College Park.

Timothy T. Jeunnette is currently a junior at Cleveland State University and works part time at NASA Lewis Research Center as a research assistant. He is majoring in mechanical engineering and plans to co-op at Cleveland Pneumatic. Upon graduation his goal is to join the automotive or aerospace field.

Judith M. Anzic is an electrical engineering student at Cleveland State University and a research assistant at NASA Lewis Research Center. Her work on solar dynamic space power systems includes laser diffraction instrumentation and the characterization of graphite epoxy composites.

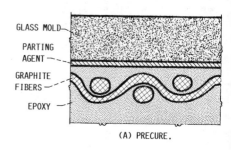

(A) PRECURE.

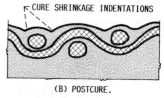

(B) POSTCURE.

FIGURE 1.

Schematic diagram showing print-through.

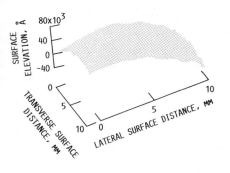

FIGURE 2.

Contour of the specimen
surface.

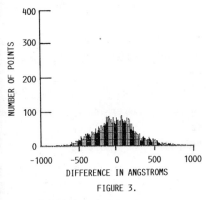

FIGURE 3.

Successive differences
histogram of the specimen
shown in figure 2.

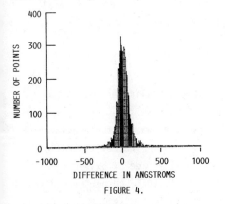

FIGURE 4.

Successive differences
histogram of glass treated
with Frekote 33.

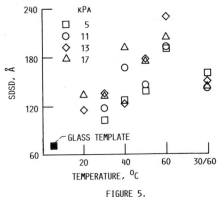

FIGURE 5.

Plot of SDSD vs. temperature
at four different pressures.
Specimens cured in a
temperature gradient are
indicated by the notation
30/60.

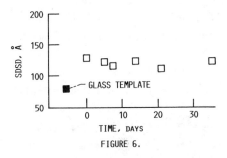

FIGURE 6.

Plot of SDSD vs. time.

PRECISION FABRICATION OF MMW TWT CIRCUIT
WITH SOLID-LIQUID TRANSITION BRAZE

T. G. Teng
Electron Dynamics Division
Hughes Aircraft Company
P.O. Box 2999
Torrance, CA   90509-2999

Abstract

To meet the high power requirements of millimeter-wave TWTs, an improved technique of RF circuit fabrication was required. Standard brazing techniques have not been successful on millimeter-wave tubes. This is because the thinnest braze foil is limited to .0005 inches which results in an uncontrollable amount of braze material buildup in circuit cavities. Because the circuit parts are small and dimensional accuracies of 70 microinches or smaller are required, the performance of the tube depends on minimizing the cavity buildup due to braze material. Diffusion bonding technique is the common practice for millimeter-wave TWT circuit fabrication. However, it can not result in a vacuum envelope and is mechanically fragile. The Solid-liquid Transition Braze (STB) technique consists of sputter-depositing a thin film of gold onto copper circuit pieces to be brazed, assembling the circuit pieces and heating them to a sufficient high temperature to cause solid state diffusion between the copper and the gold. This forms an alloy interface composition that has a melting point at or below the diffusion temperature. The STB joint requires significantly less gold, provides excellent dimensional control, eliminates braze form, avoids braze flow into unwanted areas, and has the potential of producing a vacuum envelope.

1.   INTRODUCTION

A typical millimeter wave (MMW) traveling wave tube (TWT) coupled-cavity slow wave structure is shown in Figure 1. The cavity sections are usually made of oxygen-free electronic (OFE) copper brazed together to form a structure consisting of many cavities in cascade. The schematic sectional view in

Figure 1 shows the joints where the individual cavities are brazed together. The hole in the center of the structure is the electron beam hole through which the electron beam passes. The dimensions of the cavity determine the frequency of operation for the TWT. The coupling hole in the wall of each cavity serves to couple RF energy from one cavity to the next. Note that the coupling holes are oriented on alternate sides of the beam hole so RF energy is directed through one cavity before being coupled to the adjacent cavity. The bandwidth of the TWT is determined by the size and shape of the coupling hole. The design of the coupled-cavities is tailored to the frequency and bandwidth for each application.[1]

The cavity sections are made of OFE copper because of its high thermal conductance, which enables the coupled-cavity structure to handle much higher power levels than the other slow-wave structure, i.e., the helix structure.

To meet the high power requirements of MMW TWTs, an improved fabrication technique for RF circuit was required to provide stringent control of dimensions. Standard brazing techniques have not been successful on millimeter wave TWTs because the thinnest braze foil is limited to 0.0005 inches, which results in an uncontrollable amount of braze material buildup in each cavity,

Figure 1. Because the circuit parts are small, dimensional accuracies of ± 70 microinches or smaller are required for circuit assemblies. The performance of the MMW TWTs dependents on minimizing the cavity buildup due to braze material.

In the past, medium-power MMW TWTs were assembled using diffusion bonding technique. Diffusion bonding does not result in a vacuum envelope and is mechanically fragile. As a result, an external stainless steel sheath has to be incorporated in the brazing procedure to create a vacuum envelope and for mechanical strength. However, these TWTs are limited in power output because of their less-than-optimal thermal interfaces. The ultimate solution was to design an integrally brazed circuit with vacuum integrity.

2. SOLID-LIQUID TRANSITION BRAZE (STB)

The solid-liquid transition braze consists of sputter depositing a thin film layer of gold onto copper surfaces to be brazed. Assembling the parts and heating them to a sufficiently high temperature to cause solid-state diffusion between the copper and the gold is the prerequisite to a successful STB. This forms an alloy interface composition that has a melting point at or below the diffusion temperature. To transform the solid-state interface alloy to a liquid-state alloy the diffusion temperature has to be above 911°C and can not be too high to melt or deform the circuit parts during the process. The Au-Cu phase diagram is shown in Figure 2. Since the diffusion rate of gold into copper can be very rapid at the braze temperature, the heating rate of the braze assembly has to be fast enough to assure that the temperature of the interface alloy, which varies its composition continuously during solid-state diffusion, reaches or exceeds the liquidus line of the Au-Cu phase diagram. When a liquidus state is reached, gold concentration in the interface alloy will be further reduced. If the gold content in the alloy is lower than 80 weight percent, further reduction of gold content will raise the melting temperature of the interface alloy, Figure 2. When the melting temperature of the alloy is above the brazing temperature, solidification will begin. At this time, cooling of the coupled-cavity circuit piece assembly should start right away to prevent extended solid-state diffusion. Excessive solid-state diffusion can create voids because of difference in diffusion rate between gold and copper, (known as Kirkendall effect).

The STB process offers the following advantages that traditional braze processes do not have; the joint requires significantly less gold, provides much better dimensional control, eliminates braze form, simplifies assembly, and avoids braze flow into unwanted areas. Diffusion bond techniques are able to provide necessary dimensional control, but a strong joint cannot be obtained. A typical diffusion bond joint is shown in Figure 3.

3. STB PROCESS DEVELOPMENT AND RESULTS

In light of the complicated mechanism of the transition braze, process parameters have to be appropriately controlled to obtain a strong braze joint. These process parameters include: gold coating thickness, heating rate, brazing temperature, pressure during braze, and brazing duration. To obtain the right combination of these parameters, numerous experiments are required to establish statistical confidence. During the development effort, various deposition techniques were evaluated. Cross sections of coated circuit pieces were made to investigate the thickness and uniformity of the gold layer. Finally, sputter-coating of a very thin layer of gold on the surface of the cavities was achieved. The gold thickness layers exhibited uniformity within 5 microinches across the circuit parts. Figure 4 shows a spacer circuit part and a web circuit part. Test parts were then deposited with varying thickness of gold ranging from 20 to 100 micro-inches. These parts were subjected to various temperatures, pressures, and durations in the brazing cycles. As a result of these controlled experiments, test assemblies were vacuum-checked and cross-sectioned to evaluate the quality of the braze joint.

Certain pressure perpendicular to braze joints has to be applied to the circuit assembly to permit a uniform and efficient diffusion between gold and copper at the very initial stage of the STB process. This is the prerequisite to allow a successful solid-liquid transition braze.

Finally, the gold sputtering thickness and brazing schedules were optimized to yield the required quality braze joint. The optimized processing parameters include: thickness of Au sputtered on circuit piece. brazing temperature, brazing time, and weight applied onto the circuit assembly.

Brazed assemblies have been achieved with the optimized STB process parameters in production retort furnaces. A MMW TWT coupled-cavity circuit assembly brazed with the developed STB process is shown in Figure 5. The braze assemblies exibited virtually no cavity growth in thickness and vacuum tight braze joints were achieved. Figure 6 shows a cross-section of a MMW TWT

coupled-cavity circuit assembly. There was no excess braze material buildup in cavities. The braze joints were vacuum tight. A 50X magnification photo of typical braze joints received with STB process is shown in Figure 7. A typical diffusion bond assembly has numerous voids along circuit piece interfaces, Figure 3, which limit the power level that can be reached by a MMW TWT. Tensile tests indicated that circuit assemblies that were joined with the STB process were superior to the conventional diffusion bond assemblies.

4. CONCLUSION

Hughes Aircraft Company, Electron Dynamics Division, has established an innovative joining method, the Solid-Liquid Transition Braze, for precision fabrication of MMW TWT coupled-cavity circuit structure assemblies. This development offers excellent circuit structure integrity, dimensional tolerance control, and improved thermal conductance that translate into a significantly improved power level of a traditional MMW TWT design. Such improvements have been incorporated in a number of Hughes EDD MMW TWTs.

5. REFERENCES

[1]Hansen, J.W., Lange, G.A., Rostad, A.S., and Woods, R.L., Hughes Aircraft Company, Electron Dynamics Division Applications Note

- System Aspects of Communications TWTs., August 1982.

(2)Metals Handbook, Vol. 8, 8th Edition, American Society for Metals.

5. BIOGRAPHY

Dr. T. G. Teng, Senior Staff Engineer; Parts, Materials & Processes Department; Electron Dynamics Division; Hughes Aircraft Company, is responsible for the research and development programs in materials and processes that will improve performance of Division products and/or reduce manufacturing costs without compromising quality of products. Dr. Teng received his Ph.D. degree in Applied Science from University of Delaware and M.S. Degree in Material Science from State University of New York at Stony Brook.

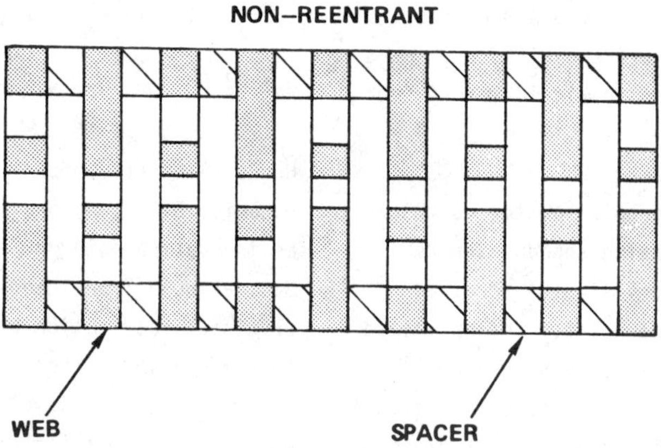

NON—REENTRANT

WEB   SPACER

Figure 1.   Schematic of a brazed MMW TWT coupled-cavity RF circuit structure.

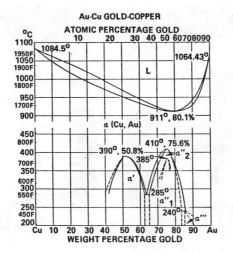

Figure 2.   Au-Cu phase diagram.   (2)

Figure 3.   Typical diffusion bond joints in a
circuit structure assembly.
50X Magnification.

(2) Spacer circuit piece   (b) Web circuit piece

Figure 4.   Ferruleless MMW TWT coupled-cavity
circuit pieces.

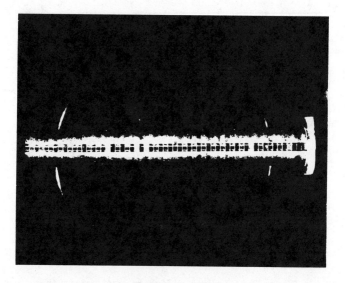

Figure 5.   MMW TWT coupled-cavity circuit
braze assembly.

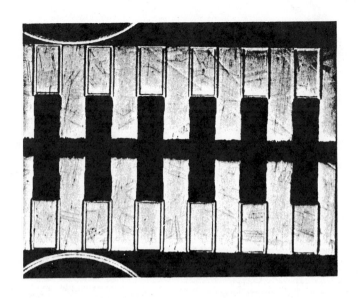

Figure 6.   Cross-section of a MMW
TWT circuit assembly
brazed with STB process.
10X MAGNIFICATION.

Figure 7.   STB joint-etched.
50X Magnification.

POTENTIAL APPLICATIONS OF MMC & ALUMINUM LITHIUM ALLOYS IN CAMERAS FOR CRAF SPACECRAFT

Marc Lane, Cheng Hsieh, and Lloyd Adams

Jet Propulsion Laboratory
California Institute of Technology
4800 Oak Grove Drive
Pasadena, California

Abstract

Recently at the Jet Propulsion Laboratory, design of a 2000 mm focal length camera for the Mariner Mark II series of spacecraft has required consideration of various new materials. Since the camera images in the near UV and visible wavelength band and the optical requirements are high, requirements for dimensional and thermal stability are severe. To avoid scattered light interference, internal surfaces may not be reflective and thus any material used must be capable of being blackened. Since cleaning is not possible in deep space, surfaces must not outgas or corrode. Since the camera must survive launch loads and not deform its optics under thermal stress, high stiffness and strength are important. Mass is also an important concern in an instrument this size (one meter long), as is cost.

Metal matrix composites and aluminum-lithium alloys have excellent mechanical properties and unique physical characteristics, such as low density, low thermal expansion coefficient, high specific stiffness, and good thermal conductivity. These properties make these materials potentially good candidates for use in optical instruments.

JPL's Mariner Mark II spacecraft camera is typical of optical instruments for which the above mentioned properties are important. The potential benefits of using metal matrix composites and aluminum-lithium alloys will be discussed based on thermal, mechanical, and optical requirements of the instrument. additional properties required for the eventual application of these materials will also be explored.

1. INTRODUCTION

The Jet Propulsion Laboratory is presently developing a near ultraviolet and visible wavelength imaging science subsystem (ISS) for use on its next generation of interplanetary spacecraft, the Mariner Mark II series.

Figure 1 shows the first spacecraft proposed for the series-the Comet Rendezvous/Asteroid Flyby (CRAF) spacecraft. The Mariner Mark II (MMII) series consists of several spacecraft intended for a variety of missions using common technology and common systems wherever possible. Thus in developing the imaging system we desire a design capable of performing for a variety of missions with a variety of different requirements. This imaging system is also a next generation system compared to those which JPL has flown on previous spacecraft in that the optical prescription is more demanding of tight tolerances, as optical performance goals of broader spectral range and a light weight design are much more ambitious.

The MMII ISS consists of a narrow angle (2000 mm focal length) Ritchey-Chretien optical design camera and a wide angle (250 mm focal length) reflector optical design camera (See Figure 2). These cameras have CCD type sensors. Presently, detailed design has been completed for the narrow angle camera and we are fabricating a development model. No detailed design has yet been done on the wide angle camera.

The MMII ISS is outwardly similar to cameras flown on the Voyager series and to be flown on the Galileo spacecraft. On Voyager, the ISS consisted of a Narrow Angle (1500 mm focal length) spherical catadioptric cassegrain optical design camera and a Wide Angle (200 mm focal length) Petzval optical design camera. These cameras have vidicon sensors. The two Voyager spacecraft and their imaging systems, which were launched in August

1977, have performed successfully at Jupiter, Saturn, Uranus, and Voyager 2 is expected to have a successful Neptune encounter in August of 1989. On Galileo, the Solid State Imaging (SSI) subsystem consists of just one narrow angle (1500 mm focal length) spherical catadioptric cassegrain optical design camera. It has a CCD type sensor. Galileo is set for launch in October of 1989 and is intended to explore Jupiter and its many moons. The spherical catadioptric cassegrain optical design was chosen for the narrow angle cameras because a change in bulk temperature of the system results only in movement of the focal point, which can be compensated for passively by special camera design.

For simplicity of design, operation, and for mass and cost reasons, these cameras do not have an active focus mechanism. Once launched, only a few electric heaters can be used to keep the cameras in focus. These control temperature gradients which may occur during operation. For bulk temperature changes the cameras have an "athermalizing system". This system uses Invar "metering rods" which allow the elements to move relative to the camera and to themselves in such a way as to remain in their optimal positions as the temperature of the system varies.

As JPL has gained experience at building these cameras, it has become more ambitious in its goals. These goals call for a diffraction limited optical system - one in which resolution is limited only by the aperture size and not by any mechanical feature or defect. The goal of the MMII optical design was to achieve a lower mass than the Voyager design and increase the spectral range while maintaining the diffraction limited performance of the Voyager design. For MMII ISS, an optical design which reduces the number of refractive elements is used. This allows for a greater imaging wavelength range as well as reduced mass - the spherical catadioptric cassegrain design required two large correctors mounted in the front of the camera. The elimination of aperture correctors and the use of aspheric surfaces on the mirrors makes the design much more sensitive to dimensional errors. Allowable motions are equal to those caused by uncompensated thermal expansion from a temperature change of only a few degrees centigrade. Stress on optical elements caused by their mounts (due to fabrication errors or temperature changes) becomes a problem even at extremely small levels. Of course fabrication tolerances are also extreme. To achieve a diffraction limited system, fabrication curvature errors must be kept below 1/4 wavelength (one millionth of an inch). Primary to secondary distance must be kept accurate to less than 0.005 mm (2 ten thousandths of an inch), and this distance changes with temperature. Since scattered light is a significant problem, surfaces must be as black as possible in the full wavelength range. Occurrences such as slippage of the elements, or changes in dimension of camera parts over a period of years, would be catastrophic for the systems.

Degradation of performance from contamination of optical elements by outgassing or flaking of material from camera surfaces, is irreversible. One can see the effects of dirt specs which have fallen the detector window in many of the Voyager pictures. At the same time, the requirement for absolute reliability remains. Since these instruments deliver images the public sees, mistakes can be quite embarrassing!

2. REQUIRED MATERIAL PROPERTIES

It should be apparent that a number of materials constraints fall upon the MMII ISS cameras, making the MMII ISS materials selection a major challenge. Materials with well known (and preferably linear) thermal expansion properties are required. Since missions can last ten years, and can take years to get launched, materials with high dimensional stability and high micro-yield strengths are required. Strength and light weight are always critical on a spacecraft, as is fracture toughness. On manned launch vehicles fracture toughness rules are especially stringent. Materials which can be blackened throughout the imager's wavelength range are required for internal surfaces. Since the optical elements must remain perfectly clean for the duration of the mission, materials which outgas, corrode, flake, or peel are excluded. Materials which can be bonded and attached such that outgassing, corrosion, and flaking do not occur, are required.

Good thermal conductivity is a desirable property for many of the camera parts. Thermal gradients along camera parts are difficult to design against. Using materials with high thermal conductivity can help to keep a more even temperature throughout the camera. The CCD's used in the Galileo and MMII cameras need to be cooled to approximately -110 degrees C to keep dark current from interfering with the image. In these designs the CCD's are attached to a radiator using a "cold finger" which conducts heat out from the CCD. Obtaining high thermal conductance while keeping the size of the cold finger reasonable requires a material with high coefficient of thermal conductivity.

In the past, Aluminum and Invar have proved to be excellent materials for spacecraft optics applications. For those parts where low coefficient of thermal expansion (CTE) is required, Invar has worked well. When dimensional stability is also required, Invar can be given a "stabilization anneal" heat treatment with only a small sacrifice of CTE. For those parts where low CTE is not so critical, and low weight is desired, aluminum is used. Aluminum 6061 has excellent dimensional stability. It can also be anodized. The new process Martin Optical Black, blackens very well throughout the visible wavelength band. In fact, even after its micro surface structure is destroyed (by a thumb print for example) it is still superior to the traditional anodize process. It is highly desirable for candidate materials to accept the Martin Optical Black process.

Of course both of these materials meet all the requirements mentioned above, and it is against these we compare the new materials. Other traditional materials which we considered but which failed to meet all of the above criteria include: Beryllium (too brittle), and Magnesium (bad corrosion).

3. CANDIDATE MATERIALS

A key technology for the new generation of spacecraft is the development of high strength-to-weight ratio materials. The application of such materials will allow spacecraft under strict weight constraints to accept more instruments than possible using conventional materials and to maximize the mission goals. Advanced materials systems such as polymer matrix composites, metal matrix composites (MMCs), rapidly solidified metals, carbon-carbon composites and aluminum-lithium alloys are some of the materials that offer potential benefits for spacecraft applications. MMCs stand out as a more developed system than carbon-carbon composites and rapidly solidified metals and have advantages over polymer matrix composites in the areas of moisture absorption, outgassing or contamination, fire resistance, radiation resistance, high temperature strength retention, and electrical and thermal conductivities (References 1 and 2). The low thermal expansion coefficient and good thermal conductivity of the MMCs make these materials good candidates for use in applications requiring good dimensional stability, such as optical instruments. In addition, metal matrix composites offer the opportunity to tailor a material with a combination of properties unavailable in any single material, such as combining high strength and high elastic modulus of fibers with the good ductility of aluminum and magnesium. A specific coefficient of thermal expansion can be achieved with the judicious combination of matrix material and reinforced material such as silicon carbide particles. On the other hand, aluminum-lithium alloys have been shown (References 3 and 4) to possess very high specific properties (property to density ratio) and have high fracture toughness and have the additional advantage of being able to be fabricated by conventional techniques. Therefore, metal matrix composites and aluminum-lithium alloys are chosen as primary candidate materials for the Narrow Angle Optics for the Mariner Mark II spacecraft ISS camera. The components most likely to use MMCs and aluminum-lithium alloys are the mirror barrel, athermalizing rods, secondary mirror hood, primary baffle support and primary mirror housing.

Table I shows the typical properties of some metal matrix composites, aluminum-lithium alloy 2090 and other conventional materials. One can easily see that MMCs and Al-Li alloy 2090 have higher specific properties over conventional materials.

4. POTENTIAL BENEFITS OF USING MMCS AND ALUMINUM-LITHIUM ALLOYS

The potential benefits of using metal matrix composite and aluminum-lithium alloys are discussed based on the particular requirements of some of the components proposed to be constructed of these materials.

4.1 Athermalizing Rods

The athermalizing rods are the primary component of the athermalizing system which allows the positions of a pair of optical elements to be controlled to compensate for bulk temperature changes. The rods are made of low CTE material and extend from one optical element to the next a distance greater than the distance between them. A high CTE material doubles back to pick up the second element. By varying the lengths of the materials involved element position can be fixed for two different temperatures. Hopefully, the element positions will be close to their desired positions in between these temperatures! The athermalizing rods must have excellent dimensional stability in addition to low CTE because they alone control the distance between elements. Normally Invar is used for the rods, however, one problem with the Invar rods is that their magnetism can potentially interfere with other instruments on the MMII spacecraft.

Zero or near-zero thermal expansion coefficient of the graphite fiber unidirectionally reinforced 6061 aluminum composite has made this material an ideal candidate for this application. The size of the rods are about 0.25 inches in diameter which may be at the lower size limit of the present technology development. Similarly, an end connection to Invar rod is presently required such that a threaded joint can be made. This requires special design as to how the rod is going to be fabricated. Adhesive bonding or integrally manufactured Invar rod ends during Gr_f/6061 consolidation are the possible approaches. Since the matrix material is 6061, it is expected to be blackened by Martin Black like the conventional 6061 aluminum.

The use of Gr_f/6061 composite would reduce the mass of the athermalizing rod which is presently made of Invar. The high axial thermal conductivity of Gr_f/6061 is also an important advantage in that it aids the temperature equalization of the camera barrel. Unfortunately, experience with Grf/6061 is limited, and we have not been able to get good estimates of microcreep behavior over an extended period of time. Since the dimensional tolerances which the rod must hold over a period probably exceeding 10 years is so tight, we are reluctant to commit to this material at present.

4.2 Radiator Plate

To keep the camera sensor (CCD) cooled to the required -110 degrees C, a radiator is required for heat dissipation to cold space. High specific thermal conductivity and high specific stiffness are major requirements of the radiator plate. Aluminum honeycomb with face sheets is an attractive candidate for its high specific stiffness but its thermal conductivity is low. Magnesium alloys (See Table I) have good specific stiffness and good specific thermal conductivity but poor corrosion and stress corrosion cracking resistance which hinder their usage. Conventional aluminum alloys have reasonable specific thermal conductivity and specific stiffness but graphite fiber reinforced 6061 aluminum composite appears to offer one of the best combinations for both properties (See Table I). Graphite/aluminum sheet at $[45,-45]_{8s}$ construction has been proposed for this application. Using Gr_f/6061 radiator plate, several lbs of weight savings can be realized.

4.3 Camera Barrel

The camera barrel is the primary structural element of the camera. The mounting struts attach to it, and it supports both the front and rear parts of the instrument. Inside, the barrel must provide baffling to counter stray light. In the present design it is a single machined piece.

The 7% lower density and 15% higher stiffness of aluminum-lithium alloy 2090-T8E41 over the conventional aluminum alloy 6061-T6 makes this alloy an excellent candidate for this particular application which demands weight reduction and high stiffness. Preliminary stress corrosion cracking data showed this material to have only moderate resistance (Reference 5).

As mentioned previously the ability of a material able to be coated to have low reflectivity in the full range of wavelength is an important requirement for its usage. Preliminary investiga-

tion at JPL has shown that
2090-T8E41 can be anodized
with Martin Black even though
the reflectivity is not as
low as 6061-T6, it is still
lower than all other methods
such as Cat-A-Lac black
paint. Another point worth
mentioning is that the Martin
Black surface still had very
low reflectivity even when
the surface was intentionally
smeared by fingers. A
comparison of various black
coatings is given in Figures
3 and 4. Even though 2090
aluminum-lithium is
relatively new and there is
not much experience on Martin
Optical Black coating, the
spectral reflectance of this
coating is still much lower
than other coatings and is
less than 5% from 0.2uM to
1.1uM wavelength.

4.4 Camera Barrel Rings

Silicon carbide particulate
reinforced 6061-T6 aluminum
composite is the logical

replacement for conventional
6061-T6 for this application.
With 30% of silicon carbide
reinforcement, this composite
has a strength of about 550
MPa (80 ksi), a stiffness of
103 GPa (15 msi),and an
almost similar density as
6061 aluminum. Microcreep
behavior of some silicon
carbide reinforced aluminum
alloys are known (See Table 2
and Reference 6). It is
higher than 6061 aluminum
(Reference 7) and compares
favorably with beryllium, a
material that has been a
preferred one for high
stiffness applications. A
large weight savings can be
realized. This composite can
be machined using the
conventional techniques
except some minor
adjustments.

5. ADDITIONAL PROPERTIES REQUIRED

In order to fulfill the
stringent requirements of the
future spacecraft, in
addition to the advantages,
such as high specific
strength, high specific
stiffness, and a tailorable
thermal expansion, often
cited for metal matrix
composites, several
additional properties have to
be demonstrated or a data
base has to be established
before practical applications
of these materials can begin.
These properties are
microyield strength and
microcreep properties to meet
the requirements of long term
dimensional stability
(graphite fiber reinforced
composites and aluminum-
lithium alloy 2090),thermal
conductivity and thermal
expansion coefficient

properties for the
temperature range of -100°C
to +50°C.

Corrosion resistance of 2090
in comparison with 6061 has
to be achieved. Surface
treatments such conversion
coating, anodic treatment
have to be evaluated.
Vassey-Glandon et al
(Reference 8) has reported
that both conversion coated
and anodized 2090-T8E41 are
superior to that of 7075 and
2124. However,preliminary
investigation at JPL on the
corrosion resistance of
chromate conversion coated
2090-T8E41 via salt spray
test per ASTM B117 has shown
it is not as an effective
protection for 6061.
It is believed that a
modification of the bath
formulation is necessary to
achieve the performance of
conversion coating on 6061
aluminum. In addition,

corrosion tests have to be conducted to learn the possible galvanic corrosion between graphite fiber and the aluminum or magnesium matrix alloys. And if so, potential remedies such as coatings have to be investigated.

2090-T8E41 is an excellent material in terms of specific strength and fracture toughness. But no information at all exists on its dimensional stability. Stress relieving treatment to obtain a more dimensionally stable condition such as the cryogenic treatment (Reference 9) for the conventional aluminum alloys has to investigated. Microyield strength and microcreep properties have to be measured to strengthen its credibility for replacing 6061 or 7075 aluminum alloys.

Some microyield strength and microcreep properties of metal matrix composites are available but are still sparse. Additional systematic measurements have to be made such that a critical evaluation can be conducted for these materials.

As mentioned previously the metal matrix composites with aluminum alloys as matrix materials are believed to behave the same the matrix materials in terms of accepting black coatings. However, actual experiments have to be conducted to verify this contention.

6. CONCLUSIONS

The new metal matrix composite materials and aluminum alloys have properties which promise important advances in quality and performance of many manufactured products. In spacecraft (and many other) applications, where cost of materials makes up a very small part of a system's total cost, use of these new classes of materials is warranted. In fact, for most projects, it is beneficial at least to research these new materials before selecting the more common materials in use today.

In designing the MMII Imaging Subsystem, metal matrix composites, and aluminum-lithium alloys were considered as candidate materials. Many of the advantages of these materials, such as high specific stiffness, high specific thermal conductivity, high specific strength, and low coefficient of thermal expansion, are of utmost importance to a good camera design. This paper discussed the potential benefits of using these new materials systems However, we also pointed out a great obstacle to selecting these materials has been the lack of information regarding long term dimensional stability. Science, reliability, and engineering considerations make an active focus camera unacceptable. Also, positional tolerances of the optical elements are extremely small - primary to secondary distance (approx. 300 mm or 12 inches) must be maintained accurate to 0.005 mm (2 ten thousandths of an inch) over a possible 10 year camera lifetime. Therefore materials of proven long term dimensional stability are required for many of the camera applications. Hopefully the immense potential of the materials systems can be put to use when the gaps in the database are filled.

7. DISCLAIMER

This paper was prepared as an account of work sponsored by an agency of the United States Government. Neither the United States Government nor any agency thereof, nor any of their employees, makes any warranty, express or implied, or assumes any legal liability of responsibility for the accuracy, completeness, or usefulness of any information, apparatus, products, or process disclosed, or represents that its use would not infringe privately owned rights.

Reference herein to any specific commercial product, process, or service by trade name, trademark, manufacturer, or otherwise, does not necessarily constitute or imply its endorsement, recommendation, or favoring by the United States Government or any agency thereof. The views and opinions of the authors expressed herein do not necessarily state or reflect those of the United States Government or any agency thereof.

8. ACKNOWLEDGEMENTS

This work was performed at Jet Propulsion Laboratory/ CALTECH under a contract with NASA.

9. REFERENCES

1. Lewis, C., "The Exciting Promise of Metal-Matrix Composites,"Materials Engrg., May 1986

2. Zweben, C., "Metal Matrix Composite Overview," DOD Metal Matrix Composites Information Analysis Center Publication No. 253, February, 1985

3. Hsieh, C. et al, "Cryogenic Mechanical Properties of Advanced Composite Materials," SAMPE International Technical Conference Minneapolis, October, 1988

4. Hsieh, C. et al, "Fracture Toughness of Discontinuously Silicon Carbide Reinforced Metal Matrix Composites and An Aluminum-lithium Alloy," SAMPE International Technical Conference, Minneapolis, October, 1988

5. Cieslak, S. J., "Alcoa Alithalite Alloy 2090 Technical Information," 17th SAMPE International Conf., October, 1985

6. Hall, E., "Microyield and Microcreep Properties of Discontinuous Metal Matrix Composites," Proceedings of 6th Metal Matrix Composites Technology Conf., May, 1985

7. Marschall, C. et al, "Dimensional Instability," Pergamon Press, 1977

8. Vassey-Glandon, et al, "Aluminum-Lithium Alloys for Fighter Aircraft Applications," 2nd SAMPE Metals and Metals Processing Conf., August, 1988

9. Metals Progress, "How Cold Stabilization Can Reduce Residual Stresses?," July, 1985

BIOGRAPHIES

Mr. Marc Lane is a Member of the Technical Staff in JPL's Advanced Spacecraft Development Group. He received his M.S. in Mechanical Engineering from Rensselaer Polytechnic Institute in 1983.

Dr. Cheng Hsieh is a Member of the Technical Staff in JPL's Materials Technology Group. He received his Ph.D. in Materials Science from SUNY at Stony Brook in 1972 and has worked with fracture mechanics, metallurgy, stress corrosion and metal matrix composites. His professional society affiliations include SAMPE, ASTM, and American Society for Metals.

Mr. Lloyd Adams is a Member of the Technical Staff in JPL's Imaging Systems Section. He has been an active member of the imaging system design teams of Voyager and Galileo spacecraft.

TABLE I

TYPICAL MATERIAL PROPERTIES AT ROOM TEMPERATURE

Material		Density, ρ (lb/in³)	Tensile Strength (ksi)		Thermal Expansion Coefficient, α (10⁻⁶in/in/°F)	Thermal Conductivity, k K (Btu/hr/ft/°F)	Elastic Modulus, E (MSi)	σtu/ρ	K/ρ	E/ρ
			Ultimate (σtu)	Yield (σty)						
Al Alloys	2090-T8E41 (Al/Li alloy)	0.093	78	72	9.0	48 - 53	11.3	839	516-570	131.5
	Al2024-T8	0.101	70	66	12.6	87.5	10.6	693	866	105
	Al6061-T6	0.098	45	40	13.5	97	10.6	459	990	102
	Al7075-T73	0.101	73	63	13.7	70	10.4	722	636	103
Metal Matrix Composite	30v/oSiC/6061-T6 (P100 fiber)	0.108	80	63	6.9	45	17.5	741	417	162
	50v/oGr/6061-T6	0.080	-100		0.5	-180	>45	-1250	-2250	>563
Polymer Matrix Composite	Gr/Epoxy	0.056	110		0.5	27	28	1964	482	500
	Fiberlass/Epoxy	0.070	150		4.5	0.5	6	2100	7	85
Glass	Fused Silica	0.08			0.31	0.8	10.2		10	129
Magnesium Alloys	AZ31B-H24	0.064	34	24	14.0	44	6.5	531	688	102
	ZK60A-T5	0.064	50	40	14.0	70	6.5	781	1094	102
Steel	AISI C1020	0.283	85	60	8.3	27	29	297	95.4	102
	15-5 PH-H1025	0.29	155	145	6.2	10.3	28.5	534	35.5	98
	Invar 36	0.29	65	40	-0.7	6.1	20.5	224	20.9	71
Be Alloy	Be S200	0.067	40	30	6.4	104	42.5	597	1552	627
Ti Alloy	Ti-6Al-4V	0.16	160	145	4.9	4.2	16	1000	26	100
Cu Alloys	102 Oxygen free Cu	0.323	35	11	9.8	226	17	108	700	53
	172 Be-Cu	0.297	180	150	9.3	70	19	606	236	64
Ni Alloy	Inconel 718	0.296	180	150	7.2	6.5	29	608	22	98

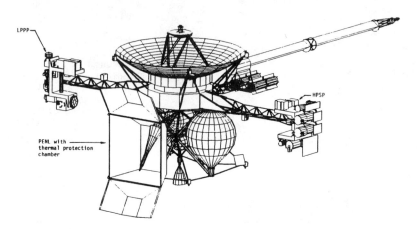

FIGURE 1-MMII/CRAF SPACECRAFT CRUISE CONFIGURATION

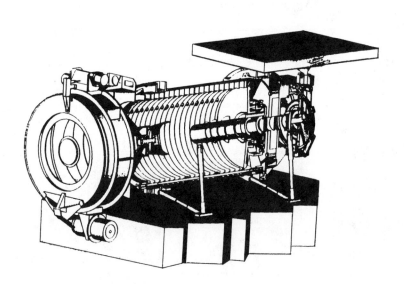

FIGURE 2-MMI/CRAF ISS NARROW ANGLE CAMERA

FIGURE 3

REFLECTANCE CURVES

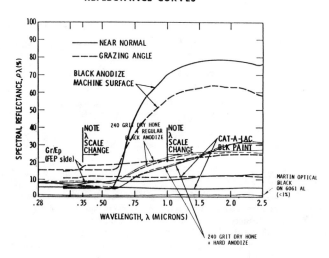

FIGURE 4

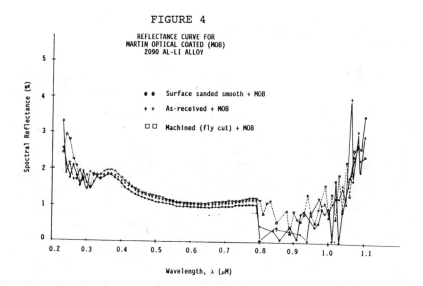

REFLECTANCE CURVE FOR
MARTIN OPTICAL COATED (MOB)
2090 AL-LI ALLOY

● ● Surface sanded smooth + MOB

+ + As-received + MOB

□ □ Machined (fly cut) + MOB

ON-ORBIT FABRICATION OF SPACE STATION STRUCTURES

Dr. Jonathan Colton, Jed Lyons, Bob Lukasik, John Mayer,
Stefan Witte, and Dr. John Muzzy
Georgia Institute of Technology
Composites Processing Laboratory and
George W. Woodruff School of Mechanical Engineering
Atlanta, Georgia 30332-0405

Abstract

The on-site fabrication of space station trusses from carbon fiber-reinforced thermoplastic composites would greatly enhance the flexibility to produce any size or shape structure desired. Current delivery vehicles limit both the size and shape of items which are placed into orbit. Pultrusion is one technique currently being studied for the on-orbit production of space structures, but pultruded parts are limited in size and shape by the pulling force which results from the frictional forces developed in the die. Die- and mold-less techniques would greatly increase the flexibility of fabrication techniques.

A novel mold-less processing technique has been developed which uses gas pressure and bladders to produce tubular structural members out of which one can construct space truss structures. A woven or braided prepreg preform is produced on Earth and brought into orbit. Integral to the preform is an inner bladder which contains the gas pressure used in consolidation, and an outer layer which produces the counter-force needed for consolidation. Solar heating is used in conjunction with the gas to process the preforms into the final parts. This technique allows for the most efficient use of resources while providing for the flexible production of a wide size range of structures.

1. INTRODUCTION

The Space Station is a critical component in many of the leadership initiatives of America's civilian space program. Planned to be operational by the end of 1990's, it will provide a platform from which to study and characterize the earth, maintain facilities to store large quantities of propellant, and assemble large inter-space vehicles [1]. The current baseline configuration for the Space Station consists of a truss network on which a power system, experiments, and pressurized modules are attached [2]. An erectable truss design was selected over a deployable design because the former is capable of growth in all three dimensions and can accommodate changes in operational needs [3]. Consequently, a major consideration in the design of the Space Station is on-orbit construction.

1.1 Space Truss Construction

On-orbit construction methods must overcome the difficulties presented by the space environment. Without a strong gravity field or a firm base on which to attach, some mechanisms which operate well on earth would send the machine and its operator spinning out into space. Consequently, moving masses must be counterbalanced. Components must function under extreme temperature variations, as they are alternately exposed to the sun's radiation and shielded in the shadows of the earth and of other components. The absence of a breathable atmosphere limits the amount of time that an astronaut has to perform extra-vehicular activities (EVA), and his pressurized suit affects the types of tasks that can be performed by restricting his movements. Automated processes are therefore preferred.

A key consideration for on-orbit fabrication of space structures is the cost of delivering materials and machines to the construction site. This will be performed by the Space Shuttles, which can deliver only what will fit into their 4.5 meter diameter cargo bay [3]. Hence, materials and machines must be packaged efficiently so that a minimum number of Shuttle missions are required.

NASA has conducted detailed studies on various approaches for constructing the Space Station on-orbit [2,3,4] and has chosen an erectable structure approach. Individual struts and connecting nodes are completely fabricated on earth and shipped into space. The Station is then erected strut by strut in orbit by the astronauts. The concept was proven feasible by the success of the ACCESS demonstration. In this experiment, a 10-bay truss was erected on an assembly fixture which was attached to the Space Shuttle. The assembly time for the 96 member truss was only 25 minutes, indicating the practicality and economy of on-orbit erected trusses [5]. A major disadvantage of this approach is the low packaging density of the prefabricated struts during transport.

A pultrusion process has also been proposed to fabricate the Station [6]. In concept, coiled stock material consisting of thermoplastic/graphite fiber prepreg is manufactured on earth. On-orbit manufacture of the structure is performed by pultrusion, using the coiled stock material. The finished pultruded sections are then cut to length and ultrasonically welded together to form the completed truss. This process has the advantage that the prepreg material would have a high storage density during transport. However, pultruded parts are limited in size and shape by the pulling force which results from the frictional forces developed in the die. Furthermore, a welded design prohibits replacement of truss members which are damaged by meteorites or accidental overloads. Repair procedures would require additional astronaut training and EVA time.

1.2 Proposed Preform Approach

A novel processing technique which forms unconsolidated earth-manufactured preforms into tubular space station truss members is described herein. The design calculations for this process can be found in reference [7].

As the material is not consolidated during transportation to orbit, 70% increases in storage density can be attained. The preform has three layers: an inner vacuum bag bladder, a woven or braided commingled thermoplastic and carbon fiber tube, and an outer bag to provide diameter control during consolidation. The outer layer could also provide protection from solar radiation.

The on-orbit consolidation process is essentially vacuum bag molding. The unconsolidated preform is gripped by inflation

chucks which are inserted into the free ends. Gas is then injected into the inner bladder of the preform, which supplies the pressure necessary for consolidation. Focused solar energy is used to melt the thermoplastic and process the preform into the final shape. The composite is then shielded from the sun and is quenched by radiation cooling to black space.

Upon consolidation, end connector fittings are attached. The connectors allow the Space Station to be constructed strut by strut; therefore, the design is compatible with existing NASA plans. Structural design changes are easily accommodated because the struts can be removed and/or replaced with the same techniques used to erect the truss.

2.0 THE PREFORM

The consolidation process is essentially vacuum bag molding, with the vacuum on the outside and pressure applied internally. The unique design of the preform results in self-consolidating tubular composite structures.

2.1 Materials and Fabrication

Carbon fiber reinforced polyetheretherketone (PEEK) composites were introduced several years ago by ICI, Ltd. [8]. The thermoplastic PEEK matrix has an indefinite shelf life and can be rapidly formed under pressures as low as 70 kPa [9]. The structural layer of the preform is an arrangement of woven or braided commingled thermoplastic fibers and carbon fibers.

The fabrication process, shown in Figure 1, begins with a mandrel upon which the inner bladder is placed. The first ply is woven or braided around the bladder. Multiple layers are then braided on top of each other, and stitched together as needed. The preform is then enclosed in the outer bag.

The inner bag is a polyimide film, such as is used in vacuum bag forming. When internally pressurized on-orbit, this bladder becomes an expanding die during consolidation of the preform. The outer bag provides the shape and outer diameter control for the tube as the composite is consolidated. Therefore, it must be strong enough to contain internal pressures up to 620 kPa, while being heated to the processing temperature of 380°C.

A recent study [10] showed that the orbital temperature variations in tubular space structures can be reduced from 111°C to 22°C by protecting the exterior tube surface with a low solar absorbance, low infrared emitting layer. The surface of the outer layer could be tailored to protect the load-bearing composite from radiation damage. Alternately, a radiation shield could be attached to the tube after consolidation.

2.2 Packaging

As the preform is not consolidated until it reaches the orbital construction site, it remains flexible, and is collapsed after it is woven. This saves precious space in the Shuttle cargo bay. The volume savings over the same amount of solid tubes increases with decreased preform stiffness. This is illustrated using the notation on Figure 2. If the 51 mm diameter preform is compressed so that the wall is bent to a 12 mm bend radius, then a space savings of 40% is realized. A preform wall bend radius of 6 mm radius yields a 70% savings.

Preforms can be packaged in continuous lengths rolled onto spools, or in discrete lengths pressed into boxes. Both of these methods are illustrated in Figure 3. The spooled preform has an end connector attached to the free end, which is preconsolidated. This assists in the on-orbit consolidation processes described later.

The canister with the collapsed preforms has an opening through which the preforms are grabbed. In the bottom of the canister is a springback that pushes the preforms against the opening as the top one is removed. The grommets attached to the inside edge of the ends are manufactured of a spring material, which ensure that the preform ends can be grabbed by the deployment and consolidation machinery.

2.3 Deployment

Preform deployment is the first process which is performed on-orbit. Before the preform can be consolidated, it must be removed from its packaging. The processing equipment and the preform packaging are combined in order to develop automatic deployment equipment. The overall machine configuration is shown in Figures 4 and 5. The entire system can be collapsed flat, and telescoped towards the preform containers, for ease of transport into space. This configuration also provides for ease of deployment once the system is in space. All of the telescoping members lock into place with spring loaded ball-locks, as the members reach their final positions.

2.3.1 Semi-Continuous Process

The spooled preform package is desirable if it is necessary to make consolidated struts of any length. The preform is deployed in a semi-continuous manner. First, a tube conveyor attaches to the existing end connector and pulls the preform off of the spool. The tube conveyor pulls the end of the tube to the inflation chuck. At this point, the motor moving the conveyors stops and the spool is stopped by a damper. The inflation chuck is constructed such that it expands as the middle section is retracted. The expansion creates a seal between the chuck and the inner bag of the preform tube. The center section of the chuck is simply a hollow steel tube used to inject the gas into the tube. This is also used to release the gas after consolidation. The movement of the inflation chuck is accomplished using ball screws fitted with counterbalances to counteract the torque effects. The ball screws are turned by electric motors.

Simultaneously with the injection of the inflation chuck into the front end of the tube, a pinch mechanism constricts the aft end of the tube. This pinch mechanism provides for the seal of the inner bag at the aft end. The pinch mechanism works by using two oppositely threaded screws between flat plates which squeeze down on the preformed tubes.

2.3.2 Discrete Process

The exact size and shape of each part of any space station truss will be designed long before the astronauts get into space. This fact makes the deployment and consolidation of the preform more feasible. Figure 5 illustrates how the precut lengths of the preform material would be consolidated on orbit. Cartridges which contain collapsed preforms are plugged into the chucking assembly. The cartridges are designed so that the next preform pops up into position as each one is removed.

Inflation chucks move inside both of the opened ends, gripping the preform, as described above. A mechanism then removes the gripped preform and translates it to the consolidation position, which is directly above the preform cartridge.

3. CONSOLIDATION

Consolidation is the use of elevated temperatures and pressures to melt the resin and densify the different layers of the preform into a void-free tube. This process determines the quality of the product. The three major processing areas requiring control are as follows:
1. pressure application
2. consolidation heating
3. component cooling.

3.1 Pressure Application

Structural foams, gases, and fluids all have the potential to provide the internal pressure necessary for consolidation of the pomposite tubes. A liquid pressurizing media would be essentially incompressible, requiring a storage volume equal to the volume needed for processing. One of the advantages of using a gas media is its shipping economy. The evaporation of a liquified gas is accompanied by an large increase in volume for the pressure ranges under consideration. An effectively large processing volume could be transported into space as a compact, bottled liquid.

3.1.1 Gas Selection

The choice of which particular gas to use is influenced by factors such as economy, compatibility with the process, and availability. Another factor to be considered is the possible reuse of the media in other parts of the system, such as maneuvering jets or environmental supply. Nitrogen is an inert gas and is readily available in liquid form at a moderate cost. Another possibility is liquid oxygen. A problem with oxygen use which could occur at the elevated process temperatures is the formation of explosive mixtures or a reaction with the composite. These could preclude oxygen as a choice. As a result, nitrogen was chosen as the model gas for the calculations.

3.1.2 Pressurizing Media

The equipment necessary to employ gas in the manner needed for processing requires no new technology. The media is simply allowed to escape from the containment bottle through a pressure regulator. The correct mass of gas for processing is indicated by a flow meter. The amount of gas is chosen so that the internal pressure is maintained below the rupture strength of the constraining layer, over the range of process temperatures. Once the consolidation has progressed to the point at which the internal pressure is unnecessary, the gas is allowed to discharge to a holding reservoir. From here the gas could be discharged through jets for attitude correction, or recovered with a pump for another process run. For the preform shown in Figure 2, approximately 21 grams of nitrogen per tube would provide a consolidation pressure of 550 kPa at a processing temperature of 425°C. With this amount of gas, an internal tube pressure of 390 kPa would be retained through the composite's solidification temperature of 200°C. These calculations show that a large enough pressure can be maintained to assure complete consolidation of the preform.

Also important is the effect of the gas on the cooling rate of the compacted preform. Here, the thermal mass of the nitrogen would be 0.2% of that of the tube, so the effect on composite heating and cooling rates is negligible.

3.2 Consolidation Heating

The largest energy requirement for the process is the heating of the preform to the consolidation temperature. Heating alternatives include the following:
(1) The use of radiating electrical resistance elements.
(2) Direct electrical resistance heating using the carbon fibers in the preform as the heating elements.
(3) Focused solar radiation.

While panels of solar cells can easily be used to power other devices on the space station when the process machinery is not in use, the conversion of solar radiation to electricity and then back to radiation heat is inefficient. Direct electrical resistance heating was ruled out because of non-uniform heating and of the fact that hot-spots might develop, resulting in a poor product. The use of focused incident solar radiation eliminates losses associated with conversion to other forms of energy.

3.2.1 Heating Process Description

Figure 6 shows how solar radiation could be focused on the preform. The primary collection mirror is a curved trough the same length as the strut being processed. It is constructed of a reflective fabric stretched over a telescoping framework, facilitating ease of machine deployment. A secondary mirror provides for the uniform heating of all sides of the preform. The position, size and shape of the focusing surfaces can be readily changed to process different sizes of struts.

3.2.2 Radiation Requirements

The required energy density for the focused radiation is dictated by the radiative power of the heated composite member. For the preform described, approximately 12,250 W/m^2 of energy must be focused onto the tube to counterbalance the maximum radiative heat loss. Using a coefficient of thermal absorption of 0.9, and taking into account the fact that the surface of the tube is round and that the input radiation is parallel, this requirement increases to 21,400 W/m^2.

A final increase in the size of the collection mirror is needed to account for the degree of reflectivity of the mirror surface. The final magnification factor is approximately 16:1 (mirror area:focal spot size). For a 51 mm diameter tube, the required mirror diameter is approximately 970 mm.

3.3 Component Cooling

Cooling of the consolidated composite is one of the stages that most greatly affects the overall system design. The material being processed imposes restrictions on the allowable cooling rate. Poor material properties can result from heat removal rates that fall outside of the range $10°C/min.$ to $700°C/min.$. This restriction, coupled with the desire for an economical solution, directs the choice of cooling methods. Heat can be removed from the members by three different means: radiation, conduction, or convection to a fluid. Of these three methods, direct radiation to black space requires no additional equipment.

To determine the feasibility of radiative cooling, an analysis of the heat removal rate was performed. Modeling the heat transfer process required the determination of the cooling mode. The considered preform has a Biot modulus of 0.52. As this is less than one, the cooling rate analysis is based on the assumption of Newtonian cooling. By equating the rate of change of internal energy of the strut to the rate of radiative transport to black space, the following cooling rate equations are derived:

$$\rho cV \, dT/d\tau = A\epsilon\sigma T^4 \tag{1}$$

$$d\tau = \rho cV/A\epsilon\sigma * dT/T^4 \tag{2}$$

$$\tau = -1/3T^3 * \rho cV/A\epsilon\sigma \quad \text{from } T_{LOW} \text{ to } T_{HIGH} \tag{3}$$

where:

ρ = mass density of strut (1600 kg/m^3)
c = specific heat (1750 J/kg K)
V = material volume (0.00302 m^3)
A = surface area (0.817 m^2)
T = material temperature (K)
τ = cooling time (sec)
ϵ = emissivity (0.9)
σ = Stephan-Boltzman constant

An investigation of the thermal system indicates that radiative cooling is feasible. For the preform of Figure 2, the above equation and data predicts a cooling rate of $35°C/min$ which will lead to an appropriate amount of crystallization of the PEEK matrix.

4. CONCLUSIONS

A potential process has been designed for the on-orbit fabrication of the structural members of the Space Station from braided thermoplastic composite preforms. The consolidation process developed is similar to autoclave and vacuum-bag molding. Integral outer and inner temperature resistant membrane layers serve as vacuum bags

when the preform is internally pressurized. The process uses focused solar radiation to supply the heat for the consolidation of the composite. Heat transfer analysis results show that the composite can be effectively quenched by radiative cooling to black space.

Two methods were developed which deploy the required length of preform material to the consolidation position. The semi- continuous approach uses rolls of continuously braided preform. Discrete lengths are consolidated and then cut off from the roll. The collapsed preform packages occupy less volume than an equivalent number of preconsolidated tubes. The second approach processes preforms which are cut to length on earth and collapsed into a cartridge box. Preform deployment is less complicated than in the semi-continuous method, with an equivalent volume savings.

There are several areas of the proposed process which would benefit from additional research. An experimental, earth-based apparatus should be constructed which consolidates braided preforms. This would demonstrate the feasibility of the process as well as provide materials for the determination of the strut's mechanical properties.

Alternative pressurizing media should be investigated further. A high temperature structural foam which expands during consolidation might provide sufficient pressure. The foam could also be added after consolidation for additional strut stiffness.

The attachment of the radiation protection sheath could be eliminated if a material was developed which possessed a high emissivity (for fast radiative cooling) and a low absorption (for environmental protection). Such a material could be included as part of the earth-manufactured preform, simplifying on-orbit consolidation.

5.0 REFERENCES

[1]   Ride, Dr. Sally K., Leadership and America's Future in Space, A Report to the Administrator (NASA), August 1987.

[2]   Mikulas, M. M., et. al., Deployable/Erectable Trade Study for Space Station Truss Structures, NASA Technical Memorandum 87573, July 1985.

[3]   Mikulas, M. M., Jr., and Bush, H. G., Design, Construction and Utilization of a Space Station Assembled from 5-Meter Erectable Struts, NASA Technical Memorandum 89043, October 1986.

[4]   Jackson, L. R., et. al., Operational Modules for Space Station Construction, NASA Technical Memorandum 85772, April 1984.

[5]   Heard, W. L., et. al., Results of the ACCESS Space Construction Shuttle Flight Experiment, AIAA Paper No. 86-1186-CP, June 1986.

[6]   Wilson, M. L., MacConachie, I.O. and Johnson, G.S., "Space Structures ...Built in Space", Modern Plastics, August, 102-110 (1988).

[7]   Lyons, J.S., et. al., On-Orbit Fabrication of Space Station Structures from Continuous Fiber Reinforced Thermoplastic Composites, Complex Systems Design Final Report, George W. Woodruff School of Mechanical Engineering, Georgia Institute of Technology, August 1988.

[8]   Mark, H.F., et. al, "Composites", Encyclopedia of Polymer Science and Engineering, 2nd Edition, Vol. 3, 776-820 (1985).

[9]   ICI Fiberite Data Sheet 5: Fabricating with Aromatic Polymer Composite, APC-2.

[10] Foss, R. A., Thermal Control of Tubular Composites In Space, No. 4508, NASA Technical Memorandum 89037, 93-94.

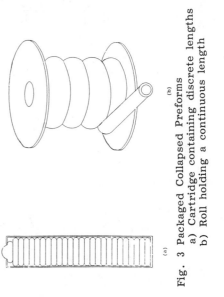

(b)

(a)

Fig. 3   Packaged Collapsed Preforms
a) Cartridge containing discrete lengths
b) Roll holding a continuous length

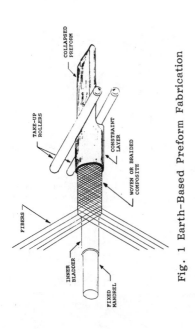

COLLAPSED PREFORM

TAKE-UP ROLLERS

CONSTRAINT LAYER

WOVEN OR BRAIDED COMPOSITE

FIBERS

INNER BLADDER

FIXED MANDREL

Fig. 1 Earth-Based Preform Fabrication

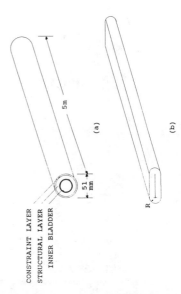

CONSTRAINT LAYER
STRUCTURAL LAYER
INNER BLADDER

5 m

51 mm

(a)

R

(b)

Fig. 2   The Preform: a) Inflated, b) Collapsed

815

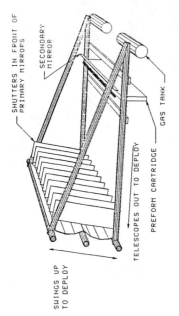

Fig. 4 On-Orbit Semi-Continuous Preform Consolidation Device

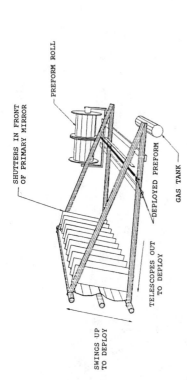

Fig. 5 On-Orbit Discrete-Length Preform Consolidation Device

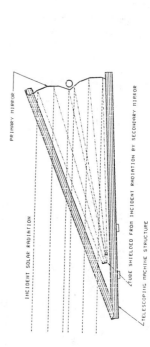

Fig. 6 Solar Radiation Ray Diagram for Consolidation Heating

A NEW INFILTRATION PROCESS FOR THE FABRICATION
OF METAL MATRIX COMPOSITES

M. K. Aghajanian, J. T. Burke,
D. R. White, and A. S. Nagelberg
Lanxide Corporation
Newark, Delaware 19714-6077

Abstract

A novel liquid metal infiltration technique for the production of metal matrix composites containing various reinforcements is described. The technique is unique in that by proper control of the process conditions, infiltration occurs spontaneously, without the aid of pressure or vacuum. The required process conditions are described and the effects of the process variables are determined using a model system comprising an aluminum alloy matrix reinforced with Al_2O_3 particles.

1. INTRODUCTION

Aluminum matrix composites have been produced by various liquid phase processes, including the mixing of molten metal and ceramic particles followed by casting (i.e., compocasting), and the infiltration of molten metals into compacts of reinforcing material via the use of a pressure or vacuum assist. Similarly, solid state processes, such as the mixing of metal and ceramic powders, followed by hot pressing, and the lamination of metal foils and ceramic fibers via diffusion bonding, have been utilized to produce such materials. The liquid phase processes are potentially more economical; however, the solid state processes have been the most successful to date, with the liquid phase processes limited by the non-wetting nature of most ceramics and molten aluminum.[1]

The present paper describes a novel liquid metal infiltration technique for the fabrication of aluminum matrix composites. By proper control of the process conditions excellent wetting is obtained, thus allowing the infiltration to occur spontaneously, without the application of pressure. With no pressure or vacuum apparatus required, this technique provides cost effective processing, and, due to the favorable wetting, pore-free composites with high structural integrity can be produced. Enhanced wetting typically results in an increased strength at the metal-ceramic interface, thus enhancing the mechanical properties of the composite.[2]

The bounds of the process have been studied via systematic examination of the experimental variables and are presented herein. The combination of the present data and the metal/ceramic wetting information available in the literature allows possible mechanisms to be proposed. This information, along with infiltration kinetics data, appears elsewhere[3] and thus will not be discussed in this paper. The mechanical properties of composites produced in this fashion are presented in a companion paper.[4]

2. EXPERIMENT

The experimental lay-up employed in this work consisted of an aluminum alloy ingot, measuring about 50 x 25 x 12 mm, placed on top of a permeable mass of ceramic reinforcing material that was contained within a refractory vessel (a 99.9% sintered Al_2O_3 tray measuring about 100 x 45 x 20 mm). In each case there was sufficient alloy to infiltrate all of the reinforcing material.

The alloy-ceramic assembly was heated to the process temperature in a controlled atmosphere furnace in the presence of a flowing nitrogen-containing gas. To inhibit unwanted gases from entering the furnace, the exit gas was bubbled through a column of oil measuring 25 to 50 mm. After cooling, the extent to which infiltration had occurred was noted and the samples were sectioned and examined microstructurally. The lay-up is shown schematically in Figure 1A, and a typical product is shown in Figure 1B.

A.

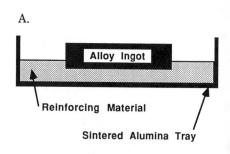

B.

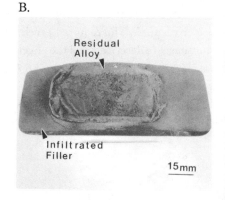

Figure 1. Experimental arrangement employed in infiltration experiments: A) schematic and B) sample after processing, removed from the Al_2O_3 tray.

During the infiltration process, aluminum nitride may form due to reaction of the molten Al with the nitrogen-containing atmosphere. The quantity of nitride that formed in the samples was determined by measuring the unit weight gain (change in weight of the sample divided by the original alloy weight). For comparison, the weight gain obtained when pure aluminum totally converts to AlN is 52 percent.

3. RESULTS AND DISCUSSION

Initial experimentation identified that there exist two requirements for the spontaneous infiltration to occur, namely (i) that the aluminum alloy contain Mg and (ii) that the atmosphere contain nitrogen and be nominally oxygen-free. However, meeting these two requirements does not ensure infiltration. The correct combination of the various process variables, such as the alloy composition, the process temperature, the process time, and the nitrogen content of the atmosphere, must be employed.

To determine the effect of the Mg content in the alloy on infiltration, alloys with Mg contents ranging from 1 to 10 weight percent were placed atop beds of 220 grit fused Al_2O_3 particles (38 Alundum, Norton Co.) and were brought to temperatures ranging from 700 to 1000°C for 10 hours in a 96% N_2/4% H_2 atmosphere.

The data, shown in Table 1, demonstrate that higher alloyed amounts of Mg result in infiltration at lower temperatures, and that under a given set of process conditions there is a critical level of Mg required to induce infiltration. For instance, at 900°C under the current process conditions no infiltration occurred with 3 weight percent Mg and full infiltration occurred with 5 weight percent Mg.

Additionally, the data show that process temperature affects the infiltration kinetics. Under otherwise constant process conditions, full infiltration occurred with alloy Al-5Si-10Mg at 800°C, whereas only partial infiltration occurred

Table 1: Effect of Mg Content on Temperature Required for Infiltration

| | Infiltration (yes/no/partial) | | | |
	700°C	800°C	900°C	1000°C
Al-5Si-1Mg	—	No	No	Partial
Al-5Si-3Mg	—	No	No	Yes
Al-5Si-5Mg	—	No	Yes	Yes
Al-5Si-10Mg	partial	Yes	Yes	—

at 700°C. No infiltration has been obtained with alloys containing no Mg.

The effect of the nitrogen content of the atmosphere on the infiltration process was determined by fabricating samples in atmospheres ranging from 100% N_2 to 100% Ar. Using alloy 520.0 (nominally Al-10Mg) a 220 grit fused Al_2O_3 bed and process conditions of a four hour soak at 800°C, no infiltration occurred in 100% Ar, only partial infiltration occurred in 10% N_2/90% Ar and full infiltration occurred when the N_2 content equalled or exceeded 25%.

In addition to affecting the process kinetics (i.e., only partial infiltration occurred with an atmosphere of 10% N_2/ 90% Ar), the atmosphere affected the quantity of nitride that formed within the product. Figure 2 plots the unit weight gain versus the percent nitrogen in the atmosphere for all of the samples where full infiltration occurred. At high percentages of N_2, where infiltration was rapid, little nitride formed, whereas in dilute atmospheres, where infiltration was slow, observable levels of AlN formed. Figure 3 shows the microstructures obtained in 100% N_2 and in 10%

Figure 3. Effect of furnace atmosphere on product microstructure: A) 100% N and B) 10% N_2/90% Ar.

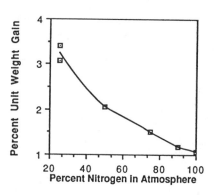

Figure 2. Dependence of unit weight gain (measure of nitride formation) on percent N_2 in a N_2/Ar atmosphere.

N$_2$/90% Ar. There is little AlN discernible in the micrograph of the 100% N$_2$ sample; however, fine AlN particles (as marked on the figure) are visible in the micrograph of the 10% N$_2$/90% Ar sample.

In a similar fashion, the process temperature significantly affects the quantity of nitride that forms within the aluminum alloy matrix. Figure 4 plots

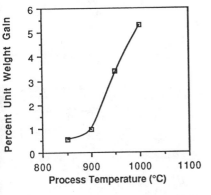

Figure 4. Relationship between process temperature and nitride formation (unit weight gain) in Al alloy matrix.

unit weight gain versus process temperature for samples fabricated using alloy Al-5Si-3Mg-3Fe, a 220 grit fused Al$_2$O$_3$ bed and process conditions of a 5 hour dwell at temperature in 96% N$_2$/4% H$_2$. The results demonstrate that increased process temperatures result in increased quantities of nitride formation, and that the increase is nearly linear from 900 to 1000°C.

Thus, the AlN content of the resultant Al alloy matrix can be tailored by selecting the appropriate atmosphere and process temperature. In turn, this allows the resultant properties of the composite to be tailored without changing the alloy chemistry or the filler loading. For instance, increases in the AlN content of the aluminum alloy matrix will decrease the coefficient of thermal expansion and increase the stiffness of the composite.

Also evident from Figure 4 is that infiltration occurred into the fused Al$_2$O$_3$ at 900°C with alloy Al-5Si-3Mg-3Fe. At the same process temperature alloy Al-5Si-3Mg did not infiltrate the Al$_2$O$_3$ (Table 1), demonstrating that Fe can promote infiltration at lower temperatures.

The spontaneous infiltration technique is applicable to the production of composites containing a wide range of reinforcement types. Examples of Al$_2$O$_3$ particle reinforced composites are shown in Figure 3. Figure 5 shows examples of Al$_2$O$_3$ agglomerate (C-75UNG, ALCAN Co.) and continuous fiber (Fiber FP®, DuPont Co.) reinforced aluminum alloy matrices. It was found that filler geometry did not significantly affect the infiltration process.

Similarly, the spontaneous infiltration process is applicable to many filler chemistries. Examples of reinforcement materials that have been utilized include SiC, TiB$_2$, MgO, SiC coated (chemical vapor deposition) graphite, and AlN. Microstructures of composites containing 220 grit SiC (39 Crystolon, Norton

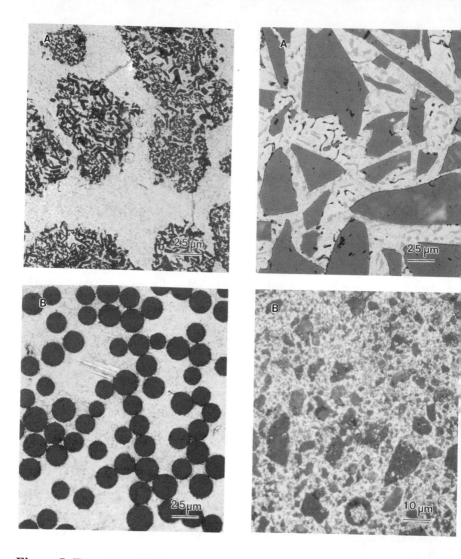

Figure 5. Examples of Al_2O_3 reinforced Al alloy matrix composites: A) agglomerated particles and B) continuous fibers.

Figure 6. Examples of particle reinforced Al alloy matrix composites: A) SiC and B) AlN.

Co.) and 3.3μm AlN (Grade A-200, Advanced Refractory Technology) are shown in Figure 6.

4. SUMMARY

A novel process for the production of metal matrix composites containing either continuous or discontinuous reinforcement is reported. The process involves the infiltration of molten aluminum alloys into loose beds or compacts of reinforcing material without the aid of pressure or vacuum (i.e., spontaneously) by proper control of the process conditions.

Using the model system of Al_2O_3 particle reinforced aluminum, the effects of the process variables on infiltration were examined. It was shown that there exist two requirements for wetting to occur, namely (i) that the alloy contain Mg and (ii) that the atmosphere be nitrogenous.

The required process temperature for infiltration to occur was shown to be strongly affected by the Mg content of the alloy, with alloys containing low levels of Mg requiring higher process temperatures. AlN precipitates were found to occur within the aluminum alloy matrix, particularly in atmospheres with low contents of nitrogen and at high process temperatures. Although the effect of filler chemistry was not quantified, the process is applicable to a wide range of filler materials.

5. ACKNOWLEDGMENTS

The authors gratefully acknowledge the technical assistance of W. R. Steininger, R. J. Wiener and K. A. Bacon of Lanxide Corporation.

6. REFERENCES

(1) Martinis, G. P., Olsen, D. L., and Edwards, G. R., Met. Trans. 19B, 95 (1988).

(2) Delannay, F., Froyen, L., and Deruyttere, A., J. Mat. Sci. 22, 1 (1987).

(3) Aghajanian, M. K., Burke, J. T., and Rocazella, M. A., J. Mat. Sci., to be published.

(4) Burke, J. T. and Aghajanian, M. K., this proceedings.

HONEYCOMB SANDWICH PRIMARY
STRUCTURE APPLICATIONS
ON THE BOEING MODEL 360 HELICOPTER

Steven Llorente
Boeing Helicopters
Philadelphia, Pennsylvania

Abstract

This report presents information regarding the use and evaluation of
sandwich structure throughout development and support of the Boeing
Model 360. Kevlar sandwich panels,
which are significantly more impact
resistant than comparable graphite
panels, were utilized in both side
skin panels (with and without windows) and crown skin panels.
Sandwich construction was also used
in frames and longerons to maximize
bending efficiency. The rotor blades
of the Model 360 utilize graphite and
fiberglass over Nomex honeycomb core.

Extensive testing and service experience has previously demonstrated the
damage tolerance, repairability, and
reliability of this type of rotor
blade. The results of an experimental evaluation of different panel
edge types for fuselage structure are
presented. The effects of severe
environment and damage were also
evaluated. Corrosion damage encountered in some military aircraft
containing aluminum honeycomb was
found not to be applicable to the use
of nonmetallic cores such as Nomex.
Finally, the development of advanced
sandwich structure concepts taking
place at Boeing Helicopters is described. These advanced concepts
offer the potential of reduced
weight, improved damage and environmental tolerance, and repairability.

1. INTRODUCTION

Composites have been accepted structural materials for many years in,
among others, the aerospace, automotive, and marine industries. For
over thirty years Boeing Helicopters
has used composites, and particularly
composite sandwich construction
utilizing Nomex honeycomb, in primary
structure with great success. Composites, when used properly, are more
efficient than metals. Their generally anisotropic nature allows the
designer to tailor the composite to
the individual application at hand.

This, and the lower density of composites, results in significant weight savings in most structural applications.

A sandwich structure yields the best possible strength to weight ratio for certain applications. Sandwich panels are also expected to have increased damage tolerance due to the presence of two separated load carrying facesheets and a core providing energy absorption and stability. This type of structure has yielded substantial advantages in terms of reduced manufacturing costs, improved specific strength and stiffness, and high damage tolerance.

2. MODEL 360 FUSELAGE

The Boeing Model 360, shown in Figure 1, utilizes composites in many primary structural components including the fuselage, rotor blades, hubs and drive shafts. The entire fuselage and the rotor blades utilize sandwich construction. The fuselage sandwich panels are manufactured from two ply Kevlar skins attached to a Nomex honeycomb core. This report will discuss the development tests and proof test conducted to verify the design of the fuselage structure. The rotor blades are discussed in another report.

An attempt was made to simplify the airframe design from the outset. Frames are one piece rings designed to support concentrated loads and distribute these loads to the fuse-

lage shell. They are located only at those points where major loads enter the fuselage such as the rotor support locations and the aft fuselage splice. Other frames support the longerons and skin panels and redistribute concentrated loads from the cargo hooks, floor/fuel tanks, and side panel cutouts. The longerons are attached to the frames and are sized to carry overall fuselage lateral and vertical bending loads. As shown in Figure 2, the large modular skin panels, designed to carry fuselage shear and torsion loads, are then connected to the longerons and frames from the outside, between each frame.

C91331

Figure 1.   Boeing Model 360 Helicopter

Figure 2.   Fuselage Assembly

The frame flanges and skin panel edges are reinforced to accept fasteners for load transfer between structural elements. A room temperature curing adhesive is used between skin panels and frames or longerons, and is designed to carry ultimate loads. Bolts are then used to provide pressure during the adhesive cure and are spaced to carry design limit loads, as a redundant load path. Figure 3 shows the efficient interface between skin panels and frames or longerons. This design approach has resulted in clean external and internal lines for the fuselage, as shown in Figure 4.

Figure 4. Fuselage Interior During Assembly

3. TEST PROGRAM

Engineering and manufacturing technology development on the Model 36 fuselage proceeded hand-in-hand with the following objectives: reducing part count, meeting weight targets, simplifying tooling, and using composites whenever possible. The test program described below was conducted to verify that the objectives were met while assuring the structural integrity of the fuselage.

3.1 Full Scale Panels

Five full size panels representing actual portions of the fuselage were manufactured and tested to examine the stability and strength of the crown and side panels. The first two panels were 63 inch by 70 inch curved side panels with windows and graphite reinforcement straps. The basic construction of these side panel

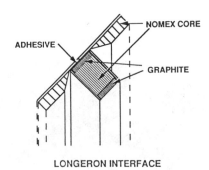

LONGERON INTERFACE

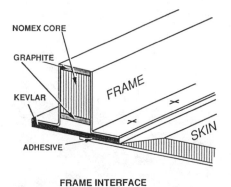

FRAME INTERFACE

Figure 3. Skin Panel Interfaces

shown in Figure 5, utilized two-ply Kevlar skins layed up in ±45 degree directions. One ply of style 120 fabric and one ply of style 285 fabric yields the basic 0.015 inch skin thickness. A one ply +45 degree Kevlar doubler (0.005 inch) was applied on the exterior skins on all four sides of the window region. Graphite straps, 4 plies thick and 2 inches wide, were added in the vertical direction. Straps were also added in the horizontal direction where they were three plies thick and 3 inches wide. The basic frame and longeron configurations were utilized and attached to the panels on all four sides.

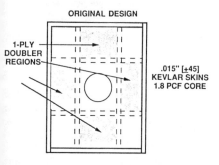

Figure 5.　Curved Side Panel Original Design

The third side panel, shown in Figure 6, included a window reinforcing ring. In this side panel configuration, the graphite straps and one-ply Kevlar doubler were omitted. The reinforcing ring utilized a 16-ply quasi-isotropic graphite fabric skin over 3 PCF Nomex. The edge of the Nomex nearest the window was sealed and the inner graphite reinforcement tapered to 9 plies in this region.

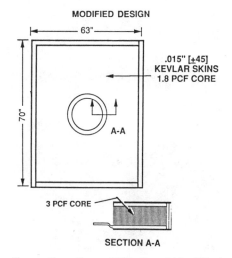

Figure 6.　Curved Side Panel Modified Design

A fourth curved panel was manufactured to represent the crown units. It's dimensions were 57.5 inches by 63 inches in dimension. See Figure 7. As shown, the crown panel utilizes the same two-ply Kevlar skins over a 1-inch thick 1.8 PCF Nomex core. Finally, an additional side panel with straps was manufactured, damaged, and repaired to evaluate the repairability of the basic fuselage concept. This panel, both before and after repair, is shown in Figure 8.

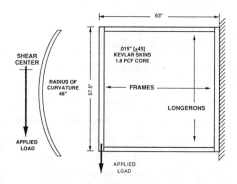

Figure 7.　Skin Panel Shear Tests Curved Crown Panel

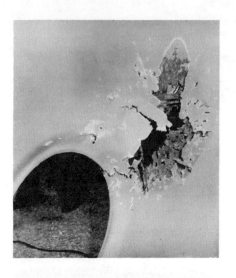

FINAL REPAIR — OUTBOARD SIDE

C49974

Figure 8.   Repaired Side Panel

3.1.1 Manufacturing

The full scale sandwich panels and picture frame panels utilized in the Model 360 test program were cocured, meaning that the facesheets were cured while being bonded to the core material. Cocuring saves manufacturing time and effort compared to the practice of precuring the facesheets and subsequently bonding them

to the core. It also allows laminates with unsymmetrical facesheets to be produced. Graphite straps, frame sections and longerons were manufactured separately and bonded or bolted to the sandwich structure. The repaired panel was shot with a 23 MM HEI round. It required only 14 manhours, to repair the 25 inch by 27 inch damaged area using field-level repair tools. The patch required 10 hours of applied external heat.

3.1.2 Testing

Full-scale airframe panels were tested by applying a downward load at the calculated shear centers of panels having their opposite vertical side fixed to a rigid steel I-Beam. The specimens were loaded in 2,000 pound increments. Load was maintained at each increment for a minimum of 20 seconds while strain and deflection data were acquired.

The first two curved side panels with windows and graphite reinforcement straps failed at 200 lb/in and 257 lb/in. The repaired side panel of this same configuration failed at 253 lb/in. The first panel failure resulted from lower longeron instability at the end fitting. The failure may have resulted from load introduction misalignment. In the second specimen, failure was prompted by a local instability around the window edging-to-shear redistribution strap interface. This local buckling failure resulted in the redesign of the window region to incorporate the window reinforcing ring. The panel having this ring failed at 326 lb/in. A compression failure line extended diagonally from the top corner to the reinforcing ring and continued on the other side of the ring to the bottom. This failure is shown in Figure 9. Finally, the curved crown panel failed at 317 lb/in due to a failure of the lower longeron end fitting. The face wrinkling failure occurred subsequently to the fitting failure.

C49752

Figure 9.   Side Panel Failure

3.2   Picture Frame Shear Panels

In-plane shear tests of fuselage structure were conducted to determine the shear allowables applicable to the design and development of full-scale aircraft structure. Once full-scale panel tests showed that the failure mode of the fuselage panels was not related to global or overall stability, it became possible to conduct further in-plane shear tests using smaller test sections. The picture frame shear test method was used to determine the required allowables.

A total of 31 picture frame panels were manufactured to determine the effects of edge treatment, facesheet type, core type, impact damage, and environmental conditioning on panel strength.   The first twelve tests were used to determine the basic Model 360 configuration.   Initially, four edge treatments were evaluated. Three of these four are shown in Figure 10. Edges were either bevelled with an edge band and doubler, or squared with a Z-shaped section, edge band and doubler to transfer loads to frames, longerons and neighboring skin panels. Two doubler widths in the bevelled panels and two square edge types (precured Z vs. cocure Z) were evaluated. Panels with bevelled edges were evaluated with both 1.8 PCF and 3 PCF Nomex cores.

BEVELLED EDGE 2.0"/4.5" DOUBLER

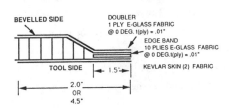

SQUARED EDGE WITH PRECURED Z

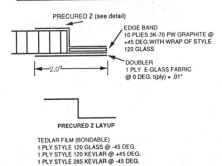

Figure 10.   Panel Edge Treatments

829

An alternate facesheet type was evaluated with both core types and bevelled edges. Instead of two ply Kevlar facesheets, the flat side (outer fuselage facesheet) incorporated a Kevlar/graphite hybrid and the bevelled side consisted of one ply of graphite fabric.

Elevated temperature tests were performed on panels with precured Z edges which were first conditioned at 120 °F and 95 percent Relative Humidity (RH) to 2.8 percent moisture content by weight. Conditioning took approximately 7 days. One test was performed at 140 °F and one at 160 °F to evaluate test temperature sensitivity.

Finally, the remaining 19 tests were performed as part of a damage tolerance evaluation of the final Model 360 configuration. Four sandwich laminate configurations were chosen for this investigation. The first two were based on the configuration of the Model 360 fuselage utilizing two ply [±45] Kevlar fabric facesheets and either a 1.8 PCF or 3 PCF Nomex core. The remaining two used two ply [±45] graphite fabric facesheets with the same cores to evaluate facesheet material effect.

3.2.1 Manufacturing

Nineteen 23.5-inch by 23.5-inch flat sandwich panels comprising the four sandwich configurations were manufactured. The majority of the damaged specimens were impacted in their center at their corresponding deter-mined visible damage energy level. Two panels, one graphite/1.8 PCF Nomex and one Kevlar/1.8 PCF Nomex, were impacted at different energy levels to evaluate the sensitivity of residual strength with respect to degree of damage. Six of the nineteen panels were tested in an undamaged state.

The Kevlar sandwich specimens used in this investigation were made from Hexcel Kevlar 49/F155-71, utilizing one ply each of styles 120 and 285. The Nomex core was one inch thick. The core near the edges of the full scale panels and some of the picture frame panels was bevelled. In the picture frame panels with precured or cocured Z edges, the core remains square. A layer of film adhesive was placed between each facesheet and the core. An edge band was incorporated in order to reinforce the area where load was introduced into the test specimen. The assembled laminate was cured in an autoclave at 250 °F. The graphite configurations were made from T300/F593 which is a 3K-70-PW type fabric cured at 350 °F.

3.2.2 Testing

The test setup for the picture frame panels consisted of a picture frame fixture, two clevises, and a load cell held in a steel enclosure. The picture frame test fixture consisted of eight steel straps held together in a square by six bolts along each side. The composite test panels were held in this fixture by 17 quarter-inch bolts per side. A 0.2-inch wide slot approximately 1.5 inches in length was machined in each corner to alleviate the high corner stresses in the panels. Damage tolerance specimens were impacted in this fixture. Load was applied at a rate of 0.05 inch per minute in all tests. Load, deflection, and elapsed time were recorded throughout the test. For the undamaged panels, strains were also recorded. The specimens were monitored visually and any audible emissions were recorded along with the corresponding load level.

The test results from the evaluation of edge treatments are given in Figure 11. As shown the large doubler width results in a 20 percent increase in failure load. The use of the precured Z edge does not result in significant strength improvement over the 4.5-inch doubler length. However, the cocured Z does result in the largest failure load of the shear panel tests at 770 lb/in. Failure in panels with square Z edges initiated with a crack in the corners of the specimen. Face wrinkling failure subsequently occurred. The alternate facesheet material comparison results are given in Figure 12. Failure in panels with one ply graphite bevelled facesheets occurred on the bevelled side as a local buckling failure similar to the all Kevlar panels. The hybrid panels are the only ones where the failure initiated on the bevelled side.

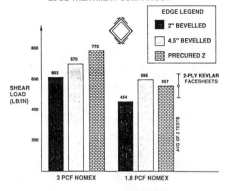

Figure 11. Edge Treatment Results

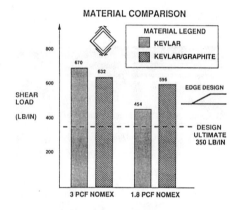

Figure 12. Facesheet Comparison Results

The environmental test results are shown in Figure 13. There is a 36 percent reduction in strength in the 140 °F wet test panel. The higher 160 °F temperature of the second test does not result in significant further reduction in strength. The conditioned panels behave similar to the dry panels except that the face wrinkling failure was accompanied by several compression face creases on both surfaces. These creases do not appear to involve the core, unlike the wrinkling failure. This is shown in Figure 14.

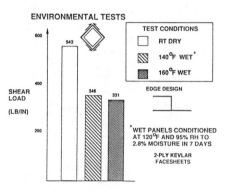

ENVIRONMENTAL TESTS

TEST CONDITIONS

☐ RT DRY

▨ 140°F WET *

▩ 160°F WET

EDGE DESIGN

* WET PANELS CONDITIONED AT 120°F AND 95% RH TO 2.8% MOISTURE IN 7 DAYS

2-PLY KEVLAR FACESHEETS

Figure 13. Environmental Test Results

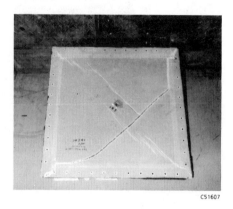

C51607

Figure 14. Wet Panel Failure

The remaining 19 tests were performed as part of a damage tolerance evaluation of the final Model 360 configuration (see Reference 1 for more details). The average shear failure loads for the undamaged Kevlar and graphite sandwich panels with 3 PCF Nomex core were 784 lb/in and 1,363 lb/in, respectively. The damaged panels failed at 626 lb/in and 1,022 lb/in, respectively. Table 1 presents the results of these tests. The average failure loads for the Kevlar and graphite sandwich panels with 1.8 PCF Nomex core were 598 lb/in and 968 lb/in, respectively. The damaged panels with easily visible damage failed at 451 lb/in and 610 lb/in, respectively. Similarly, the damaged panels with barely visible damage failed at 529 lb/in and 629 lb/in, respectively. Table 2 presents the results of these tests. As with the 3 PCF panels the extensional strains of these laminates are small when compared to the shear-strain, indicating that these laminates are in a nearly pure shear state at the center.

Table 1. 3 PCF Test Results

TEST TYPE	PANEL ID	APPLIED LOAD	SHEAR LOAD
KEVLAR			
UNDAMAGED	1	25,495 LB	767 LB/IN.
UNDAMAGED	2	26,589 LB	800 LB/IN.
DAMAGED (CV)	3	20,253 LB	609 LB/IN.
DAMAGED (CV)	4	18,500 LB	556 LB/IN.
DAMAGED (CV)	5	22,141 LB	666 LB/IN.
DAMAGED (CV)	6	20,065 LB	604 LB/IN.
GRAPHITE			
UNDAMAGED	1	45,286 LB	1363 LB/IN.
DAMAGED (BV)	2	34,260 LB	1031 LB/IN.
DAMAGED (BV)	3	33,680 LB	1013 LB/IN.

NOTES: BV, CV ARE BARELY OR CLEARLY VISIBLE DAMAGE

Table 2. 1.8 PCF Test Results

TEST TYPE	PANEL ID	APPLIED LOAD	SHEAR LOAD
KEVLAR			
UNDAMAGED	1	19,910 LB	599 LB/IN.
UNDAMAGED	2	19,870 LB	598 LB/IN.
DAMAGED (CV)	3	15,344 LB	462 LB/IN.
DAMAGED (CV)	4	14,939 LB	450 LB/IN.
DAMAGED (CV)	5	15,141 LB	456 LB/IN.
DAMAGED (CV)	6	14,484 LB	436 LB/IN.
DAMAGED (BV)	7	17,573 LB	529 LB/IN.
GRAPHITE			
UNDAMAGED	1	32,165 LB	968 LB/IN.
DAMAGED (BV)	2	20,892 LB	629 LB/IN.
DAMAGED (CV)	3	20,265 LB	610 LB/IN.

NOTES: BV, CV ARE BARELY OR CLEARLY VISIBLE DAMAGE

In all of these tests, a compression failure line (face wrinkling) extended diagonally across the panel from top to bottom. The compression failure in the undamaged panels occurred instantaneously extending vertically from corner to corner to the edge of the doubler region. A 3 PCF graphite panel with this type of failure is shown in Figure 15. Continued loading of the undamaged Kevlar panels resulted in a similar compression failure of the bevelled side at a load level lower than initial face wrinkling on the tool side. The same tool-side compression failure occurred in the damaged Kevlar panels. However the damage grew visibly, in a stable way, in the load direction from the initial indentation (caused by the impact) until it was approximately three to four inches in total length. At this point the face wrinkle extended to the doubler edge. As shown in Figure 16, continued loading of the panels resulted in a facesheet tension failure at a higher load than the initial compression failure.

Figure 16. 3 PCF Kevlar Panel Failure

As a result of the observable growth of the damaged region, it appears that the impact damage causes a transverse compression failure of the impacted facesheet. After this failure, since the panel can still carry tension load, a secondary tensile failure can occur and generally did. There was no visible failure on the back face of the Kevlar panels. However, in the undamaged graphite panel and one of the damaged graphite panels, a tension failure occurred on both the bevelled and tool side along with the compression failure.

3.3 Longerons and Frames

Both the section properties and joint configurations were evaluated to ensure that design loads could be carried. A typical longeron section is shown in Figure 17. The caps are

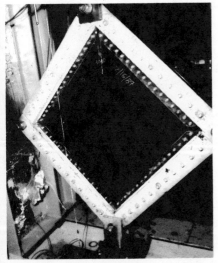

Figure 15. 3 PCF Graphite Panel Failure

made of unidirectional graphite tape(T300/5209), 52 plies thick (0.338 inch). Of those, 77 percent are 0 degree plies and 23 percent are ±45 degree plies. Each web is two plies of style 120 Kevlar fabric layed up at 0 degrees . The core is 3 PCF Nomex honeycomb. Specimens were fabricated to test the cap laminates with 0.25-inch diameter holes. Cap strength was evaluated in tension, compression, bearing, and combined tension and bearing. Two manufacturing types were evaluated; specimens utilized either precured cap laminates or laminates cocured with their Nomex honeycomb core. Finally, both Room Temperature Dry (RTD) and Elevated Temperature Wet (ETW) cap strength was evaluated. ETW specimens were conditioned to 1.1 percent moisture weight gain and then tested at 160 °F. A complete longeron assembly was also manufactured to evaluate the stability of a 63-inch section attached to skin panels.

A typical frame section is shown in Figure 18. The cross section geometry allows an efficient interface with the airframe panel edges. The caps are made of 0 degree unidirectional tape 27 plies thick (0.149 inch). The webs were graphite fabric. Typically, the 3 PCF Nomex core was 0.75-inch wide by 1.25 to 1.375 inches long depending on the particular frame section. Finally, a Kevlar strap 0.125 inch thick is applied where the frame is attached to the skin panels. Short beam shear test specimens and flexure specimens were made from full-scale frame sections cut from the flat bottom portions of two representative frame sections.

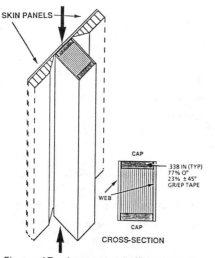

Figure 17. Longeron Full-Scale Test Schematic

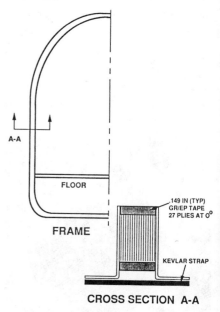

Figure 18. Model 360 Frame Section

3.3.1 Manufacturing

Frames and longerons were also cocured. Tooling development took place at Boeing Helicopters to improve part quality by reducing void content through good compaction of cap plies. A typical elastomeric tool which resulted in improved compaction of frame sections is shown in Figure 19. Pressure is provided by the expanding tool surfaces as well as by the internal autoclave pressure.

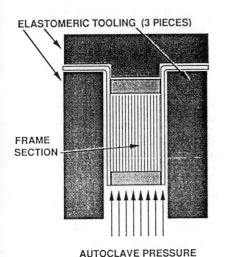

ELASTOMERIC TOOLING (3 PIECES)

FRAME SECTION

AUTOCLAVE PRESSURE

- PRESSURE FROM RUBBER "INSIDE-OUT"
- VOIDS REDUCED
- IMPROVED COMPACTION AND COMPRESSIVE STRENGTH
- IMPROVED SHEAR BETWEEN FACE ANGLES AND CAPS

Figure 19. Frame Tooling Concept

3.3.2 Testing

Longeron cap tests were performed on the specimens shown in Figure 20. The tension and compression specimens are identical, being 8 inches long with a 2-inch test section. The bearing specimen, also shown, is 5 inches long and loaded through the

0.25-inch bolt hole. Finally, the combined tension and bearing specimen was 12 inches long. All specimens have 0.064-inch aluminum loading tabs to introduce the load into the test section. They were tested statically to failure in a standard tensile test machine.

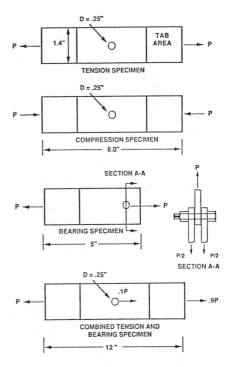

Figure 20. Longeron Cap Test Specimens

Frame sections were tested in shear and bending. Figure 21 shows the two frame section specimens. The 10-inch shear test specimen was loaded in 3-point bending. The frame bottom flanges were first removed flush with the bottom cap so that they would not interfere with load introduction. Three 0/90 doublers were applied to the webs of the specimen ends and center. A loading pad was also used to contact the web doublers. The 48-inch frame bending specimens utilized a similar load introduction methodology in a 4-point bending test.

FRAME BOTTOM SECTION

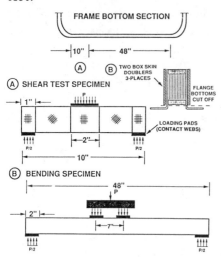

(A) SHEAR TEST SPECIMEN

(B) BENDING SPECIMEN

Figure 21. Frame Section Tests

Eighteen longeron cap tests were performed on the final Model 360 longeron configuration. Both cocured and precured cap specimens were tested. ETW specimens (conditioned to 1.1 percent moisture gain by weight and tested at 160 °F) were also evaluated. Test results are given in Table 3. Room temperature tension specimens normally failed at the notch. However, the ETW specimens experienced grip tab bond failures. There was no significant difference in failure loads between the two manufacturing types. Both specimens exceeded maximum design loads. Both compression specimens also failed at the notch, with the cocured specimen at a higher load level. ETW testing results in a 50 percent loss of compressive strength.

Table 3. Longeron Cap Test Results

TEST TYPE	FAILURE LOAD (LBS)		STRENGTH REDUCTION (PERCENT)
	ROOM TEMP. DRY	ELEV.TEMP WET 1.1% MOISTURE 160°F TEST	
TENSION	C 38000 C 33500 P 37900 P 34200	P 29800 P 31500	-15
	AVG=35900	AVG=30650	
COMPRESSION	C 42000 P 33100	P 18800 P 18600	-50
	AVG=37550	AVG=18700	
BEARING	C 6000 P 7560	P 5190 P 6600	-13
	AVG=6780	AVG= 5895	
COMBINED TENSION & BEARING	C 29600 P 22500	P 26535 P 27800	—
	AVG=26050	AVG= 27167	

NOTE: C = COCURED WITH HONEYCOMB
P = PRECURED CAP

Bearing specimens failed due to shear out of the 0 degree plies and elongation of the hole. A failed bearing specimen in the test apparatus is shown in Figure 22. ETW testing results in a 13 percent loss in bearing strength. Both manufacturing methods have large margins of safety, based on these bearing failure loads. Finally combined tension and bearing specimens failed across the hole region. This net-tension failure was accompanied by some elongation of the hole. ETW testing did not result in any strength reduction. However, the environmental test specimens did experience grip tab bond failures along with the net-tension failure.

C50980

Figure 22. Bearing Specimen Failure

Frame long flexure specimens generally failed due to compression in the cap laminates. Compressive strength was very dependent on quality of compaction (voids) in the frame caps. Investigation of lower failure load specimens generally showed poor quality cap laminates. Improvements in frame tooling resulted in specimens failing above design bending moments (18,775 in-lb). Shear tests of specimens with Kevlar webs failed due to web-cap debonding at lower loads than those with graphite webs which failed due to buckling of the webs.

3.4 Fuselage Proof Test

The fuselage assembly was subjected to a proof load test in order to substantiate the integrity of the airframe for the planned flight test and demonstration envelope. In this test, shown in Figure 23, maximum loads were applied successfully at the two rotor hub locations and three cargo hooks on the underside of the fuselage.

C70269

Figure 23. Proof Load Test

4. CONCLUSIONS

The airframe full-scale proof load test was successfully conducted on the Model 360, verifying the structural integrity of the assembled fuselage. Based on full-scale airframe panel tests, this final design incorporated 1.8 PCF Nomex core, and a window reinforcing ring. These tests were necessary to evaluate overall panel stability, demonstrate repairability, and assist in this final design configuration selection. The repaired panel failed at 10 percent higher load than the virgin side panel. Picture frame sandwich panel tests showed that the simplified bevelled edge treatment was strong enough for the maximum design shear loads, while having the least weight and cost of the four concepts evaluated.

The following additional conclusions are drawn from the investigations:

1) The Kevlar sandwich panels were significantly more impact resistant than the graphite panels. Obtaining barely visible or visible damage in the Kevlar panel required approximately two to four times the impact energy required of the graphite panel.

2) The sandwich panel tests show approximately a 20 - 22 percent reduction in strength due to impact damage in both the graphite and Kevlar test panels with 3 PCF Nomex core, and a 25 - 37 percent reduction

837

for the test panels with 1.8 PCF core, respectively.

3) Model 360 large panel test results confirm that the fuselage panels are face wrinkling critical (as opposed to buckling critical). These results combined with the damaged picture frame test results demonstrate that Model 360 type airframe panels are damage tolerant; all Kevlar panels tested (1.8 PCF or 3 PCF core) in this investigation withstood the maximum (ultimate) design shear load of 350 lb/in with easily visible damage. Since easily visible damage should be detectable in a walkaround inspection of the airframe, the strength requirement is limit load rather than ultimate load. The 1.8 PCF damaged Kevlar panels were able to carry maximum design shear loads (more load than initial failure load) after the initial face wrinkling failure, constituting a soft failure mode.

4) The recently proposed Bell/Army Design criteria for damage-tolerant helicopter primary structure speci- fies damage caused by 3 ft-lb as the minimum durability requirement (requiring no repair) and damage caused by 5 ft-lb as the minimum damage tolerance requirement (re- quiring repair) for an aircraft exterior[2]. This implies that a sandwich structure as tested utilizing two ply Kevlar skins (Model 360) would meet the durability requirements and that two ply

graphite would not meet the re quirements.

Composite sandwich structure prese the rotorcraft industry with t opportunity to reduce weight; impro safety, reliability, and maintair ability; and lower production costs Compared to a skin-stringer alumint fuselage, the Model 360 has an 8 percent reduction in fasteners (bolt and rivets), an 86 percent reductio in parts, a 90 percent reduction i tooling costs and a 50 percent reduc tion in the number of man-hour needed to fabricate the helicopter[3] Boeing Helicopters has taken thes improvements and demonstrated them i the largest flying advanced composit helicopter in the industry.

5. ACKNOWLEDGEMENTS

The authors wish to acknowledge grtefully the contributions of R. Wiesner, C. Gunther, M. Niederer, A. Bertolazzi and other personnel of Boeing Helicopters who assisted in the completion of this investigation

6. REFERENCES

1. Llorente, S. G., and Gunther, C. K., "Damage Tolerance Evaluation of Sandwich Shear Panels", Presen- ted at the National Technical Spec- ialists Meeting of the American Helicopter Society, Williamsburg, Virginia, October 25-27, 1988.

2. Rogers, C., Chan, W., and Martin, J., Design Criteria for Damage Tolerant Helicopter Primary Structure of Composite Materials", USAAVSCOM-TR-87-D-3A, Ft. Eustis, VA, June 1987.

3. Grina, K. "The Boeing Helicopter Model 360 Advanced Technology Helicopter", Vertiflite, Vol. 34, No. 1, January 1988.

IN-SITU FABRICATION OF
ADVANCED COMPOSITES SANDWICH STRUCTURE

Hossein Saatchi, Ph.D.
Sundstrand ATG
4747 Harrison Ave.
Rockford, Il 61125

Abstract

Innovative methods have been developed to fabricate complex shapes with continuous and/or short fiber-reinforced thermoplastic and thermoset sandwich structures having thermoplastic foam core. Methods developed are isostatic pressure processing (IPP) and/or in-situ component fabrication using a nonreactive foaming gas to provide consolidation pressure. In these operations, raw core materials are mixed and sandwiched between laminated skins. In IPP, the core mix is poured into the heating chamber cylinder and/or in the mold to separate the skins (commingled or braided preform) and the melt injected into the assembly in the mold. The melt consolidates the preform against the mold cavity by:
- the injection piston pressure
- the internal gases developed due to thermal decomposition of the foaming agent

The polymeric matrix materials used in these processes are high-temperature thermoplastic.

In-situ fabrication eliminates several secondary processes such as core fabrication, machining, and bonding. During in-situ fabrication, while the foaming reaction produces a foam core, the core will also bond to the skins by molecular bonding. All compression and flexural samples tested failed in the skin and crack propagated in the skin and/or foam. No skin/foam interfacial crack was detected in the samples tested. Also, composite sandwich panels with and without the flame-protection layer were subjected to a 1,093°C (2,000°F) horizontal flame impingement test.

1. INTRODUCTION

In-situ composite sandwich panel fabrication is preferable in comparison to conventional fabrication processes (1 through 4). In conventional sandwich structure fabrication, the skins and core are made separately, then the core is machined and bonded to the skins. In in-situ fabrication, most of the secondary processes are eliminated and the core and skins are made in one heating cycle. If the core material is similar to the skin matrix material, a molecular bond will develop between skins/core; and this will enhance the bond strength of the sandwich, which is considered the weakest section of the component.

To fabricate composite sandwich structure in in-situ fashion, powder compaction and vacuum bagging (PC/VB) or PEEK® foaming in place is used (1). In these methods, it is possible to produce complex geometry in a composite sandwich or monolithic form with simple equipment such as cold compaction press, oven, and vacuum pump and vacuum bagging materials. To fabricate a sound structure, 41 MPa (6 ksi) pressure is necessary to cold compact PEEK powder. Such a compaction pressure may crash low-density hollow carbon or glass microspheres. Low-pressure injection machine can eliminate the microsphere crashing.

Other advantages of the low-pressure injection molding and/or IPP in comparison with standard injection molding are:

- In-situ fabrication of sandwich structure
- 40% to 80% less clamp tonnage
- Consistent, repeatable shot weight
- Elimination of packing which creates stress
- Accommodation of molding in place textile, foam, padding, delicate decorative film, metal mesh, etc.
- Elimination of costly secondary operations
- Increase of cycle times
- Thermoplastic cellular molding with no crashing of low density microspheres
- Capability of injection small or large shots

The purpose of this study was to design and construct an IPP system and to fabricate and test thermoplastic sandwich structure in a one-step heating operation (In-situ).

2. EXPERIMENTAL

2.1 Materials

The commingle skins are carbon/polyetheretherketone (PEEK) 8HS fabric (GPK-100-18 in) and unidirectional tape (GPK-171-18 in) from Textile Technologies, Inc.

PEEK is used in powder (Grade 150 PF) or granular (D150G) forms, both purchased from ICI America. Graphite hollow microspheres are either Type E or Type L of Versar Mfg. Inc. Type E microsphere contains hollow carbon particles with an average diameter of 21 microns (0.82 mil) and density of 373 kg/m³ (0.0134 lb/in³.), and Type L with density of 154 k/m³ (0.0055 lb/in³.) with an average diameter of 50 microns (1.96 mils).

Polyetherimide (PEI) resin is unreinforced grade 1000 Ultem pellets, a product of GE. Polyphenylene sulfide (PPS) is Fortron powder, a product of Celanese.

Short fibers are 0.00317m (1/8 in.) length and mil size (CH-3 cm 018-18 and MI-3CO-MIL-CROO), products of Fortafil Fibers Inc. Mold release materials are XK-22 (of Releasomers) or FRP Release Interface (of the Hysol).

2.2 Fabrication Processes

Isostatic pressure processing (IPP) is

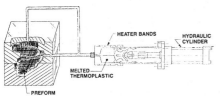

Figure 1. Schematic of Isostatic Pressure Process

Figure 2. IPP Machine

similar to low-pressure injection molding with capabilities to control the rate of molten material injection, and pressure buildup in the mold.

Sundstrand has designed and fabricated an IPP system (Figures 1 and 2).

Initially, an epoxy (a room temperature processable) system is injected into a matched-metal mold to cast a hat-section part. Then low-temperature thermoplastics such as polyethylene and acrylic (Dyna-Purge of Philip Shuman & Sons, Inc.) resins with and/or without carbon fillers are molded (Figure 3).

Fortron®, Ultem® and PEEK hat-sections were made in a similar manner.

To fabricate a sandwich panel, the raw core materials such as PEEK powder, foaming agent, and other fillers as needed are mixed and poured in the IPP chamber.

Figure 3. Molded IPP Parts. Raw Material (Top) and Polyethylene/Graphite Ultem, and Fortron Hat Sections (Bottom)

Also, the same core mixture materials are placed between a preform (commingle or braided carbon/PEEK) in the mold. The short fibers and/or carbon microspheres are added to the core materials to decrease thermal shrinkage, which causes cracks; and to enhance the strength and stiffness of the core.

The IPP chamber and the mold are heated to melting temperature of the resin. PEEK, Ultem, and Fortron processing temperatures are 400°C (750°F), 360°C (675°F), and 315°C (600°F), respectively. The processing variables are different in

Figure 4. Hat Section of Carbon/PEEK Skins and PEEK Foam Core

Figure 5. Pseudo In-Situ and In-Situ Carbon/PEEK, PEEK Foam Core and Carbon/Epoxy Parts

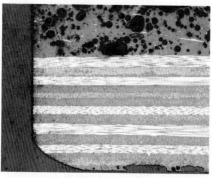

Figure 6. In-Situ Carbon/PEEK and PEEK Foam Core Panels

sandwich and/or foam with thick skins fabrication. In fabrication of sandwich having carbon reinforced PEEK skins, a minimum of 20 minutes at 400°C (750°F) is required to consolidate the commingle and/or braided preform.

Figure 4 shows the carbon/PEEK and PEEK foam sandwich structure.

Figure 5 shows a flat carbon/PEEK and PEEK foam core which was fabricated in pseudo in-situ fashion. In this process, skins and foam are molded and bonded with an adhesive.

Figure 6 shows a flat carbon/PEEK and PEEK foam core panel which was fabricated in in-situ fashion.

3. TESTING

3.1 Density of Sandwich

Densities of the composite sandwich, skin, and foam were obtained using ASTM method D1622 and method D792, and the following equations.

$$W_{cs} = W_s + W_f \tag{1}$$

where:

W_{cs} = weight of composite sandwich

W_s = weight of skin

W_f = weight of foam

$$\varrho_{cs} = \frac{W_{cs}}{V_{cs}}, \ \varrho_f = \frac{W_f}{V_f}, \text{ and } \varrho_s = \frac{W_s}{V_s} \tag{2}$$

where:

ϱ_{cs} = density of composite sandwich

ϱ_f = density of foam

ϱ_s = density of skin

V_{cs} = volume of the composite sandwich

V_f = volume of the foam

V_s = volume of the skin

$$V_{cs} = t_{cs} \times A \tag{3}$$

t_{cs} = thickness of the composite sandwich

A = area of the composite sandwich

While the A is similar in sandwich, foam, and skins, then, from equation (1), (2) and (3), equation (4) is derived:

$$\varrho_{cs} = \frac{\varrho_t t_f + \varrho_s t_s}{t_{cs}} \text{ or}$$

$$\varrho_f = \frac{\varrho_{cs} t_{cs} - \varrho_s t_s}{t_{cs} - t_s} \tag{4}$$

The composite sandwich and the skin densities were measured by ASTM method. To obtain the foam density of an in-situ fabricated panel, the measured densities of the composite sandwich and the skins were used in equation 4. Tables A and B show the densities of ten carbon/PEEK skins with PEEK, microspheres, and short graphite fibers core.

The density of the sandwich can be varied by variation in the foaming agent content, pressure, and number of commingle skins.

Table A.
Densities of Sandwich Panels
and Foam Fabricated in In-Situ Fashion

	Densities g/cc (lb./in. cu)				Total Skin
	Foam	Sandwich	Skin	Plies (#)	Thickness Cm. (In.)
1.	0.99 (0.036)	1.15 (0.041)	1.56 (0.056)	12	0.313 (0.1235)
2.	1.04 (0.037)	1.19 (0.043)	1.56 (0.056)	12	0.309 (0.1220)
3.	0.87 (0.031)	1.07 (0.038)	1.56 (0.056)	12	0.308 (0.1216)
4.	0.74 (0.026)	0.85 (0.031)	1.56 (0.056)	6	0.157 (0.0620)

Table B.
Flexural Strength of the PEEK Foam,
and the Carbon/PEEK Sandwich With
PEEK Foam Core

	Type of Facing	Number of Plies	Maximum Stress Pa (psi)	Density g/cc (lb/cu ft)
1.	PEEK Foam	*	19,037 (2,763)	0.68 (0.024)
2.	APC-2	15	178,383 (25,880)	1.00 (0.036)
3.	APC-2	6	136,373 (19,793)	0.83 (0.029)
4.	Woven Commingle	6	93,104 (13,513)	0.86 (0.030)
5.	Woven Commingle	3	65,661 (9,530)	0.81 (0.029)
6.	Unidirectional Commingle	9	171,395 (24,876)	0.97 (0.034)

*Average of Three Samples of PEEK Foam With No Facing

3.2 Mechanical Test

Compression strengths of the foam and the composite sandwich were evaluated using ASTM C365. The samples were 2.54 cm x 2.54 cm x 1.27 cm thick (1 in. x 1 in. x 0.5 in. thick). The overall compressive strength of the sandwich panels is higher than foam panels.

Flexural strength of the foam and the composite sandwich panels were evaluated according to ASTM D790, method I (A three-point loading), to center loading of a simply supported beam. The specimen rests on two supports and is loaded by a loading nose midway between the supports. The maximum axial fiber stresses occur on a line under the loading nose. This stress was calculated by the following equations:

$$S = 3PL/2bd^2 \tag{5}$$

where:

S = stress in the outer fibers at midspan

P = load at a given point on the load deflection curve

L = support span

b = width of the beam tested

d = depth (or thickness) of the specimen

Maximum strain and tangent modules calculated using following equation:

$$r = 6Dd/L^2 \tag{6}$$

$$E = L^3 m/4bd^3 \tag{7}$$

where:

r = maximum strain in outer fiber

D = maximum deflection of the center of the beam

E = modulus of elasticity

M = slop of the tangent to the straight-line portion of the load-deflection curve

Sample size was 1.25 cm x 1.25 cm x 22.86 cm (0.5 in. x 0.5 in. x 9 in.). Figures

7, 8 and 9 show the schematic, side, and top views of the compression and the flexural samples before test. Figures 10, 11, and 12 show typical compressive and flexural load-deflection of sandwich and foam panels. In both tests (compression and flexural) of composite panels, the crack initiated in the skins or the foam which is indication of a strong skin/core bond. Figures 13 and 14 show the fractographs of the specimens tested to 2% and higher deflections.

In the compression specimens tested, no crack was detected in the foam or bond line. Cracks mainly initiated in the 0 degree and 90 degree commingle skins (see Figure 15).

In flexural test a crack initiated on the top surface of the skin. Figure 16 shows crack initiation and skin buckling on the surface, and crack propagation through the skin. No cracks at the skin and foam interface or in the foam were detected. Tables B and C show the flexural and compressive strengths of six panels with different facings.

3.3 Flame Test

Carbon/PEEK skins with PEEK foam with and without Vermiculite (ICI Fiberite Fortiglass product) coated glass were flame tested at 1,093°C (2,000°F) for 10 minutes (see Figure 17). Samples were 10 cm x 10 cm x 1.27 cm thick (4 in. x 4 in. x .5 in. thick). The back side and middle section temperatures of the sandwich panel reached 204°C (400°F) and 537°C (1,000°F), respectively. These temperatures

dropped to 165°C (330°F) and 348°C (660°F) with the addition of a Vermiculite fortiglass ply on the flame side.

The test was a modified version of FAR 70 Part 25 paragraph 25.1351(e), a horizontal flame impingement test. Figure 18 shows the test apparatus set up and sample tested

4. CONCLUSION

An IPP for in-situ fabrication of composite sandwich structure was designed and fabricated. Several thermoplastic materials were molded including carbon/PEEK faced sandwich composite with a composite PEEK foam core. These processes and materials are considered to be very promising for aircraft or second-generation Space Shuttle structural applications. Due to in-situ fabrication, most of the secondary operations were eliminated. Also, the foam core is strongly bonded to the facings through a molecular bond, and no delamination was detected when specimens were tested in compression or flexural tests. This is an indication of the transfer of the load from skins to the core. Most of the fracture occurred in the skin, and this may be caused by lack of sufficient resin in the skins. This can be resolved by adding PEEK fibers in the commingle fabric. Carbon/PEEK facings with PEEK core samples were subjected to 1,093°C (2,000°F) horizontal flame. The back and middle temperatures dropped from 537°C (1,000°F) and 204°C (400°F) to 348°C (660°F) and 176°C (350°F) for samples that were fabricated with a layer of Vermiculite, respectively.

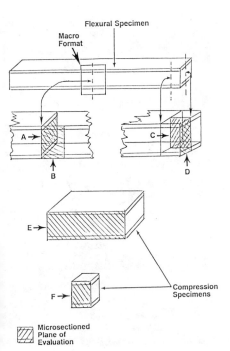

Figure 7. Schematic of Flexural and Compression Specimens

Figure 8. Side Section of Flexural (Top) and Compression (Bottom) Specimens Before Test

Figure 9. Top View of Flexural (Top) and Compression (Bottom) Specimens

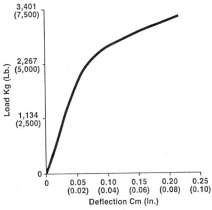

Figure 10. Typical Flatwise Compressive Load Deformation of Commingle Carbon/PEEK Skins Facing With PEEK Foam Core — Fifteen Unidirectional Commingle Facing

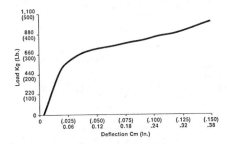

Figure 11. Typical Flatwise Compressive Load Deflection Diagrams of a Carbon/PEEK Unidirectional Commingle Facing With PEEK Foam Core

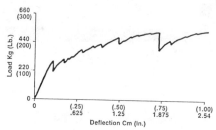

Figure 12. Typical Flexural Load Deflection Diagram of the Woven Commingle Carbon/PEEK Facings With PEEK Foam Core

Figure 13. Compression Specimens. Top Specimens are 2.54 cm x 2.54 cm x 1.27 cm (1 in. x 1 in. x 5 in.) and Bottom Specimens are 0.64 cm x 0.64 cm x 1.27 cm (0.25 in. x 0.25 in. x 0.5 in.)

Figure 14. Flexural Specimens After Test. Sample Sizes are 20.3 cm x 1.27 cm x 1.27 cm (8 in. x 0.5 in. x 0.5 in.)

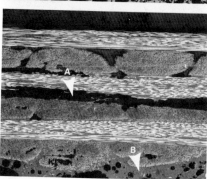

Figure 15. Fractograph of a Six Ply Commingle Carbon/PEEK Facing With PEEK Foam Core After Compression Test. Arrow "A" Shows Cracks in the Skin and Arrow "B" Shows the Skin/Foam Interface. Top Fractograph (x12.5) and Bottom (x50).

Table C.
Compressive Strength of the PEEK Foam, and Carbon/PEEK Sandwich With PEEK Composite Foam Core

Type of Facing	Number of Plies	Stress Pa (psi)	
		2% Strain	10% Deformation
PEEK Foam	*	2,636 (3,827)	29,089 (4,222)
APC-2	15	39,955 (5,799)	43,779 (6,354)
APC-2	6	27,615 (4,008)	30,205 (4,384)
Woven Commingle	6	45,708 (6,634)	45,970 (6,672)
Woven Commingle	3	32,231 (4,678)	34,105 (4,950)
Unidirectional Commingle	9	32,534 (4,722)	36,813 (5,343)

*Average of Six Samples of PEEK Foam With No Facing

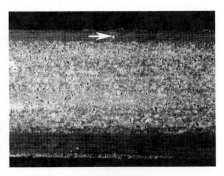

Figure 16. Fractographs of a Six Ply
Commingle Carbon/PEEK
Facing PEEK Foam Core After
Flexural Test. Top Fractograph
Shows Crack Initiation in the
Top Skin and Bottom
Fractograph Shows Crack
Propagation and Skin Buckling

Figure 17. Carbon/PEEK Facing With
PEEK Composite Foam Core
Subjected to 10 Minutes
1,093°C (2,000°F) Flame

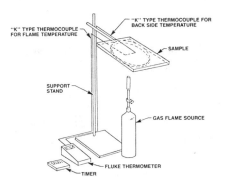

Figure 18. Schematic of the Horizontal
Flame Test Apparatus Setup

5. REFERENCES

1. Saatchi, H., Okey, D., and Murray, P.,
   "Thermoplastic Graphite Skin/Foam
   Sandwich Structure Fabrication,"
   Proceeding of 5th Annual Composite
   Technology Conference, SIU
   Carbondale, April, 1988.

2 Sundstrand Aviation, Saatchi, H.,
   "Composite Foam Sandwichs",
   High-Tech Materials Alert, Vol. 5, No. 7,
   July, 1988.

3. Sundstrand Aviation, "Aerospace
   Materials: Fibers and Foam From Hybrid
   Sandwich," *Aerospace America*, a
   publication of The American Institute of
   Aeronautics and Astronautics, October,
   1988, P42.

4. Saatchi, H., "One-Step Advanced
   Composite Sandwich Structure
   Fabrication," presented at the
   FIBER-TEX 88, Greenville, SC,
   September, 1988 (will be published as
   an ITAR NASA publcation in 1989).

HOSSEIN SAATCHI

Earned a B.S. in Metallurgical Engineering (1973), an M.S. (1975), and a Ph.D. (1978) in Materials Engineering from Drexel University and an MBA from Lake Erie College (1987). As postdoctorate fellow at the University of Pennsylvania (1978), he worked on intercalation of graphite fibers and polymer composites.

At Martin Marietta Aerospace, he developed probes and methods for nondestructive testing and repair of composites. At Gould Defense Systems, he coordinated the efforts of the organic composite group in the development, fabrication, and testing of several composite products, such as pressure vessel, missile fin, torpedo drive shaft, and ablative coating. Since 1986, he has worked for Sundstrand Advanced Technology Group in the area of advanced composite materials.

Dr. Saatchi has authored eight technical publications and holds seven patents in the area of composite technology. He has received several awards, served as the chairman of Electronic Materials, ASM Cleveland Chapter (1984-1986) and is listed in Jane's Who's Who in Aviation and Aerospace, and the International Directory of Distinguished Leadership.

34th International SAMPE Symposium
May 8-11, 1989

RECENT HONEYCOMB DEVELOPMENTS

Peter W. Borris, Mark S. Caldwell, Juan I. Castillo, Thomas N. Bitzer
Hexcel Corporation
Dublin, California

Abstract

Some new honeycomb core types promise to achieve wide acceptance in the future. These include graphite fabric with phenolic, polyimide, epoxy and thermoplastic resin matrices; layered silicate, polyester and nonwovens; non-metallic Tube-Cores; and several new cell configurations such as Double-Flex, Vari-Cell, and Iso-Core. Mechanical properties and potential applications of the new materials are discussed.

1. INTRODUCTION

Hexcel's R&D laboratory is developing a number of new core types and configurations, using a variety of novel material, resins, and core geometries. This paper describes the mechanical properties and some possible applications of these new core types, and discusses some of the criteria used in honeycomb toughness assessment.

2. GRAPHITE HONEYCOMB

Last year a graphite/phenolic core was introduced which was the first nonmetallic honeycomb to achieve properties similar to those of aluminum (see Table 1). At that time the cost of the material was approximately $350 per board foot (12" x 12" x 1"). Reduced cost of graphite fabric, improved efficiency of manufacture, and increased volume have brought that

cost down more than half, to approximately $150 per cubic foot. It is now highly competitive with conventional skin-and-stringer structures.

Graphite honeycomb eliminates galvanic corrosion; its specific strengths and moduli -- particularly its shear modulus -- are very high. It has been used in a classified military space based optical bench program, and is a candidate for applications in the next generation of military and commercial aircraft. Obviously, it is attractive for retrofit parts in situations where weight and corrosion are problems.

The results of recent tests of thermal conductivity of HFT-G-1/4-5.0 graphite honeycomb are presented, together with comparable data for other honeycomb types, in Table 2. The test cores were one inch thick and were tested in Dynatech's Guarded Heat Flow Meter Box (ASTM C518).

Since this core is used in space applications, it may be necessary to vent the cells to allow the escape of air. This is accomplished by drilling a small hole in each of the cell's free walls (see Figure 1).

Table 3 displays the percentage of original properties maintained by

849

half-inch-thick HFT-G-1/4-5.0 with
.075" vent holes. Compressive
properties are unchanged, while
shear strength is reduced by about
forty percent. This penalty will
of course vary as a function of
hole diameter and core thickness.

Graphite honeycomb can be
fabricated with polyimide resin to
provide very good retention of
strength -- particularly shear
strength -- and stiffness at high
temperatures (Table 4).

Table 5 shows mechanicals for
graphite honeycomb with toughness
enhanced by Ultem 1000 and F593
epoxy resin systems. Both resins
yielded tougher cores, with the
Ultem 1000 core appearing
particularly interesting.

3. SILICATE HONEYCOMB

Twenty-five years ago Hexcel made
an asbestos core for nonstructural
parts in a high altitude supersonic
aircraft. It was required to
withstand temperatures of 750°F for
long periods. Present health
regulations make it all but
impossible to produce this core, so
we have developed a replacement,
HRH-750, using layered silicate
paper (see Figure 2). Mechanical
properties and heat aging
characteristics for this material
are shown in Table 6 and Figure 3.

HRH-750 consists of mica layered
silicate paper and silicone resin.
The core is made by the corrugation
process, using a high purity
alumina-based node adhesive and a
subsequent resin dip of the entire
core block. Prototype quantities
of this core have been manufactured
in our Dublin, California R&D labs
and potential customers have been
contacted.

Because of its ability to withstand
high temperatures for long periods

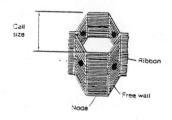

Figure 1

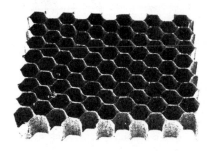

SILICATE HONEYCOMB

Figure 2

of time, HRH-750 is a candidate for
use in sandwich flame barriers and
heat exchangers.

4. POLYESTER HONEYCOMB

A nonwoven honeycomb for non-
aerospace applications has been
developed. It can replace WRII (a
Kraft paper/phenolic core) where
better toughness is required, and
HRH-10 (Nomex/phenolic) where cost
is an issue. This polyester
honeycomb. designated HRH-60, has
properties somewhat lower than
those of the strong but brittle
WRII material and the very tough
but relatively expensive (in non-
aerospace terms) HRH-10 core.
Table 7 shows mechanical properties
for two core products currently

HRH 750-3/8-4.5 (LS-9203)   0.50" T
ROOM TEMPERATURE PROPERTIES AFTER BEING CONDITIONED
AT 750 F FOR VARIOUS TIMES

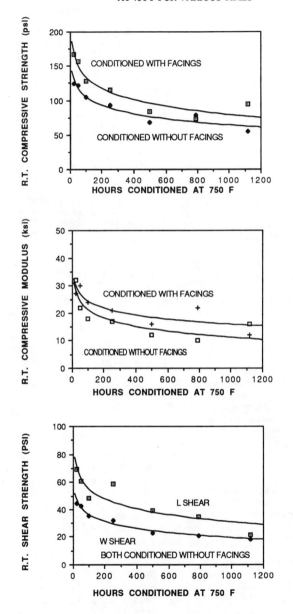

Figure 3

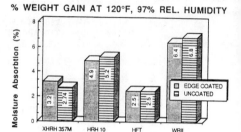

being produced with this material, HRH 60-1/4-3.5 and HRH 60-3/16-4.5.

5. ADVANCED NONWOVEN HONEYCOMB

HRH-10 aramid/phenolic honeycomb core exhibits excellent toughness and good compressive and shear strengths, and has become one of the most widely used honeycomb core materials on the market. Its toughness is obtained, however, at the expense of modulus; it has only about half the compressive modulus of glass-fabric-reinforced core, and 40% of the shear modulus. HRH-10's moisture absorption is also greater than that of glass-fiber reinforced products (see Figure 4).

Hexcel is currently developing a promising honeycomb material using an innovative advanced nonwoven substrate. As shown in Table 8, which is based on preliminary testing, this material exhibits compressive and shear moduli 50% to 100% superior to those of HRH-10. At the same time, its moisture absorption is 40% lower, putting it in a class with glass-fiber-reinforced core. The impact tolerance of this new material is currently under evaluation, and is expected to be significantly superior to that of high-modulus glass products. Production capability is now being developed.

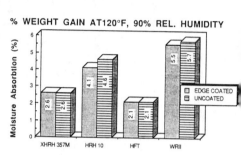

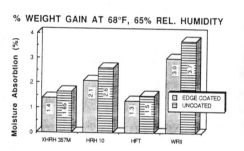

Figure 4

6. NON-METALLIC TUBE-CORE

Honeycomb is normally used in lightweight structural sandwich panel applications where strong, stiff structures are required; but it also has a unique ability to absorb energy in a uniform and predictable manner. Tube-Core is a very efficient energy-absorbing material made of alternate layers of corrugated and flat sheet coiled around a mandrel. Until recently all Tube-Core products were made of aluminum but now fiberglass and

Nomex Tube-Cores are under development (see Figure 5). As can be seen from Table 9, they are not as efficient as aluminum, but are suitable for use in applications where a non-metallic core is desired.

7. MICRO-CELL HONEYCOMB

Hexcel manufactures an aluminum honeycomb called Micro-Cell with a cell size of only 1/16 inch. It is supplied in 6.5, 9.5 and 12.0 pcf densities in 5052 aluminum, and 6.5

and 9.5 pcf in 5056. Recently
Hexcel has achieved the same cell
size in a Nomex core, HRH 10-1/16-
3.4(1.5) (see Figure 6). The core
is made of 1.5 mil Nomex paper and
dipped in a phenolic resin.

The small cell size reduced markoff
(cell outlines showing through thin
skins), greatly increases the bond
area between facings and core, and
provides a more impact-resistance
core. In co-cured sandwich panels
with composite prepreg facings, it
offers superior support and
produces a better laminate.

8. NEW CELL CONFIGURATION

Three new cell configurations that
have been developed are shown in
Figure 7.

Double-Flex is a large cell Flex-
Core which can easily be formed
into compound curvatures. The
large cell size ensures a low-
density core. Double-Flex is
currently supplied in aluminum and
Nomex.

Vari-Cell is an unusual honeycomb
configuration using different cell
sizes in a single sheet. Designed
for sound attenuation applications,
it attenuates several frequency
ranges by the Helmholtz Effect, the
cells of different sizes acting as
resonators for difference
frequencies.

Iso-Core is the result of changing
the honeycomb cell configuration to
meet specific customer
requirements (see Figure 8). In
conventional honeycomb, the L shear
properties are about double the W
properties. In Iso-Core, the core
may be made isotropic -- that is,
with L and W properties the same.
Hexcel has developed formulas and
computer programs to adjust L and W
shear properties as desired. As
Table 10 indicates, Iso-Core also

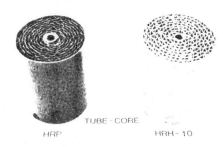

TUBE-CORE

HRP HRH-10

Figure 5

HRH-10-1/16-3.4(1.5)

Figure 6

NEW CELL CONFIGURATIONS

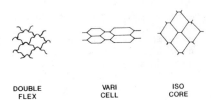

DOUBLE FLEX

VARI CELL

ISO CORE

Figure 7

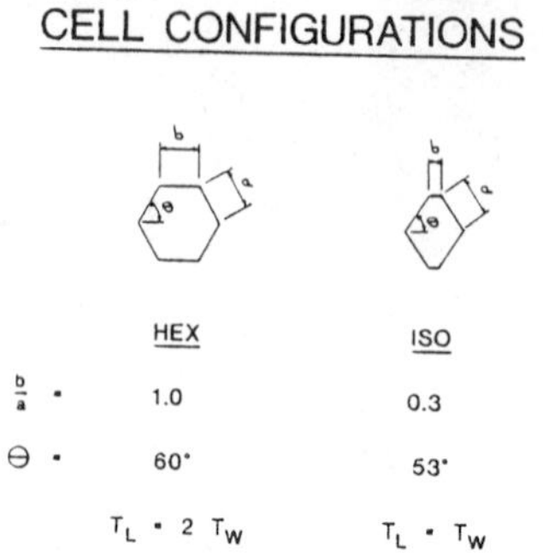

CELL CONFIGURATIONS

	HEX	ISO
$\frac{b}{a}$ =	1.0	0.3
Θ =	60°	53°
	$T_L = 2\ T_W$	$T_L = T_W$

Figure 8

offers a slightly higher compressive strength than aluminum honeycomb in a standard configuration.

Shear isotropy is useful on flooring panels where all four edges are supported; in this case the required core density is a function of the lowest shear strength along any axis. Iso-Core also provides isotropic electrical properties, an asset in low-observable application.

9. HONEYCOMB SANDWICH TOUGHNESS

Toughness is generally agreed to be a desirable quality in many honeycomb applications, but the term is ambiguous. "Toughness" is often used as a synonym for "damage resistance": a measure of the amount of energy needed to damage the panel. To withstand a heavy local impact without damage, a sandwich must have a thick skin and a high-density core -- not a desirable combination for an efficient structure.

A second aspect of toughness, however, is "damage tolerance", which is probably of greater practical importance. Damage tolerance is a measure of the panel's retention of its baseline structural properties after damage. What is desired is that the bond between core and facings remain intact and that the core deform elastically or plastically without rupture. If these criteria are met, the panel can still support considerable loads although damaged.

HRH-10 Nomex cores are extremely tough and resilient, and when used with the proper facings provide a highly damage-tolerant panel. Hexcel currently has an active research program to develop a tough fiberglass honeycomb, and expects to achieve a fiberglass core with improved damage-tolerance qualities in the near future.

10. SUMMARY

Many of the cores discussed in this paper will undoubtedly play important roles in future structural design and manufacture.

In particular, graphite fabric cores with phenolic, polyimide, and thermoplastic resins provide exciting possibilities for high strength, high modulus nonmetallic honeycombs, and silicate paper core appear to offer very good structural properties over long periods of elevated temperatures.

Controlling L and W shear properties by varying cell geometry offers sandwich panel designers new opportunities for increased strength - and stiffness-to-weight ratios, as well as electrical optimization for low-observable applications, while current research in damage-tolerant fiberglass cores promises to yield useful enhancements in the near future.

11. BIOGRAPHIES

Peter Borris is Group Leader for Honeycomb and Bonded Panel Development in the Structural Division of Hexcel. Mr. Borris received a B.S. from Humboldt State University in 1971. His experience at Hexcel, where he has been employed for 15 years has included development of adhesives and advanced composite materials. He has held his current position for the past 5 years.

Mark Caldwell is a Research Specialist in the Honeycomb and Bonded Panel Development Group at Hexcel where he has been employed for 4 years. He has been primarily involved with the development of honeycomb products from new materials and the development and introduction of new aircraft flooring panels. He has a B.S. in Chemical Engineering and a M.S. in Mechanical Engineering from the University of California, Berkeley.

Juan I. Castillo is a Research Specialist for the Honeycomb Group in the Structural Products Division of Hexcel. He's currently working on new applications of layered silicate paper and graphite honeycomb and composites products. He received his B.S. in Chemistry from San Jose State University in 1981 and is currently working on a M.S. program in Materials Engineering.

Tom Bitzer is the manager of Hexcel's R&D Testing and Engineering Group where he has been involved in the testing and design of honeycomb sandwich panels for over 22 years. He has a masters degree in Structural Engineering from the University of California in Berkeley, a Ph.D from Century University and is a registered Civil Engineer.

HONEYCOMB PROPERTY COMPARISONS
(ALL 5.0 PCF, 0.50"T CORES)

CORE TYPE	COMPRESSION STABILIZED		PLATE SHEAR "L" DIRECTION		"W" DIRECTION	
	STR. (PSI)	MOD. (KSI)	STR. (PSI)	MOD. (KSI)	STR. (PSI)	MOD. (KSI)
GRAPHITE (HFT-G)	940	103	455	92	290	35
ALUMINUM (5052)	645	180	410	78	262	34
FIBERGLASS (HFT)	775	60	400	36	200	13
NOMEX HRH-10)	810	45	325	11	175	5

Table 1

THERMAL CONDUCTIVITY BTU-IN/HR-FT^2-°F
1" THICK CORE 75°F MEAN TEMPERATURE

CORE TYPE	"T"	"L"	"W"
HFT-G-1/4-5.0	.78	.58	.46
HFT-1/8-5.5	.46	.35	.30
HRP-3/16-4.0	.55	.38	.36
HRH-10-1/8-3.0	.45	.34	.32

Table 2

HFT-G-1/4-5.0 DRILLED HONEYCOMB
0.50" THICK .075" DIAMETER HOLE

PROPERTY	% RETENTION
COMPRESSIVE STRENGTH	100%
COMPRESSIVE MODULUS	100%
L SHEAR STRENGTH	62%
L SHEAR MODULUS	100%
W SHEAR STRENGTH	59%
W SHEAR MODULUS	70%

*NOTE: PERCENT RETENTION WILL BE AFFECTED BY
CORE THICKNESS AND HOLE DIAMETER*

Table 3

HFT-327-G-1/4-5.0 GRAPHITE/POLYIMIDE

PROPERTY	R.T.	500 °F	550 °F	600 °F
COMPRESSIVE STR.	990 PSI	70%	63%	50%
COMPRESSIVE MOD.	83 KSI	71%	62%	53%
L SHEAR STR.	480 PSI	99%	92%	72%
L SHEAR MOD.	76 KSI	-	-	-
W SHEAR STR.	300 PSI	97%	92%	76%
W SHEAR MOD.	31 KSI	-	-	-

NOTE: TESTED AT TEMP. AFTER 30 MINUTE EXPOSURE

Table 4

HFT-G-1/4-5.0 R.T. PROPERTIES

RESIN SYSTEMS

	ULTEM	EPOXY	PHENOLIC
COMPRESSIVE STR.	930 PSI	890 PSI	940 PSI
COMPRESSIVE MOD.	75 KSI	62 KSI	103 KSI
L SHEAR STR.	580 PSI	590 PSI	455 PSI
L SHEAR MOD.	66 KSI	71 KSI	92 KSI
W SHEAR STR.	300 PSI	370 PSI	290 PSI
W SHEAR MOD.	22 KSI	29 KSI	35 KSI

Table 5

HRH-750-3/8-4.5

PROPERTY	R.T.	750 °F
COMPRESSIVE STRENGTH	112 PSI	89 PSI
COMPRESSIVE MODULUS	26 KSI	14 KSI
L SHEAR STRENGTH	64 PSI	61 PSI
L SHEAR MODULUS	21 KSI	-
W SHEAR STRENGTH	42 PSI	45 PSI
W SHEAR MODULUS	9 KSI	-

NOTE: 0.50" THICK, 30 MINUTES AT TEMPERATURE

Table 6

HRH-60 POLYESTER PAPER/PHENOLIC CORE
0.50" THICKNESS R.T. PROPERTIES

PROPERTY	HRH-60-1/4-3.5(3)	HRH-60-3/16-4.5(3)
COMPRESSIVE STR.	320 PSI	530 PSI
COMPRESSIVE MOD.	22 KSI	31 KSI
L SHEAR STR.	150 PSI	200 PSI
L SHEAR MOD.	6 KSI	8 KSI
W SHEAR STR.	75 PSI	110 PSI
W SHEAR MOD.	3 KSI	4 KSI

Table 7

ADVANCED NONWOVEN/PHENOLIC HONEYCOMB
0.50"T R.T PROPERTIES

PROPERTY	XHRH-357M-4.5 PCF	HRH-10-4.5 PCF
COMPRESSIVE STR.	795 PSI	685 PSI
COMPRESSIVE MOD.	51 KSI	33 KSI
L SHEAR STR.	245 PSI	280 PSI
W SHEAR STR.	130 PSI	155 PSI
L SHEAR MOD.	23 KSI	10 KSI
W SHEAR MOD.	8 KSI	6 KSI

Table 8

TUBE-CORE R.T. CRUSH STRENGTHS

DENSITY	HRP FIBERGLASS	HRH-10 NOMEX	5052 ALUMINUM
11 PCF	-	670 PSI	1000 PSI
16 PCF	960 PSI	-	1650 PSI

Table 9

ISO-CORE HONEYCOMB
ALUMINUM 3.7 PCF DENSITY

	ISO-CORE	HEXAGONAL
L SHEAR STRENGTH	230 PSI	260 PSI
W SHEAR STRENGTH	230 PSI	170 PSI
COMPRESSIVE STRENGTH	490 PSI	420 PSI

Table 10

EFFECT OF CURE CYCLE PARAMETERS
ON 350°F COCURED EPOXY HONEYCOMB CORE PANELS
T. H. Brayden and D. C. Darrow
LTV Aircraft Products Group
Dallas, Texas

Abstract

Experimental data descriptive of the differences between similar panels, cured by alternative cure cycles, is presented and discussed. The discussion explains the observed variations in terms of vector force diagrams, the ideal gas equation and the effect of volatiles on the cure of 350°F thermosetting epoxy resins.

1. INTRODUCTION

Current production on certain programs includes a variety of honeycomb core panels. Historical data for the honeycomb sandwich panels with a core ramp show that a number of them experience core collapse during autoclave cure. This is particularly true of low density core with a thickness of 1.0 inch or more and/or a relatively steep angle on the core ramp. Core collapse in these panels occurs as a result of the action of the autoclave pressure.

The textbook definition of pressure is force per unit area. On a core with a sloped ramp, the force can be represented as a vector quantity perpendicular to the surface of the ramp. See Figure 1. This vector can be decomposed into two components. One component is perpendicular to the tool surface, and the other is parallel to it. The perpendicular force tends to reduce the columnar height of the core. The parallel force shoves the core together like an accordion. Given a 20+/-3 degree angle on the core and an autoclave air pressure of 45 lbs/in^2, the parallel force on the core is 13.2 to 17.6 lbs/in^2.

The forces resisting the parallel force are the compressive strength (lateral) of the core and the force exerted by the gases filling the core volume. The resolution of forces, and the net force, is shown schematically in Figure 2. The pressure of the air inside the core varies as the temperature of the autoclave rises according to the equation

$$PV = nRT$$

. where P = air pressure in atmosphere
   V = core volume
   n = number of moles (1) of air in the core
   R = universal gas constant
   T = temperature in degrees Kelvin

Figures 3 shows the variation of the air pressure inside the core with the air temperature of the autoclave. This is calculated by the use of the combined gas laws of Boyle and Gay-Lussac assuming that the core is essentially sealed and is of a constant volume. Application of full autoclave pressure at the start of the cycle can exceed the resisting force and result in a net positive force tending to collapse the core. As the temperature increases and the air pressure inside the core rises, the layup can withstand a higher autoclave pressure without collapsing.

The external force and the temperature are both variables related to the cure cycle. Choices involved in the cure cycle include:
(a) The rate of rise of temperature
(b) The time pressure is applied
(c) The magnitude of the pressure applied
(d) The use of vacuum during all or a portion of the cure cycle
(e) Holds for a specified length of time at certain temperatures

Considering the number of alternatives, there are several different paths (cure cycles) leading from the initial (uncured) to the final (cured) state. A common cure cycle calls for application of 45 psi pressure at the start, venting the bag, a 3-5°F/min.rate. of rise to 280°F, a hold at 280°F for 60 minutes, a 3-5°F/min. rate of rise to 350°F, and a hold at 350°F for a minimum of 2 hours.

Honeycomb core panels, of the configuration shown in Figure 4, particularly those with 3 and 4 lb/ft³ core, undergo core collapse/movement when processed by this cure cycle.

In order to reduce the incidence of core movement/collapse, a modified cure cycle was considered. Possible modifications to this basic cure cycle involve:
(a) Lowering the initial pressure at the beginning of the cure cycle
(b) Use of partial vacuum during earlier portions of the cure cycle
(c) Changing the hold temperature

These modifications to the basic cure cycle suggest themselves through several different avenues; vector force diagrams such as Figure 1, and past experiences with the effects of volatiles on the cure of 350°F thermosetting resins.

Past experiences with the effects of

volatiles, particularly water vapor present during cure, on the properties of cured article include
(a) Surface roughness
(b) Porosity in the OML and IML skins
(c) Brownish yellow spots indicative of small local exotherms
(d) Frothing of the cured resin-leading to ultra-sonic rejection
(e) Adhesive mode of failure of honeycomb peels

2. EXPERIMENTAL

Reasoning in this particular vein leads to the generation of several testable hypotheses. Chief among these, since it deals with both vector forces and the control of volatiles, is the investigation of the effects of a partial vacuum during the early stages of the autoclave cycle prior to the cure of the resin.

If these modifications to the cure cycle produce a significant effect, then there must be some method of post-autoclave testing to show this. A variety of tests were performed on cured articles. These evaluations consisted of:
(a) Microscopic examination
(b) Use of a UV black light
(c) Surface roughness measurements
(d) Mechanical strength tests
(e) Destructive examination
(f) Visual examination
(g) Load deflection testing

Another important hypothesis requiring examination is the one covering the build-up of pressure inside the core volume.

2.1 Alternative Cure Cycles

In order to evaluate the effect of alternative cure cycles on core movement/collapse, several panels susceptible to core collapse were selected to be evaluated by the cure cycles diagrammed in Figures 5 and 6. Table I summarizes the information on four different test panels.

The panels were laid up and cured totally by Manufacturing personnel. After cure, the parts were visually inspected, x-rayed, painted, ultra-sonically tested, load deflection tested, and finally subjected to destructive mechanical testing.

2.2 Visual Examination

Cured panels were examined by qualified inspectors for indications of core collapse/movement looking for such items as edgeband dimensions in excess of blueprint and wrinkles in the IML skin.

2.3 Microscopic Examination

Cured panels were examined using a microscope at magnifications ranging from 8x to 40x. Attention was paid to such things as; surface morphology/roughness, porosity, cracking or crazing of the resin, wetting of the surface.

2.4 Ultraviolet Light Examination

Cured articles were examined using a UV light source. UV inspection emphasizes/reveals details not apparent under ordinary light.

2.5 Surface Roughness

Surface roughness measurements were performed using a Surtronic 3P profilometer made by Taylor-Hobson. This instrument gives measurements of surface roughness in units of μ inches and μ meters.

2.6 Load Deflection Testing

The uncut panels were subjected to a uniform load on one surface. Deflection of that surface away from its equilibrium position was noted as a function of the applied load. The apparatus for doing this is shown in Figure 8.

2.7 Destructive Examination

Panels were sectioned using a carbide blade band saw. Sections of interest were first examined under ambient conditions and later, selected ones were mounted and polished for microscopic examination.

2.8 Mechanical Strength

Mechanical testing was done on tensile specimens cut from the OML and IML skins. Specimens were prepared by cutting out skin sections, separating the skins from the core and sanding the core side to remove any embedded pieces of core. Overall shape of the specimens was that of a 10 inch dog bone with a gauge length of 2.0 inches. See Figure 7.

2.9 Pressure Within Internal Core Volume

A section of 3 lb Nomex core measuring 12" wide x 12" long x 2" thick was placed on top of 3 plies previously laid down on a platen sheet. A hole was left in the skin plies to accommodate the placement of a vacuum foot with a quick connect on one end. The foot of the vacuum attachment sat directly on top of the core. The gap in the skin was closed by sealant. The quick connect end protruded through the upper skin and the bag, and was connected by a vacuum/pressure sensor line to a gauge on the autoclave console. See Figure 9. A vacuum of 13 to 18 inches of Hg was maintained under the bag and autoclave pressure was held in the range of 10 to 20 psi.

3. DISCUSSION OF RESULTS

Table II catalogs the results of the visual inspection of the four test articles. Figure 10 is a photograph of panels number 1 and 2 for the purposes of a side by side comparison. The immediate conclusion is that the common cure cycle produces core collapse while the modified cure cycle does not. The differences between these 2 cure cycles is in:

(a) The application of full autoclave pressure from the start vs. reduced autoclave pressure at the start

(b) Venting of the bag after the application of full pressure vs. a partial vacuum under the bag until the end of the hold cycle

The results shown in Table II and Figure 10 are explainable in terms of a resolution of vector forces. Figure 2 shows the balance of forces necessary for core stability. The net force as diagrammed in Figure 2 is given by

$$F_{net} = F_a \sin \alpha \quad -F_i - F_c - F_f \quad (2)$$

Equation (2) says there will be a net positive force if the term $F_a \sin \alpha$ is large compared to the other factors. The magnitude of the first term is balanced or opposed by the other 3 terms. Of these factors, only F_i is of any appreciable magnitude. F_c is on the order of 6 psi. F_f is an order of magnitude less than F_c. With these thoughts in mind, it is seen that the application of full autoclave pressure of 45 psi, over a wide surface area, at the beginning of the cure, before the autoclave air temperature is sufficient to give a large F_i, would result in a large positive value of F_{net}. A positive value of F_{net} implies a translation of the core - i.e., core movement/collapse. Reducing the autoclave pressure at the beginning of the cure cycle avoids this problem. At low values of temperature where F_i is low, the term $F_a \sin \alpha$ is also small because F_a is purposely kept at a low value.

Figure 11 consists of sketches of the resin surfaces as seen under a microscope at a magnification of ca. 40x. Observationally, the surface morphology produced by the common cure cycle can be described as flat surfaces of a similar height above irregularly shaped areas of a lower height - canyons and mesas. The modified cure cycle produces a uniform coverage of the surface with occasional small symmetrical knolls rising slightly above the surface - a flat plain with small rises scattered about. The overall impression is that one surface has been more or less evenly wetted while the other was not. Differences in surface morphology can be explained in terms of volatiles present/absent during the thermosetting cure reaction. In addition to the autoclave pressure difference, these two cure cycles also have a difference in the use/application of vacuum. The common cure cycle vents to the atmosphere at the start of the cure cycle and hence the layup cures in the presence of whatever volatiles that emerge during the heat-up from room temperature to the hold temperature. The modified cure cycle on the other hand keeps a partial vacuum on the layup until the end of the hold cycle and therefore the layup cures without the presence of volatiles.

Surface irregularities are detectable by means other than microscopic examination. Differences in surface texture should show up in measurements of surface roughness. Surface roughness measurements on panels prepared by the two different cure cycles are 3.52 μm(common) and 1.03 μm(modified).

Careful observation of the surfaces also shows that the cured surface produced by the common cycle is slightly darker in color than that produced by the modified cure cycle. This is apparent especially on Kevlar/epoxy panels. It can also be seen on graphite/epoxy panels when viewed at the proper angle. These subtle differences become much more pronounced when viewed under a UV light source. The surface appearance of the panels cured by the common cure cycle now takes on a mottled chocolate-brown appearance that is lacking in the panels cured by the modified cure cycle.

Explanation of these phenomena need to be sought in relation to the variables in the experiment. The design of the experiment is such that these observational differences are related to either a pressure or a vacuum/volatiles factor. The pressure factor is obviously relatable to the core collapse/movement. A connection between pressure and surface morphology seems to be remote. The other choice is the vacuum/volatiles factor. The question then becomes one of how volatiles present during the cure could produce the observed effects. Previous work has indicated that the presence of moisture has a catalytic effect upon the thermosetting cure reaction (1). The effect is to lower the temperature at which the exotherm begins and to increase the intensity of the exotherm (2). Under such circumstances, the curing resin would be fluid for a shorter time and would not flow and wet the surfaces as well (3). If the volatiles are removed, and the resin is fluid for a longer time, then it will have a greater ability to flow and cover the surface evenly (4).

The effects of volatiles and an assessment of the degree of wetting ought to be confirmed by looking for foaming/frothing in the cured resin, signs of local exotherming, the formation of fillets and the consequent effect on mechanical properties such as climbing drum peel strengths.

The climbing drum peel strength for panels prepared by the two different methods are 27 pounds per 3 inch width (common) and 40 pounds per 3 inch width (modified). Examination of the failure surfaces shows adhesive failure with little or no embedded core fragments (common) vs. cohesive failure with fragments of core embedded in the resin on the underside of the skin of the panel cured by the modified cure cycle. Cross sectional cuts allow for an evaluation of the amount of filleting occurring between the resin on the underside of the skin and the core with which it is in contact. Fillet formation for the modified cure cycle is definitely better than that for the common cure cycle. See Figure 12.

The explanation of the success of

the modified cure cycle is in part connected with the term F_i in equation (2). The claim is made that F_i opposes the external autoclave pressure and prevents the collapse of the core. However, at the same time, there is a partial vacuum present under the bag. A reasonable question under the circumstance is, "How can there be pressure buildup in the core if there is a vacuum under the bag?" Figure 9 shows an experimental arrangement for testing the build-up of pressure in the core volume while maintaining a vacuum under the bag. Figure 13 is a plot of pressure within the core vs. the autoclave air temperature. The actual values measured are somewhat higher than those calculated from the perfect gas law equation. The overall shape is consistent with an increase in temperature producing an increase in pressure of gas in a container of constant volume. The drop off of the curve at higher temperatures could indicate the loss of volatiles through the skin plies as the resin becomes fluid.

The combination of an internal force opposing a reduced external autoclave pressure results in less dimpling of the skin down into the core cells. The net result is that the fibers in the skin plies for the modified cure cycle ought to be less distorted than those for the common cure cycle. Figure 12 shows the amount of dimpling that occurs. Figure 14 shows the values for tensile specimens prepared from the skins of panels prepared by the two different methods. The conclusion is that the specimens with a lower degree of fiber distortion produces skins with higher tensile strength.

An important design criterion is stiffness. How much will the panel be displaced away from its equilibrium position when it experiences a typical in-flight load? These questions can be answered by loading the surface and measuring the displacement of the surface. Figure 8 shows the experimental arrangement for load deflection testing. Table III shows the results of load deflection testing of two representative panels of similar construction but processed by different cure cycles. The load deflections for the panel cured by the modified cure cycle are superior to those cured by the common cure cycle.

4. CONCLUSIONS

Slight changes in the cure cycle have pronounced effects on the cured panels. Keeping the pressure low at the beginning of the cure cycle prevents core collapse. Later on, at the end of the hold, when the internal pressure has built up enough to oppose the external autoclave pressure, the autoclave pressure can be increased to the full value without core movement. The presence of a partial vacuum during the early stages of the cure cycle removes volatiles from contact with resin during cure. The absence of volatiles during the cure insures better wetting and filleting, prevents local exotherms and lowers porosity in the cured skins. The combination of lowered pressure at the start and the build-up of an internal pressure results in less dimpled stronger face sheets.

The modified cure cycle permits the production of honeycomb panels with low density core without core movement/collapse. The success of this cure cycle is explainable in terms of vector force diagrams, the

perfect gas law and the effects of volatiles on the cure of a common 350°F thermosetting epoxy resin.

5. REFERENCES

(1) Shechter, L. and Wynstra, J., Ind. Eng. Chem. 48, 86 (1956)

(2) Darrow, D. C., Ayers, J. A. and Brayden, T. H., 31st Int. SAMPE Symposium, 374 (1986)

(3) Hinrichs, R. and Thuen, J., 25th National SAMPE Symposium, p. 126 (1980)

(4) Susman, S. E., 25th National SAMPE Symposium, p. 251 (1980)

6. BIOGRAPHY

Thomas H. Brayden is a Senior Quality Assurance Engineer in LTVAP Materials Test Technology unit. Current responsibilities include directing work in the chemical analysis of resin systems and cure monitoring. Academic background include a Ph.D. in physical chemistry from LSU.

Donald C. Darrow is a Quality Assurance Specialist in Process Control Engineering at LTVAPG. His responsibilities include performing failure analyses and resolving problems in composites and bonding. His academic background includes a Bachelor's Degree in chemistry from the University of Hawaii.

Figure 1   Diagram of Vector Forces Due to Autoclave Pressure

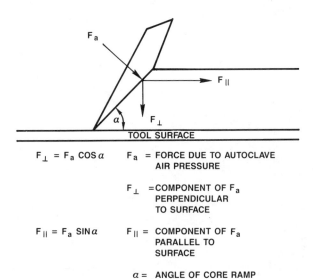

$$F_\perp = F_a \cos\alpha \qquad F_a = \text{FORCE DUE TO AUTOCLAVE AIR PRESSURE}$$

$$F_\perp = \text{COMPONENT OF } F_a \text{ PERPENDICULAR TO SURFACE}$$

$$F_{\parallel} = F_a \sin\alpha \qquad F_{\parallel} = \text{COMPONENT OF } F_a \text{ PARALLEL TO SURFACE}$$

$$\alpha = \text{ANGLE OF CORE RAMP}$$

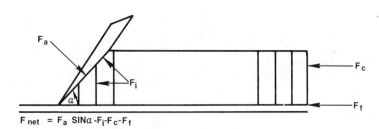

$$F_{net} = F_a \sin\alpha - F_i - F_c - F_f$$

α = CORE ANGLE

F_a = FORCE DUE TO AUTOCLAVE AIR PRESSURE

F_i = FORCE DUE TO INTERNAL GAS PRESSURE

F_c = FORCE ARISING FROM INHERENT STRENGTH OF CORE IN THE LATERAL DIRECTION

F_f = FORCE RESISTING MOVEMENT DUE TO FRICTION

Figure 2   Conditions Governing Core Stability

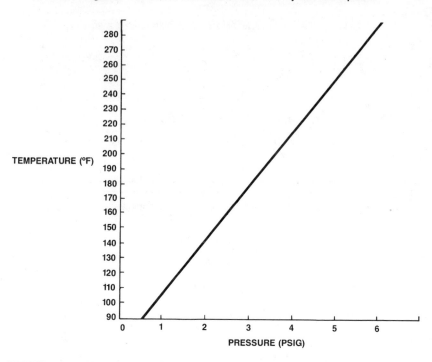

Figure 3 Increase in Gas Pressure over 70°F by Gas Law Equation

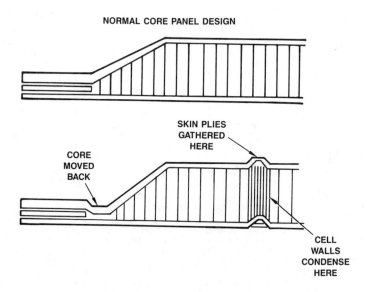

Figure 4 Effect Common Cure Cycle on Honeycomb Sandwich Panels with Low Density Core

Figure 5   Common Cure Cycle

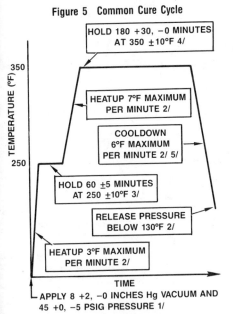

TEMPERATURE (°F)

350
250

HOLD 180 +30, −0 MINUTES
AT 350 ±10°F 4/

HEATUP 7°F MAXIMUM
PER MINUTE 2/

COOLDOWN
6°F MAXIMUM
PER MINUTE 2/ 5/

HOLD 60 ±5 MINUTES
AT 250 ±10°F 3/

RELEASE PRESSURE
BELOW 130°F 2/

HEATUP 3°F MAXIMUM
PER MINUTE 2/

TIME

APPLY 8 +2, −0 INCHES Hg VACUUM AND
45 +0, −5 PSIG PRESSURE 1/

NOTES: 1/ VENT VACUUM BAG TO ATMOS-
PHERE AT A RATE OF 2 INCHES Hg
EVERY 2 MINUTES WHEN PRES-
SURE REACHES 10 PSIG. CONTINUE
INCREASING DURING VENTING.

2/ HEATUP AND COOLDOWN RATES
FOR ALL PART THERMOCOUPLES
SHALL BE IN THE SPECIFIED
RANGE AND SHALL BE BASED ON
THE LAGGING PART
THERMOCOUPLE.

3/ THE 250°F HOLD PERIOD SHALL
BEGIN WHEN THE LAGGING PART
THERMOCOUPLE IS AT 240°F.

4/ THE 350°F HOLD PERIOD SHALL
BEGIN WHEN THE LAGGING PART
THERMOCOUPLE IS AT 340°F.
NATURAL DEPRESSURIZATION IS
PERMISSIBLE AT THE END OF THE
HOLD.

5/ BACKPRESSURE REQUIREMENTS
ARE NOT APPLICABLE DURING
COOLDOWN SEGMENT.

Figure 6   Modified Cure Cycle

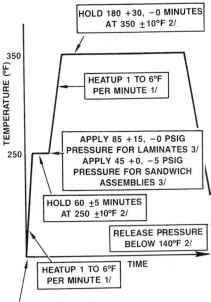

TEMPERATURE (°F)

350
250

HOLD 180 +30, −0 MINUTES
AT 350 ±10°F 2/

HEATUP 1 TO 6°F
PER MINUTE 1/

APPLY 85 +15, −0 PSIG
PRESSURE FOR LAMINATES 3/
APPLY 45 +0, −5 PSIG
PRESSURE FOR SANDWICH
ASSEMBLIES 3/

HOLD 60 ±5 MINUTES
AT 250 ±10°F 2/

RELEASE PRESSURE
BELOW 140°F 2/

HEATUP 1 TO 6°F
PER MINUTE 1/

TIME

APPLY 5 +5, −0 INCHES Hg VACUUM AND
10 +5, −0 PSIG PRESSURE

NOTES: 1/ HEATUP RATES FOR ANY PART
THERMOCOUPLE SHALL BE IN THE
SPECIFIED RANGE.

2/ BASED ON LAGGING PART
THERMOCOUPLE

3/ VENT VACUUM BAG TO ATMOSPHERE
AT A RATE OF 2 INCHES Hg EVERY
2 MINUTES WHEN PRESSURE
REACHES 20 PSIG.

339-1052-6-1

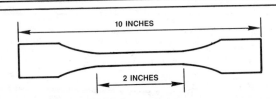

10 INCHES

2 INCHES

Figure 7   Tensile Specimens Prepared from Skins of Test Panels

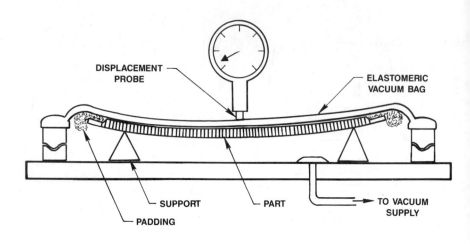

Figure 8   Setup for Load Deflection Testing

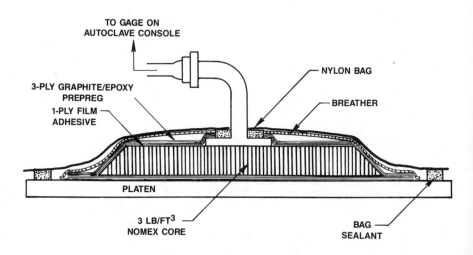

Figure 9   Experimental Arrangement for Measuring Internal Pressure Buildup within Internal Core Volume

Figure 10 Panels Cured by the Common (Foreground) and Modified (Background) Cure Cycle

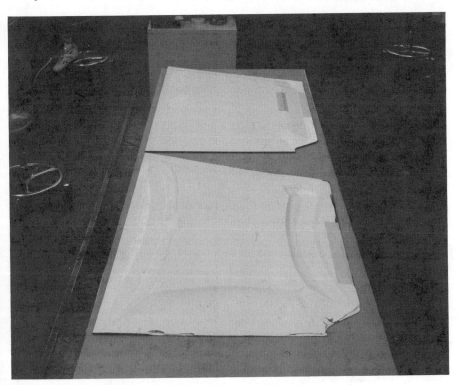

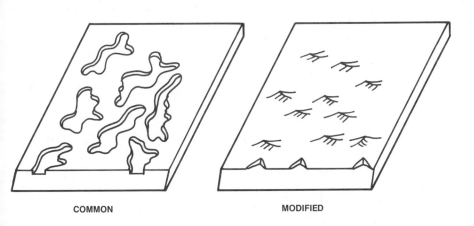

COMMON   MODIFIED

Figure 11 Sketches of Surface Morphologies Resulting from the Common and Modified Cure Cycles
(Approximately 40X)

871

Figure 12 Comparison of Filleting and Dimpling Produced by the Common and Modified Cure Cycles (Approximately 8X)

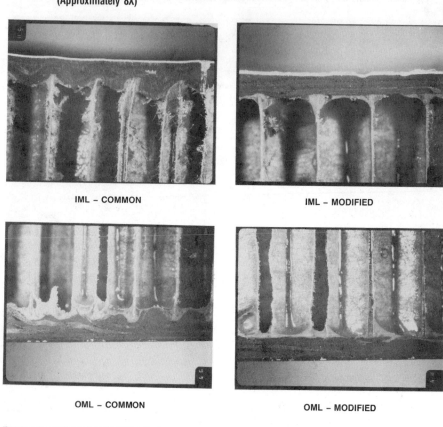

IML – COMMON

IML – MODIFIED

OML – COMMON

OML – MODIFIED

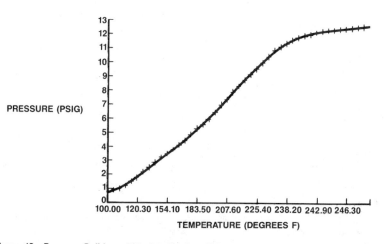

PRESSURE (PSIG)

TEMPERATURE (DEGREES F)

Figure 13 Pressure Buildup within Interior Core Volume versus Autoclave Air Temperature

TABLE I CURE CYCLE TEST PANELS CONFIGURATIONS

PART NO.	CURE CYCLE	CORE DENSITY (LB)	STABILIZATION	CORE THICKNESS (IN.)
1	COMMON	3	NO	1.3
2	MODIFIED	3	NO	1.3
3	COMMON	4	PERIPHERY AROUND 1/2 OF CORE	1.0
4	MODIFIED	4	PERIPHERY AROUND 1/2 OF CORE	1.0

TABLE II VISUAL INSPECTION OF TEST PANELS

PART NO.	DEFECTS		
	CORE MOVEMENT	PLY WRINKLING	DELAMINA-TION
1	CORE MOVED BACK 0.83 INCH AT STATION LINE YTE60. SIX AREAS OF CORE MOVEMENT UP TO 1.35 INCHES	WRINKLE 39 x 0.5 x 0.19 INCHES (LxWxH)	DELAMINATION OF ALL EDGEBAND PLIES FOR 43-INCH LENGTH NEAR SQUARE END OF PANEL
2			
3	UP TO 4.6 INCHES TOWARD CENTER ON ALL FOUR SIDES	PROTRUDING WRINKLES UP TO 0.090-INCH HIGH ON ALL FOUR SIDES, INCLUDING EDGE-BANDS AND TOP OF CORE	DELAMINATION OF EDGEBANDS ON ALL FOUR SIDES
4			

873

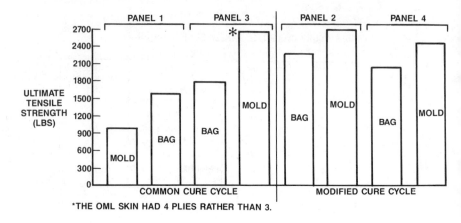

Figure 14   Tensile Strength of Dog-Bone Specimens Taken from the 3-Ply Skins

*THE OML SKIN HAD 4 PLIES RATHER THAN 3.

TABLE III   LOAD DEFLECTION TESTING OF PANELS NO. 1 AND 2

LOAD (PSI)	DEFLECTION (IN.)	COMMENTS
PART NO. 1 (COMMON CURE CYCLE PROFILE). PANEL LOADED WITH TOOL SURFACE (OML) UP:		
2	0.1364	
4	0.3046	
6	0.4495	
8	0.6066	
10	0.7020	CRACKING SOUNDS
SAME PANEL LOADED WITH BAG SURFACE (IML) UP:		
2	0.1256	
4	0.2993	
6	0.4767	
8	0.6750	CRACKING SOUNDS
10	0.8922	LOUD CRACKING SOUNDS
PART NO. 2 (MODIFIED CURE CYCLE PROFILE). PANEL LOADED TOOL SURFACE (OML) UP:		
2	0.0546	NO
4	0.1275	CRACKING
6	0.1895	AT
8	0.2502	ANY
10	0.3096	LOAD
SAME PANEL LOADED WITH BAG SURFACE (IML) UP:		
2	0.0469	NO
4	0.1111	CRACKING
6	0.1697	AT
8	0.2343	ANY
10	0.2954	LOAD

NOTE: ALL DEFLECTION TESTING WAS INITIATED USING A 0.5 PSI PRELOAD TO SEAT THE PANEL ON THE SUPPORT FRAMES AND TO ZERO THE MEASUREMENT DEVICE.

STUDY ON THE EPOXY RESIN SYSTEM MODIFIED
USING POLYETHERSULPHONE
Hua Youqing, Wang Huiqong and Zhang Xiping
Beijing Institute of Chemical Technology,
Beijing, China

Abstract

A heat-resistant and toughness polymer
(PES) was used to modify the toughness of
the epoxy resins (Ag-80(30)/F-51(70)/DDS,
Ag-80(30)/618(70)/DDS) in this paper. The
kinetics of the curing reaction for the
system was investigated by DSC; the
mechanical properties and glass
transition temperatures (Tg) of those
castings were determined by UTM and TMA
respectively; the phenomenon of phase
seperation and the morphology of the
fracture surface for the systems were
investigated by DMS and SEM respectively.
The results show that there is a
coordination effect for the curing
reaction after the two epoxy resins are
mixed, but addition of PES to the epoxy
resin matrix is no effect on the curing
reaction. It is also found that after
adding proper amounts of PES to the
matrix, the ultimate elongation and
fracture energy will increase, but the
modulus and Tg will not have any change
almost or have small decrease . The
toughened effect of PES was confirmed by
the characteristics of phase separation
investigated by DMS and by the morphology

of the fracture surface observed by SEM.

1. INTRODUCTION

In order to obtain the epoxy resin matrix
used for fiber composites with good
heat-resistance and toughness, there are
mainly three methods to be applied, (1)
Blended system of epoxy resins. Because
epoxy resins have a wide range of
properties due to their different
molecular structures, it is possible to
obtain the matrix resin with better
comprehensive properties through mixing
two or more kinds of epoxy resins in
proper ratio; (2) Adding some kinds of
thermoplastic polymers, such as PES, PSF,
PEK, PEI etc.[1,2,3], to the epoxy
resin system. Because the thermoplastic
polymers have better toughness, higher
modulus and good heat-resistance, so they
can modify the epoxy resin and will not
affect the modulus and heat-resistance of
the epoxy resin; (3) Modifying the
chemical structure of the crosslinked
networks. For example, introducing some
kinds of "flexiable segments" into the
crosslinked networks or using the curing

agents with flexiable molecular structure and so on. Usually, according to the references, a homogenous system can be formed by adding PES to the tetrafunctional epoxy resin/DDS system, in which the modulus and Tg do not decrease almost, but the fracture toughness is not improved. In this paper, PES was used to modify the matrix (Ag-80/F-51/DDS, Ag-80/618/DDS). The curing reaction and its kinetics were investigated by DSC; effect of the amount of PES on the thermal and mechanical properties of the castings were determined by UTM and TMA; the phenomenon of phase seperation and the characteristics of the morphology of the each system were studied by DMS and SEM. All above results show that PES has toughened effect on the blended epoxy mentioned above.

2. EXPERIMENTS

2.1 Materials

The structure of materials are as follows:

Ag-80

618

F-51

DDS

PES

Ag-80 epoxy resin with epoxy value of 0.76 obtained from Shanghai Research Institute of Synthetic Resin; F-51 epoxy resin with epoxy value of 0.51 provided by Wuxi Synthetic Resin Factory; 618 resin with epoxy value of 0.51 produced by Shanghai Synthetic Resin Factory; Thermolplastic modifier PES is produced by the factory of Jilin University, $[\eta]$ =5.12 in DMF at 25℃; DDS is produced by Shanghai Third Chemical Reagent Factory.

2.2 Methods

The curing reaction of the epoxy resin was investigated by Perkin-Elmer DSC-2C. The preparation procedure of the sample is, the resins was preheated for 10 min. at 75℃ and then stirred for 5 min. or heated and stirred until PES was dissolved in the epoxy resin completely. Then DDS was added at equivalent and the homogeneous mixture was obtained by stirring. The samples prepared above were placed into a vacuum oven to be degassed for 15 min. at 70℃, then sealed up and preserved at about 4℃. The amount of the sample once used is 5 mg, and the nitrogen flow rate is 20 ml/min. The calculating methods of curing kinetics are given as,
Kinetic software,

$$\ln(d\alpha/dt)=\ln Ko-Ea/RT+n\ln(1-\alpha)$$

Kissinger method,

$$\frac{d\ln\phi/Tp^2}{d(1/Tp)}=-\frac{Ea}{R};$$

$$n=1.26S^{1/2}=1.26(a/b)^{1/2}$$

Ozawa method:

$$d\ln\phi/d(1/Tp)=-1.052Ea/R$$

The castings were prepared by the hot melt method. The epoxy resin system or the modified epoxy resin system was degassed for 0.5-1.5 hr. at 100℃, and then casted into the mould and degassed again. Finally the samples prepared above were placed in a oven to be cured according to the curing program fixed.

The mechanical properties, such as the ultimate elongation, were determined by Instron-1121 Universal Testing Machine according to the standard of GB2568-81. Tg was tested by RJ-1 TMA produced by Chenguang Research Institute of Chemical Technology; $\phi=5℃/min.$; pressure is 4.9×10^7 Pa.

The dynamic mechanical spectroscopy (DMS) of the systems was determined by MAK04 viscoelastic spectroscopy made in France. The size of the sample is $3\times7\times20$ mm^3, the test temperature is within the range of 170-300℃ ; the frequency is 160Hz. The morphology of fracture surfaces of the extension samples and frozen samples in liquid N2 was observed by DX-3A SEM made in China.

3. RESULTS AND DISCUSSIONS

3.1 The curing reaction and its kinetics

The several curing plots of the systems determined by DSC are given by Fig.1-4. The kinetic parameters were calculated using the kinetic software method, the relative curing temperatures and the heat of the curing reaction are presented in Table 1.

The results show that:

a. Comparing the system of Ag-80/DDS with F-51/DDS, it is found that the initial reaction temperature(Ti) of the former is higher than that of the later, but the finished temperature(Tf) of the former is lower than that of the later, the heat of the curing reaction (△H) for the former is larger than that for the later. It is also found that the apparent activation energy (Ea) of the former is higher than that of the later. Because the Ag-80 is a kind of tetrafunctional epoxy resin and the F-51 is a kind of phenolic epoxy resin, the steric effect of the former is stronger than that of the later, that results in the lower activity of the former. And because the epoxy value of the Ag-80 is larger than that of the F-51, so the value of △H is larger than that of F-51. Besides, for the Ag-80/DDS system the reaction order (n) decreases with the value of φ increased, the mean value of n is 1; and for the system of F-51 the value of n has little dependence on the value of φ, the mean value of n is 1.5.

b. The value of Ti, Ton and Tf of the system of Ag-80(30)/F-51(70)/DDS is very close to those of F-51/DDS, that means the curing reaction of the Ag-80/DDS is carried out in the curing temperature range of the F-51/DDS at the same time, but it can not be distinguished because there is only a difference of 19℃ between the two curing temperatures. △H for the blended system is larger than that of the linear plus of two kinds of resins in weight ratio. For example, when △H of the former is 93 cal/g, △H of the later is 80 cal/g. And Ea of the blended system is lower than that of the both pure epoxy resin systems, Ea of the former is 66.0 KJ/mole and Ea of the later is 122.5 and 100.6KJ/mole, resp., that means that there is an coordination effect for the curing reaction after the two epoxy resins are blended.

c. The addition of PES to the matrix resin has not any obvious effect on the curing temperature, the heat of the curing reaction and the kinetic parameters. All mentioned above means PES has not any distinct catalytic effect on the curing reaction.

d. Plotting the Ti, Ton, Tp and Tf vs. φ and extrapolating φ to zero, the extrapolating temperature is 405, 418, 456 and 516 K, resp. The results provide a reliable theoretical basis for determining the curing conditions of the castings. The curing condition of the system mentioned above is,

120-125℃	2hr
140-145℃	2hr
160-165℃	2hr
180-185℃	2hr

It should be indicated that the kinetic parameters of the curing reactions calculated by the kinetic software method are based on the kinetic equation of n order reaction. For different curing systems of epoxy resin the reaction mechanisms are complicated. So, the calculating results have the comparative meaning only.

The calculating results by Kissinger, Ozawa method are listed in Table 2, and compared with those by the kinetic software method. It is shown that, for the

system of Ag-80/DDS and F-51/DDS the values of Ea obtained from the Kissinger and Ozawa methods are very similar to each other, but lower than that obtained from the kinetic software method; the values of n obtained from the kinetic software method and Kissinger method are pretty close each other; for the system of the epoxy resin modified using PES the apparent kinetic parameters obtained from the three methods are consistent basically.

3.2 The mechanical and thermal preperties of the castings

The mechanical and thermal properties of the castings are shown in Table 3.

In general, the fracture toughness will not be increased by adding PES to TGDDM/DDS system. But it is found that adding 2-8 parts of PES to the 100 parts of resins matrix(Ag-80(30)/F-51(70)/DDS) will result in the increase of the ultimate elongation and fracture energy and no changes of the modulus and Tg. When the amount of PES arrives at 12%, the thermal and mechanical properties of the system will reduce. The reason is not very clear and need further researches.

For the system of Ag-80(30)/618(70)/DDS, adding 8% PES to it will result in that the ultimate elongation is raised to the value of 3%, the fracture energy is increased to the value of 2.1 J, the modulus and Tg have no obvious changes The reasons, that PES can toughen the system of Ag-80(30)/F-51(70)/DDS and the toughened effect can be increased by replacing F-51 with 618, are mainly determined by the ductility of the continuous phase, the better the

878

ductility of the continuous phase, the better the toughened effect of the dispersion phase.

3.3 The miscibility and morphology

Fig.5 and 6 are the dynamic mechanical aspectroscopy of above toughened samples at higher temperatures, resp.

The Fig. 5 shows that the main transition peak temperature of PES is about 212°C that is consistent to the reports by the references[4][5] and that of the Ag-80(30)/F-51(70)/DDS is about 265°C, that confirms the phenomenon of the phase seperation in the system.

The Fig. 6 also shows the facts of phase seperation in Ag-80(30)/618(70)/DDS/PES system.

The phnomenon of phase seperation can not be observed using the high multiple SEM to examine the fracture surfaces of the modified materials mentioned above. The reason may be that the sizes of the particles are too small to be distinguished[4,5]

It is known that the phase seperation is controlled not only by thermodynamic but also by kinetic factors[4][5], and the final morphology of the curing product is also controlled by curing kinetics and its effect on the flow property of the phase seperation components, different phase seperation and morphological characteristics must result in different mechanical properties.

The SEM photographs of the fracture surfaces for the frozen samples are presented in Fig.7. It is found that, for the system of Ag-80(30)/F-51(70)/DDS, the rough part of fracture surface is smooth and has only some fine and straightly river lines; for the system of Ag-80(30)/F-51(70)/PES(8)/DDS, the rough part of fracture surface has many fine crooked river lines that indicates the toughened effect of PES in the curing system. Meanwhile, it is found that the river lines in the fracture surface for the Ag-80(30)/618(70)/PES(8)/DDS system are more crowed than those for the Ag-80(30)/618(70)/DDS system, the graftings of the river lines for the former are also more obvious than those for the later. The two results can also indicate that the addition of PES modifies the toughness of the system.

The results of SEM observation of the fracture surfaces for the tension samples are consistent to the results mentioned above.

4. CONCLUSIONS

a. E_a of Ag-80/DDS system is larger than that of 618/DDS system. The n values of the two systems is 1 and 1.5, resp.

b. T_i, T_{on} and T_f of Ag-80/618/DDS system are similar to those of 618/DDS system, $\triangle H$ of Ag-80/618/DDS system is larger than that of the linear plus of the two kinds of epoxy resins.

c. The addition of PES to Ag-80/618/DDS system has no obvious effect on the curing reaction.

d. The ultimate elongations of Ag-80(30)/F-51(70)/DDS and Ag-80(30)/618(70)/DDS systems both increase by adding proper amounts of PES to them, resp., and the modulus and Tg of the two systems do not have observable decrease.

e. The characteristics of the phase seperations for Ag-80(30)/F-51(70)/PES(8)/DDS and Ag-80(30)/618(70)/PES(8)/DDS systems are revealed by DMS. The toughened effect of PES on the two systems are confirmed by the morphology of the fracture surface through SEM.

5. REFERENCES

(1) U.S. Patant 564,393, Thermoplastic Modified Epoxy Composition, 1983.
(2) Cecere, J.A., Mcgrath, J.E., Polymer Preprint 27(1), 299(1986)
(3) Diamant, J., Moulton, R.J., SAMPE Quarterly, Oct., 13(1984)
(4) Bucknall, C.B., Partridge, L.K., Polymer 24, May, 639(1983)
(5) Bucknall, C.B., Partridge, L.K., Polymer Engineering and Science, 26(1), 54(1986)
(6) Zheng Shanying, Zhang Fengfan, Shen Tongtang, the Symposium of Composite Materials of China, Aviation Society of China, 1988, pp.133-135
(7) Turi, E.A., Thermal Characterization of Polymeric Materials, New York, Academic Pr., 1981, pp.540-544
(8) Cizmecigly, M., Gupta, A., SAMPE Quarterly, Aprol., 16(1982)
(9) Ning Rongchang, the Symposium of Composite Materials and Resins of China, China Aviation Society, 1987

6. Biography

Hua Youqing is an associate professor at Beijing Institute of Chemical Technology. She graduated from Speciality of Polymer Science in Chemical Department of Nanjing University in 1962 and engages in teaching and research in polymer physics.

Wang Huiqiong is an associate professor at Beijing Institute of Chemical Technology and graduated from Chengdu University of Science and Technology in 1958. She has been doing teaching and research work in polymer synthesis and fiber composites since 1958.

Zhang Xiping, an assistant engineer, graduated from the Worker's College of Shanghai Chemical Research Institute in 1982 and engaged in polymer synthesis and fiber composites in Beijing Institute of Chemical Technology.

Table1 the DSC curing data of the blend and toughened systems of Ag-80/DDS and F-51/DDS

system	ϕ (°C/min)	Ti	Ton	Tp	Tf	$\triangle H$ (cal/gram)	lnKo	Ea (KJ/mol)	n
				characteristic peak temp.(K)					
Ag-80/DDS	2.5	439	448	473	509	-101.4	34.2	154.3	1.29
	5	443	461	490	525	-131.1	26.6	128.2	1.08
	10	457	475	511	542	-135.7	24.6	122.5	0.89
	20	459	491	533	562	-142.2	23.2	118.5	0.72
F-51/DDS	2.5	407	425	456	513	-57.4	19.3	94.5	1.52
	5	424	439	473	532	-48.3	22.1	106.5	1.54
	10	427	450	493	563	-55.5	20.1	100.6	1.62
	20	432	466	512	582	-55.6	20.5	103.8	1.50
Ag-80(30) /F-51(70) /DDS	10	423	450	501	561	-98.8	10.6	66.0	0.8
Ag-80(30)	2.5	405	425	458	517	-116.8	5.6	47.7	0.78
/F-51(70)	5	418	435	484	546	-107.2	6.6	51.0	0.75
/PES(2)	10	421	446	503	557	-104.6	8.4	56.8	0.73
/DDS	20	427	462	540	582	-102.1	9.5	61.9	0.69

Table2 the comparision of apparent dynamic parameters calculated by the three methods

system	Ea(KJ/mol)			n	
	Software method(*)	Kissinger method	Ozawa method	Software method(*)	Kissinger method(*)
Ag-80/DDS	130.8	71.1	66.0	1.0	1.0
F-51/DDS	101.2	66.0	61.9	1.5	1.4
Ag-80(30) /F-51(70) /PES(2) /DDS	54.3	50.6	44.7	0.7	0.8

(*) The average of different ϕ used in experiments

881

Table3 The mechanical and thermal properties of 6 kinds of castings of epoxy resin

epoxy system	PES (%)	tensile strength (MPa)	tensile modulus (MPa×10³)	ultimate elongation (%)	fracture energy (J)	Tg (℃)
Ag-80(30) /F-51(70)/DDS	0	73.3	3.8	2.2	1.35	238
	2	80.9	4.9	2.3	1.36	235
	8	82.1	3.7	2.6	1.65	243
	12	76.9	4.4	2.2	1.31	225
Ag-80(30) /618(70)/DDS	0	86.1	4.1	2.5	1.83	235
	8	82.5	3.8	3.0	2.1	225

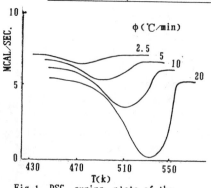

Fig.1 DSC curing plots of the Ag-80/DDS at different heating rates

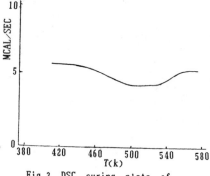

Fig.3 DSC curing plots of Ag-80(30)/F-51(70)/DDS (φ=10℃/min)

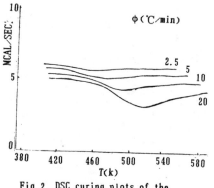

Fig.2 DSC curing plots of the F-51/DDS at different heating rates

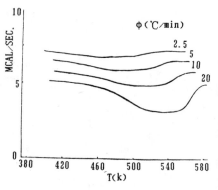

Fig.4 DSC curing plots of Ag-80(30)/F-51(70)/PES(2)/DDS

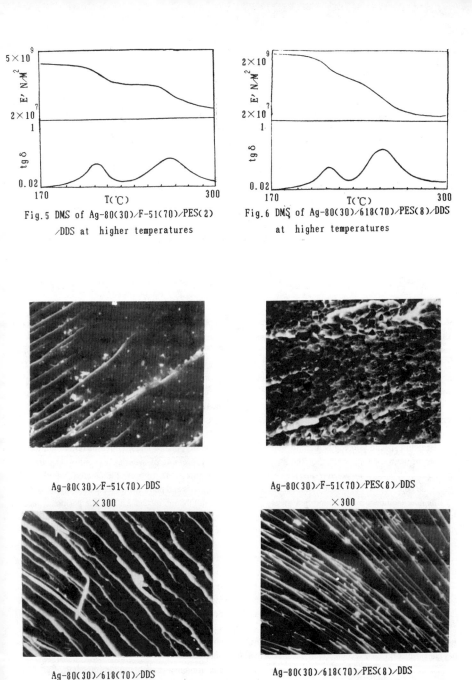

Fig.5 DMS of Ag-80(30)/F-51(70)/PES(2)
/DDS at higher temperatures

Fig.6 DMS of Ag-80(30)/618(70)/PES(8)/DDS
at higher temperatures

Ag-80(30)/F-51(70)/DDS
×300

Ag-80(30)/F-51(70)/PES(8)/DDS
×300

Ag-80(30)/618(70)/DDS
×300

Ag-80(30)/618(70)/PES(8)/DDS
×300

Fig.7 the fracture surfaces of several epoxy resin systems with SEM

PHASE DIAGRAMS OF RUBBER-MODIFIED EPOXIES BY
RAYLEIGH-BRILLOUIN SCATTERING AND THERMODYNAMICALLY REVERSIBLE
AND IRREVERSIBLE CONTROL ON MORPHOLOGY OF MULTIPHASE SYSTEMS

Henry S.-Y. Hsich
Lord Corporation
Thomas Lord Research Center
405 Gregson Drive
Cary, NC 27512

Abstract

Morphology and properties of polymer alloys can be controlled by thermodynamically reversible (structure frozen-in) or irreversible (structure locked-in) processes by simultaneously manipulating miscibility, mechanisms of phase separation, glass transitions, and cure kinetics of polymer systems. A new method of using Rayleigh-Brillouin laser light scattering experiments for constructing phase diagrams consisting of the binodal and spinodal curves has been developed. The Brillouin spectra also can be used to study cure kinetics of thermosetting materials. The miscibility of an epoxy/CTBN (carboxyl-terminated butadiene acrylonitrile copolymer) rubber system has been studied by this new method. It was found that this system has an upper consolute temperature. An increase in the acrylonitrile content of the CTBN rubber improves the miscibility and depresses the consolute temperature of this polymer system. It was found that the immiscibility region is expanded during cure. The morphology of this epoxy/CTBN system can be controlled by simultaneously manipulating the kinetic processes of phase separation and curing reactions.

1. INTRODUCTION

Recently the technology of polymer blends and alloys has gained a world-wide recognition as a cost-effective means of solving design problems and meeting changing specifications. Alloys and blends are revolutionizing the materials suppliers' ability to offer an eclectic balance, or combination, of properties in response to specific customer requests. The new sophisticated materials management now integrates material, design, and processing into a materials system approach. Fusing together engineering and the science of chemistry and physics produces a new approach to the understanding and development of materials.

This new approach is based upon the recognition of the full complexity of microstructure and the fact that properties depend upon structure. The relationships between structure and properties, and between properties and performance, become the touchstone of modern materials developments. Such a structural approach to material developments and applications, of necessity, placed major emphasis on the fabrication and processing of materials to control structure and properties. There grew the clear recognition that properties and performance were the consequences of the full thermo-mechanical and compositional history of materials. As our understanding of the materials science and technology grew, it stimulated a competition among materials, and a competition between processings, and consequently materials and processing technologies became an equally dominant factor.

Improving scientific understanding of alloying and blending mechanisms is the key for exploding utilization of polymers and composites. Polymer blends and polymer alloys are often used synonymously; however, thermodynamically speaking, there is a distinction between these two terms. Polymer alloys are conditionally miscible thermodynamically. This means that the components of the alloy are homogeneous (single phase) under at least one specific set of thermodynamic conditions. Alloys as such provide the opportunity to change morphology and properties through variations in thermal history. Polymer blends, however, do not form single phase systems under material processing and application conditions.

Their properties are largely dependent on mechanical despersion and are usually tied to the arithmetic average of the values, at most, of the components. Polymer alloys can be synergistic polymer systems. As such, their properties can exceed a simple arithmetic averaging value (additive rule) of multicomponent systems.

In the integration of polymer alloying technology, it considers: (1) phase diagrams composed binodal and spinodal curves, (2) enhancing miscibility, (3) phase separation via nucleation and growth, spinodal decomposition, and Ostwald ripening process, (4) structural relaxation (glass transition) and/or cure reaction, and (5) composite mechanics and mechanical spectrum. The initial state for processing alloy systems starts from a homogeneous state of a single-phase condition. Then the morphology of end-products can be either single-phase or multiphase depending upon the kinetics of phase separation and structural relaxation/cure reaction. On the other hand, in the integration of polymer blending technology, it pays attention to: (1) compatibilizing agents (miscibility), mechanisms of interface mixing and co-vulcanization, (3) interdiffusion and adhesion, (4) dynamic vulcanization, (5) rheology and morphology in multiphase fluid systems, and (6) chemorheology. The system is in a multiphase state during material processing, and the morphology or domain structure is controlled via rheology and chemorheology of multiphase fluids in Banbury mixers, extruders or other processing equipments. In this report, we will discuss polymer alloying technology, while the blending technology will be discussed elsewhere.

2. BACKGROUND

2.1 Phase Diagrams and Phase Separation of Multiphase Systems

Critical solution phenomena and miscibility in multicomponent systems were discussed extensively by Prigogine and Defay [1]. Recently Krause [2] and Kwei et al. [3] also gave a review on polymer systems. Phase diagrams of multiphase polymers can be a system with (a) an upper critical solution temperature (UCST), (b) a lower critical solution temperature (LCST), (c) a LCST above an UCST, (d) a closed two-phase region, and (e) a bell-shaped two-phase region. For a system containing a simple miscibility gap of high consolute temperature (UCST system), at a constant temperature above the consolute temperature T_c (sometimes called critical temperature), the Helmholz free energy G must curve upward everywhere. As the temperature drops below T_c, the Helmholz free energy at a given temperature T_0 will vary with composition, c, as depicted by the top curve of Figure 1. The points of common tangency to this curve (f and g, Fig. 1) define the composition of two coexisting phases at T_0 (**binodal points**). If the composition lies between the compositions a and b, the lowest free energy is a two-phase mixture with one phase having composition a and the other b. In addition, there two inflexion points at which $(\partial^2 G/\partial^2 c)$ vanishes, these two points occur at d and e and are called the **spinodal points** for the temperature T_0, lying somewhere between a and b. Between these two spinodal points, $(\partial^2 G/\partial^2 c)$ is negative, and the mixture is said to be in an unstable state, because any infinitesimal composition fluctuations will cause a decrease in the free energy and hence phase separation. The metastable region exists between the spinodal and the binodal curve (phase boundary). If the single phase is cooled from above the phase boundary into this region, it would be metastable and would only decompose into the two phases if the second phase can nucleate. Any attempt by the system to separate into regions differing only slightly in composition will raise the system free energy. If, however, the single phase is brought within the unstable region (between points d and e) the system can continuously lower its free energy by continuous compositional change until it reaches a two phase state at a and b.

The mechanism of phase separation in the two regions, metastable and unstable, are radically different. In the unstable region, the mixture is unstable to infinitesimal fluctuations. There is no thermodynamic barrier to phase transformation, and thus, separation should occur by a continuous and spontaneous process. Since the mixture is initially uniform in composition, this spontaneous process must occur by a diffusional flux against the concentration gradient, that is, by uphill diffusion with a negative diffusion coefficient. There is no sharp interface boundary between the phases in the initial stage of this type of phase separation. This process is called **spinodal decomposition** (SD). On the other hand, in the metastable region, because the mixture is stable to all infinitesimal composition fluctuations, a finite fluctuation is required for a phase transformation. The new phase starts from small nuclei which then proceed to grow and extend. The molecules that feed the new phase follow ordinary transport phenomena by downhill diffusion with a positive diffusion coefficient. This process is called **nucleation and growth** (NG).

2.1.1 Nucleation and Growth

The theory of phase transition α to δ has been discussed by Turnbull [4]. In general, this transition does not occur homogeneously. Rather, small domains of phase δ first become distinct at various points separated by many molecular spacings. These domains then propagate at the expense of α. Thus, the transformation α to δ takes place only at the α and δ interfaces. This mode of reaction is known as nucleation and growth, the birth of domains being called **nucleation**. However, if the compositions making up α and δ are markedly different (as happens in phase separation of multicomponent systems), the growth of δ may be governed by the diffusion of its components in α rather than by processes at the α–δ interface. The total rate of a phase change is determined by two constants: the rate of nucleation of δ domains and their rate of growth after nucleation.

In the metastable region, two basic stages of phase development may be distinguished. The first is the nucleation and growth stage during which concentration fluctuations produce nuclei of the new phase which grow from the super-saturated matrix. The second stage is the coalescence process (Ostwald ripening stage). During this coarsening stage, the total surface of the dispersed phase is reduced. Fluctuation effects play a negligible part in this stage. In this stage, the average diameter, D, of the particles are seen to obey a kinetic law of the Lifshitz-Slyozov-Wagner asymptotic law [5-7]. The equation for the asymtotic law can be expressed as:

$$D^3 - D_0^3 = g\,(t - t_0) \quad (1)$$

where D_0 is the diameter of the particle corresponding to the time t_0 from which relation (1) starts to be obeyed, and g is the rate constant.

(ii) Spinodal Decomposition

Spinodal decomposition is one of the few phase transformations in which the kinetic theory has been well studied [8-12]. The reason for this is that the entire decomposition process can be treated as a purely diffusional problem and, further, many of the characteristics of decomposition, especially morphology, can be described by an approximate solution to the diffusion equation. Since Cahn [10] and Cahn et al. [11] have demonstrated that glasses may undergo spinodal decomposition (SD), there has been wide spread tendency to assume that the kinetic mechanisms for all those demixing processes which lead to textures displaying some degree of connectivity must be spinodal decomposition. This extreme view, however, cannot be justified as other mechanisms, for example - as has been suggested by Haller [13], nucleation and growth followed by coalescence, may also lead to similar formations. Conclusions reached from a mere inspection of an electron micrograph are certainly insufficient and may be grossly misleading. Only a detailed analysis of thermodynamics in the miscibility gap (or phase diagram) and the initial kinetic process can show whether, in a given case, we are indeed dealing with spinodal decomposition.

According to the theory of spinodal decomposition [8, 10], in an inhomogeneous solution the composition everywhere differs only slightly from the average composition. The free energy difference between the initially homogeneous solution and the inhomogeneous solution is given as:

$$\Delta G = \int [1/2(\partial^2 g/\partial^2 c)(c-c_0)^2 + k(\Delta c)^2]dV \quad (2)$$

Here g(c) is the free energy density of the homogeneous material having composition c, $k\,(\Delta c)^2$ is the additional free energy density if the material is in a gradient in composition, and k is the gradient energy coefficient and is positive.

The local concentration (or composition) $c(\mathbf{r}, t)$ of the solution at time t at a point in space defined by the position vector $\mathbf{r}$ may be analyzed in terms of its Fourier components by the expression:

$$c(\mathbf{r}, t) - c_0 = \Sigma \exp[\,R(\beta)t\,]\,[A(\beta)\cos(\beta\bullet\mathbf{r}) + B(\beta)\sin(\beta\bullet\mathbf{r})\,] \quad (3)$$

The summation Σ is over all wave vector β. A and B are to be evaluated at t = 0 by Fourier analyzing the fluctuations in the initial solution. The amplification factor $R(\beta)$ is given by :

$$R(\beta) = -M(\partial^2 g/\partial^2 c)\beta^2 - 2Mk\beta^4 \quad (4)$$

where M is the molecular mobility. The solution eqs. (3) and (4) tell us that any sinusoidal component present initially in the composition profile of a specimen will grow or shrink exponentially according to whether $R(\beta)$, the amplification factor, is positive or negative. Outside the spinodal region, $(\partial^2 g/\partial^2 c) > 0$; consequently $R(\beta)$ is negative for all values of β and any existing fluctuation will diminish with time. Therefore, the system should homogenize. For this reason, a continuous and spontaneous process of concentration decomposition resulting in the formation of a periodic or quasi-periodic texture can only occur in the unstable region where $(\partial^2 g/\partial^2 c)$ is negative.

In the spinodal region, the critical value wave number, β_c, is given by the value

$$\beta_c^2 = -1/2k\,(\partial^2 g/\partial^2 c) \quad (5)$$

β_c corresponds exactly to a wavelength where all the contributions to the free energy cancel each other out, and forms the boundary between positive and negative $R(\beta)$. A wave length with $\beta < \beta_c$ will grow and $\beta > \beta_c$ will shrink. The interdiffusion coefficient D is defined by the expression

$$D = M \ (\partial^2 g / \partial^2 c) \qquad (6)$$

Then formula (4) can be rewritten as

$$R(\beta) = -D \beta^2 \ [\ 1 - \beta^2 / \beta_c^2 \ ] \quad (7)$$

M is always positive, D is negative within the spinodal, which corresponds to an uphill diffusion. From eq. (7) it is seen that the maximum of $R(\beta)$ occurs for a wavenumber $\beta_m = \beta_c / \sqrt{2}$. The spatial components of wavelength $\lambda_m = 2\pi / \beta_m$ is called the spinodal wavelength of the system.

It should be mentioned here, the unique morphology created by the initial stage of its spinodal decomposition consists of an interface between two coexisting phases which is diffuse and its thickness increases with decreasing ΔT ($\Delta T = IT - T_s I$) and becomes infinite at the spinodal temperature, T_s. T_s is the temperature at the spinodal curve. The periodic domain structure, λ_m, varies with the heat treatment temperature, T, and is described by:

$$1 / \lambda_m^2 = q \ IT - T_s I \qquad (8)$$

where q is a constant depending on the system.

In the second stage of the spinodal decomposition, the domain structure becomes large and the rate of growth of the composition fluctuation amplitude is slowed down. This period corresponds to a coarsening of the texture. This process is an Ostwald ripening process where differences in solute concentration due to various particle sizes set up concentration gradients which tend to resorb smaller particles and make the large ones grow at their expense. We have discussed this type of coarsening mechanism in the section of nucleation and growth.

2.2 Rayleigh-BrillouinScattering Study on the Phase Diagrams of Multiphase Systems

In the above discussions, it was mentioned that there are two different mechanisms (nucleation & growth and spinodal decomposition) controlling phase separation. These two mechanisms will give different kinetic rates and different morphological structures. Therefore, understanding phase diagrams of polymer systems is of monumental importance for manipulating the morphology and properties of materials. In the following, we will introduce the concept of using Rayleigh-Brillouin laser light scattering for constructing the binodal and spinodal curves that make up the phase diagrams of multiphase systems. Rayleigh-Brillouin scattering has been used by Hsich et al. [14] for studying the phase separation of multiphase systems. Hsich [15] further discussed the utility of Rayleigh-Brillouin scattering experiments as an effective method for studying chemical relaxation, such as hydration reactions, dissolution of solid state reactions, or cure reactions.

From Einstein's classical theory of light scattering [16], the scattering intensity is proportional to the density fluctuation, and it can be expressed as

$$I_T(\theta) = I_0 (k_0^4 / 32\pi^2 R_0^2)(1 + \cos^2 \theta) < (\Delta \varepsilon)^2 > \quad (9)$$

For a two component system, according to the thermodynamic fluctuation theory [17], $< (\Delta \varepsilon)^2 >$ can be expressed as

$$< (\Delta \varepsilon)^2 > = (\partial \varepsilon / \partial \rho)_{T,c}^2 \ < (\Delta \rho)^2 > + (\partial \varepsilon / \partial T)_{\rho,c}^2 \cdot$$
$$< (\Delta T)^2 + (\partial \varepsilon / \partial c)_{\rho,T}^2 < (\Delta c)^2 > \quad (10)$$

where I_0 is the intensity of the incident beam, k_0 is the wave vector associated with this beam, R_0 is the distance from the scattering volume, V, to the detector, θ is the angle between the incident and scattered wave. ε, ρ and c are dielectric constant, density and concentration, respectively. $< (\Delta \varepsilon)^2 >$, $< (\Delta \rho)^2 >$, and $< (\Delta c) >$ are the mean square fluctuations of the dielectric constant, density and concentration, respectively.

For most liquids, the second term in eq. (10) is small compared with the other terms. Therefore, according to Hsich et al. [14], eq. (10) can be expressed as

$$< (\Delta \varepsilon)^2 > = (\rho \partial \varepsilon / \partial \rho)_{T,c}^2 \ (\ k_B T/V) \ \{ \ \kappa_S(\omega_B) \ +$$
$$[\ \kappa_S(0) - \kappa_S(\omega_B) \ ] + [\ \kappa_T(0) - \kappa_S(0) \ ] \ \} \ +$$
$$(\partial \varepsilon / \partial c)_{\rho,T}^2 (k_B T) / (\partial^2 G / \partial^2 c)_{P,T} \qquad (11)$$

here k_B is Boltzmann's constant, T is the absolute temperature, κ_S and κ_T are the adiabatic and isothermal compressibility, respectively, and G is the Gibbs free energy. In dispersion liquids, the dynamic compressibility $\kappa_S(\omega_B)$ will be different from the equilibrium value $\kappa_S(0)$.

There are four terms in eq. (11). The first two terms are due to pressure fluctuations. The first term is proportional to $\kappa_S(\omega_B)$ which propagates with an acoustic frequency, ω_B, and is the source of the Brillouin doublet ($2I_B$). The second term is proportional to [$\kappa_S(0) - \kappa_S(\omega_B)$] which will not propagate when the structural relaxation time of liquids is much larger than the inverse of the acoustic frequency, ω_B (such as near the glass transition or in the glassy state). This portion of the spectrum will be relaxed to the central Rayleigh component, and it is called the **Mountain-line**. The third term presents local entropy fluctuations which do not propagate and are the source of the unshifted central Rayleigh component. The last term is due to composition fluctuations which also do not propagate and are another source of the Rayleigh component (I_R). The Rayleigh intensity contributed from the composition fluctuations can be expressed as

$$I_c = I_0 (k_0^4 / 32\pi^2 R_0^2)(1+\cos^2\theta)(\partial\varepsilon/\partial c)_{\rho,T}^2 (\\ k_B T)/[a_2 (T - T_S) \qquad (12)$$

Where a_2 is the coefficient of the free energy expansion. The ratio of the intensity of the Rayleigh central component I_R to that of the Brillouin doublet 2 I_B is called the Landau-Placzek ratio which can be written as

$$R_{LP} = I_R / 2 I_B \qquad (13)$$

According to Ornstein and Zernike [18, 19], with the temperature close to the critical point, the resultants of density fluctuations or composition fluctuations can have an effect on the state of the medium at distances that are much greater then the radius of molecular interaction under normal conditions. Therefore, the Debye correlation length becomes very large. Consequently, the scattering intensity never has the chance to reach divergence as predicted by eq. (12). Nevertheless, one can construct the spinodal curve of a phase diagram for a multiphase system by calculating the Landau-Placzek ratio as a function of the temperature in doing a super-critical (above the upper consolute temperature) study of the Rayleigh-Brillouin scattering. From eqs. (11-13), the Landau-Placzek ratio can be written as a function of (T - T_S) [14]:

$$R_{LP} = \alpha^2 T v(\omega_B)^2/C_p + [v(\omega_B)^2 - v_0^2]/v_0^2 + (\partial\varepsilon/ \\ \partial c)_{\rho,T}^2 V/(\rho\partial\varepsilon/\partial\rho)_{T,c}^2 [a_2(T-T_S)]\} \qquad (14)$$

where α is the thermal expansion, C_p is the heat capacitance at a constant pressure, and $v(\omega_B)$ and v_0 are sound speed at the Brillouin frequency and zero frequency, respectively.

3. PHASE DIAGRAM AND MORPHOLO-GY OF EPOXY-CTBN RUBBER

As we have mentioned, the phase separation process, either by nucleation and growth or by spinodal decomposition, is a diffusion control process. Therefore, to be able to control morphology as discussed by Cahn [12], the miscibility gap (binodal and spinodal curves) must be at or below the glass transition temperature, T_g, or liquidus temperature. However, Hsich [20] pointed out that in thermosetting or elastomeric systems, the morphological structure can be manipulated via cure kinetics and phase separation processes even though the miscibility gaps of the polymer systems are far above the T_g of the uncured polymers. During cure, the changes of molecular weight and network structure not only cause the miscibility gap to shift but also increase T_g of the polymers. For these reasons, if cure kinetics and phase separation processes are properly manipulated, the

morphology of polymers can be controlled.

There are two different approaches, depending on whether the material is crosslinked, in controlling the morphology of multiphase systems. For a non-crosslinked polymer system, the morphology of a material is controlled by a thermodynamically reversible process (structure frozen-in) during the cooling stage to reach its glassy state. In this case, to control the morphology, one must shoose a system in which phase separation is slow compared with the time it takes to change the temperature of the samples. This type of polymer system must have a miscibility gap (phase separation temperature) near T_g. The speed of phase separation depends on the diffusion coefficient which is related to the relaxation time [21] of the glassy materials. To effectively control the morphology of these polymer systems, one must apply the miscibility gap and the structural relaxation phenomena of the polymer systems. Aspects of nonequilibrium thermodynamics and structural relaxation of the glassy state have been discussed by Davies & Jones [22], Staverman [23], and Hsich [24-26].

To control morphology of a crosslinkable material, such as epoxies or thermoset elastmeric materials, one can control the morphology of the material by simultaneously manipulating the kinetic processes of the cure reactions and phase separation (thermodynamically irreversible, structure locked-in). In doing so, the cure kinetics of the polymer systems is of vital importance. Recently, Hsich [27] and Hsich et al. [28-30] developed a kinetic model of cure which is able to predict the change of rheological and mechanical properties during the entire cure cycle. By incorporating the cure model along with the kinetics of phase separation, one can control the morphology of these multiphase systems.

Drake and McCarthy [31] found that the incorporation of low levels of a liquid carboxyl-terminated butadiene acrylonitrile copolymer (CTBN) to a normally brittle epoxy resin significantly improved the crack resistance and impact strength without a reduction in other thermal and mechanical properties. This enhancement in crack resistance and impact strength is brought about by the formation during cure of a predominately rubbery second phase. These modified thermoset resins have found wide application in structural film adhesives for metal-metal bonding in aircraft, in paste adhesives for automotive and industrial application, in electronic encapsulation, in epoxy solvent and powder coating, and in advanced aircraft and aerospace composites. However, in most epoxy applications, the final properties are strongly dependent on the morphology generated during cure of these systems. The morphology is determined by a large number of variables, such as the miscibility of the epoxy and rubber prior to cure, the cure agent, the time and temperature of cure. In some cases, optimum toughness is provided with a multi-modal distribution of particle sizes.

A selective cure agent may enchance the carboxyl-epoxy reaction and increase the interface mixing between the epoxy and the CTBN as discussed by Siebert et al.[32]; however, we believe that good mechanical properties can also be achieved by controlling the interface mixing between the epoxy and the rubber phase through a spinodal decomposition mechanism. As mentioned before, in the initial stage of spinodal decomposition a gradual mixing interface develops instead of a sharp interface boundary. We believe we can control the sizes of the rubber particles by properly manipulating the kinetic processes of phase separation. Therefore, we are more concerned with the mechanism of phase separation (spinodal vs nucleation and growth) than with specific types of chemical reactions promoted by selective cure agents. We will begin by constructing miscibility gaps (binodal and spinodal curves) of uncured epoxy-CTBN systems. Then we will study the effects of cure agents on the miscibility gaps of these systems. Finally, the morphology of these systems will be manipulated through the kinetic processes of the cure reactions and subsequent phase separation. This report is mainly concerned with the miscibility and phase diagrams of epoxy-CTBN systems. A later report will deal with correlating the morphology and mechanical properties of the systems.

3.1 Experimental

3.1.1 Sample Preparation

The epoxy resin used in this study is a low molecular weight liquid diglycidyl ether of bisphenol-A (DGE-BA), Epon 828, manufactured by the Shell Chemical Co. The rubber modifiers employed are low molecular weight copolymers of butadiene and acrylonitrile having carboxy end groups and manufactured by the B. F. Goodrich Co. under the trade name Hycar CTBN. Three different rubber systems of varying acrylonitrile content were used in this study. Chemical and physical properties and nomenclature of the rubbers are presented in Table 1. Mixtures of the rubber-modified epoxy without curatives were prepared for miscibility studies using laser light scattering. The CTBN rubber content in the mixtures was varied from 2 to 40 phr (part per hundred of epoxy resin). Samples for light scattering were prepared by hand mixing Epon 828 with CTBN (X8) at 80°C under a dry nitro-

gen environment and then degasing.

Samples for mechanical spectra (MS) and scanning electron microscope (SEM) measurements were prepared from degased mixtures of Epon 828/CTBN (X8) or Epon 828/CTBN (X13) containing curative. Curatives used were Versamid 140 (polyamide manufactured by Henkel Co.) or Jeffamine D230 (difunctional polyoxypropyleneamine manufactured by Texaco Chemical Co.) mixing was accomplished at 50°C under a dry nitrogen environment and then degassing. Test specimens were prepared by pouring the degased mixture into a vertical Teflon mold and cureing at 120°C for four hours under a dry nitrogen environment. Mechanical spectra were measured on a Rheometric Mechanical Sprectrum (RMS). Fractured samples with exposed fresh surfaces were used for SEM measurements.

3.1.2 Rayleigh-Brillouin Laser Light Scattering

The Rayleigh-Brillouin scattering set-up includes a triple-passed piezoelectrically scanned Fabry-Perot interferometer stabilized for both mirror parallelism and plate separation by a Burleigh DAS-1 system, a single-mode laser, and photo counting equipment. The signal was stored in a multichannel analyzer (1024 channels) of the DAS-1 system. A Spectra Physics model No. 20-20 argon ion laser operating in single-mode at 488 nm was used. All spectra were recorded at 90° angle scattering geometry. The free spectral range of the interferometer was set at 46.4 GHz and the total finesse of the whole spectrometer was 50 during all measurements.

The miscibility gap (or upper consolute temperature) of the epoxy/CTBN (X13) system (26% AN content in the CTBN) is far below room temperature. The miscibility gap of the epoxy/CTBN (X31) (10% AN content in the CTBN) is above 150°C. In order to obtain a system that could be conveniently studied near room temperature, epoxy/CTBN (X8) (16% AN content in the CTBN) was selected. The Rayleigh-Brillouin scattering data of Landau-Placzek ratio and Brillouin frequency Shift for Epon 828/CTBN (X8) at various CTBN rubber contents and temperatures are listed in Table II & III, respectively.

3.2 Results and Discussion

3.2.1 Phase Diagram of Rubber-Modified Epoxy

Typical Rayleigh-Brillouin Scattering spectra for an epoxy/CTBN sample at different temperatures are shown in Fig. 2. At the high temperature region (Fig. 2a), there are two symmetrical Brillouin peaks located at frequencies $(\nu_o + \nu_B)$ and $(\nu_o - \nu_B)$. ν_o is the frequency of incident light, and v_B ($\omega_B = 2\pi v_B$) is the longitudinal hypersonic wave of the sample. The Rayleigh peak is located at frequency v_o. The longitudinal velocity, V_L, and modulus, M_L, of the hypersonic wave of the sample can be calculated from the following formulas:

$$V_L = \lambda_o v_B / [\, 2\, n \sin(\theta/2)\,] \qquad (15)$$
$$M_L \approx \rho\, V_L{}^2 \qquad (16)$$

where λ_o is the wavelength of the incident light wave, θ is the scattering angle, n (≈ 1.57) and ρ (≈ 1.18) are the refractive index and density of the sample, respectively. Fig. 2a shows that the sample is in a homogeneous single phase, because a distinct and symmetrical Brillouin doublet appears in the scattering spectrum.

As temperature is decreased, an asymmetric Brillouin doublet forms as shown in Fig. 2b. This spectrum shows that the Stokes Brillouin line, at $(v_o - v_B)$, has greater scattering intensity than the anti-Stokes Brillouin line, at $(v_o + v_B)$. This spectrum indicates that the sample is near or on the binodal curve (phase separation temperature). This experiment enabled us to identify the phase separation temperature, even through the sample is still optically transparent by visual observation. The particle sizes or the domains of the sample are believed to be smaller than the incident light wavelength. This finding is of interest and importance, because it demonstrates that Rayleigh-Brillouin scattering (RBS) is a sensitive method for studying the miscibility and phase diagrams of multiphase systems. In the RBS experiment, we defined the binodal point for each composition as the temperature where the difference of scattering intensity between Stokes Brillouin and anti-Stokes Brillouin component is about 20% (Fig. 3b). Fig. 2c and 2d are to show the Brillouin sepectra of fully phase separated samples.

More than three decade ago, Debye [33, 34] and Debye et al. [35] predicted that the angular asymmetry of the strong scattered intensity in the forward direction can be observed in the vicinity of the critical point of liquid mixtures, or in inhomogeneous systems when the particle sizes (or domain structures) are larger than one-tenth of the incident light wavelength ($\approx 0.1\,\lambda_o$). Later Debye et al. [36] indeed found that a sharp increase of asymmetric scattering intensity due to incipient precipitation at the phase separation temperature, T_p, which is about $1^{\circ}C$ higher than the critical temperature (consolute temperature), T_c, in polystrene/cyclohexane system. Our findings in the Rayleigh-Brillouin spectra are consistent with the prediction of the Debye theory, i.e., at the phase separa-

tion temperature, the phenomenon of asymmetric scattering occurs. The advantage of Rayleigh-Brillouin scattering over ordinary Rayleigh scattering is that the Brillouin component is not sensitive to the impurities or inclusions of the sample (the Rayleigh component is).

The scattering spectra in Fig. 2c and 2d were taken at the temperatures below the phase separation temperature. At this temperature, the sample is fully phase separated and becomes opaque. The asymmetry of the two Brillouin components becomes very pronounced. Therefore, the binodal curves of the multi-component polymer systems can be constructed by the Rayleigh-Brillouin scattering experiment, the point in the binodal curve, as shown in Fig. 3, is at the temperature where it starts to show an asymmetry of the Brillouin doublet (Fig. 2b) in each concentration of the mixtures.

Using Rayleigh-Brillouin scattering spectra to construct a spinodal curve has been discussed by Hsich et al. [14] and been mentioned above. As shown in eq. (16), one can easily calculate the first two terms and subtract them from the experimentally determined Landau-Placzek ratio, R_{LP}. Then the remaining R_{LP} is expressed as the third term in eq. (16) which represents the contribution from the concentration fluctuations. As the temperature approaches the spinodal decomposition, T_S, the third (remaining) term, $R_{LP}(c)$, of the Landau-Placzek ratio drastically increases in accordance with the characteristics of $(T - T_S)^{-1}$. Therefore, from a super-critical study of Rayleigh-Brillouin spectra at various temperatures, one can obtain, T_S, of the spinodal curve by extrapolating to zero value of $1/R_{LP}(c)$ in a plot of $1/R_{LP}(c)$ vs. T.

One should keep in mind, that to do an accurate calculation of, T_S, one needs the physical properties in the first two terms of eq.(14) to calculate R_{LP} from the contribution of the density fluctuations. One also needs to purify the samples to eliminate the contributions from impurities or inclusions in the Rayleigh component. However, from a practical application point of view, one can roughly estimate the spinodal curve of these polymer systems without purifying the samples or measuring all of the properties for the R_{LP} calculations. To do this, eq.(14) can be simplified as:

$$R_{LP} = A\,T + [\,M_L(\omega_B) - M_L(0)]/M_L(0) + \\ B M_L(\omega_B)/(T - T_S) \qquad (17)$$

where A & B are assumed to be constants, and $M_L(\omega_B)$ and $M_L(0)$ are the longitudinal moduli at the Brillouin frequency and zero frequency, respectively.

The second term in eq.(17) is easily to calculate. From the shift of the Brillouin frequency and eqs. (15) & (16), the second term in eq.(17) can be calculated. After calculation of the second term, one can use the least squares fit to obtain the parameters of A, B, and T_S in eq.(17).

The spinodal curve of Epon 828/CTBN (X8) system was constructed from this method and is shown in Fig. (3). The temperature range utilized for each composition was $100^{\circ}C$ to the phase separation temperature (the binodal curve). In this temperature range, the dispersion of the acoustic velocity of the epoxy system is very small, except during the cure stage. The experimental data are listed in Table II. Cook and Hilliard [37] developed a semi-empirical equation for calculating the spinodal curve by using the binodal curve. The Cook-Hilliard model is written as:

$$c_s - c_c \approx (c_e - c_c)[1 - 0.422(T/T_c)] \quad (18)$$

where c_e, c_s and c_c are the concentration at the equilibrium, the spinodal and the critical composition, respectively. The results of the calculations from eq. (20) of the Cook-Hilliard model are also plotted in Fig. (3). There is a good agreement between the Cook-Hilliard model and the current model of RBS.

(ii) Morphology and Mechanical Spectra of Rubber-Modified Epoxy

As discussed above, there are two different methods for controlling morphology of multiphase systems, depending on whether cure reactions occur during material processing. In the absence of cure, the morphology can be controlled by a temperature-jump (or vaporizing the solvent) from an equilibrium and single-phase state (stable region) into a metastable, an unstable, or even another stable region. Then the formation of morphological structure will occur according to the mechanisms of phase separation as discussed above. When cure reactions predominate, the control of morphology requires one to program cure conditions in which the system begins with a homogeneous single-phase before cure reactions begin. The morphlgy of the system can be controlled in a homogeneously single-phase or in a heterogeneously separated phase by locking-in the morphological structure via crosslinking reactions during various stages of phase separation. Once cure reactions start, the molecular weight of the polymer system increases, the immiscibility zone is expanded and phase separation can occur. By properly manipulating the kinetics of cure and phase separation, desirable material properties can be obtained.

As mentioned earlier (Fig. 3), the upper critical temperature is about $65^{\circ}C$ for Epon/CTBN (X8), and is far below room temperature for Epon/CTBN (X13). However, during cure, the critical temperature (or phase separation temperature) of these two systems will increase. Phase separation can occur even for samples that are cured at a temperature higher than the critical temperature. In this study, our purpose is to demonstrate the concept of controlling morphology via kinetics of phase separation and chemorheology regardless of curative type. The concept of locked-in morphology control is to manipulate the kinetics of phase separation by use of chemorheology during cure reactions. Two curatives were selected in this study. Versamid has a high viscosity and short gel time. This curative is believed to provide chemorheological behavior which will reduce the kinetic rate of phase separation by allowing morphology lock-in at the initial stage of phase separation. On the other hand, Jeffamine D230 promotes a rapid kinetic rate of phase separation.

Figs.4-6 illustrate the mechanical spectra of Epon/ CTBN (X8). The data were measured from -80 to $120^{\circ}C$ at a frequency of 10 rad/sec and 0.3% strain. Fig.5 represents a sample of Epon/CTBN (X8)/ Jeffamine D230 having weight ratios of 100:40:32, respectively. Figs. 4-6 describe Epon/CTBN (X8)/ Versamid samples having weight ratios of 100:40:50 and 100:10:50, respectively. These samples were cured at $120^{\circ}C$ for four hours. The glass transition temperatures for both the rubber-rich and epoxy-rich phases, and dynamic mechanical properties at room temperature ($22^{\circ}C$) are listed in Table IV. As shown in Fig. 4 and Table IV, the glass transition temperature, T_g (which is defined as the temperature at the peak value of tanδ), of the rubber-rich phase is $-51^{\circ}C$ ($RT_g = -51^{\circ}C$), and the T_g of the epoxy-rich phase is $86^{\circ}C$ ($ET_g = 86^{\circ}C$). In this sample, the damping peak (tanδ) of the rubber phase is very pronounced and ET_g was not affected by the content of CTBN rubber. These results show that there was extensive phase separation in this sample. As shown in Table IV, the tanδ value for this sample is small and is close to the value obtained with zero CTBN rubber content epoxy (neat epoxy). In fact, while the storage shear modulus for neat epoxy is somewhat higher than the sample described above, the corresponding value of T_g is identical ($ET_g = 86^{\circ}C$).

The data for the Versamid cured samples are shown in Figs. 5-6 and are also listed in Table IV. Cure conditions used for these samples were the same as those used for the sample cured with Jeffamine. Both samples have an identical RT_g ($-51^{\circ}C$), but different values of ET_g which is lower than that of neat epoxy. For neat epoxies, tanδ is small and almost identical for both curatives. However, when there is an inter-mixing between the rubber phase and epoxy phase, tanδ increases and ET_g decreases as shown in the Ver-samid cured samples represented in Figs 5-6. If full phase separation occurs, as shown in the Jeffamine cured sample (Fig 4), then both values of tanδ and ET_g will be similar to that of zero rubber filled epoxy.

Figs. 7-8 are micrographs obtained from Scanning Electron Microscopy (SEM) measurements at 10,000X magnification. Two different CTBN rubbers were used in the samples (Fig. 7 represents CTBN (X8) , and Fig. 8 represents CTBN (X13)). All sam-ples contained 40 phr rubber. The samples in Figs. 7a and 8a were cured with Jeffamine while those in Figs. 7b and 8b were cured with Versamid. RT_g, ET_g, and dynamic mechanical properties at room tem-perature (22°C) are listed in Table IV. As shown in Figs. 7a and 8a, the size of the rubber particles varies with the particular CTBN chosen. For CTBN (X8) particle size is 2 μm but for CTBN (X13) particle size is only 0.5μm. Both samples are optically opaque. The morphology clearly shows a droplet structure with a sharp boundary interface between the rubber and epoxy phases. This result indicates that the mechanism of phase separation for developing these morphological structures is due to nucleation and growth. The reason for this is that, during cure, the molecular weight of the polymer system is in-creased and, consequently, the immiscibility gap in-creases. Eventually, the immiscibility gap of the polymer system is raised above the cure temperature. This causes the polymer system to change from a sin-gle-phase equilibrium state to a metastable state and, therefore, phase separation is initiated by nucleation and growth. Since the immiscibility gap of Epon/CTBN (X8) is higher than that for Epon/CTBN (X13), we would expect that phase separation in Epon/CTBN (X8) would occur earlier than that in Epon/CTBN (X13) under similar cure conditions. Thus, the particle size of the rubber phase in Epon/CTBN (X8) should be larger than that in Epon/CTBN (X13). This in fact is shown in Figs. 7a and 8a.

When Versamid was used to replace Jeffamine as cura-tive, the morphological structure was drastically dif-ferent as shown in Fig. 7b and 8b. The chemorheo-logical behavior of Versamid in rubber-modified epoxy systems tends to retard the kinetics of phase separation. Nevertheless, the immiscibility gap is raised during cure, in a manner similar to the Jeffa-mine cured samples. Eventually, the polymer system changes from a single-phase equilibrium state to a metastable state. Initially phase separation occurs by nucleation and growth, but the retarded kinetics re-sults in another change from the metastable state to an unstable state as molecular weight continues to in-crease during cure. As pointed out earlier, the kinet-ics of phase separation when governed by spinodal de-composition are very fast. Phase separation occurs continuously and spontaneously. Thus we found with the Versamid curative, the morphological behav-ior of the samples were dominated by spinodal decom-position, as shown in Figs. 7b and 8b.

Recalling Eq. (8), during the initial stages of spinodal decomposition, the particle size of the rubber particle is inversely proportional to the square root of the dif-ference between the cure temperature, T, and spinodal temperature, T_s (ie. $|T - T_s|^{-0.5}$). The spinodal curve (T_s) of Epon/CTBN (X8) is higher than that of Epon/CTBN (X13), and cure reactions will elevate the spinodal curves above the cure temperature. Once this occurs, the value of $|T - T_s|$ for Epon/CTBN (X8) is greater than $|T - T_s|$ for Epon/CTBN (X13). Consequently, the particle size of the rubber phase in Epon/CTBN (X8) should be smaller than that of Epon/CTBN (X13). This is illustrated in Figs. 7b and 8b. The particle sizes of rubber shown in Figs. 7b and 8b are 0.2 and 0.3 μm, respectively. These particle sizes are smaller than the wavelength of visi-ble light and the samples are nearly transparent.

4. CONCLUSIONS

We have demonstrated that Rayleigh-Brillouin scatter-ing is an effective method for studying the miscibility of multiphase systems. This method allows us to construct phase diagrams composed of both binodal and spinodal curves. We also demonstrated that the morphology of polymer alloys can be controlled by simultaneously manipulating the kinetics of phase separation and chemorheology of these alloys. We have found that the particle size of the rubber reen-forcement in epoxies is effected by the mechanisms of phase separation. Phase separation by nucleation and growth gives large rubber particles than correspound-ing phase separation by spinodal decomposition. This contrast in the morphology development is the consequence of controlling phase separation through the chemorheological behavior. Such control over morphology is the key to ultimately controlling me-chanical properties.

5. REFERENCES

1. Prigogine, I. and Defay, R., *Chemical Ther-modynamics* (translated by D. H. Everett),

John Willey, New York (1972), Chaps. 16 &18.

2. Krause, S., *Polymer Blends* (D. R. Paul and S. Newman, eds.), **Vol. 1**, Academic Press, New York (1978), Chap. 1.

3. Kwei, T. K. and Wang, T. T., *Polymer Blends* (D. R. Paul and S. Newman, eds.), **Vol. 1**, Academic Press, New York (1978), Chap. 4.

4. Turnbull, D., *Solid State Physics: Advances in Research and Applications*, (F. Seitz and D Turnbull, eds.), **Vol. 3**, p. 225, Academic Press, New York (1956).

5. Lifshitz, I. M. and Slyozov, V. V., *J. Phys. Chem. Solids*, **19**, 35 (1961).

6. Wager, C., *Z Elektrochem.*, **65**, 581 (1961).

7. Zarzycki, J. and Naudin, F., *Phys. & Chem. Glasses.*, **8**, 11 (1967)

8. Cahn, J. W. and Hilliard, J. E., *J. Chem. Phys.*, **28**, 258 (1958).

9. Cahn, J. W., *Acta Metall.*, **9**, 795 (1961).

10. Cahn, J. W., *J. Chem. Phys.*, **42**, 93 (1965).

11. Cahn, J. W. and Charles, R. J., *Phys. & Chem. Glasses.*, **6**, 181 (1965).

12. Cahn, J. W., *Trans. Metall.. Soc. A.I.M.E.*, **242**, 166 (1968).

13. Haller, W., *J. Chem. Phys.*, **42**, 686 (1965).

14. Hsich ,H. S.-Y., et al., *J. Chem. Phys.* **56**, 1663 (1972).

15. Hsich, H. S.-Y., *J. Mater. Sci.* **13**, 2560 (1978).

16. Einstein, A., *Ann. Physik*, **33**, 1275 (1910).

17. Landau, L. D. and Lifshitz, E. M., *Fluid Mechanics*, Academic Press, Reading, Mass. (1959), Chap. 17.

18. Ornstein, L. S. and Zernike, F., *Phys. Z.* **19**, 134 (1918).

19. Ornstein, L. S. and Zernike, F., *Phys. Z.* **27**, 761 (1926).

20. Hsich, H. S.-Y., Lord Report, CR-CD-12-87; H. S.-Y. Hsich, IR-9-87.

21. Egelstaff, P. A., *An Introduction to the Liquid State*, Academic Press, London and New York. (1967), Chap. 10-12.

22. Davies, R. O. and Jones, G. O., *Adv. Phys.*, **2**, 370 (1953).

23. Staverman, A. J., *Rheological Acta.*, **5**, 283 (1966).

24. Hsich, H. S.-Y., *Amer. Ceram. Soc.*, **60**, 485 (1977).

25. Hsich, H. S.-Y., *J. Mater. Sci.*, **13**, 750 (1978).

26. Hsich, H. S.-Y., *J. Mater. Sci.*, **15**, 1194 (1980).

27. Hsich, H. S.-Y., *J. Appl. Polym. Sci.*, **27**, 3265 (1982).

28. Hsich, H. S.-Y., Zurn, R. M. and Ambrose, R. J., *Chemorheology of Thermosetting Polymers* (C. A. May, ed.), **ACS Symposium Series, No. 227**, (1983), Chap. 16.

29. Hsich, H. S.-Y., Yanyo, L. C. , R. M. and Ambrose, R. J., *J. Appl. Polym. Sci.*, **29**, 2331 (1984).

30. Hsich, H. S.-Y., and Ambrose, R. J., *Injection and Compression Molding Fundamentals* (A. I. Isayev, ed.), Marcel Dekker, Inc., New York, (1987), Chap. 5.

31. Drake, R. S. and McCarthy, W. J., *Rubber World.*, 159, (Oct .1968).

32. Siebert, A. R. and Riew, C. K., *Org. Coat. Plast. Chem.*, **31** (No.1),55 (1971).

33. Debye, P., *J. Appl. Phys.*, **15**, 33 (1944).

34. Debye, P., *J. Chem. Phys.*, **31**, 68 (1959).

35. Debye, P. and Bueche, A. M., *J. Appl. Phys.*, **20**, 518 (1949).

36. Debye, P., Coll, H. and Woermann, D., *J. Chem. Phys.*, **33**, 1746 (1960).

37. Cook, H. E. and Hilliard, J. E., *Trans. Metall.. Soc. A.I.M.E.*, **233**, 142 (1965).

6. BIOGRAPHY

Dr. Henry S.-Y. Hsich is a Senior Staff Scientist at Lord Corporation. He received his M. S. degree in Physics from National Tsing Hua University, Taiwan, and Ph.D. degree in Applied Physics and Materials Science from the Catholic University of America, Washington, D.C. His research interests and publications include polymer processing, polymer physics and mechanics, rheology, chemorheology, morphology, and phase separation. Currently, he is working on the technology of polymer blends and alloys.

TABLE I PHYSICAL PROPERTIES OF CTBN

Hycar Polymers	CTBN (1300X13)	CTBN (1300X8)	CTBN (1300X31)
Acrylonitrile content, %	26	18	10
Molecular weight, Mn	3200	3600	3800
Viscosity, cp (27°C)	570000	135000	60000
Specific gravity	0.96	0.948	0.924
Solubility parameter	9.14	8.77	8.45
Functionality	1.8	1.8	1.9

TABLE II. LANDAU-PLACZEK RATIO OF EPON/CTBN SYSTEM

Temperature (°C)	2 phr L-R Ratio	5 phr L-R Ratio	10 phr L-R Ratio	15 phr L-R Ratio	20 phr L-R Ratio	30 phr L-R Ratio	40 phr L-R Ratio
22							
30							
35							306
40		2370				908	196
45						252	148
50	1552	983	798	616	773	128	108
55	946	455	610	498	316	68.4	73.2
60	406	473	425	230.5	168		
65			238.7	73.5	104	53.3	48
70	84.1	93.3	47.44	24.3			
80	19.8	17.4	29.61	21.4	48.6	30.1	33.7
90	11.4	15	20.74	15.3	24.9	25.6	28.4
100	8.1	13.5	17.03	14.4	20.7	23.4	24.8
					15.9	18.6	18.3

TABLE III Brillouin Frequency Shift (GHz) OF EPON/CTBN SYSTEM

Temperature (°C)	2 phr	5 phr	10 phr	15 phr	20 phr	30 phr	40 phr
22							
30						10.03	10.09
35						9.6	9.65
40		9.91				9.44	9.34
45					9.42	9.29	9.28
50	8.95	8.94	8.86	8.92	9.18		
55	8.92	8.86	8.79		9.1	8.78	8.8
60	8.71	8.59		8.71	8.65		
65			8.42	8.39	8.55	8.51	8.27
70	8.26	8.09	8.19				
80	7.69	7.69	8.13	8.18	8.04	8.02	7.81
90	7.55	7.18	7.65	7.61	7.64	7.63	7.56
100	6.92	6.96	7.17	7.12	7.09	7.24	7.03
			6.73	6.96	6.79	6.69	6.68

894

Table IV Properties of Epoxy Systems

Epoxy System	RT_g (°C)	ET_g (°C)	tanδ	G' (10^9dynes/cm^2)
Epon/Jeffamine (100:32)	*	86	0.024	11.3
Epon/CTBN(X8)/Jeffamine (100:40:32)	-51	86	0.021	5.54
Epon/CTBN(X13)/Jeffamine (100:40:32)	-32	86	0.034	6.11
Epon/Versamid (100:50)	*	121	0.023	8.29
Epon/CTBN(x8)/Versamid (100:10:50)	-51	111	0.029	7.41
Epon/CTBN(X8)/Versamid (100:40:50)	-51	106	0.036	5.36
Epon/CTBN(X13)/Versamid (100:40:50)	-32	101	0.045	5.02

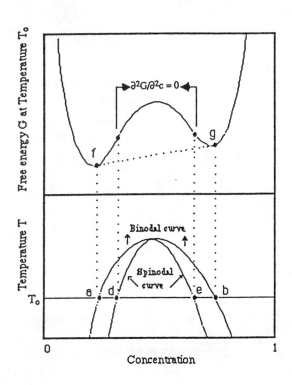

Fig. (2)   Rayleigh-Brillouin Spectra of Epoxy/CTBN System

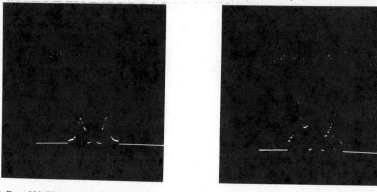

(a) Epon 828/CTBN (X8) (30 phr) at 100°C

(b) Epon 828/CTBN (X8) (30 phr) at 35°C

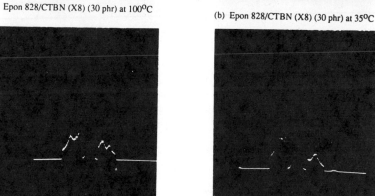

(c) Epon 828/CTBN (X8) (30 phr) at 22°C

(d) Epon 828/CTBN (X8) (2 phr) at 50°C

Fig. (3) Phase Diagram of Epoxy/CTBN

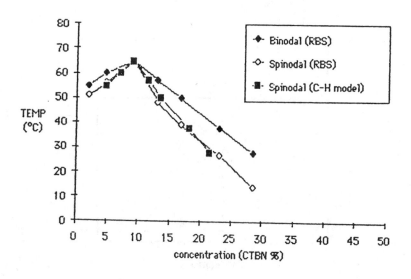

- ◆ Binodal (RBS)
- ○ Spinodal (RBS)
- ■ Spinodal (C-H model)

TEMP (°C)

concentration (CTBN %)

896

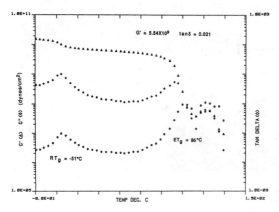

Fig. 4 Mechanical Spectrum of Epon/CTBN(X8)/Jeffamine (100:40:32)

$G' = 5.54 \times 10^9$ $\tan\delta = 0.021$

$ET_g = 86°C$

$RT_g = -51°C$

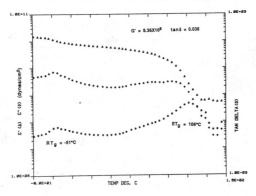

Fig. 5 Mechanical Spectrum of Epon/CTBN(X8)/Versamid (100:40:50)

$G' = 5.36 \times 10^9$ $\tan\delta = 0.036$

$ET_g = 106°C$

$RT_g = -51°C$

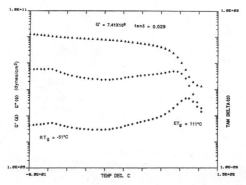

Fig. 6 Mechanical Spectrum of Epon/CTBN(X8)/Versamid (100:10:50)

$G' = 7.41 \times 10^9$ $\tan\delta = 0.029$

$ET_g = 111°C$

$RT_g = -51°C$

897

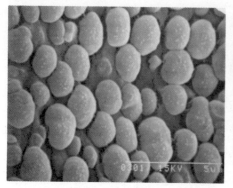 

Fig. 7a   SEM of Epon/CTBN(X8)/Jeffamine
(100:40:32)

Fig. 7b   SEM of Epon/CTBN(X8)/Versamid
(100:40:50)

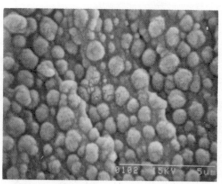 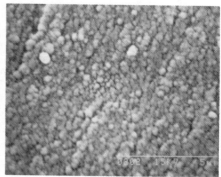

Fig. 8a   SEM of Epon/CTBN(X13)/Jeffamine
(100:40:32)

Fig. 8b   SEM of Epon/CTBN(X13)/Versamid
(100:40:50)

TOUGHENED HIGH PERFORMANCE EPOXY RESINS:
MODIFICATION WITH THERMOPLASTICS. I

Ronald S. Bauer
Shell Development Company
Westhollow Research Center
P.O. Box 1380
Houston, Texas 77251-1380

H. D. Stenzenberger, W. Römer
Technochemie GmbH-Verfahrenstechnik
(a subsidiary of Deutsche Shell AG, Hamburg)
D-6915 Dossenheim, FRG

Abstract

The approach of incorporating tough, high performance thermoplastics into brittle thermosets such as epoxides, cyanates, and bismaleimides is finding increased interest. Significantly improved damage tolerance has been achieved without compromising other critical laminate properties such as compressive strength and hot/wet performance when selected polyaromatic thermoplastics are employed.

A new epoxy resin N,N,N',N'-tetraglycidyl-α,α'-bis(4-aminophenyl)-p-diisopropylbenzene (EPON HPT® Resin 1071) cured with α,α'-bis(3,5-dimethyl-4-aminophenyl)-p-diisopropylbenzene (EPON HPT Curing Agent 1062), a new aromatic diamine curing agent, was used to study the effect of thermoplastic additives on neat resin and composite mechanical properties. The following aspects are outlined in the paper:

- Influence of the thermoplastic (backbone chemistry) and its concentration on neat mechanical properties.

- Influence of the epoxy resin/curing agent ratio on the toughenability with thermoplastics.

- Morphology of thermoplastic modified EPON HPT Resin 1071/EPON HPT Curing Agent 1062 systems.

- Preliminary composite properties for a thermoplastic modified EPON HPT Resin 1071/EPON HPT Curing Agent 1062 system.

1. INTRODUCTION

Brittleness is an inherent property of highly crosslinked polymers such as epoxy resins, bismaleimides, and cyanates. Improvements in ductility, fracture resistance, and impact strength, however, can be achieved without substantially degrading the thermal and mechanical properties of the matrix resin. McGarry and his co-workers[1] showed some twenty years ago that a liquid elastomeric carboxyl terminated butadiene-acrylonitrile copolymer, which is initially soluble in conventional bisphenol A epoxy resin, forms a second phase of dispersed particles on cure, resulting in an epoxy resin system with improved toughness. The toughness obtainable from an elastomer modified epoxy resin system depends on several factors including: the type of modifier, heterophase distribution, interfacial adhesion between the heterophase and the matrix, resin and curing agent, cure conditions and molecular weight between crosslinks in the matrix resin. A thorough and critical review of the variables affecting the toughenability of epoxy resin systems is beyond the scope of this paper. However, much has been written on the subject[2].

The use of elastomeric modifiers for toughening thermoset resins generally results in the lowering of the glass transition temperature (Tg), modulus and strength of the modified system. More recently, ductile engineering thermoplastics and functional thermoplastic oligomers have been used as modifiers for epoxy resins and other themosets. Raghava[3] found that polyethersulfone (Victrex 100P, 200P, 300P, *etc.* from ICI) modified tetraglycidyl methylenedianiline (TGMDA) cured with diaminodiphenyl sulfone (DDS) had only marginally improved toughness. In an independent study Bucknall and Partridge[4] obtained essentially the same results. They reported that a blend of polyethersulfone (Vitrex 100P) with TGMDA (MY 720 from Ciba Geigy) and triglycidyl p-aminophenol (ERL 0510 from Ciba Geigy) separately and their mixtures in various proportions when cured with either DDS or dicyandiamide (DICY) showed only very little improvement in toughness. Interestingly, they found that phase separation of the thermoplastic only occurred with the triglycidyl epoxide cured with DDS and DICY, and phase separation was not observed for TGMDA with the same curing agents as evidenced by scanning electron microscopy (SEM).

Recently it has been reported that the modification of the backbone of an aromatic thermoplastic permits control of the morphology of an epoxy resin/thermoplastic blend[5], and that the control of the morphology achieved contributes to fracture toughness. Different morphologies give rise to different degrees of toughness. Other thermosets such as polycyanates and bismaleimides have been toughened with engineering thermoplastics. Shimp[6] has reported on the toughening of polycyanates with polyetherimide, polyarylates, and polysulfone. The formation of certain morphologies, preferably, a co-continuous network of phase separated components in which modular features have 0.05 to 5 μm cross section, were found to be one essential property for achieving significant toughness improvements with minimal thermoplastic modification. Stenzenberger[7] has also obtained significant improvement in

toughness of bismaleimides using polyetherimide (Ultem 1000) and polyhydantoin (Resistherm PH-10). In the case of polyetherimide modification, the classical two-phase morphology with nodules of approximately 0.5 μm diameter was observed.

Shell Chemical Company has recently introduced a new tetraglycidyl amine/aromatic diamine curing agent system as a candidate matrix resin system for advanced composites[8]. The resin and curing agent are, respectively, N,N,N′,N′-tetraglycidyl-α,α′-bis(4-aminophenyl)-p-diisopropylbenzene (EPON HPT Resin 1071) and α,α′-bis(3,5-dimethyl-4-amino-phenyl)-p-diisopropylbenzene (EPON HPT Curing Agent 1062), the structures of which are given in Figure 1. This system has a high glass transition temperature, low water absorption, and consequently, good hot/wet performance. The performance property balance obtained with this new resin exceed that of the state-of-the-art epoxy resin systems used in advanced composites as shown in Table 1.

Although much has already been published on the thermoplastic modification of epoxy resins, no work has been specifically reported on this new high performance matrix resin system. This paper reports our initial work on the thermoplastic modification of the EPON HPT Resin 1071/EPON HPT Curing Agent 1062 system.

2. THERMOPLASTIC MODIFICATION

Three commercial thermoplastics having relatively high glass transition temperatures with chemically different backbones were used as modifiers at varying levels. The materials selected were a polysulfone (Udel P1700 from Union Carbide Corporation), a polyetherimide (Ultem 1000 from General Electric Company), and a polyhydantoin (Resistherm PH 10 from Bayer AG). Polyhydantoin Resistherm PH-10 is only available as a varnish in m-cresol. The polymer was isolated by precipitation in methanol. The chemical structures and glass transition temperature of the thermoplastics are given in Table 2.

2.1 Neat Resin Specimen Preparation

Neat resin test specimens were obtained from plaques prepared by either melt casting or compression molding. Compression molded specimens were prepared when the viscosity of the molten resin, curing agent, and thermoplastic combination was too high to pour the casting.

Melt casting specimens were obtained by dissolving the EPON HPT resin 1071 and thermoplastic in methylene chloride, and subsequently, removing the solvent under a full vacuum at 190°C. The EPON HPT Curing Agent 1062 and the resin/thermoplastic mixture were melted separately at 190-200°C, mixed thoroughly, degassed in a vacuum oven at elevated temperature, and then poured between glass plates. The Ultem modified systems were cured for 2 hours at 190°C and 4 hours at 200°C. The Udel modified systems prepared by melt casting were cured for 1.5 hours at 150°C and 4 hours at 200°C. All the test specimens prepared by melt casting were approximately 3.2 mm thick.

Compression molded specimens were obtained by first combining a solution of the EPON HPT Resin 1071 and EPON HPT Curing Agent 1062 in methylene chloride (ca. 60%w) with a solution of the thermoplastic in the same solvent and then evaporating the solvent at 35-40°C to give a residue. This residue was then B-staged by heating for 1 hour at 130°C plus 5 hours at 150°C. The B-staged material was ground to a fine powder then dried in a vacuum oven to remove the last traces of solvent and compression molded into plaques. The dried powder was compression molded at 200°C at 70 bars pressure for 30 minutes. The mold containing the powder was initially inserted in the cold press, the temperature increased to 150°C, pressure applied, and then after a being held at 150°C for 10 minutes the temperature was increased to the final cure temperature. The plaques thus obtained were then postcured for 2 hours at 200°C. All the compression molded test specimens were approximately 6.5 mm thick.

Duplicate unmodified test specimens were prepared by both the melt casting and compression molding techniques, and essentially no difference was observed in the mechanical properties of the test specimens prepared by the two different methods. However, the glass transition temperatures of the melt cast samples appear to be higher by approximately 20°C and the thicker samples absorb approximately 30% more water. For example, the data for the unmodified control in Table 3 was obtained on a compression molded specimen which had a glass transition temperature of 212°C. The glass transition temperature for the same system prepared by melt casting was 233°C. This difference could possibly be due to small amounts of residual solvent remaining in the compression molded material.

2.3 Neat Resin Properties

The mechanical properties of an unmodified resin system and the variously modified resin systems are compared in Table 3. Addition of thermoplastic to the resin results in an improvement of the RT/Dry flexural strength by 10 to 30% depending on the system. In the case of both the Udel and Resistherm modified epoxy resins, the flexural strength increases with increasing level of thermoplastic. The 6.5%w Ultem modified system has the highest flexural strength of any of the materials measured, but in this case the flexural strength decreases with increasing amounts of thermoplastic. The modulus and elongation of all of the systems at room temperature seem relatively unaffected by the type or loading of thermoplastic.

On the basis of the limited data available it appears that thermoplastic modification has only a marginal influence on the 120°C/dry mechanical properties of the systems examined. However, the Ultem and Resistherm modified resins have significantly improved properties at 175°C/dry compared to the unmodified resin system. The low value of flexural strength and modulus for the Udel modified system at 175°C may be a reflection of the lower glass transition temperature (190°C) of the polysulfone compared to the other two thermoplastics.

The fracture toughness of all thermoplastic modified epoxy resins increases with an increasing level of thermoplastic. At the 30%w thermoplastic level, Resistherm PH-10 seems to provide the highest degree of toughening of the three thermoplastics tested. Ultem ranks second and the lowest degree of toughening is with the polyethersulfone (UDEL 1700). Interestingly, low polysulfone concentrations (6.5-13%w) only provide a marginal toughness increase. As expected, toughness is improved at higher polysulfone concentrations (30%w). However, it has to be borne in mind that the samples with low UDEL-polysulfone levels (6.5 and 13%w) have been prepared by a casting process whereas the 30%w sample was compression molded. For polyetherimide and polyhydantoin, a close to linear correlation is found for the fracture energy (G_{Ic}) versus the thermoplastic concentration. However, the fracture energies for all thermoplastic modified epoxies are below the values that would be expected from the rule of mixtures.

2.4 Morphologies

Figures 1a, 1b, 1c, and 1d are SEM's of the fracture surfaces of the unmodified epoxy resin system, and the 10, 20, and 30%w. Resistherm modified systems, respectively. Figure 1a the SEM of the unmodified EPON HPT Resin 1071/EPON HPT Curing Agent 1062 system shows no discernible features and is indicative of a brittle fracture surface. In Figure 1b, the 10%w. Resistherm system, small cavities and spherical particles of 0.1 to 0.5 μm in diameter of thermoplastic can be seen. It appears, however, that there is little or no, adhesion between the matrix and thermoplastic as evidenced by the nearly spherical particles which have been pulled out of the matrix leaving clean holes. Also a few particles of thermoplastic, which appear to have been pulled out of the matrix, are just lying on the surface. Considerable plastic deformation can be seen in Figure 1c the SEM of the fracture surface of the 20%w. Resistherm modified system; but no discernible particles or nodules can be seen in the matrix. Also plastic deformation is evident in Figure 1d, the SEM of the 30%w. Resistherm modified resin system; however, irregular shaped particles or nodules of about 0.5 to 1.0 μm can readily be seen. These particles are believed to be domains of epoxy resin imbedded in a continuous phase of thermoplastic.

At levels below 20%w Resistherm, the epoxy resin appears to be the continuous phase, but above this level the thermoplastic becomes the continuous phase. When immersed in methylene chloride the system containing 30%w. Resistherm disintegrates in about 24 hours leaving an insoluble residue. This is taken as evidence that the thermoplastic, which is soluble in methylene chloride, is dissolving from around the dispersed particles of epoxy resin. There is considerable whitening of the specimen containing 20%w. thermoplastic after 24 hours immersion in methylene chloride, but no change was observed with the system modified with 10%w. thermoplastic.

3. COMPOSITES

Based on the results of neat resin fracture toughness evaluation, Resistherm PH-10 modified epoxy resins were selected for preliminary composite evaluation. Carbon fabric reinforcement (based on T300/6000-carbon fibers), style 1/7 stain weave (obtained from Interglas Ulm, West Germany) was used in these preliminary screening studies. The EPON HPT 1071/EPON HPT 1062 matrix was evaluated without thermoplastic modification and with two Resistherm levels (13 and 25%). The aim of this preliminary study was to obtain basic information on the influence of thermoplastic modifier on laminate properties such as interlaminar shear strength, flexural strength and fracture toughness (G_{Ic} and G_{IIc}).

3.1 Composite Specimen Preparation

Carbon fabric as specified above was impregnated with a methylene chloride solution of the test resin system (20%w concentration) system. Carbon fabric (32 × 32 cm square) was placed on a glass plate with dams. Resin solution was poured uniformly over the reinforcement and subsequently the methylene chloride was allowed to evaporate at room temperature, leaving a prepreg which was then dried in a circulating air oven at 70°C for one hour. The residual solvent content (volatiles) in the prepregs was below 0.8%w.

Laminates were molded via an autoclave procedure, employing a so-called restricted flow/bleed lay-up technique. The unmodified epoxy resin (with no thermoplastic modification) was cured at a pressure of 4 bars following the cure cycle given in Figure 2. The thermoplastic modified versions were also autoclaved employing the same temperature profile but the molding pressure was increased to 15 bars (200 psi). Laminates were postcured for 2 hours at 200°C in a circulating air oven.

3.2 Laminate Properties

The mechanical properties obtained for all laminates are compiled in Table 4. The properties of the unmodified EPON HPT 1071/EPON HPT 1062 system are typical for epoxy carbon fabric, fracture toughness, but are somewhat improved versus MY 720/DDS, (data not given for MY 720/DDS), in particular for G_{Ic} and G_{IIc}. For the Resistherm modified epoxy resins the flexural strength of both Resistherm levels (13 and 25%) at 177°C is marginally improved versus the unmodified base line. Shear strength, however, is slightly decreased as would be expected for a toughened resin system. The high temperature properties of the thermoplastic modified laminates are not adversely affected by the thermoplastic modifier due to the high Tg of Resistherm (>250°C). As was to be expected, the G_{Ic} and G_{IIc} values are significantly improved with increasing thermoplastic concentration.

4. CONCLUSIONS

EPON HPT Resin 1071/EPON HPT Curing Agent 1062 is a very suitable resin system for carbon fiber composites. Thermoplastics like polyethersulfone (UDEL 1700), polyetherimide (ULTEM 1000) and polyhydantoin (Resistherm PH-10) can be employed as toughening modifiers. Resistherm PH-10 provided the highest degree of toughening of all three thermoplastics tested. It was demonstrated that neat resin fracture toughness is significantly improved at thermoplastic levels of 20-30%w. When polyhydantoin is used at levels of ca. 20%w, the system undergoes a phase inversion.

Composite fracture toughness is significantly improved for the Resistherm modified epoxy resins as was demonstrated by G_{Ic} and G_{IIc} measurements on carbon fabric laminates.

5. REFERENCES

1. a) McGarry, F.J. and Willner, A.M., Dept. Civil Eng. Rep. R-68, MIT, 1968: b) McGarry, F.J. and Sultan, J.N., 24th A. Tech. Conf. SPI 1969, Section 11-b: and McGarry, F.J. and Willner, A.M., ACS Div. Org. Coat. Plast. Chem. Prep., **28**, Paper 512, 1968.

2. Siebert, R., Rubber-Modified Thermoset Resins, eds. Riew, C.K. and Gillham, J.K., p. 179, ACS Advances in Chemistry Series 208, American Chemical Society, Washington, D.C., 1983.

3. Raghava, R.S., 28th National SAMPE Symposium. p. 267, April 12-14, 1983.

4. Bucknall, C.B. and Partridge, I., Brit. Polym. Jour., 15, 71(1983).

5. Sefton, M.S., McGrall, P.T., Peacock, J.A., Wilkinson, S.P., Crick, R.A., Davies, D., and Almen, G., 19th International SAMPE Technical Conf., p. 700, October 13-15, 1987.

6. Shimp, D.A., Hudock, F.A., and Boho, W.S., 18th International SAMPE Technical Conf., p. 851, October 1987.

7. Stenzenberger, H.D., Römer, W., Herzog, M., and König, P., 33rd Internation SAMPE Symposium, 1546, March 7-10, 1988.

8. Bauer, R.S., 31st International SAMPE Symposium, p. 1104, April 7-10, 1986.

6. BIOGRAPHIES

Dr. Ronald S. Bauer obtained his Ph.D in Organic Chemistry for the University of California at Los Angeles. After graduation, he joined Shell Development Company at Emeryville, California, as a chemist where he worked in the areas of exploratory polymer synthesis, polymer characterization, polymer processing, and polymer process research. During 1971 and 1972 he was an exchange scientist at Shell's Egham Research Laboratories in Surrey, England, where he worked on the development of non-aqueous dispersions of epoxy resins. Currently, he is a Senior Staff Research Chemist at Shell Development Company's Westhollow Research Center in Houston, Texas, where he has been involved in the development of weatherable epoxy resin coatings, high solids epoxy coatings, and new epoxy resins for advanced composites and electrical applications.

Dr. Bauer has publications and patents covering epoxide, olefin, and diene polymerization involving both homogenous and heterogeneous catalysis. Also he has written a review articles on epoxy resins and has edited two books on the subject. In 1985, he was chairman of the Division of Polymeric Materials: Science and Engineering of the American Chemical Society.

Dr. Horst D. Stenzenberger received a chemical engineering degree from the Technical University of Vienna in 1967. In 1969, he received his Ph.D. in Technical Sciences from the same university. Dr. Stenzenberger joined Technochemie, a subsidiary of Deutsche Shell AG in March 1969. He is currently the Director of Research and Technical Representative for high temperature polyimide resins.

Table 1. Neat Resin Properties of
EPON HPT® Resin 1071 Cured[1]) with DDS

Curing Agent	H_2N—⟨◯⟩—$\overset{\overset{O}{\|\|}}{\underset{\underset{O}{\|\|}}{S}}$—⟨◯⟩—$NH_2$	
Resin / Properties	TGMDA[2])	EPON HPT Resin 1071
Tg (Tan δ), °C	262	249
Flexural Properties (RT/Dry)		
Strength, Mpa	138	117
Modulus, GPa	3.9	3.9
Elongation, %	5.0	3.7
Flexural Properties (Hot/Wet)[3])		
Strength, MPa	76	90
Modulus, GPa	2.5	3.0
Elongation, %	4.7	4.2
Moisture Gain, %w[4])	5.7	3.6

1) *Cured with Stoichiometric Amount of Curing Agent, Cure Schedule 2 hr at 150° and 4 hr at 200°C.*

2) *Formulation Contains 8.2 phr EPI-REZ SU-8 (Interez, Inc.).*

3) *Tested in Water at 93°C After Two Weeks Immersion at 93°C.*

Table 2. Structures and Tg of Thermoplastic Modifiers

Thermoplastic Trade Name Manufacturer	Structure	Tg, °C
Polyethersulfone (PSU) UDEL 1700 Union Carbide Corporation		190
Polyetherimide (ULT) ULTEM 1000 General Electric Company		220
Polyhydantoin (RT) Resistherm PH-10 Bayer Ag.		>250

Table 3. Properties of Thermoplastic Modified EPON HPT® Resin 1071 Cured with EPON HPT Curing Agent 1062

Property	Control	%w, Udel[a]			%w, Ultem[b]			%w, Resistherm[c]		
		6.5	13.0	30	6.5	13.0	30	10	20	30
T_g (Tan δ) °C	212	236	230	194	226	229	215	212	223	225
Flexural Properties (RT/Dry)										
Strength, MPa	109	124	131	139	145	138	125	122	133	143
Modulus, GPa	3.49	3.38	3.40	3.35	3.52	3.47	3.54	3.48	3.19	3.16
Elongation, %	3.2	4.4	4.6	4.5	4.9	4.8	3.7	3.6	4.4	5.5
Flexural Properties (120°C/Dry)										
Strength, MPa	100	—	—	103	—	—	107	112	109	117
Modulus, GPa	2.81	—	—	2.77	—	—	2.91	2.85	2.69	2.87
Elongation, %	4.19	—	—	5.34	—	—	3.91	5.35	5.53	5.58
Flexural Properties (175°C/Dry)										
Strength, MPa	52	—	—	17	—	—	74	67	71	80
Modulus, GPa	1.78	—	—	0.68	—	—	2.45	2.35	2.37	2.52
Elongation, %	4.78	—	—	>5.23	—	—	4.49	4.37	4.40	4.26
Fracture Toughness K_q, $KN/m^2 \times m^{1/2}$	520-568	607	640	1031	770	942	1314	895	1042	1351
Fracture Energy G_{1C}, J/m^2	77-95	110	121	386	169	256	488	230	321	578
Moisture Gain, %w[d]	1.41	1.01	0.98	1.38[e]	1.04	1.02	1.30[e]	1.55	1.51	1.72

a) Udel 1700 from Union Carbide Coporation. Test specimens containing 6.5 and 13%w Udel were prepared by melt casting the resin systems. The 30%w Udel sample was prepared by compression molding.

b) Ultem 1000 from General Electric Company. Test specimens containing 6.5 and 13%w Ultem prepared by melt casting the resin systems. The 30%w Ultem sample was prepared by compression molding.

c) Resistherm from Bayer AG. All test speimens were obtained by compressing molding.

d) Mositure gain was obtained on test specimens prepared by melt casting after two weeks immersion in water at 93°C, and specimens prepared by compression molding after 500 hrs at 94% relative humidity.

e) Samples were immersed in 70°C water for 500 hrs.

Table 4. Properties of Thermoplasti c Modified EPON HPT® Resin 1071/EPON HPT 1062 Curing Agent—Carbon Fabric Laminates

Thermoplastic Modifier: Resistherm PH-10
Fabric Style: Satin Weave 1/7, Area Weight 365 g/m^2

Property	HPT 1071[a] HPT 1062	HPT 1071 HPT 1062 Resistherm 13%	HPT 1071 HPT 1062 Resistherm 25%
Resin content, %v	53.49	60.67	60.70
Density, g/cm^3	1.4046	1.5338	1.4866
SBS-Strength, MPa,[b]			
23°C	65	55	60
120°C	52	43	46
177°C	45	41	39
Flexural Strength,[c] MPa			
23°C	1021	957	918
120°C	969	870	808
177°C	906	785	683
Flexural Modulus,[c] GPa			
23°C	65.17	62.59	62.51
120°C	67.90	62.16	62.83
177°C	68.52	62.33	61.66
G_{Ic} (J/m2) 23°C	680	855	1078
G_{IIc} (J/m2) 23°C	385	405	661

a) HPT 1071 100 parts + HPT 1061 61 parts.
b) SBS = Short beam shear (LS:D = 5:1).
c) Values normalized to 60%v.

Fig. 1a. SEM OF FRACTURE SURFACE OF UNMODIFIED
EPON HPT® RESIN 1071/EPON HPT CURING AGENT 1062

013490

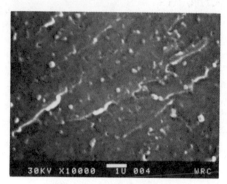

Fig. 1b. SEM OF FRACTURE SURFACE OF
EPON HPT® RESIN 1071/EPON HPT CURING AGENT 1062
MODIFIED WITH 10%w RESISTHERM PH-10

013490

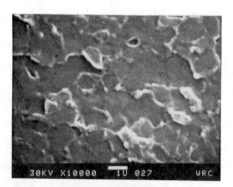

Fig. 1c. SEM OF FRACTURE SURFACE OF
EPON HPT® RESIN 1071/EPON HPT CURING AGENT 1062
MODIFIED WITH 20%w RESISTHERM PH-10

013490

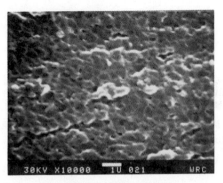

Fig. 1d. SEM OF FRACTURE SURFACE OF
EPON HPT® RESIN 1071/EPON HPT CURING AGENT 1062
MODIFIED WITH 30%w RESISTHERM PH-10

013490

○ Pull Vacuum
△ Apply Pressure [1,2]
□ Vent Vacuum and Release Pressure

1 = 4 Bars for EPON HPT 1071/HPT 1062
2 = 15 Bars for the Thermoplastic Modified Versions

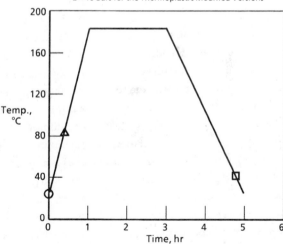

Fig. 2. AUTOCLAVE CURE CYCLE OF
EPON HPT® RESIN 1071/EPON HPT CURING
AGENT 1062 – CARBON FIBRE LAMINATES

013490-1

909

34th International SAMPE Symposium
May 8-11, 1989

AN ORTHO-THIOALKYLATED AROMATIC DIAMINE AS AN IMPROVED LIQUID HARDENER FOR CARBON FIBER REINFORCED EPOXY MATRICES (II)

Rex B. Gosnell, Ph.D.
Cape Composites Inc.
San Diego, California

Abstract

An earlier paper presented last year, revealed the potential utility and unique viscosity - reactivity relationship of this commercially available dimethyl-thiotoluenediamine (ETHACURE® 300 Curative)[1] as a hardener for epoxy matrix resins for carbon fiber prepreg. This paper presents continued studies and more specific formulations designed to take advantage of solid multifunctional epoxy resins such as EPON 1031[2], HPT 1071[2], TACTIX 742[3] and others, which usually produce resins with high glass transition temperatures. Baseline formulations are presented which exhibit classical prepreg processing behavior and take advantage of the high temperature performance of these resins when used in combination with dimethyl-thiotoluenediamine (ETHACURE® 300 Curative). Data which demonstrates the translation of shear, flexural strength and modulus, both wet and dry, in carbon fiber composites is presented. The utility of this low viscosity amine is advantageous in formulation without the need for resin advancement or "B" staging with such solid epoxy resins. The reduced hydrophylic nature of these formulations results in excellent retention of mechanical properties of carbon fiber composites upon hot-wet exposures. The chemistry provided by this amine represents a new formulation approach to high performance carbon fiber epoxy prepreg.

1) Trademark of Ethyl Corporation
2) Trademark of Shell Chemical Company
3) Trademark of Dow Chemical Company

1. INTRODUCTION

Last spring, we reported the early studies with a new liquid hardener for epoxy resins which is an isomeric mixture of 3,5-dimethylthio-2,4-toluenediamine (I) and 3,5-dimetylthio-2,6-toluenediamine (II) and sold commercially as ETHACURE® 300 Curative. This system was proposed as a viable alternative to solid amines such as diaminodiphenylsulfone commonly used in prepreg formulations.

In that reported work, it was demonstrated that this diamine system offered considerable potential as a curing agent for epoxy resins, particularly in the areas of improved high temperature mechanical properties and low water pickup.

ETHACURE® 300 Curative

NH_2 SCH_3

CH_3 —————— NH_2 (I)

SCH_3

NH_2 SCH_3

CH_3 ——————   (II)

NH_2 SCH_3

The additional work reported in this paper was designed to demonstrate the versatility of this low viscosity liquid hardener by exploring its use with solid epoxy resins, resulting in commercially acceptable tacky resins from otherwise intractable powdery epoxy systems.

Toward this purpose, three solid epoxy resins were chosen which have recognized potential as matrix systems, but suffer from the formulation disadvantage of being higher melting solids and consequently presenting a serious limitation with any prepreg resin formulation with the classical commercial solid hardener, diaminodiphenylsulfone. These three solid epoxy resins were:

Shell EPON 1031
Dow TACTIX 742
Shell HPT 1071

Shell EPON 1031 was chosen because of its recognized high temperature properties and also because of its reported unusually high reactivity with ETHACURE® 300 Curative. This phenomenon is unexplained but real. The melting behavior of EPON 1031 is such that additional liquid modifier, MY-720, is required in the formulation to result in sufficient prepreg tack.

Dow TACTIX 742 was selected also because of its high temperature capability and similarity in reactivity to Ciba ARALDITE MY-720.

Shell HPT 1071 is a blocking solid epoxy which was studied because of its high temperature capability but especially because of its high functionality.

2. OBJECTIVE

The objective of this investigation was to carry out the following development work:

* Formulate ETHACURE® 300 Curative with three solid epoxies in order to assess the curative's utility as both a hardener and a low viscosity liquid modifier.
* Prepare suitable carbon fiber prepregs from these resin systems and determine their potential and limitations as candidates for commercial prepreg.

3. FORMULATIONS

The investigations were conducted with the following formulations. A general description of handling procedures is included.

Mix 100

Shell EPON 1031	80.0 parts
Ciba ARALDITE MY-720	20.0 parts
ETHACURE® 300 Curative	28.0 parts

This formulation was prepared for off-line film casting prior to prepreg preparation, by melting together coarsely ground EPON 1031 and ARALDITE MY-72 at 350 °F. The homogeneous melt was then cooled to 200 °F and the ETHACURE® 300 Curative was mixed into the blend. The mix was stabilized at 160 - 165 °F. The flow disc diameter was 1.8" and gel time was 10 mins. at 350 °F. The resin system was cast into film on release paper using Cape's continuous casting line within 1 hour after stabilization at 160 - 165 °F. The film was stored at 0 °F until prepreg preparation. The resin lost tack after 7 days storage at room temperature but retained flexibility.

After post cure, the neat resin had a density of 1.27 gm/cc.

Mix 101

| Dow TACTIX 742 | 100.0 parts |
| ETHACURE® 300 Curative | 33.0 parts |

A melt was prepared by heating the epoxy resin at 250 °F and then adding the ETHACURE® 300. The system was advanced by holding at 250 °F for about 20-30 mins to achieve a flow disc of 1.9" and a gel time of 11 mins at 350 °F. The resin mix was cooled immediately and stabilized at 160 -165 °F. The resin was cast into film on release paper using Cape's continuous casting equipment within 2 hours. The film was stored at 0 °F.

After post cure, the neat resin had a density of 1.26 gm/cc.

Mix 102

```
Shell HPT  1071            100.0 parts
ETHACURE® 300 Curative      33.4 parts
```

This resin system was prepared for film casting by melting the resin at 250 °F and adding the ETHACURE® 300. The system was advanced at 250 °F and then cooled and stabilized at 165 °F. The resin was cast into film and stored at 40 °F. The resin mix has a surprisingly low reactivity and advancement for four hours at 250 °F, only produced a flow disc diameter of 2.4"

After post cure, the neat resin had a density of 1.19 gm/cc.

A resin film was made that was too tacky for commercial purposes, but an acceptable prepreg was prepared for lab study. This prepreg had a gel time greater than four hours. Small scale tests indicated that when cooked to the correct end point, the shelf life will exceed 10 days at 70 °F. The uncooked mix has a RT shelf life in excess of thirty days. A catalyzed version of this mix (Mix 102A) was also evaluated. This version was catalyzed with Ciba Geigy's DY-064.

4. PREPREG AND LAMINATES
Prepreg

Prepreg was prepared from the cast films of the above resins using Cape's 12" laboratory prepreg machine loaded with 60 spools of Hercules AS-4 12K. Impregnation temperature was the same in all cases at about 200 °F. Variations in the prepregging process are required from time to time and an experienced operator is always desirable in order to do the right things during prepregging a resin batch. In these experimental runs, resin content was 35-40% and the prepreg areal weight was measured at 155 ±2 gm/m². Fifteen pounds of prepreg were prepared from each resin formulation.

| | Gel Time(mins) | | Flow Disc | Resin | Fiber Areal |
	350 °F	270 °F	Diam.	Content %	Weight g/m²
Mix 100	10	42	1.8"	35	155
Mix 101	11	50	2.3"	38	157
Mix 102	>240	–	2.4"	37	153
Mix 102A	40	115	2.2"	47	141

Reactivity

The reactivity of the resins used in this study, when formulated with ETHACURE® 300 , fell in the following order of reactivity:

> Epon 1031
> Tactix 742
> MY 720
> HPT 1071

All observations with the Shell HPT 1071/ETHACURE® 300 formulation indicated that it was most definitely a slow system. Earlier work with ETHACURE® 300 suggested that it was subject to some steric blocking of reaction due to the ortho substitution. With Shell HPT 1071, this substituted glycidyl ether has some steric effects of its own and between the two components, the reaction rate is quite slow, in fact, too slow to be feasible for realistic consideration as a prepreg system. In an attempt to accelerate the reaction of Shell HPT 1071/ETHACURE® 300, a modification of Mix 102 (Mix 102A) was examined which in-cluded 0.4 phr of a mixed tertiary amine accelerator, Ciba Geigy DY 064. This resulted in apparent normal behavior in shelf life and gel time, except that high temperature properties were not acceptable. This indicates that the reactivity and mobility of epoxy sites are a problem with this system.

The observations in regard to reactivity on all of the resin systems, were based on the gel times, the shelf life, and required cooking time to achieve appropriate flow disc diameter. As a note of interest, mixing 20% of MY-720 with Epon 1031, only increased the gel time from 9 minutes to 10 minutes. This is very unexpected behavior. Gel time, flow disc diameter and prepreg information are shown above.

Laminates

Mix 100

Experimental laminates were studied in order to define a satisfactory cure schedule as follows:

Hold at 270 °F with contact pressure only for 45 minutes then gradually close mold to stops during ramp up from 270 °F to 355 °F at 25 °F/min. and hold at 355 °F for 2 hours. Cool to 150 °F. A test quality laminate was prepared using 17 plies at 5.5 mils/ply (cured thickness). Samples were tested at elevated temperature and hot-wet shear both before and after a postcure of 2 hours at 420 °F.

Mix 101

The prepreg was prepared as described above except that a reduced cook time at 250 °F was used, yielding a flow disc of 2.3 inches. Several laminates were prepared in order to define laminating conditions.

Mix 102

Film was used as described above.

This system is very slow. Staging for 15 to 20 hours at 200 °F now seems likely. This is not workable and although test laminates may be prepared with patience, a viable modification is needed for practical prepreg. A formulation with 0.4 phr of tertiary amine accelerator (Ciba Geigy DY 064) has a much faster reaction rate and such a formulation (Mix 102A) is being evaluated in further work.

Laminate Mechanical Properties

	ILS Dry				ILS Hot-Wet		
	RT	350°F	420°F		RT	350°F	420°F
Mix 100	15,700		6,000		13,500	8,000	5,000
	Flex Str		Flex Mod				
	−		−				

	ILS Dry				ILS Hot-Wet		
	RT	350°F	420°F		RT	350°F	420°F
Mix 101	14,600	−	−		−	−	−
	Flex Str		Flex Mod				
	−		−				

Mix 102   Unsatisfactory Cures

	ILS Dry				ILS Hot-Wet		
	RT	350°F	420°F		RT	350°F	420°F
Mix 102A	16,000	−	−		15,000	−	−

Odor

The odor problem with ETHACURE® 300 is of some concern. It has an odor which seems to be due to a mercaptan or similar component. Uncured prepreg has an odor and it is also generated during curing and machining of the carbon fiber composites. Unfortunately, these types of compounds are detectable by the nose at concentration levels as low as 50 ppb in air. Some of the early diamine samples received from Ethyl Corporation had significantly higher odor levels than more recent production. Ethyl is continuing efforts to identify and eliminate odorous components by production of a higher purity thioether. Prereaction with a small amount of epoxy resin, to react out odorous components, does not look encouraging. Small amounts of reodorants in the formulation are somewhat effective in masking odor.

5. SUMMARY

This isomeric mixture of dimethylthiotoluenediamines sold as ETHACURE® 300 Curative offers the prepreg resin formulator several features which are very useful in tailoring advanced prepreg systems. The reduced hydrophylic nature arising from the chemical structure of this thioether system offers attractive high temperature performance and good retention of these mechanical properties after hot-wet exposures. In addition, the low viscosity of this liquid diamine provides a useful degree of latitude in adjusting flow and tack of many of the new solid highly functional epoxy resins making them useful candidates in both the prepregging and fabrication processes.

TOUGHENABLE EPOXY RESIN FOR ELEVATED TEMPERATURE APPLICATIONS

L. M. Schlaudt, R. S. Bauer, and C. A. Blackburn
Shell Development Company
Westhollow Research Center
P. O. Box 1380
Houston, Texas 77251-1380

Abstract

A novel epoxy resin has been developed which exhibits a high glass transition temperature and low moisture absorption. This combination of attributes results in good retention of hot/wet properties up to 177°C. The resin is also amenable to toughening. The chemical structure of this resin is disclosed and the relationship between structure and toughenability are discussed. An example of a toughening approach is detailed.

1. INTRODUCTION

As composite materials are considered for use in more demanding applications, environmental resistance of materials becomes more important. Epoxy resins have often been considered unsuitable for use under hot/wet conditions because of high levels of moisture absorption (1). This has traditionally been true for resin systems containing tetraglycidyl methylenedianiline (TGMDA) and di-aminodiphenyl sulfone (DDS). More recently, the EPON HPT® resins and curing agents have demonstrated that epoxy resins can be suitable for use in hot/wet environments up to 177°C (2). The most recent addition to this product line is EPON HPT Resin 1079, the diglycidyl ether of the bisphenol of fluorenone. The structure and typical properties of this material are shown in Figure 1.

EPON HPT Resin 1079, when cured with EPON HPT Curing Agent 1062, yields a material with a high glass transition temperature (Tg) and flexural modulus, and low moisture absorption. Neat resin properties for this system are found in Table 1. EPON HPT Resin 1079 has also proven to be amenable to toughening through the use of second phase rubber particles (3). However, with its high viscosity, this resin system yields prepreg material that is dry and boardy.

A program was undertaken to formulate a model system using EPON HPT Resin 1079, in order to improve its prepreg characteristics while retaining cured properties. A toughening modifier was added to the model prepreg system to determine the impact of formulation upon the toughenability of EPON HPT Resin 1079.

2. TOUGHENING OF EPOXY RESINS

2.1 Background

It has long been known that carboxyl terminated butadiene-acrylonitrile copolymer

(CTBN rubber) improves the toughness of epoxy resins by forming a dispersed second phase in the cured matrix (4). However, highly crosslinked epoxy systems are limited in the degree to which they can be toughened. Kunz and co-workers (5) found an initial toughness increase with the addition of 5% by weight CTBN or amine terminated butadiene-acrylonitrile copolymer (ATBN) to a bisphenol A type epoxy system. However, increasing the level of rubber in the system failed to produce a corresponding improvement in fracture toughness.

The molecular weight between crosslinks (M_c) in an epoxy matrix is an indicator of the suitability of that system for rubber modication (6). M_c may be increased by increasing the amine curing agent level. Pearson and Yee (7) show an order of magnitude increase in toughness for a given CTBN level with increasing M_c, as illustrated in Figure 2.

While toughness is improved by an increasing distance between crosslinks, glass transition temperature (T_g) is reduced. Therefore, it has proven difficult to develop tough epoxy resin matrix materials with T_g's on the order of 200°C.

2.2 Toughening EPON HPT Resin 1079

The unique, stiff backboned structure of EPON HPT Resin 1079 results in a cured matrix having a T_g higher than obtainable using conventional bisphenol A type epoxy resins (8). Table 2 illustrates this by comparing EPON HPT Resin 1079, cured with selected amine curing agents, to several traditional epoxies. Due to this inherently high T_g, EPON HPT Resin 1079 has the potential to be toughened using CTBN rubber and excess amine curing agent, while maintaining good thermal resistance.

Addition of CTBN rubber to EPON HPT Resin 1079 cured with a stoichiometric amount of amine does not greatly improve toughness. However, when excess amine is added, the toughness is appreciably improved. Table 3 compares the cured resin toughness for a given level of CTBN rubber and various amounts of EPON HPT Curing Agent 1062. The T_g and selected mechanical properties for each formulation are also shown. Further improvements in toughness are achieved with the addition of higher levels of CTBN rubber, as shown in Table 4. This ability of EPON HPT Resin 1079 to form a thermally resistant, tough matrix makes it a likely candidate for inclusion in advanced composites formulations.

3. PREPREG FORMULATION

3.1 Requirements

While material performance is a driving force in the selection of resin systems for advanced applications, composites processing is also a critical concern. Tack and drape continue to be desirable qualities in prepreg materials. Because of its inherent high viscosity, it seems certain that EPON HPT Resin 1079 will find a place as a component in formulations, rather than as a stand alone matrix resin. The optimal formulation will impart improved handling characteristics to the resin while retaining good thermal resistance and mechanical performance. In order to develop recommendations on the use of EPON HPT Resin 1079 in prepreg formulations, a simple model system was developed.

3.2 Approach

Effort was concentrated on reducing the viscosity of the resin system to impart tack and flexibility to the prepreg. Thin, neat resin films were used to screen systems initially. Formulations were subjectively evaluated on their flexibility at room temperature and their surface tack. In addition to these processing characteristics, cured resin properties were evaluated by dynamic mechanical analysis.

3.3 Results

Two formulations were chosen for further evaluation. The first consisted of EPON HPT Resin 1079 blended with EPON® Resin DPL-862, a bisphenol F resin, and cured with di-(methylthio)toluenediamine (DMTDA). The second replaced half the EPON Resin DPL-862 with triglycidyl aminophenol (TGAP), a low viscosity multifunctional epoxy resin. These presented the best combinations of processing characteristics, Tg, and modulus of all formulations evaluated. The compositions of these formulations are detailed in Table 5. In both cases, a stoichiometric amount of curing agent was used.

Neat resin castings were prepared for both formulations and screening tests were performed. These tests included dynamic mechanical Tg, fracture toughness, room temperature and hot wet flexural properties, and moisture absorption. The data for the two formulations are compared to that for EPON HPT Resin 1079/EPON HPT Curing Agent 1062 in Table 6. While the Tg and moisture resistance suffered slightly from the addition of low viscosity components, the initial and hot wet flexural moduli showed improvement over the base system, though retention of properties under hot wet conditions was slightly diminished.

4. PREPREG EVALUATION

4.1 Preparation

Unidirectional prepreg tape was made from the two formulations, using sized IM6 fiber from Hercules. The viscosity of both systems dropped below 10,000 cP at 60-70°C, a suitable viscosity for film casting. At about 93°C, the viscosity fell in the range of 500-700 cP, an appropriate level for fiber impregnation. In addition, the working life of both systems at these temperatures was in excess of two hours. Enough prepreg was prepared to fabricate several laminates for limited mechanical testing. Both prepreg production and laminate fabrication were performed by Cape Composites, Inc. in San Diego.

4.2 Cure Cycle Development

Composite laminates from these prepreg formulations were cured in a heated mold contained in a press. In order to achieve the proper fiber volume, a particular viscosity profile for the matrix resin was desired to reduce bleed. The desired viscosities had been previously established (9), so temperature profiles were evaluated on these formulations to produce the desired viscosity behavior. The cure cycle which produced the desired viscosity profile consisted of a slow ramp (2°C/min.) from room temperature to 130°C, with a three hour hold at that point, followed by a slow ramp to 200°C and a one hour hold at that temperature. The viscosity profile resulting from this cure cycle is shown in Figure 3. The laminates could then be removed from the mold and postcured for one hour at

200°C and one hour at 250°C to develop properties fully. This postcure had been established at Westhollow Research Center through dynamic mechanical testing of small laminates.

4.3 Laminate Testing

Two sets of laminates, 8 plies and 16 plies thick, were fabricated from each prepreg formulation. These laminates were ultrasonically analyzed for flaws prior to postcure, machining and testing. All laminates exhibited good consolidation around the edges, with poorer consolidation and increased indications in the center of the panel. These results suggested insufficient resin flow or air entrapment during cure and increased porosity or delaminations in the center of the panels. When the laminates were postcured, the areas corresponding to the most severe indications on the C-scans delaminated, resulting in bubbles on the laminate surfaces.

The tests in progress for these laminates are 0° tension, compression (ASTM D695 method), flexure, and short beam shear. Well consolidated coupons, from delamination-free areas of panels, will be tested. Thus, fewer specimens will be available for testing, and limited data will be generated. Machining and testing are underway and data will be reported when available.

Samples of uncured prepreg will be evaluated by thermogravimetric analysis (TGA), followed by mass spectroscopy of released gases. We will attempt to determine whether moisture absorbed by the matrix during processing, or volatiles evolved during cure, are responsible for the delaminations.

5. TOUGHENING OF MODEL SYSTEM

5.1 Approach

As previously noted, two features of EPON HPT Resin 1079 which make it amenable to toughening are the stiff backbone structure and inherently high Tg. By adding viscosity modifiers to these formulations, both Tg and backbone structure are affected. It remains to be seen whether these model formulations are readily toughenable.

The system containing both EPON Resin DPL-862 and triglycidal aminophenol was carried forward into the toughening evaluations. It has the higher Tg of the two model systems and a slightly higher initial toughness. Using the system as originally developed, with a stoichiometric quantity of DMTDA, two levels of CTBN rubber were added. While it has already been shown that both rubber modifiers and excess amine curative contribute to enhanced toughness, these initial data were intended to reveal trends, not to optimize toughness. This system was evaluated against EPON HPT Resin 1079/EPON HPT Curing Agent 1062, also in a stoichiometric ratio, with the same levels of rubber modifier.

5.2 Results

Table 7 contains neat resin casting data for the formulated system with no CTBN modifier, and with 10 phr and 20 phr CTBN. The same data are presented for the EPON HPT Resin 1079/EPON HPT Curing Agent 1062 control. The formulated system suffers a 4-6% greater loss in Tg due to the added rubber than the control. However, Tg remains above 200°C for the formulation even at 20 phr CTBN. Toughness is improved to a greater degree in the control system than in the formulated material. However, the crack length was difficult to measure in these compact tension coupons because of the opaque nature of the formulated resin system. It is likely that these Kq values are conservatively low. We can therefore conclude that toughness is enhanced by the addition of CTBN rubber at both levels, even with a stoichiometric amount of curing agent, but the presence of low viscosity modifiers in the EPON HPT Resin 1079 matrix may diminish the extent of toughenability of the system. Also, thermal resistance is depressed compared to the EPON HPT Resin 1079/EPON HPT Curing Agent 1062 system as a result of adding the viscosity modifiers.

Additional data will be generated for this formulation with excess curing agent at a constant level of rubber modifier. Of particular interest will be the sacrifice of Tg with relation to increasing toughness, and whether a limit exists to the toughenability of the formulated matrix.

6. CONCLUSIONS

EPON HPT Resin 1079 is a unique epoxy resin, capable of producing a cured matrix with high Tg and modulus, and improved resistance to moisture over traditional epoxy systems. Moreover, it is amenable to toughening through the use of CTBN rubber and excess amine curative, and maintains excellent thermal resistance. This resin may be formulated using small quantities of low viscosity components to produce tacky, drapable prepreg with good thermal and mechanical properties. While such formulations remain toughenable, attention should be addressed to optimizing thermal resistance in these systems.

7. REFERENCES

1. Clancy, H. M., and Luft, D. E., 18th International SAMPE Technical Conference, October 7-9, 1986, pp. 135-141.

2. Bauer, R. S., et al., 32nd International SAMPE Symposium, April 6-9, 1987, pp. 1104-1113.

3. Bauer, R. S., 18th International SAMPE Technical Conference, October 7-9, 1986, pp. 510-519.

4. a) McGarry, F. J., and Willner, A. M., Dept. Civil Eng. Rep., R68-8, MIT, 1968.
   b) McGarry, F. J., and Sultan, J. N., 24th A. Tech. Conf. SPI 1969, Section 1-b.
   c) McGarry, F. J., and Willner, A. M., ACS Div. Org. Coat. Plast. Chem. Prepr., 28, Paper 512, 1968.

5. Kunz, S. C., Sayre, J. A., and Assink, R. A., Polymer, 23, 1987 (1982).

6. Ochi, M., and Bell, J. P., J. Appl. Polym. Sci., 29, 1382 (1984).

7. Pearson, R. A., and Yee, A. F., Am. Chem. Soc., Proc. Div. Polym. Mat., 49, 316 (1983).

8. Bauer, R. S., Am. Chem. Soc., Proc. Div. Polym. Mat., 59, 820 (1988).

9. Bauer, R. S., et al., 33rd International SAMPE Symposium, March 7-10, 1988, pp. 1385-1393.

8. BIOGRAPHIES

LAURIE M. SCHLAUDT graduated from Texas A&M University in 1984 with a B.S. degree in Mechanical Engineering. She joined the Resins Department of Shell Development Company at the Westhollow

Research Center in Houston, TX, in June, 1984. As a member of the Advanced Composites Applications Group she is involved with thermosetting resins for aerospace applications. Her current responsibilities include material test program management, database development, filament winding and technical support.

DR. RONALD S. BAUER obtained his Ph.D. in Organic Chemistry from the University of California at Los Angeles. After graduation, he joined Shell Development Company at Emeryville, California, as a chemist working in the areas of exploratory polymer synthesis, polymer characterization, polymer processing, and polymer process research. Curently, he is a Senior Staff Research Chemist at Shell Development Company's

Westhollow Research Center in Houston, TX, where he has been involved in the development of weatherable epoxy resins, high solids epoxy coatings, and new epoxy resins for advanced composites and electrical applications.

CRAIG A. BLACKBURN attended the University of Houston, where he majored in chemistry and electronics. He has seven years of experience in the analysis of metallic and organic compounds. In 1984 he joined Shell Development Company at Westhollow Research Center in Houston, TX, in the Resins Department. As a Senior Research Technician in the Advanced Composites Applications group, he is responsible for the fabrication of composite test laminates using experimental resin systems.

Figure 1. Structure and Typical Properties of EPON HPT® Resin 1079

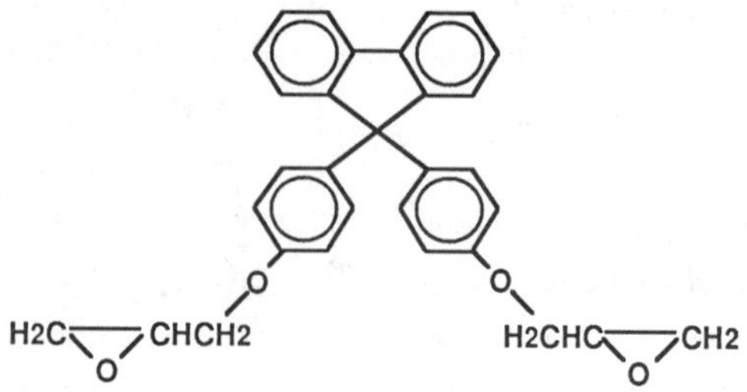

EPON HPT Resin 1079
9,9 bis(4-Glycidyloxyphenyl) Fluorene

Typical Properties of Neat Resin	
Physical Form	Glassy Solid
Epoxide Equivalent Weight	240-270
Melt Point, °C	80-82
Tg, °C	51-54
Viscosity, poise at 100°C	405
110°C	95
120°C	29
130°C	12
140°C	5
150°C	3

Figure 2. Fracture Energy (G₁c) as a Function of Molecular Weight Between Crosslinks for Unmodified and Rubber Modified Bisphenol A Epoxy Resins

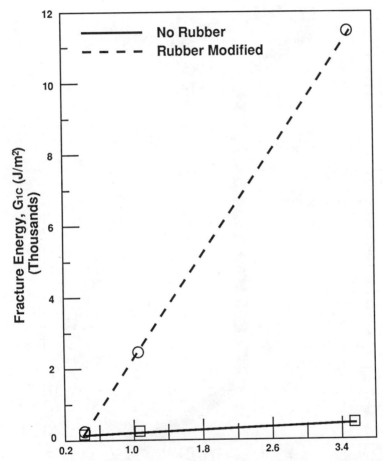

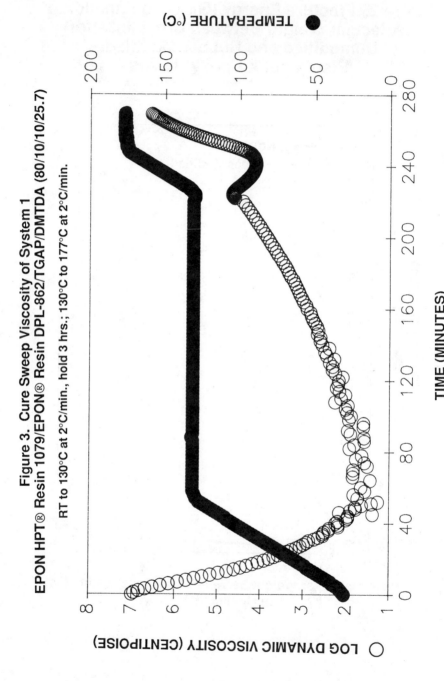

Figure 3. Cure Sweep Viscosity of System 1
EPON HPT® Resin 1079/EPON® Resin DPL-862/TGAP/DMTDA (80/10/10/25.7)

RT to 130°C at 2°C/min., hold 3 hrs.; 130°C to 177°C at 2°C/min.

Table 1. Neat Resin Mechanical Properties for EPON HPT® Resin 1079/EPON HPT Curing Agent 1062 [1]

Tg (tan delta), °C	264
Room temperature dry flexural properties	
Strength, MPa (ksi)	138 (20)
Modulus, GPa (ksi)	3.19 (462)
Elongation, %	6.4
Hot/wet flexural properties [2]	
Strength, MPa (ksi)	90 (13)
Modulus, GPa (ksi)	2.86 (415)
Elongation, %	4.1
Fracture toughness (Kq), psi√in	434
Modulus (wet/dry), % retention	90
Moisture gain, % wt.[3]	1.3

(1) Stoichiometric amount of curing agent
    Cured 2 hrs. at 150°C, 4 hrs. at 200°C
(2) Tested in water at 93°C after 2 weeks immersion at 93°C
(3) After 2 weeks immersion at 93°C

Table 2. Glass Transition Temperatures [1] of Selected EPON® Resin/Curing Agent Systems [2]

Curing Agent	EPON Resin 826 [3]	EPON Resin 828 [4]	EPON HPT® Resin 1079 [5]
Methylene Dianiline	175	163	246
Diaminodiphenylsulfone	210	195	290
EPON HPT® Curing Agent 1061	191	---	250
EPON HPT® Curing Agent 1062	171	---	243

(1) Dynamic mechanical method
(2) All systems cured with stoichiometric ratio of amine
(3) DGBPA (EEW 178-186)/Shell Chemical Company
(4) DGBPA (EEW 185-192)/Shell Chemical Company
(5) DGBPFL (EEW 240-270)/Shell Chemical Company

Table 3. Effect of Curing Agent Ratio on Neat Resin Properties of EPON HPT® Resin 1079/ EPON HPT Curing Agent 1062 with 10 phr Rubber[1]

Properties	1.00 x Curing Agent Stoichiometry	1.25 x Curing Agent Stoichiometry	1.50 x Curing Agent Stoichiometry	1.75 x Curing Agent Stoichiometry
Fracture toughness (Kq), psi√in	679	890	1092	1239
Tg (tan delta), °C	240	216	187	177
RT dry flex properties				
Strength, MPa (ksi)	124 (18)	131 (19)	131 (19)	83 (12)
Modulus, GPa (ksi)	2.9 (423)	3.1 (446)	3.2 (467)	3.4 (491)
Elongation, %	5.8	6.9	6.6	2.6
Hot/wet flex properties[2]				
Strength, MPa (ksi)	90 (13)	69 (10)	69 (10)	90 (13)
Modulus, GPa (ksi)	2.4 (346)	2.6 (371)	2.6 (376)	2.8 (412)
Elongation, %	7.6	12.5	10.6	5.0
Moisture gain, % wt.[3]	1.1	1.0	0.9	1.0

(1) HYCAR® CTBN 1300X8 Polymer (B. F. Goodrich Co.)
    Cured 2 hrs. at 150°C, 4 hrs. at 200°C
(2) Tested in water at 93°C after 2 weeks immersion at 93°C
(3) After 2 weeks immersion at 93°C

Table 4. Effect of Rubber Level[1] on Neat Resin Properties of EPON HPT® Resin 1079/EPON HPT Curing Agent 1062 at Curing Agent Level 1.25 x Stoichiometry

Properties	No Rubber	5 phr	10 phr	20 phr
Fracture toughness (Kq), psi√in	463	721	890	1173
Tg (tan delta), °C	238	225	216	209
RT dry flex properties				
Strength, MPa (ksi)	124 (18)	138 (20)	131 (19)	110 (16)
Modulus, GPa (ksi)	3.2 (458)	3.1 (453)	3.1 (446)	2.7 (385)
Elongation, %	5.1	6.8	6.9	8.4
Hot/wet flex properties[2]				
Strength, MPa (ksi)	83 (12)	103 (15)	69 (10)	69 (10)
Modulus, GPa (ksi)	2.8 (405)	2.7 (395)	2.6 (371)	2.1 (307)
Elongation, %	4.1	8.3	12.5	10.3
Moisture gain, % wt.[3]	0.9	1.0	1.0	1.2

(1) HYCAR® CTBN 1300X8 Polymer (B. F. Goodrich Co.)
    Cured 2 hrs. at 150°C, 4 hrs. at 200°C
(2) Tested in water at 93°C after 2 weeks immersion at 93°C
(3) After 2 weeks immersion at 93°C

Table 5. Model Prepreg Formulation Compositions

	System 1	System 2
EPON HPT® Resin 1079	80 parts	80 parts
Triglycidyl aminophenol	10 parts	-----
EPON® Resin DPL-862	10 parts	20 parts
Di-(methylthio)toluenediamine[1]	23.5 parts	23.5 parts

(1) Curing agent stoichiometry based on all epoxy components

Table 6. Neat Resin Mechanical Properties for Model Prepreg Formulations

Properties	EPON HPT® Resin 1079/ EPON HPT Curing Agent 1062 [1]	System 1 [2]	System 2 [2]
Tg (tan delta), °C	264	242	222
RT dry flexural properties			
Strength, MPa (ksi)	138 (20)	131 (19)	117 (17)
Modulus, GPa (ksi)	3.2 (462)	3.5 (513)	3.6 (519)
Elongation, %	6.4	5.3	3.9
Hot/wet flexural properties [3]			
Strength, MPa (ksi)	90 (13)	69 (10)	83 (12)
Modulus, GPa (ksi)	2.9 (415)	2.9 (414)	2.9 (420)
Elongation, %	4.1	2.6	2.9
Fracture toughness (Kq), psi$\sqrt{}$in	434	421	394
Moisture gain, % wt.[4]	1.3	1.4	1.2

(1) Cured 2 hrs. at 150°C, 4 hrs. at 200°C
(2) Cured 1 hr. at 121°C, 1 hr. at 177°C, 2 hrs. at 200°C
(3) Tested in water at 93°C after 2 week immersion at 93°C
(4) After 2 week immersion at 93°C

Table 7. Effect of Rubber Level[1] on Neat Resin Properties of Model Prepreg Formulation

Properties	System 1 [2]			EPON HPT® Resin 1079/ EPON HPT Curing Agent 1062 [3]		
	No rubber	10 phr	20 phr	No rubber	10 phr	20 phr
Fracture toughness (Kq), psi√in	421	620	691	434	679	845
Tg (tan delta), °C	242	214	203	264	240	236
RT dry flex properties						
Strength, MPa (ksi)	131 (19)	103 (15)	96 (14)	138 (20)	124 (18)	103 (15)
Modulus, GPa (ksi)	3.5 (513)	3.2 (469)	2.8 (403)	3.2 (462)	2.9 (423)	2.5 (359)
Elongation, %	5.3	3.9	4.2	6.4	5.8	6.2
Hot/wet flex properties [4]						
Strength, MPa (ksi)	69 (10)	76 (11)	76 (11)	90 (13)	90 (13)	76 (11)
Modulus, GPa (ksi)	2.9 (414)	2.5 (360)	2.1 (307)	2.9 (415)	2.4 (346)	2.0 (284)
Elongation, %	2.6	5.3	7.2	4.1	7.6	9.7
Moisture gain, % wt. [5]	1.4	2.0	2.0	1.3	1.1	1.3

(1) HYCAR® CTBN 1300X8 Polymer (B. F. Goodrich Co.)
(2) Cured 3 hrs. at 130°C, 2 hrs. at 200°C
(3) Cured 2 hrs. at 150°C, 4 hrs. at 200°C; stoichiometric amount of curing agent
(4) Tested in water at 93°C after 2 weeks immersion at 93°C
(5) After 2 weeks immersion at 93°C

ASSESSMENTS OF Tg'S FOR SEMI-RIGID POLYMERS
Chung J. Lee, Ph.D.

Occidental Chemical Corporation
2801 Long Road
Grand Island, New York 14072

Abstract

The assessments of Tg's for semi-rigid polymers such as Polyimides were approached using quasi-lattice theory in coupling with results obtained from quantitative assessments on Relative Bridging Effects, $R(x)$; Rotational Barrier Energy, U_R and heat capacity jump, ΔCpi contributed by various linkage groups. The results indicate Tg's of polyimides and other semi-rigid polymers, such as PQ, POXL, can be approximated using a simple equation consisting of a single structural parameter, Φ. The molecular origin of Φ and molecular mechanisms at Tg's will be discussed based on our assessments.

1. INTRODUCTION

Polyimides and many other polyheterocyclics have been known for more than 30 years, and numerous studies [1, 2, 3] have been published in dealing with qualitative Tg-structure relationships for these semi-rigid polymers. However, our understanding of underlying principles, which govern molecular processes at Tg's of these polymers are still lacking at large. Recently, some quantitative Tg-structure relationships [4] and methods for computing Tg's [5] have been presented. In the present paper, molecular mechanism and packing characteristics of these semi-rigid polyheterocyclics will be proposed.

2. METHODOLOGIES

This article deals with semi-rigid polymers consisting of rigid rotators, such as A, B, and C, which are connected with various bridging groups, such as x, y and z, as shown in the following:

$$\{ \text{(A)} - x - \text{(B)} - y - \text{(C)} - z \}$$

According to the quasi-lattice theory [6], Tg's of glass polymers can be calculated using the following equation:

$$Tg = \frac{\Sigma Ui}{\Sigma \Delta Cpi} \frac{Z_1 - Zg}{Z_1} (k') \qquad (1)$$

In the equation (1), the Ui and ΔCpi is group contribution to molar cohesive energy and to heat capacity jump ΔCp, or heat capacity change at Tg's, respectively. Z_1 and Zg is, respectively, the lattice coordination numbers of polymers liquid (rubber) and glass. And $K' = \Delta Cvi / \Delta Cpi$. The original theory suggests also $Z_1 - Zg = 1$ at Tg's. To apply this equation to the above semi-rigid polymers, one needs not only the knowledge of the ΔCpi, but also k' and Z_1.

The ΔCpi for polyheterocyclics can be derived from the following two methods. First, a ΔCpi can be calculated from ΔCp difference of a polymer-pair, which have similar compostions, except a presence or absence of a certain chemical group in their repeating units. The ΔCpi of the bridging groups in poly-quinoxalines [7] (PQXL) are obtained by this method. (See Table 1a and 1b).

The second method involves two newly derived equations relating ΔCpi to rotational barrier energy U_R and U_R to some universal structural constants, called Relative Bridging Effects, (R(x). The treatments for deriving these Universal Structural constants are very straightforward [4] [5]. For instance, an isomerization effect, Ri can be calculated from Tg ratio of a polymer-pair consisting of two isomeric monomers [4]:

$$R^i_m = \frac{Tg(m)}{Tg(o)} \qquad (2)$$

The Tg(m) and Tg(o) is the Tg of a polymer consisting of m-diamino benzene and o-diaminobenzene respectively: A Relative Bridging Effect, R(x), on another hand, can be calculated from Tg ratio of a polymer-pair consisting of different bridging groups [4].

$$R(x) = \frac{Tg(x)}{Tg(-o-)} \qquad (3)$$

For instance, the Tg(x) and Tg(-o-) is the Tg of polymer consisting of -x- linkage and -o- linkage respectively.

For comparison of various R(x) and Ri derived from all polyhetero-cyclics, the denominators used in the equations (2) and (3) are Tg's of para- or P,P' isomer and oxygen, or -o- linked polymers, respectively.

By employing these equations, we have reached the following conclusions from studying Tg's of more than 250 semi-rigid polymers:

(1) R(x) is a universal constant for a chemical group, regardless whether the -x- linkage is located in diamine, dianhydride or repeating units of PQ or PQXL.

(2) Ri for a given isomer is also a constant. For instance, R op = 0.948, Rmm = 0.931 and Rmp = 0.964 and Rmm = $(Rm)^2$.

From these observations, we conclude that the molecular mechanisms involved at Tg's of PIM, PQ and PQXL should be very similar and can be equally treated with equation (1) and assumptions we imposed on it.

We also found that the Relative Bridging Effects, R(x), of various chemical groups have a very good correlation with rotational barrier energies, U_R, published for polyimides[8]:

$$\log U^R \text{ (J/Mol)} = 10.06 \times R(x) - 9.47$$
$$(r = 0.999) \qquad (4)$$

From the existence of the conclusion (1) we reached in the last Section II, we believe the equation (4) is also equally applicable to PQ and PQXL. By applying the equation (4) to PQ and PQXL and ΔCpi data derived in Table (1b), the following equation can also be established:

$$\Delta CPI \text{ (J/Mol)} = K_{10} - K_{11} \log U_R \qquad (5)$$

In the equation (5), $K_{10} = 67.65$

J/Mol K and K_{11} is 12.38/K and U_R is in J/Mol.

By applying the equation (5) to polyimides, ΔCpi for various other chemical groups, such as CH_2 and SO_2 can then be established (Table 2).

The ΔCpi for chemical groups found in linear, flexible polymers are also evaluated for comparison. In the Table 3, the ΔCpi can be derived directly from that of the homopolymers, whereas in the Table 4, the ΔCpi's were derived from a deductive method. By assuming the ΔCp for the polymers in the Table 4 are the sum of ΔCpi (i.e., Δ Cpi), and the ΔCpi found in the Table 3 are applicable to these polymers, on can, for instance, calculate the ΔCpi's for -O-,-$C(CH_3)_2$- etc.

All the calculated Δ Cpi are summarized in the Table 5 in conjunction with cohesive energy density, Σui/ΣVi of their parent polymers. In the Table 5, the R(ΔCpi) is defined as relative ΔCpi as follows:

$$R(\Delta Cpi) = \frac{\Delta Cpi(x)}{\Delta Cpi(PIM)}$$

The ΔCpi(x) is the group contribution to heat capacity jump for a given chemical group found in polymer X.

3. MOLECULAR MECHANISMS AT Tg'S

Previously, [5] we have shown the Tg's of PIM, PQ, POXL and alikes can be approximated by the following simple equation [6]:

$$Tg = 722 - 353 \, \Phi \qquad (6)$$

The Φ is called "ether linkage density", of a repeating unit and can be calculated from the following equations (7) and (8).

$$\Phi = \frac{\Psi i}{Ni} \qquad (7)$$

$$R(x) = 1.224 - 0.448 \Psi i \qquad (8)$$

The ΣNi is total numbers of rigid rotators in the repeating units of these polymers studied.

Since the Φ, or Ψi can be correlated to ΔCpi and U_R by Equations 4, 5 and 8, the molecular mechanisms at Tg's of these semi-rigid polymers become understandable. The Ψi, then, is a relative flexibility index and the $R(x)$ is an indicator of relative rigidity of a given bridging group, such as x, y, z shown in our earlier illustration. The molecular origin of the $R(x)$ can be traced back to it's correlation with the Rotational Barrier Energy, U_R, which is obtainable from quantum chemical calculations; or to the ΔCpi, which is available from heat capacity measurement. As it can be seen, for a more rigid linkage group, its rotational barrier energy is higher and it's ΔCpi is lower at Tg's.

In addition, from the Table 5, one also notes that the ΔCpi is largely influenced by its surroundings, or the cohesive energy density of its parent polymer. It is not a constant as previously suggested (12a and b). As a matter of fact, the ΔCpi found in semi-rigid polymers, such as PIM, PQ or PQXL, can be twice as large as that observed in the linear flexible polymers. The $R(\Delta Cpi)$ can be correlated to the $\Sigma Ui/\Sigma Vi$ as shown in the Figure 1. This result is not a surprise to us since the ΔCp has also been correlated to cohesive energy density or Young's modulus at 4K, E(4K) earlier [13]. However, it does create an additional problem for the application of equation (1) to all polymers.

Our current studies indicate that k's for aromatic polymers, such as polycarbonate (k'=3.78) and polyphenyloxide (k'=5.4) are also much larger than that suggested [6] for the linear-flexible polymer (k'=1.8 ~ 2.2). Accordingly, the Z_1 seems to be still a universal constant (Z_1=8-9) for all polymers. If this is true, then the lattice volumes involved at Tg's of the semi-rigid polymer is expected to be very much larger than that suggested for the linear flexible polymers, since the cross-section areas of repeating units for the semi-rigid polymers are normally 2-5 times that of the linear flexible polymers.

REFERENCES

1. St. Clair, T.L. et al in Harris, F.W. and Seymour, R. Edt., "Structure-Property Relationships in Polymers", Academic Press (1977), p. 199.

2. Bessonou, M.I., et al edt. "Polyimides", Consultants Bureau, N.Y., London (1987).

3. Mittal, K.L., edt. "Polyimides", Vol. I & II. Plenam Press (1984).

4. Lee, C.J., "Polyimides: Quantitative Tg-Structure Relationships", Proc. 20th Intl. SAMPE Tech. Conf. (1988).

5. Lee, C.J., "Polyimides: Theoretical Assessments of their Tg's", Proc. 3rd Polyimide Conf., Mid Hudson, SPE (1988).

6. Kaelble, D.H., "Physical Chemistry of Adhesion", N.Y., Wiley-Intersi, (1971), Chapter 8.

7. Wrasidlo, W., Journ. Polm. Sci. A-2 (9), (1971), p. 1603-1627.

8a. Balagina, Y.G., et al, Vysokomol. Soedin A18(6), (1976), p. 1235-1242.

8b. Zubkov, V.A., et al, ibid, A17 (9), (1975), p. 1955-1961.

9. Tg and ΔCp data in Tables (1) and (2): Wunderlich, B., Cheng, S.Z.D., Gazzetta Chimica Italiana 116, 346 (1986); Wunderlich, B., "Recommended Data of Heat Capacities of 50 linear Macromolecules" in Bromdrup and Immergut eds., "Polymer Handbook", third edition, Wiley-Interscience, 1988.

10. Kaelble, D.H., "Computer-Aided Design of Polymers and Composites", M. Dekker, N.Y. (1985).

11. Barton, A.V.M., "CRC Handbook of Solubility Parameters and Other Cohesion Parameters", Table 4, p. 249, CRC Press (1983).

12a. Cao, M.Y. and Wunderlich, B., Journal of Polymer Science, Polymer Physics, Edt. 23, 521 (1985).

12b. Cheng, S.Z.D. and Wunderlich, B., ibid, 24 1755 (1986).

13. 1) Lee, C.J., Polymer Eng. and Science 27 (13), 1015 (1987).

   2) Pan, R.Y.L., Cao, M.Y. and Wunderlich, B., Journal of Thermal Analysis, Volume 31, 1319 (1986) and references herein.

BIOGRAPHY

Dr. Lee has over 15 years experience in polymer R&D, specializing in high temperature polymers. He is an author of 26 publications, 12 issued U.S. patents, 10 additional patent applications, a review article and a to-be-printed Monograph entitled "High Temperature Polymers: Tg-Structure Relationship" (1989). He is an invited speaker by NASA, Bell Laboratories, the governments of Japan and Taiwan and many universities on the above subject and on polyimidesiloxanes.

Table 1a THE Tgs AND Δ Cp OF

(III)

Polymer Nos.	Y	X	Z	T_g[7] (K)	ΔC_p[7] (J/K.Mole)	ΣU_i[10] (KJ/Mol)
6	H	-	-	649	77.46	115.57
8	H	SO_2	-	615	92.53	137.47
10	H	CO	-	591	100.07	122.89
12	H	O	-	579	104.68	122.39
15	H	-	$-OC_6H_4-$	576	123.94	146.19
20	H	-	$(-OC_6H_4-)_2$	508	175.85	176.87
21	H	-	$(-OC_6H_4^-)_3$	489	227.77	207.43
22	H	-	$-C_6H_4-$	578	121.84	139.37
5	C_6H_5	-	-	645	118.91	173.97
7	"	SO_2	-	618	131.15	198.87
9	"	CO	-	598	134.40	181.29
11	"	O	-	577	139.43	180.79
14	"	-	$-OC_6H_4-$	573	178.78	204.59
16	"	SO_2	"	563	188.42	276.49
17	"	CO	"	544	195.69	211.91
18	"	O	"	531	199.30	211.41
19	"	-	$-SC_6H_4-$	561	164.97	205.57

934

TABLE 1b. GROUP CONTRIBUTIONS TO HEAT CAPACITY (JIMES):

Polymer Structures	Synonym	Chemical Groups		ΔC_{pi} (J/K.Mol)	Note Data Based On
(III)	PQXL	Z = $-C_6H_4-0-$	Y= H	49.20 ± 3.85	3 polymer pairs
		"	Y=C_6H_5	59.57 ± .68	4 polymer pairs
		Y = C_6H_5*-		37.81 ± 3.72	4 polymer pairs
		X = $-SO_2-$		12.98 ± 2.92	3 polymer pairs
		= $-CO-$		18.34 ± 3.97	3 polymer pairs
		= $-O-$		23.69 ± 3.34	3 polymer pairs
		z = $-C_6H_4-$		22.14	1 polymer pair
		= $-C_6H_4S-$		45.96	1 polymer pair

*The differences between Y = H and Y = C_6H_5.

Table 2. - GROUP CONTRIBUTIONS TO HEAT CAPACITY JUMPS:

Polymer Structures	Chemical Groups	ΔC_{pi} (J/K.Mol)
(PIM structure)	-O-	21.43
	-CO-	17.57
	$-CH_2-$	21.73
	$-C(CH_3)_2-$	20.83
	$-SO_2-$	12.64
	$-Si(CH_3)_2-$	25.31
	-S-	23.66

Table 3. GROUP CONTRIBUTIONS TO HEAT CAPACITY JUMPS, Δ Cpi

Polymer Structures	Synonym	$T_g^{(9)}$ (K)	$\Delta Cp^{(9)}$ (J/K.Mol)	$\Sigma U_i^{(10)}$ KJ/Mol	Chemical Groups	ΔCpi (J/K Mol)
$(-CH_2-)$	PE	237	10.4	4.14	$-CH_2-$	10.4
$(-C_6H_4-O-)$	PPO	358	21.4	30.65	$-C_6H_4-O-$	21.4
$(-C_6H_4S-)$	PPS	363	26.3	32.06	$-C_6H_4S-$	26.3

937

TABLE 4. GROUP CONTRIBUTIONS TO HEAT CAPACITY JUMPS:

Polymer Structures	Synonym	$T_g^{(9)}$ (K)	$\Delta C_p^{(9)}$ (J/K.Mol)	$\Sigma U_i(10)$ (KJ/Mol)	Chemical Groups	$\Delta C_{p;}$ (J/K.Mol)	Note Ref (ΔC_{pi} = J/K. Mol)
$(-CH_2 -O-)$	PMO	190	30.3	10.97	$-O-$	19.9	$(-CH_2-)$ = 10.4
$(-CH_2)_2 -O-)$	PEO	206	35.2	15.10	$-O-$	14.4	"
$(-CH_2-CH\ CH_3\ -O-)$	PPO	198	32.2	23.76	$-O-$	11.4	(PP) = 20.8
$(-CH_2C(CH_3)_2-)$	PIB	200	21.3	16.04	$-C(CH_3)_2-$	10.9	$(-CH_2-)$ = 10.4
$(-C_6H_4-CH_2-CH_2-)$	PPX	286	37.6	32.08	$-C_6H_4-$	16.8	"
$\begin{array}{c} CH_3 \\ (-\overset{|}{Si}-O-) \\ CH_3 \end{array}$	PSL	152	31.5	19.64(8c)	$-Si(CH_3)_2-$	20.1~11.6	$(-O-)$ = 11.4~19.9
$(-CH_2-CH(C_6H_5)-)$	PS	206	30.7	34.24	$-C_6H_5^*$	9.9	$(-CH_2-)$ = 10.4

*A difference between $-CH\ C_6H_5-$ and $(-CH_2-)$

Table 5. COMPARATIVE GROUP CONTRIBUTIONS TO HEAT CAPACITY JUMPS

Chemical Groups	ΔCpi (J/K.Mol)	Parent Polymers	R(ΔCpi)	ΣUi [10] (kJ/Mol)	Σ_3Vi [11] (cm^3/Mol)	ΣUi/Σ_3Vi (kJ/cm^3)
$-0-$	19.9	PMO	0.84	10.9	24.9	.438
	14.4	PEO	0.51	15.1	41.4	.365
	11.4	PPO	.48	16.2	57.6	.281
	23.69	PQXL	1	~175	~350	~.500
	21.43	PIM	.90	~150	~300	~.500
$-CH_2-$	10.4	PE	.48	4.14	16.5	.251
	21.73	PIM	1	~150	~300	~.500
$-C_6H_4O-$	21.4	PPO	.43	30.65	69.9	.439
	49.20	PQXL	1.00	~175	~350	~.500✗
	59.57	"	1.20	~211	~450	~.469**
$-C_6H_4S-$	26.3	PPS	.57	32.06	76.4	.420
	45.96	PQXL	1.0	~175	~350	~.500
$-C(CH_3)_2$	10.9	P1B	.52	16.04	66.8	.240
	20.83	PIM	1.0	~150	~300	~.500
$-S_i(CH_3)_2-$	11.6~20.1	PSL	.46	12.82	57.6 (8b)	.223
	25.31	PIM	1.0	~150	~300	~.500
$-C_6H_4-$	16.8	PPX	.76	32.08	94.3	.340
	27.14	PQXL	1.0	~175	~350	~.500
$-C_6H_5$	9.9*	PS	-	-	-	*ΔCpi'($_6H_5$-H)
	37.81*	PQXL	-	-	-	

* ΔCpi(C_6H_5-H)

** Phenylated

939

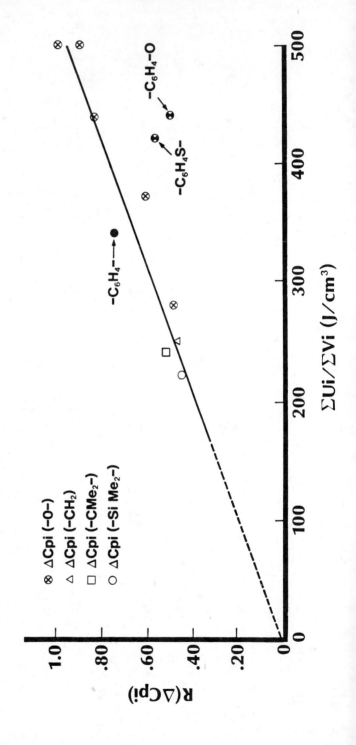

FIGURE 1

EFFECTS OF COHESIVE ENERGY DENSITIES ON RELATIVE GROUP CONTRIBUTIONS TO ΔCpi

$\otimes$ ΔCpi (−O−)
△ ΔCpi (−CH_2)
□ ΔCpi (−CMe_2−)
○ ΔCpi (−Si Me_2−)

$-C_6H_4-$
$-C_6H_4-O$
$-C_6H_4S-$

$\Sigma Ui/\Sigma Vi$ (J/cm^3)

R(ΔCpi)

940

PHTHALONITRILE RESIN FOR HIGH TEMPERATURE
COMPOSITE APPLICATIONS

Teddy M. Keller and David J. Moonay
Naval Research Laboratory
Polymeric Materials Branch
Chemistry Division, Code 6120
Washington, DC 20375-5000

Abstract

High performance organic polymers which can withstand temperatures up to 372°C (700°F) are in demand as matrix materials for advanced composites. An aromatic, diether-linked phthalonitrile resin, prepared from 4,4'-bis(3,4-dicyanophenoxy)biphenyl, exhibits excellent thermo-oxidative properties. The resin is easily processed from the melt of the monomer as a function of the amine curing agent and processing temperatures. Polymerization occurs by a cyclic addition reaction without the formation of volatile by-products. The polymerization reaction can be stopped at a pre-polymer stage. The prepolymer can be stored indefinitely at ambient conditions without further reaction. The stability of the prepolymer at ambient temperatures is particularly appealing for the preparation of prepregs and their applications as laminates for fiber-reinforced composites. The mechanical properties of the resin were found to be a function of the postcuring conditions.

1. INTRODUCTION

High performance organic polymers, which can withstand temperatures in excess of 300°C (572°F), are in demand as matrix materials for composites to replace metallic components in weight-critical aerospace applications. Such materials could bridge the gap between currently used high temperature polymers and ceramics/metals. Several commercially available polyimides are presently being considered for these applications. A major problem of the polyimide systems is the inability to process void- and blister-free components in high yield. These process problems, attributed to the evolution of volatile component formed during the polymerization condensation reaction, must be alleviated before these materials will be widely accepted for high temperature performance applications.

Considerable advances have been made in recent years concerning the synthesis and development of thermally stable polymers. The PMR polymers[1,2] have found numerous applications in the aerospace industry. The aliphatic crosslinking moiety, which is the weak linkage for thermal degradation in these resins, limits the utility of these polymers for high temperature applications. The initial weight loss in the thermo-oxidative degradation of PMR-15 has been attributed to both the nadic- and diphenylmethane-components with the nadic crosslinking unit ultimately becoming the more significant contributor to overall resin weight loss.[3]

In our studies, a new class of high performance phthalonitrile-based polymers[4-8] with superior thermo-oxidative properties has been under development. The phthalonitrile monomers are readily converted to highly crosslinked thermosetting polymers in the presence of thermally stable aromatic diamines.[5] The polymerization reaction occurs through the terminal phthalonitrile units, which are interconnected by aromatic dioxy linkages, to afford heterocyclic crosslinking products. Shaped components are easily

processed in a controlled manner by heating the polymerization mixture above its melting point or glass transition temperature (Tg) until gelation occurs. Due to the solubility properties and their indefinite stability at ambient temperatures, the prepolymers formed from these monomers are potential candidates for the preparation of stable prepregs and their applications as laminates for advanced fiber-reinforced composites. This paper is concerned with the development of a bisphenol-based phthalonitrile resin, prepared from 4,4'-bis(3,4-dicyanophenoxy)biphenyl 1[8], in terms of its synthesis, ease of processability, thermal and oxidative stability, and mechanical properties.

2.   EXPERIMENTAL

2.1 Preparation of Phthalonitrile-Based Monomer 1.

The synthesis of 4,4'-bis(3,4-dicyanophenoxy)biphenyl 1 has been described elsewhere[8]. The phthalonitrile 1 is synthesized in high yield by the nucleophilic displacement of a nitro substituent from 4-nitrophthalonitrile 3 by the dialkali salt of 4,4'-biphenol 2 in dry dimethyl sulfoxide (see Scheme I).

2.2 Polymerization of Phthalo-nitrile 1.

The monomer 1 was melted at 240°C, cooled to approximately 220°C and 1,3-bis(3-aminophenoxy)benzene (APB, 1-2% by weight) was added with stirring. The resulting dark amorphous polymerization mixture was cured by heating at 200-240°C until gelation occurred, at 280°C for 6 hours and at 315°C for 16-24 hours. The time to gelation was a function of the amine concentration and the initial cure temperature. The polymer 4 was postcured at temperatures up to 375°C to optimize physical properties. When exposed to temperatures in excess of 315°C, 4 was postcured under an oxygen-free argon atmosphere.

2.3 Curing Procedure Used For Studies

The physical properties of 4 were determined on samples which had been prepared and postcured under the following conditions: Sample A was cured by heating in air at 240°C for 16 hours, at 280°C for 6 hours, and at 315°C for 16-24 hours. Sample B was obtained by postcuring of sample A at 350°C for 4 hours. Additional postcuring of sample B at 375°C for 12 hours afforded sample C.

2.4 Thermal Analysis

The thermal characterizations were implemented using a DuPont 1090 thermal analysis system equipped with a thermogravimetric analyzer (TGA, heating rate 10°C/min), a differential scanning calorimeter (DSC, heating rate 10°C/min), and a dynamic mechanical analyzer (DMA, heating rate 5°C/min).

2.5 Mechanical Analysis

Tensile strength measurements were performed on dogbone-shaped specimens that were 2 inches long. All specimens were prepared by charging preheated molds with a prepolymer mixture. The mold assemblies were then placed in a preheated air circulating oven and cured by the prescribed curing procedure. All specimens were removed from the molds after the heat treatment at 315°C. Any additional postcuring at elevated temperatures was performed on specimens which had been removed from the molds.

The tensile specimens had an 1/2 inch gauge length. The specimens were sanded and polished to ensure homogeneous dimensions. An Instron machine was used to measure the room temperature tensile strength of 4. The tensile strength values were obtained at a strain rate of 0.02/min.

3. PROCESSABILITY

Thermosetting polymer 4 is easily processed into a shaped component or film in a controlled manner. The monomer reactivity is controlled as a function of the amount of amine curing additive. The polymerization reaction can be performed in one step by heating the melt of the 1-amine mixture until gelation occurs. Polymer 4 can be postcured at elevated temperatures to improve the mechanical and thermal properties. Alternatively, low molecular weight prepolymers, which can be stored indefinitely at room temperature, can be formed by quenching the reaction before gelation occurs. The viscosity of the prepolymer will depend on the molecular weight, which can be controlled as a function of the reaction temperature and exposure time. The amorphous prepolymers are soluble in common solvents such as methylene chloride, chloroform, and the dipolar aprotic solvents.

After the addition of the amine curing additive, the reaction mixture is rapidly converted from a crystalline into an amorphous phase. At this stage, the curing temperature can be lowered to a point above the glass transition temperature (Tg) of the material. This important observation permits the polymerization reaction to be performed in a more controlled manner as a function of both the amine concentration and curing temperature. In essence, when the polymerization reaction is performed at temperatures below the melting point (231-233°C) of 1, the processing window can be extended and larger concentrations of amine additive can be used.

4. THERMAL STABILITY

The thermal stability of 4 was assessed under dynamic and isothermal conditions. The relative stability was determined on powdered samples between 25-800°C in nitrogen and air atmospheres using thermogravimetry.

Isothermal studies were also performed to determine the thermal stability and reliability of 4 at various temperatures in an oxidative environment.

Figure 1 shows the thermal stability of 4 in nitrogen. The onset of thermal degradation and the charred residue remaining at 800°C were dependent on the postcure temperature. As the postcure temperature was increased, substantial improvements in both the thermal stability and the char yield were observed. Moreover, when cylindrical samples were aged for 24 and 100 hours, 4 exhibited an anaerobic char yield of 75% and appeared visually to be void-free.

The oxidative properties of 4 are shown in Figure 2. In an effort to enhance its stability, cured samples of 4 were postcured at various temperatures between 315-375°C in an inert atmosphere. The postcure treatments extended the crosslink density but had little effect on the thermo-oxidative stability. All of the postcured samples showed similar thermograms. Catastrophic failure consistently occurred between 525-600°C.

Isothermal measurements indicate that 4 can be expected to perform well for relatively long exposures in air at moderate temperatures between 300-357°C (572-675°F). All aging studies were performed for

100 hours in an air flow at 100 cc/min. The testing was performed on cylindrical neat samples (1 inch in diameter x 1/8 inch thick) at 300, 315, 343, 357, and 372°C (see Table 1). Oxidative weight losses were not detected when 4 was aged at or below 315°C.

5. DYNAMIC MECHANICAL ANALYSIS

Dynamic mechanical analysis (DMA) was used to follow the extent of the curing reaction and the development of the network structure and to predict the performance of 4. Dynamic mechanical properties are particularly sensitive to the increase of molecular weight, to chain entanglement, and to the crosslinking density. The testing was performed in the temperature range of 25-375°C using a programmed incremental heating rate of 5°C/min. Samples of 4 were examined which had been cured and postcured as described in the curing procedure (2.3) shown in the Experimental Section.

Typical modulus and damping curves are shown in Figures 3 and 4. Sample A showed the largest modulus change with a viscoelastic transition to the rubbery state occurring between 200-360°C. With thermal aging (compare B and C), an enhancement of the modulus was observed which declined less dramatically as the temperature rose, reflecting an increase in polymeric rigidity and loss of molecular mobility as crosslinking progresses. The damping responses were dependent on the postcure temperature. Samples A and B exhibited glass transition temperatures (Tg) of 290 and 332°C, respectively, as determined from the peak maxima of the broad primary damping peaks. As the postcure temperature was increased, the magnitude of the primary damping peak (Tg) was diminished. Sample C did not show damping responses characteristic of a viscoelastic transition to a rubbery state. Apparently, this sample had attained a high crosslink density resulting in the loss of main chain molecular mobility.

6. TENSILE STRENGTH PROPERTIES

Table 2 shows some preliminary testing results of 4 cured with 1 and 2 weight percent of APB. The value of the tensile properties cured above 315°C certainly adds credence to the expected thermal resistance of 4 relative to current state-of-the-art high temperature polymeric materials. Further tests are needed to confirm our results, but our initial observation suggests that 4 is thermally stable at temperatures up to 375°C (700°F).

7. SUMMARY

Polymer 4 is a potential candidate as a high performance material for numerous applications. The synthesis is short and potentially low-cost. The resin is easily processed into non-void components

945

and exhibits high thermal and oxidative properties. Prepolymer formation is readily achievable in a controlled manner. The payoff from the polymer could be especially high in space and military applications, where the low weight and corrosion resistance of plastics are important. When postcured at high temperatures, the polymer does not exhibit a glass transition temperature (Tg). Potential applications include its use as a matrix material for advanced composites, e.g., component design in the vicinity of an aircraft engine, and as a molding material for the fabrication of electronic devices due to the thermal stability at the required soldering temperatures[9].

8. REFERENCES

1. Serafini, T.T., Delvigs, P., and Lightsey, G.R., J. Appl. Polym. Sci., 16, 905 (1972).

2. Serafini, T.T., ACS Organic Coatings and Plastics Chemistry, 40, 469 (1979).

3. Alton, W.B., SAMPE Proc., 12, 121 (1980).

4. Keller, T.M. and Griffith, J.R., Resins for Aerospace, Am. Chem. Soc. Symp. Ser., 132, 25 (1980).

5. Keller, T.M. and Price, T.R., J. Macromol. Sci. Chem., A18(6), 931 (1982).

6. Ting, R.Y., Keller, T.M., Price, T.R., and Poranski, C.F., Jr., Cyclopolymerization and Polymers with Chain-Ring Structures, Am. Chem. Soc. Symp. Ser., 195, 337 (1982).

7. Keller, T.M., J. Polym. Sci.: Part A: Polym. Chem., 25, 2569 (1987).

8. Keller, T.M., J. Polym. Sci: Part A: Polym. Chem., 26, 3199 (1988).

9. Frisch, D. and Ciccarone, R., "Thermal Analysis for Evaluating Laminates", Circuits Manufacturing, Benwill Publishing Corporation, July 1977.

9. BIOGRAPHY

Dr. Teddy M. Keller is Principal Investigator of a novel organic polymers program at the Naval Research Laboratory. Keller, who has numerous patents and publications, received his B.S. degree from East Tennessee State University, a Ph.D. degree from the University of South Carolina, and did postdoctoral work in fluoropolymers at the University of Florida. He is currently associated with several exploratory/developmental programs including high temperature polymers for advanced composite applications, composite formulation and testing, fluoropolymers, and electrically conducting polymers.

David J. Moonay is a Research Chemical Engineer at the Naval Research Laboratory. He received his B.A. in Chemistry from Hamilton College in Clinton, New York in 1982 and an M.S. in Chemical

Engineering from the Ohio State University in 1985. He is interested in the structure-property relationships of interpenetrating polymer network (IPN) systems. He is currently involved in the development of some novel high temperature resins and blends for applications above 315°C (600°F).

Scheme I

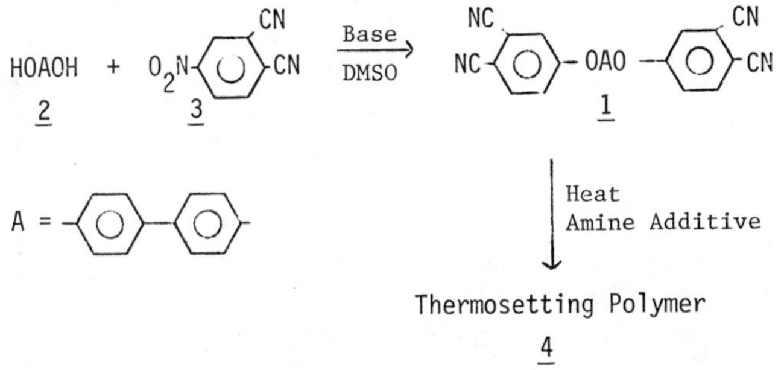

$$A = -\langle O \rangle - \langle O \rangle -$$

Heat
Amine Additive

Thermosetting Polymer
4

Table 1. Isothermal Oxidative Weight Loss Studies in Air for 100 Hours

Temp.°C	Weight Loss (%)
300	None detected
315	None detected
343	1.8
357	7.2
372	--

Table 2. Preliminary Room Temperature Tensile Strength Properties of 4

		Processing conditions[a]				
		Air(°C)			Argon(°C)	
Tensile Strength (MPa)	Wt % APB	240	280	315	350	375
46	1	16	6	24	--	--
61	1	16	6	24	4	12
55	2	16	6	16	--	--
58	2	16	6	16	4	--

[a]Hours at each temperature

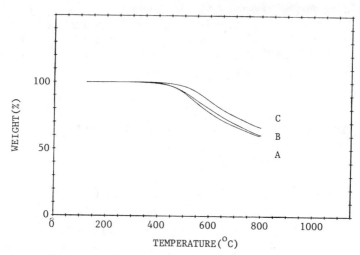

Figure 1. TGA of samples A, B, and C in nitrogen.

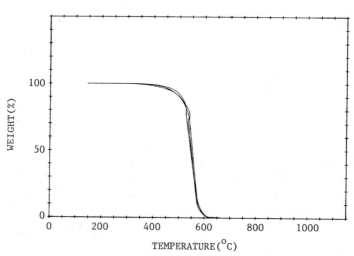

Figure 2. Samples A, B, and C show similar oxidative
properties.

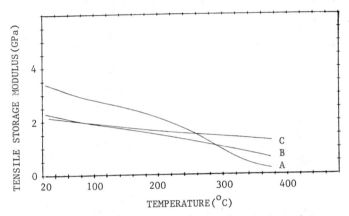

Figure 3. Modulus curves on samples A, B, and C.

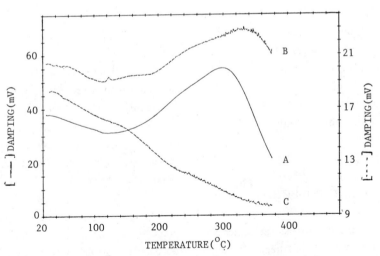

Figure 4. Damping profile on samples A, B, and C.

34th International SAMPE Symposium
May 8-11, 1989

ADVANCED GRAPHITE / POLYIMIDE COMPOSITES
FOR
HIGH TEMPERATURE FILAMENT WOUND STRUCTURES

M. W. Egerton and M. S. Tanikella
E. I. Du Pont Composites Division, Wilmington, Delaware
and
J. L. Koury
Air Force Astronautics Laboratory, Edwards, California

Abstract

A joint program with the E. I. DuPont Company and the Air Force Astronautics Laboratory (AFAL) demonstrated fiber stresses over 4137 MPa (600 ksi) in 5.75" diameter pressure bottles using a DuPont Avimid* N prepreg containing Hercules IM7 fiber. Results compare favorably with conventional polyimide matrix composite bottles. The resin used in the prepreg is a fluorinated aromatic polyimide (Tg ≥ 350 °C) with outstanding high temperature mechanical performance and oxidative stability.

1. INTRODUCTION

The aircraft and aerospace industries are continuously driving high strength to weight material systems to greater and greater temperature limits. These increased temperature limits permit improved engine performance and efficiency, allow aircraft and missiles to fly at greater speeds, and facilitate weight reductions. Many additional advantages can also be derived from material systems capable of handling harsh high temperature environments.

Fiber reinforced composites have already established their value in industry as being a solid route to making low weight high strength components. The fiber systems commonly used in high temperature components include graphite, aramid, ceramic and glass. These fibers are typically bound together by a carbon, ceramic, metal or polyimide matrix.

The polyimide matrix in Avimid® N prepregs, developed by DuPont, possesses outstanding and unique properties. Fiber reinforced laminates using this amorphous polyimide are significantly tougher than laminates made from conventional

* DuPont Registered Trademark for Fiber Reinforced Resin Composite Structures

thermosetting polyimides. More damage tolerant systems should result. Avimid® N prepregs have unparalleled thermal oxidative stability which translates into superior stiffness and strength retention at elevated temperatures. The material has demonstrated good resistance to organic fluids and absorbs only a nominal amount of moisture [1].

In working with high temperature materials there are always trade-offs between properties, cost, processability and scalability. Each factor must be evaluated before a new or different material system can be considered for an application. In developing Avimid® N prepregs the physical properties and cost have been well established. In addition, processing of stamped or pressed parts and flat or contoured panels is well under way. In the area of filament winding, however, only limited work has been done.

This paper will discuss the fabrication, testing and physical properties of 5.75" diameter filament wound pressure bottles made from DuPont's Avimid® N containing Hercules IM7 fiber. This development was a joint effort between the E. I. DuPont Company and the Air Force Astronautics Laboratory (AFAL). The work demonstrates that Avimid® N prepreg can be filament wound into a complex shape and yield fiber tensile strength translations equivalent to addition type polyimide resin systems.

5.75" diameter pressure bottles were selected as a demonstration part because these bottles have been used, per ASTM Standard D2585, to generate performance data on many high temperature material systems. This allows for a direct and fair comparison of Avimid® N composites with others. Secondarily, a domed end pressure bottle can be considered as a complex shape, introducing an added degree of difficulty in fabrication, that will build confidence in the ability to process complex parts with this material.

2. FABRICATING THE MANDREL

In order to fabricate a 5.75" pressure bottle one must begin by producing a mandrel on which to place the composite material. As described in Procedure A of ASTM D2585 a washout type mandrel with an elastomeric liner was used [2].

The mandrels were fabricated by casting two domed ends from sodium silicate and bonding the ends together to form a hollow sand shell. This shell was finished and lined on the exterior with a fluorinated elastomer. The function of the elastomer was to provide an impermeable barrier during pressure testing. After curing and finishing of the elastomeric liner metal end fittings, also called bosses, were attached using a metal-to-rubber bonding agent. The final step was to apply a second layer of elastomer locally around each boss to ensure a seal. Figure 1 shows the sand mandrel with liner just prior to bonding of the end fittings.

3. THE WINDING PROCESS

The filament winding process is done in two steps. Referring to Figure 2, fibers must be placed in the helical (or polar) direction and in the hoop direction. These two steps may

Figure 1. Typical 5.75" Sand Mandrel with Elastomer Covering Just Prior to Bonding of the End Fittings.

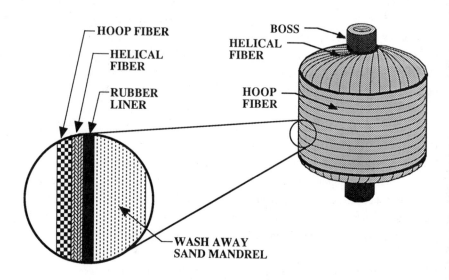

Figure 2. Pictorial Representation of a 5.75" Filament Wound Pressure Bottle Showing a Cross-Section Taken in the Barrel Region.

be done back to back or at different times depending on the desired compaction and curing stages.

The helical fiber's sole function is to prevent the domed ends from blowing off during pressurization. They add little strength to the fibers running in the hoop direction. Accurate placement of the helical fibers is critical to help prevent fiber slippage and or fiber buildup around the bosses. Stress concentrations can be created by improper or uneven placement of the helical fibers around the ends.

The helical lay down pattern of choice is a geodesic, or non-slip, path with the fibers running tangent to and just barely touching each boss. Taking the geometry of the bottle into consideration a geodesic path is best achieved by placing the fibers at $11.5°$ to the axis of the bottle. In order to minimize fiber buildup and cross over points a one circuit winding, or single band width advance, is used.

Placement of the hoop fibers is also critical in that the bottle is designed to fail in the hoop fibers. Any gaps, non-uniformities or wrinkles in the hoop fibers will cause the bottles to burst prematurely and will yield poor fiber translation strength values. Fiber translation strength is measured by comparing the hoop fiber stress at burst to the virgin tensile fiber strength as spun. Should the hoop fibers be improperly laid at the tangent lines between the barrel portion and dome portions of the bottle a stress concentration may result lowering the ultimate performance of the bottle.

Winding of the bottles can typically be done on either a helical or a tumble type winder. In this study a small tumble winder was used. Figures 3 and 4 depict a tumble winder applying helical and hoop fibers, respectively. Helical fibers are applied by holding the feed arm stationary while tumbling the bottle end for end and incrementally rotating the bottle on its axis the width of one tow band. Hoop fibers are applied by placing the bottle in a vertical position, rotating it about the spindle axis and slowly traversing the feed arm down and then up.

The ratio of hoop fiber stress to helical fiber stress, which is controlled by the amount of fiber placed in each direction, is important because this ratio will determine where the bottle will fail. This value is also important in that stress ratios must be equivalent, in different bottles, in order to accurately compare the performance of two material systems. As mentioned previously, the bottle is designed to fail in the hoop fibers. This is achieved by designing a stress ratio of 0.5 into each bottle, as determined by the netting equation [2]. In general terms an equal thickness of hoop fibers and helical fibers will yield a stress ratio close to 0.5 .

Conventional wet winding and prepreg winding techniques were used in this study. Equivalent results were obtained via the two processes. Polyimide prepregs are much newer to filament winding and are considered to be a viable means to separate the impregnation and winding steps. This tends to simplify the number of variables in the

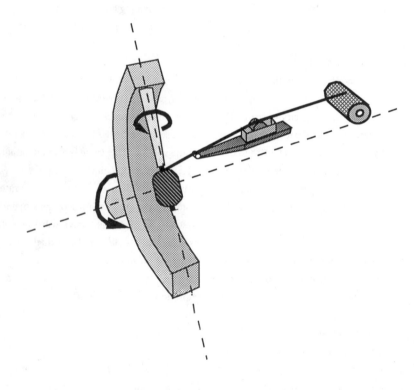

Figure 3. Schematic of a Tumble Winder
Applying Helical Wraps to a
5.75" Pressure Bottle.

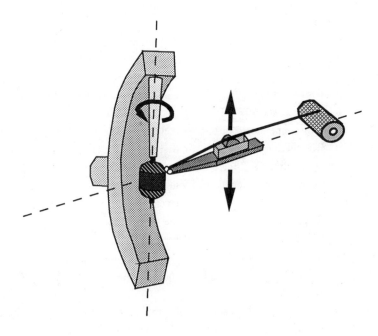

Figure 4. Schematic of a Tumble Winder
Applying Hoop Wraps to a
5.75" Pressure Bottle.

winding process and is considered, in the long run, to be the method of choice.

4. CURING THE BOTTLES

After the helical and hoop wraps have been applied the bottle is rotated on a spit until the resin has set. At this point the bottle can be handled without settling of the resin. Bagging, B-stagging and autoclave curing can now take place. Figure 5 shows typical bottles wrapped in bleeder plies of fiberglass mat prior to B-staging.

As with most condensation type polyimides Avimid® N prepreg is heated during its final cure, with hold periods at specific points, over several hours to temperatures in the range of 390° C. The relatively long cure cycles are required to allow time for the solvent material and water by-products to leave the system [1].

A key to high performance bottles is to develop bagging and curing procedures which minimize fiber movement and wrinkling. A wrinkle, buckle or non-uniformity in the composite will create a stress concentration factor that will yield low burst values.

The cure cycle is tailored to maximize the glass transition temperature (T_g) and physical properties of the matrix while minimizing void content and fiber movement. A cured bottle is show in Figure 6. The bottles made from Avimid® N exhibited T_g's $\geq$ 350 °C and showed void contents ranging from 3% - 5%.

5. BURST TESTING & CALCULATIONS

After curing is complete, bagging materials removed and the sand mandrel washed out the bottles are ready for burst testing. Each bottle is placed in a hydrostatic burst chamber, filled with water and then pressurized to burst, see Figure 7, at a rate of approximately 84 kgf/cm^2/min (1200 psi/min). A pressure verses time graph is generated.

The ultimate burst pressure is read from the graph and is used along with pre-recorded winding parameters in the netting analysis equations [2]. These equations are used to calculate helical and hoop fiber stresses and their ratio. The equations are specifically designed to compensate for expansion of the bottle under pressure and reinforcement of the hoop layers by the underlying helical layers. These equations are considered to be the standard for stress calculations in 5.75" pressure bottles.

6. COMPARISON OF BURST RESULTS

In the study done using Avimid® N composites several material and processing variables were investigated. These variables include such things as solvent system, sizing material, wet winding verses prepreg winding and curing times and temperatures. When investigating multiple variables a spread in bottle performance is expected. The burst results from the better performing bottles are presented in Table 1.

Fiber translation strengths ranging from 58% - 98% were demonstrated. This means

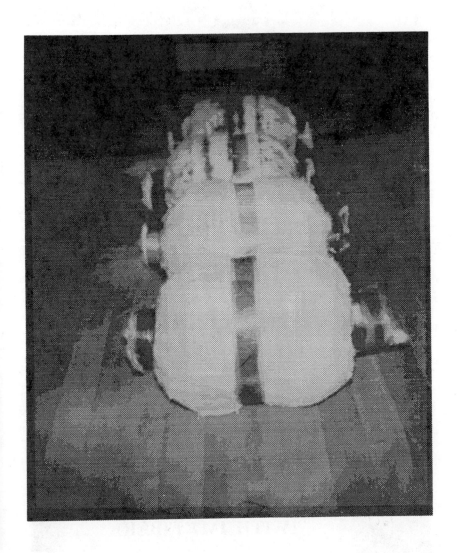

Figure 5. Typical 5.75" Pressure Bottles Wrapped in Fiberglass Mat Bleeder Plys Prior to B-Staging.

AVIMID® N

5.75" PRESSURE BOTTLE

(WITH IM7 FIBER)

Figure 6. A Typical 5.75" Pressure Bottle Made With Avimid® N, After Curing is Complete.

Figure 7. A Typical 5.75" Pressure Bottle Made With Avimid® N, After Hydrostatic Bursting.

that 58% - 98% of the virgen fiber tensile strength has been translated into and utilized by the hoop wraps in the finished part. For Avimid® N prepregs containing IM7 greater than 4137 MPa (600 ksi) tensile strength was demonstrated in multiple cases.

When comparing pressure bottles made with dissimilar materials or by different processes it is important that these bottles have equal stress ratios. Bottles based on Avimid® N prepregs with stress ratios of 0.50 - 0.58 exhibited fiber translation strengths ranging from 58% - 76%. These results are expected to compare favorably against typical addition type polyimides.

7. PHYSICAL PROPERTIES OF COMPOSITE MATERIALS FROM AVIMID® N

Avimid® N prepreg has posted neat resin properties with Tg's ranging from 340 °C - 370 °C, densities ranging from 1.43 g/cc - 1.45 g/cc, flexural moduli of 4170 MPa, flexural strengths of 117 MPa and break elongations of 6% [1].

The unique chemistry of Avimid® N prepregs imparts several beneficial high temperature properties to the resin. The material is based on an aromatic tetracarboxylic acid, 2, 2-bis (3', 4'-dicar-boxyphenyl) hexafluoropropane (6FTA). The 6FTA monomer is mixed with m-phenylenediamine (MPD) and p-phenylenediamine (PPD). Adding heat the monomers in solution will undergo a conventional imidization reaction forming the polyimide and releasing water.

This unique chemistry makes Avimid® N prepregs one of the most thermally and oxidatively stable organic polymer systems known. The polymer chain is completely aromatic with no unstable linkages. It's ability to branch or cross link is limited, reducing the potential number of weak links in the chain, and the chemically inert and bulky nature of the components in the 6FTA monomer help to prevent crystallization.

TABLE 1. Delivered Strength of Carbon Fibers in **Avimid® N** Prepregs Investigating Multiple Process and Material Variables.

Fiber Type	Tow Lot Strength MPa (ksi)	Hoop Fiber Stress MPa (ksi)	Stress Ratio	% Fiber Strength Translated
Hercules IM7	5180 (751)	2990 (433)	0.46	58
Hercules IM7	5180 (751)	3280 (476)	0.50	63
Hercules IM7	5530 (802)	3460 (502)	0.29	63
Hercules IM7	5240 (760)	3330 (483)	0.51	64
Hercules IM7	5180 (751)	3670 (532)	0.47	71
Hercules IM7	5240 (760)	3990 (578)	0.50	76
Hercules IM7	5530 (802)	4510 (654)	0.30	82
Hercules IM7	5240 (760)	4410 (640)	0.39	84
Hercules IM7	5530 (802)	5430 (788)	0.24	98

With Avimid® N prepreg's stable chemistry an impressive host of high temperature properties have been demonstrated in combination with stable reinforcing fibers. These include:

1) Maintaining 50% of the laminates original flexural strength up to 50,000 hours at 260 °C, 5,000 hours at 316 °C, and 1,500 hours at 343 °C [1].

2) Exhibiting neat resin fracture toughness values at 23 °C of 2400 J/m^2 which is 30 times more resistant to fracture than the epoxies tested and 10 times more resistant than the thermoset polyimides tested [1].

3) Showing very low weight losses in thermal aging tests, with laminates losing less that 1% of their weight after 10,000 hours at 260 °C, as compared to a 16% weight lose in conventional thermoset polyimide laminates [1].

4) Demonstrating minimal changes in laminate strengths, and no surface cracking or erosion, when exposed to 300 °C for 1000 hours [1].

5) Showing only a 30% loss in laminate compression properties after 3000 thermal cycles between (-54) °C and 218 °C. This represents 2-3 times better performance than addition type polyimides [3].

6) Performing excellently in moisture resistance, solvent resistance and weatherability tests [1].

8. COMMENTS

Taking into account that Avimid® N composites have demonstrated fiber translation strengths over 4137 MPa (600 ksi) in 5.75" pressure bottles, and that it has repeatedly shown far superior thermal and oxidative stability over addition type polyimides, makes it a leading candidate in the quest for high temperature composite systems. These results support fabricating of complex parts demanding high temperature, high strength properties from organic polyimide composites based on Avimid® N.

9. ACKNOWLEDGEMENTS

The authors would like to thank the combined efforts of the entire Composites Division at E. I. DuPont and the Air Force Astronautic Lab for their efforts in manufacturing, analyzing, testing, and documenting this work in pressure bottles made from Avimid® N. Jim Carey's help in establishing the proper cure cycle was important in eliminating fiber wrinkles. Donna Dietert's contribution's in the areas of testing and analysis at DuPont was invaluable. The guidance in stress analysis equations provided by Gerald K. Knight from Morton Thiokol's Wasatch Division was especially appreciated.

10. REFERENCES

1. Du Pont Company, "Avimid® N Composite Materials for Advanced Aircraft/ Aerospace Applications," Brochure E-75102.
2. ASTM 2585-68 (Reapproved 1985), "Standard Method For Preparation and

Testing of Filament Wound Pressure Vessels."

3. Tanikella, M. S., " Thermal Cycling and High Temperature Performance of Avimid® N," Unpublished Data, July 31, 1987.

BIOGRAPHIES

Ken Egerton is a Research Engineer with E. I. Du Pont Company working for the Composites Division at Chestnut Run Plaza in Wilmington, Delaware. He received a Masters Degree in Mechanical Engineering, specializing in robotics, from Bucknell University in 1984. His current efforts are centered in the areas of advanced composite processing techniques for thermoplastic and thermoset matrixes. Ken received the DuPont Market Director's Award for outstanding contributions to the Textile Fibers Department and is the author of three papers on Composite Processing and Properties.

Murty Tanikella is a Research Associate with E.I. Du Pont Company working for the Composites Division at Chestnut Run Plaza in Wilmington, Delaware. He received his Ph.D in Chemistry from University of Pittsburgh in 1967 and did postdoctoral research at Rice University and The National Research Council of Canada. His current efforts are focused on developing high temperature polyimide matrix materials, especially Avimid® N, for composite applications. Murty is the author of a number of patents and publications.

Jim Koury is an Aerospace Engineer with the Air Force Astronautics Laboratory working for the Aerospace Vehicle System Division at Edwards Air Force Base in California. He has a Bachelor of Science degree in Chemistry and has been working as a Project Engineer for 22 years. Current efforts are in the advancement of processing techniques for thermoplastic and thermoset composite structures. He is co-chairman of High Temperature Polymeric Plastic Laminate Evaluation (High Temple) and was chairman of the committee for Standardization for Composites for Joint Army, Navy, Air Force and NASA Composite Motor Cases. Jim is the author and co-author of a number of publications.

LARC-CPI, A NEW SEMI-CRYSTALLINE POLYIMIDE

P. M. Hergenrother
NASA Langley Research Center
Hampton, VA 23665-5225
M. W. Beltz*
University of Akron
Akron, OH 44325
and
S. J. Havens
PRC, Inc.
Hampton, VA 23666

Abstract

As part of a program on high performance/high temperature structural resins for aerospace applications, work was performed with a new semi-crystalline polyimide (LARC-CPI) to improve the compression moldability while retaining high mechanical properties and thermooxidative stability. Various molecular weight versions of LARC-CPI polyamide acid were prepared, end-capped with different groups, converted to polyimide and evaluated for film

properties, thermooxidative stability and melt flow. One controlled molecular weight, end-capped version of LARC-CPI was evaluated more comprehensively in adhesive and composite work and exhibited good compression moldability, reasonable crystallization rates and high mechanical properties.

*Research Associate position at
NASA Langley Research Center

1. INTRODUCTION

A major part of our effort has focused on the development of high temperature structural resins for aerospace applications. These materials are needed to perform for hundreds to thousands of hours around the engines on commercial aircraft where the temperature may be as high as 370°C depending on the application. High speed aircraft structures demand tens of thousands of hours at temperatures of 230°C and higher. Space vehicles require performance for hundreds of hours at temperatures of 300°C and higher. Structural resins for use in these applications require a unique combination of properties such as processability, environmental stability and high mechanical properties. Several experimental polymers have shown good adhesive and composite properties for thousands of hours at 230°C and for hundreds of hours at 300°C [1,2]. However, only a few high temperature organic polymers are commercially available as adhesives tapes [3] or prepregs [4-6]. Recently a new series of semi-crystalline polyimides were reported [7]. One particular polyimide, LARC-CPI, exhibited excellent adhesive and film properties [8]. However, high molecular weight LARC-CPI required high pressures at 400°C to fabricate adhesive specimens and composites. In an attempt to improve the compression moldability of LARC-CPI, several different molecular weight end-capped versions were prepared and evaluated. Molecular weight control and end-capping to improve melt flow and stability is commonly used with compression and injection moldable, commercially available, high performance thermoplastics.

2. EXPERIMENTAL

2.1 Polymer Synthesis

3,3',4,4'-Benzophenonetetra-carboxylic dianhydride (BTDA) was reacted with a stoichiometric amount of 1,3-bis(4-aminophenoxy-4'-benzoyl)benzene (1,3-BABB) at ambient temperature in N,N-dimethylacetamide (DMAc) under nitrogen at 15% solids content to yield a viscous solution of high molecular weight poly(amic acid). Lower molecular weight versions of LARC-CPI were prepared by offsetting the stoichiometry of either BTDA or 1,3-BABB by either 2.5 or 5.0 mole percent and subsequently end-capping with a stoichiometry amount of aniline, phthalic anhydride, n-hexylamine, 4-(n-hexyl)aniline and naphthalic anhydride. The end-capping agent was added either in the beginning of the polymerization or after 4 h of reaction. Only slight differences in the inherent viscosity were observed as a function of when the end-capper was added. Portions of the DMAc solutions were used to cast films which were thermally converted to polyimides.

To obtain polyimide for adhesive and composite evaluation, BTDA was reacted with a 5 mole % excess of 1,3-BABB in a mixture of bis(2-methoxyethyl)ether (diglyme) (77.8%) and DMAc (22.2%) at 25% solids content at ambient temperature under nitrogen for 18 hours to yield a poly(amide acid) with an inherent viscosity of 0.69 dL/g. Ten mole % of phthalic anhydride was added and after stirring the solution at ambient temperataure under nitrogen for 4 and 18 hours, the inherent viscosity decreased to 0.60 and 0.57 dL/g, respectively. The solution was used to prepare adhesive tape and unsized AS-4 prepreg.

LARC-CPI powders were obtained by chemically imidizing the poly(amide acid) in solution with acetic anhydride and a small amount of pyridine at 120°C for 16 h under nitrogen. The polyimide was precipitated in methanol and subsequently chopped in a high speed blender. A yellow powder was isolated and subsequently dried at 200°C in forced air oven overnight.

2.2 Films

The poly(amide acid) solutions (15% solids concentration) prepared using exact stoichiometry and also from the end-capping studies were centrifuged, the decantate cast onto plate glass using a 30 mil doctor blade and dried to a tack-free form in a dust-free chamber. The films on glass were then thermally converted to the polyimide by heating in air at 100, 200 and 300°C for 1 h at each temperature. In some cases, boiling water was required to remove the films from the glass plates. Mechanical properties of the 2.0-2.5 mil thick films were determined according to ASTM D882 using four to six specimens per test condition.

2.3 Thermooxidative Stability Test

Dry films of approximately 0.3 g were placed in crucibles and heated at 300°C in circulating air for 500 h. Weight loss, film flexibility and color were recorded periodically.

2.4 Adhesive Specimens

The as-made poly(amide acid) solution in a mixture of diglyme and DMAc were used to brush coat 112 E-glass, with an A-1100 finish, secured on a frame. Each coat was dried in air for ~ 1 h each at 100 and 200 which converted most of the poly(amide acid) to the polyimide. Generally, 5 coats were required to provide ~ 14 mil thick boardy tape which contained ~ 2.7% volatiles. Titanium (Ti, 6Al-4V) to Ti tensile shear specimens with Pasa-Jell 107 surface treatment were fabricated by heating to 375 to 400°C during ~ 45 min. under 200 psi and held at temperature under 200 psi for 15 minutes followed by cooling under pressure. Three specimens were tested for each condition according to ASTM D1002.

2.5 Composites

Unsized AS-4 fiber was coated on a drum winder with a poly(amide acid) solution [25% solids (w/v) in diglyme and DMAc from BTDA and 1,3-BABB upset by 5 mole % in favor of 1,3-BABB and end-capped with 10 mole % of phthalic anhydride]. The wet unidirectional prepreg was dried on the drum for 18 h at ~ 60°C to a tack-free form and subsequently cut into pieces and further dried in a circulating air oven for 1 h each at 100, 150 and 200°C. The prepreg was boardy, curled, resin rich on the non-drum side and had a volatile content of 2.1%. The curled prepreg was flattened in a press under mild pressure at ~ 220°C prior to use. Small unidirectional composites (3 in x 7 in x 10 to 16 plies) were fabricated with and without bleeder plies in a stainless steel mold by heating from ambient temperature under 300 to 500 psi to 365 to 400°C during ~ 1 h and maintaining at 365 to 400°C under 300 to 500 psi for 15 minutes followed by a postcure under pressure for 3 hours at 300°C. The laminates were C-scanned and cut into flexural and short beam shear specimens and tested according to ASTM D790 and D2344 respectively.

2.6 Polymer Characterization

Inherent viscosities were measured on 0.5% solution (w/v) in DMAc at 25°C. Differential Scanning Calorimetry (DSC) was preformed at a heating rate of 20°C/min with the apparent glass transition temperature (T_g) taken at the inflection point of the ΔT vs temperature curve and the crystalline melt temperature (T_m) taken at the peak of the endotherm. Wide angle x-ray scattering data (WAXS) was obtained on thin film specimens of the polyimide. With the x-ray diffractometer operated at 45 kV and 40 mA, using copper radiation with a flat sample holder and a graphite monochromator, the intensity of 1 s counts taken every 0.01° (2θ) was recorded on hard disk for the angular range 10-40° (2θ). An external quartz standard was used in goniometer alignment. Flow tests were conducted by heating powder samples (0.10 g) sandwiched between aluminum foil under various pressures to 400°C and measuring the relative flow. Two determinations were performed for each polymer. Although this test is subjective, a ranking of relative flow was obtained.

3. RESULTS AND DISCUSSION

3.1 Polymer Synthesis and Characterization

Several end-capped versions of LARC-CPI as listed in Table 1 and 2 were prepared by the solution polymerization of BTDA and 1,3-BABB by upsetting the stoichiometry by 2.5 and 5.0 mole percent in favor of both monomers. The poly(amide acids) were then end-capped with a stoichiometric amount of an appropriate end-capper using n-hexylamine, aniline, 4-hexylaniline, phthalic anhydride or 1,8-naphthalic anhydride. Portions of the poly(amide acids) were thermally and chemically converted to the corresponding polyimides. The synthesis of LARC-CPI is depicted in Eq. 1. The inherent viscosities of the poly(amide acids) in Table 1 and 2 suggest two molecular weight levels for each end-capped polymer. However, the molecular weight distributions of the poly(amide acids) was not determined. A few polyimides films exhibited good flexibility whereas other polyimide films prepared from poly(amide acids) with higher inherent viscosities were brittle. For example, the naphthalic anhydride end-capped polyimide film from poly(amide acid) with an inherent viscosity of 0.50 dL/g (Table 2) was flexible whereas the phthalic anhydride end-capped polyimide film from poly(amide acid) with inherent viscosity of 0.55 dLg/ was brittle. The difference may be due to different degrees of crystallinity as well as different molecular weight distributions.

All of the polyimides were semi-crystalline with T_gs from 217-229°C and T_ms between 345-370°C. The T_gs and T_ms from the end-capped polyimides are similar to those values obtained for LARC-CPI. However, there is a slight increase in T_ms for the end-capped polymers. This shift in the T_ms is probably due to an increase in crystallinity associated with lower molecular weight. Lower molecular weight polymers crystallize more readily than higher molecular weight polymers. In fact the polyimides end-capped with aniline exhibit this behavior very distinctly. High molecular weight LARC-CPI has a T_m at 350°C. When the anhydride terminated poly(amide acid) was end-capped with aniline at the 5, 10 and 15 mole % level (of aniline), the T_ms of the thermally converted polyimides were 360, 370 and 375°C respectively. At the 10 and 15 mole % level, films of the polyimides were brittle.

High molecular weight LARC-CPI film is slow to crystallize after heating to 385°C. However, aniline or phthalic anhydride end-capped lower molecular weight, LARC-CPI films (stoichiometry upset by 5 mole % in favor of BTDA or 1,3-BABB and end-capped with 10 mole % of aniline or phthalic anhydride) were held at 385°C for 0.5 hour and subsequently annealed at ~ 300°C for 0.5 hour to induce about the same degree of crystallinity as in the original films. Reasonable crystallization kinetics are desired so crystallinity can be induced into LARC-CPI adhesive panels and composites in a relatively short time.

The thermooxidative stability of films of high molecular weight and various end-capped versions of LARC-CPI (stoichiometry upset by 2.5 mole % and 5 mole % of end-capper used) are summarized in Table 3. LARC-CPI end-capped with 5 mole % of naphthalic anhydride exhibited the best thermooxidative stability with a 5.4% weight loss after 500 hours at 300°C. The n-hexylamine end-capped version exhibited the lowest stability as evidenced by a weight loss of 13.7% at 300°C after 500 hours.

Melt flow tests were performed on powders of high molecular weight and various end-capped versions of LARC-CPI obtained by chemical cyclodehydration of the poly(amide acids) and subsequently dried at 200°C for 18 hours. The end-capped LARC-CPI samples were prepared by upsetting the stoichiometry by 2.5 mole % and end-capping with 5 mole % of the appropriate reactant. Powder samples (0.1 g) were sandwiched between aluminum foil and introduced into a preheated press at 400°C. About 200 psi was applied at 400°C for 10 minutes and the relative flow of each sample obtained. The diameter of the resulting films ranged from 0.61 to 0.79 in. with aniline end-capped LARC-CPI exhibiting the most flow and phthalic anhydride end-capped LARC-CPI showing the least flow for the end-capped polymers. High molecular weight LARC-CPI consolidated well but exhibited little flow. All of the pressed films were flexible except the n-hexylamine and 4-hexylaniline end-capped LARC-CPI. Since melt flow of these polymers were considered marginal for adhesive and composite fabrication, other end-capped polymers were prepared by upsetting the stoichiometry by 5 mole % and using 10 mole % of end-capping agent. Under the same melt flow determination as previously used, the diameters of the flexible flow discs were 0.98, 1.22 and 1.30 in. for the phthalic anhydride, naphthalic anhydride and aniline end-capped LARC-CPI respectively.

Films were prepared by casting poly(amide acid) solutions onto plate glass and subsequently drying through 300°C. All films were slightly opaque and crystalline as evidenced by WAXS and DSC. Representative DSC curves and an X-ray diffractogram are presented in Figures 1 and 2 respectively. However, only the films cast from poly(amide acids) prepared by upsetting the stoichiometry by 2.5 mole % were tough and flexible with one exception. The naphthalic anhydride end-capped poly(amide acid) prepared with a 5 mole % upset in stoichiometry gave a film having a low degree of crystallinity that was tough and flexible. The mechanical properties of unoriented representative films are presented in Table 3. Generally, the tensile strength and tensile modulus of the lower molecular weight, end-capped LARC-CPI films were lower than that of high molecular weight LARC-CPI film. The moduli of the naphthalic anhydride end-capped polyimide film are noticeably less than that for most of the other films presumably due to lower levels of crystallinity.

High molecular weight LARC-CPI poly(amide acid) was used to cast a film which was subsequently converted to polyimide by heating for 1 hour each at 100, 200 and 300°C. The film was subsequently unaxially oriented at ~ 240°C.[9] The properties of the unaxially oriented LARC-CPI film were excellent as shown in Table 4. All of the other films in Table 4 are biaxially oriented. The elongation of LARC-CPI film is low presumably due to the quality of the film. No special care was exercised to remove foreign particles in the poly(amide acid) solution by filtration or to avoid dust particles during the film casting. Further optimization of LARC-CPI film should provide higher mechanical properties, especially elongation, and better thermooxidative stability.

3.2 Adhesives

Adhesive and composite work primarily used the phthalic anhydride end-capped LARC-CPI. In retrospect, aniline or naphthalic anhydride end-capped LARC-CPI may have been a better choice since these polyimides exhibited better melt flow and comparable thermooxidative stability as the phthalic anhydride end-capped LARC-CPI. However, films of the naphthalic anhydride end-capped LARC-CPI exhibited low levels of crystallinity. Future work will involve the evaluation of the aniline and naphthalic anhydride end-capped versions in adhesive and composite work.

The Ti/Ti tensile shear strengths of LARC-CPI from prior work [8] are summarized in Table 6. The strengths were excellent but the bonding conditions, especially pressure (1000 psi), were too stringent for practical consideration. As part of the prior work, a lower molecular weight version of LARC-CPI was bonded under 200 psi at 400°C and gave Ti/Ti tensile shear strengths of 5450 psi at 25°C and 2510 psi at 232°C. In continuing this effort to improve the compression moldability of LARC-CPI, a new, controlled molecular weight, end-capped version was evaluated in adhesive work. In spite of thick bondlines (12-13 mils), Ti/Ti tensile shear specimens gave ~ 5500 psi at 25°C and ~ 4400 psi at 177°C (Table 7). Excellent strengths (3960 psi) were also obtained at 200°C for those specimens exposed to temperatures of 300°C for several hours. Annealing at 300°C presumably induces more crystallinity into the polyimide, allowing it to exhibit higher strength at 200°C. The bond strengths at 232°C were disappointing (1600 psi) since in previous work [8], 232°C strengths of 2800 to 3670 psi were obtained. All 232°C tested specimens in Table 7 failed adhesively. The adhesive tape used in this work was thick and under the bonding pressure of 200 psi, resulted in bondline thicknesses of 12-13 mils. Generally, specimens with bondline thickness of 12-13 mils exhibit low strength. Other versions of LARC-CPI are being evaluated as adhesives.

3.3 Composites

Composite work focused on unidirectional laminates fabricated from solution coated, poor quality, unsized AS-4 unidirectional tape which was dried to a volatile content of 2.1%. Laminates were fabricated with and without bleeder plies at final temperatures of 365 to 400°C under 300 to 500 psi. The best consolidated laminates (via C-scan) were fabricated without bleeder at a final temperature of 365°C under 500 psi followed by a postcure at 300°C under 500 psi for 3 hours. As presented in Table 8, initial flexural properties at 25, 177 and 204°C were respectable. The initial 232°C values were lower than expected since DSC analysis showed the matrix to have a fair degree of crystallinity. The short beam shear strengths (SBSS) are low presumably due to the poor quality of the prepreg (non-uniform resin distribution, fiber misalignment, poor fiber wetting,etc.). This is commonly encountered in initial work on new thermoplastics composites, especially with solution coated drum-wound prepreg. The initial 177°C SBSS was low apparently due to a small amount of residual solvent. Upon aging at 316°C for 100 hours, 177°C SBSS increased significantly with the 232°C SBSS retaining 60% of the 25°C value. The flexural properties at elevated temperatures also increased as a result of increased crystallinity from aging at 316°C. A flexural strength of 209 Ksi at 232°C(above the T_g of the polyimide)was observed. Future composite work will involve further optimization of LARC-CPI to increase the rate of crystallization, improve prepreg quality and obtain better mechanical properties, especially SBSS.

4. CONCLUSIONS

The chemical resistance and mechanical properties of LARC-CPI filims were excellent. The compression moldability and crystallization rate of LARC-CPI neat resin improved considerably by controlling the molecular weight and end-capping. Preliminary adhesive and composite work using a controlled molecular weight, phthalic anhydride end-capped, LARC-CPI was very encouraging.

The use of trade names or manufacturers does not constitute an official endorsement of such products or manufacturers, either expressed or implied, by the National Aeronautics and Space Administration.

5. REFERENCES

1. P. M. Hergenrother, Chemtech, August, 496 (1986)
2. P. M. Hergenrother and N. J. Johnston, Proceedings of Div. Org. Coat. Plast. Chem. 40, 460 (1979)
3. Product Data Sheets on FM-34, 35 and 36, American Cyanamid Company, Aerospace Products Dept., Havre de Grace, MD 21078
4. Product Data Sheets on Cypac 7005 and 7156-1, American Cyanamid Company, Aerospace Products Dept., Havre de Grace, MD 21078
5. PMR-15 prepreg available from Ferro Corp., Culver City, CA 90232; Fiberite Corp., Winona, MN, 55987; Hysol, Pittsburg, CA 94565 and U.S. Polymeric, Santa Ana, CA 92707
6. Avimid prepreg available in experimental quantities from DuPont, Composites Center, Wilmington, DE 19898
7. P. M. Hergenrother, N. T. Wakelyn and S. J. Havens, J. Polym. Sci.: Pt. A: Polym. Chem. 25, 1093 (1987)
8. P. M. Hergenrother and S. J. Havens, SAMPE J. 24(4), 13 (1988)
9. R. Kovar and R. Lusignea, Foster-Miller, Inc., Watham, MA; NASA Contract NAS1-18636, Final Report, August 1988

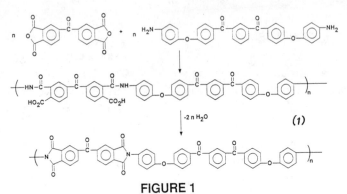

FIGURE 1

DIFFERENTIAL SCANNING CALORIMETRIC CURVES

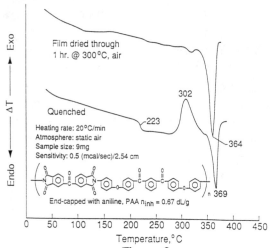

Film dried through
1 hr. @ 300°C, air

Quenched

302

-223

Heating rate: 20°C/min
Atmosphere: static air
Sample size: 9mg
Sensitivity: 0.5 (mcal/sec)/2.54 cm

364

369

End-capped with aniline, PAA n_{inh} = 0.67 dL/g

Temperature,°C

Figure 2

X-RAY DIFFRACTOGRAM OF POLYIMIDE FILM

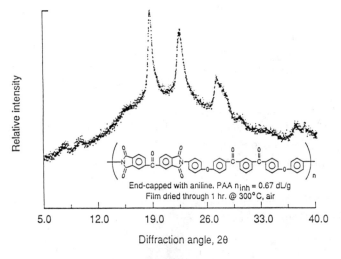

End-capped with aniline. PAA n_{inh} = 0.67 dL/g
Film dried through 1 hr. @ 300°C, air

Diffraction angle, 2θ

Table 1

End-capped LARC-TPI Using Amines

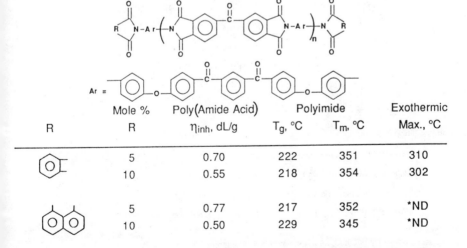

$Ar =$

R	Mole % R	Poly(Amide Acid) η_{inh}, dL/g	Polyimide T_g, °C	T_m, °C	Exothermic Max., °C
--	--	0.81	222	350	
$CH_3(CH_2)_5-$	5	0.93	222	355	304
	10	0.68	218	355	292
C_6H_5-	5	0.67	222	365	312
	10	0.44	218	370	310
$CH_3(CH_2)_5$⟨⟩	5	0.65	219	354	314
	10	0.50	217	360	302

Table 2

End-capped LARC-CPI Using Anydrides

$Ar =$

R	Mole % R	Poly(Amide Acid) η_{inh}, dL/g	Polyimide T_g, °C	T_m, °C	Exothermic Max., °C
⟨⟩	5	0.70	222	351	310
	10	0.55	218	354	302
⟨⟨⟩⟩	5	0.77	217	352	*ND
	10	0.50	229	345	*ND

*ND - Not Detected

Table 3

Stability of LARC-CPI Films at 300°C (air)

LARC-CPI Film[1]	% Weight Loss After Hours				
	48	144	240	408	500
High molecular weight	0.6	2.0	2.4[2]	3.2	5.9
n-Hexylamine end-cap	2.0	3.4[2]	5.9	8.8	13.7
Aniline end-cap	0.3	1.3[2]	2.2	5.4	6.9
4-Hexylaniline end-cap	0.9[2]	1.7	1.7	4.7	9.0
Phthalic anhydride end-cap	0.6	1.5[2]	2.1	4.2	6.9
Naphthalic anhydride end-cap	0.1	0.6	1.2[2]	5.3	5.4

[1]Amount of end-capper used was 5 mole %, all films were dried under same conditions through 1 hour at 300°C

[2]Became brittle and darker in color

Table 4
LARC-CPI Thin Film Properties at 25°C

End-cap	Tensile Strength, psi	Tensile Modulus, psi	Elongation, %
None-high molecular weight	19,400	615,500	4.4
5% n-hexylamine	16,600	478,000	4.9
5% Aniline	18,000	526,000	4.6
5% 4-Hexylaniline	19,800	533,000	5.9
5% Phthalic Anhydride	14,200	527,000	3.0
5% Naphthalic Anhydride	18,100	466,000	18.5
10% Naphthalic Anhydride	16,000	425,000	10.2

Table 5

Polyimide Film Properties at 25°C

Film	Tensile st., psi	Tensile mod., psi	Elong., %	Weight loss (%) after 500 h at 300°C (air)
Kapton® (DuPont)	25,000	430,000	70.0	4.4
Apical® (Allied-Signal/Konagafuji)	28,000	405,000	90.0	--
Upilex® S (ICI/Ube Chem.)	56,900	1,280,000	30.0	1.7
Novax (Mitsubishi Chem.)	49,800	996,000	50.0	30.6
LARC-CPI (Foster-Miller)*	45,900	1,360,000	4.0	5.9**

*Uniaxially oriented, all other films biaxially oriented

**Unoriented film

Table 6

LARC-CPI Ti/Ti Tensile Shear Data*

Test Condition	Strength, psi	Failure
25°C	6250	> 95% Cohesive
25°C after 3-day water boil	5140	~ 90% Cohesive
25°C after 72 hr hydraulic fluid soak	5590	~ 70% Cohesive
25°C after 1000 hr @ 232°C	7120	~ 100% Cohesive
25°C after 5 hr @ 300°C, 100 psi	6130	> 95% Cohesive
25°C after 100 hr @ 316°C	4590	~ 70% Cohesive
177°C	4510	> 95% Cohesive
177°C after 4 hr @ 300°C, 100 psi	4690	~ 100% Cohesive
232°C	590	~ 95% Adhesive
232°C after 100 hr @ 232°C	1840	~ 50% Cohesive
232°C after 1000 hr @ 232°C	2740	~ 50% Cohesive
232°C after 5 hr @ 300°C, 100 psi	2800	~ 80% Cohesive
232°C after 100 hr @ 316°C	3670	> 95% Cohesive

*Ref. 8; Pasa-Jell 107 surface treatment; inherent viscosity of poly(amic acid) = 0.50 dL/g; bonding conditions, 400°C, 1000 psi, 15 min; 112 E-glass tape contained 0.1% volatiles, bondline thickness 5-6 mils

Table 7

Adhesive Properties of LARC-CPI*

Bonding Condition	Ti/Ti Tensile Shear Strength, Psi (Failure Mode)**			
	25°C	177°C	200°C	232°C
400°C, 200 psi, 15 min	4200 (90% C)	4630 (100% C)	2650 (80% C)	600 (95% A)
375°C, 200 psi, 15 min	5650 (100% C)	4050 (95% C)	2430 (75% C)	----
375°C, 200 psi, 15 min + 18 hr at 300°C unrestrained	5380 (100% C)	4370 (95% C)	3920 (70% C)	1600 (95% A)
375°C, 200 psi, 15 min + 1 hr @ 310°C under 200 psi	5500 (100% C)	4330 (100% C)	2700 (75% C)	920 (95% A)
375°C, 200 psi 15 min + 100 hr @ 316°C unrestrained	4800 (95% C)	----	3960 (75% C)	1560 (95% A)

*Controlled molecular, phthalic anhydride end-capped version, 112 E-glass tape contained 2.7% volatiles, Pasa-Jell 107 surface treatment, bondline thickness 12-13 mils   **C = cohesive, A = adhesive

Table 8

LARC-CPI Unidirectional Unsized AS-4 Laminate Properties*

Test Temp., °C	Exposure	Flexural St., Ksi	Flexural Mod., Msi	Short Beam Shear St., Ksi
25	None	267	15.0	8.7
177	None	212	14.4	3.0**
204	None	196	14.4	---
232	None	110**	11.9	---
25	100 hr @ 316°C, air	265	14.3	8.9
177	100 hr @ 316°C, air	----	----	6.9
204	100 hr @ 316°C, air	214	14.0	5.9
232	100 hr @ 316°C, air	209	13.3	5.3

*Fiber volume ~ 53%; fabricated by heating to 365°C under 500 psi, holding 0.5 hr @ 365°C under 500 psi, and postcuring at 300°C for 3 hr under 500 psi
**Thermoplastic failure

POLYIMIDE MATRIX COMPOSITES: POLYIMIDESULFONE / LARC-TPI (1:1) BLEND

NORMAN J. JOHNSTON, TERRY L. ST. CLAIR,
ROBERT M. BAUCOM, AND TIMOTHY W. TOWELL*
NASA LANGLEY RESEARCH CENTER
HAMPTON, VA 23665-5225

Abstract

Polyimide matrix composites were fabricated from unidirectional unsized AS-4 carbon fiber and a doped 1:1 blend of two polyimides: benzophenone dianhydride-3,3'-diaminodiphenylsulfone ($PISO_2$) and benzophenone dianhydride-3,3'-diaminobenzophenone (LaRC-TPI). To enhance melt flow properties, the molecular weight of the $PISO_2$ was controlled by end-capping with phthalic anhydride and addition of five percent by weight p-phenylenediamine-phthalic anhydride bisamic acid dopant. Prepreg was drum-wound using a diglyme slurry comprised of the soluble polyamideacid of $PISO_2$, the soluble bisamideacid of the dopant, and the insoluble imidized LARC-TPI powder. Melt flow studies with a rotary rheometer and parallel plate plastometer on neat resin and prepreg helped develop an optimum cure cycle. Composite mechanical properties at room and elevated temperatures, dry and moisture-saturated, were evaluated, including short beam shear strength and flexure, tensile, shear, and compression properties. Two 18" x 24" skin-stringer panels were fabricated, one of which was tested in compression to failure.

1. INTRODUCTION

Polymer research at NASA Langley Research Center has emphasized the development of high temperature thermoplastics such as polyimides and polyarylene ethers. They offer attractive mechanical properties at elevated temperatures for adhesive and composite matrix applications involving high speed aircraft. The purpose of this paper is to continue the evaluation study reported previously[1] on polyimide blends as matrices for carbon fiber reinforced composites.

In that study, a large number of compositions were investigated involving LARC-TPI, 1, polyimidesulfone. ($PISO_2$), 2, Figure 1, and blends of LaRC-TPI preimidized powder in polyamideacid diglyme slurries of 1 and 2. The study revealed that the slurry technique provided an excellent method for fabricating prepreg from otherwise insoluble polymer powders and afforded well-consolidated void-free composites with outstanding properties. The use of polyimide blends and bisamideacid additives to improve processability was also demonstrated.

Further research has shown that slurry blends with LaRC-TPI preimidized powder in $PISO_2$ polyamideacid solution demonstrated better melt flow characteristics than blends of the same powder in LaRC-TPI polyamideacid solution.[2] Therefore, this paper will deal only with the 1:1 slurry composition of $PISO_2$:LaRC-TPI preimidized powder in diglyme. This ratio proved to be the best compromise between melt flow, derived primarily from the preimidized LARC-TPI powder, and the ability to prepreg thick

*Research Associate from Old Dominion University, Norfolk, VA, working at NASA Langley Research Center

slurries.

2. EXPERIMENTAL*

2.1 Starting Materials

The PISO$_2$ polyamideacid solution, endcapped with phthalic anhydride, was obtained commercially from High Tech Services as a 30 percent solution in diglyme, inherent viscosity (0.5 percent in dimethylacetamide at 30°C) 0.57 dl/g. Its synthesis has been reported elsewhere.[1,3,4] The LARC-TPI 2000 polyimide powder was obtained in several lots from MTC, Inc. According to MTC assay, depending on the lots, imide content varied from 85 to 94 percent, polyamic acid from 5 to 15 percent, and isoimide from traces to 4 percent. The bisamideacid used to dope the slurries was prepared from one mole of p-phenylenediamine and two moles of phthalic anhydride as described elsewhere. (5)

Stable slurries were formulated by diluting the 30 percent PISO$_2$ solution to 15 percent and adding LARC-TPI powder to achieve a 1:1 ratio by weight of polymer solids. Concentrations ranging from 24-26 percent solids afforded slurries that were stable for several hours at room temperature. The bisamideacid dopant was added as a diglyme solution at a w/w concentration of 2.5 percent.

2.2 Prepreg/Composite Fabrication

Slurries were prepregged by passing a single tow through a dip tank and onto an 18-inch diameter multiple speed drum winder as described previously.[1] Fiber areal weights could be varied from 145 to 200 g/m^2 and resin contents from 38 to 50 percent, w/w. Unsized Hercules AS-4 12K tow carbon fiber was used exclusively in this study. Prepreg volatile content ranged from 5 to 15 percent before oven drying. Because the prepreg dried so easily at room temperature, it was immediately removed from the drum and cut as required while still tacky and drapeable. Oversize plies were further dried in a circulating air oven under restraint at 204°C and stored at room temperature. SEM photomicrographs

* Use of trade names or manufacturers does not constitute an official endorsement, either expressed or implied, by the National Aeronautics and Space Administration.

showed the 2-6 micrometer particles of LARC-TPI powder to be rather evenly distributed through the thickness of the tow and along the fiber axis.

The dried plies were trimmed to size and stacked in a closed mold between Kapton^R film spray-coated with Frekote^R 33. No bleeder cloths were employed since polymer flow was minimal. Moldings were done in a 25 ton four post upacting press containing 12 inch electrically heated platens. The press was outfitted with a linear voltage differential transformer (L.V.D.T.), cantilevered over the side, to measure platen movement during ply consolidation. Heating and cooling rates of about 7°C per minute were employed. From the L.V.D.T. response, the following cure cycle was developed and used exclusively: at 300 psi, ramp to the following temperatures, 260°, 276°, 300°, and 343°C, and hold at each temperature until flow as detected by the L.V.D.T. stops. Hold times varied with part thickness. However, the hold at 343°C was always one hour.

Panels were evaluated ultrasonically as previously described[1] at a preestablished sensitivity level adequate to detect microvoids in T300/5208 carbon fiber/epoxy composites. Composite fiber weight percentages and fiber volumes were calculated from experimentally determined values of fiber areal weight, panel dimensions and weight, and fiber density.

2.3 Characterization Equipment

DSC, TMA, mechanical test machine, and DCB test procedures and equipment were described previously.[1] Flexure tests were run at a 32:1 span:depth ratio. Scanning electron micrographs were taken with an Hitachi Model S-510 SEM. Procedures for longitudinal and transverse tension and iosipescu shear tests on unidirectional specimens have been reported.[6] Compression tests were made on O$_{48}$, 1.5 in. x 1.75 in. fully instrumented specimens as described by Shuart.[7] Neat resin GIC values were obtained on miniturized specimens using a procedure reported by Hinkley.[8]

The Rheometrics System 4 rheometer was used to measure isothermally the melt viscosity of LARC-TPI powders . The standard torsional mode at an oscillatory frequency of 10 rad/sec was employed after the sample pellet had melted, wetted the platens, and reached temperature. Similar measurements on LARC-TPI powders have been reported. [9] Melt flow properties were also studied with a Tinius Olsen parallel plate plastometer modified as described elsewhere.[10] All measurements were taken at 300 psi using a 3°C heating rate, the same conditions employed for composite fabrication. L.V.D.T. displacements were corrected for apparatus thermal expansion. Densified specimens used in the study were press molded at RT from powders which were either obtained commecially or precipitated from solution, washed and dried.

3. RESULTS AND DISCUSSION

3.1 Characterization of LARC-TPI 2000 Powder

Melt viscosities of the various lots of LARC-TPI 2000 powder were difficult to measure because, when heated, the reactive powders gave off volatiles and increased in viscosity. Volatiles apparently come from cyclodehydration of polyamideacid and reactive end group chain propagations. The optimum processing window for composite fabrication appears to be during the early stages of the melt before viscosity buildup reaches 10^5-10^7 poise and the volatiles cannot be removed. In later lots of the 2000 powder, lots 25-801 and 25-802, the melt viscosity during an isothermal measurement at 347°C increased from 200 poise to a maximum 40,000 poise over 40-50 minutes. These lots were the most extensively used in this study. Melt viscosity studies of some previous lots have been reported.[9]

A series of DSC curves of lot 25-801 powder is shown in Figure 2. The undried as-received material displayed a very strong crystalline melt endotherm centered at 282°C. On reheating, the Tm is not seen; only a Tg at 219°C is observed. Apparently, after a 350°C exposure the material remains amorphous. The composite cure cycle was adjusted upward to take advantage of this fact. DSC studies on similar LARC-TPI powders have been reported.[9]

Moldings were made by first preheating the powder in an open die in an oven at 300°/0.5 hour and 350°C/1 hour to remove all volatiles. The die was then transferred to a 350°C preheated press, the die closed, and 300 psi applied for 1 hour at 350°C followed by rapid cooling under pressure. X-Ray diffraction patterns of the moldings showed only the standard halo typical of amorphous materials. Void-free plates up to 6 in. x 6 in. x 0.3 in. were made by this procedure.

Table I lists tensile properties, fracture toughness, and Tg values for neat resin plates made from powder lots 92-712 and 25-801 and from consolidated commercial LARC-TPI film. Tensile properties from the two sources of LARC-TPI were in excellent agreement. Moduli were higher than those reported by Bell and coworkers[11] for 300°C air-cured LARC-TPI film (540 Ksi), an indication that some chemical/physical interaction may be occurring in the powder at the higher cure temperature. The Tg value of the molding was lower than that obtained from film,[11] probably because the molecular weight was somewhat lower. Glc values were extremely high (15.9 in-lb/in^2), reflecting the toughness observed in many similar thermoplastic materials.[12]

3.2 Characterization of Blended Powder

DSC curves of the blended powder from the doped polyimide formulation are shown in Figure 3. The powder was predried at 204°C to remove solvent and help imidize polyamideacid. The DSC of the predried powder displayed two very strong endotherms centered at 225° and 284°C. The former is attributed to the Tg of partially imidized PISO$_2$ and to imidization reactions,[3,10] the latter to the Tm of the LARC-TPI. When reheated, the powder afforded a DSC featured only by a broad complex endotherm from 225° to 260°C, assigned to overlapping Tgs of the PISO$_2$ and LARC-TPI polyimide structures. As expected, no evidence of a Tm was seen.

3.3 Parallel Plate Plastometer Studies on Neat Resins

3.3.1 Background

Repeated attempts were made to mold void-free PISO2:LARC-TPI composites at 300 psi utilizing flow information from the L.V.D.T. attachment to the press. Panels of highest consolidation were obtained when isothermal holds were placed at critical "flow transitions" during heat-up. These holds were maintained until platen movement subsided. The complex ramp/hold cure cycle described in Section 2.2 resulted. Such a procedure has been extremely helpful in determining molding cycles of low flow, difficult-to-process matrix materials.

However, to screen the flow properties of new materials and develop preliminary consolidation cycles under rheological conditions simulating press/autoclave conditions, a miniturized test was needed. Parallel plate plastometer procedures were developed to conduct preliminary flow/consolidation studies on small neat powder and prepreg samples at various heating rates and pressures. The technique helped correlate the melt flow behavior of neat powders of LARC-TPI, PISO$_2$, and their blends and prepregs with the successful complex ramp/hold cure cycle used to fabricate PISO$_2$:LARC-TPI (1:1) composites. This information was then used to optimize that cycle.

3.3.2 Melt Flow Studies

Plastographs of LARC-TPI (lot 25-801) and PISO$_2$ powders are shown in Figures 4 and 5. The LARC-TPI curves are characterized by a rapid rate of platen closure at 250°C, just below Tm. Total squeeze out of resin is observed. The PISO$_2$ powder dried at 204°C is characterized by rapid platen movement in the 225°-260°C range near Tg. Total loss of resin is observed. For the powder predried at 300°C, rapid platen movement occurs at 250°-260°C but does not afford total squeeze out. The curve levels out at 32 percent of the original gap indicating that some chemical/physical reaction which increases resin stiffness must occur when PISO$_2$ is exposed at 300°C in air for an hour. Obviously, predrying to 300°C is not desired for either material. Further, the data indicates that holds should be built into the molding cycle to take advantage of the rapid flow exhibited by each material at specific temperatures.

This data was utilized to interpret the plastographs in Figure 6 of the doped polyimide blend. The ramp/hold cycle shown in Figure 6 is the one optimized for composite fabrication, except the duration of each isothermal hold was reduced for experimental convenience. No flow is seen at 204°C, the predry condition. Flow begins at about 225°C, coincident with the Tg of partially imidized PISO$_2$. Although LARC-TPI has a Tg in this region, the effect on

flow would be insignificant due to its semi-crystalline nature. Flow associated with the Tg of imidized PISO$_2$ is expended during the hold at 260°C. A temperature rise to 276°C initiates melting of LARC-TPI crystallites and the hold there expends the majority of the flow produced by Tm. Above 276°C, some flow is incurred from additional melting and thermoplastic flow under 300 psi pressure. The holds at 300° and 343°C, while producing no further flow, prevent recrystallization during cool-down and probably initiate some chain extension and chemical/physical interactions which increase stiffness.

During the entire cycle, polyamideacid is converting to polyimide and chain extension is taking place, both of which occur with concomitant evolution of water of cyclodehydration. The latter, if not properly removed, can be the source of microvoids in the finished part. The holds permit dramatic drops in viscosity which, in turn, allow volatiles to be evolved at a controlled rate and consolidation to occur before chemical/physical reactions build the viscosity to undesired levels.

3.4 Composite Studies

3.4.1 Prepreg Melt Flow Study

Figure 7 shows a series of 5 plastographs, each made with a billet of stacked (0/90/0/90/0) prepreg, AS-4/PISO$_2$:LARC-TPI (1:1)/2.5% dopant, each billet predried at a different temperature for one hour. Runs were made with the optimized ramp/hold cure cycle. The initial platen movement in the 3 prepregs dried below 204°C was attributed to loss of solvent and imidization. In the temperature range from 220° to 260°C, platen movement was similar in all plastographs to that observed for the neat resin blend in Figure 6, except the rate of movement increased as the drying temperature was increased. Platen movement at Tm was relatively small compared to that of the neat resin in Figure 6. Apparently, fiber loading increases with decreased platen separation until most of the applied load is carried by the fibers and no further movement is observed. This study clearly demonstrates that the prepreg must be predried to 204°C to remove volatiles and prevent premature flow associated with imidization. Such flow at an early stage in the cycle is undesirable; it prematurely loads the fibers such that flow due to Tg and

Tm cannot be fully exploited. The latter is critical to help remove air and water of cyclodehydration and wet the fibers.

3.4.2 Additional Composite Cure Studies

Figure 8 contains C-scans of four 3 in. x 3 in. AS-4/PISO$_2$:LARC-TPI(1:1) O$_{20}$ panels. All scans were run at the same signal amplitude and gain. The panel in scan 8a contained 2.5 percent dopant and was processed by the optimized ramp/hold cure cycle. The scan is virtually transparent except for a few voids at the edge and 3 triangularly positioned black spots caused by bolts supporting the panel in the water bath. The panel in scan 8b contained the same polyimide-doped matrix but was processed by a straight-up cure cycle using a 5°C/min. heating rate. The poor quality of the panel shows that this cure condition is unsatisfactory.

The scan in Figure 8c was made from a panel containing the undoped polyimide blend and processed by the optimized ramp/hold cure cycle. The poor quality of the laminate demonstrates the effect a 2.5 percent (w/w) addition of bisamideacid dopant has on polyimide resin melt flow properties[5] and ability to consolidate plies and fabricate void-free parts. The panel in scan 8d contained the same undoped polyimide and was processed by a straight-up cure cycle. As expected, the panel was of poor quality. Additional studies with 3 in. x 3 in. O$_{20}$ laminates where the optimum holds were either eliminated or altered generally afforded panels whose C-scans indicated unacceptable levels of voids. The effect of these on mechanical properties, especially at elevated temperature, will be determined.

3.4.3 Composite Properties

A description of each of the composites whose mechanical and toughness properties are reported herein is given in Table II. Short beam shear strengths and flexure properties at 4 temperatures, dry and moisture saturated, are listed in Table III. Tensile and shear properties at two temperatures, dry and moisture saturated, are given in Table IV and compression properties at room temperature dry are given in Table V.

The flexure properties were generally higher than those observed for undoped AS-4/PISO$_2$:LARC-TPI (2:1) composites in the earlier study.[1] Retention of both dry and

wet strength at elevated temperatures was outstanding. About 80 percent retention of room temperature dry flexure strength was observed at 177°C/wet. Short beam shear strengths were relatively low compared to those for epoxy composites and for undoped polyimides in the earlier study.[1] This is in contrast to the iosipescu shear strengths, Table IV, which were outstanding. Both shear strength and modulus values at the 3 conditions shown in Table IV were higher than those of many selected thermoplastic and thermoset composites, including APC-2, 8551-7, and 2220-1 and -3.[6]

Longitudinal tensile values were standard for AS-4 fiber-reinforced laminates. Transverse properties were reasonably low, probably because of relatively poor fiber/resin interfacial adhesion. Compression tests were run at room temperature on thick specimens using a newly developed technique, so very little comparative data is available except that shown in Table V.[7]

The compression strengths for epoxy appear to be very low when compared to values obtained from other widely-used compression test methods. However, they appear to be reasonable for a test where interlaminar shearing is the dominate failure mode for unidirectional specimens. Both the epoxy and the polyimide specimens failed by this mechanism. Interestingly, the 118 Ksi value for the polyimide is approximately 87 percent of the epoxy value, whereas in other compression tests, thermoplastic compression strengths are only about 70 percent of those observed for thermosets.[12] Considering the quality of the drum-wound prepreg (e.g., fiber alignment, resin distribution, etc.), the polyimide value is very good. It is also notable that compression strength drops about 10 percent (118 to 106 Ksi) when specimens contain microvoids.

The mode I fracture toughness of a O$_{24}$ composite was measured using the double cantilever beam test. Values were 6.2 in-lb/in^2 (initiation) and 8.8 in-lb/in^2 (propagation). The initiation value is close to that predicted from the relationship of neat resin Glc versus composite Glc.[13]

3.4.4 Skin-Stringer Panel

Two 18 in. x 24 in. T-bar structural test panels were fabricated according to the schematic in Figure 9. Conventional drum-wound AS-4/PISO$_2$:LARC-TPI (1:1)/2.5% doped prepreg was used having a fiber areal weight of about 135 g/m^2, a thickness of 6 mils, and solvent (diglyme) content of approximately 5-15 percent to maintain tack and drape. Steel tooling was sprayed with a fluorocarbon release agent and baked at 232°C/1 hour. Prepreg was applied in a (0/45) layup to tooling bars arranged in opposed "C-channels" comprising the web and flanges of the stiffener. Additional prepreg in a (0/90/45) layup was applied to the cap of the stiffener and the stiffener element was placed on the preplied skin, a (90/45/0) layup. The entire assembly was placed on a steel caul sheet, vacuum bagged with 3 mil Kapton^R film and high temperature strip sealant, and autoclaved at 300 psi according to the optimum ramp/hold cure cycle discussed above. Photos of the planform and edge of a trimmed panel are shown in Figures 10 and 11, respectively. One panel was instrumented for a compression test and failed at 30.7 Ksi compression load. An identical AS-4/3502 epoxy panel failed at 41.9 Ksi.

4. CONCLUDING REMARKS

Well-consolidated high quality unidirectional and angle-plied carbon fiber reinforced composites were fabricated from a 1:1 blend of LARC-TPI preimidized powder slurried in PISO$_2$ polyamideacid diglyme solution doped with 2.5 percent (w/w) bisamideacid of p-phenylenediamine/2 phthalic anhydride. A complex optimized cure cycle was developed for this blend using information from parallel plate plastometry, melt viscosity, and DSC studies. Considerable effort was made to perfect characterization tools and methodology to aid in the fabrication of low flow matrices. The flexural, shear, and tensile properties at room and elevated temperatures, dry and wet, demonstrate the potential of this blend as a matrix material. Further research is required to improve melt flow characteristics and reduce the thermally induced volatiles of these low flow, thermally stable systems.

5. ACKNOWLEDGMENTS

The authors gratefully acknowledge Dr. J. R. Pratt for the synthesis of the bisamide acid dopant, Dr. J. H. Starnes, Jr., for help in the design and test of the skin-stringer panel, and Dr. M. J. Shuart for help in running the compression tests.

5. REFERENCES

1. N. J. Johnston and T. L. St. Clair, Intl. SAMPE Tech. Conf. Series, 18, 53 (1986); SAMPE J., 23(1), 12 (1987).
2. N. J. Johnston, unpublished results, NASA-Langley Research Center.
3. T. L. St. Clair and D. A. Yamaki in Polyimides, K. L. Mittal, Ed., Plenum Pub. Co., NY, 1984, Vol. 1, P. 99; NASA TM-84574, 1982.
4. J. F. Dezern amd P. R. Young. Int. J. Adhesion and Adhesives, 5(4), 1985, 183.
5. J. R. Pratt, T. L. St. Clair, H. D. Burks, and D. M. Stoakley, Sci. Adv. Matl. Proc. Eng. Series, 32, 1036 (1987).
6. S. L. Coguill and D. F. Adams, Final Technical Report for NASA Grant NAG1-277, Dec. 1988. U. of Wyoming Report UW-CMRG-R-88-114, Dec. 1988; NASA CR-xxxxx, February, 1989.
7. M. J. Shuart, AIAA Paper No. 88-2293, AIAA/ASME/ASCE/AHS 29th Structures, Structural Dynamics and Materials Conf., Williamsburg, VA, April 18-20, 1988.
8. J. A. Hinkley, J. Appl. Polym. Sci., 32, 5653 (1986).
9. H. D. Burks, T. H. Hou, and T. L St. Clair, SAMPE Quart., 18(1), 1 (1986).
10. T. H. Hou and T. L. St. Clair, SAE Technical Paper Series, SP-748, 31 (1988).
11. V. L. Bell, B. L. Stump, and H. Gager, J. Polym. Sci.:Polym. Chem., 14, 2275 (1976).
12. N. J. Johnston and P. M. Hergenrother, NASA TM-89104, Feb. 1987; Sci. Adv. Matl. Proc. Eng. Series, 32, 1400 (1987).
13. D. L. Hunston, R. J. Moulton, N. J. Johnston, and W. D. Bascom, ASTM STP-937, 1987; D. L. Hunston, Composites Tech. Rev., 6, 176 (1984).
14. J. N. Dickson, S. B. Biggers, and J. H. Starnes, Jr., Seventh DoD/NASA Conf. on Fibrous Composites in Structural Design, Denver. CO, June 17-20, 1985.

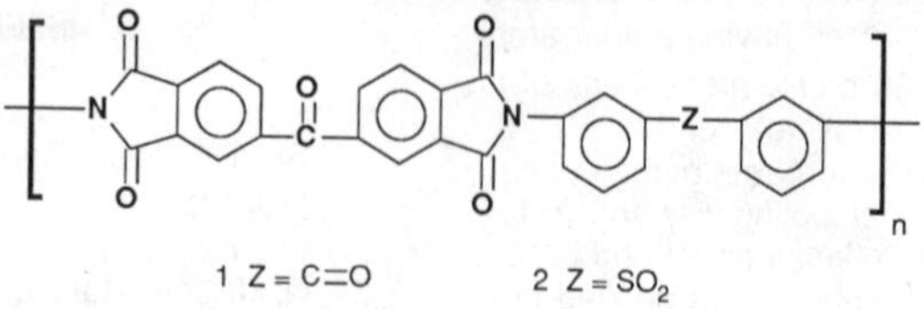

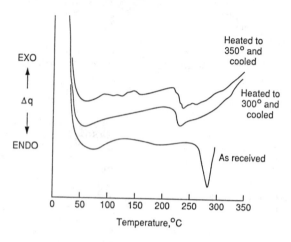

FIGURE 1. MOLECULAR STRUCTURE OF LARC-TPI, 1, AND PISO$_2$, 2.

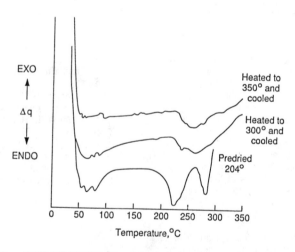

FIGURE 2. DSC OF LARC-TPI PREIMIDIZED POWDER (MTC LOT 25-801).

FIGURE 3. DSC OF POWDER PRECIPITATED FROM DIGLYME BLEND OF PISO$_2$:LARC-TPI(1:1)/2.5% DOPANT

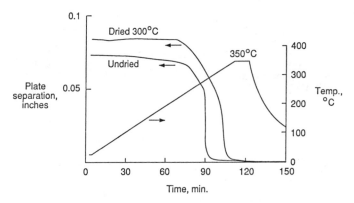

FIGURE 4. PLASTOGRAPHS OF LARC-TPI PREIMIDIZED POWDER (MTC LOT 25-801).

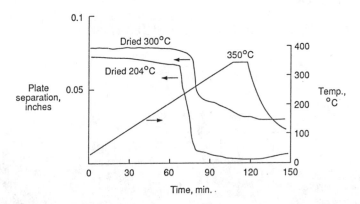

FIGURE 5. PLASTOGRAPHS OF PISO$_2$ POWDER PRECIPITATED FROM DIGLYME SOLUTION.

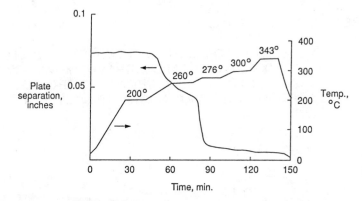

FIGURE 6. PLASTOGRAPH OF POWDER PRECIPITATED FROM DIGLYME BLEND OF PISO$_2$:LARC-TPI(1:1)/2.5% DOPANT.

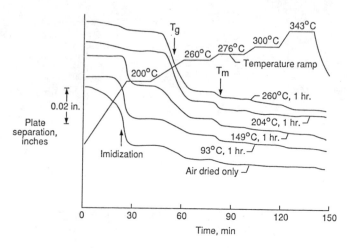

FIGURE 7.   PLASTOGRAPHS OF PREPREG MADE WITH AS-4 FIBER AND
            PISO$_2$:LARC-TPI(1:1)/2.5% DOPANT BLEND. CURVES
            OFFSET ALONG THE ORDINATE FOR DISPLAY PURPOSES.

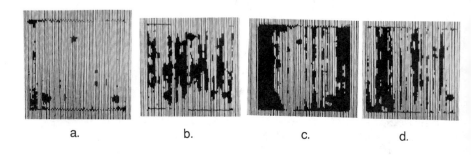

a.   b.   c.   d.

FIGURE 8.   C-SCANS OF 3"X3" (0)$_{20}$ AS-4/PISO$_2$:LARC-TPI(1:1)
            COMPOSITES.
            a. 2.5% DOPED FORMULATION, OPTIMIZED CURE CYCLE.
            b. 2.5% DOPED FORMULATION, STRAIGHT-UP CURE CYCLE.
            c. UNDOPED FORMULATION, OPTIMIZED CURE CYCLE.
            d. UNDOPED FORMULATION, STRAIGHT-UP CURE CYCLE.

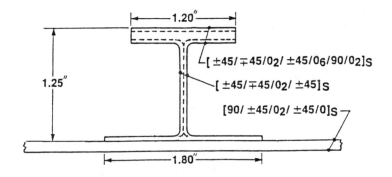

FIGURE 9.   END VIEW SCHEMATIC OF THE STRINGER PORTION OF THE
18"X24" POLYIMIDE SKIN-STRINGER PANEL.

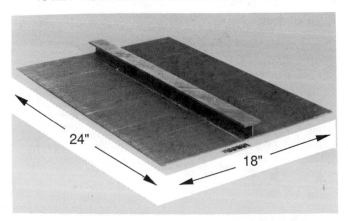

FIGURE 10. PHOTOGRAPH OF THE18"X24" POLYIMIDE SKIN STRINGER-
PANEL.

FIGURE 11. END VIEW PHOTOGRAPH OF THE STRINGER PORTION OF THE
18"X24" POLYIMIDE SKIN-STRINGER PANEL.

Table I

Neat Resin Properties of Molded LARC-TPI[1]

Property	Molded Powder	Molded Film
Tensile Strength, Ksi	16.5[2]	16.9[5]
Tensile Modulus, Ksi	659	630
Tensile Strain-to-Failure, %	3.1	3.2
G_{Ic}, in-lb/in^2	15.9[3,4]	-
T_g, °C (DSC)	255[4]	-

[1] Molded tensile bars 4 in. long, gauge length 1 in.; average of 3 specimens; tensile data courtesy of J. T. Hartness, BASF Structural Materials, Inc.

[2] LARC-TPI powder lot 92-712

[3] Average of 4 specimens; Std. Dev. 3.3 in-lb/in^2

[4] LARC-TPI powder lot 25-801

[5] Film from MTC, Inc.

Table II

Description of AS-4/PISO$_2$:LARC-TPI (1:1)/2.5% Doped Composites[1]

Panel No.	Layup	Test	Thick., in.	Fiber Vol., %	Fiber Wt., %	Tg, °C dry/wet	C-Scan
GD-747	0_{10}	Flex.	0.059	57	65	247/231[2]	good
GD-793	0_{20}	SBS	0.113	52	60	237/220[2]	good
GD-837	0_{48}	Compr.	0.315	47	56	-	bad
GD-840	0_{48}	Compr.	0.267	51	59	-	fair
GD-841	0_{48}	Compr.	0.268	54	61	-	good
JS-325	0_{24}	DCB	0.182	58	66	-	good

[1] All panels were 6 in. x 6 in.

[2] Estimated from TMA, expansion mode

Table III

Short Beam Shear and Flexure Properties of
AS-4/PISO$_2$:LARC-TPI (1:1)/2.5% Doped Composites

Test Temp., °C	Specimen Condition	SBS[1] St., Ksi	Std. Dev., Ksi	Flex.[2] St., Ksi	Std. Dev., Ksi	Flex. Mod., Msi	Std. Dev., Msi	Defl., %
RT	dry	10.3	0.8	307	13	16.2	0.65	2.1
RT	wet	10.1	0.5	303	5	16.1	0.56	2.0
93	dry	10.3	0.9	283`	5	16.9	0.53	1.8
93	wet	8.6	1.1	261	9	15.3	0.21	1.7
150	dry	7.4	0.9	247	18	16.6	0.17	1.6
150	wet	6.9	0.5	256	5	16.7	0.81	1.6
177	dry	7.4	0.6	249	4	16.5	0.27	1.6
177	wet	5.4	0.3	244	14	16.4	0.54	1.5

[1] Panel GD-793

[2] Panel GD-747; moisture wt. gain 0.30%

Table IV

Tensile and Shear Properties for Dry Unidirectional
AS-4/PISO$_2$:LARC-TPI (1:1)/2.5% Doped Composites[1]

Test	Test Temp., °C	Specimen Condition	Strength, Ksi	Modulus, Msi	Strain-to-Failure, %
Axial tension[2]	23	dry	256	17.4	1.35
	100	dry	239	19.6	1.13
	100	wet	227	17.3	1.30
Transverse	23	dry	4.8	1.19	0.48
Tension[3]	100	dry	6.4	1.33	0.47
	100	wet	3.9	1.40	0.30
Iosipescu	23	dry	19.1	0.95	>7
Shear	100	dry	16.0	0.78	>14
	100	wet	14.7	0.82	>18

[1] Data from U. of Wyoming, Grant NAG1-277, Dr. D. F. Adams, PI
[2] Poisson's Ratio: 23°C dry, 0.31; 100°C dry 0.30; 100°C wet, 0.44
[3] CTE, 10^{-6}/°C: 23°C and 100°C dry, 22.3

Table V

Composite Compression Properties

Material	Strength, Ksi	Std. Dev., Ksi	Modulus, Msi	Std. Dev., Msi	Number Specimans	C-Scan
PI[1]	118	3	16.0	0.1	4	good
PI[1]	106	-	14.6	-	2	bad
Epoxy[2]	135	-	19.5	0	2	good

[1] AS-4/PISO$_2$:LARC-TPI(1:1)/2.5% Doped Composite
[2] AS-4/3502

FIBER GLASS MOLDABLE BLANKET FOR
PRODUCTION OF NON-METALLIC PARTS

R. Michael Fay
Philip F. Miele
Manville Corporation
Denver, Colorado

ABSTRACT

A unique moldable fiber glass blanket material has been developed for fabrication of high strength and high modulus structural non-metallic parts. The new material effectively combines 55-70% glass fibers with 30-45% phenolic resins in a blanket form that is stable for three months at room temperature. This blanket material is molded using techniques and cycle times similar to SMC but yields parts with excellent surface finish and superior strength. Parts also exhibit the low smoke and low toxicity well known for Phenolic-SMC.

This paper describes the novel approach of producing this moldable material in-line as the glass is fiberized and formed into a blanket. Physical properties of molded parts from this material and potential applications are also discussed.

1. INTRODUCTION

Many technologies exist which combine fiber glass and thermosetting resins to produce non-metallic molded parts and panels for the transportation industry. Structural and semi-structural applications of these materials often require high fiber glass contents to meet the increased strength and modulus needs. Structural Reaction Injection Molding (SRIM) and Resin Transfer Molding (RTM) utilize fiber glass preforms to achieve these desired high glass contents. Fabricating and handling preforms is time consuming and requires additional steps to fabricate a molded part.

A new Fiber Glass Moldable Blanket (FMB) has been developed which incorporates these desired high glass contents and a thermosetting resin in one package. FMB is produced in eight foot wide blanket form typically containing 55-70% glass and 30-45% phenolic resin. Phenolic resins were selected for use in the initial FMB development but several alternate resins would work equally well. FMB can be molded similarly to Sheet Molding Compound (SMC) at 3.4-6.9 MPa (500 - 1000 psi) in a male/female tool for 120 seconds. The resulting FMB parts exhibit flexural modulus in excess of 14 GPa (2 x 10^6 psi) and notched Izod impact strength exceeding 500 J/m (9.4 ft-lb/in). Under proper conditions, molded parts have been shown to provide a near Class A automotive paintable surface.

2. MANUFACTURE

Fiber Glass Moldable Blanket (FMB) is an extension of a product sold by the fiber glass industry as Uncured Wool. Uncured Wool is a fiber glass blanket containing 14-16% uncured liquid phenolic binder. Uncured Wool is typically used in the automotive industry to mold hoodliners and as a component of headliners. FMB is essentially a modified high binder content version of Uncured Wool.

Fiber Glass Moldable Blanket is produced using a rotary fiber glass manufacturing process similar to those used throughout the building products industry to produce residential insulation batts and rolls. In this process the phenolic resins are combined with the glass as it is being fiberized. Other additives such as chopped glass strand reinforcing fiber, silane coupling agents and catalysts are also introduced at this point. A schematic of this process is shown in Illustration I. A typical moldable composition which has been produced by this process combines the following:

48%	5 Micron Bulk Fiber
28%	Phenolic Resin Powder
12%	Liquid Phenolic Binder
12%	13 Micron Chopped Glass Reinforcing Fiber

Uniform dispersion of all the above components is controlled by a proprietary combination of rotary glass fiberization, binder spraying, and reinforcing fiber chopper systems. These components are collected on a moving fine mesh chain and usually combined with additional layers of FMB from one or more fiberization modules. This modular approach allows production of multi-layer constructions with different fiber glass/phenolic resin/ reinforcing fiber ratio's for certain applications. One such application would involve high phenolic resin content in exposed layers for optimum molded part surface finish and higher glass content in the inner layers for maximum stiffness.

Illustration II shows the multiple layers of FMB being produced. After the layers are combined a compaction step is necessary to reduce the lofted fiber bulk and improve handling. At this point the product can be in-line molded or packaged for use later.

3. MOLDING AND STRENGTH TESTING

Molding parts from FMB requires heat and pressure to cause the phenolic resin to flow and cure. Cure cycles of 90 seconds or longer are required depending on the type of phenolic resin selected. The phenolic resins used in FMB are a combination of a powdered high molecular weight phenol formaldehyde resin such as Varcum 29 - 217* and a liquid phenolic binder. The liquid phenolic binder is primarily a low molecular weight resole type phenol formaldehyde resin combined with catalyst, silane coupling agent, and water. For purposes of product development, a single glass fiberization module was used to prepare several variations of single layer FMB.

* BTL Specialty Resins Corp

Table I shows some of the resin/glass variations that are capable of being produced. FMB made with only liquid phenolic is extremely tacky and difficult to handle. However, by combining the liquid and dry phenolic resins in the proper proportions, an uncured FMB is produced with no dust, no room temperature tackiness, no need to outgas parts during cure, and up to three months of room temperature storage life.

Samples of each of the uncured FMB variations listed in Table I were molded into 0.25m x 0.25m (10 in. x 10 in.) plaques by compressing five layers at 5.5 MPa (800 psi) for two minutes at 149°C (300°F) to a cured thickness of 3.3 - 3.6mm (0.13-0.14 inches). The sample plaques exhibit a yellow to tan appearance which has been shown to darken with UV exposure. The strength properties of the sample plaques are presented in Table II. The strength data shows the importance of adding a percentage of chopped strand reinforcing fiber to the FMB to improve impact resistance.

4. FIRE HAZARD PROPERTIES

The low smoke, low flammability and low combustion toxicity of phenolic sheet molding compound has been previously demonstrated[1]. Parts molded from FMB enjoy similar performance. The Limiting Oxygen Index values for FMB parts depend on the phenolic content. At phenolic contents of 35% and 43% the Limiting Oxygen Index values are 49 and 45 respectively. Figure I shows Specific Optical Densities, D_{max}, of molded FMB in the NBS Smoke Chamber are less than 45. Combustion toxicity results detailed in Table III show no halogenated by-products and only small traces of HCN. Formaldehyde was present at <2 ppm.

5. APPLICATIONS

FMB has been successfully used to mold a two piece automotive hood, and an exterior door panel. Molding of contour shapes with deep draws presents problems similar to molding with SMC. Additional automotive parts being investigated are floor pans and trunk compartment panels. Other transportation applications for FMB, such as aircraft interiors, are also being explored.

FMB is projected to be slightly more expensive than SMC, but significantly less expensive than SRIM or RTM.

6. SUMMARY

A new moldable material containing high glass content and phenolic resin has been developed and characterized. Fiber Glass Moldable Blanket can be readily molded under high pressure and moderate heat to form medium to large structural reinforced plastic parts with excellent surface finish. FMB offers an attractive alternative for non-metallic applications for the following reasons:

- Ease of Use
- Fast Cycle Times (90-120 seconds)
- Long Shelf Life (>3 months @ R.T.)
- Low Smoke (D_{max} <45)
- Low Toxicity
- Excellent Surface Finish
- Low Cost
- Modular Approach Allows Versatility

The drawbacks and limitations to FMB are

related to the need for high tonnage presses and steel tools to mold parts.

7. REFERENCES

1. Gupta, M.K., D.W. Hock, and J.F. Keegan, "Low Smoke and Low Toxicity Phenolic Sheet Molding Compound," 42nd Annual Conference, Composites Institute, Cincinnati, Session 11A (Feb 1987).

8. BIOGRAPHIES

R. Michael Fay is a Senior Research Chemist in the Engineered Products Division at Manville Corp. He is a 1977 graduate of Colorado State University and has been involved in fiber glass product and process development for the past 10 years. His research interests include adhesives, laminates, and coatings as well as insulations used at the two temperature extremes. Mr. Fay's efforts have resulted in several patents.

Philip F. Miele is a Senior Research Chemist with the Fiber Glass Division of the Manville Corp. in Denver, Colorado. Mr. Miele is a 1970 graduate of Northeastern University in Boston, MA. Since joining Manville in 1977 Mr. Miele has been responsible for the development of thermosetting resins and binders for various fiber glass applications.

Illustration I

FMB ROTARY FIBERIZATION MODULE

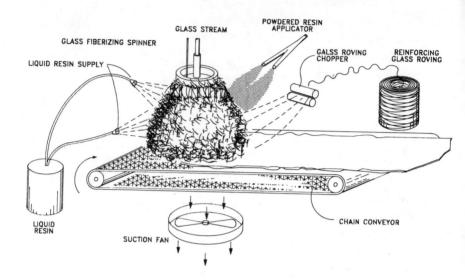

Illustration II

MULTILAYER FMB PRODUCTION PROCESS

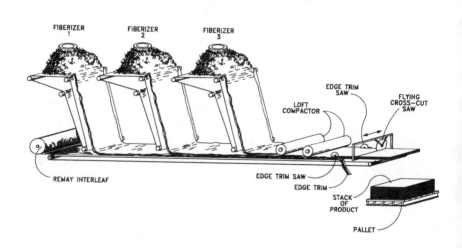

TABLE I

VARIATIONS OF FIBER GLASS MOLDABLE BLANKET

Percent Bulk Fiber Glass	Percent Phenolic Resin		Percent Chopped Glass Strand Reinforcing Fiber
	Dry	Liquid	
55	0	45	0
65	0	35	0
70	19	11	0
48	28	12	12
53	29	12	6

TABLE II

PHYSICAL PROPERTY COMPARISON OF VARIOUS FMB PLAQUES

Ratio of Bulk Fiber Glass/ Phenolic Resin/ Reinforcing Fiber	Molded Plaque Density g/cc	Flexural Strength MPa (psi)	Flexural Modulus GPa (x 10^6 psi)	Notched Izod Impact Strength J/m (ft-lb/in)
55/45/0	1.70	141 (20,500)	14.1 (2.05)	69 (1.3)
65/35/0	1.42	159 (23,100)	11.6 (1.68)	75 (1.4)
70/30/0	1.65	160 (23,200)	16.8 (2.44)	-- --
48/40/12	1.70	161 (23,300)	14.7 (2.13)	518 (9.7)
53/41/6	1.74	131 (19,000)	16.3 (2.37)	208 (3.9)

TABLE III

COMBUSTION TOXICITY DATA FOR MOLDED FMB*

COMPOSITION OF ATMOSPHERE (PPM)

Hydrogen Chloride	0
Formaldehyde	<2
Ammonia	0
Carbon Monoxide	243
Carbon Dioxide	2925
Nitrous Oxide	37
Hydrogen Cyanide	<2

* Test conducted per MIL-M-14G at
U.S. Testing Company Inc. on FMB
containing 43% phenolic/57% glass

FIGURE I

SPECIFIC OPTICAL DENSITY OF FMB
PLAQUE WITH 43% PHENOLIC AND 57% GLASS *
(ASTM   E 662-83)

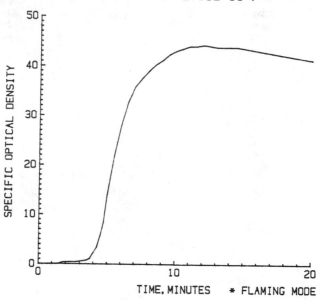

TIME, MINUTES   * FLAMING MODE

ON THE USE OF CURE MODELING IN HONEYCOMB PROCESSING

Leroy Chiao and Peter W. Borris
Hexcel Corporation
Structural Division
11711 Dublin Blvd.
Dublin, CA 94568

Abstract

A general cure model for honeycomb core based on physical principles has been applied to both aramid paper and fiberglass fabric honeycomb coated with phenolic resin. The cure model was used to design cure cycles which are much shorter than those currently used in industry, but advance the resin to the same degree of cure, as verified by microdielectrometer experiments. Plant trials show that these modified cure cycles result in core with equivalent mechanical properties to those which go through the standard cure cycles.

The model was also used to predict cure reaction runaway (exotherm) behavior. This information is useful in analyzing regions of the honeycomb block where the airflow is poor and also situations of sudden airflow loss.

1. INTRODUCTION

Honeycomb is an important aerospace material used predominantly as a core in very lightweight and stiff sandwich structures. Two widely used non-metallic cores are phenolic/aramid paper and phenolic/fiberglass fabric composites. The honeycomb is coated by dipping in a solution of phenolic resin and then cycling through a cure oven. This process is repeated until the core reaches the specified density. Because the cure of the resin is exothermic, the cure cycle must be carefully designed to expedite the cure process without causing reaction runaway (uncontrolled exotherm).

A general honeycomb cure model (HCM) based on physical principles has been developed, which successfully describes observed laboratory and plant experiments (Chiao and Borris, 1988). This model has been used to design modified cure cycles for phenolic/aramid and phenolic/fiberglass core which require typically about 50% shorter ramp/dwell times than the standard cure cycles currently used in industry. Microdielectrometer experiments verify that the modified cure cycles advance the resin to the same degree of cure as the standard cycles and plant trials show that the mechanical properties are equivalent.

The HCM was shown to correctly model observed behavior in reduced airflow regions of the honeycomb block during cure (Chiao and Borris, 1988). These dead airflow zones arise from blocked cells, poor airflow baffling and general oven design. During the shorter intermediate cure cycles, these regions are undercured. However, during the longer, high-temperature cure cycles, these regions can exotherm. Using the HCM, various scenarios are analyzed and potential dangers exposed.

2. MODEL DESCRIPTION

Because of the geometry of honeycomb, a block of core can be modeled in a relatively straight forward manner. Since a detailed development of the HCM appears elsewhere (Chiao and Borris, 1988), only the general concepts and equations are presented here. Honeycomb can be treated as a bundle of roughly tubular chemical reactors, with the reactant on the walls. Since each "tube" shares common walls with its neighbors, it is a good assumption that within a bundle through which the same velocity air flows, the heat generation per tube is equal. Due to the symmetry of the bundle across each "tube" wall, the heat flux is zero in the center of each wall. Thus, each tube can be modeled as an adiabatic reactor, with an exothermic reactant on the inner wall (Figure 1).

In modeling the cure process, one must include mass and energy balance equations for the resin layers, as well as an energy balance for the gas phase in the honeycomb cells. Also, evaporation of solvent must be accounted for. The physical equations appear below. Refer to Figure 2.

Mass Balances: $d\alpha_j/dt = R(\alpha)_j$ (1a)

Initial Conditions: $\alpha_j(0) = \alpha_j^\circ$ (1b)

Gas-Phase
Energy Balance: $dT_g/dt = A_5(T_{gi}-T_g)$
$\qquad + A_6(T_r-T_g)$ (1c)

$A_5 = Q/V_g$ (1d)

$A_6 = (ha)/(\rho_g C_{pg} V_g)$ (1e)

Initial Condition: $T_g(0) = T_g^\circ$ (1f)

Resin/Substrate
Energy Balance: $dT_r/dt = A_7(-\Delta H_r)$
$\qquad \Sigma_j (M_j R_j) + A_8(T_r-T_g)$
$\qquad -A_9 m(\Delta H_v)$ (1g)

$A_7 = 1/(M_r C_{pr})$ (1h)

$A_8 = (ha)/(M_r C_{pr})$ (1i)

$A_9 = 1/(M_L C_{pr})$ (1j)

Initial Condition: $T_r(0) = T_r^\circ$ (1k)

The variables T and t represent the temperature and time, α is the degree of cure, $R(\alpha)$ is the reaction rate expression, ρ and C_p denote the density and heat capacity, and ΔH_r is the enthalpy of reaction. The remaining variables Q, V, ha, m, ΔHv and M are the volumetric gas flowrate, the honeycomb cell free volume, the convective heat transfer variable, the mass transfer rate of the solvent, the solvent vaporization enthalpy, and the resin mass. The superscript "0" denotes initial conditions, while the subscripts "r" and "g" refer to resin and gas properties. The subscript "j" is used as a dummy variable to index the resin layers, with j=L representing the resin layer which contacts the gas flow. The rate law used was of the form proposed by Kay and Westwood (1975) for a phenolic resin.

Thermophysical properties of air

were correlated from Incropera and Dewitt (1981). Resin properties were obtained from the Encyclopedia of Polymer Science and Technology (1981) and heat transfer coefficients were calculated from established equations (see Chiao and Borris, 1988). Ordinary differential equations (ODE) were integrated using the RKF45 subroutine (H.A. Watts and L.F. Shampine, Sandia National Laboratory), a fourth-fifth order Runge-Kutta-Fehlberg method. This subroutine uses extrapolation for sixth-order local accuracy, and performs relative and absolute integration error checking. Code was developed and run on an Apple Macintosh SE with a Radius accelerator (16 MHz 68020/68881) as well as a Compaq 386/20 (20 MHz 80386), equipped with a Weitek 1167 floating point accelerator.

3.SIMULATION GUIDED CURE CYCLE DESIGN

In processing honeycomb which requires more than one dip/cure iteration, usually a low temperature cure cycle is used to partially stage the "intermediate" resin dips to save processing time and a high temperature cure cycle is used on the "final" resin dip which ensures full cure of all resin layers. For high density blocks which go through many dip/cure iterations, final cure cycles are used periodically throughout the densification step to avoid the buildup of large masses of unreacted resin. Otherwise, these large masses could exotherm.

Several factors must be considered when designing the cure cycles. If process temperatures are too high, then resin degradation could occur. Moreover, the potential for uncontrolled exotherm increases at elevated temperatures. Using the HCM, modified cure cycles were designed which advance the resin to the same degree of cure as the standard cure cycles. The modified

cycles call for shorter cure times (typically ~50%) at elevated cure temperatures. Figures 3 and 4 compare the modified cure cycles to the standard cycles. These plots show that the processing times can be cut approximately in half. Two modified final cycles (MF) were designed. MF1 calls for a higher temperature cure than MF2. MF1 was used to prove that a high temperature final cure cycle can be safe and practical. In production, MF2 would be used because the lower cure temperature provides additional cushion for exotherm prevention with only a small increase in processing time.

Production blocks were manufactured in the plant using both modified and standard cure cycles. Two different composite honeycombs were analyzed, an aramid/phenolic and a fiberglass/phenolic. Blocks which required two dip/cure cycles were used for the aramid/phenolic evaluation. Four experiments were run:

1. Standard intermediate/standard final cure cycles (SI/SF).
2. Modified intermediate/standard final cure cycles (MI/SF).
3. Modified intermediate/modified final cure cycle 1 (MI/MF1).
4. Modified intermediate/modified final cure cycle 2 (MI/MF2).

The first experiment was run as a control block, for comparison purposes. The second experiment isolates the intermediate cure cycle, the third and fourth examine the modified intermediate and the two final cycles.

The blocks were examined after coming out of the intermediate cure cycle and compared to several other production blocks of the same product. Visually, there were no differences. The colors were judged identical by the technicians and operators working in the area. Dead zones of airflow were evident on all the blocks, both experimental and production, along the upper edge, with a prominent concentration at the upper corner of the blocks nearest to the loading door. In these regions, the resin was undercured, as evidenced by lighter color. The positions of these dead zones were identical on the experimental blocks as well as the production blocks. This suggests a systematic airflow problem, not unique to the modified cure cycles. After the final cure cycles, the blocks were again compared. The block for experiment #3 was slightly darker in color than the others. As was the case for the intermediate cycles, dead airflow zones were observed along the top of the blocks, this time as temperature excursions during cure (dark zones). The blocks for experiments #2 and #4 were visually identical to the control and other production blocks.

Mechanical tests were run on the experimental blocks. The room temperature test results (Table 1) show that the modified cycles yield core with essentially equivalent properties, within experimental error. Some of the averaged MI/MF1 block properties are slightly lower than those for the other experiments. This may be due to minor heat damage in the low airflow regions of this block where thermocouples recorded some exotherm activity. L and W properties refer to the ribbon and expanded directions of the honeycomb, which are orthogonal. In stabilized compression tests, facing material is first bonded onto the honeycomb in order to stabilize the cells, before load application. For bare compressive tests, no facings are used. Elevated temperature tests, where the test samples are heated to 350°F for 30 minutes appear in Table 2. Again, the mechanical properties are equivalent

within experimental error. Note that the averaged properties for the MI/MF1 block are much closer to the other blocks at elevated temperature than at room temperature.

For the fiberglass/phenolic tests, a block was run through four dip/cure cycles using the modified intermediate cure cycle for the first three and the modified final cycle MF2 for the fourth. In addition, a standard postcure which is prescribed for this product was used. This block was compared to a production block on which all cure cycles used were standard. Comparison of the room temperature mechanical properties (Table 3) again shows that the two blocks are essentially equivalent, within experimental error. For the MI/MF2 core, the averaged L-shear properties are slightly higher and the W-shear properties slightly lower than those for the SI/SF block. This is because the cell configuration on the MI/MF2 test block was slightly more biased in the L-dimension.

The dead airflow zones are of particular interest. During the ramp portion of the cure cycle, the temperatures in these zones lag the rest of the block. Consequently, after the intermediate cycle, these regions are undercured. During the final cure however, the dead zone temperatures can reach a critical point, where the cure reaction begins a thermal runaway. That is, at a certain temperature, the curing resin is generating heat faster than it can be transferred away. Two things can happen: Either the reaction will reach completion, which stops the heat generation, or the block will reach its ignition temperature. It is also interesting to note that there is a critical airflow range for a given cure cycle. If the airflow in the dead zone is very low, then the temperature will not reach the critical point during the cycle, since the heating rate is too low. If the airflow is sufficiently high, then the excess heat generated during the early stages of runaway will be transferred away before it can accumulate. Thus there is a critical operating range of airflow, which allows a sufficient heat up rate to reach the critical runaway temperature, but is insufficient to transfer the excess generated heat away to prevent exotherm. It was shown in earlier work that these dead zones can be modeled using the HCM (Chiao and Borris, 1988). The HCM proved to be capable of accurately predicting temperature lag during low temperature cures and exotherm peak height and location during high temperature cures. Thus the process engineer can determine by simulation whether a cure cycle will cause an exotherm. In this work, the final cure cycles are evaluated for two potential exotherm situations. The first study focuses on dead zone behavior, where the measured and predicted airflow is only approximately 12% of normal. These dead zones are caused by any combination of factors, including improper baffling of oven airflow, cell blockage and cell damage during handling. The second examines the resin temperature response to sudden loss of airflow at cure temperature. Such a situation could arise if power is lost to the cure ovens, or if the blowers fail. Figure 5 shows predicted dead zone behavior of the final cure cycles during the second dip cure of an aramid/phenolic core. The certain loss level represents the point above which, loss of the block to fire is certain. This level was estimated based on past plant experiences. As can be seen, all of the final cycles should be safe. However, MF2 is a better choice for production than MF1 because of the additional cushion available between the maximum

temperature overshoot and the certain loss level. Moreover, MF2 requires only slightly more processing time than MF1 (Figure 4). In the event of total airflow loss at cure temperature, there is little that can be done. Figure 6 contains the temperature responses to this situation, as predicted by simulation. It is evident that loss of airflow during the final cycle would lead to temperature overshoots in excess of the certain loss level, regardless of which cure cycle is used (SF, MF1, MF2). If airflow cannot be restored quickly, then fire deluge systems should be immediately engaged.

Up to this point, the honeycomb cure model has been shown to be capable of designing shorter, more efficient cure cycles which yield core with equivalent mechanical properties. Also, it has been used to predict behavior of the process under extreme operating conditions. It is desirable to experimentally verify that the modified cure cycles actually advance the chemical degree of cure to the same point as the standard cycles. A common method for estimating degree of cure of an exothermic thermoset is differential scanning calorimetry (DSC), an extremely useful thermal analysis technique for studying cure reactions (for example, Morgan et al., 1985). The ratio of the residual enthalpy of a partially staged sample to the ultimate enthalpy of an unstaged sample is subtracted from unity. However, for reactions such as condensation phenolics, the water formed during reaction vaporizes and interferes with the calorimetry. One solution is to use high pressure DSC to prevent the formed water from vaporizing (for example, Kay and Westwood, 1975). Under high pressure, though, the chemical rates may be different than under atmospheric conditions.

An alternative method is to monitor the resin cure via it's dielectric properties. For this work, a Micromet II microdielectrometer was used to compare the dielectric properties of the phenolic resin staged by the cure cycles being studied. This technique involves the imposition of a sinusoidally varying electric field upon the resin sample, and work done has demonstrated that it is more sensitive than DSC (e.g. Day and Shepard). Free ions and dipoles respond to the periodic electric field depending on the state of the material. This technique may be thought of as an electrical analogy to dynamic mechanical analysis (DMA), wherein a sample is put through periodic mechanical deformation and the material properties tracked, as a measure of the material state. One of the properties used to monitor cure through dielectrometry is the loss factor, E". The loss factor is a measure of the work expended to align the charged species. During the early stages of the cure, the work (the product of the force and the displacement) done increases as the resin softens and becomes less viscous (more displacement). As the resin chains extend and crosslink, the matrix begins to freeze and the work done decreases because the charged species are becoming much less mobile (less displacement). Thus, the loss factor passes through a maximum with time as the cure proceeds. After the maximum, the loss factor approaches an asymptotic limit as the resin approaches full cure.

For this work, the loss factor was monitored for the different cure cycles. Figure 7 is a comparison of the loss factors measured during the intermediate cure cycles. As can be seen, the modified intermediate cycle advances the resin to the same point as the standard cycle. For

this experiment, a high-conductivity parallel plate sensor was used at an oscillation frequency of 1 Hz. Although it is not practical to estimate an actual degree of cure with these data because of the nature of the resin (volatile reaction products emitted during cure) comparison of the values of the loss factor is a valid measure of the relative degree of cure between the two cure cycles. The HCM estimates that the degree of cure after the intermediate cycles is relatively low, approximately 7%. The same experiment was performed to compare the standard final cure cycle (SF) to MF2, using a low-conductivity integrated circuit sensor at 1 Hz. Figure 8 shows that at this relatively high degree of cure (HCM estimated at approximately 65%), the two cure cycles yield the same final loss factor values. The curve for MF2 dips near the endpoint because, the sample was cooled to the same temperature as the SF cured sample for the final loss factor measurement. Like other material properties, the loss factor is highly temperature dependent. These experiments demonstrate that the modified cure cycles advance the resin to the same point as the standard cycles, for both the intermediate and final cures. Confidence in these results is enhanced by the fact that equivalence was observed for both low and high degrees of cure (estimated 7% and 65%). These dielectric results compliment the mechanical test results and temperature-time measurements in validating the cure cycles designed with the honeycomb cure model. Moreover, verification of equivalent resin state ensures equivalent chemical resistance.

4. CONCLUSIONS

A general honeycomb cure model has been applied to both aramid/

phenolic and fiberglass/phenolic composite honeycomb. This model has been used to design modified cure cycles which reduce the required ramp/hold cure times by approximately 50%. Plant trials show that the honeycomb blocks cured by the modified cycles have equivalent mechanical properties as standard product in both room temperature and elevated temperature tests. Moreover, dielectric measurements verify that the modified cycles advance the resin to the same point as the standard cure cycles. This enhances confidence in the modified cure cycles and ensures equivalent chemical resistance. Simulations based on the HCM were also used to analyze the cure cycles and predict temperature-time behavior under extreme operating conditions. Dangerous operating envelopes were defined and avoided. In this work, the overall utility of the honeycomb cure model was demonstrated.

5. REFERENCES

Chiao, L. and P.W. Borris, 1988, "Honeycomb Cure Modeling", SAMPE Quarterly, 20, 1, pp. 33-37.

Day, D.R. and D.D. Shepard, "Cure Monitoring: A Comparison of Dielectric and Thermal Analysis", Internal publication # CA0001, Micromet Instruments, University Park, 26 Landsdowne St., Suite 150, Cambridge Mass., 02139.

Encyclopedia of Polymer Science and Technology, Volume 13, 1970, John Wiley and Sons, pp.780-781.

Incropera, F.P. and D.P. Dewitt, 1981, Fundamentals of Heat Transfer, John Wiley and Sons.

Kay, R. and A.R. Westwood, 1975, "DSC Investigations on Condensation Polymers-I Analysis of the Curing Process.", European Polymer Journal, 11, pp. 25-30.

Morgan, R.J., C.M. Walkup and T.H. Hoheisel, 1985, "Characterization of the Cure of Carbon Fiber/Epoxy Composite Prepregs by Differential Scanning Calorimetry.", Composites Review, 7, No. 1, pp. 17-19.

6. Biography

Leroy Chiao is currently a composites processing researcher in the Chemistry and Materials Div. at Lawrence Livermore National Laboratory. Prior to this, he was a Research Specialist in the Structural Division of Hexcel Corp.

Dr. Chiao earned his degrees in Chemical Engineering. He worked as a Postdoctorate researcher, studying transient systems with chemical reaction and has authored over a dozen technical publications.

Peter Borris is Group Leader for Honeycomb and Bonded Panel Development in the Structural Division of Hexcel. Mr. Borris received a B.S. degree from Humboldt State University in 1971.

His experience at Hexcel, where he has been employed for 15 years has included development of adhesives and advanced composite materials. He has held his current position for the past 5 years.

Table 1 R.T. Mechanical Properties
Aramid/Phenolic

<u>Data</u> <u>Normalized</u> <u>to</u> <u>3.0</u> <u>pcf</u> <u>Sample</u> <u>Size</u> = <u>5</u>

	<u>SI/SF</u>	<u>MI/SF</u>	<u>MI/MF1</u>	<u>MI/MF2</u>
L-Shear (psi)	153	151	160	159
Std. dev.	0.8	4.3	6.0	1.7
C.V. %	0.5	2.9	3.8	1.1
Modulus (ksi)	5.1	5.1	4.2	5.0
Std. dev.	0.2	0.2	0.3	0.3
C.V. %	3.9	3.7	7.3	5.7
W-Shear (psi)	86	82	85	89
Std. dev.	1.0	1.9	3.4	1.2
C.V. %	1.1	2.3	4.0	1.4
Modulus (ksi)	3.2	2.7	2.6	3.4
Std. dev.	0.1	0.2	0.1	0.1
C.V. %	3.5	7.0	3.8	2.3
Bare Cmp. (psi)	272	280	249	250
Std. dev.	31.5	17.6	5.8	10.1
C.V. %	11.6	6.3	2.3	4.0
Stab. Cmp. (psi)	348	346	308	367
Std. dev.	15.0	21.2	30.8	17.3
C.V. %	4.3	6.1	10.0	4.7
Modulus (ksi)	19.9	18.4	18.6	21.2
Std. dev.	0.5	0.8	1.4	0.9
C.V. %	3.0	4.3	7.3	4.1

SI - Std. Intermediate Cycle   SF - Std. Final Cycle
MI - Mod. Intermediate Cycle   MF1 - Mod. Final Cycle #1
                               MF2 - Mod. Final Cycle #2

Table 2 350°F Mechanical Properties
Aramid/Phenolic

Data Normalized to 3.0 pcf Sample Size = 5

	SI/SF	MI/SF	MI/MF1	MI/MF2
L-Shear (psi)	109	98	115	104
Std. dev.	2.2	3.5	4.1	2.7
C.V. %	2.0	3.6	3.6	2.6
Modulus (ksi)	4.7	4.8	4.7	4.1
Std. dev.	0.2	0.2	0.8	0.2
C.V. %	4.5	5.1	17.4	4.4
W-Shear (psi)	65	60	64	68
Std. dev.	0.6	1.1	0.8	1.6
C.V. %	0.9	1.9	1.3	2.4
Modulus (ksi)	2.8	2.8	2.7	2.9
Std. dev.	0.1	0.2	0.3	0.1
C.V. %	2.4	8.6	10.0	4.4
Bare Cmp. (psi)	211	213	203	207
Std. dev.	8.4	7.3	3.0	8.6
C.V. %	3.8	3.4	1.5	4.2
Stab. Cmp. (psi)	257	213	225	258
Std. dev.	7.8	22.1	18.5	9.7
C.V. %	3.0	10.4	8.2	3.8
Modulus (ksi)	14.9	9.7	12.1	18.5
Std. dev.	0.3	2.3	1.7	2.4
C.V. %	2.2	23.7	13.8	12.7

SI - Std. Intermediate Cycle   SF - Std. Final Cycle
MI - Mod. Intermediate Cycle   MF1 - Mod. Final Cycle #1
                                MF2 - Mod. Final Cycle #2

Table 3 R.T. Mechanical Properties
Fiberglass/Phenolic

Data Normalized to 3.2 pcf Sample Size = 5

	SI/SF	MI/MF2
L-Shear (psi)	193	212
Std. dev.	13.3	15.7
C.V. %	6.9	7.4
Modulus (ksi)	21.7	23.0
Std. dev.	2.1	7.0
C.V. %	9.7	30.3
W-Shear (psi)	93	84
Std. dev.	3.9	2.0
C.V. %	4.2	2.4
Modulus (ksi)	6.1	5.4
Std. dev.	0.5	0.4
C.V. %	7.4	8.1
Stab. Cmp. (psi)	314	347
Std. dev.	28.4	28.0
C.V. %	9.0	8.1

SI - Std. Intermediate Cycle   SF - Std. Final Cycle
MI - Mod. Intermediate Cycle   MF2 - Mod. Final Cycle #2

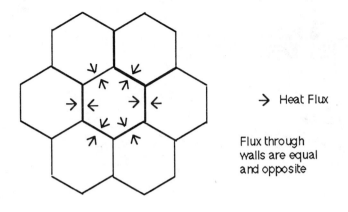

→ Heat Flux

Flux through
walls are equal
and opposite

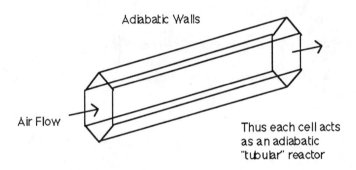

Adiabatic Walls

Air Flow

Thus each cell acts
as an adiabatic
"tubular" reactor

Figure 1. **Honeycomb Modeling Analogy.**

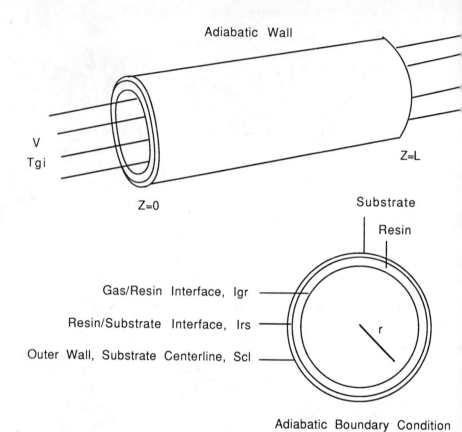

Adiabatic Wall

V
Tgi

Z=0

Z=L

Substrate

Resin

Gas/Resin Interface, Igr

Resin/Substrate Interface, Irs

Outer Wall, Substrate Centerline, Scl

r

Adiabatic Boundary Condition

<u>Notation</u>

Cp - Heat Capacity, J/Kg-K
h - Heat Transfer Coefficient, W/m^2-K
ΔH_r - Heat of Reaction, J/Kg
ΔH_v - Heat of Vaporization, J/Kg
k_T - Thermal Conductivity, W/m-K
M - mass, Kg
m - Mass Transfer Rate, Kg/s
R - Reaction Rate Expression, 1/s
T - Temperature, K
t - Time, s
α - Degree of Cure, dimensionless
ρ - Density, Kg/m^3

<u>Subscripts, Superscripts</u>

g - Gas Phase
i - Boundary Value, Z=0
j - Resin Layer Index
L - Outer Resin Layer
0 - Initial Value, t=0
r - Resin/Substrate

<u>Figure 2</u>.   Adiabatic Reactor Diagram and Notation.

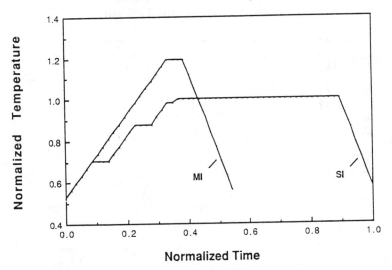

Figure 3. Comparison of Intermediate Cure Cycles.
SI≡Standard Intermediate Cycle, MI≡Modified Intermediate Cycle.

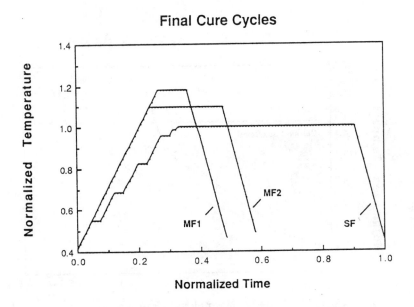

Figure 4. Comparison of Final Cure Cycles. SF≡Standard Final
Cycle, MF1≡Modified Final Cycle 1, MF2≡Modified Final Cycle 2.

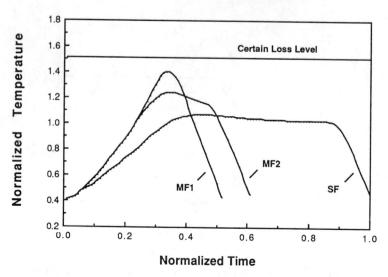

Figure 5. Second Dip Final Cure Cycle Temperature Profiles for 12% Airflow Conditions.

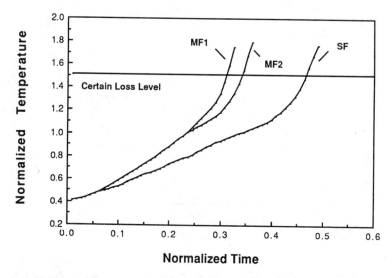

Figure 6. Second Dip Final Cure Cycle Temperature Response for Airflow Loss at Cure Temperature.

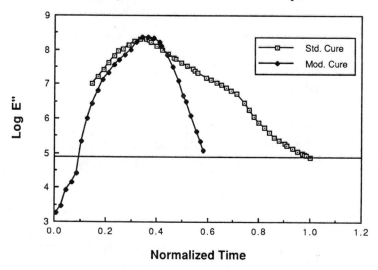

Figure 7. Loss Factors During Intermediate Cure Cycles.

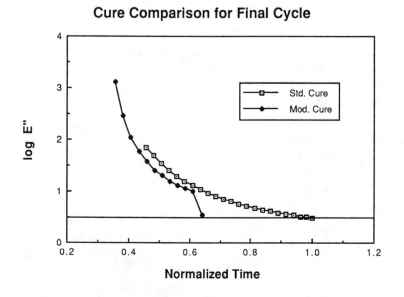

Figure 8. Loss Factors During Final Cure Cycles.

Comparison Between SF and MF2.

STACKING METHOD OF THICK COMPOSITE LAMINATES
CONSIDERING INTERLAMINAR NORMAL STRESS

C. S. Hong and D. M. Kim

Department of Mechanical Engineering

Korea Advanced Institute of Science and Technology

P. O. Box 150, Cheongryang, Seoul, Korea

Abstract

Global–local laminate variational model is utilized to investigate the characteristics of interlaminar stresses in thick composite laminate under uniform axial extension. Various laminates with different fiber orientations and stacking sequences are analyzed to observe the behavior of interlaminar normal stress. From this result, the interlaminar normal stress distribution along the laminate interfaces is examined and discussed with an existing approximation model. The repeated stacking of Poisson's ratio symmetric sublaminate is found to be the best stacking method of thick composite laminate to reduce the magnitude of interlaminar normal stress for the prevention of the free–edge delamination.

1. INTRODUCTION

The interlaminar stresses near the free–edge region of composite laminates play an important role in the initiation of damage at the free–edge. These interlaminar stresses are caused by the mismatches of Poisson's ratio, shear-coupling properties, and thermal expansional coefficients between layers[1]. The differences of engineering properties between layers develop fully three dimensional state of stress in the vicinity of the free–edge.

Extensive work has been done in the analysis of this complicated behavior of the finite–width composite laminates subjected to uniform axial strain. These works include finite difference method[2], finite element method[3], boundary–layer theory[4], global–local variational model[5], etc[6,7]. These analytical works have been reported mostly on the interlaminar stress distributions in thin laminates (e.g., 4– and 8–ply laminates). Many practical laminates, however, those for compressive structures and primary structures, consist of numerous layers (e.g., 100–ply laminate). In thick composite laminates, it is incapable or difficult to calculate interlaminar stress using a conventional numerical method.

The design of thick laminated structures needs to determine fiber orientation, stacking sequence, and ply thickness. Especially, the stacking sequence is an important design parameter related to the free–edge delamination[8]. For the practical design application, a more complete under-standing of the interlaminar stress behavior altered by stacking sequences of thick composite laminates.

For the prevention of free–edge delamination, some techniques have been reported. Free–edge cap reinforcement[9], stitching along the free–edge[10], and using adhesive layer[11] are these attempts. Even though these techniques can suppress free–edge delamination, they reduce laminate stiffness or strength and require extra work. The best way to prevent the free–edge delamination of thick composite laminates is to determine the optimum stacking sequence.

In this paper, a good stacking me-thod for the construction of thick lami-nate considering interlaminar normal stress is suggested. Since thick laminate can be constructed by repetition of sublaminates, the suggested stacking method based on the concept of sublami-nate approach to suppress interlaminar stress of thick laminate[12]. Global-local laminate variational model[5] is utilized to analyze various laminates for exami-ning interlaminar normal stress behavior and to verify this stacking method. An existing approximation model[13] for interlaminar normal stress is discussed with the global–local solution.

2. THE BEHAVIOR OF INTERLAMINAR NORMAL STRESS

2.1 Laminate analysis

Fig.1 shows the laminate geometry and stress components in the free–edge region of a multi–layered composite laminate subjected to uniform axial strain. The laminate is symmetric about the mid–plane and assumed to be consisted of perfectly bonded layers. The thickness-to–width ratio of the laminate, $(2h)/(2b)$, is $1/4$. Assuming the laminate is long in the axial x–direction and considering the laminate symmetry about mid–plane, only a quarter of the laminate is modeled to analyze (quasi–3D modeling surface in Fig.1).

For the stress analysis of this problem, global–local laminate varia-tional model[5] is utilized. This analysis is based on Reissner's variational equation. The analysis is formulated to include global region(g) and local region(l) in order to facilitate the solution of problems involving laminates with many layers. The global region is formulated from an assumed displacement field and leads to the definition of effective (or smeared) laminate moduli, is not sufficiently accurate for stress field computation. The local region is formulated to give detailed response in a region of interest.

The 8–ply quasi–isotropic laminate with fiber orientations of 0, 90, 45, and −45 degrees has been analyzed to examine the behavior of interlaminar normal stress. Material properties used for the stress analysis are given in Table 1. There are twelve distinct combinations of layers in this quasi–isotropic laminate. Fig.3–Fig.5 show interlaminar normal stress distributions along each interface for $[45/-45/0/90]_s$, $[45/0/-45/90]_s$, and $[0/45/90/-45]_s$ laminates.

2.2 The behavior of interlaminar normal stress

As can be expected, Fig.3–Fig.5 show that the same laminate with different stacking sequences gives different interlaminar stress distributions. It is seen that the $[45/-45/0/90]_s$ and $[45/0/-45/90]_s$ laminates develop large tensile interlaminar normal stresses at z=0 and z=t, where t is one ply thickness. Along these interfaces, σ_z exists in well known form. From the center line (y=0) to the free–edge, σ_z has one extreme point, changes the sign, and increases with extremely steep stress gradient toward the free–edge. In the case of $[0/45/90/-45]_s$ laminate, in Fig.5, the magnitude of σ_z is considerably small and σ_z exists in narrow regions than the other two laminates.

3. AN APPROXIMATION MODEL FOR INTERLAMINAR NORMAL STRESS

When a laminate with free–edge is subjected to uniform axial extension (Fig.1), in the region remote from a boundary, the in–plane stress component σ_y can be calculated by classical laminate theory (CLT). To satisfy the boundary condition of laminate, σ_y leads to zero at the free–edge. So, interlaminar normal

stress σ_z is induced in a free–edge boundary zone to satisfy laminate moment equilibrium with σ_y. This relationship is given as follows at $z=z_k$.

$$\int_{z_k}^{h} \sigma_y(z) \, z \, dz$$
$$= \int_0^b \sigma_z(y) \, y \, dy = M(z_k) \quad (1)$$

where $M(z_k)$ is induced moment by σ_y which can be calculated by CLT.

Interlaminar normal stress σ_z also satisfies the force equilibrium in z–direction.

$$\int_0^b \sigma_z(y) \, dy = 0 \quad (2)$$

From equations(1,2), σ_z exists in the form of pure couple along an interface.

Pagano and Pipes approximated the distribution of σ_z associated with free–edge problem in laboratory type tensile coupons[13]. They gave the magnitude of σ_z at the free–edge as following equation by using equations(1,2) and assumed distribution of σ_z.

$$\sigma_m = \frac{45}{14h^2} M(z_k) \quad (3)$$

In Fig.6 through–the–thickness distributions of σ_z at the free–edge of quasi–isotropic laminate are plotted. Solution obtained by global–local model is average value of σ_z over one ply thickness from the free–edge.

$$\bar{\sigma}_z = \frac{1}{t} \int_{b-t}^{b} \sigma_z(y) \, dy \quad (4)$$

It has been reported that the onset of delamination predictions based on this average stress procedure agree closely with the experimental findings[14].

As shown in Fig.6, the approximation model suggested by Pagano and Pipes is very convenient and useful to rank the stacking sequence and determine the sign of σ_z.

4. THE STACKING METHOD FOR THICK LAMINATE

As shown in Fig.3 and Fig.4, at the interfaces which have relatively big magnitude of σ_z than the other interfaces, the σ_z distribution is in the category of the form assumed in reference (13). In this case, the magnitude of σ_z at the free—edge is proportional to the induced moment $M(z_k)$. Therefore, a stacking sequence should be determined to reduce the magnitude of $M(z_k)$. And a stacking sequence which accumulates $M(z_k)$ toward a certain interface should be avoided. Considering these conditions, a thick laminate should be constructed by repeating sublaminate groups which shows the optimum stacking sequence to prevent the free—edge delamination. Fig.2 shows the construction of thick laminate by sublaminate approach.

The optimum sublaminate to suppress interlaminar normal stress is the Poisson's ratio symmetric sublaminate. Poisson's ratio symmetric sublaminate means that the Poisson's ratio is symmetric with respect to the mid—plane of the sublaminate. Poisson's ratio of a layer is even function of fiber orientation. $[\theta_n/\varphi_m/-\theta_n]$ sublaminate, for example, can not be a symmetric sublaminate, but can be a Poisson's ratio symmetric sublaminate. For thick laminate, there can be obtained many possible combinations of Poisson's ratio symmetric

sublaminates.

The effect of this stacking method was determined by analyzing three related laminate groups: $[(\pm\theta)_2/90_2]_s$, $[\pm\theta/90]_{2s}$, and $[\theta/90/-\theta]_{2s}$. And θ is chosen 0, 15, and 25 degrees. When θ is 0 degree, the laminates does not have mismatch of coupling properties. When θ is 15 and 25 degrees, the laminates have maximum shear coupling effect and have maximum Poisson's ratio mismatch with respect to 90 degree layer, respectively.

Fig.7 shows through-the-thickness distribution of σ_m calculated by equation(3). Given $(\sigma_m)_{max}$ values are σ_m values of $[(\pm\theta)_2/90_2]$ laminates at the mid—plane. $(\sigma_m)_{max}$ of $[(\pm\theta)_n/90_n]_s$ laminate becomes small at the rate of $1/n$ for $[(\pm\theta)_n/90_n]_s$ laminate which is constructed by repeated stacking of $[\pm\theta/90]$ sublaminate. The maximum σ_m value of $[\theta/90/-\theta]_{ns}$ laminate which is constructed by Poisson's ratio symmetric sublaminate is reduced at the rate of $1/(8n)$ compared with $[(\pm\theta)_n/90_n]_s$ laminate. When a laminate is constructed by repeated stacking of Poisson's ratio symmetric sublaminates, σ_m is zero at the interfaces of repeating groups and does not increase to a certain interface but cyclically oscillates.

Fig.8—Fig.10 show through-the-thickness distributions of $\bar{\sigma}_z$ calculated by global—local model. In this analysis, all six layers are taken as local regions. Independent of fiber orientation θ, $\bar{\sigma}_z$ distributions are very similar. These figures also show that the repeated stacking of Poisson's ratio symmetric sublaminate suppresses interlaminar normal stress dramatically.

When Fig.8–Fig.10 are compared with Fig.7, considerable difference can be found in $[\pm\theta/90]_{2S}$ laminate, especially at z=2t (0.33h). Fig.11 shows the distributions of σ_z along z=2t for $[0_4/90_2]_S$, $[0_2/90]_{2S}$, and $[0/90/0]_{2S}$ laminates. The distribution of $[0_2/90]_{2S}$ laminate is quite different from the assumed distribution by Pagano and Pipes. For $[0_2/90]_{2S}$ laminate, there exist two extreme points along z=2t. This type of σ_z distribution is also found in Fig.3 and Fig.4 along z=2t and z=3t. In this case, approximation model does not give reasonable solution.

As shown in Fig.12 and Fig.13, $[45/0/-45/90]_S$ and $[0/45/90/-45]_S$ laminates have considerably large magnitude of σ_z near the free–edge of laminate mid–plane. For these quasi-isotropic laminates, the repeated stacking of Poisson's ratio symmetric sublaminate also reduces the magnitude of σ_z considerably. Upper four layers are smeared in global region (g) for analyzing these laminates.

5. CONCLUSION

Along the interfaces which have relatively big magnitude of induced moment than the other interfaces, interlaminar normal stress distribution is in the category of the distribution assumed by Pagano and Pipes. In this case, the magnitude of interlaminar normal stress at the free–edge is proportional to the induced moment.

When constructing thick composite laminate, sublaminate approach is good stacking method to prevent delamination induced by interlaminar stresses. The optimum sublaminate to suppress interlaminar normal stress is Poisson's ratio symmetric sublaminate which has Poisson's ratio symmetry with respect to the sublaminate mid–plane. In the laminate constructed by the repeated stacking of Poisson's ratio symmetric sublaminates, interlaminar normal stress does not increase toward a certain interface but regularly down to zero at the interfaces of sublaminate groups. To suppress interlaminar normal stress for the prevention of the free–edge delamination in thick composite laminate, the best stacking method is the repeated stacking of Poisson's ratio symmetric sublaminates.

6. REFERENCES

[1] Herakovich,C.T., "On the Relation ship Between Engineering Properties and Delamination of Composite Materials," Journal of Composite Materials, Vol. 15, pp. 336–348 (1981)

[2] Pagano,N.J. and Pipes,R.B., "Inter laminar Stresses in Composite Lami nate Under Uniform Axial Extension," Journal of Composite Materials, Vol. 4, pp. 538–548 (1970)

[3] Wang,A.S.D. and Crossman,F.W., "Some New Results on Edge Effect in Symmetric Composite Laminates," Journal of Composite Materials, Vol. 11, pp. 92–106 (1977)

[4] Tang,S. and Levy,A., "A Boundary Layer Theory – Part II : Extension of Laminated Strip," Journal of Compo site Materials, Vol. 9, pp. 42–52 (1975)

[5] Pagano,N.J. and Soni,S.R., "Global-Local Laminate Variational Model," Int. J. Solid Structures, Vol. 19, pp. 207–228 (1983)

[6] Wang,S.S. and Choi,I. "Boundary-Layer Effects in Composite Laminates: Part 2 — Free–Edge Stress Solutions and Basic Characteristics," J. of Applied Mechanics, Vol. 49, pp. 549–560 (1982)

[7] Kassapoglou,C. and Lagace,P.A., "An Efficient Method for the Calculation of Interlaminar Stresses in Composite Materials," J. Applied Mechanics, Vol. 53, pp. 744–750 (1986)

[8] Pagano,N.J. and Pipes,R.B., "The Influence of Stacking Sequence on Laminate Strength," Journal of Composite Materials, Vol. 5, pp. 50–57 (1971)

[9] Heyliger,P.R. and Reddy,J.N. "Reduction of Free–Edge Stress Concentration," Journal of Applied Mechanics, Vol. 52, pp. 801–805 (1985)

[10] Mignery,L.A., Tan,T.M., and Sun, C.T., "The Use of Stitching to Suppress Delamination in Laminated Composites," Delamination and Debonding of Materials, ASTM STP 876, pp. 371-385 (1985)

[11] Soni,S.R. and Kim,R.Y., "Analysis of Suppression of Free–Edge Delamina tion by Introducing Adhesive Layer," The Proceedings of the Sixth ICCM combined with the Second ECCM, pp. 5.219–5.230 (1987)

[12] Hong,C.S., "Suppression of Inter laminar Stresses of Thick Composite Laminates Using Sublaminate Approach," 32th International SAMPE Symposium April 6–9, pp. 558–565 (1987)

[13] Pagano,N.J. and Pipes,R.B., "Some Observation on the Interlaminar Strength of Composite Laminates." International Journal of Mechanical Science, Vol. 15, pp. 679–688 (1973)

[14] Kim,R.Y. and Soni,S.R, "Experi mental and Analytical Studies On the Onset of Delamination in Laminated Composites," Journal of Composite Materials, Vol. 18, pp. 70–80 (1984)

7. BIOGRAPHY

Dr. C.S. Hong is professor of aeronautical engineering at Korea Advanced Institute of Science and Technology, Seoul, Korea. He received Ph.D. degree (1977) from Pennsylvania State University. He was an NRC-NASA research associate at Langley Research Center during 1977–1979. He has held his position at KAIST since 1979. He was a visiting professor at Washington University in St. Louis (1986) and a visiting scientist at Air Force Wright Aeronautical Laboratories in Wright-Patterson Base(1987).

D.M. Kim is a Ph.D candidate in Aeronautical Engineering Department at KAIST. He received his M.S. degree (1986) from KAIST. His major interest in composite material is the failure behavior of thick composite laminate under various loading conditions.

Table 1. Material Properties

E_{11} = 137.8 GPa (20 Msi)
$E_{22} = E_{33}$ = 14.5 GPa (2.1 Msi)
$G_{12} = G_{13} = G_{23}$ = 5.9 GPa (0.85 Msi)
$\nu_{12} = \nu_{13} = \nu_{23}$ = 0.21

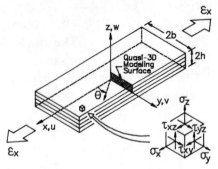

Fig.1 Laminate geometry and stresses

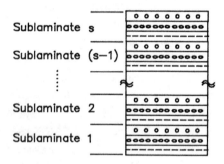

Fig.2 Thick laminate construction by sublaminates

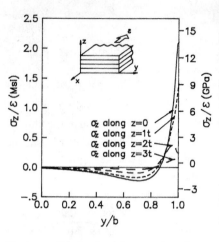

Fig.4 σ_z distribution along various interfaces for [45/0/−45/90]s laminate

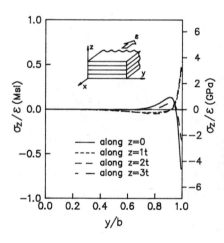

Fig.5 σ_z distribution along various interfaces for [0/45/90/−45]s laminate

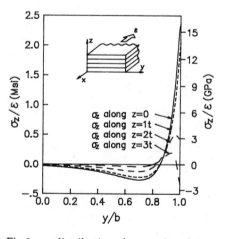

Fig.3 σ_z distribution along various interfaces for [45/−45/0/90]s laminate

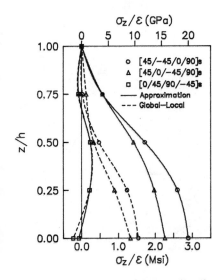

Fig.6　Through–the–thickness distribution of σ_m and $\bar{\sigma}_z$

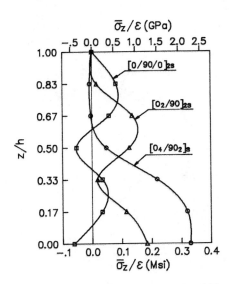

Fig.8　Reduction of the magnitude of $\bar{\sigma}_z$ by sublaminate approach for (0/90) laminate family

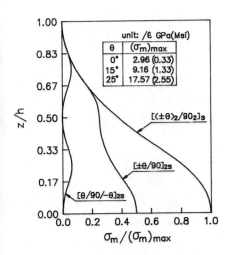

Fig.7　Reduction of the magnitude of σ_m by sublaminate approach

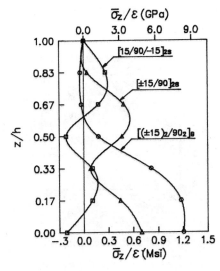

Fig.9　Reduction of the magnitude of $\bar{\sigma}_z$ by sublaminate approach for (±15/90) laminate family

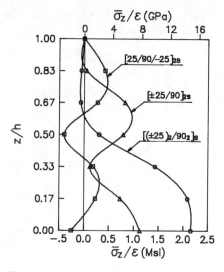

Fig.10 Reduction of the magnitude of $\bar{\sigma}_z$ by sublaminate approach for $(\pm 25/90)$ laminate family

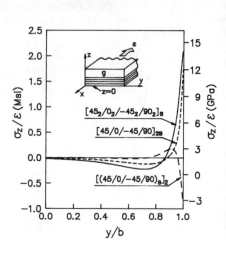

Fig.12 σ_z distribution along z=0 for $(45/0/-45/90)$ laminate family

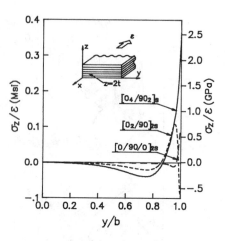

Fig.11 σ_z distribution along z=2t for $(0/90)$ laminate family

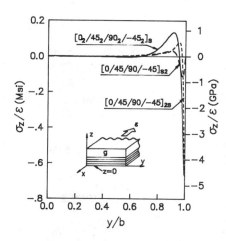

Fig.13 σ_z distribution along z=0 for $(0/45/90/-45)$ laminate family

34th International SAMPE Symposium
May 8-11, 1989

TOTAL CAPABILITY CONTRACTING

FOR A FLIGHT CRITICAL STRUCTURE

Duncan J.Wardrop and Robert M.Allanson
Westland Aerospace
East Cowes, Isle of Wight, England

ABSTRACT

Components, using a combination of aluminium skins, ribs and honeycomb or Graphite/epoxy and nomex honeycomb bonded into an assembly, have been designed and manufactured for some years.
Aerospace marketing found that a number of major aircraft companies were querying the use of honeycombs for various reasons and were expressing the need for other techniques to be developed.
This paper reviews the novel solution to a problem which involves the use of Graphite/ epoxy composite material and structural foam which replaces the conventional bonded skin, rib, honeycomb combination designs.
This paper includes the current design and manufacturing routes available for the Graphite/epoxy and foam materials and the solutions that were developed to ensure the concept was brought to a successful conclusion.

1.   PREAMBLE

1.1   The problem presented to Westland Aerospace was to design and manufacture a Flap Vane in composite materials without resorting to the use of a honeycomb configuration and without the use of mechanical fastening where feasable - that is to use adhesive methods for assembly.
The final component had also to be interchangeable with the existing metal design, and withstand all of the loading criteria given by the customer.

1.2 The design that you will see unfold is such that no redesign of the basic Flap or Wing Structure geometry was necessary.

1.3 This particular vane is also required to have a joint configured near the centre of its length.

1.4 Three arrangements were considered:

1.4.1 Graphite epoxy skins with a foam core and a pair of ribs at each Flap track attachment position.

1.4.2 Graphite epoxy skins with two spars, a foam core and a pair of ribs at each Flap track attachment position.

1.4.3 Graphite epoxy skins with two spars, no core and a large number of ribs between track positions as well as a pair of ribs at each Flap track attachment position.

1.5 All three of these arrangements use metallic components only for fittings and fastenings in order to avoid fatigue and corrosion as well as to save weight.

1.6 All three of these arrangements were to use film and some foaming adhesives for bonding the skins, ribs and foams together.

1.7 The greatest emphasis was allocated to weight and cost within the constraints of the customer procurement specification so, as shown in Figure No.1, this gave the indication that this was the configuration which gave the best overall solution.

1.8 A typical diagramatic section, in between ribs, evolved as shown in Figure 2, comprising pre-machined foam and pre-cured graphite epoxy skins.

1.9 A typical diagramatic section at the rib station, see Figure No.3, shows the graphite-epoxy ribs either side of the aluminium box fitting to which the gooseneck flap track fittings are attached.

1.10 It was decided that

from the initiation of the contract all design would be carried out using three dimensional Computer Aided Design.

The Westland system is CAD 20.1.2, a three dimensional colour system.

2. MASTERING AND TOOLING

From the inception of the contract two major decisions were made by Production Engineering.

2.1 All mould tooling would be matched to master shapes. The masters were machined from solid light alloy billets using appropriate outside surface data supplied direct from the Computer Aided Design system in use at Westland Aerospace.

2.2 The mould shells were made 7mm thick from Graphite Epoxy tooling prepreg. These were pre-cured at 100 psi, 212°F (100°C) and a graphite epoxy egg-crate structure bonded on using silicone adhesive. This structure was then de-moulded, supported and post-cured in stages to 365°F (185°C). These were then set on rigid steel frames and loosely attached with slip bolts to allow for the different expansion coefficients of the materials. The completed moulds were then checked for vacuum integrity and release coated.

2.3 All assembly tooling would be matched to master tooling supplied by our customer to ensure inter-changeability of components.

3. THE SKINS

3.1 There are only two main skins, one upper, one lower, manufactured using Graphite with an Epoxide matrix and joined at the trailing and leading edges.

3.2 The skin material is preimpregnated woven, five harness satin weave cloth, cured at 350°F in an appropriate mould - the mould face being the outer face of the component.

3.3 To ensure surface integrity and to reduce any filling requirment prior to painting after final assembly, the first layer of material layed into the mould was a thin (0.005 inch) laminate of light weight film adhesive. This avoids the weight adding filling, required to give a good non-pitted cosmetic appearance to the finished article when painted. Peel plỳ was used on any face that had to be subsequently bonded.

3.4 The skins comprise three laminations generally and up to eight laminations where reinforced at the rib positions. They are laid 0 - 45 - 0 to give the configuration desired by the stress engineers.

4. THE RIBS

4.1 These ribs are manufactured on male steel tools using airpad intensifiers. The intensifiers are required to give consistent flange thickness and to prevent porosity and voiding in the corner radius. As expected, springback was encountered, and the moulds were adjusted to compensate for this. This exercise became very complex, due to the changing angles of the rib flanges and the requirement for good fit-up to the skins. A change to female tooling is being investigated as this method may give a more consistent outer profile. However, it would require a more complex suite of tools, including internal intensifiers, or new novel processes which are under investigation.

4.2 With regard to the ribs at the joint; because of the loads involved they were required to be of Aluminium material and to form an interchangeable joint. As you can see in Figure No.4 the fittings at the outboard end of the inner section and the inboard end of the outer section are lap joints aft of the nose with the shear loads being taken by the spigot and bush pre-assembled to the Vane prior to the bonding phase.

Now we come to the main part of this design.

5. THE FOAMS

5.1 It was decided to use structural foam because it can withstand the design loads in the Vane and the processing pressure during bonding of skins. (Honeycomb would tend to collapse where edgewise pressure was applied.) Also the foam is easily machined to the complex profiles required and Westland have experience in the use of these materials on other components.
Bonding is carried out at 250°F (125°C) 25 psi. and Rohacell 51 WF and 71 WF was chosen because of its very low compressive creep characteristic when fully heat treated. In fact, during bonding, the actual compresive creep is less than 0.010" over a 3" core thickness.

5.2 The foam is a qualified material, and when in a heat-treated and stabilized condition can operate at temperatures of 365°F (180°C) and for brief periods up to 392°F (200°C). Tensile and compressive strength increases marginally at low temperatures, down to -320°F (-196°C). Elongation is lowered from 4.0% for Rohacell 51 at room temperature, down to 1.4% at .320°F (-196°C).
The densities range from 3.11 to 4.4 lbs/ft.sq.

5.3 An extensive structural test program has been carried out by Westland to establish the characteristics of Rohacell foam. This involved compression and shear tests at normal room temperature and at elevated temperature in order to establish strength and stiffness properties. Tests with various degrees of moisture absorption were also carried out. Rohacell foams are hydroscopic, and the properties are significantly reduced with moisture absorption, so rigid criteria had to be established for storage, handling and drying operations.

5.4 The foam is manufactured in specific block sizes and as sizes required could not be supplied to cover the dimensional configuration we carry out a block bonding operation to get to the billet sizes needed.

The aerofoil profiles are CNC machined to a program on a purpose built machine, although a subcontractor was used to manufacture the initial batch.

5.5 Because of the nature of the material and the profile required, a series of tests were carried out to check expansion character- istics under heat and the surface finish of the foam after machining.

As ball ended cutters had to be used because of the geometry of the cores, they will leave cusps on the curved surface and it was the height of these and the distance between them that had to be ascertained in order to produce a good bond joint to the skin. The result was that plus 0.010" cusps at 0.5" pitch were found to be acceptable.

5.6 The surfaces also had to be machined to allow for various additional strength- ening laminations at the ribs stations and at the

ends to fit into the composite ribs.
Allowances were also made for compression set during autoclave processing and for film adhesive thickness.

6. THE MACHINED FITTINGS

6.1 Housings
These are fittings to which the flap track goosenecks are attached on assembly. Because of interchange- ability requirements for the goosenecks having to be replaceable the attachment holes are not full size at this stage.

The pilot size and facing allowance was as a result of some calculations and research into past experience as to the expansion/contraction of the whole system during curing and these holes and the face depth are finally machined during the mechanical assembly stage.

The housing material is QQA-200-11 (7075-T6511) aluminium.

6.2 Gooseneck Fittings
These are fittings which assemble to the housings and

hold the flap vane into the tracks on the main flaps. These fittings are interchangeable and the material is MIL-S.8844 300M (280-300KSI) steel.

6.3 Splice Fittings

These are metal ribs which are assembled at the joint between the two parts of this outer vane and enable the two parts to be assembled together. These fittings are manufactured in QQA250/12 (7075-T7351) aluminium.

7. THE ADHESIVE ASSEMBLY

7.1 Having thus produced a 'Kit of Parts' we then proceeded to carry out bonding trials by dry runs, to check fit ups of individual details and film and foam adhesive thickness allowances.

7.2 For initial production it was intended to make the Vanes in three bonding stages for close scrutiny of fit-up i.e.
(1) Foam Cores to Rib Assemblies
(2) Foam Assemblies to Lower Skin

(3) Top Skin
However, the expansion coefficient difference between foam and the tool caused jig pin failure. Therefore a two stage bond was used i.e.
(1) Foam Cores,
    Rib Assemblies,
    Bottom Skin
(2) Top Skin
Other modifications during the development phase included removing the foaming adhesive connection between foam cores and ribs, as some problems were noticed with migration into film adhesive glue lines. Film adhesive was used and the foam cores were machined dead size +0.010" lengthwise. Sufficient bonding pressure was applied by the expansion of the foam cores.

7.3 After the bonded assembly was complete the units were subjected to various N.D.I. techniques to check for non bond and/or voided areas.

8. NON DESTRUCTIVE INSPECTION

8.1 A combination of 'C'

and 'A' scan techniques are used to check for voids, delaminations, foreign objects, on the composite details and the final bond stage.

8.2 Mechanical straightness to profile checks are carried out in the assembly jig prior to the machining of the gooseneck fitting holes and faces, and the splice joints.

9. QUALIFICATION TESTING

9.1 Testing

Qualification testing was carried out at both the structural element and component levels.
Structural element tests were carried out to failure to establish the strength of the gooseneck fitting to Flap Vane attachment and the splice joint to Flap Vane. Durability and damage tolerance tests were also carried out at structural element level on a two dimensional specimen which incorporated two gooseneck fitting supports.
Component level tests were carried out on a full

specimen of the Outboard Flap Vane Assembly to confirm the static proof load performance. These tests were followed by durability, damage tolerance and failure tests.
The proof test was carried out prior to the damage tolerance tests to ensure compliance with the requirement to fulfil the proof test program three months prior to the aircraft first flight.
I will not go into detail regarding figures and the definitive results as I am a Production Engineer not a Design Engineer, but will just say that the Vane conformed to the tests as predicted.

10. CONCLUSION

10.1 In conclusion, the Westland Aerospace team have designed and manufactured composite Flap Vanes with benefits of weight saving and no corrosion compared to a comparable design in metal.

11. ACKNOWLEDGEMENTS

The authors wish to acknowledge the contributions of several colleagues at Westland Aerospace, made in the course of this work, particularly Mr.Phil Grainger and Mr.Deryck Jones, also the MCDonnell Douglas Aircraft Company.

BIOGRAPHIES

Duncan J.Wardrop is Deputy Chief Engineer at Westland Aerostructures Ltd, a Division of Westland Aerospace.
Duncan Wardrop started his engineering career with the original Fairey Aviation Company in 1944 and studied to eventually become a member of the Institute of Mechanical Engineers, and a Chartered Engineer in England. He is currently involved in Advanced Material Manufacturing Resource Requirements for the Westland Aerostructures Facility in the next decade.

Robert M.Allanson is Head of Production Development at Westland Aerostructures, a Division of Westland Aerospace.
Robert Allanson started his engineering career at British Hovercraft Corporation, on design and development of flexible structures, then worked on manufacturing development of advanced composites. He is currently involved in the transition period of the hand-over of the development of the Flap Vanes to the production environment and the research to introduce production techniques necessary to manufacture components.

FIG.1 BASIC STRUCTURE

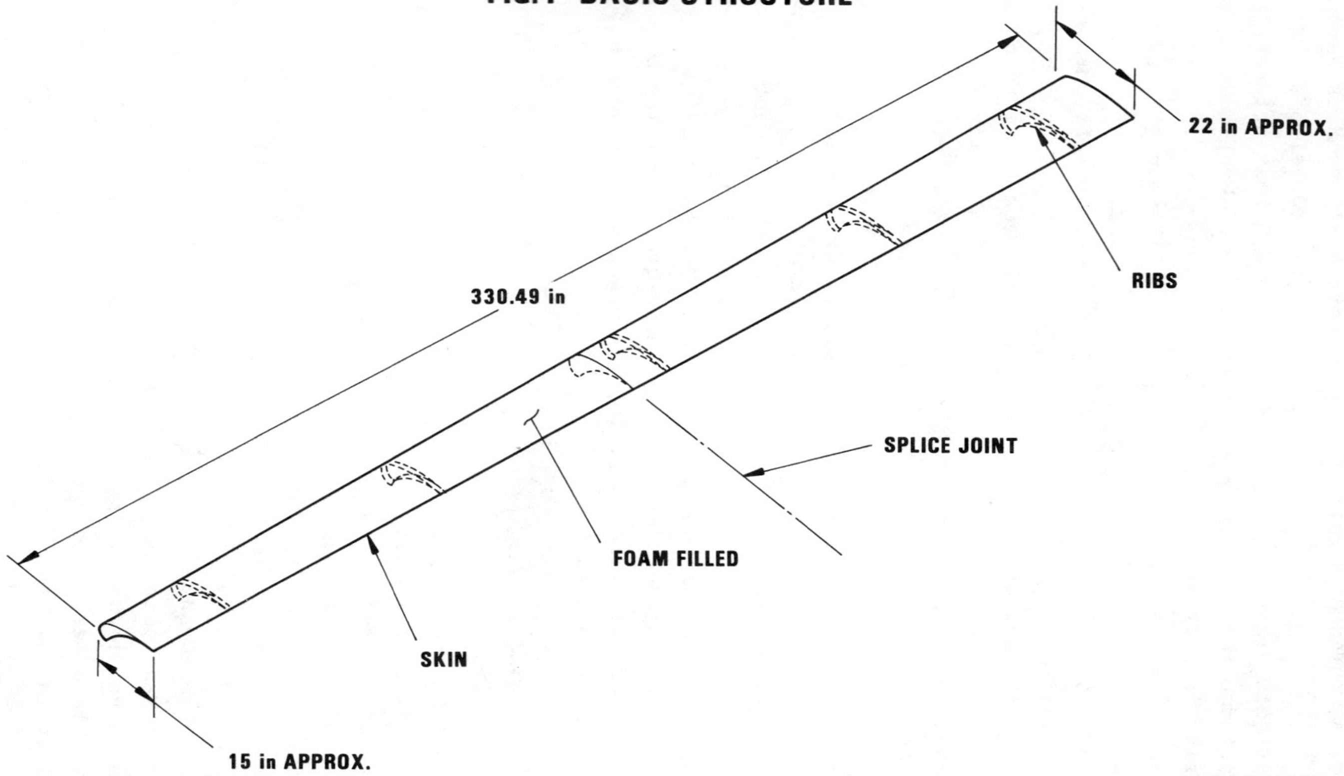

22 in APPROX.

RIBS

SPLICE JOINT

FOAM FILLED

330.49 in

SKIN

15 in APPROX.

WESTLAND
AEROSPACE

MD-11 OUTBOARD FLAP VANE

Westland Group plc

1028

FIG.2 SKIN LAY-UPS AND JOINTS

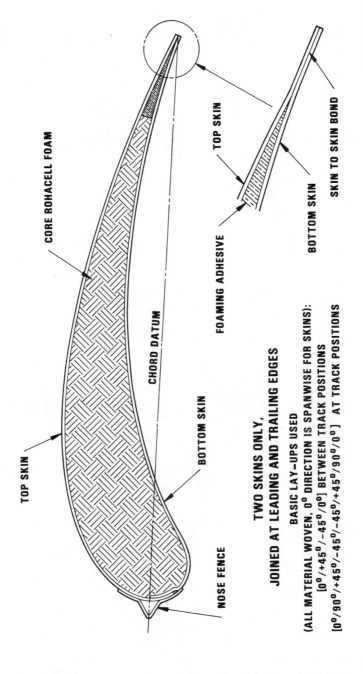

TOP SKIN

CORE ROHACELL FOAM

CHORD DATUM

BOTTOM SKIN

NOSE FENCE

FOAMING ADHESIVE

TOP SKIN

BOTTOM SKIN

SKIN TO SKIN BOND

TWO SKINS ONLY,
JOINED AT LEADING AND TRAILING EDGES
BASIC LAY-UPS USED
(ALL MATERIAL WOVEN, 0° DIRECTION IS SPANWISE FOR SKINS):
$[0°/+45°/-45°/0°]$ BETWEEN TRACK POSITIONS
$[0°/90°/+45°/-45°/-45°/+45°/90°/0°]$ AT TRACK POSITIONS

Westland Group plc

MD-11 OUTBOARD FLAP VANE

WESTLAND
AEROSPACE

1029

FIG.3 RIBS

MACHINED POCKET
BONDED AND RIVETED TO RIBS

SIMPLE CHANNEL SECTIONS,
LAY-UP UNIFORM AROUND SECTION

TYPICAL ARRANGEMENT AT A TRACK POSITION

MD-11 OUTBOARD FLAP VANE

Westland Group plc

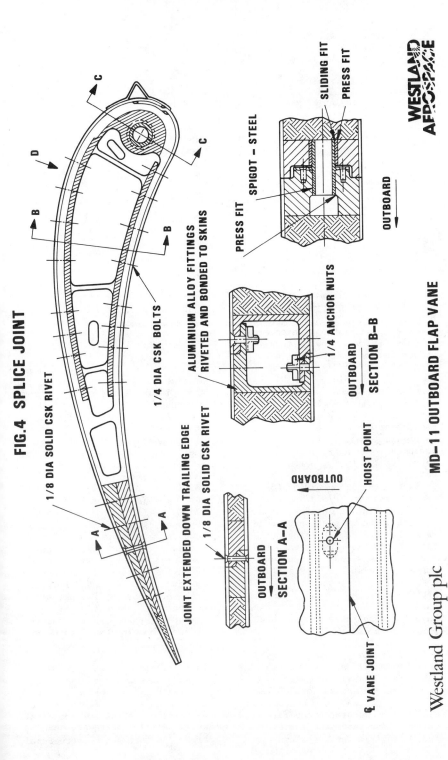

FIG.4 SPLICE JOINT

1/8 DIA SOLID CSK RIVET

1/4 DIA CSK BOLTS

ALUMINIUM ALLOY FITTINGS
RIVETED AND BONDED TO SKINS

JOINT EXTENDED DOWN TRAILING EDGE

1/8 DIA SOLID CSK RIVET

OUTBOARD
SECTION A–A

OUTBOARD

HOIST POINT

₵ VANE JOINT

1/4 ANCHOR NUTS

OUTBOARD
SECTION B–B

PRESS FIT

SPIGOT – STEEL

SLIDING FIT

PRESS FIT

PRESS FIT

OUTBOARD

MD–11 OUTBOARD FLAP VANE

WESTLAND
AEROSPACE

Westland Group plc

1031

STRUCTURAL RESIN TRANSFER MOLDING
OF HIGH TEMPERATURE COMPOSITES
John E. Stockton
U.S. Composites Corp.
Rensselaer Technology Park
Troy, NY   12180

Abstract

Recent developments in bismaleimide and cyanate ester based resin systems have produced formulations which are processible via low viscosity processes such as wet filament winding, wet braiding, and resin transfer molding (RTM). A program has been completed at U.S. Composites Corp. to evaluate the RTM processing considerations of these materials and to extend equipment capabilities to fabricate actual parts. Two resin systems have been evaluated, Shell Compimide 65FWR (BMI) and Dow XU71787 (Cyanate Ester). Flat plates and complex geometry parts have been fabricated with each. The parts fabricated have been evaluated for dimensional accuracy, surface finish, fiber wetting and void content (via photomicrograph and image analysis). Results thus far have demonstrated that high performance 241°C T_g composites are producible via RTM. Fiber volume fractions of 50% have been produced, and no technical barriers are foreseen to achieving in excess of 60% V_f. Higher temperature equipment with more accurate temperature control than that used for epoxy and vinyl ester systems is required. High temperature

applications for the process include nose cones, gear boxes, leading edges, and rocket motor cases.

1. INTRODUCTION

As new resin systems have become available, the use of advanced composites is moving from secondary structures and moderate temperature applications into hotter and more structurally demanding applications. The use of Bismaleimide systems is bridging the temperature gap between epoxies (120°C Wet) and polyimides (315°C). With the new resin systems available, 175°C to 232°C use temperature is achievable. These systems, however, not only represent an increase in raw material costs, but also a longer more energy intensive cure cycle than epoxy systems. To compound the cost problem, most Gr/BMI parts are currently fabricated by hand lay-up of prepregs followed by vacuum bagging and autoclave cure.

Increasingly, aerospace, industrial and recreational products fabricators are looking to lower cost manufacturing methods such as resin transfer molding. While still relatively new to high performance structural composites, RTM has demonstrated its viability in this area, particularly with low viscosity vinyl ester and epoxy systems.

To reduce the fabrication cost of $175^{\circ}C$ to $232^{\circ}C$ service temperature composites it is desirable to extend RTM technology to handle BMI and cyanate ester based resin systems.

U.S. Composites Corp. has a significant technology and experience base in RTM with vinyl ester and epoxy resin systems. Specialized computer controlled pumping systems and computer controlled multizone heating systems have been developed. These systems have been applied successfully with integrally heated molds to produce high fiber volume fraction parts (up to 60 % V_f) with void contents of less than 1%. Complex geometries including flanged sections, male and female threads, multihollow sections (Figure 1), and foam cored structures have all been produced successfully. This paper describes a program to extend these capabilities into higher temperature systems through the selection and evaluation of 2 test resins, and the fabrication of some sample parts.

2. RESIN SYSTEMS SELECTION

Prompted by interest from our customers and support from the manufacturers, the following two resin systems were selected:

Shell Compimide 65FWR

Dow XU71787

Shell Compimide 65FWR is a one component reactive toughened BMI. It is heat curable without the addition of a catalyst.

The $5^{\circ}C$/min. cure viscosity sweep (Figure 2) shows that

viscosities as low as 100 cps can be achieved at approximately $135^{\circ}C$. Examination of the viscosities vs. time isothermals (Figure 3) showed that although viscosity at this temperature builds quickly, it would take approximately 60 minutes to reach 500 cps. The 65FWR is supplied as a resolidified melt and is solid at room temperature. The resin supply and pumping system must therefore be heated to melt and pump the resin.

The Dow XU71787 is a cyanate ester of dicyclopentadiene phenol novolac. The pure resin is a solid at room temperature. Vinyl toluene is added as a reactive diluent to modify the viscosity for the particular application. As expected, increased vinyl toluene reduces the T_g of the cured resin. The effect of vinyl toluene concentration on T_g and viscosity is shown in Table 1.

TABLE 1

XU71787 T_g vs. Vinyl Toluene Concentration

Weight % Vinyl Toluene	Neat Resin T_g
0%	266 $^{\circ}C$
5%	253 $^{\circ}C$
10%	241 $^{\circ}C$
15%	235 $^{\circ}C$
20%	227 $^{\circ}C$

The XU71787 uses a cobalt curing agent. Two cobalt curing agent systems were available from Dow; Cobalt Napthanate (CoNap) or Cobalt AcetalAcetone (CoAcAc). The CoNap is relatively reactive with the cyanate ester and builds viscosity too quickly for large RTM applications. The CoAcAc, however, is more latent.

The XU71787 catalized with 400 ppm of CoAcAc is well suited for large structure RTM. Even with vinyl toluene levels as low as 5%, viscosity below 500 cps can be maintained at less than 100°C for up to 8 hours.[1] This system, while somewhat complicated by the mixing of three components is extremely flexible for RTM because of its long pot life and formulation flexibility. The processing challenge when working with the XU71787 is to minimize the amount of vinyl toluene used to maximize T_g.

3. PUMPING SYSTEM REQUIREMENTS

Based on the available data on the selected resin systems and discussions with Dow and Shell, the upgrade requirements requirements for our RTM equipment were identified. The following system upgrades were implemented:

o Resin supply and pumping system capable of 100°C.

o Means of heating and controlling pumping system temperature.

o Heated resin feed lines capable of 2 MPa (300 PSI).

o Integrally heated, self-contained mold.

o Uniform temperature control of each portion of the system to eliminate cold or hot spots.

A schematic of the RTM system is shown in Figure 4.

4. FLAT PANEL FABRICATION

The ability to mold 65FWR and XU71787 was first tested in a small flat plate mold. The processing data from these tests would be compared to an existing data base of epoxy test results.

The mold used was a perimeter fill, center vent 125 mm dia. disc mold which produces 6.4 mm thick specimens.

Mold temperature was controlled with each system to achieve an in mold resin viscosity of less than 300 cps. As expected, mold pressures were comparable to those experienced when working with epoxy systems and similar in mold viscosities. Each system was shot as a single component and delivered to the mold at constant volumetric flow rate. The fiber reinforcement used was Fortafil UDF. This is a true unidirectional dry reinforcement held together with a thin, permeable polyamide veil. 25 plies were used to achieve a 55% V_f. The fill times for the 5 inch disc mold were in the 5 to 10 minute range which eliminated concerns about premature resin gelation.

The initial cure for each system was conducted in the mold, followed by a free standing postcure. Each molded specimen exhibited a surface finish comparable to that of the aluminum female cavity tool.

5. REPRESENTATIVE PART SELECTION

In the flat plate we had the advantage of working with a small simple tool with which we had much experience. The success indicated, however, that with the system upgrades to high temperature, high pressure equipment, more complex parts fabrication with the 65FWR and the XU71787 would be possible.

The next task was to extend the flat panel experience into the fabrication of some actual parts. The fabrication of these parts was to demonstrate the ability to mold some of the features that previously had been molded successfully with more conventional epoxy systems. The exact part configurations molded to date are proprietary. The parts have been in the range of .5 to 2.5 Kgs finished weight and would fit into 60 cm cube.

The goals of the part molding were to demonstrate:

o Reasonable Cost Tooling.

o Economical Preform Fabrication.

o Dimensional Accuracy.

o High Quality Surface Finish IML & OML.

o $\geq$ 50% V_f Gr/BMI and Gr/XU771787.

6. TOOLING

The tool design utilized an inner male mandrel, female cavity, and two end plates. To achieve our economic goals, an aluminum casting was designed and procured and then finish machined on a tracer equipped vertical turret lathe. Tool design accounted for differential CTE of the aluminum tool and the carbon reinforced laminate in an effort to achieve our dimensional accuracy goals. Net trim lines were incorporated into the tool for transfer to the molded parts.

7. PREFORM FABRICATION

Three preforming techniques have been considered:

o Lay-up and adhesive securing of precut woven or stitch bonded cloth.

o Filament winding.

o Triaxial braiding.

Thus far most of the work has utilized textile braiding for preform fabrication.

The use of precut cloth was successfully demonstrated in the flat panel moldings. For more complex part fabrication the automated fiber placement techniques of braiding or filament winding are more desirable. Adhesive binders had been successfully used for preform fabrication for epoxy RTM, but the compatibility of available adhesive binders with either of our selected resin systems was unknown.

U. S. Composites has both braiding and filament winding capabilities. For the applications investigated thus far, braiding proved to be the most attractive option for preform fabrication. In comparison to filament winding, it had the following advantages:

o Computer controlled braiding can accurately change the bias fiber angle over a changing cross section to produce a constant wall thickness.

o Triaxial braiding automatically incorporates 0° reinforcement.

o Braiding was expected to produce a satisfactory preform with the least time "in the machine". This helped satisfy our goal of economical preform fabrication.

In most RTM operations, there is no post impregnation compacting or consolidation operation. The fiber volume fraction of the molded part is completely determined by the amount of fiber in the preform and the volume of the mold cavity. Complementing automated fiber placement with accurate predictive tools can minimize the number of molding iterations to arrive a a satisfactory part.

U.S. Composites "BRAID" program[2], developed for automated

wet braiding has been used successfully as a predictive tool for RTM preform fabrication. In addition to generating important braider control file data, the BRAID program also calculates fiber volume fraction of the structure. Rapid iterations of modelling are performed to eliminate costly iterations of molding and testing. Once a satisfactory preform is defined using the BRAID program, the necessary braiding parameters are used to generate a control file for the CNC Braiding station. The mandrel portion of the tooling is loaded into the braiding machine and a preform is produced.

The braided preform is seamless and dimensionally stable. It may be trimmed as necessary and is reasonably resistant to "unravelling". Identical preforms were fabricated for parts to be molded from compimide 65FWR and XU71787.

8. PART FABRICATION RESULTS

All molding trials were successful. Epoxy, BMI, and cyanate ester parts produced with identical preforms and molding conditions optimized for the peculiarities of each resin system produced similar quality parts.

Shoot Conditions:

o All preforms @ 50% V_f.

o Mold and resin feed lines temperature controlled to produce in mold viscosities $\leq$ 300 cps.

o Pumping system run at constant delivery rate (as opposed to constant pressure).

o Maximum permissible pressure = 2 Mpa (300 PSI)

The largest parts produced to date had mold fill times of 45 to 55 minutes. For successful processing each of the two high temperature resin systems had their own peculiarities.

Compimide 65FWR

o Short pot life at temperatures necessary to produce optimum molding viscosities. Extra precautions were taken to assure mold fill prior to gelation.

o Susceptible to resolidification. Cold spots in system and mold can produce blockage and dry reinforcement areas.

o Does not form volatiles or contain any high vapor pressure ingredients.

XU71787

o Vinyl toluene diluent has a relatively high vapor pressure. Extra care must be taken with the application of the combination of heat, pressure, and vacuum to eliminate void formation.

o Once mixed with vinyl toluene,the system in no longer solid at room temperature. This reduces the demands on the RTM system temperature uniformity.

o Extremely long useable pot life.

When handled properly, each system produced high quality parts.

o Void content (determined by image analysis of photomicrographs) was less than 1%. See photomicrograph, Figure 5.

o Wall thickness of specimens was within $\pm$ .05 mm.

o Part fiber volume fractions = 50%.

o Good transfer of net trim lines from mold to part.

9. CONCLUSIONS

Carbon fiber reinforced parts with fiber volume fractions of 50% have been produced. Based on parellels drawn to epoxy experience, no barriers are forseen to producing parts with 60% V_f.

Reasonable molded part tolerances may be held with moderate cost aluminum tooling. (Chrome plated tool steel is recommended for long production runs.)

The results of the high temperature resin transfer molding program have been very successfull. Resin systems and equipment are now available which are capable of producing high performance, high temperature, resin transfer molded composites. No limitations in part geometry compared to epoxy or vinyl ester capabilities are expected.

10. BIOGRAPHY

Mr. Stockton is currently Program Manager at U.S. Composites. He has been active in the development and installation of RTM equipment, mold theory and design, and composite structure design. Prior to joining U.S. Composites, he was Engineering Project Leader at Head Racquet Sports where he developed a Resin Transfer Molding process for high volume production of racquet products. He received his BSME from RPI.

11. REFERENCES

(1) Pucket, P.M., 34th. International SAMPE, (1989).

(2) Kruesi, A. H., and Hasko, G.H., 32nd. International SAMPE, (1987), p. 309.

FIGURE 1

MULTIHOLLOW RTM PANEL AND TOOLING

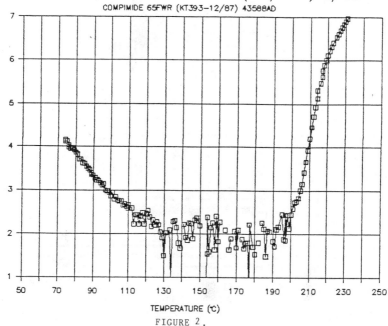

FIGURE 2.

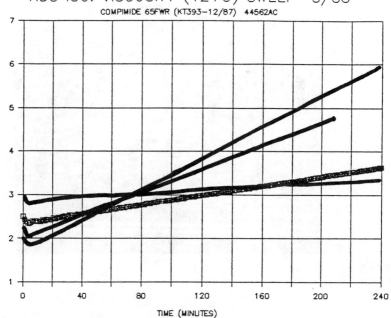

FIGURE 3.

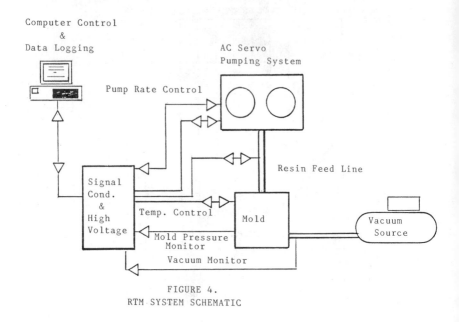

FIGURE 4.
RTM SYSTEM SCHEMATIC

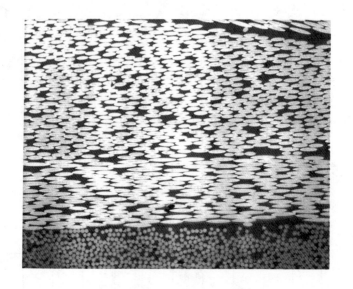

FIGURE 5.
200X, BRAIDED RTM PHOTOMICROGRAPH

AN APPARATUS TO PREPARE COMPOSITES FOR REPAIR

E. A. Westerman

P. E. Roll

Boeing Advanced Systems

Abstract

Damaged composite structures can be repaired using several mechanically fastened or bonded techniques. Mechanically fastened composites are repaired with a methodology similar to that of metallic structures. Bonded composite repairs require preparation techniques generally not used with metallics.

Bonded repair joints consist of scarf, step and overlap types. Overlap joints are common to both composite and metallic structures and usually do not require any special preparation techniques. Scarf joints require sanding or cutting to bevel or taper the material around the damaged area. Scarf joint preparation is a time consuming, tedious process that is difficult to control. Step joint preparation consists of peeling away each ply of structural material to form a terrace around the damaged area. This process is also time consuming and difficult to control.

A fixture has been developed to rapidly and accurately prepare a damaged area for a scarf or step repair. This fixture contains a standard router, router guides, rotating assembly and a vacuum attachment mechanism. The fixture is fully adjustable for both scarf angle and depth of cut. It can be attached to any smooth surface with suction cup feet and is easy to setup and operate.

The mechanical scarfing apparatus has been demonstrated on graphite/epoxy, graphite/BMI, and graphite/PEEK structural panels. Testing has shown that scarfing time can be reduced by 50% and scarf angle accuracy can be improved by 150%. Additional development work is planned to prepare a contour following device that would improve the scarf angle to structure interface.

1. INTRODUCTION

Damaged aircraft structures, constructed from advanced composite materials, are typically restored using fiberglass repair techniques. Repairs generally consist of defining the damaged area, removing the damage, and securing a patch. Damaged material is removed to eliminate defect propagation and to aid in identifying additional defects. The material removal process also prepares the damaged area for a repair patch. Composite repair patches are typically bolted and/or bonded in place and come in either overlap or flush styles. In addition, bolted repairs require a flange area in which to attach the fasteners. Figure 1 shows the typical repair types.

Removal of damaged material and preparation for the repair is dependent on the type of repair selected. Structurally acceptable repairs require quality preparation methods. Current repair preparation is typically performed by a skilled technician using hand held power tools to remove material. This process is time consuming and often results in a less than ideal repair surface.

A mechanical scarfing apparatus (MSA) has been developed which eliminates the variability associated with the hand held material removal process. The apparatus significantly reduces repair preparation time and increases the surface quality of the prepared area. The apparatus is portable, easily assembled and can be used in any orientation making it ideal for use in shops, factories and directly on aircraft surfaces.

2. PROBLEM

Impact is the typical cause of damage to composite structures and often creates unseen defects. A repair to composite structures generally begins by establishing the dimensions of the defect using a variety of non-destructive inspection methods including visual, acoustic, and ultrasonic techniques. The defect must then be removed to eliminate the potential for damage propagation. Damage removal also aids in identifying additional hidden defects before the structure is repaired. The area being repaired is then prepared to receive the patch. The patch is then bolted and/or bonded into place. Bonded

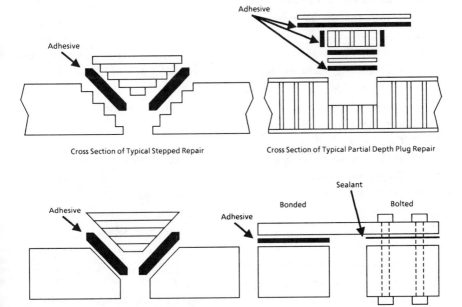

Cross Section of Typical Stepped Repair

Cross Section of Typical Partial Depth Plug Repair

Cross Section of Typical Scarf Repair

Cross Section of Typical Overlap Repair

Figure 1. Typical Repair Types

patches are typically cured using heat and pressure to ensure a good bond.

Composite repairs are time consuming and require highly skilled personnel. Engineers designing or specifying repairs are concerned that the repairs achieve the desired structural efficiency. Analysis of the entire repair process led to the conclusion that improvements in the preparation of the damaged area for repair would address these concerns. The following factors affecting repair area preparation were identified:

1) Quality of cut
2) Portability of tools
3) Elapsed time
4) Personnel skill
5) Equipment suitability

3. RESEARCH GOALS

The development of improvements to the repair preparation process focused on identifying a portable process or device that can be used by semi-skilled personnel to rapidly prepare high quality repair surfaces. Several goals were defined for the developmental program.

1) The quality parameters of the prepared surface must assure a straight, controlled, and smooth finished cut of predetermined size around the damaged area. Figure 2 illustrates these quality parameters.

2) The device must be lightweight, portable, and easily handled by one person.

3) Time to prepare the damaged surface for repair must be reduced 50% from that of the present day process.

4) The device must be easy to use and adjust. It should require minimal skill on the part of the operator. A person should be able to use the device without training or practice.

5) The device must be suitable for use in multiple environments, able to grow with the user's needs and must not damage or alter the structure before, during, or after operation.

6) The device must operate on any structural configuration in vertical, horizontal, and inverted modes.

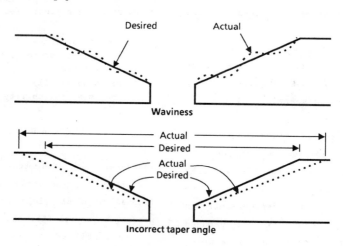

Figure 2. Quality Parameters

The successful completion of these goals is paramount in rapid and reliable preparation of damaged areas for high quality repairs.

4. DEVELOPMENT

The MSA evolved through a traditional design development program. The first task was to identify the cutting options for material removal. Three power-driven concepts were considered: sawing, sanding, and routing. Weight, functionality, speed, and quality of the repair preparation led to the selection of an air powered router as the cutting instrument. The only operational parameter for this instrument is selection of the cutting speed, thereby supporting simplicity.

The prototype of the MSA was designed to use an "off the shelf" router that would be compatible with existing cutting bits to reduce the overall cost. The router is supported by and slides along a beam that can be easily adjusted to any desired scarf angle. The beam is mounted on a pivot that allows the router assembly to rotate freely in a plane around the damaged area. The rotation coupled with the sliding on the beam allows the cutter to make a precise conical cut through the damaged area. The router beam and pivot assembly are supported by a gantry that is, in turn, supported by a framework. The gantry can slide along the top frame rails to produce oval or "race track" cutouts. The entire MSA is supported by active vacuum suction cup feet allowing it to be attached firmly to a table, a component, or the aircraft.

The design of the MSA allows it to prepare scarf or step repairs in all types of materials. It can also be configured to remove damaged honeycomb core. Figure 3 shows the assembled MSA.

5. RESULTS

The basic prototype design of the MSA has been developed to improve the quality, decrease the preparation time, provide reproducible results, and reduce the skill level required to perform a scarf, step, and/or honeycomb core cutout. The MSA has met the first five developmental goals identified for the device but is currently limited to simple structural configurations.

Figure 3. Mechanical Scarfing Apparatus
(Patent Pending)

5.1 Testing

The prototype was constructed out of 2024 aluminum stock material. The material was machined and then assembled to its present design configuration. Operational trials included moving the router in a radial motion sliding it along the beam toward the center of the damaged area. It was discovered that this action required a steady hand and a good deal of skill to achieve the proper feed rates. This led to the conclusion that the cutting motion being used would not meet design goals. The prototype was modified to allow the cutter to be positioned radially on the beam and rotated around the center of the damage thus following a stepped circular or spiral pattern. Additional testing showed that this technique was much easier to control. In addition, technicians can pick up a feel for the proper cutting and feed rates in just a few minutes. A full spiral motion would be used in an automated, feed controlled configuration. Figure 4 shows the various motions tested.

The prototype has been used successfully on a graphite/BMI filament-wound cylinder, a graphite/PEEK hard plank-soft skin wing box and several flat test coupons. Operating features for the MSA prototype include an infinitely adjustable scarf ratio of ±2-to-1, maximum scarf diameter of 43 cm (17 in.), vacuum attachment to structure, and infinitely adjustable routing control paths.

5.2 Test Results

Quality of Scarf. The MSA can maintain and control angles or tapers up to ±2-to-1. Surface smoothness and waviness can be easily controlled to get results comparable to those obtained using a NC machine. Surface finish is dependent on cutter type, rotational speed, and feed rate. This accurate router movement allows the repair technician to closely control the thickness of the adhesive layer between the patch and the parent material.

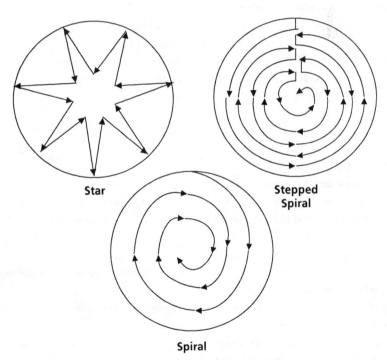

Star

Stepped Spiral

Spiral

Figure 4 Cutting Motions

Structural integrity and performance are increased when scarf quality is maintained.

Portability. The prototype of the MSA is designed such that it can be disassembled and placed into an 20cm x 30 cm x 102 cm (8" x 12" x 40") carrying bag. The assembly weighs about 17 kg (35 lbs). Assembly or disassembly takes less than 10 minutes and the entire prototype device can be easily transported by commercial aircraft. Larger versions, used for larger cuts, will still remain easily transported by one or two persons.

Time. The actual cutting time for any particular scarf is dependent on the size, material, cutter type and feed rates used. Table 1 shows a comparison of times achieved with the MSA compared to handscarfing times. Optimized cutter types are dependent on the materials to be prepared. The MSA also produces a scarf of superior quality to that of the handscarfing method.

User Skill. The design of the MSA prototype used a "tinker toy" approach to make set up and alignment quick and easy for semi-skilled personnel. Set-up and alignment have been accomplished in less than 10 minutes by personnel with no prior training or practice. The circumferential cutting pattern used allows the technician to develop a feel for the proper feed rate in the first couple of revolutions around the periphery of the repair area. Operator fatigue is minimal due to the low reaction forces of the cutter. One or two fingers can apply enough force to rotate the router assembly around the repair area.

Equipment Suitability. The design of the MSA allows the use of different routers and cutters depending on specific applications. Operating costs are minimized by reducing cutting time and cutter bit wear. The design has the ability to grow with the needs of the user. The MSA can be supported on the aircraft in an upright or inverted position through the use of vacuum attaching feet, thus eliminating the need to remove the part for repair.

6. CONTINUING DEVELOPMENT OF MSA

Throughout the construction and testing of the MSA, several areas have been identified as needing additional developmental work.

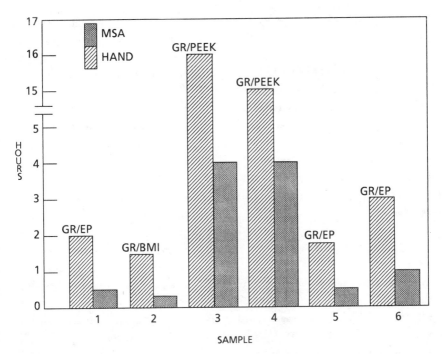

Table 1 — Scarfing Time Comparison

Panel Edges. Early use of the MSA showed that the initial design could not be used to scarf panel edge damage because the suction cup placement would be outside the planform of the component. Offset blocks would allow the gantry to be cantilevered out over the edge of the work piece thereby allowing scarfing out to the very edge of the work piece.

Contour Following. The current design of the MSA is limited to flat or very large radius curved surfaces. While this will solve most of todays limited contour repair problems, it has been recognized that some form of contour following capability is necessary to prepare complex curved surfaces.

Thick Laminates. The MSA has greatly improved the rate of material removal when compared to hand sanding. However, in the case of very thick laminates, material removal can take hours or days instead of minutes. Several concepts for rapid removal of large amounts of material are being pursued and will be tested in the near future.

7. CUTTING BIT OPTIONS

As mentioned earlier, cutting bit types and sizes will need to be optimized to determine the optimum cutting bit and feed rates for different material types. This optimization process will continue as required.

8. CONCLUSIONS

The MSA is a device that permits the rapid high-quality preparation of damaged areas for repair and addresses the concerns that users and repair design engineers have with the current process.

- The quality of the scarf is several orders of magnitude better than hand scarfs.

- The MSA allows precise control of bondline thickness.

- The MSA is easily portable and can be transported, set up, and operated by one person.

- The MSA will produce scarf cuts in 50% or less of the time required for hand sanding of a scarf.

- The MSA can be operated by semi-skilled or unskilled personnel with minimal instructions.

- The MSA can be used to prepare parts in any orientation, including inverted, without alteration or damage.

- The MSA is a very valuable tool that can be put in use today to reduce the cost of repairing composite structures. However, as with any device in the early stages of development, additional work needs to be done to assure it achieves its full potential.

9. BIOGRAPHIES

Everett A. (Bud) Westerman

Mr. Westerman is currently a senior maintainability engineer responsible for the integration of composite supportability into several Boeing Advanced Systems programs. He is principal investigator on several independent and contracted R&D activities. He has several patents pending that will improve the state of the art in aircraft structural maintenance. Mr. Westerman received his BSME/BSBA from the University of Nevada/Reno. He has been with Boeing for four years.

Phillip E. Roll

Mr. Roll is currently working as an engineer responsible for integrating maintainability into structural and aircraft electromechanical systems on a Boeing Advanced Program. He is the co-inventor for two inventions that will improve the aircraft maintenance process. He has been instrumental in defining the goals for the KC-135R and 757/767 power plant programs. Mr. Roll received his BSME from Michigan Technological University. He has been with Boeing for six years.

REPAIR ADHESIVES: DEVELOPMENT CRITERIA FOR FIELD LEVEL CONDITIONS

Michael J. Cichon
Dexter Adhesives & Structural Materials Division
Hysol Aerospace Products
Pittsburg, California

ABSTRACT

Aircraft are generally kept in service beyond their normal expected service lives, as such the repair of aircraft has received national attention. A great deal of that attention has focused upon the commercial airline industry. The military is also an area where many aircraft have been overhauled or upgraded beyond their expected service lives. This trend is expected to continue since the cost of upgrade is often much lower than the purchase of new planes. The need for repair materials which will provide a high level of service along with improved handling qualities is becoming more evident.

Hysol has been involved with the development of repair materials throughout the aerospace industry over the last twenty years. Of current interest to Hysol has been the development of new repair materials which are more tolerant of the variable conditions present in a repair environment. This development effort has yielded adhesives which have more tolerance for variations in bond line thickness and mix ratio, while providing high temperature performance with wide processing curves. In addition, handling features have been improved with a major goal of room temperature storage of these materials for one year being attained.

Hysol's adhesive system EA 9394 is highlighted in this paper although the concepts presented are applicable to most repair adhesives. Data is presented which measures adhesive performance relative to bond line thickness, elevated long-term storage conditions, variations in cure temperatures, cure schedules, surface preparation and mix ratio.

1. INTRODUCTION

The aerospace industry has always been concerned about repair methods and materials. With respect to adhesives usage in a repair environment, the material is tested to a specification before it is qualified for its particular repair application. Since aerospace users often demand the ultimate in both product quality and performance, it is important to also identify those factors at the user's level which influence the quality of the repair.

Typically, individuals involved with the actual repair of aircraft select the adhesive from those specified by the manufacturer of the aircraft. This adhesive specification is normally developed by a materials and process group, with the repair methods determined through a separate design group. The adhesive manufacturer primarily develops materials around this performance oriented specification with a secondary goal of incorporating user friendly handling characteristics in the adhesive.

One of the key product development goals is to increase the products processing window without sacrificing performance. Additionally, repair industry personnel, both commercial and military, are seeking materials which are environmentally safe, easy to handle, and which can withstand ambient storage for an extended length of time while providing a low energy cure.

One of Hysol's first adhesives used in a variety of repair environments for metal bonding was Hysol EA 934. This system was developed over twenty-five years ago and is still qualified to over one hundred specifications. While EA 934's replacement product EA 934NA is still a very popular product, there is a need for new materials which are more tolerant of conditions in a repair environment. This need has led to the development of several new classes of epoxy resin formulations which feature significant improvements over this older chemistry.

2. BACKGROUND

2.1 Materials Quality in Repair Applications

A great deal of attention has been given to the writings of Taguchi[1] on the development of quality control in products and processes. Product quality according to Taguchi's methods is "determined by the economic losses imposed upon society."[1] Therefore, the user defines quality. Losses include a failure of the material as well as costs associated with pollution, waste disposal and maintenance.

Hysol provides products which meet an agreed upon specification. This specification outlines the material's expected performance characteristics under a given set of conditions. Realistically, our products may be used under more variable conditions and typically, the product's secondary character-istics such as handling and field processing variables are not as defined. These variables are important to the end user since they determine the product's suitability from a user's perspective.

Operating environment variables in a repair environment such as humidity and temperature are examples of external operating factors which can cause deviations in the product's performance. Product deterioration and repair process imperfections are two categories of internal operating factors. Repair process imperfections such as adherend surface preparation, variations in cure temperature, or vacuum pressure also influence the quality of the repair since variations in this area affect bond line thickness, cure and adhesion.

EA 934NA has some limitations in the repair environment. It currently requires freezer storage, possesses no toughness, has a pot life of only 40 minutes for a 450 gram mass, and has a more narrow processing window as compared to EA 9394. As with many materials, there are trade-offs which must be made in order to develop a material which is ideal for the widest variety of users.

Hysol's goal is to maintain or exceed existing repair materials' performance characteristics while improving the handling parameters for end users. This combined effort will provide for a higher quality repair.

Primary Adhesive Need	Trade-off
• High Temperature Performance	• Sacrifice toughness, mostly brittle systems.[2]
• One Part System with Room Temperature Storage	• Need for higher cure temperature.
• Low Cure Temperature	• Need for freezer storage, limited outtime or two part system.
• Environmental Resistance Performance	• Cost, processability.
• Mix Ratio Insensitivity	• Lower performance.
• One to One Mix Ratio	• Lower performance due to filler levels.
• Increased Toughness	• Sacrifice upper temperature performance.
• Safer Materials	• May influence performance or handling conditions.
• Improved Moisture Resistance	• Cost, toughness.

2.2 Processing Variables Associated with Repair Adhesives

There are three defined levels of repair - depot, field and battle damage repair.[3] Since battle damage repair is normally a temporary repair often with constraints on the flight envelope, we have focused on field and depot level repairs for our development efforts.

Field level and depot level repairs try to achieve the same objective - to return the plane to unrestricted service. However, if one looks at the repair processes in a depot versus field repair one can find significant differences. Typically, a repair depot may have capabilities which duplicate the original manufacturer's facilities.[3] Controlled environmental conditions, autoclaves and a full range of equipment would be considered normal operating conditions. Repairs in this environment are often quite extensive and extend beyond areas which would be considered suitable for a field repair. Film adhesives are the predominant repair material as a result of the larger nature of these repairs.

In a field repair, one may find more variation in both skill level and in the repair environment. In addition, equipment limitations for curing and storing the adhesives may exist. Freezer storage would be a limiting factor and an autoclave cure would most likely be unavailable. The majority of repairs would utilize a heating blanket since the repair must normally be performed on the aircraft without disassembly. Time may also be more of a factor in a field repair since the plane is not in for scheduled service.[4] The repair may be temporary, although many are permanent. Surface preparation procedures may also be more limited. Paste adhesives are the preferred materials due to storage and usage considerations. Additionally, repair materials and processes may be different from the original materials and processes.

A review of literature written about adhesive repair, along with visits to repair facilities, indicates some differences in repair philosophy and a need for practical information on adhesive performance.

Some of the questions commonly asked about repair adhesives at a user level relate to handling characteristics and processing parameters. As expected, these are the key user variables which affect the quality of the repair. Common questions are:

a. How thick should the bond line be and how do I ensure this thickness?

b. How much pressure should be applied to the part?

c. What is the cure cycle? Are there alternative cure schedules?

d. What is the effect of exceeding the cure temperature?

e. How fast can I ramp up to the cure temperature?

f. What is the minimum cure time at a given temperature?

g. What would be the minimum or maximum recommended pressure during cure?

h. What type of surface preparation should be used? Is one better than another?

i. What is the effect of variations in the mix ratio?

j. How does moisture affect the bond?

k. How does pot life affect adhesive performance?

l. How soon can I machine the part?

m. How safe is the adhesive to handle or dispose?

If the questions are grouped together, one can see that the questions refer to specific processing parameters associated with epoxy adhesives. These parameters can be segregated by cure schedule, surface preparation, handling characteristics and substrate variation.

We reviewed the basic variables surrounding adhesive bonding and associated them with the repair environments. Based upon this matrix, we developed adhesives which will operate more consistently across a wide variety of operating parameters.

During the development stages for some of our newer adhesives, Hysol concentrated on optimizing properties which made the adhesive more consistent to use, while still attaining 350°F service. One criteria for the development of an adhesive used in repair was that the structural performance of the materials it would be replacing would not be compromised.

3. PROCESSING AND HANDLING VARIABLES

3.1 Storage Stability

Ambient storage stability of a system is a desired feature for field repair. It eliminates the need for freezer storage and allows transportation flexibility. The term room temperature storable is not sufficient since room temperature could vary from 77°F-120°F. Temperatures as high as 120°F for six weeks could represent storage conditions on a container ship in the Indian Ocean. This indicates that an ideal adhesive for repair should be able to withstand the harshest of these requirements.

Storage life of the adhesive is defined as the point where the resin doubled in viscosity. This bulk property measure was also verified through mechanical tests at the end of the adhesive's storage life. This data is presented in Exhibit A, which illustrates the viscosity change of the EA 9394 Part A at 77°F, 90°F and 120°F. The data illustrates the stability of the system at 77°F for one year. In addition, the data presented shows the stability of the system for nine months at 90°F and over four months at temperatures as high as 120°F.

3.2 Mix Ratio

Ideally, in a repair environment, one would prefer a film adhesive or a one part paste in order to avoid mixing errors. However, a one part paste or film is a difficult goal to attain while providing a complete cure at temperatures under 200°F and providing storage stability at temperatures of 90-120°F. This requirement was met only through the use of a two part system. The development of a two part system requires an adhesive which is tolerant of mix ratio variations. We examined tensile lap shear performance against variations of ±15% of Part A and B ratios, and chose a mix ratio and system which would provide the closest results to the control. See Exhibit B.

Another way to eliminate mix ratio errors is to provide the two part system in a custom package such as a cartridge kit or a divider bag. In a custom package, the two parts are weighed which eliminates the need for measuring the two components. The package is used for storage, mixing and dispensing. Additionally, the kit type package is suited for the smaller usage normally found in field repair and provides for a safer way to use and dispose of the unused adhesive.

3.3 Process Variables - Work Life
Work life or pot life of an adhesive is determined by the point at which the adhesive reaches a viscosity where it is no longer able to be applied. The recommended pot life for EA 9394 is 70 minutes for a 450 gram mass. Exhibit C verifies the tensile lap shear performance at the end of its pot life, since it is possible for an adhesive to have a performance pot life different from its handling pot life.

3.4 Process Variables - Surface Treatment

The majority of adhesive failure in repair can be traced to inadequate surface preparation, and this can be further compounded in the repair environment. We examined a variety of surface preparations and primers using EA 9394. Initial data was generated to review the differences in tensile lap shear performance on a PAA aluminum against a primed surface versus a sandblasted/MEK wiped surface. Results were encouraging as seen on Exhibit D, with slightly lower properties at room temperature on the sandblasted/MEK wiped surface. Results at 350°F indicate the sandblasted surface slightly better than the control, however, it has been documented that long-term durability is sacrificed with the sandblasted method of surface preparation. Additional testing with only a MEK wipe gave significantly lower results when compared with etched surfaces, however, 1000 psi tensile lap shear performance was maintained up to 300°F. See Exhibit E. A review of data generated with EA 9394 against primed versus unprimed PAA etched surfaces illustrates little or no differences as illustrated in Exhibit F.

One other factor present in repair environments is exposure to prebond humidity. In this test, we examined PAA aluminum which was exposed to 85% relative humidity for three hours prior to bonding. Results indicate a loss in tensile lap shear strength of approximately 35-45%, however, 1,000 psi was still maintained at 350°F. See Exhibit G.

3.5 Cure Variables - Temperature, Pressure and Bond Line Thickness

Since the cure cycle is another area where there can be processing variability, we looked at variations in cure temperature, cure pressure and bond line thickness data.

We tested the adhesive at 5 psi to simulate an inadequate seal on vacuum bag. The results show good tensile strength with cure pressures as low as 5 psi. See Exhibit H. We compared this data against bond line thickness data which indicated an ideal bond line thickness of 3-5 mils. This is representative of the thickness of this adhesive under 20 psi pressure pressure with no bond line control. The results in Exhibit I indicate good strength with bond lines as thick as 17 mils.

The recommended cure cycle for EA 9394 is 5-7 days at room temperature or one hour at 200°F. In a repair environment, a repair might require a cure under a shorter time period or with a cure temperature in excess of 200°F. The majority of our testing in this area involved looking at tensile lap shear properties under a variety of cure conditions. The goal of this development work was to provide a system which could be cured under a wide processing window.

In addition, some of the variations within a field repair may involve cure temperature. The ability to make this processing window wide assured a good cure. Exhibit J illustrates the results of five different cure schedules against tensile lap shear performance. In metal bond repair and more so with honeycomb and composite repair, moisture in the bond line is a factor, so cure schedules ideally are kept under 200°F to prevent liberation of moisture in the bond line. A cure schedule of 1/2 hour at 180°F was sufficient to affect a complete cure.

We also examined the amount of time required to achieve handling properties of EA 9394 at 125°F. This testing was done to simulate conditions encountered in a deep section repair where the maximum heating blanket temperature at the surface would be limited to 200°F. The results indicate a set time of 45 minutes to achieve 100% of the tensile lap shear strength at 77°F. See Exhibit K.

In some repair situations time is of the essence, therefore, we also reviewed the adhesive under a short elevated cure cycle. As seen in Exhibit L, a cure cycle of 5 minutes at 200°F or at 300°F is sufficient to produce good tensile lap shear results.

There is also the possibility of overcuring the adhesive in a repair environment. In this test, we exposed the adhesive to a ramp of 5° per minute up to 450°F. This temperature was held for 40 minutes and then the specimen was removed from the heat source. Some loss of 77°F and 200°F properties was noted, but the adhesive lost less than 25% of its room temperature strength. See Exhibit M.

4. CONCLUSION

Typically an ideal repair resin will have the following characteristics:

- Storage stability at temperatures up to 120°F.
- Mix ratio insensitivity.
- Wide cure temperature processing window.
- Ability to cure quickly.
- Ability to cure at temperatures lower than 200°F.
- Bond line thickness insensitivity.
- Good processing characteristics.
- Long pot life.

EA 9394 possesses these characteristics as evidenced through the testing completed to date. These same characteristics also make EA 9394 a good material for production usage as well.

The challenge is to provide materials which allow consistency in the manufacturing and repair environment. This data indicates the development of repair materials which operate consistently over a wide range of conditions can positively influence the quality of the repair.

As an added feature, this adhesive is produced in several versions; unfilled (EA 9396), non metallic filled (EA 9395), and aluminum filled (EA 9394). Designed for wet lay-up repair, composite repair and metal repair, respectively.

5. REFERENCES

1. Quality Engineering in Production Systems, Genichi Taguchi, Elsayed A. Elsayed, Thomas Hsiang, McGraw Hill- New York, 1989, p3.

2. Adhesive Bonding of Aluminum Alloys, Edward W. Thrall, Raymond W. Shannon, Marcel Dekker, 1985. Marcel Dekker, Inc. New York.

3. Adhesive Bonded Aerospace Structures, Standardized Repair Handbook, Wright Patterson, Sept. 1978.

4. Composite Repairs, SAMPE
   Monograph #1. 1985 Covina,
   CA.

6. BIOGRAPHY

Michael J. Cichon is a Market
Development Specialist in Dexter's
Adhesives & Structural Materials
Division. His responsibilities
include bringing Hysol's
developmental products into
aerospace applications and
markets. Academic background
includes a B.S. from the
University of Connecticut.

7. ACKNOWLEDGEMENTS

The author would like to
acknowledge the efforts of Frank
J. Seeno and Todd Fitton for the
preparation and testing of
specimens. Their assistance was
greatly appreciated.

EA 9394 VISCOSITY VERSUS
TIME AND TEMPERATURE

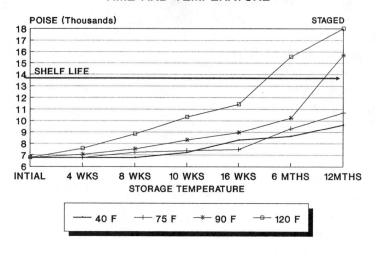

EFFECT OF MIX RATIO ON
TENSILE LAP SHEAR RESULTS

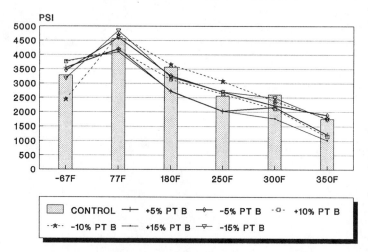

EA 9394

EXHIBIT C

EA 9394 TENSILE LAP SHEAR
EVALUATION AFTER 70 MINUTES OUTTIME

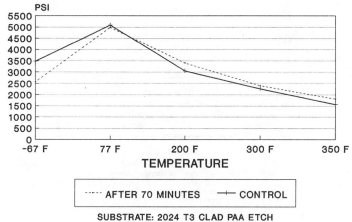

SUBSTRATE: 2024 T3 CLAD PAA ETCH
EA 9394 CURE: 7 DAYS AT 77F
450 GM MASS MIXED & APPLIED AFTER 70 MIN

EA 9394 TENSILE LAP SHEAR
VERSUS SURFACE PREPARATION

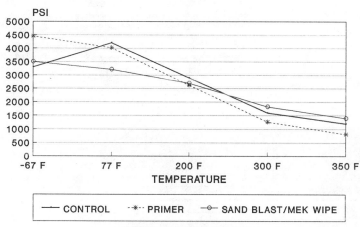

SUBSTRATE: 2024 T3 CLAD
PRIMER: HYSOL EA 9228
CURE: 1 HR AT 200 F @ 15 PSI

TENSILE LAP SHEAR VERSUS
SURFACE PREPARATION METHOD

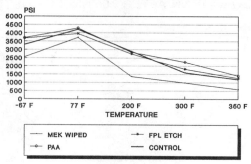

SUBSTRATE: 2024 T3 CLAD
EA 9394 CURE: 77F FOR 7 DAYS

EA 9394 PRIMED
METAL PERFORMANCE

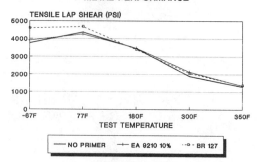

PRIMER CURE: 1 HR AT 250F
PRIMER THICKNESS: .2 MILS
UNPRIMED - PAA 2024 T3

EA 9394 AFTER SUBSTRATE
EXPOSURE TO 85% HUMIDITY

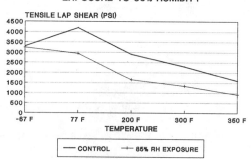

SUBSTRATE: 2024 T3 CLAD PAA
CURE: 7 DAYS AT 77 F
SUBSTRATE EXPOSED TO 85% RH FOR 3 HOURS

EA 9394 TENSILE LAP SHEAR
VERSUS BOND LINE PRESSURE

EXHIBIT H

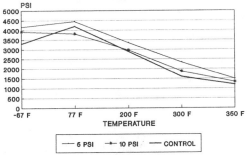

SUBSTRATE: 2024 T3 CLAD
CURE: 1 HR AT 200F

EFFECTS OF BONDLINE THICKNESS
TENSILE LAP SHEAR RESULTS (PSI)

EXHIBIT I

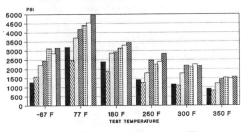

EA 9394
EA 9394 TENSILE LAP SHEAR
STRENGTH vs CURE TEMPERATURE

EXHIBIT J

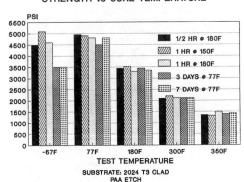

SUBSTRATE: 2024 T3 CLAD
PAA ETCH

TIME FOR COMPLETE CURE
AT CURE TEMPERATURE OF 125F

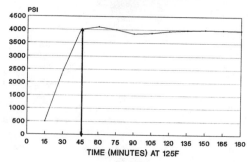

EA 9394
SUBSTRATE: 2024 T3 CLAD

EA 9394
SHORT ELEVATED CURE

EXHIBIT L

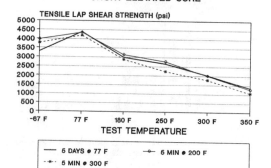

EA 9394 TENSILE LAP SHEAR STRENGTH
VERSUS EXCESSIVE CURE TEMPERATURE

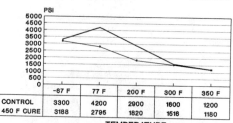

	-67 F	77 F	200 F	300 F	350 F
CONTROL	3300	4200	2900	1600	1200
450 F CURE	3188	2795	1820	1516	1180

TEMPERATURE

— CONTROL   — 450 F CURE

SUBSTRATE: 2024 T3 CLAD
CONTROL CURE: 7 DAYS AT 77 F
HIGH TEMP CURE: 450 F FOR 40 MINUTES

ADHESIVE-BONDED COMPOSITE-PATCHING REPAIR
OF CRACKED AIRCRAFT STRUCTURE

Ching-Long Ong, Shyan Shen
Chung-Shan Institute of Science and Technology
P.O. Box 90008-11-12
Taichung, Taiwan, R.O.C.

Abstract

The development of quick and reliable repair technology for damaged aircraft structures for field operation is one of the most important issues to keep high availability for any Air Forces. Aero Industry Development Center (AIDC), R.O.C., has been engaged in developing and validating a composite-patching repair technology for cracked aircraft structures. In this paper, three room-temperature-cure adhesives were evaluated with single-lap shear test and fatigue test. The effects of the application of adhesion promoter and primer on the adhesive strength were also determined. After adhesive-bonded repairs with carbon or boron-fiber composite patches, the fatigue life of cracked aluminum panels has been extended 60 to 100 times. Three repairs of structural cracks on the AT-3 full scale fatigue test article experienced 18,000 simulated flight hours without failure. Therefore, it is believed that this composite patching repair with room-temperature-cure adhesive is proven to be reliable and economical.

1. INTRODUCTION

Metallic aircraft components are susceptible to fatigue and/or stress-corrosion cracking in service, and cause a lot of maintenance problems. Several repair methods have been developed in recent years, such as bolted or bonded repair with metallic or composite patches[1-3]. Among them, the composite-patch bonding is the most effective and economical method for field repair.

The use of composite patches made of boron/epoxy (b/ep) or graphite/epoxy (gr/ep) has many advantages such as designed directional stiffness, better fatigue strength, and good formability. In addition, the crack growth under the patch can be monitored using eddy current instrument[4]. Furthermore, the adhesive bonding uniformly and effectively transfers stress between the cracked component and the patch around the

crack tip with minimum stress concentrations which are often caused by rivet or bolt repairs[5].
The success of composite-patch-bonding repair largely depends on good control of surface treatment procedures and correct selection of adhesive systems. Different tank surface treatments have been evaluated in Aero Material Laboratory[6]. In the continuation of the work, the non-tank surface treatments have been evaluated recently[7]. They are abrasion, phosphoric acid non-tank anodizing (PANTA), Pasa-Jell 105, hydrofluoric acid/alodine 1200 chemical conversion (HF-A), and gelled sulfuric acid/sodium dichromate treatment (GFPL). Through Boring wedge test and long-term environmental tests, PANTA has the best results. The initial bond strength of FM 73 film adhesive for the five treatments are almost the same, but a six months aging in water, hydraulic oil, or JP-4, the residual bond strength of abrasion, GFPL, and HF-A treatments were dramatically dropped to about 40 percent of the initial strength. On the other hand, Pasa-Jell and PANTA treatment remain 80% and 90% of their initial strengths, respectively. Furthermore, the fatigue tests for the certification of the repair of real structures shall be conducted. In this paper, the evaluation and selection of the adhesive system is presented, and followed by the fatigue tests of repair panels. Finally, the room-temperature-

adhesive-bonding repair of gr/ep patch on three cracked components of the AT-3 full-scale fatigue test article are described.

2. ADHESIVE SELECTION

High-temperature-cure adhesives have been extensively used because of higher bond strength and better environmental resistance than the room-temperature-cure adhesives. They would be more suitable as bonding agent for patch repairs. However, they have to be cured under more severe conditions including heating rate control, higher curing temperature and pressure to gain strength and durability. These requirements can be easily achieved in manuafcturing shops but hard in field operations. In addition, due to the large difference of the thermal expansion coefficients between aluminum structures and composite patches, the application of the high-temperature-cure adhesives will induce thermal residual stress[8]. Therefore, it is necessary to find a curing cycle of relatively lower temperature to alleviate the residual stress and provide proper bond strength and durability for the repair work. On the other hand, strong room-tempeature-cure adhesives can also be used. Some papers have presented the achievements of room-temperature-cure adhesives for repair works[4],[8],[9].

In this study, the high-temperature-cure film adhesive FM 73 (by American Cyanamid) was chosen to find its optimum curing cycle for field repair.

At the same time, three room-temperature-cure adhesives, namely, AV138/HV998 epoxy adhesive (138/998; Ciba-Geigy)[4], Versilok 201 acrylic adhesive (V201; by Lord Corp.)[9], and Permabond F241 acrylic adhesive (by Adhesives and Resins Pty. Ltd.)[8] were evaluated.

For FM 73 with standard curing conditions of 121°C/276 KPa/1 hr, the differential scanning calorimetry (DSC) technique was first used to measure the degree of cure (DOC) at different temperature/time conditions.

$$\text{Degree of Cure} = (1 - \frac{\Delta H_c}{\Delta H_u}) \times 100\%$$

ΔH_c: ΔH peak area of cured film adhesives.

ΔH_u: ΔH peak area of uncured film adhesive.

The results showed that the cure of FM 73 could be completed at much lower temperature with longer curing time. Secondly, the lap shear test per Federal Specification MMM-A-132 was employed to determine the temperature/time condition giving the best bond strength for both aluminum-to-aluminum and aluminum-to-gr/ep bonding under 600 mmHg vacuum curing pressure. Finally, the fatigue behaviors of the standard cured and the best low-temperature cured specimens were tested per MMM-A-132. For the three room-temperature-cure adhesives, single lap shear tests and fatigue tests were carried out to choose the best one for field repair. All the bonding surfaces of bare 2024-T3 aluminum specimens were treated with sulfuric acid/sodium dichromate/Carb-o-sil gel (GFPL)[7] before bonding. The gr/ep specimens were 12 plies of zero degree laminate of HY-E 1076E (by Fiberite) and surface sanded in water with 120 grit sandpaper.

In order to determine the improvement of the bond strength by the application of the adhesion prometer A-187 (by Union Carbide) and primer BR-127 (by American Cyanamid) for the room-temperature-cure adhesives, single-lap shear of aluminum-to-aluminum specimens were tested. The aluminum specimens were GFPL treated and brushed with A-187 or BR-127, then adhesives were applied and cured for three days at room temperature. The effect of A187 and BR-127 were determined from the single lap shear data.

3. ALUMINUM PANEL REPAIR TEST

The effectiveness of composite patching repair was certified by tension-tension fatigue test of alclad 2024-T3 panels of 2.54mm thickness. The 15 mm initial crack was produced from a 5 mm edge-cut with the configuration shown in Figure 1. The cracked panels were GFPL treated prior to patch bonding. Composite patches were seven-layer unidirectional laminate made from both HY-E 1076E gr/ep and 5521/4 b/ep (by AVCO). The curing conditions of gr/ep and b/ep were 177°C/2 hr and 121°C/1 hr, respectively. In order to reduce inter-laminar shear and peel stresses, the thickness of patches were internally stepped with

3mm per ply, i.e., the largest layer was on outside (see Figure 1). Before bonded to cracked panels, patches were sanded in water with 120 grit sandpaper. Finally, the patches were bonded to cracked panels with different adhesives similarly to the preparation of the single lap shear specimens.

The tension-tension fatigue of patched panels were tested on Instron Model 1333 with 138 MPa peak stress, 10 Hz frequency, constant amplitude, 0.01 Ratio, and sine wave cycling. Crack growth was monitored with 25mm crack gages automatically and eddy current instrument EM-6300 (by Sperry Automation) manually. The difference of crack growth measured between both measuring methods was smaller than 1mm. The accuracy of the crack length can be measured with EM-6300 is ±1mm.

4. REPAIR OF AIRCRAFT STRUCTURES

Three repairs of structural cracking on the AT-3 full scale fatigue test article have been performed.

4.1 The Fitting of Front Spar Root of Vertical Tail

There was a 15 mm crack on the fitting of front spar root of vertical tail after 11,250 simulated flight hours. The cracked area was sanded and GFPL treated, then bonded with a gr/ep patch by the room-temperature adhesive V201. The pressure needed for bonding was applied with "C" clamps. The patch was eight-layer unidirectional laminate with fibers perpendicular to the crack (see Figure 2).

4.2 Lower Bulkhead Attached to Speed Brake

There was a 19 mm crack on the lower bulkhead which was attached to speed brake after 11,852 simulated flight hours. Because of the complexity of the structure, there is no good traditional repair method can be applied However, the patch bonding repair can easily and effectively demonstrat its superiority in this case.

First, aluminum molds were made to match the geometry of the cracked structure. Secondly, two gr/ep patches of four-layer unidirectional laminates were cured on these molds. These patches were also internal stepped and bonded with fiber direction perpendicular to the crack. Thirdly, the cracked surfaces and the composite patches were GFPL treated and sanded in water, respectively. Finally, two patches were bonded to the crack with AV138/HV998 adhesive and "C" clamp pressurization for 24 hours curing (see Figure 3).

4.3 Firewall Web of the Aft Fuselage

There was a 20 mm crack on the firewall web of aft fuselage at 6022 simulated flight hours and was stop-drilled. But two new cracks were initiated from this stop-drilling hole and both grew to 10 mm long at 11,852 simulated flight hours. This result showed that the stress of this area was very high and the stop-drilling method did not work. Therefore, the composite patching repair was applied.

With the space limitation around the firewall, the room-temperature bonding repair was chosen instead of the high-temperature bonding methods. Since these three cracks grew in different directions, the patches covering them from both sides of the web were designed as $(0/\pm45/0)_s$ of gr/ep laminate and internally stepped with 3 mm per two plies. All the surface treatment, adhesive, and bonding processes were the same as the preceeding bulkhead repair except the pressure was applied by hand for 30 minutes (see Figure 4).

5. RESULTS AND DISCUSSIONS

5.1 Adhesive Selection

Figure 5 shows the degree of cure (DOC) of FM 73 adhesive at different temperatures for different periods of time. These curves depict that the lower limit of the curing temperature is 70°C for eight hours. In order to reduce the thermal residual stress of the components around the crack, the lower temperature is chosen but not lower than 70°C. Furthermore, the single lap shear strength at different curing conditions proves that the 70°C/8hr curing will provide good bond strength closing to the result of standard 121°C/1hr curing (see Figure 6). With the same adhesive FM 73, a higher curing temperature, namely 80°C, has been reported by baker[8]. The effects of adhesion promoter A-187 and primer BR-127 on room-temperature adhesives are presented in Table 1. The adhesion promoter and primer both have negative effects on AV138/HV998 and V201. But the bond strength of F241 is highly enhanced by A-187 and BR-127.

The single-lap shear strength of room-temperature-cure adhesives is shown in Figure 7 with the reference data of FM 73. The Al-Al bond strength is in the order V201>AV138/HV998>>F241, but the Al-gr/ep bond strength is AV138/HV998>V201>>F241. So, AV138/HV998 was chosen for composite patching repair.

Figures 8 and 9 show the fatigue behaviors of the Al-Al and Al-gr/ep FM 73 bonded specimens. In the consideration of the fatigue strength at one million cycles, both Al-Al and Al-gr/ep of 70°C/8hr/vacuum pressure bonded are very close to those of 121°C/1hr/vacuum pressure bonded, although the static strength of the former is lower.

The fatigue behaviors of AV138/HV998 and V201 adhesives with Al-Al bonding specimens are presented in Figure 10. The fatigue strength of AV138/HV998 at one million cycles is 6.9 MPa and higher than those of V201 (5.2 MPa) and FM 73 (5.9 MPa). Therefore, AV138/HV998 was selected as the best one among the three room-temperature-cure adhesives for repair work because of its high strength, stable results, and easy application.

5.2 Patching of Cracked Panels

Figure 11 shows the fatigue test results of cracked-panels bonding-repaired with different patch materials and procedures. For the 2.5 mm thick aluminum panels, the non-repaired one can only stand for 620 cycles. With a stop-drilling hole of 2.4 mm diameter, the life was prolonged to about fifteen times (9000 cycles). Furthermore, the composite-patching-repairs with room-temperature-cure adhesives provide additional life: the gr/ep patch/AV138 adhesive repair is 37,000 cycles, the b/ep patch/AV138 repair is 58,000 cycles and the gr/ep patch/V201 adhesive is 90,000 cycles. Comparing with non-repaired one, they provide 60, 95, and 145 times life, respectively.

In order to make comparison, a theoretical crack growth curve with 1.3 mm initial crack was derived from the finite element method. This theoretical curve provides a reference of fatigue behavior of the intact panel. The fatigue life of the different composite-patching-repairs are all above half of the theoretical value.

With the same epoxy adhesive AV138/HV998, b/ep patch repair has longer life than gr/ep patch repair. This can be attributed to the higher modulus of b/ep which is about 1.5 times of gr/ep. For the same gr/ep patch, V201 adhesive provides longer fatigue life than that of AV138/HV998.

In addition to the achievement of the extension of the life cycle, the crack growth rate after repair is very important. For the composite patching repaired panels, all the cracks grew at slow rate from the re-initiation to failure (see Figure 11). In actual repair conditions, the slow crack growth rate will provide enough opportunities for

periodical inspection to determine whether the patch still works or has to be replaced. At the same time, the eddy current instrument has been proved to be able to detect the cracks under composite patches. This is the major advantage of composite patching repair over the traditional metal patch under which crack growth can not be detected.

5.3 Structural Repairs

All the three repairs were inspected after four life time fatigue test (about 30,000 simulated flight hours) of the full scale article. The eddy current method were used to inspect the crack growth under the composite. The crack on the fitting of front spar root of vertical tail frew from 15 mm to 19 mm after 18,700 simulated flight hours (about 2.4 life time span).

After 18,000 simulated flight hours, the crack on the lower bulkhead attached to the speed brake grew from 19 mm to 20 mm. After peeling the patches, it was found that the bond-line thicknesses were not uniform. This may be caused by the uneven bonding pressure from "C" clamps during the repair. It should be emphasized that this structure is highly curved and short edged, and can not be repaired by any traditional methods. Furthermore, replacement of the structure will be very time-consuming and infeasible for the fatigue test schedule. But the composite patching repair only take three days and last for eighteen thousand simulated flight hours.

Therefore, the composite patching repairs are proved to be fast, durable, and economical.

After 18,000 simulated flight hours, the two cracks on the firewall web of aft fuselage grew from 10 mm to 16 mm and 42 mm, respectively. The large crack growth in this case can be explained as follows:

(1) This structure is curved and could not be tightly matched by flat patches.

(2) The space is too limited to apply vacuum-bagging pressure or "C" clamps, and the hand-pressure is not adequate for good bonding.

(3) The stress level in this area is too high.

The initial crack of 20 mm long was repaired by stop-drilling hole, but grew to two new cracks of 10 mm long only after 5,800 simulated flight hours. Then the composite patching repair was applied and lasted about 18,000 simulated hours (nearly 2.5 life time). These results can clearly demonstrate the merit of the composite patching repair methods on real structure.

6. CONCLUSIONS

The results of this program indicate the following conclusions:

(1) Both of adhesion promoter A-187 and primer BR-127 could enhance the bond strength of F241 acrylic adhesive only.

(2) The high-temperature-cure film adhesive FM 73 could be applied at 70°C/8hr/vacuum pressure curing with similar bond strength at 121°C/1hr/vacuum pressure curing.

(3) AV138/HV998 has been selected as the best one from the three room-temperature-cure adhesives for composite patching repairs. It provided almost the same fatigue strength as FM 73 at one million cycles.

(4) Composite-patching repair could extend the life 60 to 140 times of the cracked panels with 15 mm initial cracks. The repair efficiency of b/ep patch is better than that of gr/ep patch.

(5) The crack growth of the composite patching repair can be easily inspected by the use of the eddy current technique. The slow crack growth rate after repair will provide enough opportunities for periodical detections and enhance the safety of repairs.

(6) The system of gr/ep patch, GFPL surface treatment, and AV138/ HV998 adhesive provided good repair efficiency on three structures of AT-3 full scale fatigue test. They apparently demonstrated how durable and economical the composite patching repair technology was. At the same time, all the three repairs could hardly be done by traditional repair methods.

In summary, the composite patching repair will be adequate for repair of typical lightly loaded aircraft structures. High-temperature-cure film adhesives should be first considered to apply with minimum curing temperature for their high strength and good durability. But if the conditions are limited, room-temperature-cure adhesives would be suitable for composite patching repairs.

7. BIOGRAPHY

Dr. Ching-Long Ong is Chief of Aero Material Department at Aeronautical Research Laboratory, AIDC. He is in charge of material and process for the IDF aircraft development program. He is specialized in non-metallic materials applications and developments, especially in the fields of composites and adhesive bonding technology. Dr. Ong received his B.S. in Chemical Engineering from Chung Cheng Institute of Technology, Taiwan in 1970, and M.S. in Chemical Engineering from university of Washington in 1975. During the period from June 1978 to June 1983, he received M.S. in computer science and Ph.D. in the field of polymer material application and computer simulation from University of Washington, Seattle, Wash.

Mr. Shen is an Assistant Research Engineer at Chung Shan Institute of Science and Technology. He is specialized in surface treatment, adhesive bonding of aircrafts, and has been engaged in aircraft repair technology for several years. He has the B.S. degree in chemistry from Tamkang University and the M.S. degree in polymer science from Tsing Hua University, Taiwan, R.O.C.

8. REFERENCES

1. Sandow, F.A., and Cannon, R.K., "Composite Repair of Cracked Aluminum Aircraft Structure," AFWAL-TR-87-3072, Air Force Wright Aeronautical Laboratories, Sept. 1987.

2. Stone, R.H., "Field-Level Repair Materials and Processes," Lockheed-California Co., Burbank, California, Proceedings of 28th National SAMPE Symposium, Apri. 1983, pp. 210-222.

3. Dastin, Sam, Machine Design 58, 86 (1986).

4. Baker, A.A., Composite Structures 2, 153 (1984).

5. Shen, S., Ko, T.C., Chu, R.C., Ong, C.L., "Reinforcement of Aircraft Structures with Advanced Composite Materials," ARL-76C-013, Aeronautic Research Laboratory, Taichung, Taiwan, R.O.C., Oct. 1987.

6. Shu, W.Y., and Ong, C.L., "The Evaluation of Surface Treatment for Bond Durability," Aero Industry Development Center, Taichung, Taiwan, R.O.C., Proceedings of the 18th International SAMPE Technical Conference, Oct. 1986, pp. 888-895.

7. Shu, W.Y.,Shen, S., and Ong, C.L., "The Evaluation of Non-tank Treatments for Aluminum Bonding," Journal of Adhesion Science and Technology, in press.

8. Baker, A.A., Composites 18, 293 (1987).

9. Zalucha, D.J., "Aircraft Field Repair," Lord Corp., Erie, Pennsylvania, Proceedings of 30th National SAMPE Symposium, March 1985, pp. 1419-1423.

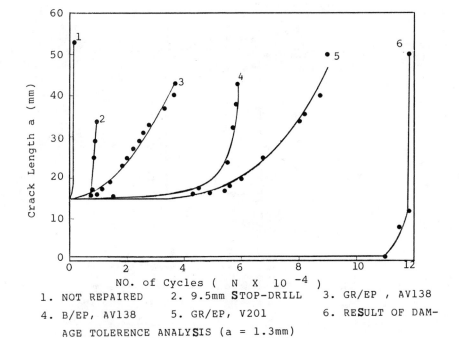

1. NOT REPAIRED   2. 9.5mm STOP-DRILL   3. GR/EP , AV138
4. B/EP, AV138   5. GR/EP, V201   6. RESULT OF DAM-
AGE TOLERENCE ANALYSIS (a = 1.3mm)

Figure 11. Fatigue Test of Repair Panels

Single lap shear ; MPa / Surface Improvement \ Adhesives	AV138/HV998	V 201	F 241
None	14.7	20.4	10.2
A-187	13.6	16.7	13.9
BR127	13.4	10.2	17.3

Table 1: The Compatibility of Adhesion Promoter A-187
         and Primer BR-127 for Room-temperature-cure
         Adhesives.

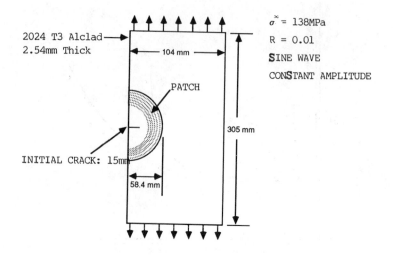

$\sigma^{\infty} = 138\text{MPa}$

R = 0.01

SINE WAVE

CONSTANT AMPLITUDE

2024 T3 Alclad
2.54mm Thick

104 mm

PATCH

305 mm

INITIAL CRACK: 15mm

58.4 mm

Figure 1: The Configuration of Repair Test Panel.

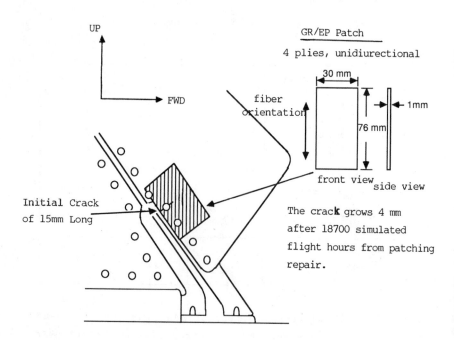

UP

FWD

fiber orientation

GR/EP Patch

4 plies, unidiurectional

30 mm

76 mm

1mm

front view   side view

Initial Crack
of 15mm Long

The crack grows 4 mm
after 18700 simulated
flight hours from patching
repair.

Figure 2: Repair of the Fitting of Front Spar Root
of Vertical Tail.

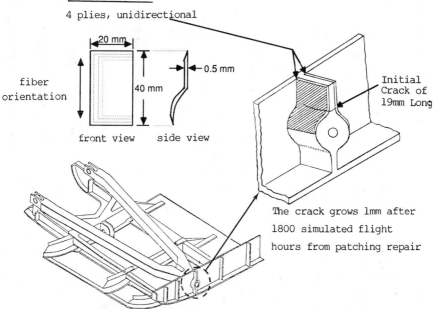

GR/EP Patch

4 plies, unidirectional

20 mm

0.5 mm

fiber orientation

40 mm

front view   side view

Initial Crack of 19mm Long

The crack grows 1mm after 1800 simulated flight hours from patching repair

Figure 3. Repair of the Lower Bulkhead Attached to Speed Brake.

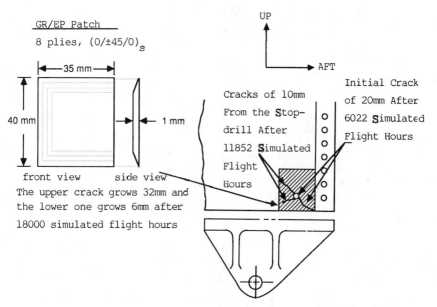

GR/EP Patch

8 plies, $(0/\pm45/0)_s$

35 mm

40 mm

1 mm

front view   side view

The upper crack grows 32mm and the lower one grows 6mm after 18000 simulated flight hours

UP

AFT

Cracks of 10mm From the Stop-drill After 11852 Simulated Flight Hours

Initial Crack of 20mm After 6022 Simulated Flight Hours

Figure 4. Repair of the Firewall Web of Aft Fuselage.

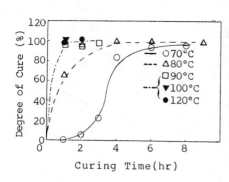

Figure 5. Degree of Cure of FM 73 Film Adhesive in Different Curing Condition by DSC

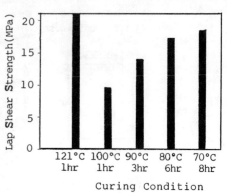

Figure 6. Single Lap Shear Strength of FM 73 Film Adhesive.

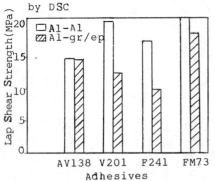

Figure 7: Evaluation of Room-Tempaerature-cure Adhesive. (With FM 73 for Reference)

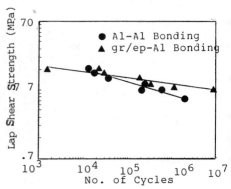

Figure 8: S-N Curves of FM 73 Adhesive Cured at 121°C /1hr/Vacuum Pressure.

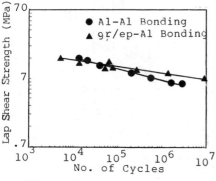

Figure 9: S-N Curves of FM 73 Adhesive Cured at 70°C/ 8hr/Vacuum Pressure

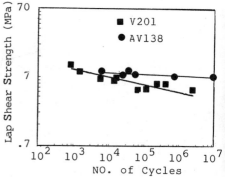

Figure 10: S-N Curves of Room-Temperature-cure Adhesives.

JANNAF INTERIM MECHANICAL TEST STANDARDS FOR
FILAMENT WOUND COMPOSITES

MAJ Richard Price and Terry Vandiver
Composite Structures and Materials, Structures Directorate
U.S. Army Missile Command, Redstone Arsenal, AL 35898

Abstract

The history and progress to date of interim JANNAF test standards to determine mechanical properties of filament wound composite structures are presented. An industry-wide survey of test methods in use was conducted. Standardization of test methods for uniaxial loading of 90° filament wound cylinders is being pursued. Test specifications, fixture geometry and specimen fabrication information are presented for three Interim JANNAF Standard Test Methods; "Transverse Tensile Properties of Unidirectional Fiber/Resin Composite Cylindrical Sections" (90° Filament Wound), "Transverse Compressive Properties of Unidirectional Fiber/Resin Composite Cylindrical Sections" (90° Filament Wound), and "Torsion Properties of Unidirectional Fiber/Resin Composite Cylindrical Sections" (In-Plane Shear, 90° Filament Wound). Milestones are outlined for the conduct of validation Round Robin Testing to determine precision, repeatability and reproducability of these tests.

1. INTRODUCTION

A need exists for industry wide standards for determining material properties of filament wound composite motor cases, launchers and other cylindrical sections. At present, the majority of standard test specifications are for flat laminate properties. The mechanical behavior of filament wound structures is typically different from the behavior of flat laminate structures. Differences result from the type of cure, resin void content, microcracking, and free edge construction. However, filament wound structures require the same mechanical property data for design and analysis as general laminated structures. The majority of filament wound structures of interest to the Joint Army Navy NASA Air Force (JANNAF) Interagency Propulsion Committee are used in the rocket motor case community and most test specimens are in the form of cylinders or bottles which approximate the geometry of the structures to be designed and analyzed. There are numerous in-house test methods to determine the desired properties of cylindrical sections, but none have been standardized.

2. OBJECTIVE

The objective of the Round Robin Test Working Group of the JANNAF Composite Motor Case Subcommittee (CMCS) is to establish standard test specifications for determining mechanical proper-

ties of filament wound structures which can be used industry-wide for design and analysis of composite structures.

3. BACKGROUND

The CMCS of the JANNAF Interagency Propulsion Committee was formed in November, 1983. It originally consisted of four working panels; Test and Inspection, Design and Analysis, Processing and Materials. In October, 1987, the Materials and Processing Panels were combined to form the Processing and Fabrication Panel. Concurrently, another panel, Damage, was formed. The charter of the CMCS is to consolidate and assist dessimination of the pool of interagency information on the design, analysis, testing and fabrication of composite rocket motor cases and gun tubes. The decision to pursue standard test methods was made at that time. This decision was based on the fact that there were no industry-wide standards for determining mechanical properties of filament wound composite structures. Key events in the evolution of the Round Robin Test effort supporting JANNAF interim standard test methods are outlined in Figure 1.

Most major filament winding contractors had in-house methods for evaluating material properties of cylinders but there was no standardization of these test methods which allowed comparison of results between agencies, nor a method to gauge real improvement of mechanical properties due to changes in materials or processing methods. A working group under the Composite Motor Case Subcommittee was established to pursue standardization of test methods which could be used industry-wide for filament wound composite structures. For this purpose an industry-wide survey was conducted to determine the tests being used by industry and government agencies. In December, 1985, chairmen were selected for each of the types of test methods under investigation; tension, compression, and shear. At the same time, results of the survey were presented and a CMCS panel of experts from industry was chosen to recommend test methods which JANNAF would attempt to standardize. In February, 1986, 15 invited papers were presented at a JANNAF sponsored CMCS workshop in Lancaster, California. The papers identified six tensile, three compression and six shear test methods. In April, 1986, the CMCS panel of experts evaluated the presentations and the survey data, and recommended six test method types (seven test methods) to determine the desired properties. In December, 1987, an all-government decision meeting was held to solidify funding and interagency support for the standardization effort. It was decided to pursue the standardization of test methods to determine uni-axial material properties through conduct of a Round Robin Test conducted along the guidelines of MIL-Handbook 17 (6) and ASTM (1). Funding was allocated for contractor support in fabrication, a portion of the testing effort, and the selection of a secretariat for the Round Robin Test (RRT) coordination.

In May, 1988, the Round Robin Test Kickoff Meeting was held in conjunction with the JANNAF CMCS Presidio, California, meeting (5). The RRT Working Group decided at that time to pursue the four tests which used 90° filament wound tube specimens. A meeting was set up for December, 1988, at which time the Design and Analysis panel would present final recommendations on specimen geometry and RRT fixture design, the Test and Inspection Panel would present final recommendations for RRT specifications, and the Processing panel would present a final recommendation for a RRT processing specification and processing mandrel design. A series of panel meetings were conducted prior to the December meeting.

In September, 1988, the contract for secretariat of the Round Robin Test effort was awarded to Materials Science Corporation (MSC), Spring House, PA. This was beneficial since MSC is also the secretariat for MIL-Handbook 17.

In December, 1988, the recommendations were presented and final concensus recommendations were approved for three of the four tests; 90° Tension, 90° Compression and In-Plane Shear. Discussion of the relative merits of the NOL Ring and the pressurized tube test required

scheduling a decision meeting to be held in May, 1989, to determine which test JANNAF would pursue as an interim standard for 0° Tension.

4. SURVEY

To determine the state of testing, a survey of industry was conducted to determine what in-house tests were being used, the purpose of those tests, and the specific properties determined by those tests. Approximately 35 agencies participated in this survey including representatives of major filament winding contractors, interested government facilities, and research organizations. Survey results are summarized in Figure 2. From this survey, it was determined that approximately 17 different tensile tests, 17 compressive tests and 16 shear tests were being used in various forms for design and analysis, screening, quality control, aging, damage tolerance, material development, processing effects, environmental effects, statistical data base, and other uses.

5. TEST SELECTION

The next step was to determine the mix of tests most used in the industry which would provide the desired properties for the design and analysis of filament wound structures. The desired material properties are: E_{11} and E_{22} in tension and compression, μ_{12} and μ_{21} in tension and compression, G_{12} for in-plane shear, and G_{23} for transverse shear. A call for papers was made for the JANNAF Workshop on Test Methods for the Mechanical Characterization of Filament Wound Composites in February, 1986, and input was requested on which test methods could be standardized and give the material properties desired. The results were published as CPIA Publication 448 (Reference 3). It was decided to pursue a logical progression of selecting uniaxial loading conditions for the first test methods investigated. If this effort was successful, then biaxial and triaxial loading conditions could be investigated.

From this input a set of six test types were chosen which would produce the desired material properties (Figure 3). The tests for transverse shear and 0° compression utilize flat laminate specimens and are in the process of being standardized by ASTM, so these tests were not pursued by the JANNAF CMCS RRT Workgroup. From this list it can be seen that standard test methods needed to be developed for 0° and 90° Tension, 90° Compression and In-Plane Shear for composite thin walled cylinders. Three of the test types had only one specimen candidate used by industry, therefore, interim JANNAF standard test specifications were written for the 90° Tension, 90° Compression, and In-Plane Shear tests. The decision to choose either an NOL ring or pressurized 90° wound cylinder test for determining 0° Tensile properties will be made at a workshop meeting to be held coincident with the May JANNAF Propulsion Meeting. Both test methods have distinct advantages and disadvantages which make evaluation of pure 0° tensile properties difficult.

6. TEST SPECIMENS

The three test methods for 90° Tension, 90° Compression and In-Plane Shear are now Interim JANNAF Test

Methods and will be published in a CPIA Publication. For the conduct of the Round Robin Test, a particular specimen geometry, layup, material selection and fabrication process has been determined. The specimen geometry is shown in Figure 4. The same specimen was selected for all three of the test methods for ease of test fixture and specimen fabrication as well as standardization. The test fixture for the tension and compression test is the same, as can be seen in Figure 5. An attachment to the fixture in Figure 5 provides torsional loading for the in-plane shear test as shown in Figure 6.

Specimens will be manufactured by a contractor selected through competitive bidding by Materials Science Corporation, secretariat for both the Round Robin Test effort and secretariat for MIL Handbook 17. Fabrication and parting mandrels were designed to be sent to the fabrication contractor. Mandrels and test fixtures are to be manufactured by government agencies.

7. ROUND ROBIN TESTING

Once the specimens and test fixtures are fabricated the Round Robin Test can be conducted. The present plan calls for six testing agencies, both government and contractor, to test specimens in accordance with all three interim JANNAF standard test specifications. Results can then be pooled and evaluated for bias due to test facility, specimen lot, repeatability of test and reproducibility from one test facility to another. Once the round robin test results are evaluated, it can be determined whether the interim test standards have the precision required for pursuing standardization of these tests through ASTM and for inclusion in MIL-Handbook 17. The milestones for conduct of the Round Robin Test and analysis of data are shown in Figure 7. Throughout the RRT effort, coordination has been maintained with MIL Handbook 17, ASTM Committee D30 on High Modulus Fibers and their Composites, the DOD Standardization Program for Composites Technology (CMPS) and the Intersociety Forum Communications and Coordination Committee (5).

8. CONCLUSIONS

Several items of interest have been learned throughout this process of attempting to standardize tests. In summary, the process is time-consuming, expensive, and requires an organization dedicated to devoting the time, assets, and leverage to keep the standardization process moving.

It is believed that the effort toward standardization of these tests will be beneficial to both government agencies and contractors. It has been rewarding to see the amount of intra-contractor sharing of information and the spirit of cooperation among those involved in this process. Any attempt to move toward tests which provide data on the actual shapes being used in composite case design will be beneficial in providing real design properties rather than having to extrapolate properties from flat laminate data.

9. REFERENCES

1. The American Society for Testing and Materials, ASTM Standards and Literature References for Composite Materials, 1st Ed., Philadelphia, PA, 1987.

2. Chemical Propulsion Information Agency Publication 418, 1984 JANNAF CMCS/ S&MBS Joint Subcommittee Meeting, Pasadena, California, Johns Hopkins University, Applied Physics Laboratory, Laurel, MD, 1984.

3. Chemical Propulsion Information Agency Publication 448, Test Methods for the Mechanical Characterization of Filament Wound Composites, Lancaster, California, Johns Hopkins University, Applied Physics Lab, Laurel, MD, 1986.

4. Chemical Propulsion Information Agency Publication 489, 1988 JANNAF Composite Motor Case Subcommittee Meeting, Pasadena, California, Johns Hopkins University, Applied Physics Lab, Laurel, MD, 1988.

5. MIL-HDBK-17, Proceedings of the Polymer Matrix Composites Coordination Group, 18th Meeting, Newport, RI, Coordinated by US Army Material Technology Lab, Watertown, MA, Oct 1988.

6. MIL-HDBK-17B, Military Handbook, Polymer Matrix Composites, Volume 1: Guidelines, Naval Publications and Forms Center, Philadelphia, PA, Coordinated by US Army Material Technology Lab, Watertown, MA, 1988.

<u>Figure 1. Key Events in the Round Robin Test Evolution</u>

<u>Date</u>   <u>Action</u>

Nov 83   JANNAF Interagency Propulsion Committee formed
           the Composite Motor Case Subcommittee (CMCS) with
           4 panels: Test & Inspection, Processing, Design &
           Analysis, and Materials.

Apr 84   First T&I Panel meeting. Survey sent out to 35
           contractor and government agencies.

Nov 84   JANNAF CMCS/S&MBS Joint Meeting-survey results
           reviewed and more detailed information requested
           from respondents (2).

Dec 85   Screening survey evaluated, panel of experts
           selected, and test method chairmen selected.

Feb 86   Technical Papers presented on possible test
           methods, resulting in CPIA Publication 448 (3).

Apr 86   Six test methods selected to determine uniaxial
           properties.

Dec 87   All Government Meeting to solidify funding and
           agency support for Round Robin Test (RRT) Effort.

May 88   RRT Kickoff and decision to concentrate on four
           tests -- 0° and 90° Tension, 90° Compression and
           In-Plane Shear (4).

Sep 88   Secretariat Selected and Contract Awarded for
           RRT --- Materials Science Corporation.

Dec 88   RRT Workshop. Final recommendations made and
           accepted for Test Specifications, Specimen
           Geometry, Test Fixtures, Processing Fixtures, and
           Processing Specifications for 90° Tension, 90°
           Compression and In-Plane Shear Test Methods.
           Decision on NOL versus Pressurized Tube type test
           methods for 0° Tension will be made in May 1989.

Figure 2. Summary of Survey Results.

Test Specimen Type	Test Data	Properties

0° Tension Tests

Test Specimen Type	Test Data	Properties
Flat Laminate (0° Layup)	σ_{11}, ϵ_{11}	E_{11}, μ_{12}
Elongated Ring	σ_{11}, ϵ_{11}	E_{11}, μ_{12}
Pressurized NOL Ring	σ_{11}, ϵ_{11}	E_{11}, μ_{12}
Pressurized Tube (90° Wound)	σ_{11}, ϵ_{11}	E_{11}, μ_{12}

90° Tension Tests

Test Specimen Type	Test Data	Properties
Flat Laminate (90° Layup)	σ_{22}, ϵ_{22}	E_{22}, μ_{21}
Tube (90° Wound)	σ_{22}, ϵ_{22}	E_{22}, μ_{21}

0° Compression

Test Specimen Type	Test Data	Properties
External Pressurized Tube	σ_{11}, ϵ_{11}	E_{11}, μ_{12}
Flat Laminate 0°	σ_{11}, ϵ_{11}	E_{11}, μ_{12}

90° Compression

Test Specimen Type	Test Data	Properties
Flat Laminate 90°	σ_{22}, ϵ_{22}	E_{22}, μ_{21}
Tube (90° Wound)	σ_{22}, ϵ_{22}	E_{22}, μ_{21}

In-Plane Shear Tests

Test Specimen Type	Test Data	Properties
±45° Layup Tension Laminate	τ_{12}, Γ_{12}	G_{12}
±45° Helical Filament Wound Tube	τ_{12}, Γ_{12}	G_{12}
90° Filament Wound Thin Tube	τ_{12}, Γ_{12}	G_{12}
Rod (Torsion)	---	G_{12}
Iosipescu	τ_{12}, Γ_{12}	G_{12}
Asymetric 4-Point Bend	τ_{12}, Γ_{12}	G_{12}
4-Point Ring Twist	---	G_{12}

Transverse Shear

Test Specimen Type	Test Data	Properties
Iosipescu	τ_{23}, Γ_{23}	G_{23}
Asymetric 4-Point Bend	τ_{23}, Γ_{23}	G_{23}
Torsion Rod	---	G_{23}
±45° Compression	τ_{23}, Γ_{23}	G_{23}

Note: Test Methods shown provide the properties desired for JANNAF uniaxial loading conditions. Other tests were screened out due to biaxial or triaxial loading states.

Figure 3.   JANNAF Test Methods Selected by RRT Work Group

Test Type	Specimen Type	Test Data	Properties
0° Tension	NOL Ring		
	ASTM D 2291 (1)		
	Pressurized Tube	σ_{11}, ϵ_{11}	E_{11}, μ_{12}
90° Tension	Tube	σ_{22}, ϵ_{22}	E_{22}, μ_{21}
0° Compression	Flat Laminate		
	ASTM D 3410 (1)	σ_{11}, ϵ_{11}	E_{11}, μ_{12}
90° Compression	Tube	σ_{22}, ϵ_{22}	E_{22}, μ_{21}
In-Plane Shear	Torsion Tube	τ_{12}, Γ_{12}	G_{12}
Transverse Shear	Flat Laminate		
	Iosipescu	τ_{23}, Γ_{23}	G_{23}

Note: All tubes are 90° filament wound cylinders.
Orientation of stresses is shown below in accordance with
MIL-HDBK-17B, Polymeric Matrix Composites, Table 6.6.9.

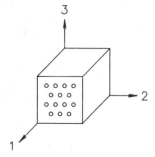

A) FLAT LAMINATE PROPERTIES ORIENTATION

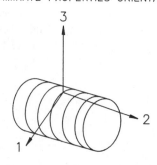

B) CYLINDRICAL PROPERTIES ORIENTATION

Figure 4. ROUND ROBIN TEST SPECIMEN

MATERIAL:

IM7,T40 OR EQUIVALENT FIBER
FIBER VOLUME = 60±2%
WET FILAMENT WINDING PROCESS
VOID CONTENT < 5%
12 PLIES OR 6 LAYERS
BAND ADVANCE = 0.10"
FIBER TENSION = 4±0.5 #/TOW
FIBER WIND ANGLE = 90°

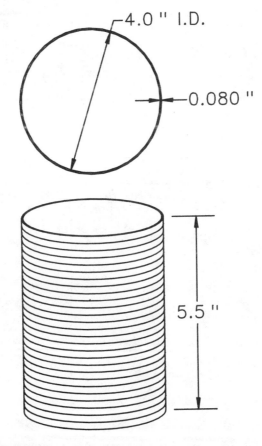

Figure 5. ROUND ROBIN TEST FIXTURE FOR TENSION AND COMPRESSION TESTS

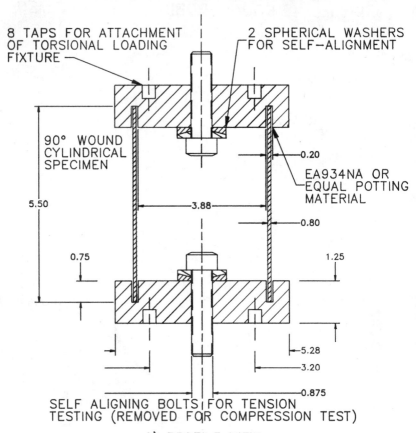

8 TAPS FOR ATTACHMENT OF TORSIONAL LOADING FIXTURE

2 SPHERICAL WASHERS FOR SELF-ALIGNMENT

90° WOUND CYLINDRICAL SPECIMEN

EA934NA OR EQUAL POTTING MATERIAL

0.20

0.80

5.50

3.88

0.75

1.25

5.28

3.20

0.875

SELF ALIGNING BOLTS FOR TENSION TESTING (REMOVED FOR COMPRESSION TEST)

A) PROFILE VIEW

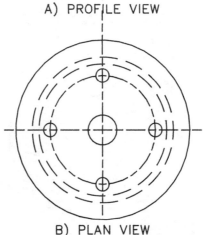

B) PLAN VIEW

1090

Figure 6. TORSION (IN-PLANE SHEAR) TEST FIXTURE ATTACHMENT

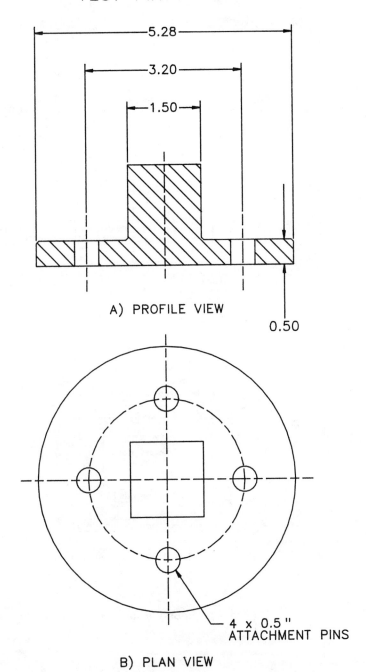

A) PROFILE VIEW

B) PLAN VIEW

4 x 0.5" ATTACHMENT PINS

Phase I

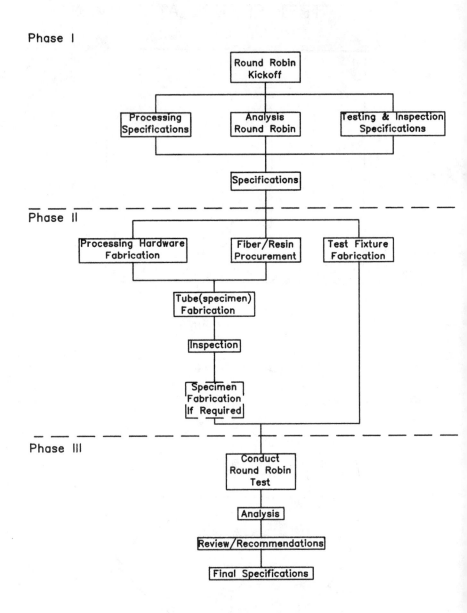

Phase II

Phase III

Figure 7.   Round Robin Test Milestones

10. BIOGRAPHIES

MAJ Richard Price is a career regular army officer in the Corps of Engineers. He graduated with a BSCE from the Citadel in 1971, received his MS in Structures from the University of Texas, El Paso, in 1977, and his PhD in CE from Clemson University in 1988. He is a registered professional engineer and has served in numerous command and staff assignments in the US and overseas. He is presently serving as the Research and Development Coordinator, Structures Directorate, US Army Missile Command, Redstone Arsenal, AL.

Mr. Terry Vandiver is currently Task Chairman of the JANNAF CMCS Round Robin Test Working Group and is Chairman of the Test and Inspection Panel of JANNAF CMCS. He has over 15 years of experience in design, analysis and testing of composite rocket motor cases with the US Army Missile Command, Redstone Arsenal. He received his BA in 1972 and his BSME degrees from the University of Alabama, Huntsville, in 1978 and is certified as an EIT in Alabama. He has been an integral part of the CMCS since its inception in 1983.

EVIDENCE OF LOAD SHARING IN FILAMENT WOUND PRESSURE VESSELS USING KEVLAR®-49 OR T-40 CARBON FIBER EPOXY PREPREG

Larry K. Reynolds, M. Reed Haddock and Darrel G. Turner
Strategic Operations, Morton Thiokol Inc.
P. O. Box 689
Brigham City, Utah 84302-0689

Abstract

This paper reports the results of tests conducted at Morton Thiokol, Inc. on the fiber strength averaging effect using Kevlar®-49 or T-40 carbon fiber in filament wound pressure vessels. The data is presented as evidence of load sharing between high and low strength material and the premise that the fiber under load in a filament-wound pressure vessel will perform at some average strength under load.

The testing consisted of using spools of Kevlar®-49 or carbon T-40 fiber epoxy resin prepreg with high and low strength to fabricate 5.75-inch and 18-inch diameter pressure vessels. The mean strength from the individual high and low strength spools was compared to the delivered fiber strength from the pressure vessels fabricated using both the high and low strength material together. The comparison showed that the strength predicted from the mean of the individual spools equaled the delivered fiber strength and supports the concept that the load sharing mechanism is in operation affecting the pressure vessel performance.

1.0 INTRODUCTION

A question was raised whether a pressure vessel with interspersed spools of fiber would fail at the ultimate strength of the weakest spool (weak link) or if some load sharing mechanism exists which causes the vessel to perform at the average strength of all the spools used.

The objective of this paper is to present test results as evidence that load sharing between individual spool rovings is the determining mechanism in pressure vessel burst strength performance.

2.0 EXPERIMENTAL DESIGN

All of the testing for this evaluation was conducted with 5.75-inch and 18-inch diameter filament wound pressure vessels. The 5.75-inch diameter pressure vessel is commonly used in the aerospace industry to determine fiber/resin performance. A typical bottle is made by winding polar and hoop plies as shown in Fig. 1. The design of the pressure vessel is specific for each material system used. A summary of the design parameters is shown in Table I.

The common elements in all of the bottles were the mandrels, winding equipment, the winding personnel and the method of hydroburst. The 5.75-inch diameter mandrels were fabricated according to ASTM 2385 as a sand type, covered with a rubber bladder.

The materials used in the tests were Kevlar®-49 impregnated with an anhydride cured epoxy resin, a release coated Kevlar®-49 impregnated with epoxy resin and T-40 carbon fiber impregnated with epoxy resin. The release coated Kevlar®-49 consisted of fiber coated with a release agent before impregnation which effectively releases the fiber from the resin matrix in the cured composite (Ref. 1)

All of the bottles failed in a mid-cylinder hoop mode as designed. Using the netting equation a hoop fiber stress at burst was calculated for each test bottle. For a bottle wound entirely from a single spool, the hoop fiber stress was used as the

TABLE I

Material System	Kevlar®–49/ Epoxy	Release Coated Kevlar®–49/Epoxy	T–40 Epoxy
Layup Design (where X = polar layer O = hoop ply)	XOOO	XOO	XOOXOO
Polar Wind Density (tow/inch/ply)	9.47	9.47	10.00
Hoop Wind Density (tow/inch/ply)	10.05	10.05	10.80

Filament-Wound Pressure Vessel

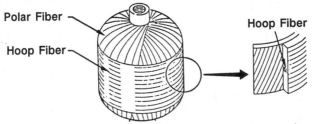

Figure 1. Typical 5.75–inch diameter pressure vessel test specimen

ultimate fiber strength of that spool. The 18–inch diameter bottles were filament wound using a multiple tow band on a sand mandrel. The burst mode was also a mid–cylinder hoop failure and the netting equation was used to determine the mean delivered fiber stress from the burst pressure.

3.0 DISCUSSION

Since each material system involved a different pressure vessel design, a separate test plan was followed for each. For the two types of Kevlar®–49 prepreg, a matrix of 5.75–inch bottles was tested and evaluated. The T–40 carbon fiber prepreg was evaluated using 5.75–inch bottles and 18–inch diameter pressure vessels. Each study is presented below.

3.1 Release Coated Kevlar®–49 Prepreg

The standard 5.75–inch diameter bottle design for the release coated Kevlar®–49 prepreg material was one polar layer covered with two hoop plies. Winding the high and low strength spools in all of the possible hoop ply positions defines a total of four winding configurations. Two of the configurations consisted of winding either the strong or weak spool in both the inner and outer hoop ply positions. The two other winding configurations consisted of winding the inner hoop ply with the strong spool and the outer hoop ply with the weak spool, then alternating the positions so that the strong spool was in the outer

hoop ply and the weak spool in the inner.

The results of the 5.75–inch diameter bottle testing for the release coated Kevlar®–49 prepreg material is shown in Table II. The mean of the high strength spool (461 ksi) and the low strength spool (404 ksi) was calculated to be 432.5 ksi. this value was compared to the combined average strength of 431.5 ksi from the two winding configurations using both high and low strength spools. The results show the average strength equals the predicted mean strength. All of the individual bottles in this matrix were burst at a strength greater than the weakest spool strength. This observation supports the premise that the weaker roving can share its load with the stronger roving to allow the delivered strength in the pressure vessel to exceed the ultimate strength of the weak spool.

Evaluating each of the winding configurations separately it was noted that the position of the weak spool in the design had an effect on the delivered fiber stress at burst. For the bottles with the strong spool wound on the inner hoop ply, the combined average strength was 421 ksi. By placing the strong material in the outer hoop ply the strength increased to 442 ksi. It is suggested that the outer hoop ply influences the failure in these two hoop ply bottles because it has no load sharing on it's outside surface. Therefore, the spool used on the outside ply (low or high) tends to bias the results in the thin bottle design.

Table II

Results of the 5.75-inch Diameter Pressure Vessel Testing
Using Release Coated Kevlar®-49 Prepreg

| Hoop Winding Configuration | | Actual Bottle Hoop | Avg (%CV) | Combined |
Inner	Outer	Strength (ksi)	ksi	Avg ksi
High	High	458,463	461	
Low	Low	405,405,403,404,403	404 (0.2)	432.5
High	High	423,418,421	421 (0.6)	
Low	Low	436,447,443	442 (1.3)	431.5

3.2 Kevlar®-49 Prepreg

The standard 5.75-inch diameter bottle design for the Kevlar®-49 prepreg material system was one polar layer followed by three hoop plies. Without the release coating on the Kevlar® fiber, the delivered fiber strength in a 5.75-inch pressure vessel is significantly lower. Winding the strong and weak spools in all of the possible positions in the three hoop plies makes a total of eight different winding configurations. These winding configurations are made by alternating the strong and weak spools between the first hoop ply, the middle hoop ply and the outer hoop ply. The combined average of all of these configurations represents a pressure vessel which was wound with multiple rovings interspersed throughout the bottle.

The test results for the Kevlar®-49 winding configurations is shown in Table III. The combined average of all of the bottles with the high and low strength spools in the different winding configurations was 325.2 ksi. This combined average strength compares to the individual spool average strength of 329.5 ksi (determined from the high strength spool of 350 ksi and the low strength spool of 309 ksi). These results were considered equal (within the variability of the test) and confirmed the results presented in the release coated Kevlar®-49 matrix.

As seen with the release coated Kevlar®-49 prepreg testing, the position of the weak spool on the outside ply in the winding configuration affected the 5.75-inch bottle performance. Also note that the 5.75-inch bottles with two hoop plies wound from the strong spool tested at a higher strength than those wound with two hoop plies from the weak spool. Using the rule of mixtures, the predicted strength for the bottles with two hoop plies wound from the weak spool would be

0.667(309 ksi) + 0.333(350 ksi) = 322.6 ksi.

The average strength of all of the bottles wound with two hoop plies from the weak spools was 322 ksi.

The same comparison can be made with the 5.75-inch bottles wound with two hoop plies from the strong spool. The average of all bottles in this group is 328 ksi. The predicted strength using the rule of mixtures is 336.6 ksi. It is suggested that the cause for the apparent bias between the predicted value and the observed value is a low test value which pulls the average down. From the bottles tested with the hoop winding configuration of high-low-high, one of the three tests burst with a fiber stress of 309 ksi. While no cause for the low burst could be deter-

Table III

Results of the 5.75-inch Diameter Pressure Vessel Testing Using Kevlar®-49 Prepreg

| Hoop Winding Configuration | | | Actual Bottle Hoop | Ave | (%CV) | Combined |
Inner	Middle	Outer	Strength (ksi)	ksi		Avg ksi
high	high	high	357,335,357	350	(3.6)	
low	low	low	306,311,309	309	(0.8)	329.5
low	high	high	340,341,324	335	(2.8)	
high	low	high	309*,334,330	324	(4.1)	
high	high	low	330,317,330	326	(2.3)	
low	low	high	318,327,339	328	(3.2)	325.2
low	high	low	324,326,312	321	(2.4)	
high	low	low	310,324,316	317	(2.2)	

*Suspect Value

mined from examination of the post tested bottle, the value does not appear to be consistent with the trends shown in all of the other testing. Eliminating this value from the population, the combined average for the bottles wound with two strong hoop plies is 331.0 ksi. This average compares better with the predicted value from the rule of mixtures.

3.3 Carbon T-40 Prepreg

In the characterization of carbon fiber T-40 epoxy prepreg both 5.75-inch and 18-inch diameter pressure vessels were hydroburst tested. The 18-inch diameter pressure vessel was wound with a four tow band which disperses the tows from four spools equally throughout the entire bottle. It was hypothesized that if the individual tows shared the load in the pressure vessel, the burst could be predicted by the average strengths of the individual spools used to wind the 18-inch bottle.

The strengths of individual spools were determined in 5.75-inch diameter bottle tests. The average of the individual spools comprising the18-inch diameter bottle and the low strength spool value were then compared to the delivered fiber stress from the 18-inch bottle (see Table IV). The plots of the predicted fiber stress, the 18-inch bottle delivered fiber stress,and the low performing spool used in the 18-inch bottle, are shown in Fig. 2. By visual examination of the plot it is obvious that the 18-inch bottle delivered fiber stress, more closely follows the average of the individual spools than the low strength spool used in the 18-inch bottle fabrication. The average difference (Δ) between the average of the individual spools and the delivered fiber stress of the 18-inch bottle is 14.6 ksi SD = 7.6. In contrast, the average difference between the 18-inch bottle delivered fiber stress and the low strength spool used in the 18-inch bottle is 36.1 ksi SD = 17.5.

The fact that the delivered fiber strength can be more accurately predicted by the average of the individual spools suggests that a load sharing mechanism is in operation.

Table IV

Lot Acceptance Data T-40 Prepreg 5.75-inch and 18-inch Diameter Bottles

MTI Lot No.	Number of Spools	5.75-inch Bottles		18-inch Bottle Strength ksi
		Low Spool	Avg ksi	
5379-0003	3	695	708	726
5379-0004	3	704	707	717
5379-0007	3	697	723	724
5379-0008	3	694	709	725
5379-0009*	3	632	664	677
5379-0010*	3	612	675	686
5379-0011	3	689	711	701
5241-0018	3	705	743	731
5241-0039	4	680	692	725
5241-0044	4	709	727	746
5241-0050	4	690	706	725
5241-0053	4	686	730	743

*Reject lots

4.0 CONCLUSION

The results from the pressure vessel testing support the premise that: weaker individual roving can share its load with adjacent stronger material to perform at some average ultimate strength; that average strength can be represented by the average of the individual spool strengths used in the pressure vessel fabrication. In the 5.75-inch diameter pressure vessel where the high and low strength material was not interspersed throughout the design, the ultimate delivered fiber strength was sensitive to where the weak material was used. This sensitivity is expected to be a nonsignificant factor as the material becomes more interspersed in pressure vessels wound with the multi-roving bands and multiple layers or plies.

Because the fibers will perform in a pressure vessel at some average strength, the lot average fiber strength is a critical parameter for acceptance of prepreg material.

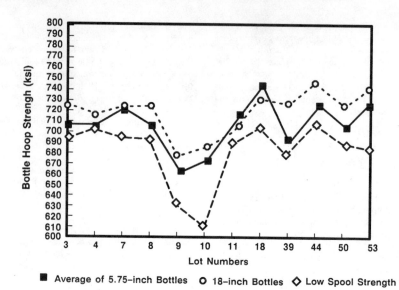

Figure 2. The arithmetic average strength of the individual spools predicts the delivered fiber stress at burst in the 18-inch diameter pressure vessel

REFERENCES

1. Mumford, N. A.; Hopkins, P. C.; Lloyd, B.A.; "Matrix/Fiber Interface Effects on Kevlar®-49 Pressure Vessel Performance", J. Spacecraft, Vol 20, No. 4, July–August 1983, p. 399.

TORSIONAL IMPACT OF FILAMENT WOUND TUBES

Dietmar P. Wurzel
German Aerospace Research Establishment (DLR)
Stuttgart, West Germany

Abstract

A drop weight impact test facility and a specially designed load introduction were used to subject filament wound tubes to torsional loads. The tube material was glass fiber reinforced plastic (GFRP), a few specimens were made from carbon fiber reinforced plastic (CFRP). The tubes were manufactured with a constant inner diameter but different ply and wall thicknesses, and lengths. Fiber orientations were predominantly +/-45 degrees, but some other orientations were also employed. Test parameters were varied by using different loading velocities and loading energies, e.g. drop heights and drop weight masses, which mutually influenced strain rates. The tubes were designed to fracture before buckling. Strain rates ranged from approximately 1 to 10 1/s.

A total of 200 tube specimens were tested under static and dynamic loading. The impact test results indicated an average increase of 10% in fracture strength for the GFRP tubes and a somewhat smaller increase for the CFRP tubes compared to static tests. Fracture strains also increased, resulting in a higher energy absorption till failure. Some tubes were repeatedly tested with loads slightly below the fracture load levels. These loadings neither reduced the fracture strength nor the stiffness. Static failure of the tubes could fairly well be predicted with a quadratic interaction failure criterion.

Supplemental tensile impact testing of longitudinally reinforced GFRP coupons with fiber and matrix composition corresponding to the tube specimens showed a linear increase in tensile strength with strain rate. Strain rates ranged from 0.2 to 200 1/s, leading to a 45% increase in strength. Calculations and test results show that the higher dynamic strength in fiber direction does not contribute exclusively or predominantly to the higher torsional strength of the tubes under dynamic loading. Also, test results showed a marked infuence of the material quality achieved in the winding process on the strength. Tubes constructed of more, thinner plies showed greater failure strength than tubes of equal wall thickness made of fewer, thicker plies. Matrix cracking happened well below the failure levels but did not have an apparent influence on strength and stiffness in the tests performed.

Introduction

During their lifetime fiber reinforced plastic parts and structural elements will be exposed to impact loadings either by design or by accident. Many studies have been done in the last 30 years to learn about the behavior of composite materials under impact loading, employing various kinds of testing machines with a wide range of strain rates. From these we know that especially, though not exclusively, some fiber reinforced material properties are strain rate dependent, e.g. tensile strength and energy absorption increase with higher strain rates. Many of the tests involved dynamic loading of unidirectional tensile test coupons which supposedly causes a "simple" stress state. But what was obtained were often widely scattered, sometimes even contradictory results. Most of the problems were caused by inadequate load introduction into the specimens, indicating that impact tests must be carefully planned and executed.

In this work, filament wound GFRP tube specimens were subjected to torsional impact loads. The stress state in tubular specimens under torque is well defined. In isotropic walls a pure shear stress will develop outside the clamping area; the same applies for orthotropic walls as long as the wall thickness is small compared to tube diameter and length. In the special case of orthotropically laminated tubes with fiber orientations under +/-45 degrees, the fibers follow the principal stress/strain directions and will be subjected only to tensile and compressive loads. Tubular specimens, therefore, though not as simple as flat coupons, are ideal for testing basic material properties. Also, tubes are often used in structural applications like driving shafts or control rods where they may be exposed to sudden changes in torsional loading as simulated in this study.

Glass fiber reinforced plastic material was chosen as it shows a notable dependence of fiber dominated properties on strain rate; it also offers superior energy absorption capability. Due to the material's transparency, damages can easily be observed in test specimens.

Material Selection and Specimen Fabrication

The fiber material selected was E-glass EC 10-800 K43 from Gevetex. The 4000 filament roving had a cross section of 0.314 mm^2 and a 3.3% strain at failure. For comparison a few tubes were reinforced with T300 B 3000x40 graphite fibers - 3000 filaments, cross section 0.115 mm^2, failure strain 1.2%. The matrix material was an araldite LY 556/HY 917/DY 062 epoxy resin from Ciba-Geigy. The tubes were filament wound on a preheated mandrel 1.2 m in length. The resin was heated to 45 degrees C; the roving was prestressed to achieve uniform quality. To remove excess resin the tubes were bandaged and then cured/postcured at 80/120^0 C for four-hour periods. Later the mandrels were removed and cloth ribbons impregnated with cold-curing resin were added in the load introduction areas. The tubes were cut to yield six tube specimens of standard length. The reinforcements at each end were machined to provide cones for clamping, Fig. 1.

All tube specimens had an inside diameter of 25 mm. The "standard tube" was 155 mm long, the fibers were oriented under +/-45^0 in two "plies", each ply consisting of 40 rovings in each direction. The average fiber volume content was 66%. To study their influence a couple of variations were introduced:

Fig. 1: Tube specimens

◆ 45: Standard tube
◆ 45-3L: 50% increase in wall thickness by adding a third ply
◆ 45(3): Three, but thinner plies (reduced roving number per ply), standard wall thickness
◆ 45(4): Four plies, standard wall thickness
◆ 45-90: Additional 90° ply inside and out
◆ 45-UD: For unidirectional plies under +/- 45° (no filament crossovers), standard wall thickness
◆ 30: Fiber orientation +/-30°, standard wall thickness
◆ 90: Fiber orientation 90°, 100% increase in wall thickness
◆ 45-L: "Long" tubes (178 mm)
◆ 45-K: "Short" tubes (122 mm)
◆ C45: CFRP tubes, standard thickness

(Due to the lower cross section of the CFRP roving, three plies with 60 rovings each were needed to obtain the standard wall thickness.)

To determine the strength and stiffness parameters static tests were performed on flat and tubular specimens. The flat coupons were cut from unidirectional reinforced plates manufactured by the filament winding process to achieve corresponding material properties. With an average wall thickness to diameter ratio of 0.05 the "thin wall" criterion was fulfilled. Accordingly, the laminated plate theory was used to calculate the engineering constants of the different tube versions. Two sets are listed in the table. The first set was based on the initial shear modulus of the UD-ply. The starred values used in the failure analysis were based on a secant modulus that was derived from shear tests for shear angles corresponding to those at fracture of the tubes, the failure modulus was used for the 90° tubes.

Test Set-Up

To do the tests a drop weight facility was designed and installed that allowed dropping rail-guided weights, variable between 2.5 and 60 kg, from as high as 15 m, delivering a maximum velocity of 17 m/s. The facility featured a motorized winch, a solenoid release, two adjustable pairs of infrared light barriers and a hydraulic dashpot to catch the weight, Fig. 2.

Also a clamping and loading device for the tube specimens was designed and built, Fig.

Table 1: Material Properties
(Nomenclature follows [1])

Engineering Constants	GFRP	CFRP
E_x [kN/mm²]	44.8	146.5
E_y [kN/mm²]	15.99	8.8
E_s [kN/mm²]	6.6	6
($E_{s\ failure}$[kN/mm²]	1.86	1.5)
v_x [-]	0.29	0.31
Material Strengths		
X [N/mm²]	1350	1805
X' [N/mm²]	543	693
Y [N/mm²]	28.5	46
Y' [N/mm²]	125	156
S [N/mm²]	80	90

Table 2: Engineering Constants of Tube Specimens

Tube Version	45	45-90	30	90	C45
E_1 [kN/mm²]	19.33	18.97	28.68	15.99	20.90
E_2 [kN/mm²]	19.33	30.39	16.06	44.80	20.90
E_6 [kN/mm²]	13.28	10.42	11.61	6.60	37.68
v_{21} [-]	0.47	0.25	0.52	0.10	0.74
E_1^* [kN/mm²]	10.29	15.52	21.43	15.99	14.56
E_2^* [kN/mm²]	10.29	25.89	11.18	44.80	14.56
E_6^* [kN/mm²]	13.28	8.87	10.71	1.86	37.69
v_{21}^* [-]	0.72	0.33	0.87	0.10	0.82

3 and 4. Static tube tests had been conducted to obtain data to help lay out the fixture.) Great care was taken to obtain a compact device and low inertial moments and to limit elastic deformations and vibrations. To perform the tests the tube ends were pushed onto shaft butts; a clamping ring with conical inserts at each end was bolted to a flange. The inside surfaces of the inserts were grooved to permit an even tighter grip. Clamping was favored over bonding or even integrated metallic fittings due to the large number of tubes to be tested. The rear flange sat on a pivot; a sleeve bearing was considered sufficient as no relative movements occured. On one side the flange had a lever-like extension which rested on a load cell to measure the torsional moment. The front flange/shaft unit was supported by two needle bearings. The double bearing block could be adjusted to accommodate different tube lengths. An "impact lever" was mounted between these bearings; its task was to turn the translatory motion of the passing drop weight into a rotational movement to twist the tube. The lever was designed as short as possible to obtain high angular velocities and to keep its mass and vibrations down. It was long enough, however, to be in contact with the drop weight loading fin till after the tube had failed. A removable shoe was used to protect the impact area. All bearings allowed horizontal movements to prevent constraints along the tube's symmetry axis.

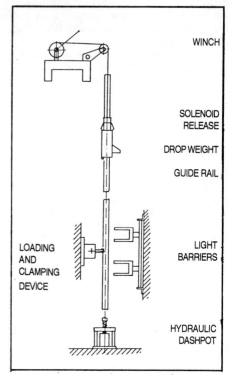

WINCH

SOLENOID RELEASE

DROP WEIGHT

GUIDE RAIL

LOADING AND CLAMPING DEVICE

LIGHT BARRIERS

HYDRAULIC DASHPOT

Fig. 2: Drop weight facility

Instrumentation, Data Registration and Analysis

Two pairs of light barriers measured the velocity of the drop weight just before it touched the impact lever and after failure had occured. The height difference between the light barriers, the velocity difference and the drop weight mass allowed determination of the energy the drop weight lost during impact. An accelerometer was mounted on the drop weight. The velocity measurement before impact and integration of the deceleration gave the velocity variation during the test and consequently the angular velocity during the loading of the tube. The angle of rotation and/or shearing deformation were registered via a precision differential capacitor at the free end of the flange/shaft unit (designed for a maximum angular velocity of 18,000/s) and also via strain gauges on the tube (maximum

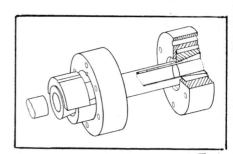

Fig. 3: Load introduction into tube specimen

capacity three gauges per tube). The angular pickup values were more stable but less accurate than the strain gauge measurements as one or more gauges failed prematurely because of cracks. (The comparison of both measurements helped to better determine the energy absorption in the tubes up to failure because deformations inside the clamping area could be estimated.) The torsional moment was determined from the lever arm length of the rear flange and the load measured by the

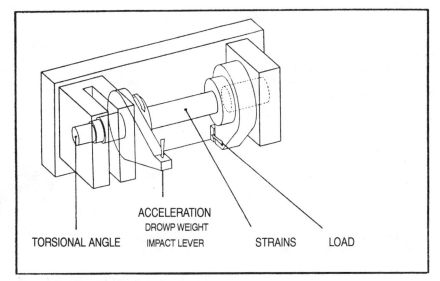

Fig. 4: Loading and clamping device

piezoelectric-load cell; this led to the shear stress in the tube. Finally an accelerometer mounted on the impact lever delivered the signal to trigger the test data registration, increasing the total number of registration devices to seven, Fig. 5.

To handle the data registration during the short duration of the test a digital eight-channel, 5 MHz transient recorder was employed. Depending on testing parameters the total time till failure of the tubes lasted between 1.4 and 7.2 ms. The sample rate was set to between 1 and 3.5 µs, with a 4 K storage capacity of each channel this resulted in observation windows between 4 and 15 ms.

The data were evaluated with an IBM 1130 computer. The following (time dependent) information about the drop weight and the tube specimen was obtained:

◆ drop weight velocity
◆ angle of torsion (from angular capacitor)
◆ longitudinal, transverse and shear strains (from strain gauge measurement)
◆ shear stress
◆ shear modulus
◆ deformation energy.

To facilitate further evaluation and comparisons, four or five sets of diagrams were plotted for each test specimen:

◆ drop weight velocity over time
◆ shear stress over strains, shearing deformation
◆ shear stress over angle of torsion
◆ deformation energy over angle of torsion
◆ shearing deformation (from strain gauges) over angle of torsion (from angular capacitor); this information was obtained on a limited number of tests.

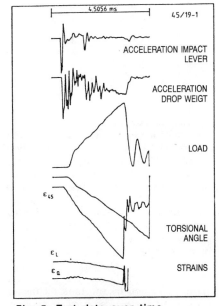

Fig. 5: Test data over time

1103

Due to the short test duration and the necessarily high resolution in the data registration, differences in location and sensitivity of the registration devices led to different response times (e.g. about 200 μs between strain and load measurements). In order to match measurements to obtain the above diagrams, the signals had to adjusted on an equal time basis. Due to a hum no "point" is easily defined where the signal flank starts from the offset level; also, there is a gradual build-up in signal strength, so the computer program had to define a "rise point" to coordinate the signals. The evaluation program then determined the time to failure by checking the load signal for a sudden drop off. This led to an "evaluation window" that lasted from the onset of loading to the failure of the tube.

Test Program

The test program comprised static and dynamic tests. The same clamping and loading fixture was used in both test series. A hydraulic testing machine and its load measuring device were used in the static tests. All tube configurations were statically tested. The dynamic tests consisted of three parts.

ing rate, it also reduced the loading time and the decrease in angular velocity was less. An increase in mass basically resulted in shorter loading times and the deceleration was also less. A drop height of 3 m was used to test the influence of the tube parameter changes described earlier. To judge on the influence of the matrix, 90^0 tubes were also tested with a drop height of 0.5 m. On average, 4 tubes were tested per measuring point.

Finally a couple of tubes were subjected to impact loads at and just below the failure level. Altogether, 206 tubes were tested and 134 glass/epoxy tubes were impact tested. About three to four hours were required per test, including computer evaluation.

Test Results

All tubes generally exhibited similar damage patterns: One or two ribbons of severe damages followed tensile loaded fibers; in the ribbon area compression loaded fibers often were broken. Delaminations and extensive cracks extended from the ribbons. No concentration of damages towards the load introduction areas was observed. Outside the visible damage zones microscopic observation revealed numerous

Table 3: Overview of Major Tube Tests

Height [m]	Mass [kg]	Specimen Version
0.5	18, 34, 51	45, 90
1.5	18	45
3	18, 34	45
3	18	45-3L, 45-UD, 45(3), 45(4), 45-L, 45-K, 45-90, 30, 90, C45
6	18, 34, 51	45
9	18	45

The standard tube was used to determine the influence of the loading velocity on the tube behavior. An 18 kg mass was dropped from five different heights, ranging from 0.5 to 9 m. The actual velocity range of the drop weight on first contact with the impact lever was between 3 and 13 m/s. (Though fictitious these figures correspond to initial rotational speeds of 370 to 1600 rpm.) Additionally, the mass was increased to 34 and 51 kg at three of these height levels. An increase in height resulted in a higher angular velocity of the loaded tube end. As the energy absorbed by the tube till failure proved to be nearly independent of the load-

transverse cracks primarily in layers with compression loaded fibers. The crack density increased when ply thickness decreased; it was higher in plies with a ply on each side, surface plies showed fewer cracks. The cracks originated mostly from voids or other irregularities. Tubes loaded close to but under the fracture level showed identical transverse crack densities, confirming that transverse cracks happen at an earlier stage.

Under the testing conditions described strain rates of 1.8 to 9.4/s were achieved in the tube specimens. The fracture

Table 4: Test Results for Standard Tubes (+/-45°)

Test	τ_B [N/mm²]	G_B [N/mm²]	A/V [10^{-3} J/mm³]	ε_{45} [%/10]
Static Test	264	13050	2.3	10.8
0.5 m, 18 kg	283	12270	3.0	12.7
34 kg	288	12290	3.1	12.7
51 kg	278	12000	3.0	13.0
1.5 m, 18 kg	287	11930	3.3	13.6
3.0 m, 18 kg	299	12750	3.2	12.2
34 kg	292	12960	3.0	13.3
6.0 m, 18 kg	300	11940	3.7	14.1
34 kg	292	12710	3.2	12.9
51 kg	326	13500	3.3	13.9
9.0 m, 18 kg	296	11430	3.7	13.4

Table 5: Test Results for Different Tube Configurations

Version	τ_B [N/mm²]	G_B [N/mm²]	A/V [10^{-3} J/mm³]	ε_{45} [%/10]
45	299 (264)	12750 (13050)	3.2 (2.3)	12.2 (10.8)
45-3L	342 (310)	12260 (12240)	4.2	14.2 (11.6)
45(3)	332 (283)	12760 (12650)	4.3 (2.9)	13.3 (11.0)
45(4)	341 (302)	11880 (12900)	4.6	13.6 (12.9)
45-UD	298 (273)	12880 (15040)	3.2	13.5 (9.1)
45-K	296 (264)	13340 (12500)	3.0	12.4 (10.6)
45-L	257 (233)	13000 (13400)	2.3 (1.8)	11.0 (10.0)
45-90	286	8250	4.7	17.1
30	219 (216)	9230 (13150)	2.4 (1.6)	11.1 (8.6)

(Static values in brackets)

Table 6: Test Results for 90° Tubes

Test	τ_B [N/mm²]	G_B [N/mm²]	A/V [10^{-3} J/mm³]	ε_{45} [%/10]
Static Test	80	1860		23
0.5 m, 18 kg	80	3500	1.1	12.3
3.0 m, 18 kg	87	3000	1.4	14.5

strength proved to be strain-rate dependent, higher strain rates resulted in higher fracture strengths. The fracture strengths of the dynamically tested standard tubes averaged 110% of the static fracture strengths. Measurements of the shear modulus at failure indicated rather constant or slightly lower values during impact loading. Accordingly, the increase in fracture strength was accompanied by an increase in failure strains. All tube configurations with fiber orientations under 45°, standard tubes as well as their variations, in principle exhibited similar differences under static and dynamic loading. Strength of tubes with fiber orientations of +/-30⁰ remained basically unchanged. The same applied for circumferentially wound tubes, here the shear modulus under impact, however, was markedly higher than the static value. Tables 4 to 7 give the torsional strength τ_B, the shear modulus G_B, the energy absorption till fracture per volume element A/V and the failure strain ε_{45} m measured under 45⁰ (i.e. in fiber direction for 45⁰ tubes and variants).

The buckling strength generally surpassed the material strength. The buckling strength coincided with material strength in versions 45-L and 30, but test data do not indicate buckling prior to failure. The Tsai/Wu quadratic interaction failure criterion[1] was used to estimate the static failure of the tubes. The static failure loads of the GFRP tube configurations corresponded to the calculated last ply failure values or surpassed these slightly.

A number of tubes were intentionally (reduced drop heights) and unintentionally (slippage in the gripping devices) loaded close to their ultimate strength without fracture actually occurring. When these tubes were subsequently tested with impact loads leading to failure, identical stress-strain values and no lower fracture levels than in previously unloaded tubes were obtained. This confirmed that the cracks observed did not result in a stiffness degradation. This also confirmed that, for the GFRP tube configurations under study, the application of a failure criterion beyond first ply failure was permissible. Keeping service load levels within the first ply failure envelope would leave the strength potential vastly unexploited.

The CFRP tubes showed a less pronounced increase in fracture strength with strain rate. Contrary to the glass/epoxy tubes the failure shear modulus decreased noticeably below the static value, accompanied by a higher shear angle at failure. As fiber dominated properties of CFRP materials are considered unrelated to strain-rate variations this points to the contribution of the matrix to the strain-rate dependent behavior. The CFRP tubes also failed closer to the first ply failure limit, cracks and delaminations reduced the stability of the layers and led to failure of the tubes. The inherently different behavior of composite materials places emphasis on conducting both analytical and experimental studies on an equal basis.

A series of longitudinal tensile impact tests were conducted in parallel on filament-wound unidirectional GFRP coupons; 160 test coupons with a cross section of 6.4 mm were tested with a 25 kN-hydropulse testing machine. The coupon ends were directly gripped by specially designed clamping heads to avoid problems often encountered with bonded load introductions. The strain rates realized in the tests covered a range from 2.3×10^{-1}/s to 2.1×10^{2}/s, i.e. three orders of magnitude. An evaluation of the test results indicated a linear relation of the unidirectional tensile strength to the strain rate. Fracture strength was about 20% above the static level at the low end and 45% at the high end.

The same strain rate that resulted in a 10% increase in the torsional strength of the GFRP tube caused the longitudinal tensile strength of the glass fiber to increase twice as much. A recalculation of the failure envelopes using increased fiber strength showed that improved fiber properties only marginally account for the increase in torsional strength. Higher values of the matrix

Table 7: Test Results for CFRP Tubes

Test	τ_B [N/mm²]	G_B [N/mm²]	A/V [10^{-3} J/mm³]	ε_{45} [%/10]
Static Test	360	32000		
3.0 m, 18 kg	386	26500	2.5	7.3

dominated transverse tensile and compressive strengths however would result in an improved torsional strength. Also accentuating the influence of the matrix was the fact that the maximum strains in the tube at failure did not come close to the failure strains of the fibers.

Great care has to be used during the filament winding process. Voids, insufficient impregnation of the fibers and other irregularities have a negative influence on material performance. Building up the tube walls of three or four plies instead of two increased the torsional strength and limited damage propagation. Microscopic observation revealed fewer voids when thinner layers were used. Standard tubes and 45-UD tubes did not differ in torsional strength. Additional circumferential layers greatly improved the energy absorbing capability, a good solution when stiffness is not the dominating design criterion. Overall, the higher strength and better energy absorption under impact conditions make tubular glass/epoxy elements attractive candidates in the design of crash structures.

References

(1) Tsai, S. W., Hahn, H. T.: Introduction to Composite Materials. Technomic Publishing Co. (1980)
(2) Wurzel, D. P.: Beitrag zur schnellen Torsion von Wickelrohren. Institut für Flugzeugbau der Universität Stuttgart (1986)

Bibliography

Dietmar P. Wurzel studied mechanical engineering at the Technical University Aachen and aeronautical engineering at the University of Stuttgart, where he received his "Diplom-Ingenieur" and doctorate. In 1974 he joined the Institute of Structures and Design of the German Aerospace Research Establishment (DLR) in Stuttgart to work on composite materials. From 1982 to 1983 he was a visiting scientist at the Materials Laboratory at Wright- Patterson AFB in Dayton, OH. Back in Germany, he headed a consultant group established at the institute for composite technology. In 1987 he came to Washington, D.C., where he now heads the DLR Washington Office.

ADVANCES IN POWER TRANSMISSION USING FILAMENT WOUND COMPOSITES

Brian E. Spencer
Addax, Inc.
Lincoln, Nebraska

Abstract

Filament wound composites are now being applied to a broad range of power transmission applications which are outside the defense, military and automotive industries. Examples include high speed, high torque pump and compressor couplings, quill shafts and cooling tower shafts. In addition to the composite shafts, flexible couplings which allow higher angles of misalignment have been developed using advanced composites. The advantages of composites over steel shafts and traditional flexible couplings include: cost, weight, higher critical speeds, ability to torsionally tune system, vibration damping, lower bearing loads and corrosion resistance.

This paper discusses the design and fabrication of composite shafts and flexible couplings for power transmission. Applications discussed include an 18,000 horsepower pump coupling, a torsionally tuned quill shaft and cooling tower

shafts and couplings.

1. INTRODUCTION

The use of high performance oriented fiber composites is identified with the defense and aerospace communities. Oriented fiber composites can provide high strength and stiffness in a light weight component. The technology developed by the defense and aerospace industries is now being applied to industrial power transmission applications. The composite drive shaft was first introduced to the cooling tower industry in early 1986. The first production composite shaft was put in service in mid-1986. By the end of 1988, over 300 large cooling tower fans were being driven successfully with composite shafts. The largest shafts being eleven inches in diameter and over eighteen feet long. Composite shafts are being used in cooling towers, pump drives and engine driven compressors. Flexible elements have also been developed utilizing the advantages of composite materials. These composite elements can tolerate high misalignments and torque loads and significantly dampen noise and mechanical vibrations.

This paper describes the technology used in the design and fabrication of composite drive shafts and flexible elements and several applications of these products.

2. THE FILAMENT WINDING PROCESS

The filament winding process is used in manufacturing both the composite drive shaft and flexible element. The filament winding process is the machine controlled technique of applying a controlled amount of resin and oriented fiber on a mandrel that provides the finished component shape. The mechanics of filament winding is illustrated in Figure 1. The tensioned fiber bands are accurately placed on the mandrel using numerically computer controlled or chain and gear mechanical winding machines. Figure 1 shows the fiber being pulled from tensioned spools through the delivery eye onto the rotating mandrel. The resin can either be pre-applied on the fiber in an off-line operation (pre-impregnation, prepreg) or applied during the winding operation (wet winding). Prepregging usually requires storing the material at low temperature until required for winding to retard the curing process. Wet winding uses a resin bath, along the fiber path between the tensioning system and the delivery eye, in which the dry fibers are pulled through. Both wet winding and prepreg winding are widely used. The choice of technique depends on the application.

3. MATERIALS

Composites used to fabricate the composite drive shafts and flexible elements are a combination of two materials: fibers and resin where neither would be adequate alone. The combination of these two components results in a strong, tough, fatigue and corrosion resistant material. Table 1 shows the properties of common fibers and resin used in filament winding. Table 2 compares the specific strength, specific stiffness and cost of metals and some fibers. Table 3 presents typical properties for unidirectional composites. These tables illustrate the potential of composites. Composite parts can be lighter, stronger, stiffer and, in some cases, less expensive than the corresponding metal part. Composites are orthotropic, which allows tailoring the design to meet requirements that may be conflicting for metals. (An orthotropic body has material properties that are different in three mutually perpendicular directions and three mutually perpendicular planes of material symmetry).

Many types of resin systems are available for use in filament winding. They can be classed in two broad groups; thermosets and thermoplastics. Thermosetting resins (once cured cannot be remelted) have been the most widely used. Within this group, epoxies are used for most applications. They are easy to process and are inexpensive ($1/lb to $5/lb). Epoxies can have use temperatures up to 350°F and are resistant to most chemicals and solvents. Polyimides, another thermosetting resin class, can be used up to 600°F, but are difficult to filament wind and are expensive ($15/lb to $25/lb). Techniques for filament winding with thermoplastic resin (they can be remelted and reformed as needed) are now being developed. As materials and processes improve, this class of resin will be used increasingly. Thermoplastics offer reduced manufacturing labor, improved toughness, reduced scrap costs, and ease of field repairs. The price for thermoplastics suitable for filament winding are moderately expensive ($5/lb to $50/lb).

Resins and fibers are continually being improved. The resulting improved properties will make composites attractive for even more applications.

4. APPLICATIONS

With over two years of application experience, the composite coupling (drive shaft assembly) has demonstrated its advantages over metal couplings in industrial applications. Those advantages include:
- High misalignment tolerance
- Corrosion resistance to caustic and acidic atmospheres
- Low bending loads on bearings
- Long single spans
- No fretting failures
- Fatigue resistance
- Shafts which eliminate thermal expansion
- Light weight
- Ability to torsionally tune system
- Noise and mechanical vibrations attenuation

4.1 Composite Cooling Tower Fan Couplings

A typical cooling tower fan coupling is shown in Figure 2. The assembly consists of stainless steel hubs, composite flexible elements, composite spacer flange and composite spacer tube. These single span couplings take advantage of composite graphite's high specific stiffness by allowing significantly longer coupling shafts than can be tolerated from metal. These long single span shafts require neither intermediate bearing support nor additional flexible couplings. The shaft diameter, ranging from 4 to 12.5 inches, depends on the shaft length.

Because of the high specific strength of filament wound composites, the composite shafts, if properly designed, are usually speed critical not strength critical. The shafts are capable of transmitting many times the torque used in cooling tower applications. The safety margin on critical speed is designed to customer requirements.

The single piece flexible element is also filament wound. The design utilizes the high strength of continuous fibers while providing the design flexibility of a filament wound composite. These single piece elements have no faying surfaces, therefore no fretting wear. The materials used are essentially inert.

The ideal flexible coupling will connect and transmit torque between two rotating shafts, but isolate each machine from the other under adverse alignment conditions. The Addax composite flexible element is designed with large torque and misalignment capacity, yet produces low bending forces on the connected shafts and bearings. The unique combination of high strength with great flexibility and low reaction forces in each composite coupling cannot be equalled by any metal disc or diaphragm-type coupling. Other flexible elements for metal disc couplings consist of a number of thin laminated discs, which exhibit a tendency to develop fretting corrosion with increased misalignment. Although the composite element appears to be similar in design to popular disc-type couplings, significant advantages and differences set this coupling apart from the rest. The proprietary composite element is designed as a single part, thus avoiding the fretting corrosion problems associated with disc-type couplings.

The composite materials in the element are more flexible than metal discs, producing a softer coupling. The materials are both corrosion and fatigue resistant. The flexible element has been fatigue tested with misalignment at 300 hp and 1000 and 3000 rpm. Laboratory testing and field units have shown the capability of the flexible element design. The first flexible elements were put in service in May 1988 and have been running continuously since. The laboratory testing has been conducted with angular and axial misalignment. The cooling tower element is rated at ± 1 degree angular and .2 inches of axial misalignment simultaneously. Fatigue testing has demonstrated these ratings with tests to date conducted with over 4 degrees angular misalignment without failure.

4.2 Pump Drive Couplings

Many high speed, high torque turbine driven boiler feed pumps are closely coupled and have little misalignment between machines. But due to the high horsepower and high speed, all metal couplings, due to their weight, input a high load into the machines bearings which reduces life. The composite couplings reduce weight, thus reducing the bearing load. The composite flexible elements also dampen vibrations which effectively isolates the motor from the pump, which is desirable. Figures 3 and 4 show two pump drive couplings. Both transmit over 200,000 in-lbs of torque. Figure 3 is a boiler feed pump which has very little mis-alignment but is transmitting 18,000 horsepower at 5600 rpm. Figure 4 shows an axial flow pump coupling. This assembly operates at 1200 horsepower and 300 rpm but is misaligned approximately two degrees. This coupling sees substantial torque pulsations produced by blade passing frequencies. The composite assembly substantially dampens these vibrations which are detrimental to the machines.

4.2 Engine Driven Compressor Couplings

Many coupling applications require a specific torsional stiffness of the coupling assembly so that critical frequency problems can be reduced or eliminated. Figure 5 shows a composite shaft that was designed in a specific envelope with the required strength and torsional stiffness. A steel shaft could not be designed to operate under the required conditions because of conflicting stiffness and strength requirements. A composite shaft was designed and built that had the required strength yet was torsionally soft. This shaft transmits 200,000 in-lbs of torque in a gas compressor speed increaser. This shaft is also unique in that the metal end fittings drive the shaft across a hexagonal shaped internal inter-face in the composite shaft. No fasteners are used.

5. SUMMARY

Composite couplings have been in service for over two years in industrial plants. This experience has proven the advantages of composite over metal couplings. With the reduction in cost of graphite and economies of increased production, composite couplings can now be purchased for prices approaching metal couplings. The benefits, such as reduced maintenance costs, lighter weight, corrosion resistance, improved fatigue life and high misalignment tolerance, which are inherent in composites, can greatly reduce life cycle costs.

BIOGRAPHY

Brian Spencer is the Engineering Manager and one of the founders of Addax, Inc., Lincoln, Nebraska. He is responsible for all engineering aspects including proposal preparation, design, development, tooling and fabrication. Mr. Spencer received a B.S. in Agricultural Engineering from the University of Nebraska in 1970; an M.E. in Industrial Engineering from the University of California-Berkeley in 1971; an M.E. in Mechanical Engineering from the University of

California-Davis in 1980; and a
Ph.D. in Engineering Mechanics from
the University of Nebraska in 1988.

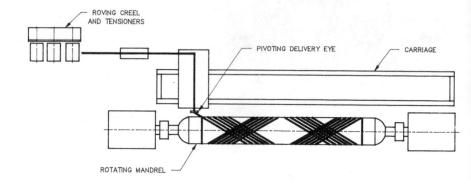

FIGURE 1.   Layout of a filament winding machine

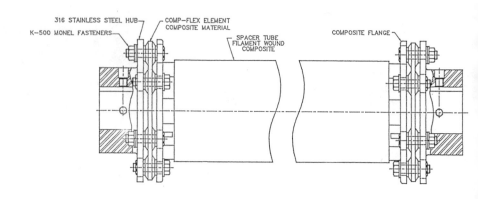

Figure 2.   Schematic drawing of composite
            cooling tower coupling

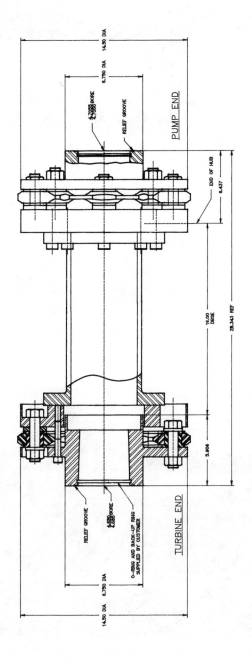

FIGURE 3. Boiler feed pump coupling

1115

FIGURE 4. Axial flow pump coupling

FIGURE 5. Compressor coupling

TABLE 1 - Fiber and Resin Properties

FIBER PROPERTIES

	S-2 Glass	34 MSI Graphite	40 MSI Graphite	50 MSI Graphite	Kevlar
Density, lb/in^3	.090	.065	.065	.065	.054
Strand Tensile Strength, KSI	665	600	820	350	525
Modulus of Elasticity, MSI	12.6	35	40	50	19.2
Coefficient of Thermal Expansion per $^{\circ}$F x 10^{-6}	3.1	-.3	-.3	-.4	-1.1
Tensile Elongation, percent	5.4	1.7	2.0	.6	2.7

Source: Manufacturers Product Literature

1. Owens Corning S-2 Fiberglass
2. Amoco T-600
3. Amoco T-40
4. Amoco T-50
5. DuPont

MSI = Modulus x 10^6 PSI

RESIN PROPERTIES
Epon 828 Based Epoxy

Density, lb/in^3	.0433
Tensile Strength, KSI	12
Tensile Modulus, KSI	440
Percent Elongation	7.0
Compressive Strength, KSI	20
Compressive Modulus, KSI	660
Shear Strength, KSI	8
Shear Modulus, KSI	470
Coefficient of Thermal Expansion, per $^{\circ}$F x 10^{-6}	30

ALL PROPERTIES AT ROOM TEMPERATURE

TABLE 2 - Comparative Properties - Fibers vs. Metals

Fiber	Density Lb/In	Strand Tensile Strength KSI	Specific Strength Strength/Density In x 10	Tensile Modulus MSI	Specific Modulus Modulus/Density In x 10	Cost $/lb	Cost $/in
Kevlar	.054	525	9.7	19.2	356	20.00	1.08
IM6	.063	700	11.1	40.0	634	43.00	2.71
AS6	.066	600	9.1	35.0	530	42.00	2.77
XAS	.065	550	8.5	33.0	508	13.00	.85
T-40XS	.065	820	12.6	40.0	615	60.00	3.90
HMS	.065	350	5.4	50.0	769	50.00	3.25
S-2 Glass	.090	665	7.4	12.6	140	3.94	0.35
Aluminum	.100	80	.80	10.4	104	5.00	0.50
Titanium	.160	150	.94	16.0	100	7.00	1.12
4340 Steel	.283	220	.78	29.0	102	4.00	1.13

* The effect of the resin which would be present in a composite
is not included in these numbers. Most high performance composites
have a 60% fiber volume.

TABLE 3 - Typical Unidirectional Properties of Epoxy Composites
(Fiber Volume = .60)

Elastic Constants	34 msi Graphite	50 msi Graphite	40 msi Graphite	S-2 Glass	Kevlar
Longitudinal Modulus, msi	20.60	30.20	24.20	7.70	11.6
Transverse Modulus, msi	1.50	1.60	1.50	1.80	.8
Shear Modulus, msi	.75	.80	.77	.96	.42
Poisson's Ratio, V_{LT}	.32	.32	.32	.32	.32

Strength Properties Allowables					
Longitudinal Tensile Strength, ksi	230	195	285	210	200
Transverse Tensile Strength, ksi	10	5	6	6	4.3
Longitudinal Compressive Strength, ksi	100	85	140	100	2.5
Transverse Compressive Strength, ksi	23	20	20	20	20
In-plane Shear Strength, ksi	9	9	9	9	low

Ultimate Strains					
Longitudinal Tension, Percent	1.10	.78	1.20	2.7	1.7
Transverse Tension, Percent	.57	.29	.40	0.3	.54
Longitudinal Compression, Percent	.48	.26	.58	1.1	0.2
Transverse Compression, Percent	1.30	1.20	1.30	1.1	2.5

Physical Properties					
Density, lb/in^3	.057	.057	.057	.072	.050
Longitudinal Coefficient of Thermal Expansion per $^\circ F \times 10^{-6}$	-.21	-.35	-.21	3.7	-1.1
Transverse Coefficient of Thermal Expansion per $^\circ F \times 10^{-6}$	19.5	19.5	19.5	19.5	19.5

34th International SAMPE Symposium
May 8-11, 1989

PREDICTING THE STRENGTH OF FILAMENT-
WOUND SPECIMENS WITH SURFACE CUTS

D. H. Morris
Department of Engineering Science and Mechanics
Virginia Polytechnic Institute and State University
Blacksburg, Virginia 24061

C. E. Harris
Mechanics of Materials Branch
NASA Langley Research Center
Hampton, Virginia 23665

Abstract

The notched strength of filament-wound composite specimens was determined for coupons with various sized semi-elliptic surface notches. When the part-through notches did not cut the first 0° layer the strength was independent of the size of the notch and was equal to the unnotched tensile strength. When the cut penetrated 0° layers specimens failed in a two-part failure mode. The first part of the failure was modeled using fracture mechanics and a straight line tangent to the fracture mechanics solution, and the second part of the failure was modeled using a failure criterion that accounted for the moduli of 0° and helical layers.

1. INTRODUCTION

The purpose of this paper is to present a summary of efforts to develop an analytical model to predict the strength of tensile specimens with surface cuts. The surface cuts were selected to simulate surface damage due to low velocity impact. The cuts were semi-elliptic in shape, and varied from very shallow to very deep. The strength models depended upon the depth of the cuts.

2. EXPERIMENTAL PROGRAM

Test specimens were cut from a graphite/epoxy cylinder that was 35.6 mm (1.4 in.) thick and 0.76 m (30 in.) in diameter. The cylinder was manufactured by Hercules, Inc., and had the following asymmetric layer orientations (outside to inside):

$(\pm 56.5)_2/0_3 \ [(\pm 56.5)_2/0_3]_3/$
$[(\pm 56.5)_2/0_3]_7/(\pm 56.5/0_6)_4/$
$(\pm 56.5)_2/(90/0)$

The 0° layers are in the longitudinal direction of the cylinder and the ±56.5° layers are helical layers. The ± 56.5° layers are about 1.6 times as thick as the other helical layers. The fibers are Hercules Inc. AS4W-12K and the resin is Hercules Inc. HBRF-55A, except for the 0° layers where the resin was Hercules Inc. MX-16. The helical layers were wet-wound and the 0° layers were hand-laid.

Test specimens were cut in the longitudinal (0°) direction of the cylinder, and thus had slightly curved faces. In order to insure uniform gripping pressure during testing, aluminum spacers were placed between the surfaces of the test specimens and grips. One side of the spacers was flat to match the grips and the other side was either concave or convex to match the curvature of the test coupons. Load was transferred from the testing machine to the test coupons through friction. Slip was prevented by placing an abrasive screen between spacers and test coupons.

Semi-elliptic surface notches were cut in the outer surface of the test coupons by an ultrasonic cutting tool with a 0.406 mm (0.016 in.) thick blade. The border of the cut had a radius of 0.203 mm (0.008 in.); no attempt was made to further sharpen the notches. The cuts were perpendicular to the 0° layers (and to the direction of loading).

The size of test coupons depended upon the strength and the testing machine capacity. Some test coupons were straight-sided (Fig. 1), and some coupons were machined with a 235 mm (9.25 in.) radius grinding wheel which resulted in the tapered coupon shown in Fig. 2. For a homogeneous isotropic material, Poe, Illg and Garber[1] found the stress concentration factor for the tapered coupon to be no more than 1.04.

Since the laminate was asymmetric, stretching-bending coupling may be induced by the applied load. However, Poe, Illg and Garber[1] and Harris and Morris[2] found that the stiff grips of the testing machine prevented most of the strains due to the coupling effect. Poe, Illg and Garber[1] found that the modulus calculated from strain gages was about 12% greater than the modulus predicted by assuming clamped ends.

All tests were conducted at a constant cross head displacement rate of 0.042 mm/s (0.01 in./min). Two or three replicate tests were conducted for each test condition. The values of a/t (Fig. 1) varied from 0.0335 to 0.491, and 2c/a varied from 1.0 to 4.0.

3. TYPES OF FAILURE

Specimens with shallow notches (the cut depth did not penetrate the first 0° layers) failed catastrophically. The strength of these specimens was the same as for unnotched specimens, and the notched strength was independent of the size of the semi-elliptic cut.

Failure was in two parts when the cut depth pierced 0° layers. This type of failure is shown schematically in Fig. 3. For first ligament failure fibers broke in the plane of the notch, over a thickness equal to the depth of the notch, and the load suddenly dropped. Zinc iodide enhanced X-ray photographs showed the existence of matrix cracks along the helicals and some delaminations. The matrix cracks and delaminations were in the vicinity of the notch, and did not extend below a plane at the bottom of the notch. The delamination at the bottom of the notch was small but extended toward the grips as the load was increased to remaining ligament failure. Even at approx-

imately 95% of the remaining ligament failure load the delamination was small; the delamination extended to the grips when the remaining ligament failed. When the bottom of the cut was in a helical layer, the delamination (Fig. 3) started at the cut depth, but turned toward and ran parallel to the next deepest 0° layer at remaining ligament failure. These delaminations never crossed a 0° layer. Also, it was observed that the deeper the cut the more extensive the associated delamination. Further increases in load caused the remaining ligament, of thickness (t-a), to fail.

To summarize, when the cut depth did not pierce the first 0° layer specimens failed catastrophically and the failure stress was independent of cut size. When 0° layers were cut specimens failed in a two-part manner.

4. STRENGTH PREDICTION MODELS

Two models are needed to predict the strength when specimens failed in two-parts; one for first ligament failure and one for remaining ligament failure.

4.1 First Ligament Strength

Linear elastic fracture mechanics was used to predict failure of this ligament. For a homogeneous isotropic material, Newman and Raju[3] present a fracture mechanics solution for a specimen with a semi-elliptic surface flaw loaded by remote tensile stress. The equation relates the stress intensity factor (K) and the remote uniform applied tensile stress (S) as

$$K = S\sqrt{\pi a/Q}\ F(a/c, a/t, c/2B, \phi) \quad (1)$$

The symbols a, c, t, 2B and ϕ (elliptical angle that specifies the location on the border of the cut) are defined in Fig. 1. Equations for the ellipse shape factor (Q) and the boundary correction factor (F) are given by Newman and Raju[3].

It was assumed that failure occurred when the maximum stress intensity factor reached the fracture toughness (K_Q). Since the function F varies along the border of the cut, the maximum value of F was used in the analysis. This occurs at $\phi = 0^o$ or $\phi = 90^o$, depending upon the size of the cut. This is similar to procedures used in predicting notched strength of metals.

By letting $K = K_Q$ and $S = \sigma_N$ (notched strength) in Eq. (1), first ligament failure occurs when

$$\sigma_N = \frac{K_Q}{\sqrt{\pi a/Q}\ F} \quad (2)$$

The fracture toughness (K_Q) was not measured. Thus, the general toughness parameter model developed by Poe[4] was used to estimate the fracture toughness. The general toughness parameter (Q_c/ε_{tuf}) was found to be relatively constant for a large number of laminates. This parameter is given by

$$Q_c/\varepsilon_{tuf} = 1.50\sqrt{mm}\ (0.298\ \sqrt{in.}) \quad (3)$$

In Eq. (3), ε_{tuf} is the fiber failing strain, and Q_c is given by

$$Q_c = K_Q\ \xi_1/E_x \quad (4)$$

The term ξ_1 is given by $\xi_1 = 1 - \nu_{xy}\sqrt{E_y/E_x}$, where ν_{xy} is the laminate inplane Poisson's ratio, E_x is the laminate modulus in the loading direction, and E_y is the laminate modulus in the transverse inplane direction. The laminate properties were calculated using lamination theory from lamina properties supplied by Hercules Inc. The laminate was assumed symmetric to represent the rigid grips which allow little bending. Further details may be found in the report of Harris and Morris[2].

The fiber failing strain (ε_{tuf}) was estimated from the unnotched strength (σ_o) and E_x by $\varepsilon_{tuf} = \sigma_o/E_x$, and was 0.0124[2]. The stress-strain curve was essentially linear to failure.

Combining previous equations, K_Q is calculated using

$$K_Q = \frac{1.50\ \varepsilon_{tuf}\ E_x}{\xi_1} \quad (5)$$

Harris and Morris[2] estimated the fracture toughness to be 945 MPa $\sqrt{mm}$ (27.2 ksi $\sqrt{in}$). Using this value and Eq. (2), first ligament strength can be calculated (note than σ_N is based on gross area).

4.2 Remaining Ligament Strength

It is assumed[5] that stress is uniform in the remaining ligament, of thickness $(t-a)$. Then, at failure the remaining ligament stress (σ_ℓ) is

$$\sigma_\ell = P/[2Bt(1-a/t)] = \varepsilon_{tuf}E_{xr} \quad (6)$$

where P is the applied load and E_{xr} is the modulus in the loading direction of the remaining ligament. The values of E_{xr} were calculated using lamination theory, with the laminate being assumed symmetric, as previously discussed. The gross stress at failure is $\sigma_R = P/2Bt$. Thus, Eq. (6) becomes

$$\sigma_R = \varepsilon_{tuf}E_{xr}(1-a/t) \quad (7)$$

and accounts for the fact that the 0° and helical layers have different moduli. Predictions were made at each interface of the 0° and helical layers.

To summarize, Eq. (2) was used to predict first ligament strength and Eq. (7) was used to predict remaining ligament strength.

5. RESULTS

Predicted and experimental values of first ligament strength are compared in Figs. 4,5 and 6, for notch aspect ratios (2c/a) of 1.0, 2.0 and 4.0, respectively. Experimental values represent the average of two or more tests. Circles represent data from 25.4 mm (1.0 in.) wide specimens and squares for 50.8 mm (2.0 in.) wide specimens. For the 25.4 mm wide specimens, σ_N was based on the gross area at the notched section. Notched strength was normalized by the unnotched strength of 379 MPa (55.0 ksi)[2]. The location and size of the 0° and helical layers are shown on the abscissa.

Three prediction curves (for a given specimen width) are shown in Figs. 4-6. For cuts that did not penetrate the first 0° layer the strength ratio is 1.0, that is, the notched strength is independent of the cut. Similar results were found for a filament-wound cylinder,[6] where the authors indicated that performance would not be lost should the outer helical layers be damaged.

When 0° layers were cut, two prediction equations are necessary. For the deeper cuts (deep depends upon the value of 2c/a), Eq. (2) gives a good estimate of notched strength. For less deep cuts, Eq. (2) greatly overpredicts the experimental data. For these cuts the data is represented quite well by a straight line drawn from the outer surface of the first 0° layer and tangent to the fracture mechanics solution, Eq. (2). These lines are called tangent lines in Figs. 4-6. The tangent line approach is similar to that of Feddersen.[7]

Figure 7 compares experimental and predicted values of

remaining ligament strength. The location and size of the 0° and helical layers are shown on the abscissa. The predicted curve, found using Eq. 7, has a stair-step appearance. This is due to the fact that the modulus of the helical layers is less than the 0° layers, and thus the strength is reduced more when the 0° layers are cut. As before, strength is normalized by the unnotched strength. Equation (7) over-predicts the strength; the maximum difference is approximately 10%. Bending stresses are the probable cause for experimental strength values being less than predicted values. (Recall that Eq. (7) assumed uniform stress in the remaining ligament.)

6. CONCLUSIONS

Strength prediction models were developed for tensile specimens with part-through cuts. The specimens were taken from a filament wound cylinder, and the cuts were semi-elliptical. Prediction models depended upon the type of failure. When the cut did not exceed the thickness of the outer helical layers, the strength was equal to the unnotched strength and was independent of the size of the cut. When 0° layers were cut, specimens failed in two stages. First ligament failure was for a sublaminate with thickness equal to the depth of the cut, and remaining ligament failure was for

a sublaminate of thickness t-a. For the deepest cuts, first ligament strength was approximated by a linear elastic fracture mechanics solution. For cuts of intermediate depth, first ligament strength was approximated by a straight line tangent to the fracture mechanics solution and extending to the outer surface of the first 0° layer. Remaining ligament strength was approximated by assuming uniaxial stress in this ligament; the model accounted for the differences in moduli of the 0° and helical layers. Bending probably accounted for experimental data lying below the prediction curve.

ACKNOWLEDGEMENT

The first author would like to acknowledge the financial support provided by a grant from the NASA Langley Research Center.

REFERENCES

1. Poe, Jr., C. C., Illg, W. and Garber, D. P., "A Program to Determine the Effect of Low-Velocity Impacts on the Strength of the Filament-Wound Rocket Motor Case for the Space Shuttle," NASA Technical Memorandum TM-87588, 1985.

2. Harris, C. E. and Morris, D. H., "Preliminary Report on Tests of Tensile Specimens With a Part-Through Surface Notch for a Filament Wound Graphite/Epoxy Material," NASA Contractor Report NASA-CR-172545, 1985.

3. Newman, Jr., J. C. and Raju, I. S., "Stress-Intensity Factor Equations for Cracks in Three-Dimensional Finite Bodies," Fracture Mechanics: Fourteenth Symposium - Volume 1: Theory and Analysis, ASTM STP 791, J. C. Lewis and G. Sines, Eds., 1983, pp. I-238-I-265.

4. Poe, Jr., C. C., "A Unifying Strain Criterion for Fracture of Fibrous Composite Laminates," Engineering Fracture Mechanics, Vol. 17, 1983, pp. 153-171.

5. Harris, C. E., Morris, D. H. and Poe, Jr., C. C., "The Fracture Behavior of Filament Wound Cylinders With Surface Flaws," presented at the 26th Structures, Structural Dynamics and Materials Conference, AIAA/ASME/ASCE/AHS, Orlando, Florida, April 15-17, 1985.

6. Beckwith, S. W., Morgan, M. E., Kapp, J. R. and Anderson, G. P., "Damage Tolerance/Fracture Control Approach to Graphite/Epoxy Filament Wound Case (FWC) for Space Shuttle Motors," Proceedings of the 32nd International SAMPE Symposium and Exhibition, Vol. 32, April 1987, pp. 1528-1543.

7. Feddersen, C. E., "Evaluation and Prediction of the Residual Strength of Center Cracked Tension Panels," Damage Tolerance in Aircraft Structures, ASTM STP 486, 1971, pp. 50-78.

BIOGRAPHIES

Don H. Morris is a Professor in the Department of Engineering Science and Mechanics at the Virginia Polytechnic Institute and State University, Blacksburg, Virginia. He received B.S. and M.S. degrees in Mechanical Engineering from Mississippi State University (1962, 1964) and a Ph.D. in Engineering Mechanics from Iowa State University (1971). He has been engaged in research related to the fracture behavior of thick composite laminates, and the viscoelastic behavior of composites.

Charles E. Harris is Head of the Mechanics of Materials Branch at the NASA Langley Research Center, Hampton, Virginia. He received a B.S. in Aerospace Engineering (1972), and M.S. (1973) and Ph.D. (1983) degrees in Engineering Mechanics from the Virginia Polytechnic Institute and State University. He has been engaged in research related to developing a damage dependent constitutive model for laminated composites, and the fracture of thick composite laminates.

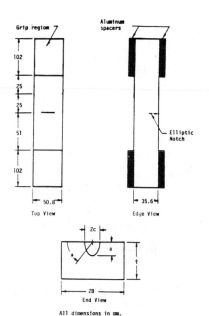

Grip region
Aluminum spacers
102
25
25
51
102
Elliptic Notch
50.8
35.6
Top View
Edge View
2c
a
t
2B
End View
All dimensions in mm.

Fig. 1 Straight-sided test specimen

Grip region
102
51
235
51
25.4
102
50.8
All dimensions in mm.

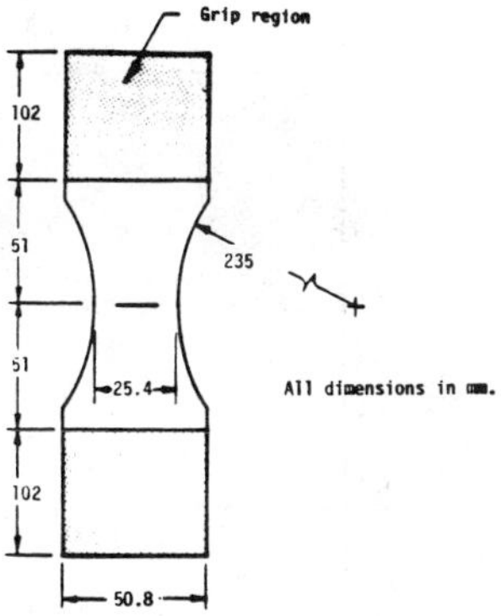

Fig. 2 Tapered test specimen

First ligament failure
Remaining ligament failure
Load
Cross head displacement
Broken fibers
First ligament
Delamination
Remaining ligament
FIRST LIGAMENT FAILURE
REMAINING LIGAMENT FAILURE

Fig. 3 Schematic of two-stage failure

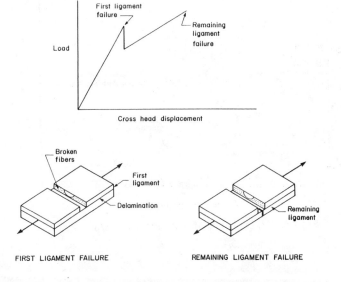

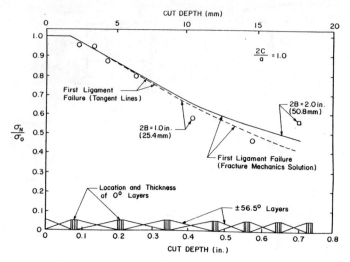

Fig. 4 First ligament failure for 2c/a = 1.0

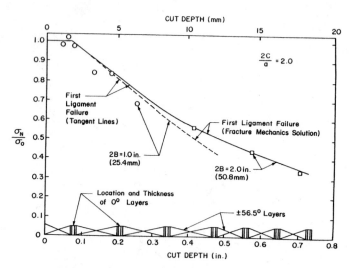

Fig. 5 First ligament failure for 2c/a = 2.0

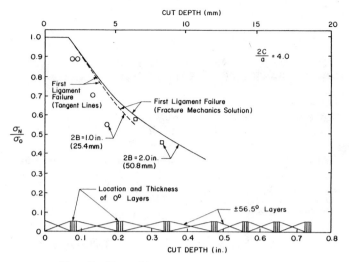

Fig. 6 First ligament failure for 2c/a = 4.0

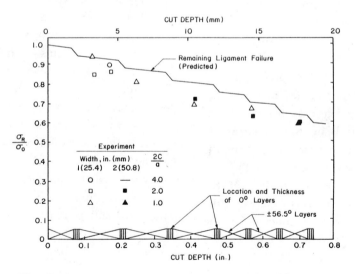

Fig. 7 Remaining ligament failure for 2c/a = 1.0, 2.0, 4.0

ON THE MECHANICS OF FILAMENT WINDING
PART I: A GENERALIZED MODEL

Hechmi Hamouda, Tae J. Kang and Aly El-Shiekh
College of Textiles and Mars Mission Research Center
North Carolina State University
Raleigh, N.C. 27606-8301

Abstract

In this paper the filament winding process was analyzed to relate process variables to structural parameters. An analytical model has been developed for a filament wound preform by determining the necessary geometric and kinematic conditions. An equation of motion of winding was developed to predict layer by layer geometry using the mandrel shape as the initial boundary condition. This model provides the laws of motion of the traverse stroke relative to the mandrel to ensure that the filament laydown is of the predetermined geodesic path over the mandrel, that the winding density is distributed over the mandrel in the prearranged manner, and that the winding build is being formed to reproduce the pre-assigned shape or contour of the preform. From this analysis, the winding process parameters can be controlled accordingly to produce any given shape. The analytical model was used to produce computer simulation of the winding process. The dynamic simulation of the winding process visualizes and inspects the layer by layer path of the tow and provide process variables required to produce preforms of optimum structural parameters. The Computer simulation will be presented later in part II of this series

1. INTRODUCTION

Attempts to one-step filament winding of revolution shapes directly with no prearrangement phase has been less successful then those preceded by adjustments attempts especially for large vessels. Although by trial and error, wound product can be made, because of the approach used, such manufactured items are difficult to reproduce with acceptable quality. The main reason is the empirical method used to determine the process variables. The need and usefulness of analyzing the mechanics of filament winding is required by the need for readily automated equipment leading to the manufacture on an industrial scale of wound products with high mechanical properties as well as excellent structure reproducibility.

A number of different approaches to formulate and analyze the filament winding process has been carried out to establish a fundamental understanding of the mechanics of such processes. Germane analysis has been initially stimulated by winding of textile yarn on bobbins (or packages)[1]. The kinematics of such processes were analyzed for cylindrical, conical and complex shaped packages[2]. In all cases the package have no side support, special consideration were given to the process analysis to provide self support of the yarn when it is wound at the free sides of the package[3]. Recently more stimulus for filament winding analysis, was generated by various industry sectors manufacturing pressure vessels, tanks, and piping systems. Although enduses of wound yarn packages and wound pressure vessels are quite different, the winding process variables are very similar. On the other hand, most of the published work related to filament winding pertains mostly to testing and performance evaluation of end products from a structural or material point of view. Other related published works emphasize the effect of specific structure behavior subsequent to the windings process such as the effect of crazing or cracks on a particular end use of wound products. Another group of publications deals with the process itself from control and design optimization point of view.

Existing programmable filament winding machines are based on either by a trial-and-error emperical formulae or simple numerical estimate of the delivery eye position based on the static geometry of the process[4]. In most cases a track is defined for the delivery eye movement, then according to the laydown path position relative to the mandrel geometry, the succeeding delivery eye position coordinates will be approximated. Aided with computer based simulation, the process will then be fine tuned through a simulated visual inspection prior to the actual filament winding process. Complexity of a thorough analysis often forces filament winding manufacturers to apply simple expressions beyond their intended applicability or, in some instances, alternative forms of fibrous structure formation and reinforcement where the composite behavior is more easily understood[5]. In modeling the filament winding process attempts[6], emphasis was aimed at selected variables associated with the wound product. These variables were limited to the fiber motion and position on the mandrel after laydown, coupled with thermochemical and stress models through material properties. The actual funcional movement of the delivery eye as dictated by the shape being wound, was omitted from all process analysis. Another approach used to overcome the complexities of such process with the usage of a numerical control winding machine[7] to provide an optimum fiber path along each layer to achieve a minimum thickness build-up for the changing circumference. As far as the motion relationship between the delivery eye and the laydown path is concerned only an empirical approach was used based on graphic simulation preceding the actual process.

The latest development in filament winding included a new generation computer controlled system[8]. The equipment is configured such as it relies on real time control of several servo axes, analog outputs, digital output and tension controllers. The system operates based on numerical pattern data that can be transferred from other sources. Motions needed for the process are "taught" to the system based on a "stepping" technique viewed on a simulated pattern screen. Alternate winding techniques were tried to remove the major constraint of the conventional winding methods using netting approach imposed by a fixed domed shapes. To the size the final high composite bulge on the end of the dome, an incremental laydown process[9] is used. The process consist of shifting the fiber laydown according to several families of geodesic paths. The only indication about the parameters defining the winding process is that these parameters are reproduced by programming the different moves of the machine with admittance that some small differences might appear between the theoretical data and the real parameters of the satellite layers.

2. PROCESS FORMULATION

Filament winding on a cylindrical mandrel is basically provi-ded by three separate movements. Rela-

tions among these movements dictate the final shape of filament trajectory on the mandrel as well as the shape of the final product. To formulate the process of filament lay-up on a rotating body of revolution, some definitions of the process variables and parameters are made. All possible linear movements and rotations of the forming process are considered in this formulation. For the sake of definition clarity lets assume, for the moment, that only the beginning formation of one layer is being considered. Vectors, points, distances and principal motions showing on Figure 1 illustrate the geometrical and kinematic parameters and variable which defining the process.

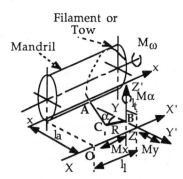

Figure 1. Multiaxial filament winding variables and parameters.

Two axis x-x' and X-X' run parallel to each other. They define respectively the path of point A where the filament first coincides with the mandril, and the longitudinal movement path of point B connected to the delivery eye through a solid arm of length R. The first axis x-x' is the generator axis where the wound structure is being generated, the latter one X-X' is the longitudinal delivery axis where the filament is being delivered to the process. The remaining axis are used to define two additional movement possibilities. Y-Y' is the axis of transverse delivery movement allowing a perpendicular movement of the delivery arm relative to the mandril. Z-Z' is the axis around which the delivery arm can rotate. Although this additional rotation movement $M\alpha$ can be compensated by simultaneously combining X and Y movement, it is useful when and if additional incremental relative movement is required while both linear movements M_x and M_y are occurring in regular cyclic mode.

In addition to R the length of the delivery arm, another geometrical component of the process is l_a the distance between longitudinal delivery axis and generator axis. The position of the delivery eye C is defined, relatively to the origin O, by distances l_l and l_t both in the longitudinal (X) and transverse (Y) directions. The angle of rotation α at B around axis Z-Z' of the delivery arm R is also a component of the geometrical definition of the process. For the following analysis R is set as a parameter with a fixed length. On the other hand, angle α, and lengths l_l and l_t are variables. The equation of motion of point C can be defined function of time t as:

$$C = C(t) = C[x(t), Y(t), \alpha(t), R] \quad (1)$$

Lets assume $x = x(t)$ a given equation of motion of the winding point A. The longitudinal winding point velocity $V_x = \dfrac{dx}{dt}$, parallel to the generator axis x-x', combined with the rotational velocity ω dictates the magnitude of the winding angle θ. A geometrical analysis of two dimensional view of the winding process, illustrated in figure 2, leads to the following relation:

$$\tan\theta = \frac{V_o}{V_x} \quad (2)$$

V_o is the transverse winding velocity of point A (this velocity is relative to the mandrel's motion) and perpendicular to the generator axis x-x'. If ω is the mandril angular velocity and r is the radius of the filament layer being wound, V_o can be expressed as:

$$V_o = \omega r \quad (3)$$

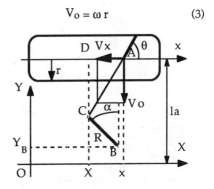

Figure 2. Two dimensional projection of cylindrical filament winding.

According to figure 2 the winding angle θ can also be geometrically expressed as the ratio of distances CD and AD:

$$\tan \theta = \frac{CD}{AD} \qquad (4)$$

Differential equation (5) is obtained by combining equations (2) and (4) and replacing both the longitudinal and transverse velocities of the winding point A by their values mentioned above. This differential equation relates the motion equation $x(t)$ of the winding point A to the delivery eye (point C) motion equation $X(t)$ and to other parameters and variables of the process.

$$\frac{dx}{dt} = \pm \frac{\omega r}{l_a - Y_B - R \cos \alpha} (X - x) \qquad (5)$$

where:

la distance between the mandril axis ox and the traverse axis OX, and

Y_B ordinate of the pivot point B of the delivery eye.

The plus sign is used when the delivery eye is moving to the right. Y_B is the linear transverse motion of the delivery point support, a is the rotational motion of the delivery arm. Using the differential equation of (5), the delivery movement $X(t)$ can be determined if a linear winding motion $x(t)$ is predetermined. The latter motion can be determined from shape and density of the winding to be performed. If the filament laydown geodesic path over the mandrel is predetermined, $x(t)$ is only the the linear component (in the mandril axis direction) of the geodesic filament path. The differential equation of mo-

tion introduced by Emerov[1] represents only a particular case ($\cos \alpha = Y_B = 0$) of equation (5).

3. LOW ANGLE WINDING

To cover all the cylinder surface with tows layed side by side, (all the circumference length of the cylinder $2\pi r$ should be covered) the necessary minimum number m of two is[9]:

$$m = 2 \pi \left(\frac{r}{b}\right) \cos\theta \qquad (6)$$

where:

r the layer's winding radius, and
b the width of the tow used.

Equation (6) is obtained by equating the tow covered circumference length to the number of projected tow widths covering the same circumference (projection parallel to the cylinder axis). Figure 3 shows the variation of the minimum number of tow as function of the ratio of layer radius to tow width varies for different values of θ.

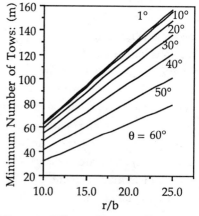

Figure 3. Effects of layer radius on its minimum number of tows.

A more accurate way to determine the number of turns n of the mandril needed to cover all the surface, assuming that the tow is layed down side by side, can be expressed as[9]:

$$n = \frac{2\pi \pm \beta}{2(\phi + \psi) \pm 2\pi k} \qquad (7)$$

where:

β rotation angle for a tow width,

φ rotation angle for one tow length,

ψ rotation angle during traverse motion direction change, and

k integer number depending on the size of angle φ.

Angles φ and ψ (see Figure 4) are determined if the condition n being an integer is satisfied. If not, φ and ψ are adjusted until n becomes an integer. The winding angle θ is determined from the following relationship for a cylinder of length L.

$$\theta = \tan^{-1} [\phi \frac{r}{L}] \qquad (8)$$

Equation (8) can be modified such as n is directly related to θ the winding angle. The modification is made through expressing angle β as the ratio of b the tow width and r cosθ.

$$n = \frac{2\pi \pm \frac{b}{r}\cos\theta}{2[\psi + \frac{L}{r}\tan\theta] \pm 2\pi k} \qquad (9)$$

A condition on θ is necessary to achieve complete coverage of the cylinder surface area: the number m defined in equation (6) should be an integer. The conditional angle θ_c for complete surface coverage should be:

$$\theta_c = \cos^{-1} [\frac{m}{2}(\frac{b}{r})] \qquad (10)$$

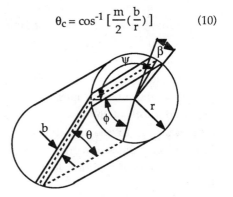

Figure 4. The geometry for low angle winding.

Relationship between the conditional winding θ_c angle and the winding radius expressed by equation (10) is shown in Figure 5 for various fixed number of covering tows m.

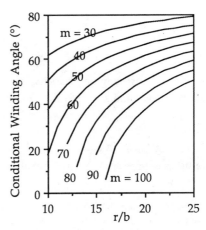

Figure 5. Effect of preform radius on tow helix angle.

4. HIGH ANGLE WINDING

High angle winding of preforms is used for certain applications. The cylinder can be covered either partially or totally. For a total coverage of the cylinder surface certain geometrical conditions pertain to the winding process. To avoid overlapping of the tow by laying it down side by side the winding pitch, or delivery eye advance per turn, should correspond to the projected width of the tow (projected perpendicular to the mandril axis). The maximum winding angle imposed by this condition is defined as:

$$\theta_{max} = \cos^{-1}\left[\frac{1}{2\pi}\left(\frac{b}{r}\right)\right] \qquad (11)$$

Equation (11) can be expressed in term of the mechanical winding charac-teristics rather than in terms of winding angle θ. Using the definition of the winding angle θ:

$$\theta = \tan^{-1}\left(\frac{\omega r}{V_x}\right) \qquad (12)$$

where:
ω the mandril angular velocity, and
V_x the tow velocity parallel to the mandril axis.

Replacing θ_{max} in equation (11) by its value as expressed above will result in:

$$\left(\frac{\omega b}{V_x}\right)_{max} = \sqrt{4\pi^2 - \left(\frac{b}{r}\right)^2} \qquad (13)$$

Relationships expressed by equations (11) and (13) and relating the maximum winding angle or the maximum operating ratio to the radius of winding should be taken into consideration when winding cylin-

drical shapes with rapidly varying diameters. (e.g. conical, spherical, etc..) Figure 6 ullistrates the effects of the winding radius on the maximum winding angle and the maximum winding velocity.

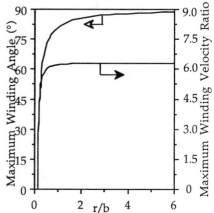

Figure 6. Effect of layer radius on maximum angle and maximum winding speed.

Equation (11) requires that $\cos\theta_{max}$ should be less than or equal to unity which impose a minimal winding radius function of the tow width. This relation can expressed as:

$$r \geq \frac{b}{2\pi} \qquad (14)$$

For the winding to be possible, the minimum winding radius r/b should correspond to exactly $1/2\pi$. When r/b reaches this minimum, the following condition prevails:

$$\frac{\omega b}{V_x} = \tan\theta = \theta = 0 \qquad (15)$$

Expression (15) is valid only for $\omega = 0$ which is no longer filament winding.

Unlike low angle winding, the total number of turns needed to cover the whole cylinder surface depends on the length L of the cylinder being wound. From the geometry of the winding, the total number m can be obtained by equating the total length of pitches to the cylinder length, m can be expressed as:

$$m = (\frac{L}{r}) \frac{\tan\theta_{max}}{2\pi} \qquad (16)$$

or

$$m = (\frac{L}{b}) \sin\theta_{max} \qquad (17)$$

Both expressions (16) and (17) can lead to determine the number m depending on either the radius of the layer or the width of the tow being used.

5. TOW VOLUME FRACTION

When a tow is wound side by side with no overlapping nor uncovered space between two consecutive tows, the tow volume fraction V_t is unity. Because of the following assumption, the terminology tow volume fraction is used here rather than fiber volume fraction V_f: the fibers forming the tow are completely packed with no void in between. This assumption is far from reality since there are always voids between the fibers forming the tow. The volume fraction mentioned here represents an ideal situation as described above. To calculate V_f, V_t should be multiplied by the packing factor of the tow being used.

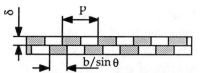

Figure 7. Idealized sectional view of two consecutive wound layers.

From the idealized geometry shown in figure 7, the tow volume fraction can be expressed as:

$$V_t = \frac{1}{2\pi \cos\theta} \frac{b}{r} \qquad (18)$$

The expression of the winding angle θ in equation (13) imposes the following condition on the minimum dimensionless radius of winding for each given tow volume fraction.

$$(\frac{r}{b})_{min} = \frac{1}{2\pi V_t} \qquad (19)$$

Figure 8 illustrates the above codition between the minimal winding radius andthe tow volume fraction.

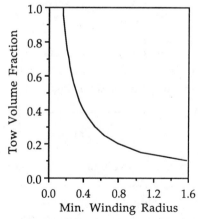

Figure 8. Effects of the minimal winding on the tow volume fraction.

Figures 9 shows the variation of the tow volume fraction V_t when the winding angle θ is maintained constant. These variations were computed based on equation (18). The relationship was plotted for different winding angles.

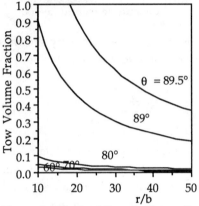

Figure 9. Effects of the winding radius and angle on tow volume fraction.

It should be noticed that equation (18) will produce volume fractions V_t greater than 1 when the winding angle θ is higher than θ_{max} which correspond to tow overlapping. Overlapping was not taken into account in modelling the tow volume fraction.

Replacing θ by its value according to equation (12) in equation (18) will lead to the following:

$$\frac{\omega b}{V_x} = \sqrt{4\pi^2 V_f^2 - (\frac{b}{r})^2} \qquad (20)$$

When the tow volume fraction becomes unity ($V_t = 1$), the resulting winding velocity ratio is the minimal allowable one expressed in equation (13).

The relationship expressed by equation (20) and relating the winding velocity ratio to the dimensionless radius of winding and to tow volume fraction is necessary to be considered when a constant tow volume fraction is to be maintained during the winding operation. As shown in figures 10, a specific variation profile of the winding velocity ratio has to be followed specially while winding cylindrical shapes with rapidly varying diameters. (e.g. conical, spherical, etc..).

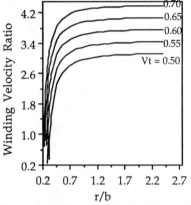

Figure 10. Effects of the winding radius and the tow volume fraction on the winding velocity ratio.

6. COMPLEX PREFORM FORMATION

When winding complex shapes, the design considerations dictate that the mandrel should have a certain angular velocity profile, while the synchronized traverse carriage moves back and forth with different strokes in a geodesic path to ensure the consistency of the preform build. The stroke periods and its amplitude are designed to change with both the thickness of the preform being formed and the relative position of the carriage to the mandrel. Thus the various profiles of stroke modification of the traverse movement give different shape of contours, winding angle, and winding density of the composites. The layup kinematics are determined from the geometrical consideration of the winding pattern of the preform. It is possible to determine analytically the law of motion of the traverse and mandrel to produce a filament wound preform with preassigned structural parameters.

The first researcher that dealt with this sort of problem was Emerov in a serie of papers[1-3,10-16] related to textile packages. Emerov's analysis can be applied to filament winding as shown below.

To link the motion of the traverse carriage to the mandrel position and its rotational speed as the winding process progress, two systems of coordinates are selected, one, a stationary system (x,y,z) and other, a system x', y', z' which rotates together with the axis of the mandrel as shown in Figure 11. Equation of motion (21) of the winding point N for non-cylindrical shapes, is derived, from the differential equation of winding[1] and expressed as:

$$\frac{dx}{dt} = \frac{r(\frac{d\phi}{dt} - \frac{d\gamma}{dt})}{\sqrt{Y^2 + Z^2 - [r + (X-x)\frac{dr}{dt}]^2}}(X - x) \quad (21)$$

where

ϕ rotation angle of the mandrel,

γ angle between the radius of point N and xy plane,

X,Y,Z delivery point M coordinates,

x,y,z winding point N coordinates.

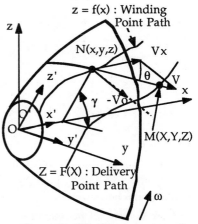

Figure 11. Winding geometry for complex shapes.

Equation (21) defines the movement of the winding point, yarn lay down path, mandrel rotational speed, and modes of traverse movement for all preform shapes. Assuming that the dimension of the bobbin remains constant during one stroke of transverse movement, and that the movement of the transverse delivery point M is defined for building cylindrical preform as:

$$X = \begin{cases} vt; \text{ for } 0 \le t \le \tau \\ -vt + 2L; \text{ for } \tau \le t \le 2\tau \end{cases} \quad (22)$$

where

L length of the traverse movement path,

V traverse speed, and

τ half-period of the traverse stroke,

then the movement of the winding point N can be described from the following equations:

$$X = \begin{cases} vt - \dfrac{dv}{r\omega} + \dfrac{2dv}{r\omega}\exp\left(-\dfrac{r\omega}{d}t\right) \\[4mm] -vt + 2L - \dfrac{2dv}{r\omega}\exp\left[-\dfrac{r\omega}{d}(t-\tau)\right] \end{cases}$$

; for $0 \le t \le \tau$

; for $\tau \le t \le 2\tau$ \qquad (23)

where

d distance between the traverse delivery point and winding point,

r radius of the build, and

ω angular Velocity of the mandrel.

The variables Y and Z are expressed in relation to X(t) of the equation of the motion as:

$$Y = Y(X) \qquad (24)$$

$$Z = Z(X) \qquad (25)$$

The winding point variable y, z can, therefore, be expressed in terms of X, Y, Z and x to obtain the equation of yarn winding on a surface of mandrel which makes possible a complete analysis of the building process.

$$Y = \frac{r}{Y^2 + Z^2}\left\{ Y\left[(X-x)\frac{dr}{dt} + r \right] - Z\sqrt{Y^2 + Z^2 - \left[(X-x)\frac{dr}{dt} + r \right]^2} \right\} \quad (26)$$

$$Z = \frac{r}{Y^2 + Z^2}\left\{ Z\left[(X-x)\frac{dr}{dt} + r \right] - Y\sqrt{Y^2 + Z^2 - \left[(X-x)\frac{dr}{dt} + r \right]^2} \right\} \quad (27)$$

Therefore a filament wound preform of given geometric winding parameters can be produced by determining the necessary geometric and kinematic relations from the equation of winding. However, in the filament winding process, maintaining the equilibrium of the winding process on the surface should be carefully considered.

Differential equations 21, 26 and 27 can be solved numerically for complex shapes and will lead to obtain an approximate equation of motion of the delivery point which will produce the needed preform shape. It is felt however that some results can be achieved by analyzing the situation where the delivery eye moves in a preassigned geodesic path similar similar to that of the preform profile (see figure 12).

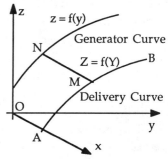

Figure 12. Geometric representation of a curved preform.

Analysis of this problem is under way and a computer simulation for such case will follow in a later presentation.

7. CONCLUSION

This paper used a reasonable and schematic approach in analyzing the process of filament winding. From the analytical relations presented filament winding can made more accurate by programming various drive mechanisms to generate a speed profile based on the geodesic shape of the structure. The equations presented are useful in determining the resulting volume fraction of wound structures as affected by the process parameters, the tow or filament size and the packing factor.

8. ACKNOWLEDGMENT

This work was partially supported by NASA Headquarters through control # 8061C.

9. REFERENCES

[1] Emerov. E.D, *Differential Equation of Motion of the Winding Point,,* Tech. of Textile Industry USSR 1960, No. 2, pp. 91-96.

[2] Emerov. E.D., *The Movement of the Traverse in Building a Complex Shaped Package,* Tech. of Textile Industry USSR, 1966, No. 6, pp. 70 - 75.

[3] Emerov. E.D., *The Yarn-Winding Parameters on a Cylindrical Bobbin as a Basis for the Design of a Winding Motion,* Tech. of Textile Industry USSR., 1962, No. 6, pp. 82-92.

[4] Evans D.O., *Simulation of Filament Winding,* 30th National SAMPE Symposium, March 19-21, 1985, pp. 1255 - 1274.

[5] Ecklod G. C., *A Design Method for Filament Wound GRP Vessels and Pipework,* 1985 Butterworth & Co. (Publishers) Ltd., Composites Vol. 16, No. 1, January 1985.

[6] Caluis, E. P. and G. S. Springer, *Modeling of the Filament Winding Process,* in Proceeding of the 5th International Conference on Composite Materials (ICCM-V), San Diego, CA, July 30 - August 1, 1985, pp. 1071-1088.

[7] Maheshwari, M., *Filament Winding of Non Axisymetric Fuel Tank* 31st International SAMPE Symposium, April 7-10, 1986, pp. 880 - 899.

[8] Roser, R. R. et al., *New Generation Computer Controlled Filament Winding,* 31st International SAMPE Symposium, April 7-10, 1986, pp. 810-821.

[9] Barbalat, C., et al., *Design and Filament-Winding of Structure by an Incremental Method,* 30th International SAMPE Symposium, March 19-21, 1985, pp. 1265-1274.

[10] Emerov. E.D, *Movement of the Winding Point along the Generator of a Cylindrical Bobbin,* Tech. of Textile Industry U.S.S.R. 1962, pp. 90-102.

[11] El'Shaev, V.N., *Investigation of the Yarn Position on the Winding Drum during the Building Process,* Tech. of Textile Industry U.S.S.R. 1966,pp. 94-99.

[12] Emerov. E.D., *The Equilibrium Condition of the Yarn Turn at the*

Winding-on Point, Tech. of Textile Industry U.S.S.R., 1970, p. 79-83.

[13] Karezo, V.D., *The Density Distribution in a Cross-Wound Cylindrical Bobbin*, Tech. of Textile Industry U.S.S.R., 1970, pp. 76-80.

[14] Vulfson, I.I., *The Optimal Equation of Motion of the Yarn Guide in the Reversing Section*, Tech. of Textile Industry U.S.S.R., 1971, pp. 51-55.

[15] Emerov. E.D., *The Movement of the Yarn Traverse for Given Conditions of Equilibrium for the Yarn in Winding*, Tech. of Textile Industry U.S.S.R., 1972, pp. 62-66.

[16] Emerov. E.D., *The Equation of Yarn Winding on a Surface of Rotation*, Tech. of Textile Industry U.S.S.R., 1965, pp. 76-80.

10. BIOGRAPHY

Hechmi Hamouda is assistant professor of Textile Engineering, Chemistry, and Science at North Carolina State University. He holds a Ph.D. in Mechanical Engineering from State University of New York at Buffalo, an M.S. and B.S. in Mechanical Engineering from L'École Nationale d'Ingénieurs de Tunis. He has over three years experience in analyzing Textile processing dynamics and evaluation and characterization of Textile structures.

Tae J. Kang is assistant professor of Textile Engineering at Seoul National University. He holds a Ph.D. in Polymer Sciences from North Carolina State University. He has over five years experience in textile processes including filament winding.

Aly El Shiekh is professor of Textile Engineering, Chemistry, and Science at North Carolina State University. He holds a B.Sc. from Alexandria University, an M.S. in Textile Technology, the MechE and ScD in Mechanical Engineering from MIT. He has over 25 years experience in research including the analysis of fibrous structures, their mechanical properties, and process and equipment development. Since 1988 he is a member of the Mars Research Center directing 3-D braiding and filament winding of composite materials.

MATERIALS RESISTANCE TO LOW EARTH
ORBIT ENVIRONMENTAL EFFECTS

H. G. Pippin and L. P. Torre
Boeing Aerospace
Seattle, WA. 98124-2499

and

R. G. Linton and A. F. Whitaker
NASA-MSFC
Marshall Space Flight Center, AL.
35812

Abstract

A number of flexible polymeric materials have been considered as candidates for protective coatings on Kapton film. These coatings have been tested under a variety of environments, each of which simulates one or more aspects of the low earth orbit space environment.

Mass loss rates vs. fluence and temperature, optical properties, and surface characteristics under exposure to the various environments will be presented. Kinetics data on Kapton and other materials is interpreted in terms of bond strengths and relative thermodynamic stabilities of potential products. Activation energy for degradation of Kapton by oxygen atoms was determined to be 30KJ/MOL $\pm$5KJ/MOL.

Materials tested include silicones, fluorosilicones, fluorophosphazenes, fluorocarbons, and hydrocarbons.

INTRODUCTION

Discovery of unexpected degradation of thermal control paints on early shuttle flights and subsequent identification of atomic oxygen as the reactive specie[1] has lead to serious concerns about the long term survivability of certain material types exposed to low earth oribt (LEO) conditions. Boeing has carried out investigations on the suitability of different materials for use as external materials on Space Station since 1984. Starting in late 1985 much of this work has been performed under an advanced development contract "Space Station Protective Coating Development", supported by NASA-MSFC.[2] Data reported in this paper is primarily from the NASA contract.

Spacecraft in low earth orbits face two environmental factors not found at other orbits; a significant flux of atomic oxygen onto surfaces facing the direction of motion (ram direction) and thermal cycling due to traverse through the earth's shadow. These effects, acting in concert with solar particle and photon radiation, high energy cosmic rays, impact by micrometeoroids and debris, and complicating factors of contamination by outgassing, rocket motor exhaust, and EVA's, must be overcome in order for spacecraft to survive for reasonable periods of time in LEO's.

To be useful at LEO, materials must survive (retain mass) and carry out the function for which they are selected. Many external surface materials serve a thermal control function and must be oxidation resistant to maintain their absorptance to emittance ratio. Some coating materials also serve a simultaneous protective function for organics and/or organic based composite substrates, and certain metals. Seals, lubricants, solar panel materials, heat radiator panels, antennas, and mirrors are hardware which will be exposed to the space environment. Work discussed in this paper focussed upon transparent and white pigmented protective coatings for Kapton thin film substrate.

OXYGEN EXPOSURE

Two mil. thick uncoated Kapton H was used as the baseline material and served as internal standard for these experiments. Selected materials were exposed to atomic oxygen fluxes of between 1 and $5 \times 10^{+16}$ atoms/cm^2-sec for varying periods of time. The apparatus used for these measurements is described in detail in a companion paper published in these proceedings. Mass loss of Kapton was acquired over several temperatures. Data for Kapton, shown in Table 1, was fit to an Arrhenius equation. The values of the activation energy and pre-exponential factor are shown in Table 2. For contract data the mass loss rates reported for each temperature are from least square fits to all available data obtained at the particular temperature. The data point for the lowest temperature was obtained by NASA Ames Research Center.[3]

Mass loss of selected materials relative to Kapton under simultaneous exposure conditions are shown in Table 3. Silicone based materials performed relatively best in tests done for the contract. A siloxane based polymer, CV1-1144, is predicted to have a lifetime at LEO longer than other flexible polymeric materials. A silicone polyimide co-polymer also survived atomic oxygen exposure well. Compared on a mass loss per time under exposure, film coatings of plasma polymerized hexamethyldisiloxane/tetrafluoroethylene provided good atomic oxygen resistance. However, the coatings made by the plasma polymerization process are many times thinner than the other coatings investigated and the absolute lifetimes are short. After short periods of exposure, x-ray photoelectron spectra (XPS) show nitrogen. XPS is a surface technique; and HMDS/TFE does not contain nitrogen. The nitrogen detected is from the Kapton substrate, indicating the coating has been compromised. Scanning electron microscopy photos show HMDS/TFE coatings with cracks in some areas and other areas in which the coatings have flaked off at different times during the exposure. A specimen of HMDS/TFE was exposed to atomic oxygen for 96 hours and then examined with a scanning electron microscope. An SEM from this specimen is shown in Figure 1. The Kapton has "steps" notched in it due to differing amounts of oxidation by atomic oxygen.

Cracking occurred in several materials after exposure to the combined effects environments and/or atomic oxygen exposure. Fluorocarbon materials exhibited varying degrees of resistance;

TFE showed no changes in mass or surface elemental composition over long exposure times when exposed to neutral atomic oxygen. However, when placed within a plasma, TFE specimens lost mass at a greater rate than Kapton.

OPTICAL PROPERTIES

The in situ absorptance of materials show large changes after relatively short term exposure to simultaneous proton, electron and simulated solar UV exposure. Exposure conditions for this test are shown in Table 4. The absorptance measurements are shown in Table 5, along with ex situ measurements of emissivity of the same specimens. A comparison done with a white silicone paint shows a large change in absorptance of the area exposed to all the combined effects, and very little change after exposure to only electrons. The vacuum UV exposure provided by Lyman- radiation was provided in the on-off sequence shown in Table 4. The data indicates some effect in the initial rate of absorptance change. Table 6 shows data from an earlier combined effects test. Both tests show the expected changes in absorptance of white pigmented coatings where the radiation doses include a component of protons.

Little change in optical properties occurred for most materials as a result of exposure to alternating sequences of vacuum thermal cycling and simulated solar UV exposure. Conditions for this test are shown in Table 7 and the results in Table 8. With one exception, materials tested for flexibility subsequent to this exposure by bending over a small radius (0.040 and/or 0.015") showed an increased tendancy to form microcracks. The exception was a fluorosilicone(CV-3530). HMDS, HMDS/TFE, a siloxane, and a fluorophosphaszene were also tested.

X-RAY PHOTOELECTRON SPECTRA RESULTS

Results from a number of XPS are shown in Table 9. Data are included from control specimens, specimens with previous atomic oxygen exposure, and specimens with previous vacuum thermal cycling/UV exposure. The siloxane-polyimide co-polymer shows considerable decrease in the relative carbon content upon atomic oxygen exposure, indicating preferential oxidation of the polyimide sections.

DISCUSSION

Extensive analysis of surfaces exposed to atomic oxygen show cracking; many show increased oxygen content on the surface, and recession occurring just under the cracks. Such observations are consistent with a surface oxidation of the materials, leaving the bulk properties relatively unchanged.

Initial changes in absorptance due to exposure to simultaneous protons, electrons, and UV were rather large for most materials. The rate of change decreased considerably over the test duration, leaving the possibility that a limiting value of absorptance may eventually be reached. However the tests were too short to verify this point.

Atomic oxygen recombination to form molecular oxygen releases about 5ev of energy. Therefore one expects that materials with chemical bonds stronger than 5ev will make good coating candidates. However, under atomic oxygen exposure, as the system tends toward equilibrium the most stable species possible will be formed. Under the conditions of interest this will often be the most stable oxide. This oxidation will occur unless the material is already the most stable species under the ambient conditions, or a large activation energy is required, in which case the oxidation will still occur, but at a very slow rate. Hydrocarbons react with atomic oxygen rather easily because the oxygen can abstract hydrogen atoms and because other potential products, carbon monoxide and carbon dioxide, are thermodynamically relatively stable. Similarly, fluorine atoms are not abstracted by oxygen atoms because the O-F bond is very weak compared with other fluorine bonds. Siloxanes appear to be stable coatings because the oxidation to silica is relatively slow; but it does occur.

Materials used for LEO applications face an extremely severe environment. The simulations used to produce the data repeated here provide a necessary screening function. Those materials which do not perform well in these tests cannot be expected to survive the LEO conditions for sufficient lengths of time. Spacecraft survivability at LEO remains a materials issue. Additional data on this subject may be found in the contract final report for the NASA advanced development contract NAS8-36586, "Space Station Protective Coating Development".

REFERENCES

1. Leger, L. J., NASA Technical Memorandum 58246, May 1982.

2. Pippin, H. G. and Hill, S. G., NAS8-36586 "Space Station Protective Coating Development", final report, January, 1989.

3. Golub, M. A. and Wydeven, T. Polymer Degradation and Stability 22 (1988) Pp 325-338.

Table 1 Mass loss rate of Kapton as a function of Temperature

Source	Temperature(K)	1000/T	Mass Loss Rate
Boeing	468	2.14	1.89
	458	2.18	0.89
	422	2.37	0.85
	373	2.68	0.44
	358	2.79	0.10
	346	2.89	0.13
NASA AMES			
	295	3.39	0.014

Mass loss rates from Boeing data are least square fits
to data at each temperature

Table 2 Arrhenius parameters for reaction of
Kapton with atomic oxygen

Arrhenius fit to data	Range
$A = 4.5 \times 10^3$ (10^{-24} cm^3/atom)	$1.7 - 12. \times 10^3$
$E_a = 30.7$ (KJ/Mol-K)	$28 - 34$

Table 3 Mass loss of selected coatings on Kapton relative to Kapton mass loss

Exposure Time(Hr)	Mass Loss Ratios at 85C	
	CV1-1144(65)	Fluorophosphazene(58)
6	0.08	0.15
10	0.07	0.13
15	0.05	0.10
20	0.06	0.18
25	0.05	0.15

Exposure Time(Hr)	Mass Loss Ratios at 196C		
	HMDS/TFE(52)	Silicone-Polyimide(93) copolymer	RTV Fluorosilicone(101)
6	0.13	0.13	0.45
10	0.14	0.12	0.20
14	0.41	0.08	0.11

Table 4 Irradiation parameters and test sequence for combined effects exposure, summer 1988

Exposure Time(hours)	Average UV Suns	ESH Dose	Lyman Alpha	Particle Fluences	
				Protons	Electrons
62	1.6	100	ON	0.35	0.77
122	1.6	200	OFF	0.71	1.2
226	1.5	360	ON	1.1	2.2
336	1.5	520	OFF	2.0	3.3
471	1.8	760	ON	2.5	4.2
606	1.8	1000	OFF	3.1	4.9
100 HOURS LYMAN ALPHA ONLY			ON	10^{+15} p/cm^2	10^{+15} e/cm^2

Table 5 In situ absorptance and ex situ emissivity measurements of materials exposed to combined effects test sequence, summer 1988

Material	Exposure Time (ESH)							
	0	100	200	360	520	760	1000	1000
Aluminum								
Foil	0.117		0.123		0.128		0.125	0.02
Evaporated	0.094		0.102	0.099	0.106	0.098	0.100	-----
Kapton	0.389		0.427		0.452		0.456	0.77
HMDS	0.338	0.365	0.370	0.377	0.388	0.391	0.399	0.80
	0.350	0.373	0.375	0.386	0.397	0.401	0.408	0.79
HMDS/TFE	0.365	0.392	0.395	0.404	0.413	0.418	0.425	0.76
CV1-1144	0.345	0.386	0.398	0.419	0.443	0.464	0.486	0.67
	0.345	0.387	0.398	0.420	0.444	0.464	0.487	0.66
fluorophosphazene	0.476		0.492		0.539		0.573	0.87
S11G/LO	0.197	0.284	0.322	0.377	0.424	0.455	0.485	0.88
S13G/LO	0.195		0.314		0.412		0.466	0.88
DSET Silicone	0.190	0.279	0.315	0.375	0.425	0.460	0.491	0.90
with H+	0.191						0.433	0.91
without H+							0.224	-----
"Thin" HMDS	0.355	0.403	0.416	0.439	0.460	0.479	0.498	0.67
Silicone-Polyimide	0.386	0.428	0.438	0.458	0.475	0.490	0.506	0.79

Table 6 Solar absorptance values for selected materials as a function of combined radiation effects dose level. Data from spring 1987 test

Equivalent sun hours of UV	0	200	500	1000
35 kev proton fluence +15 2 units 10 /cm	0	1.1	3.3	6.0
30 kev electron fluence +15 2 units 10 /cm	0	0.9	2.5	5.4

Material

	0	200	500	1000
Witness OSR	0.070	0.072	0.076	0.081
Kapton(1)	0.360	0.394	0.441	0.489
HMDS(67)	0.363	0.380	0.397	0.416
HMDS/TFE(69)	0.362	0.379	0.396	0.419
Fluorophosphazene(82)	0.360	0.412	0.507	0.577
S13G/LO-1	0.234	0.288	0.378	0.445
CV-1144	0.338	0.357	0.380	0.407
CV-3530	0.334	0.356	0.400	0.444

Table 7 Conditions for combined vacuum thermal cycling/UV exposure(TC/UV), spring 1988

VACUUM THERMAL CYCLING	ULTRAVIOLET EXPOSURE
811 CYCLES	503.9 HOURS OF EXPOSURE
Vacuum 1-7X10 Torr	Vacuum 1-6x10 Torr
Temperature -80C to +80C (+-3)	Temperature +109C to +115C
Cycle Period 39-41 minutes(typical)	Intensity 1.5-1.6 Solar Constants (0.40 to 0.25 micron range)

Table 8 Optical properties of selected materials before and after TC/UV exposure, spring 1988

Material	Initial	After Exposure	Initial	After Exposure
Kapton	0.276	0.276	0.557	0.556
FEP	0.284	0.284	0.680	0.672
TFE	-----	0.055	0.512	0.511
HMDS	0.253	0.252	0.565	0.563
HMDS?TFE	0.251	0.259	0.518	0.528
CV1-1144	0.243	0.259	0.686	0.692
CV-3530	0.246	0.248	0.787	0.802
Si-Polyimide	0.236	0.309	0.560	0.211
F-Phosphazene	0.244	0.392	0.654	0.782

Table 9 Surface composition of selected materials determined using
X-ray Photoelectron Spectra

Material (Hrs exposure)	Element (Mol %)					
	O	C	Si	F	N	P
HMDS						
0-AO	20	47	33	-	-	-
25-AO	47	21	31	-	0.3	-
48-AO	42	30	28	-	-	-
TC/UV	21	54	25	-	-	-
HMDS/TFE						
0-AO	18	49	30	3	-	-
96-AO	31	47	21	0.8	-	-
96-AO	30	50	18	-	2	-
TC/UV	22	52	24	1.4	-	-
Siloxane-Polyimide						
TC/UV	23	51	26	-	-	-
6-AO	38	30	32	-	-	-
51-AO	43	20	36	-	-	-
CV-3530						
TC/UV	11	52	11	27	-	-
0-AO	14	45	15	26	-	-
1-AO	40	20	31	9	-	-
24-AO	33	25	24	17	-	-
CV1-1144						
0-AO	21	52	27	-	-	-
48-AO	29	39	32	-	-	-
48-AO	33	37	30	-	-	-
Fluorophosphazene						
0-AO	20	42	7	27	-	3.6
49-AO	16	68	9	0.9	3.7	3.1
49-AO	23	40	14	17.6	2.7	3.2
TC/UV	13	30	2	45	5.0	5.9
"Thin" HMDS						
TC/UV	19	57	21	2.8	-	-
3-AO	13	75	5.5	4.5	1.6	-
9-AO	21	71	1.6	0.8	6.0	-
Kapton						
"Polyimide"	17	76	-	-	7	-
1-AO	25	58	-	-	4.5	-
4-AO	24	63	-	-	5.4	-
49-AO	23	67	-	-	4.8	-

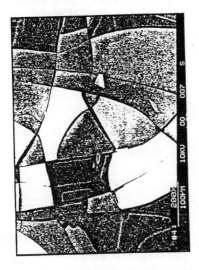

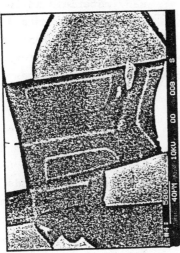

Figure 1   Photographs of HMDS/TFE coating taken using a scanning electron microscope. Sample previously exposed to atomic oxygen for 96 hours

APPLICATION AND PERFORMANCE OF SILICON-BASED
ATOMIC OXYGEN PROTECTIVE COATINGS
J.H. Sanders, P.B. Lloyd and B.J. Tatarchuk
Chemical Engineering Department
Auburn University, Alabama

Abstract

Silicon-based coatings, applied in the form of sputtered silica overlayers or in the form of "paint-on" silicone fluids, provide resistance to the corrosive effects of atomic oxygen encountered in LEO. In this study, conversion electron Mössbauer spectroscopy (CEMS) has been used as a diagnostic technique to evaluate overall coating effectiveness by measuring substrate oxidation below coatings to better than monolayer sensitivity. Iron/silver layered specimens were used as substrates and 30 nm silica coatings were found to significantly decrease substrate oxidation. Preferential separation of silver from coated and uncoated specimens was noted. Silicone fluids were also found to provide good protection of silver foils.

1. INTRODUCTION

Atomic oxygen degradation is a serious problem encountered by many materials in low earth orbit (LEO). Metals such as silver and osmium, which have been considered for use as reflecting surfaces in solar dynamic power systems, are highly reactive with atomic oxygen so that property changes render them inadequate to perform desired functions for extended periods [1,2]. Also, Kapton, a polymide used for solar array blankets, undergoes significant mass losses of ca. 2130 $\mu g/(cm^2\ yr)$ at anticipated Space Station altitudes of 500 km. Under such conditions, typical Kapton materials will provide lifetimes of ca. 15 years [3]. The use of protective coatings is a method for circumventing the problems associated with atomic oxygen degradation. Protective coatings, however, require careful selection and application to ensure that they are thin enough to retain critical substrate properties while thick enough to provide adequate protection.

This study is comprised of work on various silica-based coatings in an attempt to deduce mechanisms for protection as well as to develop coatings for enhanced performance of space-borne materials. One of the most common coatings presently used to retain optical properties in LEO is sputtered silica [4]. The addition of small amounts of polytetrafluoro-ethylene by co-deposition yields more flexible coatings. Such coatings, however, are subject to the formation of defects produced during manufacture, transport, and/or deployment, as well as by contact with micrometeriods and space debris [5,6].

Current efforts concentrate on the use of backscatter conversion electron Mössbauer spectroscopy (CEMS) as a diagnostic tool to evaluate coating performance and substrate lifetime, as well as to reveal chemical information at the coating/substrate interface in a non-destructive fashion. Also, low vapor pressure silicone fluids are investigated to determine their use as flexible coatings which can be used in tandem with rigid materials.

2. EXPERIMENTAL

2.1 Background

CEMS can be used as a diagnostic technique to investigate coating/substrate interfaces. This technique involves the application of a Doppler shift to a gamma-ray source which can excite daughter nuclei within a specimen. For ^{57}Fe daughter nuclei, subsequent relaxation occurs via the emittence of photons as well as K-, L- and M-shell conversion electrons, as depicted in Figure 1. Relaxation of core holes proceeds via KLL, LMM and lower energy Auger events as well as by shakeoff processes. The net effect of a single relaxation event is the expulsion of ca. 5 electrons from within the topmost 0.3 μm. These electrons contain electronic, magnetic and chemical information, revealed

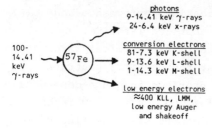

Figure 1. I= 3/2 ---> 1/2 nuclear relaxation scheme for a ^{57}Fe nuclei.

in the form of spectra plotted as the electron intensity versus gamma-ray energy.

To investigate coating performance using CEMS, substrates must be fabricated using ^{57}Fe. Oxidation of ^{57}Fe is an easily distinguished transition as the metallic iron sextuplet is converted to a quadrupole doublet. The relative spectral area of each component allows the extent of oxidation to be calculated based on known ^{57}Fe concentrations. Simulated space environments were obtained using a 13.6 MHz Plasmod plasma asher operated at 80 watts with air at 380 mtorr as the oxygen source. Calibration of the ashing conditions by Kapton was performed and used to estimate an atomic oxygen flux of 2 x 10^{17} O atoms/(cm^2 s) based on fluence and scaling factors found in the literature [7]. This flux is such that 1 h in the plasma asher is equivalent

to ca. 1 yr at an altitude of 500 km.

2.2 Sample Preparation

Iron/silver layered substrates were chosen as atomic oxygen "counting substrates." Iron alone was found to passivate in the presence of atomic oxygen, while silver continuously oxidized as shown in Figure 2. The role of

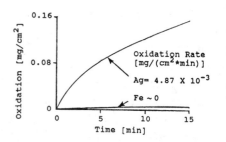

Figure 2. Mass gain versus ash time for iron and silver foils.

silver in the detector substrate was to provide a turbulent subsurface environment in the presence of atomic oxygen so that enhanced iron oxidation would occur. The data in Figure 2 were obtained by ashing known surface area samples of both silver and iron and weighing these samples at intermittent ash times.

Specimens were prepared in a high vacuum evaporation chamber operated at a base

pressure of ca. 1×10^{-7} Pa.
Enriched [57]Fe (67%, Oak Ridge
National Laboratory) and
silver (99.9999%, AESAR) were
evaporated successively as 3
nm layers onto optically flat
fused quartz substrates (W.A.
Sales Co.) for a total of 27
nm, as shown in Figure 3. All
substrates were precleaned
with organic solvents and
heated to 500 K in vacuum
immediately prior to
evaporation to remove adsorbed
gases. Materials were
evaporated using a 3 KW
electron beam gun and
thicknesses were controlled
using a calibrated Inficon XTC
crystal monitor and a
pneumatic shutter assembly. A
30 nm silica coating was
subsequently applied to
selected substrates.*

Two silicone fluids were also
applied to silver foils and
analyzed as atomic oxygen
protective coatings. Dow
Corning DC 976 and DC 705 were
dissolved in benzene at a
concentration of about 3
mg/ml. Solutions were then
spread onto silver foils
(99.9999%, AESAR) and the
solvent allowed to evaporate.
This procedure results in a
thin surface film of silicone

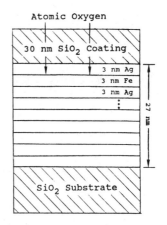

Figure 3. Sample preparation
of iron/silver layered
specimens.

estimated to be on the order
of a micron in depth. All
silver foils were polished and
cleaned with organic solvents
prior to the application of
silicone fluids.

2.3 Analysis

All sputtered specimens were
analyzed using CEMS, X-ray
photoelectron spectroscopy
(XPS) and scanning electron
microscopy (SEM). XPS and SEM
analyses were obtained after
extensive plasma ashing of
both the uncoated and silica
coated Fe/Ag specimens. Only
SEM was used to analyze the
silver substrates coated with
silicone fluids.

CEMS data were collected in an

*Coating procedures performed at NASA-Lewis Research Center, by
D. Gulino, Electro-Physics Branch.

UHV chamber equipped with 7 spiraltron electron multipliers operated at ca. 10^{-8} Pa. Seven spectra were obtained simultaneously in the constant acceleration mode and summed to increase effective counting rates. A 200 mCi ^{57}Co/Pd source was used with positive velocity defined as the source approaching the absorber and zero velocity referenced to the centroid of a metallic iron spectrum. Further details of the spectrometer and the data fitting routine have been described elsewhere [8]. All spectra were recorded at room temperature.

XPS spectra were collected using a Leybold-Heraeus LHS-10 system operated at a base pressure of ca. 10^{-8} Pa. An aluminum anode was used for these studies. Lattice oxygen (@ 531.0 eV) within the specimen was generally used to calibrate the work function of the analyzer.

SEM micrographs were obtained using an ISI Model 5540 SEM operated at a beam energy of 5 kV.

3. RESULTS

3.1 Sputtered Silica Coatings

CEMS spectra for uncoated and 30 nm SiO_2-coated Fe/Ag specimens are shown in Figure 4. A sextuplet dominates spectra for both specimens before ashing. These sextuplets have hyperfine fields of 330 kOe and are representative of bulk metallic iron. After only 2 minutes of ashing, the uncoated specimen has a CEMS spectrum with 26% spectral area contained in a Fe^{+3} doublet having an isomer shift of 0.4 mm/s and a quadrupole splitting of 1.0 mm/s. Continued oxidation results with increased ashing, until about 60% of the original metallic iron spectrum has been converted to Fe^{+3}. The

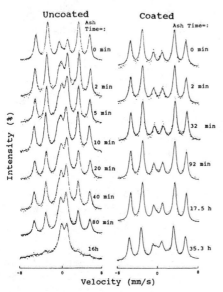

Figure 4. CEMS spectra for uncoated and coated specimens after the indicated ash times.

coated specimen undergoes very little oxidation as verified by the dominance of the sextuplet. After 35.3 h ashing, only 13% of the total spectral area can be associated with an Fe^{+3} doublet.

Figure 5 is a plot of the extent of oxidation versus ash time for the CEMS data shown in Figure 4. As can be seen,

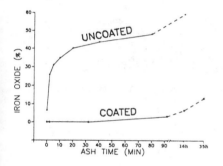

Figure 5. CEMS Iron oxide spectral area versus ash time for uncoated and coated specimens.

the uncoated specimen oxidizes rapidly with over 40% oxidation taking place in less than 20 minutes. The coated specimen has no traces of oxidation until about 90 minutes of total ashing. Comparison after 16 h of ashing shows that 7.2 nm of iron was oxidized in the uncoated specimen while only 0.7 nm of the iron (about 2.5 atomic layers) was oxidized in the coated specimen.

SEM micrographs of coated and uncoated specimens are shown in Figure 6. Micrographs of both specimens reveal a significant amount of area in the form of "popcorn" structures on the surface. These structures comprise 12% and 7% of the areas of coated and uncoated specimens, respectively. Based on the size distribution of the popcorn structures, and assuming the volume of each structure to be 25% the volume of a hemisphere (defined by a mean radius determined from the area taken off a micrograph), these structures account for all the silver present in the coated specimen and 26% of that located within the uncoated specimen. The surface of the uncoated specimen has a rough texture while the coated specimen appears more smooth.

XPS scans for both specimens were obtained after ashing procedures. Ag $3d_{3/2-5/2}$ and Fe $2p_{1/2-3/2}$ scans are shown in Figure 7. Silver peak positions for both specimens indicate Ag^{+2} on the surface. Iron was detected in the +3 valence state for the uncoated specimen with Si^{+4} being the most prominent species detected on the coated specimen. For the uncoated

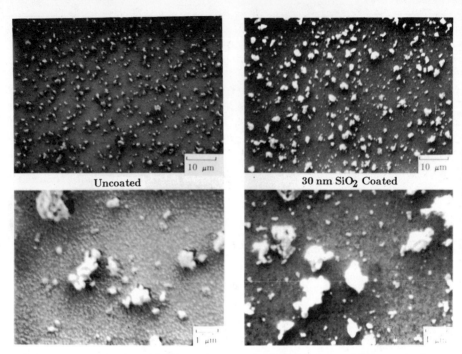

Figure 6. SEM micrographs of uncoated and 30 nm SiO_2-coated specimens after extensive plasma ashing.

specimen a Ag/Fe atomic ratio of 4.6 was calculated, and for the coated specimen, a Ag/Si atomic ratio of 0.077 was calculated.

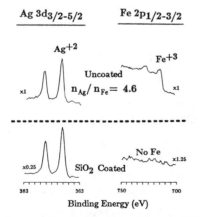

Figure 7. Iron and silver XPS scans of coated and uncoated specimens after plasma ashing.

3.2 Silver Foils Coated with Silicone Fluids

SEM micrographs of silicone coated silver foils prior to and after 10 minutes of ashing are shown in Figure 8. DC 976 forms a discontinuous coating with large unidentified particles within the coated regions. These particles are less pronounced after ashing, however, the nonuniform coating allows significant atomic oxygen degradation of the silver foil. DC 705 provides a more uniform coating and does not show evidence of degradation within the coated regions.

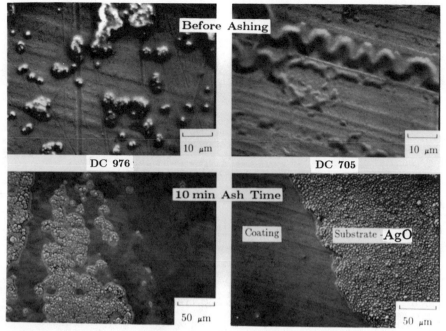

Figure 8. SEM micrographs of silicone fluids prior to and after 10 minutes ashing.

4. DISCUSSION

Figure 5 provides evidence that oxidation of iron in the detector substrate is essentially eliminated by a 30 nm silica coating. Investigation by SEM indicates phase separation of iron and silver in the substrate. Determination of the composition of the "popcorn" structure as being AgO was obtained using XPS and supports a mechanism for the phase separation wherein silver migrates out of the layered specimen toward pinhole defects.

Schematics of both the coated and uncoated specimens are presented in Figure 9. Whether the formation of AgO initiates at the outer surface of the specimen or within the subsurface region has yet to be determined. For the latter situation, the 50% volumetric expansion associated with metallic silver oxidation may create a subsurface increase in pressure, forcing AgO through defect sites and forming "popcorn" structures at the surface. For such a mechanism to be operative, it seems logical that with the extrusion of all the underlying silver, some iron

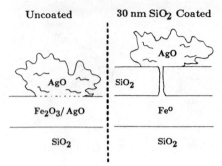

Uncoated	30 nm SiO₂ Coated

Figure 9. Schematic of "popcorn" structures formed on both coated and uncoated Fe/Ag substrates after extensive plasma ashing.

would also be carried to the surface. Since this is not the case, a mechanism where silver migrates through defect sites and oxidizes at the coating surface must also be considered.

It is interesting to note that "popcorn" structures form on both coated and uncoated specimens. The mechanism in which silver oxidizes below the coating and causes pressure build-up is easily understood for the coated specimen where the rigid silica overlayer creates a closed system. A similar explanation for the uncoated specimen can also be valid if the iron layers form rigid oxide skins upon ashing.

Further experimentation is planned to clarify the mechanism(s) of phase

separation. If silver migration toward pinholes occurs, addition of the correct amount of silver in coatings may prove beneficial for obtaining self-plugging systems. New coating techniques may involve a thin pre-coating of silver or silica/silver co-sputtering.

From the SEM micrographs in Figure 8, it is apparent that DC 705 provides a more uniform atomic oxygen resistant coating than DC 976. The boiling point for DC 705 is 518 K at 66 Pa, therefore, this fluid would not survive applications on surfaces exposed to high temperature environments. However, future efforts will attempt to use DC 705 to block pinhole defects in more rigid silica-coated specimens. Such technology would be beneficial for many reasons including, (i) the repair of rigid coatings after deployment, (ii) the reduction of rigid coating thicknesses since pinhole densities may be reduced, and (iii) the production of more flexible silica coatings.

5. CONCLUSIONS

CEMS is a sensitive and nondestructive diagnostic technique useful for determining substrate lifetimes below protective coatings. Coating/substrate interfaces can be monitored for less than one atomic layer of oxygen infiltration. The use of 30 nm silica coatings was found to increase the expected lifetimes of substrates as much as an order of magnitude.

Silver migration toward pinhole defects was also found to occur in iron/silver layered specimens. This phase separation resulted in AgO decoration of the pinholes at the surface of the coating. No iron was detected by XPS at the surface. Preferential separation of silver may prove beneficial for developing coating materials with self-plugging characteristics.

The silicone fluid, DC 705, was found to provide continuous and uniform coverage against atomic oxygen degradation when applied to a silver foil as a dilute solution from an organic solvent. Although this substance is not thermally stable, it may be applied over rigid silica coatings to plug defect sites and enhance overall coating performance at reduced loadings and outgassing rates compared to full siloxane overlayers.

6. REFERENCES

1. Peters, P.N., Linton, R.C., and Miller, E.R., Geophysical Research Letters 10, 569 (1098).
2. Peters, P.N., Gregory, J.C., and Swann, J.T., Appl. Optics 40, 1290 (1986).
3. Banks, B.A., et al., Proceedings of the 18th IEEE Photovoltaic Specialists Conference, IEEE, New York, 1985, pp 381-386.
4. Banks, B.A., et al., Ion Beam Sputter-Deposited Thin Film Coatings for Protection of Spacecraft Polymers in Low Earth Orbit, NASA TM-87051, 1985.
5. Gulino, D.A., The Survivability of Large Space-Borne Reflectors Under Atomic Oxygen and Micrometeoroid Impact, NASA TM-88914, 1987.
6. Gulino, D.A., Effect of Hard Particle Impacts on the Atomic Oxygen Survivability of Reflector Surfaces With Transparent Protective Overcoats, NASA TM-88874, 1987.
7. Miller, W.L., Mass Loss of Shuttle Space Suit Orthofabric Under Simulated Ionospheric Atomic Oxygen Bombardment, NASA TM-87149 (1985).
8. Zabinski, J.S., and Tatarchuk, B.J., Nucl. Instr.

Methods Phys. Res. <u>B31</u>, 576
(1988).

BIOGRAPHIES

Jeffrey H. Sanders is a
graduate student at Auburn
University where he is
completing his PhD research in
Chemical Engineering. His
research involves the use of
surface and subsurface
analytical techniques to study
buried interfacial reactions.
He received a NASA-Graduate
Student Researchers Program
Fellowship for three years.
He earned a BS in Chemical
Engineering from Georgia Tech
in 1983.

Peter B. Lloyd obtained a BS
in Chemical Engineering from
North Carolina State
University in 1986. He began
graduate studies at Auburn
University the same year in
the Chemical Engineering
Department in the fields of
surface science and catalysis.
He is the recipient of a
Southeastern Regional
Fellowship and a NASA Graduate
Student Researchers Program
Fellowship.

Bruce J. Tatarchuk is a
faculty member in the Chemical
Engineering Department and
Space Power Institute at
Auburn University.

34th International SAMPE Symposium
May 8-11, 1989

EVALUATION OF ATOMIC OXYGEN RESISTANT PROTECTIVE COATINGS FOR
FIBERGLASS-EPOXY COMPOSITES IN LEO

Sharon K. Rutledge
NASA Lewis Research Center
Cleveland, Ohio

Phillip E. Paulsen
Cleveland State University
Cleveland, Ohio

Joyce A. Brady
Sverdrup Technology
Middleburg Hts., Ohio

Abstract

Fiberglass-epoxy composite masts are the prime structural members for the Space Station Freedom solar array. At the altitude where Space Station Freedom will operate, atomic oxygen atoms are the most predominant species. Atomic oxygen is highly reactive and has been shown to oxidize organic and some metallic materials. Tests with random and directed atomic oxygen exposure have shown that the epoxy is removed from the composite exposing brittle glass fibers which could be easily removed from the surface where they could contaminate Space Station Freedom Systems. Protection or fiber containment systems; inorganic based paints, aluminum braid, and a metal coating; were evaluated for resistance to atomic oxygen, vacuum ultraviolet radiation, thermal cycling, and mechanical flexing. All appeared to protect well against atomic oxygen and provide fiber containment except for the single aluminum braid covering. UV radiation resistance was acceptable and in general, thermal cycling and flexure had little to no effect on the mass loss rate for most coatings.

1. INTRODUCTION

Fiberglass-epoxy composites have many potential space uses such as a mast material for Space Station Freedom. Space Station Freedom will utilize photovoltaics for the primary power generation system in the first phase of operation [1]. The photovoltaic cells are mounted to a flexible polyimide Kapton HN® blanket which provides support for the cells as well as the interconnecting circuitry. A fiberglass-epoxy mast is used to extend and retract the solar array blanket and provide structural support. There are two main fiberglass-epoxy components to the mast: the battens and the longerons. There are three longerons per mast. They are continuous and extend the full length of the array (approximately 30.5 m (100 ft). As the mast is retracted, the longerons coil into a canister for storage where they are under conditions of significant flexural stress. Battens are the cross braces which provide internal support to the mast and are under no stress when stored. A more complete description of the solar array assembly system is given in reference 2.

When extended, the mast components will be exposed to the low Earth orbital environment. The main constituent of this environment between 180 and 650 km (97 and 351 nmi) is atomic oxygen [3]. Impact of surfaces with energetic (4.2 to 4.6 eV)[4] atomic oxygen causes surfaces to oxidize which could lead to contamination of surrounding surfaces or structural failure. Many materials including epoxy are known to be susceptible to reaction with atomic oxygen [4]. In addition to atomic oxygen, durability to other environmental hazards such as UV radiation [5], and thermal cycling [5] need to be assessed for spacecraft materials.

This paper will discuss the effect of atomic oxygen on fiberglass-epoxy composites and several candidate protective coatings and coverings. The consequences of thermal cycling, flexing, and UV radiation will also be discussed on both protected and unprotected fiberglass-epoxy surfaces. Testing concentrated on longerons since they undergo the largest amount of mechanical stress. Any technique which can provide protection for the longerons should also provide adequate protection for the battens.

2. EXPERIMENTAL PROCEDURE

2.1 Longerons and Protection Techniques

Longerons were supplied by AEC Able Engineering for testing. The longerons had rectangular cross-sections .64 by .74 cm (.25 by .29 in.) with rounded edges. Samples for atomic oxygen plasma exposure, flexure testing, and thermal cycling were 12.7 cm (5 in.) in length while samples for UV exposure and directed atomic oxygen beam exposure were 2.54 cm (1 in.) in length. Longerons contained 19 to 22 percent amine cured epoxy resin by weight; the remainder being S-2 glass fibers.

The protection systems evaluated for the fiberglass-epoxy are aluminum braid and double aluminum braid coverings (AEC Able Engineering); In-Sn eutectic coating of primer/electroless nickel/immersion coated gold/indium-tin eutectic (applied by Composite Optics Inc.); CV-1144, a silicone based paint (manufactured by McGhan Nusil and brush applied at NASA LeRC); and S13G/LO-1, a thermal control paint composed of potassium silicate treated zinc oxide pigment in a silicone elastomer vehicle (manufactured by IIT Research Institute and applied by paint spray gun at NASA LeRC on top of a brush applied organosilane ester primer). The appearance of the samples prior to exposure is illustrated in Figure 1.

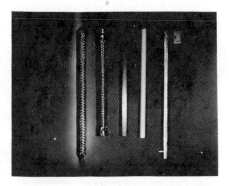

Figure 1. Protected Mast Samples (left to right): Single Al Braid, Double Al Braid, CV-1144, S13G/LO-1, and In-Sn Eutectic Covered

2.2 Dehydration

Samples were dehydrated in a vacuum chamber at a pressure between 2.7 and 9.3 Pa (20 mtorr and 70 mtorr) prior to mass measurement in order to eliminate errors due to absorbed water from the atmosphere and outgassing. The amount of time necessary for the sample to reach equilibrium ranged from approximately 5 days for unprotected fiberglass-epoxy to approximately 25 days for CV-1144 and S13G/LO-1 coated fiberglass-epoxy longerons. A detailed description of the dehydration exposure duration determination is given in reference 6.

2.3 Atomic Oxygen Exposure

Two types of atomic oxygen exposure systems were used for testing. An RF (13.56 MHz) air plasma asher (SPI Plasma Prep II) was used for durability testing of the longerons. Samples were exposed directly in the plasma at pressures ranging from 2.7 to 16 Pa (20 mtorr to 120 mtorr). The plasma contained atomic oxygen and nitrogen in various ionization and energy states. Although the various states of nitrogen are abundant, the reaction of materials with nitrogen appears to be negligible in relation to the reaction with the atomic oxygen states present [7]. Typical fluxes of atomic oxygen in the plasma ranged from $5x10^{14}$ to $2x10^{15}$ atoms/$(cm^2$-sec). These values are based on the epoxy loss rate from the longerons assuming the same erosion yield for epoxy $(1.7x10^{-24}$ cm^3/atom) as measured in space on Shuttle flight STS-8 [8].

Although the flux is accelerated to what is experienced in low Earth orbit (LEO) and the plasma energy (a few 10ths of an eV) is lower, ashers can provide a good qualitative indication of material survivability in LEO. To date, materials that have survived in an asher have also survived in LEO. The asher was used to determine initial coating durability and to evaluate durability after thermal cycling and flexing. These tests were performed sequentially in order to better simulate the actual longeron environment. (Figure 2)

The arrival of atomic oxygen on the longerons in a plasma asher is from many angles while the atomic oxygen in space is nearly unidirectional. In order to determine what difference

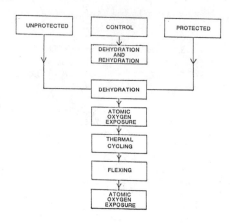

Figure 2. Longeron Test
Sequence

directionality plays in the
oxidation of fiberglass-
epoxy, an atomic oxygen
directed beam was used to
expose smaller unprotected
longeron samples for mass
loss determination followed
by scanning electron
microscopy. The directed
beam is produced by an end
Hall gridless ion source
(Commonwealth Scientific
Inc.). A mixture of O^+ and
O_2 is present in the beam
which impinges on the
samples at approximately 57
eV for an anode energy of
90 eV [9]. Pressure during
operation was approximately
.013 Pa ($1x10^{-4}$ torr) with
a base pressure of
approximately $1.3x10^{-4}$ Pa (
$1x10^{-6}$ torr). Samples were
exposed at an equivalent
atomic oxygen fluence of
approximately $9.4x10^{20}$
atoms/cm^2 based on the
erosion yield of epoxy in
LEO.

2.4 Thermal Cycling

Thermal cycling was
performed mainly to
determine if thermal
expansion mismatch between
the protective surface and
the longeron would cause
cracks or openings to occur
that would allow the
underlying surface to be
exposed to atomic oxygen.
Thermal cycling was
performed at atmospheric
pressure in a gaseous
nitrogen environment by
cycling the sample between
a chamber heated by
electric coils and a
chamber filled with cold
nitrogen gas. Transfer of
the sample between chambers
was controlled by a
thermocouple embedded in
the center of one longeron
used only for temperature
control. Up to three
longerons could be exposed
at one time on our sample
tray. Each longeron
experienced 413 thermal
cycles between a core
temperature of +80 and -80
^oC. The average time spent
in one chamber was
approximately 4 min.

2.5 Flexure Testing

Flexure testing was
performed in order to
simulate the extension and
retraction of the mast from
the mast canister. During
storage, the longerons are
coiled into a canister
whose typical diameter is
approximately 66 cm (26
in.). Longeron samples,
both protected and
unprotected, were flexed
and then straightened with
the aid of a clamping
fixture to the radius of
curvature they would
experience in the canister
for a total of 100 cycles.
This corresponds to a
surface strain per cycle of
0 to approximately 1
percent. The mast extension
and retraction may occur
only 10 to 20 times during
the life of Space Station
Freedom, so this is a more
severe test of the mast
flexural durability.

2.6 Ultraviolet Radiation
Exposure

Longerons were exposed to vacuum ultraviolet (VUV) radiation followed by exposure to atomic oxygen in the asher to determine if VUV radiation would affect the protective coating such that cracks or defects would be formed in the coating and the underlying surface would be degraded by atomic oxygen. Samples were exposed on one side. VUV radiation was provided by a deuterium lamp in a water cooled chamber inside a vacuum belljar. Pressure during operation was $5x10^{-5}$ Pa ($4x10^{-7}$ torr) to $2.7x10^{-4}$ Pa ($2x10^{-6}$ torr). The sample exposure level was 5 equivalent suns for approximately 1000 equivalent sun hours (ESH). Sample temperature during exposure was between approximately 21 and 32 $^{\circ}$C (70 and 90 $^{\circ}$F). By using a deuterium lamp in vacuum for UV exposure, an accelerated UV exposure is achieved in the 100-200 nm (3.9x10-6 to 7.9x10-6 inches) wavelength range with a less than real time exposure closer to the visible region of the spectrum. Since the wavelength region that is accelerated contains the most damaging radiation, the test is more severe and UV damage should be more evident.

3. RESULTS AND DISCUSSION

3.1 Durability Testing of Unprotected Fiberglass-Epoxy

Unprotected fiberglass-epoxy longerons were exposed to atomic oxygen in a plasma asher for 1747 hr which corresponds to an equivalent atomic oxygen fluence of $8.8x10^{21}$ atoms/cm^2 based on the erosion yield of epoxy in LEO. The mass loss per unit area for two longerons exposed at different spatial locations in the plasma was recorded as a function of time along with the mass loss per area of a sample of polyimide Kapton® included for comparison (Figure 3).

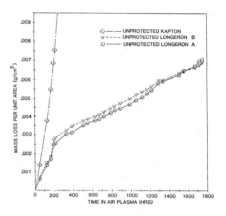

Figure 3. Mass Lost From Unprotected Fiberglass-Epoxy as a Function of Plasma Exposure Time

From previous asher tests and data obtained in space, it is known that glass and other metal oxides are very resistant to attack by atomic oxygen [8]. Therefore, the mass loss observed is most likely from the epoxy in the composite and not the S-2 glass fibers. The drastic change in slope that occurs at approximately 200 hr is consistent with the change in mass loss rate which would occur if the epoxy on the surface had been removed leaving a mix of epoxy and glass fibers on the surface in a proportion equivalent to the fill ratio. The most alarming thing about this data is that the mass loss rate does not eventually decrease as would be expected if the fiberglass on the surface shielded the deep, visually hidden, underlying epoxy. This appears to indicate that the fiberglass-epoxy would not become self protecting once the glass fibers were exposed. For a 15 year exposure in a constant density environment for Space Station Freedom, the average fluence that the mast surfaces are likely to be exposed to would be approximately half of the front and back solar array exposure or 2.1×10^{22} atoms/cm^2 [10]. This exposure would correspond to approximately 4220 hours in the asher based on an equivalent asher fluence. Assuming that the oxidation depth is small in comparison to the longeron diameter, and the rate of epoxy loss remains constant beyond 1747 hours in the asher, the depth of oxidation can be approximated by calculating the loss from a flat fiberglass-epoxy surface with a surface area percentage of 31% epoxy after approximately 200 hours of asher exposure. In this manner, it was determined that the outer layer of epoxy covering the fibers for these particular samples was approximately .0016 cm (6.3×10^{-4} in.). The depth of oxidation below the outer epoxy layer was approximately .0285 cm (.011 in.). Since the glass fibers are approximately 10 microns (3.9×10^{-4} in.) in diameter, this depth would correspond to approximately 29 fiber diameters. In terms of overall depth, this would correspond to only 5% of the longeron diameter with an overall longeron mass loss of 2% over the life of Space Station Freedom. These numbers are not very large and would not cause great concern. However, the glass fibers which are exposed

could break off and contaminate Space Station Freedom systems, or could cause difficulty in mast retraction if the loose fibers created friction in the track of the extension and retraction mechanism. Figure 4 shows an unexposed fiberglass-epoxy longeron and one that was exposed to atomic oxygen in the plasma asher for an equivalent fluence of 8.8×10^{21} atoms/cm^2 which is approximately 41% of the Space Station Freedom life. Individual fibers can be seen that have lifted off of the surface.

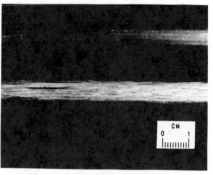

Figure 4. Unexposed (Top) and Plasma Exposed (Bottom) Fiberglass-Epoxy

The actual depth of oxidation and amount of fiber exposure may not be as severe in LEO since the plasma atomic oxygen exposure is omnidirectional while the actual exposure would be better simulated by a sweeping directed beam. Therefore, a directed beam of atomic oxygen ions was used to bombard the samples to determine if there are differences between directed and random exposure. Scanning electron photomicrographs in Figure 5 show fiberglass-epoxy exposed to the air plasma at an equivalent fluence of 5×10^{20} atoms/cm^2 and exposed to the directed beam at an equivalent fluence of 9.4×10^{20} atoms/cm^2. The plasma exposed sample appears to have a more porous epoxy surface remaining with the fibers loosely adherent to the underlying surface, while the epoxy surrounding the fibers in the directed beam exposed sample has taken on the highly filamentous and textured surface as observed with ram exposed polymers on Shuttle flight experiments in LEO [11]. The epoxy also seems to be more intact underneath the fibers due to the directionality of the oxidation.

a. Exposed in Air Plasma Asher

b. Exposed in Atomic Oxygen Directed Beam

Figure 5. Atomic Oxygen Exposed Fiberglass-Epoxy

While the directed beam exposure was performed on one side of the sample, the actual mast will experience a directed beam which will sweep all the way around it because the mast must rotate to maintain alignment of the solar cells with the sun. It would be expected that a more complete exposure of the surface would occur which would remove more of the epoxy underneath the glass fibers. The actual exposure is probably somewhere between the asher and the directed beam with the penetration depth of the atomic oxygen being much shallower for the beam and space exposures. Longer exposures with the beam are needed to verify this. The possibility of fiber removal would still be a serious problem.

The concern over the extent of fiber removal is severe enough that a means of coating or covering the surface may be needed to prevent the removal of fibers from the surface by either containing them at the very least, or preventing epoxy removal. The protection required must also be able to survive the surface strain levels (approximately 1%) experienced by the retracted longeron.

3.2 Durability Testing of Protected Fiberglass-Epoxy

All 5 types of protected longerons and an unprotected specimen were exposed to the air plasma for an equivalent fluence of approximately 4.6×10^{20} to 8.5×10^{20} atoms/cm^2 for initial durability evaluation. All coatings and coverings except the single aluminum braid appeared to provide some protection to the longeron (Figure 6).

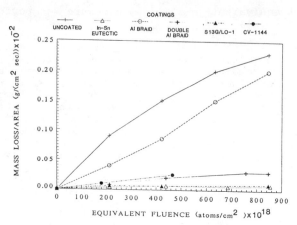

Figure 6. Mass Loss of
Protected and Unprotected
Fiberglass-Epoxy as a
Function of Fluence

The single aluminum braid
is very open which allows
the fiberglass-epoxy to be
directly exposed to the
atomic oxygen. The braid
openings are also large
enough that the fibers
could not be contained on
the surface of the
fiberglass-epoxy after they
are exposed. The mass loss
rates for the unprotected
and aluminum braid
protected fiberglass-epoxy
composites are very similar
and scanning electron
micrographs of the surface
under the braid were
identical to those for the
unprotected fiberglass-
epoxy. The addition of a
second braid layer reduced
the mass loss rate further.
The CV-1144 experienced
some mass loss and this was
attributed to areas where
the paint did not
completely cover the
surface (Figure 7). This
coating also seems to
remain tacky after coating
and exposure. The S13G/LO-1
and indium-tin eutectic
coated samples experienced
very little mass loss after
exposure to atomic oxygen.

Figure 7. Scanning Electron
Photomicrograph of a CV-
1144 Coated Longeron After
Exposure to an Atomic
Oxygen Fluence of
Approximately 4.6×10^{20}
atoms/cm^2

Longerons coated with CV-
1144, In-Sn eutectic, and
S13G/LO-1 were exposed to
UV radiation followed by
ashing in order to
determine if UV could break
down the protective nature
of the coating. The 1000
ESH exposure appeared to
have no effect on the mass
loss rate of the longerons
during ashing (Figure 8).
A slight darkening of the
S13G/LO-1 after UV exposure
was the only observable

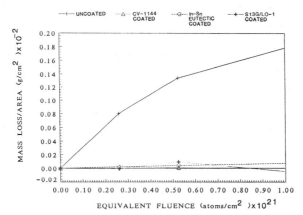

Figure 8. Mass Loss of
Protected and Unprotected
Fiberglass-Epoxy Exposed
to an Air Plasma After
1000 ESH of VUV Exposure

effect. The CV-1144 performed slightly better in this test. This is possibly due to a more continuous coating on this sample.

Some of the protected samples and the unprotected sample from Figure 6 as well as a second unprotected sample were thermal cycled and then flexed before a second exposure to atomic oxygen in order to determine if the protective coatings could withstand these conditions and still protect against attack by atomic oxygen. Unprotected sample # 1 and the indium-tin eutectic coated sample were exposed at the same time. The remaining three were exposed together in a later exposure. Mass loss per unit area data for these exposures are shown in Figure 9.

The mass loss per unit area data for the unprotected and single aluminum braid protected longerons during the second atomic oxygen exposure agree fairly well with the data for the first atomic oxygen exposure.

This also appears to be true for the CV-1144 and the first 1.8×10^{20} atoms/cm^2 exposure of the indium-tin eutectic. The eutectic appears to lose a large amount of mass at greater fluence levels which is unexplained. The rate of loss is very close to that for unprotected epoxy, but there was no unprotected portion of the longeron visible as in the case of the CV-1144. There was also very little cracking of the surface observed. If the coating itself is being removed because it is being oxidized, the mass loss should have been observed earlier. S13G/LO-1 coated and double aluminum braid coated samples will be exposed in the future along with a verification exposure of the In-Sn eutectic.

4. CONCLUSIONS

Even though the total amount of epoxy removed from fiberglass-epoxy composites in low Earth orbit is not significant

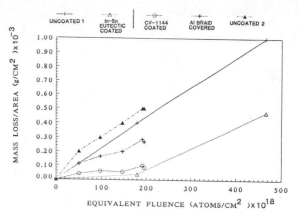

Figure 9. Mass Loss Per
Unit Area for Unprotected
and Protected Fiberglass-
Epoxy Exposed to an Air
Plasma After Exposure to
Thermal Cycling and
Flexure

for most applications, the contamination problems that could result from loss of glass fibers from the surface is of great concern. Preliminary tests with directed and random atomic oxygen sources indicate that fiber exposure is highly likely at the atomic oxygen fluence levels that Space Station will experience. Therefore some means of protection to either prevent loss of epoxy at best or provide fiber containment at the very least is needed. Of the coatings evaluated to date, CV-1144, S13G/LO-1, and In-Sn eutectic appear to provide good protection against atomic oxygen with a double aluminum braid covering being slightly worse. The single aluminum braid offered little to no protection and also seemed to provide no fiber containment ability. The ability to protect, however is very dependent on the continuity of the coating coverage. Vacuum ultraviolet radiation appeared to have no effect on the ability of the coatings to resist atomic oxygen attack. Flexing and thermal cycling also appeared to have little effect on the mass loss rates of the braid covered samples and CV-1144 coating. The In-Sn eutectic coating exhibited an increase in mass loss which would indicate coating failure, however no visual indication of failure was observed. This coating and S13G/LO-1 will be tested in the future. CV-1144 appears to provide good fiber containment and atomic oxygen resistance if applied uniformly to the surface. S13G/LO-1 and In-Sn eutectic appear promising, however, more testing is needed.

5. ACKNOWLEDGEMENTS

The authors would like to thank Russ Hart of NASA Lewis Research Center for the use of his thermal cycling facility.

6. REFERENCES

1. Baraona, C.R., The Space Station Power System, NASA TM-88847, Fifth Conference on Photovoltaic Generators in Space, European Space Agency, Noordwijk, Netherlands, September 30 to October 4, 1986.

2. Ciancone, M.L., Rutledge, S.K., Mast Material Test Program (MAMATEP), AIAA Paper 88-2475, AIAA Issues of the International Space Station Conference, Williamsburg, Virginia, April 21-22, 1988.

3. NOAA, ANSA, and USAF, U.S. Standard Atmosphere, 1976.

4. Banks, B.A., Mirtich, M.J., Rutledge, S.K., and Nahra, H.K., Protection of Solar Array Blankets from Attack by Low Earth Orbital Atomic Oxygen, 18th IEEE Photovoltaic Specialists Conference, Los Vegas, Nevada, October 21-25, 1985.

5. Rauschenbach, H.S., Solar Cell Array Design Handbook, Van Nostrand Reinhold Co., New York, 1980.

6. Rutledge, S.K., Paulsen, P.E., Brady, J.A., and Ciancone, M.L., Oxidation and Protection of Fiberglass-Epoxy Composite Masts for Photovoltaic Arrays in the Low Earth Orbital Environment, NASA TM-100839, Spring Meeting of the Materials Research Society, Reno, Nevada, April 5-9, 1988.

7. Rutledge, S.K., Banks, B.A., DiFilippo, F., Brady, J., Dever, T., Hotes, D., An Evaluation of Candidate Oxidation Resistant Materials for Space Applications in LEO, NASA TM-100122, Workshop on Atomic Oxygen Effects Sponsored by NASA JPL, Pasadena, CA, November 10-11, 1986.

8. Banks, B.A., Rutledge, S.K., and Brady, J.A., The NASA Atomic Oxygen Effects Test Program, Proceedings of the 15th Space Simulation Conference, Williamsburg, Virginia, 1988.

9. Kaufman, H.R., Robinson, R.S., Seddon, R.I., End-Hall Ion Source, J. Vac. Sci. Technol. A 5 (4), Jul/Aug, 1987, pp 2081-2084.

10. Leger, L., Visentine, J., Santos-Mason, B., Selected Materials Issues Associated with Space Station, 18th International SAMPE Technical Conference, October 7-9, 1986.

11. Banks, B.A., Mirtich, M.J., Rutledge, S.K., and Swec, D.M., Sputtered Coatings for Protection of Spacecraft Polymers, NASA TM-83706, 11th International Conference on Metallurgical Coatings Sponsored by the American Vacuum Society, San Diego, CA, April 9-13, 1984.

BIOGRAPHIES

Sharon K. Rutledge is a Research Engineer with the Electro-Physics Branch at NASA Lewis Research Center where she currently works in the areas of atomic oxygen simulation, atomic oxygen durability evaluation of materials for Space Station Freedom and other missions, and high emittance radiator surfaces for spacecraft. She has received her M.S. in Materials Science and Engineering from Case Western Reserve University, Bachelors Degree in Chemical Engineering from Cleveland State University and is a member of Tau Beta Pi. She has been on the staff of NASA 8 years.

Phillip E. Paulsen is an undergraduate research assistant for Cleveland State University working at NASA Lewis Research Center. Presently, he is evaluating the atomic oxygen durability of coatings and surfaces for Space Station Freedom. He is a member of Tau Beta Pi and expects to graduate with a dual degree in Mechanical Engineering and Economics in December of 1989. He has been employed by Cleveland State University approximately 2 years.

Joyce A. Brady is a research engineer for Sverdrup Technology's Lewis Research Center Group. Presently, she is investigating the effects of vacuum ultraviolet radiation and temperature cycling on proposed spacecraft materials. She is also assisting with the coordination of the LeRC sponsored Atomic Oxygen Effects Test Program whose purpose is to increase the understanding of material erosion characteristics in ground based atomic oxygen exposure facilities through a data collection program. She is pursuing a Master's degree in Materials Science and Engineering from Case Western Reserve University and has earned a B.S. in Chemistry from Cleveland State University. She has been employed by Sverdrup Technology approximately 2 years.

RADIATION AND THERMAL EFFECTS ON THE TIME-DEPENDENT
RESPONSE OF T300/934 GRAPHITE/EPOXY

Robert N. Yancey
Advanced Research and Applications Corporation - ARACOR
Sunnyvale, CA 94086

Marek-Jerzy Pindera
Civil Engineering Department
University of Virginia
Charlottesville, VA 22901

Wayne Slemp
Joan G. Funk
Applied Materials Branch
NASA-Langley Research Center
Hampton, VA 23665

Abstract

Previous work on T300/934 graphite/epoxy composites has suggested that radiation, in conjunction with elevated temperature, may lead to an increase in the time-dependent response of the material under mechanical loading. This paper outlines the results of an investigation into the effects of radiation and temperature on the time-dependent response of the same composite system. Creep tests on irradiated and nonirradiated T300/934 composite specimens and bulk 934 resin specimens were carried out at room temperature and +121°C. The irradiated resin and composite specimens were exposed to 1 MeV electrons for a total dose of 10,000 Mrads to simulate a 30 year exposure in geosynchronous orbit (GEO). The experimental results indicate that electron radiation has little effect on the creep response of the composite and bulk resin specimens at room temperature while at +121°C the electron radiation exposure resulted in a significant increase in the creep response observed in the initial stages of loading. The initial increase in the creep response is accompanied by a decrease in the glass transition temperature (T_g) of the irradiated specimens. The extent of creep decreases with increasing exposure time to elevated temperature and is accompanied by an increase in T_g.

The magnitude of recovery of T_g after long exposure times to +121°C suggests that the irradiated material is capable to healing itself to some degree but cannot totally recover from exposure to radiation at +121°C.

1. INTRODUCTION

The use of resin matrix composites has become quite common in the aerospace industry. The most commonly mentioned advantages that composites enjoy over conventional materials are superior strength-to-weight and stiffness-to-weight ratios but other advantages are just as important. The other advantages include low thermal conductivity, low thermal expansion, and the ability to tailor composites to meet specific needs. Today, engineers look to composite materials not only to save weight but also to design structures that meet requirements that were previously thought unrealistic with conventional materials such as metals and plastics. These additional advantages make resin matrix composites ideal for space structures.

The space environment presents many harsh conditions for structural materials. The effects of vacuum, thermal cycling, and radiation on the performance of a candidate material must be completely evaluated before the material can be utilized in long-term space structures. In geosynchronous orbit (GEO), a spacecraft or structure will be in an almost perfect vacuum, experience temperatures as cold as -157°C and as hot as +121°C, and be subjected to ultraviolet, proton and electron radiation [1]. All these conditions may have a potentially significant effect on the performance of many structural materials.

Milkovich, et al [2,3] and Reed, et al [4] have conducted tests on T300/934 graphite/epoxy under simulated space environment conditions. Constant strain-rate, quasi-static and cyclic tension tests have been performed on graphite/epoxy coupons at -157°C and +121°C after the specimens were exposed to a radiation dose in vacuum equivalent to a 30-year exposure in GEO. The quasi-static tests performed by Milkovich, et al, and the cyclic tests performed by Reed, et al, suggest that radiation, coupled with elevated temperature, may lead to an increase in the time-dependent component of T300/934 under mechanical loading. This hypothesis is consistent with dynamic mechanical analyzer (DMA) data obtained by Milkovich, et al, which indicated that radiation reduced the glass transition temperature of the composite to near the elevated testing temperature of +121°C. Milkovich, et al, attributed the reduction in T_g to be the result of radiation-induced molecular chain scission and separation of low molecular products in the epoxy network.

The present investigation was undertaken to determine the combined effect of radiation and temperature on the time-dependent response of T300/934 graphite/epoxy. In order to meet this objective, creep tests on baseline (nonirradiated) and irradiated T300/934 graphite/epoxy specimens with different fiber orientations were conducted at room and elevated (+121°C) temperature. Creep tests also were carried out on bulk 934 resin specimens that were subjected to the same total radiation dose as the composite specimens. DMA and thermomechanical analysis (TMA) tests were conducted on the baseline and irradiated specimens to gain an understanding of the changes at the molecular level caused by radiation exposure and test temperature.

2. EXPERIMENTAL PROGRAM

Unidirectional coupons having fibers oriented at 0°, 10°, 45° and 90° with respect to the longitudinal axis were cut from panels laid up and cured at the NASA-Langley Research Center according to standard T300/934 graphite/epoxy cure procedures.

The panels were scanned ultrasonically before the specimens were cut in order to avoid possible defective regions. The coupons were 152.4 mm long and 12.7 mm wide. These dimensions were dictated by the maximum aspect ratios of the coupons that could be efficiently placed in the radiation facility. Bulk 934 resin specimens were manufactured following procedures outlined by Herakovich, et al [5]. These specimens had the "dog-bone" geometry (type 5) outlined in ASTM Standard D638-82a [6].

Half of all the specimens (composite and bulk resin specimens) were subsequently exposed to 1 MeV electrons at a dose rate of 50 Mrads per hour for a total dose of 10,000 Mrads which simulates a "worst case" exposure of 30 years in GEO. The radiation exposure was performed at the NASA-Langley Research Center's Space Materials Durability Laboratory. The specimens were irradiated with a 254 mm diameter beam from an electron accelerator. An aluminum plate attached to the system's water-cooled backplate was used for holding the specimens in place. A thermocouple and Faraday cup were connected to the backplate to monitor the temperature and electron dosage rate, respectively. During irradiation, the maximum temperature that the specimens experienced was +38°C;

in general, the temperature was maintained at +35°C.

After irradiation, fiberglass tabs were bonded to the composite creep test specimens and the specimens were instrumented with 45° rosette strain gages. Figure 1 shows a schematic of the composite coupon prepared for testing.

The creep tests on irradiated and nonirradiated specimens were conducted at room temperature and +121°C. Four test conditions were, therefore, associated with each type of specimen, namely: NR (nonirradiated, room temperature), IR (irradiated, room temperature), NE (nonirradiated, elevated temperature), and IE (irradiated, elevated temperature). Henceforth, the above two-letter code will be used to identify the different specimens tested at the four conditions. Three specimens of each type were tested at each condition.

The creep response of each type of specimen was determined at four different load levels. Wherever possible, the load levels were approximately 20%, 40%, 60% and 80% of the ultimate load for the given configuration based on the data reported by Milkovich, et al. The specimens were held at each load level for two hours. At the end of the two-hour period, the load was removed and the specimen was allowed to recover for two hours.

This process was repeated four times, each time at a successively higher load level. The entire load sequence is illustrated in Figure 2. A listing of the load levels used for each specimen type is given in Table 1. In the majority of cases, these load levels are approximately equal to the percentages of the ultimate loads enumerated above. However, it should be mentioned that they were also influenced by the weights available for use in the creep frames, and the desirability to compare the creep response of different types of specimens at the same load level.

The creep tests on 10°, 45° and 90° composite coupons were performed on lever arm creep frames located in the Laboratory for Experimental Mechanics and Non-Metallic Materials Characterization at Virginia Polytechnic Institute and State University. The specimens were aligned and clamped with steel grips that were tightened with socket-head cap screws. The load was applied with steel pins going through the grips and the load frame. Due to the very high strength of the composite in the fiber direction, the creep tests on 0° composite coupons were conducted on a United Testing System (UTS) screw-driven loading frame operating in a load control mode. The bulk resin tests were performed using a dead weight fixture specially designed for this purpose [7].

The temperature of the elevated temperature tests was monitored with a thermocouple attached to the grips holding the test specimens. Generally, the temperature was maintained between +118°C and +124°C; it rarely fluctuated more than 1°C during each test. Each specimen was maintained for an hour at the elevated temperature before being tested to allow it to reach thermal equilibrium. Temperature was not monitored for the room temperature tests but all tests were run in temperature-controlled rooms that were maintained between +22°C and +24°C. Although humidity varied from day to day, all tests were conducted on specimens freshly removed from a vacuum chamber.

The glass transition temperature of irradiated and nonirradiated composite specimens was determined using the DuPont 981 Dynamic Mechanical Analyzer (DMA) following the procedure outlined by Milkovich, et al. The DMA technique is based on the fact that internal damping of a polymer greatly increases near T_g. The shape of the damping vs temperature curve can be qualitatively related to the molecular weight and cross-link density. The following general observations are useful in interpreting DMA results: increasing heights of damping peaks indicate decreasing average molecular weights, right-

ward shifts (to higher temperatures) of the damping peaks indicate higher cross-link densities, and wider damping peaks indicate wider distributions of molecular weights. Due to the size and brittle nature of the epoxy specimens employed in this investigation, the glass transition temperature of bulk resin specimens was determined using the TMA technique. DuPont 942 Thermomechanical Analyzer was employed for this purpose, again following the procedure outlined by Milkovich, et al.

3. EXPERIMENTAL RESULTS

Due to space limitations, only selected results will be presented in this paper which are most pertinent to the discussion of the effects of space radiation and temperature on the time-dependent response of T300/934 graphite/epoxy. The presentation will begin with the discussion of the creep response of the composite specimens tested at the four conditions. This will be limited to the response of 10° and 90° tensile coupons. The fiber dominated 0° coupons did not exhibit noticeable creep in the time frame tested, indicating that graphite fibers are practically elastic in the considered temperature range before and after irradiation. It will be recalled that the contribution of the matrix phase to the longitudinal response of 0° coupons is negligible for graphite/epoxy composites. On the other hand, the longitudinal and shear response of the 45° off-axis coupons exhibited similar trends as the response of the 10° off-axis coupons and thus will not be discussed.

The presentation of the creep response of composite specimens will be followed by the creep response of bulk resin specimens. Next, additional creep data on irradiated 10° off-axis coupons tested at +121°C that have been maintained for different periods of time at the elevated temperature prior to testing will be presented. This will be followed by DMA and TMA data on irradiated composite and bulk resin specimens, respectively, that were also presoaked at the elevated temperature for different periods of time. The interested reader is referred to reference (7) for a more detailed outline of the experimental results.

Figure 3 illustrates the longitudinal creep response of the irradiated and nonirradiated 10° off-axis coupons tested at room temperature. The load levels for both types of specimens were identical. The response is illustrated for the entire loading sequence. It is seen that the creep response for the irradiated and nonirradiated specimens is nearly identical except for a slight difference in the elastic response. Differences in the elastic response are most likely due to slight variations in the cross-sectional areas of the individual specimens. The creep strains at each load level are rather small for both types of specimens. It is observed that a small permanent strain remains after the loading/recovery cycle at each load level for both conditions.

Figure 4 illustrates the longitudinal creep response of the irradiated and nonirradiated 10° off-axis coupons tested at +121°C. In this case, only the first two load levels are the same for both conditions due to the lower strength of the IE specimens (Table 1). Nevertheless, it is seen that the response of the IE specimens is markedly different than the response of the NR specimens. The initial creep response of the IE specimen is significant and exhibits a large permanent strain at the end of the first recovery period. As the test progresses, the magnitude of the creep strain appears to diminish after each loading cycle. The magnitude of the permanent strain at the end of each recovery cycle also becomes progressively smaller in relation to the strain at the beginning of the given loading cycle. At the end of the entire loading sequence however, a large permanent strain remains. This is in contrast with the creep response of the NE specimen which exhibits little creep strain and thus little permanent strain at the end of the loading sequence even though it was exposed to higher loads than the IE specimen. The shear response of the 10° off-axis coupons presented in the principal material coordinate system is illustrated in Figures 5 and 6 for the two test temperatures. These curves were obtained by using standard transformation equations to transform stresses and strains from one coordinate system to another. The trends observed in the shear response curves are similar to those seen in the longitudinal creep response except that in this case the creep component is more pronounced. This suggests that the creep response of the 10° off-axis specimens tested at room temperature and +121°C is, in large measure, due to the shear component. This is very evident at the elevated temperature where dramatic differences are seen between the response of the NE and IE specimens. The results of the creep tests conducted on the 90° coupons, which will be discussed next, support this hypothesis.

Figure 7 illustrates the creep response in transverse tension obtained from irradiated and nonirradiated 90° coupons tested at room temperature. It is seen that the creep response for both types of specimens is very similar and not very pronounced. The end of each loading cycle is characterized by residual strain which, curiously, increases slightly during recovery of the first two loading cycles in the case of both types of specimens and in the last cycle in the case of the IR specimen. This may be due to damage occurring in the matrix during initial loading in the presence of the large tensile residual stresses produced during cool down [7].

The creep response in transverse tension for the elevated temperature tests is illustrated in Figure 8. The extent of the creep response of the NE specimen is of the same order of magnitude as for the specimens tested at room temperature. On the other hand, the IE specimen exhibits significantly more creep during the initial stages of the loading sequence which tends to decrease during subsequent loading cycles. The recovery for both types of specimens is almost complete at the end of each cycle in contrast to the preceding results. At the elevated temperature, the residual stresses are much smaller than at room temperature, thus allowing viscoelastic effects to take place instead of damage. The almost complete recovery is due to the high stiffness of the fibers which tend to spring back as the matrix stresses relax upon removal of the load. The important thing to note is that even though the creep strains increase significantly for the irradiated 90° coupons at the elevated temperature, they are still not comparable to the large shear creep strains observed in the response of the 10° off-axis coupons tested under the same conditions.

The creep response of the bulk resin specimens exhibits the same trends as the creep response of the composite specimens. Figure 9 illustrates the creep response of the four types of resin specimens (NR, IR, NE, IE) tested at the first stress level of 11.03 MPa. The NR and IR results are nearly identical, except for the elastic response, and exhibit very little time-dependent behavior. The NE specimen exhibits a slight increase in the creep response while the corresponding increase in the case of the IE specimen is very dramatic. A large permanent strain remains at the end of the first loading cycle of the IE specimen whereas the recovery for the remaining specimens is nearly complete.

At the higher stress levels, the creep response of the NR, IR and NE specimens remained small and increased proportionally with increasing load. On the other hand, the creep response of the IE specimen at the second level increased to the point where the strain gage readings became unreliable and the gages began to peel off. This occurred at approx-

imately 1.5% strain. As a result, creep tests on the IE specimens could not be performed at the higher load levels. Figure 10 illustrates the creep response of the IE specimen up to the point in the second cycle where the gages stopped producing reliable data. As is observed in the figure, the creep strain after the first 30 minutes of the second load cycle is smaller than the corresponding strain of the first cycle despite the 50% increase in the load level of the second cycle. This is consistent with the decreasing creep behavior during subsequent loading cycles observed in the time-dependent behavior of the irradiated composite specimens tested at the elevated temperature.

4. DISCUSSION AND ADDITIONAL RESULTS

As hypothesized by Milkovich, et al, radiation causes chain scission and separation of low molecular weight products. In time, the separated radicals eventually recombine and form new cross-links. As the mobility of the radicals increases with increasing temperature, the rate at which they recombine also increases. The above process is greatly accelerated at temperatures close to the glass transition temperature, and in effect "heals" the damage caused by radiation. This healing phenomenon first postulated by Tenney, et al [8] on the basis of thermal cycling and DMA data alone, which in many ways resembles a post-curing process, can be used to explain the test results obtained in the present study.

The IE results in all cases seem to substantiate the above healing effect. As illustrated, the first loading cycle always exhibited the greatest creep behavior. This was accompanied by a large apparent permanent strain at the end of the recovery period. During subsequent cycles, the relative magnitude of creep and permanent strains decreased despite increases in the applied load. The observed creep response of the IE specimens may be explained by using a schematic representation of a cross-linked molecular structure, Figure 11a, which undergoes the following sequence of events, Figure 11b-d. First, radiation causes chain scission as shown in Figure 11b. At +121°C, the broken chains are quite mobile and will slide, twist and uncurl rapidly. The free radicals are also mobile at this temperature and begin to recombine. As the specimen is strained, the molecular chains slide past each other, Figure 11c, while new cross-links are formed in the strained condition, Figure 11d. Upon recovery, the material is in a different state than when the load was initially applied since many more cross-links now exist, many of which were formed in the strained state. This creates an apparent permanent strain in the specimen upon removal of the load. During subsequent loading, the structure of the polymer is more cross-linked, more rigid and thus more resistant to creep. This explains the decrease in the creep behavior and the decrease in the permanent strains observed during subsequent load cycles.

In order to verify the above hypothesis, additional creep tests were conducted. Since cross-links are continually being reformed in the IE specimen at elevated temperature, creep tests on irradiated 10° off-axis coupons were conducted at +121°C after presoaking the already irradiated specimens for different periods of time at this temperature. Figure 12 illustrates the creep response of these specimens. The creep response of the nonirradiated specimen is included for comparison. As shown, the longer the specimen is exposed to +121°C before being subjected to mechanical load, the less creep it experiences during subsequent loading. After 8 hours at +121°C, the creep response of the irradiated 10° off-axis coupon is reduced substantially, although not to the point where it is comparable to the creep response of the material in the NR condition. This reinforces the hypothesis that some healing is taking place while the specimen is maintained at +121°C.

In order to obtain a qualitative estimate of the magnitude of healing that occurs at +121°C, DMA and TMA tests were conducted on composite and bulk resin specimens with different presoak histories. As mentioned before, glass transition temperatures obtained from these tests can be qualitatively related to the cross-link density. Figure 13 illustrates the effect of presoaking the 45° off-axis specimens for different periods of time at +121°C on the damping response as a function of temperature. The glass transition temperature of the irradiated 45° off-axis coupons as a function of presoak time obtained from the above response curves is given in Figure 14. Included in the figure are the results for the nonirradiated specimens presoaked for the same periods of time. As is observed, irradiation initially reduces the T_g by approximately 55°C and substantially broadens the damping peak, thus indicating that the radiation exposure produces a lower cross-link density and wider distribution of molecular weights. Increasing the presoak time of irradiated specimens at +121°C increases T_g for presoak times up to 40 hours. After 40 hours of presoak time, the difference between T_g of irradiated and nonirradiated specimens is reduced to approximately 28°C.

Beyond 40 hours of presoak time, no increase in T_g takes place. The increase in the T_g and the decrease of the damping curve width with increasing presoak time indicate that the polymer matrix is cross-linking with exposure to the elevated temperature. This, in turn, indicates that the irradiated material is capable of healing itself to some degree at +121°C but cannot totally recover from the exposure to radiation.

The TMA results for the bulk resin specimens illustrated in Figure 15 show similar trends. In this case, the glass transition temperatures of both the irradiated and nonirradiated bulk resin specimens are lower than the corresponding temperatures of the composite specimens. Further, healing time appears to be shorter. However, the reduction in the initial T_g due to irradiation is approximately the same as for the composite specimens, as is the increase in T_g at the end of the 8 hour period when T_g stabilizes. It is possible that the presence of fibers influences the rate of healing.

5. CONCLUSIONS

The results of the present study indicate that radiation does not significantly affect the creep response of T300/934 graphite/epoxy at room temperature. At +121°C however, electron radiation initially increases the time-dependent behavior of the

1184

composite while lowering its glass transition temperature. The increase in the creep response is substantial and is most pronounced in the presence of shear stress along the fiber direction. Radiation-induced chain scission of the epoxy network allows for increased chain mobility at the elevated temperature. Increased chain mobility increases viscoelastic behavior of the composite and also permits free radicals and ionic centers broken off from molecular chains during radiation to recombine and cross-link. Increasing the time of exposure of irradiated specimens to elevated temperature, therefore, increases the glass transition temperature by increasing the cross-link density and thus reduces the magnitude of the time-dependent response. The magnitude of the recovery of T_g after prolonged exposure of irradiated specimens to +121°C, however, is approximately 50% of the loss incurred during irradiation. This suggests that the irradiated material is capable of healing itself to some degree when maintained at +121°C but it cannot fully recover from exposure to radiation at this temperature.

6. ACKNOWLEDGEMENTS

This research was supported by the NASA-Virginia Tech Composites Program under Grant NAG-1-343 while the first two authors were associated with the ESM Department at VPI&SU. The authors gratefully acknowledge this support. The late George Sykes of the NASA-Langley Research Center was the technical monitor during the initial stages of the investigation. This investigation is a continuation of the work on radiation effects of composite materials that he, together with Professor C. T. Herakovich, initiated. Appreciation is also expressed to Professor H. Brinson for the use of testing equipment located in the Laboratory for Experimental Mechanics and Non-Metallic Materials Characterization at VPI&SU.

7. REFERENCES

1. Garrett, H.B., "Review of the Near-Earth Spacecraft Environment," SPIE, Vol. 216, Optics in Adverse Environments, 1980, pp. 109-115.
2. Milkovich, S.M., Herakovich, C.T. and Sykes, G.F., "Space Radiation Effects on Graphite- Epoxy Composite Materials," CCMS-84-08 (VPI-E-84-20), Virginia Polytechnic Institute and State University, Blacksburg, VA., June 1984.
3. Milkovich, S.M., Herakovich, C.T. and Sykes, G.F., "Space Radiation Effects on the Thermo-Mechanical Behavior of Graphite-Epoxy Composites," J. Composite Materials, Vol. 20, November 1986, pp. 579-593.
4. Reed, S.M., Herakovich, C.T. and Sykes, G.F., "Influence of Electron Radiation and Temperature on the Cyclic, Matrix Dominated Response of Graphite-Epoxy," J. Composite Materials, Vol. 21, July 1987, pp. 234-252.
5. Herakovich, C.T., Fox, F.G. and Sykes, G.F., "Degradation of Graphite-Epoxy Due to Electron Radiation," ASME J. of Engineering Materials and Technology, Vol. 110, April 1988, pp. 146-152.
6. D638-82a, "Standard Test Method of Tensile Properties of Plastics," 1984 Annual Book of ASTM Standards, Section 8, Vol. 08.01,

American Society of Testing and Materials, Philadelphia, PA, 1984.

7. Yancey, R.N. and Pindera, M-J, "Radiation and Temperature Effects on the Time-Dependent Response of T300/934 Graphite/ Epoxy," CCMS-88-02 (VPI-E-88-05), Virginia Polytechnic Insti-tute and State University, Blacksburg, VA., March 1988.

8. Tenney, D.R., Sykes, G.F. and Bowles, D.E., "Space Environmental Effects on Materials," AGARD Environmental Effects on Materials for Space Applications, Toronto, Canada, September 22-24, 1982.

Table 1. Creep Load Levels for Each Specimen Type

Specimen type	Load level 1 (MPa)	Load level 2 (MPa)	Load level 3 (MPa)	Load level 4 (MPa)
NR-Bulk Resin	11.03	22.06	33.09	44.12
IR-Bulk Resin	11.03	22.06	33.09	44.12
NE-Bulk Resin	11.03	22.06	33.09	44.12
IE-Bulk Resin	11.03	16.54	-	-
NR-10°	50.05	100.17	150.22	200.34
IR-10°	50.05	100.17	150.22	200.34
NE-10°	50.05	74.59	102.37	130.23
IE-10°	50.05	74.59	76.80	102.37
NR-45°	32.75	49.98	67.22	84.45
IR-45°	32.75	49.98	67.22	84.45
NE-45°	32.75	49.98	67.22	84.45
IE-45°	10.34	15.51	20.68	25.85
NR-90°	8.34	16.68	25.09	33.43
IR-90°	8.34	16.68	25.09	33.43
NE-90°	8.34	16.68	25.09	28.13
IE-90°	8.34	11.44	16.68	19.78

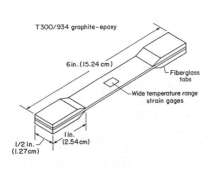

Figure 1. Specimen Geometry

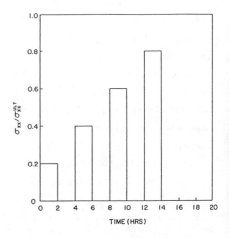

Figure 2. Loading Sequence for the Creep Tests

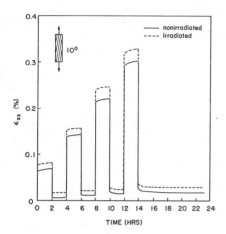

Figure 3. Longitudinal Creep
Response of 10° Off-Axis
Coupons at Room Temperature

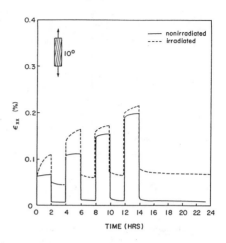

Figure 4. Longitudinal Creep
Response of 10° Off-Axis
Coupons at +121°C

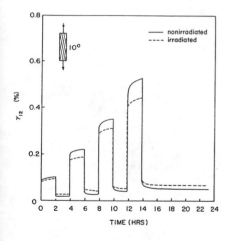

Figure 5. Shear Creep Response
of 10° Off-Axis Coupons
at Room Temperature

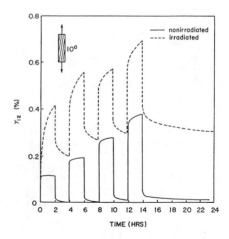

Figure 6. Shear Creep Response
of 10° Off-Axis Coupons
at +121°C

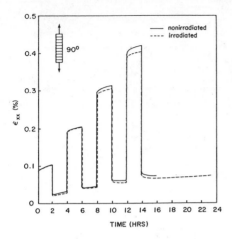

Figure 7.   Transverse Creep
Response Obtained from 90°
Coupons at Room Temperature

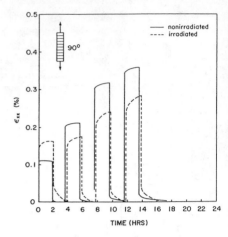

Figure 8.   Transverse Creep
Response Obtained from 90°
Coupons at +121°C

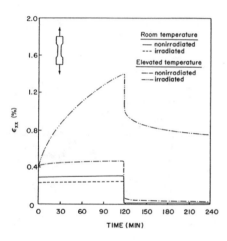

Figure 9.   Creep Response of Bulk
Resin Coupons at 11.03 MPa

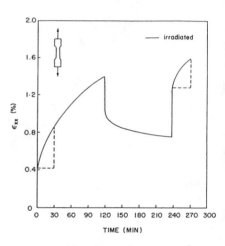

Figure 10.   Creep Response of
Irradiated Bulk Resin
Coupons at +121°C for the
Entire Loading Sequence

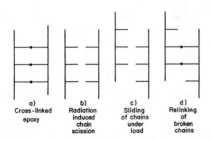

Figure 11.   Schematic Representation of the Healing Phenomenon

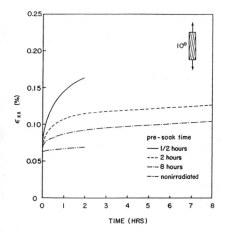

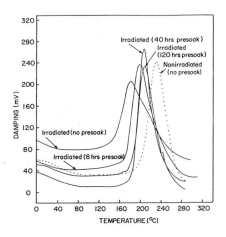

Figure 12. Effect of Soak Time at +121°C on Subsequent Longitudinal Creep Response of Irradiated 10° Off-Axis Specimens

Figure 13. Damping Response of Irradiated 45° Off-Axis Specimens with Different Presoak Times Obtained from DMA Tests

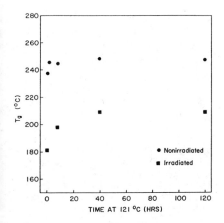

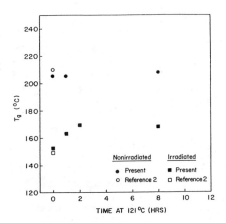

Figure 14. Glass Transition Temperature of Irradiated and Nonirradiated 45° Off-Axis Specimens as a Function of Presoak History

Figure 15. Glass Transition Temperature of Irradiated and Nonirradiated Bulk Resin Specimens as a Function of Presoak History

RESULTS OF PROTECTIVE COATING STUDIES FOR
THE HUBBLE SPACE TELESCOPE SOLAR ARRAY

R. C. Linton, R. L. Gause, R. J. Harwell, R. F. DeHaye,
H. D. Burns, Jr. and J. M. Reynolds
Materials and Processes Laboratory
NASA/Marshall Space Flight Center
Marshall Space Flight Center, AL

Abstract

Increased concerns for the erosive effects of orbital atomic oxygen on susceptible materials of the original (HEC) solar array for the Hubble Space Telescope led to the development of a second-generation array (BSFR-ATOX) composed of oxygen resistant or protected materials. A multi-disciplinary effort to develop and qualify feasible approaches for the application of protective coatings to the existing fabricated and flight-qualified HEC array was initiated in early 1987 as a contingency pending successful qualification of the BSFR-ATOX array. The results and conclusions of the comprehensive performance verification and qualification testing of candidate protective coatings are described and interpreted in the context of the unique constraints imposed by the flight-ready HEC array.

1. INTRODUCTION

Electrical power for the Hubble Space Telescope (HST) is derived from batteries charged by arrays of silicon solar cells. The original flight solar array, delivered to NASA by cooperative agreements with the European Space Agency, is known as the "High Efficiency Cell" (HEC) Array. The STSA-1 (HEC) array is flexible, consisting of 48,760 solar cells on composite blankets of adhesives, silver mesh wiring, and Kapton H (Figures 1 and 2).

As a contingency pending successful and timely qualification of the back-up array, designated STSA-BSFR (Back Surface Field Reflecting solar cells), considerations for adding atomic oxygen protection to the existing HEC array were formalized in March 1987.

The atomic oxygen susceptible materials were the Ag interconnects, the Kapton on the array backside, and the composite material hinges.

Logistics imposed a minimum operational HEC array life of three years. Revised predictions of orbital degradation of array materials susceptible to atomic oxygen were based on increased flux projections for the postponed mission (increased solar activity indices). The life limiting elements were the silver solar cell interconnectors (35 microns) and backside Kapton (12.5 microns). Orbital erosion rates for these materials were estimated from previous flight data and considerations of thermally induced rate acceleration factors.

2. MATERIALS SELECTION CRITERIA

Requirements for environmental stability governed the selection of protective coating materials, but further constraints were imposed to maintain the flight integrity of the existing HEC array. The new coating processes and properties were selected specifically for minimal impact to the HEC array deployment and retrieval mechanism, thermal design, and inherent stress relief features. Severe constraints were imposed by the nature, number, and relative inaccessibility of the silver solar cell electrical interconnectors located in the 0.9 mm wide intercell gap.

Each HEC interconnect has two "fingers" crossing between adjacent silicon cells, and each finger has a stress relief loop formed in it. Thus, the total number of interconnectors to be coated was effectively 99,520 counting two "fingers" each. Because most of the area of the Ag interconnects is protected by an overlapping cover glass, the exposed area of the silver is basically limited to the stress-relief loop (0.5 mm base width).

Since the solar cells are bonded to composite blankets, direct access to the underside of the interconnects for coating is virtually impossible, yet atomic oyxgen could reach the underside from the sides or through the holes of the interconnect mesh pattern by reflection from the underlying blanket. To provide maximum atomic oxygen protection it was necessary to select a coating that would wet the surface and migrate to the underside. This was the primary reason for the selection of the candidate coating referred to as G-1B — a distilled, non-curing derivative of the Dow Chemical dimethyl polysiloxane DC-100. Another coating material selected for qualification testing was SWS V-10, a curable, elastomeric dimethyl polysiloxane of moderate wetting capability. The limited number of available HEC array configuration blanket specimens restricted full qualification testing to only these two candidate materials. Additionally, McGhan Nusil's CV1-1144-0, a diphenyl dimethyl polysiloxane was included in as many different types of tests as practical.

3. TESTING

For qualification testing of the coating materials, most of the requirements were mandated by environmental exposure projections for the HST mission. Table 1 is a summary of the requirements of the primary tests performed to qualify the coatings for application to the HEC array. Selected test results from these requirements are reported on in this paper. In addition to these specified tests, the coating materials were investigated to determine basic compatibility to HEC materials by measurements of the coefficient of thermal expansion (C.T.E.) and thermo-gravimetric analysis to determine compatibility to HEC array materials.

Atomic Oxygen Exposure Testing

Candidate coating materials were tested for oxidation resistance in a Tegal Corporation radio frequency (RF) excited plasma generator. Specimens placed in the glass-walled reaction chamber were subjected to a continuous interaction with neutral and ionized atomic and molecular species. Controllable instrument parameters regulating the oxidation rate are pressure, RF power, specimen location, and specimen orientation. Passive temperature indicators and thermocouples were used to monitor specimen temperature during exposure to the oxygen plasma. The maximum temperature recorded for non-metallic specimens such as glass slides and Kapton was 82°C. Oxidized silver foil stabilized to a maximum of 173°C, but unoxidized, protected silver specimens reached a maximum of only about 80°C.

Acceptance criteria for the testing were based on visual observations and, for Kapton, measured mass loss. Lab measurements of plasma exposed Kapton mass loss were compared to calculated mass losses based on published Reaction Efficiency values[1] as a function of HST orbital fluence to relate lab exposure to the equivalent orbital exposure.

1191

Mechanical Cycling in Atomic Oxygen

Simulation of thermally-induced orbital flexing (wiggling) of interconnects during atomic oxygen exposure provided a rigorous test of protective coating integrity. An automated, vacuum-compatible device constructed of ceramic materials was designed and assembled. It cyclically flexed (stretched) HEC interconnects while exposing them to the laboratory-generated atomic oxygen plasma.

In the modified plasma environment, flexed interconnects were exposed to a reduced atomic oxygen fluence equivalent to less than 1/3 of normal operational exposure.

Ultraviolet Testing

Requirements for ultraviolet stability of the candidate coatings were primarily based on HEC array thermal design considerations. Specimens of coated Kapton were exposed to a maximum vacuum irradiation of 2000 equivalent sun hours (E.S.H.) in accelerated (2 solar constants) tests. The specimens, mounted on a water-cooled substrate, were irradiated at a pressure of 10^{-7} torr through a sealed quartz window by a 10 Kilowatt HgXe source.[2] Estimated coating thickness ranged from 3 to 8 microns.

VCM Testing

Outgassing properties of the coating materials were investigated by conventional volatile condensable material (VCM) testing per specification MSFC.1443.[3] Supplemental test procedures included the addition of optical witness samples (OWS) adjacent to the volatile outgassing product collector plates.

Outgassing test acceptance criteria, then, included the standard maximum of 1.0% total mass loss (TML) and 0.1% volatile condensable material (CVCM) content with an additional limit of no more than 3% relative decrease in reflectance of the OWS through the selected wavelength range (120 to 200 n.mi.).

Independent outgassing tests of 24-hour vacuum exposure at 10^{-6} torr were conducted on the three candidate coating materials. Specimens were prepared from films of the coatings brushed on aluminum foil substrates.

Electron and Proton Exposure

Electron and proton irradiation tests of coated Kapton specimens provided no significant evidence of induced degradation. The exposures were conducted in a diffusion-pumped (10^{-5} pascal) chamber irradiated by a 1 MeV Van de Graaff ion accelerator.[4] These accelerated exposure tests generated a maximum integrated particle flux (fluence) of 10E15 (10^{15}) particles/cm^2 in approximately 5.5 minutes.

Thermal Cycling

On the HEC array, the solar cell electrical interconnects are looped for stress relief to withstand thermally-induced flexing caused by the predicted orbital temperature variations of -100°C to +100°C. Based on a nominal orbital altitude of 600 kilometers, the HST will undergo approximately 30,000 thermal cycles in five years.

The original thermal cycling tests for qualification of the HEC array resulted in breakage of a large (50%) number of the silver strands forming the network of the interconnect mesh. The acceptance criteria were based on maintenance of electrical continuity and performance.

Only three array test specimens (coupons) were available. Each coupon, cut from a fabricated array blanket, consisted of 12 solar cells arranged in three adjacent strings of four cells in series (14 cm by 7 cm). One coupon was used for thermal vacuum cycling at MSFC, from -100°C to +100°C in a cycle time of 17 minutes. Temperature and electrical continuity of this coupon were monitored throughout the test. Coatings were applied to the rear (Kapton) side of the coupon, and to the interconnects of the outer two

strings of solar cells. As a control, the interconnects of the
middle string were not coated.

4. PROTECTIVE COATINGS RESULTS

Contamination Assessment

For SWS V-10 and CV1-1144-0, acceptable results were obtained for the
conventional criteria of TML and
CVCM for specimens heated to 125°C.
Reflectance changes of OWS's held at
25°C in these tests indicated the
need for some caution in the use of
the coatings in the vicinity of
sensitive optical surfaces. There
was no significant absorption at
wavelengths corresponding to the
spectral response of HEC array solar
cells.

Unacceptable levels of TML and CVCM
were measured for specimens of G-1B
heated to 125°C. Visible droplets
were observed on the OWS that may
have resulted from spattering of the
liquid coating when heated under
vacuum. The OWS did not significantly degrade in the wavelength
range of the solar cell spectral
response, even with visible whitening of the droplets after subsequent
atomic oxygen exposure. A test of
G-1B in which the specimen was
heated to only 90°C resulted in
acceptable TML and CVCM levels,
although visible droplets were
observed on the OWS.

Concerns for the effects of contamination of HEC array solar cells
during coating application led to
optical transmission measurements
of solar cell cover glass samples
deliberately coated with varying
amounts of the candidate coating
materials. These spectral transmittance measurements covered the
wavelength range 250 to 2500 n.mi.
to overlap the range of HEC solar
cell spectral response (0.35 to 1.1
μm). No significant change in the
optical transmission of cover glass
samples coated with moderate amounts
of any of the candidate materials
was observed for ambient laboratory
exposure.

Exposure of the contaminated samples
to 400 equivalent sun hours (ESH)

of solar ultraviolet irradiation did
not measurably degrade the optical
transmission. Exposure of the
samples to atomic oxygen produced
visible whitening of the coating
material and degraded the optical
transmission at wavelengths that
would degrade the output of the
solar cells.

The magnitude of transmission loss
induced by atomic oxygen was found
to be generally proportional to the
cover glass surface area contaminated, ranging up to a 50% loss for
a fully covered specimen. The
atomic oxygen exposure effects were
most pronounced for G-1B compared
to the other two materials tested.

Atomic Oxygen Resistance

Effects of atomic oxygen exposure on
unprotected silver were investigated
for baseline comparison. HEC array
components, such as solar cell interconnects and connector-integrated-
cells, were provided by ESA. The
major emphasis focused on the raised
stress relief loop of HEC interconnects.

The oxidiation of Ag progresses
through several distinct stages but
quickly produces the characteristic
black appearance of fully surface
oxidized silver. SEM images (Figure
3) readily confirm underside oxide
growth comparable in magnitude to
that on the top of the loop. In
thermally stressed flight exposure,
this oxide flakes, exposing fresh
silver and accelerating the oxidation process.[5]

Experimental procedures were
developed to determine the relationship between plasma exposure and
silver depletion in HEC interconnects. Exposure of 30 minutes duration resulted in visibly dense
oxide coverage and noticeable
embrittlement. Initial estimates of
unoxidized silver thickness after
two hours of plasma exposure indicated a depletion of only 2.7
microns, using magnified cross-
sectional SEM photographs (Figure 4).
Immersion of oxidized interconnects
in NH4OH removed oxide layers without attacking unoxidized silver.

Interconnect thickness and weight loss measurements after plasma exposure and oxide removal indicated that oxide growth and silver depletion rates stabilized after 60 minutes of exposure; the oxide protected the underlying silver until the fourth hour of exposure (Table 2). Silver depletion measured by this approach was approximately six times greater than estimates from cross-sectional SEM photos.

Protective Coatings

Singular clumps of black silver oxide on coated interconnects exposed to atomic oxygen provided evidence of incomplete coating coverage or wetting, while more extensive areas of oxide growth indicated shortcomings of coating preparation such as improper mixing ratios or curing.

Cleaning of interconnects in assembled arrays is difficult, and the concave, mesh hole patterns of the exposed stress relief loops tended to dilute and thin loop top coatings. The minute (5 μl) quantity of coating material sufficient to provide five year protection of interconnects formed a syringe droplet greater in diameter than the width of the intercell gap exposing the interconnect.

The most consistent results were obtained when the materials were applied with the aid of a stereo microscope. Visual inspection of coated interconnects to verify complete surface coverage was not effective, so an UV-activated fluorescing tracer (provided by ESA) served for inspection of coated interconnects and Kapton.

The relative effectiveness of the coatings was most evident when viewed in direct comparison to unprotected specimens (Figure 5). Rough-textured oxide growth on bare HEC interconnects exposed to atomic oxygen overlapped the eyelets of the mesh pattern and eradicated the original metallic sheen. Coated HEC interconnects exposed to atomic oxygen retained the original silvery appearance.

For coated interconnects exposed to an atomic oxygen fluence equivalent to five HST mission years, optical inspections revealed no significant evidence of degradation. Some minor changes were observed with SEM imaging. Comparison with a similarly exposed bare interconnect provided graphic evidence of the relative magnitude of effects (Figure 6).

Atomic oxygen exposure during mechanical flexing resulted in the uncoated interconnects becoming densely oxidized and brittle. Most of the silver strands on top of the stress relief loop were broken, presaging imminent total breakage. Coated interconnects that were exposed to atomic oxygen throughout 30,000 cycle flexing tests were intact and visibly free of oxide.

Effective atomic oxygen protection for Kapton by the coating materials was demonstrated by comparison of weight loss measurements after plasma exposure. Typical results for coatings >3 microns thick indicated <1% mass loss for plasma exposures in excess of six hours. Thinner coatings did not consistently provide adequate protection.

The protective coatings visibly changed in appearance with exposure, developing a whitish translucence that eventually led to surface silicate formation and microcracking. These changes in transparency were most evident and potentially significant for coatings applied to glass substrates.

Inconsistent results were obtained from tests of the bubble-pattern Kapton 200H used for cushioning of HEC array solar cells in retracted array storage. Specimen weight loss rates varied from the same as that of smooth Kapton to four times that rate.

Visible deterioration usually appeared on the raised area of the bubbles. When coatings were carefully applied to compensate for raised areas, full atomic oxygen protection, comparable to results for sheet Kapton, was provided.

Thermal Cycling Response

After 14 months and 30,000 cycles of thermal vacuum exposure, the solar cell coupon retained electrical continuity, and flash-testing revealed no significant change in the power or electrical characteristics. Visual examination of the interconnects was performed with a stereo microscope at 60X magnification; <50% strand breakage was observed.

Exposure of the other two HEC coupons to ambient pressure, rapid (2.5 minutes) thermal cycling by ESA resulted in significant silver strand breakage in the coated interconnects, although electrical continuity was maintained. Inspection of a third, uncoated control coupon revealed minimal strand breakage. Significant (50%) strand breakage in the control would be expected based on the original HEC tests.

Irradiation Resistance

As noted, the levels of particulate irradiation resulted in no significant coating degradation. No measurable changes in the solar absorption, emittance, or atomic oxygen exposure resistance were detected. Similar exposure of a solar cell cover glass, completely coated with the V-10 silicone, to 10^{15} protons/cm^2 did not significantly degrade the optical transmittance (250 to 2500 n.mi.). Subsequent exposure of this specimen to atomic oxygen reduced the transmittance approximately 5%.

Ultraviolet irradiation exposure resulted in no significant change in specimen visible appearance or thermophysical properties (α,ε). In subsequent plasma exposure tests, ultraviolet irradiated specimens of both SWS V-10 and CV1-1144-0 coated Kapton retained optimal atomic oxygen resistance properties, with less than 1% measured mass loss after three equivalent HST mission years of exposure.

A previous UV exposure test to 1000 ESH at one S.C. level of irradiation resulted in hazy, dry looking specimens with significant loss of resistance to atomic oxygen, although solar absorption and thermal emittance values were not measurably changed. Inspection of control specimens revealed areas of <1 micron thickness.

The coated Kapton specimens that were resistant to the 2000 ESH ultraviolet exposure were thicker (6 to 8 microns) and more uniformly applied than the earlier affected specimens.

SUMMARY AND CONCLUSIONS

The candidate coatings were demonstrated to be adequately resistant to five-year HST mission environmental exposure, including atomic oxygen, solar ultraviolet and charged particle radiation, and thermal vacuum cycling. Effective material compatibility with the HEC array for the V-10 and CV1-1140-1 coating materials was verified by V.C.M., blocking, and thermo-optical testing and measurement.

Both atomic oxygen exposure and blocking testing were used to discriminate the relative influence of coating cure time, solvent ratios, primers, and method of application (brush or spray). Measurements of the solar absorptance (α) and infrared thermal emittance (ε) of coated specimens, including flight configuration connector-integrated-cells (CIC's) indicated no significant change due to exposure from the environmental testing.

Successful qualification of the back-up (BSFR) solar array eventually obviated the need for HEC array use, but CV1-1144-0 has been used on selected surfaces of the BSFR array (e.g., cushion roller).

REFERENCES

1. Leger, et al., Selected Materials Issues Associated with the Space Station, SAMPE Quarterly, Vol. 18, No. 2, Jan. 1987, pp. 48-54.

2. Whitaker, A. F., et al., Evaluation of Materials for High Performance Solar Arrays, NASA Technical Paper 1220, George C. Marshall Space Flight Center, 1978.

3. MSFC-SPEC-1443, Outgassing Test for Non-Metallic Materials Associated with Sensitive Optical Surfaces in a Space Environment, George C. Marshall Space Flight Center, 1987.

4. Taylor, R. A., A Space Debris Simulation Facility for Spacecraft Materials Evaluation, SAMPE Quarterly, Vol. 18, No. 2, January 1987, pp. 28-34.

5. Whitaker, A. F., et al., Protective Coatings for Atomic Oxygen Susceptible Materials - STS-41G Results.

ACKNOWLEDGMENTS

The contributions of the following are appreciated: Ted Edge, Doug Alexander, Jim Burka, Ed White, Bobby Cothren, Joey Norwood, and Bruce Glick of MSFC. The cooperation of the ESA/ESTEC is gratefully acknowledged.

Table 1

COATING QUALIFICATION TEST REQUIREMENTS

Test	Requirement
Atomic Oxygen	Fluence - 5 Orbital Years (3.6×10^{21} atoms/cm^2)
Solar Ultraviolet	2000 ESH
Electron, Proton	10^{15} particles/cm^2
Outgassing (VCM)	VCM (TML, CVCM), Optical
Thermal Vacuum Cycling	-100 to +100°C 30,000 Cycles
CTE, Thermal Shock	-100 to +100°C
Blocking	1 Newton Peel

Table 2

SILVER DEPLETION IN HEC INTERCONNECTS
EXPOSED TO ATOMIC OXYGEN

Interconnect No.	Asher Exposure (minutes)	Silver Depletion (microns)
01-01-038	30	8.7
01-01-039	60	16.3
01-01-040	90	16.9
01-01-041	120	16.8
01-01-042	150	17.0
01-01-043	240	20.1

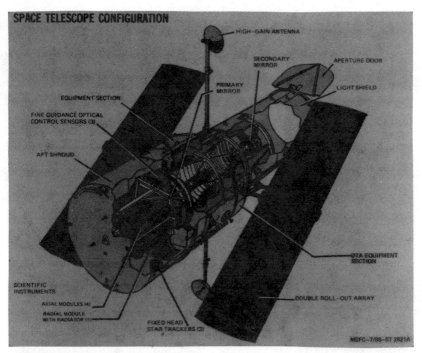

Figure 1. Hubble Space Telescope Configuration

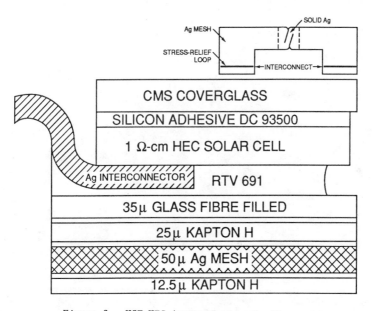

Figure 2. HST HEC Array Blanket Configuration

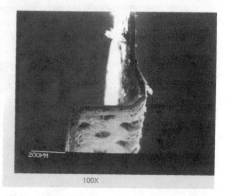

Figure 3. Silver Oxide Growth on Unprotected HEC Interconnect
Exposed to Atomic Oxygen

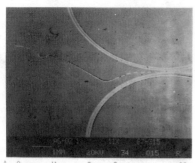
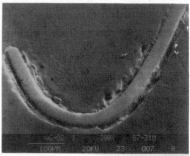

A. OVERALL VIEW OF CROSS SECTION   11x   C. STRESS RELIEF LOOP   34.7UM THICK   200x

Figure 4. Cross-Sectional Appearance of Unprotected HEC
Interconnect Exposed to Atomic Oxygen

Photomicrograph
HST HEC I/C
3 HRS AO Exp (3-5-87)

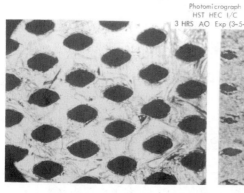
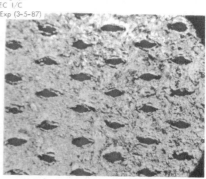

Figure 5. Visual Comparison of Coated to Uncoated HEC
Interconnects Exposed to Atomic Oxygen

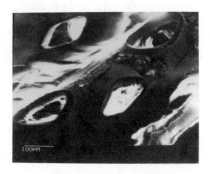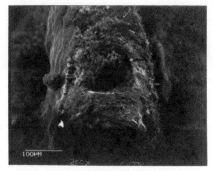

Figure 6. Magnified (SEM) Images of Coated and Uncoated
HEC Interconnects Exposed to Atomic Oxygen

Roger C. Linton

Roger Linton is a physicist in the
Engineering Physics Division of
Materials and Processes Laboratory
of the Marshall Space Flight Center.
He has 23 years of experience with
NASA, spanning vacuum UV optics,
contamination, and the effects of
atomic oxygen on materials. Mr.
Linton served as Chairman of the
MSFC team charged with the develop-
ment of protective coatings for the
HST HEC array.

Dr. Raymond L. Gause

Dr. Gause is Chief of the Engineering
Physics Division, Materials and
Processing Laboratory at the NASA
Marshall Space Flight Center. He
has been working in the contamination area for 15 years and his
experience is in both research and
applications. He developed the contamination control philosophy for
Skylab and was the Technical Manager
of the Skylab Contamination Ground
Test Program. Currently, he is
technically responsible for Space
Telescope Contamination Control and
serves as Chairman of the Space
Telescope Contamination Panel which
reviews MSFC and contractor contamination control activities.

Howard DeWitt Burns, Jr.

DeWitt Burns is a Materials Engineer
in the Engineering Physics Division
of the Materials and Processes
Laboratory at Marshall Space Flight
Center. Mr. Burns has been employed
at MSFC for six years and his major
job function has been materials
evaluation for space applications.
He is also involved in contamination
and environmental evaluation/control
for processing of space hardware.

Robert DeHaye

Mr. DeHaye is in the Materials and
Processes Laboratory at Marshall
Space Flight Center. Prior to this,
he worked in the Electronics and
Information Laboratory, also at MSFC.
He has experience in areas of vacuum
technology and processing, microelectronics design and fabrication,
and the development of microcircuit
design and inspection criteria. He
also has experience in surface coating processes for both protective
and optical uses, and in the effects
of the environment on surfaces and
surface coatings. Presently he is
continuing work on the effects of
atomic oxygen on materials.

J. R. Reynolds

Mr. Reynolds is a member of Engineering Physics Division, Materials and
Processes Laboratory at MSFC. He
has been working in the contamination
area for 20 years, is author of numerous technical papers and patents.
He is currently working on the
Orbiting Maneuvering Vehicle and the
Advanced X-Ray Telescope contamination control.

Roger J. Harwell

Mr. Harwell has served as a materials
engineer in the Materials and Processes Laboratory for 24 years. He
has been responsible for the development and characterization of thermal
protection systems and thermal control coatings from the Saturn
vehicles through present flight
experiments including the Hubble
Space Telescope.

MATERIALS SCREENING CHAMBER FOR TESTING MATERIALS RESISTANCE TO ATOMIC OXYGEN

H. G. Pippin
Boeing Aerospace
Seattle, WA. 98124-2499

and

Ralph Carruth
NASA-MSFC
Marshall Space Flight, Al. 35812

ABSTRACT

A unique test chamber for exposing material to a known flux of oxygen atoms is described. The capabilities and operating parameters of the apparatus include production of an oxygen atom flux in excess of 5×10^{16} atoms/cm^2-sec, controlled heating of the sample specimen, RF circuitry to contain the plasma within a small volume, and long exposure times.

Flux measurement capabilities include a calorimetric probe and a light titration system. Accuracy and limitations of these techniques are discussed.

An extension to the main chamber to allow simultaneous ultraviolet and atomic oxygen exposure is discussed. The oxygen atoms produced are at thermal energies. Sample specimens are maintained at any selected temperature between ambient and 200°C, to within ± 2°C. A representative example of measurements made using the chamber is presented.

INTRODUCTION

This paper describes the development and operation of a materials screening test chamber built by Boeing for the purpose of testing the resistance of materials to atomic oxygen. Subsequent to the Boeing development, a second, nearly identical chamber was built under contract[1] for NASA-MSFC. These efforts were undertaken following observations made subsequent to the earliest shuttle flights.[2] Extensive degradation of polyurethane paints, Kapton blankets, and other organic based materials occurred under exposure to low earth orbit (LEO) conditions during these flights. A primary cause of the degradation was determined to be atomic oxygen.[3]

Boeing Aerospace Materials and Processes organization initially used a commercial RF plasma source to study the degradation of materials under exposure to atomic oxygen. However, such systems do not allow separation of the effects of atomic oxygen from other variables. Acquisition of a large custom built plasma asher began a long period of development in order to characterize and control sample conditions. The specific goals of this effect were to separate the samples from the plasma, regulate the sample temperature, measure atomic oxygen flux, and allow the inclusion of other variables in a controlled manner.

APPARATUS

The apparatus described here is an improved version of a thermal atom source. A photo of the test chamber is shown in Figure 1. The system consists of a vacuum chamber, an RF electronic circuit with a Plasma Products, Inc. Model HFS-1000G power supply, metered gas flow systems regulated by two Tylan Model FC-280 mass flow controllers, two independent flux detection systems, and a controlled temperature sample holder. The vacuum chamber is separable into two compartments by a gate valve, and each is independently pumped. The gate valve allows that part of the chamber where the plasma is produced to be under vacuum at all times, minimizing the drift in plasma conditions due to changing conditions on chamber surfaces. When properly tuned, the "balanced" RF circuit delivers energy into the vacuum chamber such that some energy is absorbed into the plasma and can contribute to the production of energetic species, including oxygen atoms. Microwave sources exist which are capable of dissociating 100% of the oxygen molecules present in the plasma when such sources are run at high powers. The source described here is capable of supplying up to 1000 watts. Typical experiments are conducted using 200-300 watts, with perhaps 10% of the molecules dissociated.

The "balanced" RF circuit is designed such that there is an effective ground potential along the center axis of the 3" diameter side tube. The term "balanced" refers to symmetry of the RF voltage about ground potential. The plasma region is confined to the side tube. The sample specimens are routinely placed downstream of the plasma region and around the 90 bend between the side tube and main chamber.

The study by Linnett and Marsden[4] showed that for glow discharge plasmas the ion concentration drops to zero within a few centimeters outside the glow region. The chamber walls are thick pyrex glass and do not transmit UV radiation. The sample position is over 30 centimeters from edge of the plasma glow. At typical operating pressures of 50 milletorr and greater virtually all molecules and atoms which were placed in an electronically excited state within the plasma glow will have relaxed to the ground electronic state before reaching the sample location. Linnett and Marsden[4] made estimates of the maximum possible excited state concentration under such circumstances and found it to be less than 0.1%, the limit of detection in their experiment. Thus, during an experiment only neutral, ground state oxygen atoms and molecules reach the specimens.

The sample holder is an aluminum cross capable of holding 8 individual samples, each 1" in diameter, with 3/4" diameter circular areas exposed. The sample holder has a ribbon of heat tape attached to the back to allow precise temperature control of the samples. A small thermocouple is attached to the front of the holder. Temperatures, selected from ambient to 200C, are routinely maintained constant to within +2C over periods of many hours. These temperatures are recorded at regular intervals on a

Cole-Parmer 32 channel data logger.

Flux Measurement

Production of oxygen atoms in a plasma source is a complicated function of pressure, gas temperature, RF power absorbed by the plasma, gas purity, and conditions on the inner surfaces of the vacuum chamber. A number of methods have been developed to measure the flux of oxygen atoms through a cross sectional area in vacuum systems. Two independent methods have been chosen to measure the atomic oxygen flux in this system. These are a physical measurement using a silver oxide surface[5] and a chemical measurement using the reaction of oxygen atoms with nitrogen dioxide.[6]

The silver oxide coated calorimetric probe is heated by the recombination of oxygen atoms on its surface as well as the thermal energy of the flowing gas. This heat is dissipated primarily through radiative processes. An uncoated glass surface acts as a reference probe. This surface detects heat only from the thermal energy of the gas. Both the calorimetric probe and the glass reference lose some hest due to convection and some by conduction down the thermocouple. These processes cause virtually the same heat loss in both probes. The temperature difference between the two probes is due to the fact that the silver oxide surface is catalytic for oxygen atom recombination and the glass surface is not. About 1 to 10^{+4} atoms striking the glass surface recombine on this surface. To convert the temperature difference into a flux, one must equate the heat of reaction for recombination to the difference in emitted energy of the two probes, using the Stefan-Boltzmann law, and taking into account the fact that the emissivities of the silver oxide and glass surfaces are different. The Stefan-Boltzmann equation is:

$$E = \epsilon \sigma T^4,$$

where $\sigma = 5.67 \times 10^{-8}$ KJ/m^{2}sec-K^4,

T is the temperature in Kelvin, E is the rate of energy emitted from a source per unit area, and ϵ is the emissivity of the source. An emissivity of 0.965 was measured for the silver oxide coating and an emissivity of 0.80 was measured for the glass surface. The equation used to calculate the flux is

$$(\text{\#RXNS}) (\text{Heat per RXN}) = \sigma(\epsilon_{Ago} T^4_{Ago} - \epsilon_{Glass} T^4_{Glass}).$$

The number of reactions determined by this equation must be multiplied by two to obtain the number of oxygen atoms. There are several considerations in determining the meaning of the value determined using the equation. first, the assumption is made that 5.0 ev are available per reaction. If a product molecular oxygen is in an excited vibrational state then less energy will be deposited in the surface by that particular reaction. Second, a fraction of the oxygen atoms which impinge upon the surface will scatter and not be available to recombine. Third, while the silver oxide surface is known to be highly catalytic for recombination, an independent measure is needed to determine if the efficiency is 100% or whether it is somewhat lower.

Consideration of the above uncertainties and assumptions made using this method of determining flux leads to the conclusion that the flux is underestimated by this measurement.

The chemical technique is based on the following set of reactions.

1) $NO_2 + O \rightarrow NO + O_2$ (fast)
2) $NO + O \rightarrow NO_2^*$ (slow)
3) $NO_2^* \rightarrow NO_2 + h\nu$ (green)

This sequence has been described extensively in the literature. The success of this method depends upon the fact that reaction 1 is very fast compared with reaction 2. If NO_2 is in excess, reaction 1 will consume virtually all the O and no emission will be observed. If the O atoms are in excess, then some O will react with NO to produce the electronically excited NO_2^*. This species will emit visible radiation. Thus by increasing the flux of NO_2 until a stoichiometric mixture of NO_2 and O is achieved, the emission acts as an indicator. The intensity of the NO_2^* emission increases with NO_2 flow rates until the concentration of NO_2 at the point where the photons are being detected is half the oxygen atom concentration. As the NO_2 concentration is increased further the intensity of emission decreases because the O atoms become the limiting reagent. An EG&G 1460 optical multichannel analyzer attached to a Jarrell-Ash vis-UV spectrometer with a 1420B UV sensitized silicon photodiode array detector for light capture, is the photon counting system. The light titration puts an upper bound on the oxygen flux because the NO_2 flow rate is measured and the cross section of the chamber is known. The measured intensity is lowered because some NO_2 diffuses away from the observation point and is not detected. This can be observed visually because even when the equilibrium point is reached the green glow is visible upstream of the observation point.

PROCEDURE

A standard experiment includes 4 specimens of one coating and 4 specimens of uncoated Kapton. The sample specimens were held at 85C during the exposure. The exposed area of each specimen was 2.06 cm^2.

Prior to exposure, specimens are heated in a thermal vacuum at 150F for 1 hour. Immediately upon cooling the samples are weighed, loaded into the sample holder and placed in the vacuum chamber. The chamber is pumped to a background pressure of ~20 microns. The samples are brought to the desired temperature, the oxygen flow is started, typical flow rates being 8-10 sccm, with pressures typically 80-120 microns, and the plasma is established. Following exposure for the desired time period, the plasma is turned off, and the samples are allowed to cool. When the sample holder has reached ambient temperature the specimens are removed and weighed as rapidly as possible. Figure 2 shows a plot of mass loss of Kapton vs fluence of oxygen atoms using data obtained with test chamber.

DISCUSSION

Environmental factors which contribute to degradation of materials at LEO are atomic oxygen, solar particle (H+,e-)

and ultraviolet radiation, impacts from micrometeroids and manmade debris, thermal cycling due to spacecraft traversing through the earths shadow, and contamination from the spacecraft itself. There have been many efforts made to simulate one or more of these aspects of the LEO space environment. No one test chamber build to date simulates all significant environmental factors present at low earth orbit altitudes. A major contribution to degradation and recession of materials at LEO is due to the ambient atomic oxygen which impinges on the spacecraft. A number of laboratories have attempted to simulate this effect.

Laboratory sources of atomic oxygen are from essentially two types of apparatti.[7] First, there are beam systems which are being used to produce atoms with about 5ev kinetic energy. Systems of this type typically are limited to low flux, small cross sectional area, and/or have difficulty producing neutral species with the desired energy. Second, there are plasma sources which produce a mixture of ions, excited state neutrals, UV emission and stray RF radiation, in addition to thermal oxygen atoms. In the test chamber described here, an oxygen flux of about 10 to 80 times typical on-orbit fluxes may be produced. There is no direct exposure to charged species or UV emission from the plasma. Excited neutral species are also minimized in this test chamber. The flux is variable over a wide range by varying the pressure, input power, and sample location. The chamber may be operated continuously for long periods of time (120 hours). Due to the gate valve, the cycle time

between experiments is minimized. Construction of this chamber is one step in the development of an LEO simuluation capability. A UV source is being added to provide simultaneous atomic oxygen and UV exposure. Addition of a supersonic nozzle source to achieve a longer mean free path between collisions and capability for thermally cycling of sample specimens would be useful additions to this device. At present the chamber remains an effective source of atomic oxygen for determining the oxidation resistance of materials.

REFERENCES

1. Pippin, H.G. and Hill, S. G., NAS8-36586, "Space Station Protective Coating Development", final report, January, 1989.

2. Miller, E.R., NASA Technical Memorandum 82524, Feb. 1983.

3. Leger L. J., NASA Technical Memorandum 58246, May 1982.

4. Linnett, J.W. and Marsden, D.G.H., Proc. Roy. Soc., A234 P489 (1956).

5. Mearns, A.M., and Morris A. J., Engineering, Chemistry, and use of Plasma Reactors, Chemical Engineering Progress Symposium Series #112, 67 (1971). Bell, A. T. and Kwong, K., AIChE Journal 18 (5) Sept. 1972.

6. Elias, L. J.C.P. 44(10), May 166, P3810, and references therein.

7. See articles in 18th International SAMPE Technical Conference, Vol. 18, Oct. 1986. See also abstracts from NASA Workshop on Atomic Oxygen Effects, Jet Propulsion Laboratory, Nov. 10-11, 1986.

Figure 1 Photograph of Atomic Oxygen Test Apparatus

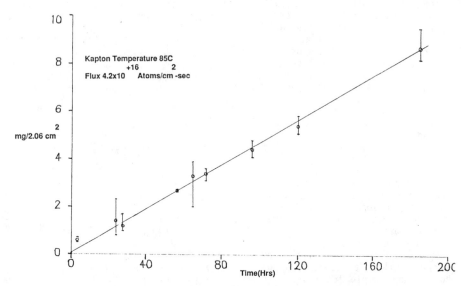

Figure 2 Mass Loss of Kapton as a Function of Exposure to Atomic Oxygen

EXTENDED THERMAL CYCLE TESTING OF GRAPHITE/EPOXY COMPOSITE STRUTS FOR SPACE STATION APPLICATIONS

Randy Jones and Rudy Lukez[1]
Morton Thiokol, Inc., Aerospace Group
Brigham City, Utah 84302-0689

Bryan Peterson[2], J. Clair Batty, and Frank J. Redd
Utah State University, Center for Space Engineering
Logan, Utah 84322-4140

Abstract

Graphite composite struts designed for the planned U.S. Space Station have successfully undergone extended thermal cycle testing. These tests were conducted as part of a continuing effort to verify that composites will survive the low-earth orbit (LEO) environment. Using equipment designed specifically for the test program, two different strut designs were subjected to 10,000 thermal cycles between 200°F and -150°F (+93°C and -101°C). Periodic inspections identified no microcracking damage. Coefficient of thermal expansion (CTE) and axial modulus tests showed that the struts were not significantly affected by the exten- sive temperature cycling. Test objectives, equipment, schedule, and results are discussed in this paper.

1. INTRODUCTION

Tentative baseline requirements for the proposed U.S. Space Station include using graphite/epoxy composite materials for the project's structural truss framework. Graphite epoxy materials offer the advantages of high dimensional stability because of relatively low CTE properties and high strength to weight ratios. Figure 1 shows the Space Station and its truss structure. During its expected 30 year life, the Space Station will experience 175,000 temperature cycles.

Figure 1. Artist's Drawing of the Space Station's Core Area Shows Struts Proposed for the Truss Structure (Courtesy of NASA)

In order to better understand the effect of extended, extreme temperature cycling on graphite/epoxy struts proposed for the Space Station, a machine was designed, fabricated, and verified to thermally cycle samples for long durations. Two graphite epoxy cylindrical specimens were thermally cycled 10,000 times from +200°F to -150°F (+93°C to -101°C). The specimens were inspected and photographed through a microscope at intervals throughout the program. At the completion of the tests, the CTEs and axial modulii of the samples were determined and compared to control samples.

The purpose of the project described above was to evaluate potential designs based on input from NASA contractors for the graphite/epoxy struts. This effort was not designed to duplicate basic microcracking research which often involves flat composite panels made from $[0_a/90_b]_c$ layups. A mathematical evaluation with comparative experimental results of microcracking using this approach is given in Ref. 1, 5.

2. SPACE ENVIRONMENT CONSIDERATIONS

The proposed Space Station will operate in Low Earth Orbit (LEO), about 250 miles above the earth's surface. Components in this orbit will typically experience temperatures from +170°F to -80°F (+77°C to -62°C) about every 90 minutes. In extreme cases, temperatures may range from +200°F to -150°F (+93°C to -101°C) (Ref. 2). The actual temperature experienced by a component depends on (1) the surface solar absorptance

to emittance ratio, (2) the type of protective coating on the exposed material, and (3) period of time exposed to solar insolation.

3. SPACE STATION REQUIREMENTS AND MICROCRACKING CONCERNS

Most Space Station designs call for a low cost, lightweight truss of struts that will support the overall configuration for a minimum of 30 years in LEO. Specific requirements for this truss are listed in Ref. 2. The effect of microcracking as it applies to these requirements is a major concern.

Microcracks (see Fig. 2) are defined as:

> Small cracks in a composite's matrix material (resin) which run through the thickness of a given ply and extend parallel to the fiber direction (Ref. 3).

Microcracks can result from combined fabrication and thermal stresses caused by mismatched thermal expansion between a composite's fiber and matrix, and between adjacent plies of different orientations. When mechanical or thermal loading is applied to a composite part, microcracks may form perpendicular to the direction of the applied load and possibly extend parallel to the fiber (Ref. 3).

If Space Station struts were to microcrack while in orbit, the ability to meet mission objectives would be impaired because a composite component's

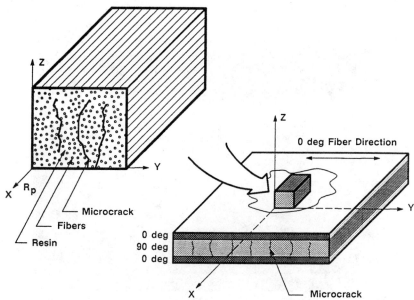

Figure 2. Typical Microcracks in a Composite

CTE changes when microcracking occurs. If strut CTEs were to change significantly, then the Space Station trusses dimensional stability would be negatively affected. Microcracked composite parts also lower a component's stiffness and change the residual strain state.

Another problem with microcracking concerns the protective coating which will be applied to the outside of composite Space Station struts. If microcracking occurs, the subsequent substrate damage may break the protective coating, such as aluminum foil, which in turn would expose the underlying composite to atomic oxygen degradation (Ref. 4).

4. TEST EQUIPMENT

Several different test configurations were conceived and evaluated. In the selected concept shown in Fig. 3, the composite specimens are transported between an electrically heated oven and a liquid nitrogen cooled chamber located about 8 ft directly beneath the oven. In this system, only the specimens experience a temperature change as they travel through tubes connecting the hot and cold chambers. The chambers and connecting tubes are filled with dry nitrogen gas under positive pressure so that all air and water vapor are eliminated from the system. The liquid nitrogen feed system that was developed provided automatic, low pressure feed at level-sensor controlled intervals (Fig. 4). The system, automated for constant operation, achieved the specified strut

temperature fluctuations in a 13.17 minute period. Shown in Fig. 5 is a photograph of the indoor components of the completed system. Note the large box at the bottom encloses the cold specimen receptacle and an elaborate insulation system to minimize liquid nitrogen boil off.

5. TESTING

5.1 Specimen Description

Two types of specimens were used for the test. Both specimen designs were similar to proposed struts for the Space Station. Each specimen was a cylinder with a 0.100 inch wall thickness, 2.0 inch inside diameter, 6.5 inches long and made from a 350°F preimpregnated graphite/epoxy resin cure system. One specimen used Amoco Performance Products T-300 fiber/Fiberite 934 resin and the other used Amoco Performance Products P-75 fiber/Fiberite 934 resin. Both struts used a $(\pm 30_2, \pm 10_3)_s$ layup. Some studies have shown that low angled composite tubes (less than 45 deg) with adjacent angle differences less the 30 deg are less susceptible to microcracking damage (Ref. 3).

5.2 Operation

A computer controlled system required minimal manual labor to operate the test. Normal operation tasks included a daily check of system function parameters and filling of the 160 liter intermediate liquid nitrogen tank. A less frequent duty was to remove the specimens from the apparatus as

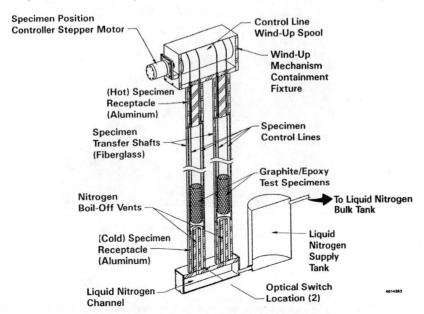

Figure 3. Thermal Cycle Test Apparatus; Basic Configuration

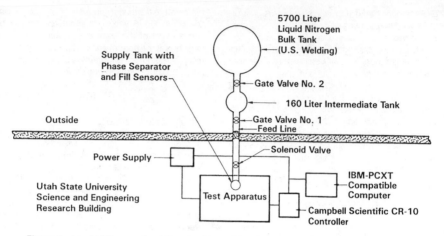

Figure 4. Liquid Nitrogen Feed System, Test Apparatus, and Control System Setup

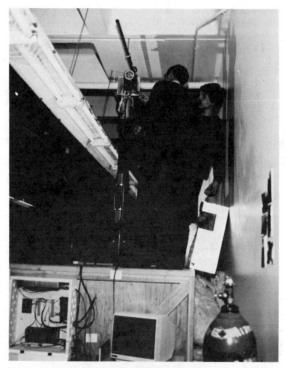

Figure 5. Indoor Portion of the Thermal Cycle Test Apparatus

shown in Fig. 6 at the specified intervals for photo microscopic examination. Start-up required purging the air from the hot chamber, repositioning the specimens to the proper location and switching on the hot chamber temperature control system. Checks were placed in the control software to ensure proper system functioning at all times.

6. TEST RESULTS

6.1 Microcracking

The tubes were removed from the cycling apparatus at 200 and 1,000 cycles, at 1,000 cycle increments up to 6,000 cycles, and again at 10,000

Figure 6. Struts Being Removed From the Hot Receptacles After Cooling to Room Temperature

cycles. Photomicrographs were taken at three circumferential locations at the axial midpoint of each tube. After completing 10,000 cycles, the ends of the tubes were cut, polished, and photomicrographed at 100X magnification. No evidence of microcracking was observed in either the side or end locations of the tubes.

6.2 CTE

Each tube specimen had a control sample cut adjacent to it before the cycling began. CTE measurements in the axial direction were made on the two cycled tubes and on the two control samples. Composite Optics of San Diego, California performed the measurements using a proprietary laser measurement technique. The cycling temperature range of -150° to 200°F was reproduced in the measurement. The results of the control and cycle specimens' CTEs are listed in Table I.

Table I. CTE Results of Control Samples and Cycled Tubes

	CTE (μ in/in/°F)	
Specimen	P-75/934	T-300/934
Control	-1.65	-0.77
Cycled	-1.79	-0.69
Delta	-0.14	0.08
Delta (%)	8.48	-10.39

The strain resolution of the equipment used is ± 0.05 μ in/in/°F and the repeatability is approximately ± 0.58 μ in./in. over the temperature range used. The change in CTE of the T-300/934 sample is within the equipment resolution tolerance and the P-75/934 is just above it.

Classical Lamination Theory (CLT) was used to predict the control samples' CTEs and upper bounds on the CTEs of tubes which are fully microcracked. These upper bounds were obtained by letting the transverse modulus (E_2) go from 100 percent to zero percent, simulating fully cracked plies with no transverse stiffness. Bowles (Ref. 5) found that this technique overpredicts the effects of physically reasonable microcracking on CTE and axial modulus and used finite element analysis for correlation with the CLT. CLT is used here simply to provide an upper bound to the expected changes. Table II lists the results of the CLT analysis on CTE.

Table II. CLT Predictions of CTE

	CTE (μ in/in/°F)	
Description	P-75/934	T-300/934
E_2 = 100%	-1.55	-0.88
E_2 = 0%	-0.52	-0.06
Delta	-1.03	0.82
Delta %	-66.5	-93.2

The control sample's actual measurements are within 13 percent of the predicted values. As Table II shows, large decreases in CTE (-66.5 percent and -93.2 percent) result when the transverse stiffness is reduced to zero.

The T-300/934 cycled specimen had a decreased CTE from the control sample so it appears that some microcracking occurred. However, since the change was within the equipment resolution, it is difficult to ascertain whether the change is because of microcracking or instrument resolution.

The P-75/934 specimens did not follow the trend of a decreased CTE after cycling that microcracking would suggest. The cycled specimen had an increased negative CTE with indicates that no microcracking took place. The fact that the cycled specimen's CTE is higher can be explained by the resolution of the measurement device or a difference in the CTEs of the two specimens that were present before the cycling began.

6.3 Axial Modulus

The two cycled tubes and the control specimens were subjected to axial compression tests at room temperature. The strain was monitored with three strain gages located at 120 degree intervals around the circumference of each tube and an average of the three was calculated. Three modulus tests were run for each tube and the results were averaged. Table III lists the results of the axial compression modulus tests.

Table III. Axial Modulus Test Results

Specimen	Modulus (msi)	
	P-75/934	T-300/934
Control	20.1	13.4
Cycled	19.1	13.4
Delta	1.0	0.0
Delta %	-5.0	0.0

CLT was again used to predict the effect a decreased transverse modulus (E_2) has on the axial modulus. The transverse modulus was input as 100 percent, then as zero percent. Table IV presents these reults.

Table IV. CLT Axial Modulus Predictions

CTE (μ in/in/°F)

Description	Modulus (msi)	
	P-75/934	T-300/934
E_2 = 100%	21.5	13.3
E_2 = 0%	18.9	12.2
Delta	2.6	1.1
Delta %	-12.1	-8.3

The change in axial modulus of approximately -10 percent versus the change in CTE of -66 percent and -93 percent indicates that the CTE is much more sensitive to microcracking than axial modulus.

The control sample's moduli were within 7 percent of the predicted values. The T-300/934 specimens showed no difference in compressive modulus indicating no change in transverse stiffness. If the -5.0 percent change of the P-75/934 specimens were due entirely to microcracking, it would indi-

cate a significant loss of transverse stiffness. Again, the sample size of one makes it difficult to ascertain whether the difference is because of the natural variation of samples, test apparatus resolution, or reduced stiffness due to microcracking.

7. CONTINUED EFFORTS

The equipment and methods developed for the work described in this paper will continue to be used for additional material investigations. Work is now underway subjecting other materials to extended thermal cycling.

8. CONCLUSIONS

It is difficult, with a sample size of one, to reach concrete conclusions as to the extent of microcracking in the cycled specimens. Of the three techniques employed to test for microcracking, the CTE measurement is the most sensitive since it considers the whole tube while a minute amount of microcracking might be missed in a visual examination. Also, CLT analysis shows that CTE is much more sensitive to microcracking than axial modulus. Table V shows a summary of the three techniques.

Table V. Results of Microcracking Determination Tests

Evidence of Microcracking

Inspection Method	P-75/934	T-300/934
Visual	No	No
CTE	No	(1)
Axial Modulus	(2)	No

(1) Change is within equipment resolution.
(2) Probably due in part to natural variation of samples.

The evidence in Table V suggests that little if any microcracking occurred in both of the cycled specimens. If there were a significant amount, it would have been detected in the visual examination

While this 10,000 cycle test is a fraction of the required 175,000 cycle life of the Space Station, the collected data is valuable for establishing confidence in the dimensional stability of a graphite/epoxy truss system.

ACKNOWLEDGMENTS

The authors wish to thank David Bowles, NASA Langley Research Center, Hampton, Virginia; and Ike Spiker, Lockheed Space Services, NASA/Johnson Space Center, Houston, Texas, for their assistance in reviewing the equipment drawings, test plans, and photographs presented in this paper.

REFERENCES

1. Adams, Daniel S.; Bowles, David E.; and Herakovich, Carl T.; "Thermally Induced Transverse Cracking in Graphite/Epoxy Cross-Ply Laminates," Journal of Reinforced Plastics and Composites, Vol. 5, July 1986.

2. Lukez, Rudy; Nelson, David R.; Teller, Volker B.; Rockoff, Harley J.; "Design, Fabrication, and Testing of Rolled Carbon/Epoxy Struts for Space Station Applications," 19th International SAMPE Technical Conference, Washington, D.C., October 1987.

3. Tompkins, Stephen S.; Sykes, George F.; Bowles, David E.; "The Thermal and Mechanical Stability of Composite Materials for Space Structures," IEEE/ASM/ASME/SME Space Technology Conference, Anaheim, CA, September 1985.

4. Leger, L.; Visentine, J.; Santos-Mason, B.; "Selected Materials Issues Associated With Space Station," SAMPE Quarterly, Vol. 18, No. 2, January 1987, pp. 54-84.

5. Bowles, David E., "Effect of Microcracks on the Thermal Expansion of Composite Laminates," Journal of Composite Materials, Vol 18, March 1984.

BIOGRAPHIES

Randy Jones is a structural analyst for Morton Thiokol's Strategic Composites Section, where he has worked on various composite structures since 1987. Mr. Jones holds a B.S. degree from Utah State University and a M.E. degree from the University of Texas at Arlington, both in Mechanical Engineering. Prior to his employment at Morton Thiokol, Mr. Jones worked for the Communications Sector of Motorola Inc. in Fort Worth, Texas.

Rudy Lukez is a composites project engineer at EDO Corporation's Fiber Science Division in Salt Lake City, Utah. When this work was done, Mr. Lukez was a design engineer in Morton Thiokol's Strategic Composites Design Section.
Mr. Lukez earned his B.S. in Mechanical Engineering at Cleveland State University, Cleveland, Ohio, in 1983. He worked for Morton Thiokol from 1984 to 1988. Prior to his employment at Morton Thiokol, Mr. Lukez worked for Hughes Aircraft Company's, Radar Systems Group in El Segundo, California.

Bryan Peterson is an engineer in the Composite Structures Certification Group of General Dynamics' Forth Worth, Texas Division. He holds B.S. and M.S. degrees in mechanical engineering, from Utah State University. His M.S. thesis project pertained to this research.

J. C. Batty is a Professor of Mechanical Engineering. He has authored or co-authored more than 70 technical publications in the thermal science area since receiving the Sc.D. degree in Mechanical Engineering at the Massachusetts Institute of Technology in 1969.

Frank J. Redd is a Research Professor of Mechanical Engineering and Director for the Center for Space Engineering Research (Utah Center of Excellence) at USU. He received his Ph.D. in Mechanical Engineering from Brigham Young University in 1975. Since that time he has directed many high technology programs supporting defense related space and ballistic systems for the Air Force as well as civilian space research at USU.

---

[1]Mr. Lukez is now employed at EDO Corporation/Fiber Science Division in Salt Lake City, Utah.
[2]Mr. Peterson is now employed at General Dynamics Corporation in Fort Worth, Texas.

COMPOSITE PARTS AND PREPREGS CONTAINING POLYBENZIMIDAZOLE (PBI) HIGH POLYMER MATRIX RESIN

Bennett C. Ward
Hoechst Celanese Corporation, PBI Products Division
P. O. Box 32414, Charlotte, NC 28232
(704)554-3068

Abstract

Polybenzimidazole (PBI) high polymer was used to make carbon and quartz fiber prepregs with good room temperature drape and tack properties. Prepregs were either woven or unidirectional, were free of tetraaminobiphenyl monomer, and achieved their drape and tack by the presence of residual N,N-dimethylacetamide (DMAc) solvent. Composite panels were fabricated from graphite fabric prepregs using either conventional heated platen compression molding or an isostatic pressing system (Thermoclave™. Composite parts were made with fabrication temperatures of 875°F (470°C) and pressures of as low as 200 psi. Lay-up and fabrication methods were developed to facilitate solvent removal during cure, and include the use of Celgard® microporous polypropylene as an antibleed material. Mechanical properties, along with some high temperature properties, of these composite panels are reported. PBI matrix resin composites have been reported to have outstanding short-term, high temperature thermal stability, making them ideal for high performance aerospace applications such as tactical missiles.

1. INTRODUCTION

Polybenzimidazoles are heterocyclic polymers which are known for their outstanding thermal and chemical stability (1). Although a wide variety of aromatic polybenzimidazoles have been synthesized and characterized since the first report in 1961 (2), the particular polymer used in all commercial and most developmental applications is poly [2,2'-(m-phenylene)-5,5'-bibenzimidazole], which is commonly referred to as PBI.

PBI

PBI resin has recently been developed as an engineering plastic with the trade name Celazole®(3). Made by a proprietary sintering process, molded PBI has been found to have the highest compressive strength (58 kpsi) of any known organic plastic, filled or unfilled. It has high tensile strength and modulus (23 kpsi and 0.85 Mpsi, respectively) and excellent hysteresis and creep properties (4). Thermal properties are also excellent, with a glass transition temperature of 800°F (425°C) and retention of usable tensile and compressive strength in neat (unreinforced) resin at temperatures of over 700°F. PBI resin does not burn in air, and is resistant to hydrolysis and most common chemical environments.

For composite applications, low molecular weight prepolymeric forms of PBI have been used for several years as the matrix material in PBI/graphite and PBI/glass prepregs. The PBI prepolymer has a very low molecular weight (inherent viscosity of approximately 0.05 dl/g as a 4% solution in 97% sulfuric acid), has a discreet melting point (less than 200°C) (5), and is hot melt applied to reinforcing fabrics, tapes or rovings. The resulting prepreg is stiff and boardy at room temperature, and must be heated to achieve drape and tack for lay-up. In addition, the prepolymeric material contains residual monomers, including tetraaminobiphenyl (approximately 5%). Its low degree of polymerization results in the formation of large amounts of condensation by-products (typically phenol and water) during cure, which means that carefully staged, high pressure curing conditions are needed to minimize void formation (Figure 1). Kuhbander has reported (6) solution impregnation with PBI prepolymer and a complex, low pressure cure cycle for composite formation. Problems with residual monomers and condensation volatile formation remain, however.

PBI matrix resin in composites was found to have excellent strength retention characteristics at temperatures of 1200°F and higher. For example, Jones et.al. (7) reported 60% and 20% flexural and tensile strength retention at 800 and 1200°F, respectively in PBI resin/T-300 or Celion 3K unidirectional laminates (8 ply). Excellent tensile and flexural modulus retention (35%) and interlaminar shear retention

(25%) was also observed at 1200°F. In contrast, polyimides exhibit little or no strength retention at 1200°F.

In addition, Kromrey (8) observed excellent dimensional stability, weight loss and erosion characteristics in a PBI/carbon fiber prototype ram jet inlet subjected to a Mach 4 wind tunnel test in which the leading edges were heated to 1440°F for 3 minutes.

Because PBI exhibits such positive short term thermal resistance in composite matrix form but has been difficult to process in the past, the PBI Products Division of Hoechst Celanese began a program to develop a viable PBI matrix resin prepreg system with good handling and processing properties, using the company's strengths in PBI polymer and solution technology.

2. PBI MATRIX RESIN PREPREG

2.1 Early, High Polymer Prepregs

Early work at Hoechst Celanese concentrated on formation of prepregs with high molecular weight PBI solutions in DMAc, with the PBI having an IV of greater than 0.6 dl/g. These prepregs were used in some early composites fabrication development work (detailed below). The high molecular weight PBI system had several disadvantages, however:

a. Use of lithium chloride (LiCl) was necessary as a DMAc solution stabilizer. In order to remove the LiCl, extensive water washing was required, which made the prepregs stiff and non-tacky. Should washing not be conducted, the residual LiCl could adversely affect thermal stability and radar observability properties.

b. Several passes through a dip bath/pregging machine were necessary to achieve target resin content (35-40%). This caused logistical problems, and would result in possible fiber damage and variability if conducted on a larger scale.

During this early program the following prepregs were made: Celion G30-500 3K (unsized), 8 Harness Satin Fabric and HITEX 46 (unsized), 3" wide unitape (9). Since each prepreg was washed to remove LiCl, no solvent remained, and the prepregs were stiff and boardy (Table 1).

2.2   Intermediate MW Polymer Prepregs

A much improved PBI matrix resin system was developed using an intermediate molecular weight (MW) PBI polymer (IV of 0.20 - 0.35 dl/g, or 10,000 to 20,000 weight average MW) in DMAc solution to prepreg unidirectional or woven reinforcing fibers. The intermediate molecular weight, or IV, of the polymer was important because solutions could be made of sufficiently high solids content and low viscosity to allow one pass prepregging of fabric or unidirectional tape. In addition, intermediate MW PBI solutions were more stable to precipitation in DMAc than high molecular weight PBI solutions, which eliminated the need for added lithium salt stabilizers. Finally, the solutioning process eliminated all traces of residual tetraaminobiphenyl monomer (to a detection level of 1 ppm). This, plus the higher molecular weight, limited the amount of condensation offgases (phenol and water) during cure compared to the PBI prepolymer system.

Prepregs were made using intermediate MW PBI matrix resin at YLA, Inc., Concord, CA, on Celion G30-500 3K (unsized) 8 Harness Satin fabric, and Astroquartz II (A1110 size) 581 8 Harness Satin fabric. Each prepreg had a resin content of 35-39% PBI (dry basis), and contained 30% residual DMAc solvent (total weight basis). Early prepregs were made which contained from 0.5 to 2% LiCl stabilizer. Later in the program, it was discovered that

LiCl could be eliminated from the system and adequate polymer solution stability could still be maintained. Consequently, prepregs and subsequent data were generated with LiCl-free intermediate MW PBI solutions. Prepreg data are summarized in Table 1.

DMAc was retained at a level of about 30%, which was found to provide an excellent degree of tack at room temperature. The amount of residual solvent in the prepreg was important. If the residual solvent level fell to 20% or less, tack was lost, but drape was maintained. Continued loss to less than 15% solvent led to progressive stiffening and formation of a "boardy" prepreg. Even though DMAc has a high boiling point (176°C) it has a relatively low vapor pressure at room temperature. Care must be taken to keep prepregs tightly wrapped during storage to prevent loss of tack and drape due to solvent loss.

3.   COMPOSITE FABRICATION

Composite fabrication efforts were conducted using both a Thermoclave isostatic press at United Technologies Chemical Systems Division (10) and heated platen hydraulic presses.

3.1   Fabrication of PBI High Polymer Prepregs With No Residual Solvent

Initial work was done in the Thermoclave comparing PBI prepolymer prepreg (Acurex 2801 PBI Prepolymer on Celion 3K G30-500, 8HS) and PBI high polymer prepreg on an identical substrate. Lay-up utilized a steel tool, followed by a layer of PTFE/glass release cloth, prepreg (8 or 15 ply), PTFE/glass release cloth, three glass bleeder plies, perforated aluminum foil, three glass bleeder plies and two plies of aluminum foil vacuum bag. Cure was conducted at a final temperature of 875°F (470°C) and 1400 psi using standard prepolymer cure conditions (Figure 1).

1216

Mechanical properties of the resulting composites are shown in Table 2, and indicate that the high polymer prepreg had equivalent density, higher tensile and flexural strength, but lower flexural modulus and short beam shear. Most mechanical properties, however, were lower than expected for a woven standard modulus carbon fiber composite.

3.2 Fabrication of Intermediate MW PBI Prepregs Containing Solvent

Initial lay-up experiments with the solvent-rich intermediate MW PBI matrix prepregs showed much improved drape and tack properties vs. both the PBI prepolymer and earlier generation PBI high polymer prepreg systems. Drape and tack properties at room temperature were such that a channel section was readily laid-up using 8 plies of woven carbon fiber prepreg, with excellent conformity in both inside and outside corners with 1/4" radii. There was no need for using a heat gun to soften the material, as was the case with PBI prepolymer prepregs.

Two precautions were necessary when working with these DMAc-containing materials. If care was not taken to minimize DMAc evaporation during the lay-up of individual plies, a gradual decrease in tackiness would occur, which would cause difficulty in laying up complex parts. This problem was avoided by keeping the individual prepreg stored in an airtight container until just before use. In addition, operators working with the DMAc-containing materials were required to wear appropriate protective equipment, including an organic vapor respirator and butyl rubber gloves, and to work in a well ventilated area, to avoid any respiratory or skin contact with the solvent.

Fabrication trials on these PBI matrix resin prepregs were conducted at Hoechst Celanese using either Tetrahedron, Wabash or Dake 30-ton heated platen presses capable of 1000°F. Either 4x4" or 6x9" panels were usually formed. The lay-up method outlined above for the Thermoclave was basically followed, with lay-up being done on a flat steel or aluminum tool equipped with a series of vacuum ports. A schematic of the bagging arrangement used is found in Figure 2.

In initial fabrication experiments the solvent rich prepregs exhibited excessive resin bleed, which resulted in resin-starved panels and poor physical properties. This problem was solved in two ways:

1. A layer of Celgard® microporous polypropylene film was placed next to, and on both sides of, the prepreg layup. Addition of Celgard to the bagging system eliminated resin bleed, maintained part densities, and resulted in substantial improvement in flexural strength and short beam shear properties.

2. A "devolatilization" step was employed at the beginning of the cure cycle, which was designed to remove most of the DMAc solvent at relatively low temperatures. The step consisted of a 3-4 hour hold under vacuum and contact platen pressure at 300°F (150°C). With most of the DMAc removed, bleed was minimized and high density, low void parts could be made at a variety of high temperature processing conditions.

Both low (200 psi) and high (1400 psi) pressure cure cycles were examined in this evaluation, which featured direct temperature ramps from 300°F to 875°F, and pressure application at 600 to 700°F. See Figure 3 for a representation of the molding conditions. The high pressure cure cycle was a derivative of the established cycle for PBI prepolymer, and replicated earlier molding efforts on high polymer composites in the Thermoclave. The low pressure cure was evaluated in an effort to make larger panels and also to determine if autoclave cures were possible.

The results (Table 3) indicated that intermediate MW PBI prepreg:

* Gave mechanical properties which were either equivalent to, or better than, the target properties expected for woven standard modulus carbon fiber composites.

* Gave better mechanical properties with a short cure cycle than either prepolymer or high molecular weight PBI prepregs.

In addition:

* Compression molding results were better than those obtained in the Thermoclave.

* Mechanical properties (tensile, flex, shear) were similar for the 200 and 1400 psi processes, which implied that an autoclave cure for intermediate MW PBI/solvent rich prepregs was in reach. Panel densities at 200 psi were significantly lower, however, indicating continued low pressure process optimization is needed.

* Removal of LiCl from the system did not affect mechanical properties.

Continued improvement is expected in mechanical properties of woven laminates as the fabric lay-down is optimized to minimize skew of the warp and fill. Also, pre-sizing the carbon fiber with PBI should improve properties.

In addition to flat panel compression molding, the intermediate MW PBI/solvent rich prepregs were successfully formed into a complex channel section in the United Technologies Thermoclave, using the lay-up, bagging and processing conditions developed for flat panels. Parts with 1/4" inside and outside radii were readily made with little or no bridging or delamination.

4. TESTING AND TECHNICAL DEVELOPMENT

Limited high temperature testing has been performed on this PBI/carbon fiber composite system. The testing that has been done suggests outstanding short-term thermal stability and resistance to thermal shock, even when wet. Data are summarized in Table 4. The results indicated minimal weight loss at short-term exposures even up to 1800°F (980°C), and no propensity to blister or delaminate, even when thermal shocked when wet at 1800°F. The specimens also maintained their structural integrity under these harsh thermal conditions, and showed little or no surface erosion.

Short-term technical development activities include determination of typical properties for the following fiber systems with PBI: Celion 3K woven, Astroquartz woven, HITEX 46 uni and filament wound glass and carbon. In addition, extensive testing will be conducted to determine compression and compression after impact properties, and flexural, tensile, compression and short beam shear behavior at 700, 1200 and 1500°F.

5. APPLICATIONS

It is anticipated that PBI matrix materials will be used primarily in high velocity aerospace applications, where lightweight and short term, very high temperature stability is a requirement. Other PBI properties of interest include the high compressive and tensile strength of the molded, unfilled resin, inherent laser resistance of PBI, and its demonstrated good adhesion to carbon fiber. Another important factor is that PBI is a fully commercial resin, with a one million pound capacity PBI fiber and resin plant currently in operation.

Aerospace applications include

major tactical missile structures, including nose cones, radomes, fins, nozzles and casings. Other applications are space reentry vehicles and other high speed projectiles, aircraft brake assemblies and radiation-resistant structures. Some non-aerospace uses under investigation are for oil recovery and down-hole applications, where both lightweight and thermal and chemical resistance are important. These applications may include light sucker rods, data logging equipment and other sealing devices.

6. ACKNOWLEDGMENTS

The author wishes to thank Robert V. Kromrey and his staff at United Technologies Chemical Systems Division, San Jose, CA, for invaluable work in Thermoclave process development for PBI, and Mike Fellman and Gary Patz at YLA, Inc., Concord, CA, for their assistance in PBI matrix prepreg development.

7. BIOGRAPHY

Bennett C. Ward is Sr. Development Chemist with Hoechst Celanese PBI Products Division in Charlotte, NC. He holds a B.S. in chemistry from Duke University and a Ph.D. in organic chemistry from the University of North Carolina, Chapel Hill. His expertise is in high temperature polymer synthesis and fabrication, composite molding processes and advanced materials testing. He is author or co-author of ten other publications and six patents on PBI.

8. REFERENCES

1. See one or more of the following references:

    a. Levine, H. H., Encylc. Polymer Sci. Technol., 11 188 (1969).

    b. Powers, E. J., Serad, G. A., in "High Performance Polymers: Their Origin and Development", Seymour, R. B., Kirshenbaum, G. S., Eds. American Chemical Soc., New York (1986), pp 355-373.

    c. Cassady, P. E., "Thermally Stable Polymers, Synthesis and Properties", Dekker, New York (1980), pp. 168-173.

    d. Critchley, J. P., et.al. "Heat Resistant Polymers", Plenum, New York, (1983), pp. 259-291.

2. Vogel, H., Marvel, C. S., J. Polymer. Sci., 50 511 (1961).

3. See:

    a. Ward, B. C., SAMPE Journal, March-April, 1989, in press.

    b. Ward, B. C., DiSano, L. P., Alvarez, E, "Polybenzimidazoles (PBI)", in Engineered Materials Handbook, Vol 2, Engineering Plastics, ASM International (1988), Metals Park, OH, pp. 147-150.

4. Dwiggins, C. F., Ward, B. C., "Creep and Hysteresis Behavior of Molded Celazole PBI Resin", concurrent paper in this issue.

5. Levine, H. H., US Patents 3,533,879 and 3,386,969 (Whittaker Corp).

6. Kuhbander, R., University of Dayton Research Institute, in AFWAL-TR-83-4026.

7. Jones, J. F., Waldrup, J. C., and Fountain, R., 29th SAMPE Symposium (1984) pp 777-783.

8. Kromrey, R. V., SPE Composites Conference, Los Angeles, CA, November, 1988.

9. HITEX Carbon Fiber supplied by Sparta/Army MTO - Materials Technology Laboratory.

10. Kromrey, R. V., US Patent 4,704,240 (United Technologies).

TABLE 1. Summary of PBI Matrix Prepregs

Polymer Type	Fiber Substrate	Resin Content	Solvent	LiCl	Comments
Prepolymer (Acurex)	Celion G30-500 3K 8 Harness Satin	35-40%	None	No	Tack and drape when heated
High MW PBI	Celion G30-500 3K 8 Harness Satin	40	None (Washed)	No	No Tack or drape
High MW PBI	HITEX 46 3" Tape (9)	36	None (Washed)	No	No Tack or drape
Intermediate MW PBI	Celion G30-500 3K 8 Harness Satin	36	30%	Yes	Drape and tack at Room Temperature.
Intermediate MW PBI	Celion G30-500 3K 8 Harness Satin	38	30%	No	Tack and drape at Room Temp.
Intermediate MW PBI	Astroquartz II 581 8 Harness Satin	37	30%	Yes	Tack and drape at Room Temp.

TABLE 2. PBI Matrix Composite Mechanical Properties from the UTCSD Thermoclave (TM) (all Celion G30-500, 3K, 8 Harness Satin)

Prepreg	Density g/cc	Tensile Strength kpsi	Tensile Modulus Mpsi	Flexural Strength kpsi	Flexural Modulus Mpsi	Short Beam Shear kpsi
PBI Prepolymer	1.45	37	--	50	7.7	6.0
High MW PBI No Solvent	1.46	48	11	75	7.2	5.2
Targets	1.50	80-120	10	100	10	8

See Table 1 for Prepreg details.

TABLE 3. PBI Matrix Composite Mechanical Properties - Hoechst Celanese Flat Platen Press (all Celion G30-500, 3K, 8 Harness Satin)

Prepreg	Density g/cc	Tensile Strength kpsi	Tensile Modulus Mpsi	Flexural Strength kpsi	Flexural Modulus Mpsi	Short Beam Shear kpsi
High MW PBI No Solvent 1400 psi process	1.45	--	--	88	8.7	6.5
Int. MW PBI 30% Solvent, LiCl 1400 psi process	1.49	--	--	110	9.6	6.2
Int. MW PBI 30% Solvent, LiCl 1400 psi process Celgard bleeder	1.49	--	--	130	8.4	10.4
Int. MW PBI 30% Solvent, No LiCl 1400 psi process Celgard bleeder	1.47	--	--	110	6.7	11.3
Int. MW PBI 30% Solvent, LiCl 200 psi process Celgard bleeder	1.42	100	9.6	115	7.3	7.9
Targets	1.50	80-120	10	100	10	8

See Table 1 for Prepreg details.

TABLE 4. Water Absorption and Ultra High Temperature Behavior on PBI Matrix Resin/Celion G30-500 8HS Composites (38% Resin Content)

Water Absorption   1.5% (100 °C immersion, 2 hours)

Weight Loss (5 minutes) Dry Specimens   Wet Specimens (1.5% water)

1300 °F (700 °C)	1.2%	1300 °F (700 °C)	2.2%
1800 °F (980 °C)	10%	1800 °F (980 °C)	13%

No blistering or delamination observed on any specimen

Testing: Thermal Protective Performance apparatus, air, 5 minutes exposure to natural gas flame and radiant heat.

All specimens

    Thickness: 0.10 in. (6 ply laminate)
    Length: 1.0 in.
    Width: 0.50 in.

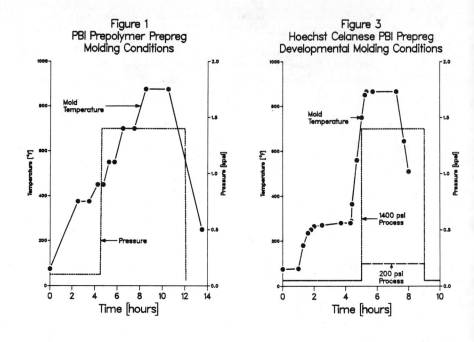

Figure 1
PBI Prepolymer Prepreg
Molding Conditions

Figure 3
Hoechst Celanese PBI Prepreg
Developmental Molding Conditions

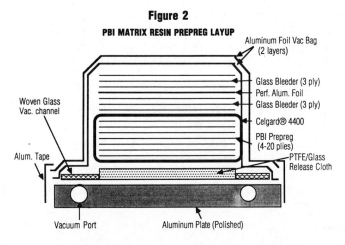

Figure 2

PBI MATRIX RESIN PREPREG LAYUP

Aluminum Foil Vac Bag (2 layers)

Glass Bleeder (3 ply)
Perf. Alum. Foil
Glass Bleeder (3 ply)

Celgard® 4400

PBI Prepreg (4-20 plies)

PTFE/Glass Release Cloth

Woven Glass Vac. channel

Alum. Tape

Vacuum Port

Aluminum Plate (Polished)

Compression Molding and Thermoclave®

34th International SAMPE Symposium
May 8-11, 1989

STUDY OF PROCESSING PARAMETERS OF PEEK/GRAPHITE
COMPOSITES FABRICATED WITH "FIT" PREPREG

Mark Thiede-Smet, Heath Tecna Aerospace Co.

Marie Liu, and Victor Ho, CIBA-GEIGY Corporation

Abstract

CIBA-GEIGY has acquired a new technology for making thermoplastic prepreg using a patented "Fiber Impregnated with Thermoplastic" ("FIT") process from Atochem/France.

Fabrics woven from "FIT" tow prepreg show a great deal of drapability.

This paper details a processing study of the "FIT" tow prepreg made of graphite fiber and Polyetheretherketone (PEEK) thermoplastic using both press and autoclave consolidation.

A statistically designed experiment was used to evaluate the effects of several processing variables and determine a recommended processing window. Molding conditions, which included temperature, pressure and time were related to part quality determined by mechanical tests, ultrasonic tests and thickness measurements. These are presented and discussed.

Scanning Electron Microscope (SEM) analysis is included to determine the fiber/resin distribution and the quality of the laminates.

1. INTRODUCTION

The purpose of this work is to understand the processing characteristics and to develop a recommended processing window for the "FIT" material based on PEEK polymer.

This work was a joint development by the Composite Materials Department of CIBA-GEIGY and Heath Tecna Aerospace Company.

2. MATERIAL

The "FIT" process was patented by Atochem in France and acquired by CIBA-GEIGY in 1988.

The "FIT" process consists of a fiber tow permeated with powdered thermoplastic, which is sheathed with the same or a different thermoplastic (see Figure 1).

The ratio of powder to sheath is adjustable. Combinations are limited only by the compatibility of powder to sheath material. Theoretically, all extrudable thermoplastics could be used for powder or sheath.

In this study Toray T-300 6K graphite fiber and PEEK 150 G

polymer were used in the tow. Total resin content was 38 - 40% by weight. The tow was then woven into a 5-harness satin fabric.

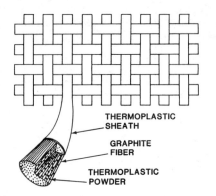

FIGURE 1:   CONSTITUENTS OF "FIT" TOW

Here is a simplified explanation of "FIT" tow manufacturing:

(1.) The fiber tow is first pulled through a set of braked, staggered cylinders that spread the fiber tow.

(2.) The fiber then enters a fluidized bed, where a controlled amount of thermoplastic powder is distributed onto it.

(3.) The powdered fiber is then passed through a cooling injector, which also centers the tow in the axis of the die.

(4.) As the fiber passes the hot die, melted thermoplastic is being extruded, enveloping the passing fiber and forming a sheath. This completes the tow manufacturing process.

Prepreg tow can be used in a variety of ways: "As is" for filament winding; woven to form a flexible prepreg fabric; or collimated to form unidirectional prepreg.

3.   STATISTICALLY DESIGNED EXPERIMENT

The methodology chosen for this work was a statistically designed experiment. The test plan was designed so that statistical analysis would determine relationships between molding conditions and tests for part quality.

Two sets of experiments were performed: a smaller experiment for autoclave consolidation, and a broader experiment for press fabrication covering an extensive range of processing.

After reviewing reports and papers concerning process development of PEEK Composites (1 - 4), a decision was made as to which processing parameters would be varied and what ranges would be explored (Table I). All other conditions were held constant.

Processing parameters for the autoclave experiment included: pressure, temperature, and time (at full pressure before the beginning of cool-down).

The choice of which processing combinations for each test panel was critical for the analysis. Our statistician recommended a "full factorial experiment" (5) which has all eight combinations of high and low process settings for the three variables.

A visual representation of a "full factorial experiment" is shown in Figure 2. Each ball indicates a combination of processing parameters at which a laminate was fabricated. Nine combinations were fabricated plus 2 replicates.

Four process parameters were explored for the press experiment: 3 for the hot

1224

TABLE I: PROCESSING VARIABLES EXPLORED

AUTOCLAVE EXPERIMENT	
TEMPERATURE	680 - 720 F
PRESSURE	120 - 180 PSI
TIME	30 - 60 MINUTES
PRESS EXPERIMENT	
HOT PRESS TEMPERATURE	670 - 750 F
HOT PRESS PRESSURE	50 - 450 PSI
TIME IN HOT PRESS	5 - 65 MINUTES
COOL PRESS PRESSURE	50 - 450 PSI

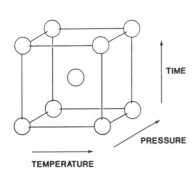

FIGURE 2:   COMBINATIONS OF PROCESSING CHOSEN FOR THE AUTOCLAVE EXPERIMENT

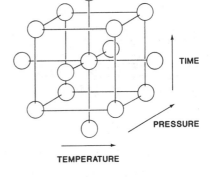

FIGURE 3:   PROCESSING COMBINATIONS CHOSEN FOR THE PRESS EXPERIMENT

press (temperature, pressure and time), and one for the cool press (pressure).

Because of the broad range of processing tested a "Box-Wilson experiment" was recommended (5). The combinations of variables for each laminate are represented in Figure 3 (three of the four variables are shown). This amounts to a "full factorial" plus selected combinations to explore the extreme values of processing. Here, 25 combinations were fabricated plus 13 replicates.

Regression techniques were performed on the panel test results. This quantified the influence of each processing parameter in a simple mathematical model. "Three dimensional" graphs were plotted to identify the desirable processing windows.

4.   TESTING

Five tests were used to measure part quality: short beam shear, compression strength, C-scan, thickness and appearance.

Short beam shear (SBS) specimens were prepared according to ASTM D-2344. Six specimens were tested at room temperature in the fabric's warp direction.

Specimens for compression testing were 3.180" x .500" tabbed coupons with a 0.188" unsupported gauge length and tested in an ASTM D695 test fixture. Five specimens were tested at room temperature in the fabric's warp direction.

The C-scan was a "through transmission ultrasonic" inspection performed submerged in water. One C-scan number describing each panel was obtained. The higher the number was, the better the quality of the panel.

For each panel, five thickness measurements were taken in separate areas, but identically for each panel.

The appearance test was a subjective, human evaluation of resin condition, fiber straightness and panel warpage.

5. FABRICATION

All laminates were flat, made from 8 plies of "FIT" fabric using the lay-up [0]4s. They measured 7.1" x.9.8".

Autoclave panels were laid up on a small plate of Comtek XS chemically bonded ceramic (CBC). The heat-up and cool-down rate of the autoclave was controlled to 8°F per minute.

For the press panels, the two-press method was chosen: a hot press to heat and compact the panel; a cool press to solidify it. A track was built between the presses, and a wheeled carriage transported the mold. The mold was composed of 0.25" carbon steel flat plates top and bottom

6. RESULTS/DISCUSSION

6.1 Autoclave Experiment

Three process variables were explored for the autoclave experiment: temperature, pressure and time. Not all the variables were significant in each mathematical model developed from these tests.

The results discussed below are summarized in Table II. This tabulates the processing variables which were

TABLE II: SIGNIFICANT PROCESSING VARIABLES AND
INTERACTIONS FOR EACH TEST

SIGNIFICANT VARIABLES	TEST METHODS							
	SBS STR.	COMPR. STR.	C-SCAN			THICK.	APPEAR.	
AUTOCLAVE		*			*			
PRESSURE	X	x		X	x			
TIME	X			X	x			
TEMPERATURE	X	x						
CORRELATION	96%	N/A	84%			N/A	N/A	
PRESS				*	*			
PRES. HOT PRESS	X	X	X	x	x	X		
PRES. COOL PRES			X	x				
TIME	X	X	X		x	X		
TEMPERATURE	X	X						
CORRELATION	48%	48%	67%			30%	N/A	

* TWO "x's" IN THIS COLUMN INDICATES AN INTERACTION BETWEEN THOSE TWO PROCESSING VARIABLES

significant in influencing each of the five tests along with any interactions between variables. A measure of the percent variability in the data that was explained by the mathematical model is also listed. This is called the correlation. The closer this is to 100%, the better the model.

6.1.1 SBS Strength

Analysis of the SBS data resulted in a mathematical model relating SBS strength to three significant variables: Temperature, pressure and time.

A three dimensional graph of this model, called a surface plot, is shown in Figure 4. Since only two processing variables can be shown on this graph, the third variable (time) is held constant at 60 minutes.

The surface plot shows SBS increasing with temperature and pressure. Time would have had a similar effect had it been shown on the graph.

SBS strengths above 13.0 ksi are achievable with proper processing.

6.1.2 Compression Strength

Analysis of the compression strength data indicated that compression strength was not significantly affected by processing parameters for the autoclave experiment.

The mean compression strength for all autoclave tests specimens was 56 ksi.

6.1.3 C-Scan

The number derived from the C-scan test showed the most sensitivity to process parameter changes compared to the other tests performed.

Only two of the three processing variables tested were significant in influencing the C-scan number: pressure and time.

The model resulting from the statistical analysis is represented by a surface plot in Figure 5. Notice that 3 of the 4 corners of the surface are at high values of C-scan; this will be contrasted with the press results.

A value of 240 C-scan points was determined to be the minimum acceptable result for the equipment used. It can be seen in the contour plot (Figure 6) of the C-scan model that the level of 240 C-scan points was not achieved within the range of processing of the autoclave experiment. This experiment will be expanded to include 200 psi and 70 minutes.

6.1.4 Thickness

Thickness measurements resulted in no trends and no significant processing variables. The mean thickness per ply was 0.015" for all panels.

6.1.5 Appearance

The appearance judgement also showed no trends and no significant processing variables. Good surface finish and fiber alignment were the norm for the autoclave panels.

6.2 Press Experiment

Four process variables were explored for the press experiment: temperature, pressure and time, all in the hot press, and pressure in the cool press. Not all the variables were significant in each mathematical model developed from these tests.

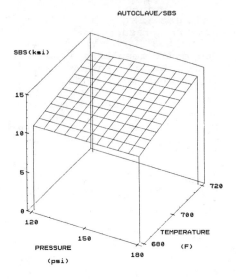

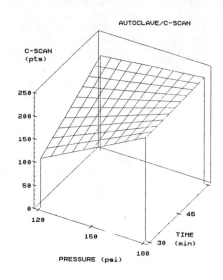

FIGURE 4: SHORT BEAM SHEAR STRENGTH WAS DEPENDENT ON PRESSURE, TEMPERATURE AND TIME FOR THE AUTOCLAVE EXPERIMENT

FIGURE 5: C-SCAN QUALITY WAS STRONGLY INFLUENCED BY PRESSURE AND TIME FOR THE AUTOCLAVE EXPERIMENT

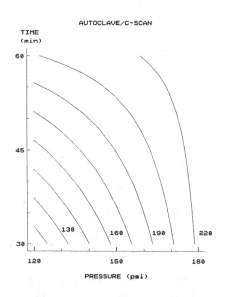

FIGURE 6: CONTOUR PLOT FOR AUTOCLAVE C-SCAN RESULTS

The results discussed below are summarized in Table II.

6.2.1 SBS Strength

Of the four processing parameters, three were statistically significant: pressure in the hot press, time, and temperature being the least important.

The mathematical model derived from the statistical analysis is shown in the surface plot in Figure 7. Since only two processing variables can be shown on the plot, the variable "time" was held constant at 50 minutes for the plot. In the model, time had an influence similar to that of pressure.

These SBS strengths showed more variation than the autoclave values due to the larger range in processing in the press experiment. SBS strengths above 14 ksi are achievable.

6.2.2 Compression Strength

The compression strength data was affected by the same processing variables as the SBS data.

The surface plot (Figure 8 with temperature constant at 730°F) indicates strengths above 80 ksi to be attainable with proper processing.

6.2.3 C-Scan

As with the autoclave work, the number derived from the C-scan test showed the most sensitivity to process parameter changes compared to the other tests performed.

All variables were signifi-cant except temperature in the mathematical model for C-scan. Two sizable inter-actions were also present. The surface plot (Figure 9)

shows the influence of hot press pressure and time, with cool press pressure constant at 400 psi. Notice that only one of the four corners of the response surface gave high C-scan values.

200 C-scan points was deter-mined to be the minimum acceptable for the press panels. This was lower than for the autoclave panels because of a low quality border, 1.2" wide, which surrounded each panel bringing the combined C-scan number down.

A contour plot (Figure 10 with time constant at 50 minutes) shows the importance of the pressure in the cool press. For best results, this should be approximately equal to hot press pressure, and both should be towards the high end of the ranges explored.

6.2.4 Thickness

Thickness did confirm an expected trend for the press panels. The higher the hot press pressure and time, the thinner the panels were. Thicknesses of 0.014" to 0.015" per ply can be expected.

6.2.5 Appearance

Again nothing statistically significant came from the appearance judgement. Press panels ranged from severely resin starved to a surface of uniform resin.

6.3 SEM Photographs

SEM photos of fracture surfaces and polished cross-sections gave additional insight to the differences in mechanical properties seen.

Figure 11, shows a cross-section from the panel having the lowest SBS and

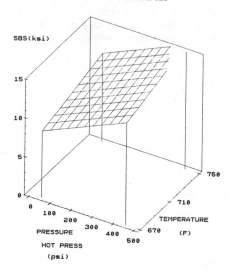

FIGURE 7: PRESSURE,
TEMPERATURE AND TIME WERE
SIGNIFICANT IN AFFECTING SBS
STRENGTH FOR PRESS PANELS

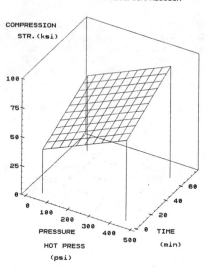

FIGURE 8: COMPRESSION
STRENGTH FOR PRESS PANELS
WAS DEPENDENT ON PRESSURE
IN THE HOT PRESS, TIME AND
TEMPERATURE

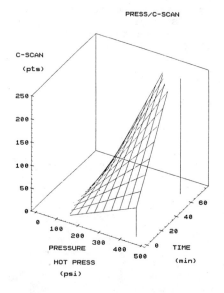

FIGURE 9: C-SCAN QUALITY
WAS GREATLY INFLUENCED BY
PRESSURE IN THE HOT AND COOL
PRESSES, AND TIME

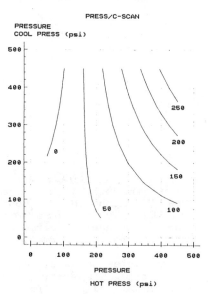

FIGURE 10: COOL PRESS
PRESSURE WAS AS IMPORTANT AS
HOT PRESS PRESSURE FOR "FIT"
LAMINATES

compression test values. It shows incomplete consolidation and a miserable fiber-resin interface. This panel was found to have a void content of 10%. Most of the process settings were on the low side of the ranges tested.

Figure 12 shows the fracture surface from the press panel which had the highest SBS and compression strengths in this study. It demonstrates good resin adhesion to the fiber and a ductile resin failure. This panel had a 0.8% void content and was processed at the highest hot press pressure.

A fracture surface from an autoclave specimen is shown in Figure 13. This indicates strong bonding between plies and a ductile resin failure

Only minor visual differences were seen between the fracture surfaces from the autoclave panels which had the highest and lowest mechanical test results.

A cross-section of an autoclave panel (Figure 14) illustrates the uniform resin distribution, and close proximity of adjacent plies. This laminate had less than .5% voids.

7. CONCLUSIONS

The statistically designed experiment proved to be an excellent analytical tool for quantifying the influence of process variations.

The surface and contour plots developed from the statistical analysis provided guidelines for selecting process settings.

The authors found that changes in process parameters significantly affected the properties of PEEK "FIT" laminates.

In general, the values of the C-scan, SBS and compression strength increased as higher pressure, time and temperature were used in fabricating the laminates.

Higher values of SBS and compression strength were achieved with the press experiment than with the autoclave experiment. This was attributed to the higher pressures used in the press experiment.

The C-scan tests revealed that double the pressure is required in the press to obtain equivalent laminate quality to autoclave panels.

The SEM photographs indicated that due to the inherent nature of the "FIT" material there was good resin distribution among the filaments and fiber tows. High quality panels can be made using proper processing.

Currently, the recommended processing window for PEEK "FIT" prepreg for autoclave consolidation is 710°F and 60 minutes at 180 psi before cooling. Work will continue to expand the autoclave experiment to 200 psi and 70 minutes.

For two-press consolidation the recommendation is a 730°F hot press at 400 psi for 50 minutes before transferring to a 250°F cool press at 400 psi.

8. REFERENCES

(1) Iaconis, J.M. "Process Variables Evaluation of PEEK APC-2 Thermoplastic Matrix Composite", 32nd SAMPE Symposium, pp. 104 - 115, April 1987.

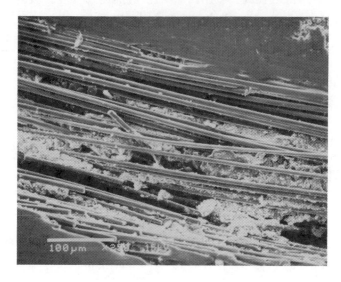

FIGURE 11:   HIGH VOID PRESS PANEL WITH POOR FIBER –
             MATRIX BONDING CAUSED BY TOO LOW PROCESS
             SETTINGS

FIGURE 12:   SUBSTANTIAL FIBER – MATRIX BONDING AND
             DUCTILE RESIN FAILURE IN PRESS PANEL WHICH
             SAW HIGHER PROCESS SETTINGS

FIGURE 13:   FRACTURE SURFACE OF AUTOCLAVE SBS SPECIMEN
              INDICATING STRONG BONDING BETWEEN PLIES AND
              DUCTILE RESIN FAILURE

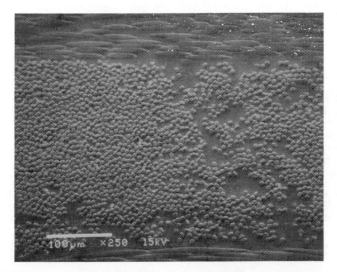

FIGURE 14:   CROSS-SECTION OF AUTOCLAVE LAMINATE SHOWING
              UNIFORM MATRIX DISTRIBUTION AND CLOSE
              PROXIMITY OF ADJACENT PLIES

(2) Silverman, E.M., Jones, R.J. SAMPE Journal, Vol. 24, No. 4, pp. 33 - 40 (1988).

(3) Kurz, J.E. "Processing Science of Thermoplastic Composites", Report to Air Force Wright Aeronautical Laboratories, March 1987, Contract F33615-85-C-5046.

(4) Naguom, T., et al. "Evaluation of PEEK Matrix Composite", 32nd SAMPE Symposium, pp. 396 - 407, April 1987.

(5) Montgomery, D.C., Design And Analysis of Experiments, John Wiley & Sons, NY, Ed. 2, 1984, pp. 445-474.

9. ACKNOWLEDGEMENTS

The authors would like to acknowledge the contributions of Dr. Shaw Lee for consultation, Craig Whittaker for statistical analysis, Jesse Gonzales and Marlo Carrillo for specimen fabrication and testing, Jeaneen Kelsay for laminate fabrication, and Drew Zimmerman for c-scan inspection.

10. BIOGRAPHIES

Mark Thiede-Smet is currently responsible for Engineering Thermoplastic Composite development at Heath Tecna Aerospace Co.. His 3 years at Heath Tecna combined with 6 years at Boeing Commercial Airplane Co. has included a variety of composite R&D programs including filament winding, pultrusion, press and autoclave processing of both thermoplastic and epoxy matrix composites.

Marie W. Liu is a Development Chemist at the Composite Materials Department of CIBA-GEIGY Corporation. She has been engaged in prepreg material development using organic matrix and carbon fibers. Ms. Liu has been with CIBA-GEIGY for 5 years. During the last two years she has been involved in thermoplastic resin-fiber composite studies. Her previous experience included development of biocompatible polymer coatings for disposable medical devices.

Victor Ho is a group leader of prepreg material development at the Composite Materials Department of CIBA-GEIGY Corporation. His current responsibilty is to manage the group developing resin matrix-fiber prepregs for various industrial applications. He has been with CIBA-GEIGY for 10 years. Mr. Ho has 20 years of experience in non-metallics and for the last 17 years has been actively involved in material and process activities on advanced organic composites, adhesives and electrical insulations.

High Temperature Polyetherimide Composites

Steven Peake , Art Maranci and Diana Megna+
American Cyanamid Company
* Discovery Research, Stamford, CT 06904-0060
+ Engineered Materials Technology, Havre de Grace, MD 21048

Abstract

Continuous fiber reinforced composites have been fabricated from a novel class of thermoplastic polyetherimide resins with glass transition temperatures greater than 250°C. These polyetherimides were screened for application as composite matrix resins on the basis of processability, laminate quality, solvent resistance, and retention of mechanical properties at 180 to 235°C (350 to 450°F). One candidate was selected for further development and a more extensive property profile was investigated. This prepreg could be consolidated at 350 to 385°C (660 to 725°F) and 1.4 MPa (200 psi). The resulting laminates showed excellent solvent resistance, and retention of mechanical properties up to 180°C (350°F/wet). This paper will describe laminate fabrication and mechanical properties of these polyetherimide composites.

1.0 INTRODUCTION

Thermoplastic polymers are receiving increasing interest as matrix resins for advanced composites. The principal reason is that thermoplastic composites may be shaped or formed using rapid forming techniques such as thermoforming. Because no cure chemistry occurs during the forming process, processing time is dependent only on the time required to achieve complete consolidation. Furthermore, the polymer properties are independent of the consolidation cycles (at least for amorphous polymers) and the laminate may be reconsolidated to correct imperfect parts. These factors should lead to lower manufacturing costs for thermoplastic composites. A second benefit is derived from the inherent ductility of thermoplastic polymers; thermoplastic matrix composites will have greater toughness as measured by post impact compressive strength than thermosets. This is particularly true when considering materials for service at 150°C/wet and above.

A wide variety of engineering thermoplastics, including amorphous and semicrystalline polymers, have been examined in continuous fiber composites. In selecting a resin for aerospace composites, many of the performance criteria are the same as for thermosetting polymers: stiffness, toughness, and retention of properties under hot/wet conditions. Issues of particular importance to thermoplastic composites are consolidation temperature and pressure, solvent resistance, melt rheology, and extent of crystallinity.

An earlier report described composites based on polyetherimides with glass transition temperatures up to 220°C.[1] These materials offer a good balance of toughness, mechanical properties and processability, but for some applications a resin with higher service temperature was needed. In cooperation with General Electric Plastics, second generation polyetherimides were screened for use in continuous fiber reinforced composites. These polymers had glass transition temperatures up to 330°C and retained thermoplastic characteristics. This paper will review the process by which the new polyetherimides were screened and will describe composite properties of candidate matrix resins.

2.0 EXPERIMENTAL

2.1 Prepreg Fabrication

For initial evaluations, small pieces of prepreg were made in the laboratory by coating AS-4 plain weave fabric (3K70P) with a solution of the resin in N-methylpyrrolidinone. The solution was approximately 30 wt. % solids and sufficient resin was added to give a fiber volume of approximately 60%. The prepreg made in this fashion had tack and drape and was amenable to autoclave processing with removal of solvent. Alternatively, the prepreg could be dried by heating in a forced air oven for 30 minutes at 150°C (300°F) followed by 15 minutes at 330°C (625°F). Unidirectional tape was made in the laboratory by setting up an array of fibers under tension with an areal weight of 145 gsm; the fibers were then coated with a solution of resin and dried as described above. Large scale evaluation was carried out on prepreg which was impregnated by a proprietary process and which contained no solvent.

2.2 Laminate Fabrication

Laminates were fabricated by compression molding of dry prepreg or autoclave processing of wet prepreg. In compression molding, the layup was placed between aluminum sheets which had been coated with a high temperature release agent. This was placed between 6.4 mm thick (0.25") caul plates and the entire assembly was placed in press which had been preheated to the molding temperature; the molding temperature was typically 100°C above the polymer's glass transition temperature.

When the layup reached the press temperature, the press was bumped (ie., repeatedly opened and closed) then 1.4 MPa (200 psi) was applied and the press was allowed to cool.

In autoclave processing, the bagging sequence shown in Figure 1 was used. For example , a 12" X 14" laminate was covered on both sides with 15" X 15" sheets of glass fabric with Teflon* coating (eg., TX 1040) then with 15.5" X 15.5" release coated 5 mil Kapton* film; tacky tape sealant was placed around the perimeter of the laminate to act as a dam. The assembly was completed by placing a 14" X 12" steel caul plate and 5 plies of glass breather cloth on top then sealing a 21"X 21" bag made from 5 mil Kapton film with tacky tape around the perimeter. The laminate was consolidated by placing in an autoclave at room temperature, applying full vacuum to the bag and 140 kPa (20 psi). The layup was heated to 130°C (260°F) at 1.3°C/min. The vacuum was released and heating continued to 180°C (350°F) at 1.3°C/min. The temperature was held at 180°C (350°F) for

2.5 hours then raised to 230°C (450°F) at 1.3°C/min. The pressure was reduced to 10 psi, raised twice to 20 psi, then returned to 70 kPa (10 psi). Heating was continued to 290°C (550°F) and this temperature was held for 30 minutes. Full vacuum was applied and heating at 290°C was continued for 30 minutes. The temperature was raised to the final temperature (typically 385°C) at 1.5°C/min, then the pressure was raised to 900 kPa (120 psi). After 20 minutes the vacuum was released and the the autoclave was cooled to room temperature at 1.3°C/min under pressure.

2.3 Physical and Mechanical Testing

A Melt Flow Index Apparatus (ASTM 1238-73) was used to determine the melt viscosity of the neat polyetherimide resins. The die capillary was 2.3 mm in diameter by 8.0 mm. Shear rates were measured by weighing the extrudate. Shear rates varied from 0.1 to 60 sec^{-1} and shear stresses were varied from 86 to 274 kPa. Neat resin shear viscosity and shear modulus as a function of temperature was determined on a Rheometrics RMS 605 Mechanical Spectrometer.

A summary of the laminate configuration and test methods is summarized in Table 1. Flexural creep was measured according to the method described by ASTM D2990. The test fixture was placed inside of an oven. Quartz rods extended from the test specimens to dial gauges located on the outside. Weight gain of composites in solvents was determined by placing 1.0 X 2.3 X 0.3 cm [0,90] fabric specimens in solvent at the appropriate temperature. The samples were wiped dry before each weighing.

Tensile properties of fiber tow were determined by ASTM 4018. The fiber tows were impregnated with a room temperature curing epoxy (Epo Mix from Buehler) at 50% resin content by weight. The specimens were allowed to cure overnight and they were tabbed with polycarbonate. Strain gauge extensometers were attached directly to the samples, and the stress-strain curve was measured in an Instron test machine.

3.0 RESULTS AND DISCUSSION

Laminates were made from a series of ten new polyetherimide resins. For several polymers, conditions could not be found which would give void free laminates. The laminates were examined microscopically and those that were void free were screened for retention of short beam shear strength at elevated temperatures after water exposure. The trade-off between laminate quality and service temperature can be seen from the plot of short beam shear strength vs. temperature for moisture conditioned laminates. The results for three composites are shown in Figure 2. Another polyetherimide composite, CYPAC 7005®[1], is shown for comparison. Composite A showed excellent retention of strength even at 235°C; however, the room temperature strength was indicative of a poor quality laminate. This was confirmed when the laminate was examined m i c r o s c o p i c a l l y ; microporosity was present within the fiber tows. Good quality laminates were made with resins B and C, and a more complete set of data was generated for these. The melt rheology of three polyetherimide resins was determined using a Melt Flow Index Apparatus (ASTM 1238). The data obtained could be fitted to equation (1) shown. The second term relates to the activation

$$\log\eta = A + 8400/T - (0.5)\log\gamma_w \quad (1)$$

Where η = viscosity, poise
       T = temperature, $^{\circ}K$
       $\dot{\gamma}_w$ = shear rate, sec^{-1}
       A = material constant
energy of flow and the third term to the power law description of the shear rate dependence of the viscosity. Within the experimental range, an activation energy of 16.8 kcal could describe the behavior of all three resins. The material constants were as follows:
Ultem* 1000 Resin: A = -8.64
CYPAC 7005 Resin: A = -7.89
Resin B   A = -6.63
A comparison of viscosities predicted by equation (1) for a particular temperature and shear rate vs. the measured viscosities is shown in Figure 3.

On the basis of the short beam shear results, resins B and C were selected for further work. In order to gain better insight into the upper use temperature, compressive strength was measured for fabric laminates. These results along with other mechanical properties are summarized in Table 2. The mechanical performance, glass transition temperatures and retention of properties under hot/wet conditions of both resins were equivalent. Both showed greater than 60% retention of the room temperature compressive strength at 180 C/wet.

These high Tg resins showed improved solvent resistance over earlier polyetherimides. The weight gain in several solvents after thirty days is shown in Figure 4. In general, resin C showed better solvent resistance although resin B showed the best resistance to dichloromethane.

Processing conditions can play a key role in obtaining high quality laminates from thermoplastic composites. In compression molding the mold surfaces must be flat, and the press platens parallel to insure even consolidation. Because of the relatively high molding temperatures, differences in the coefficients of thermal expansion between laminate and mold can lead to fiber buckling and/or laminate warpage. At temperatures above the glass transition, the resin is a viscoelastic melt which is unable to provide sustained lateral support to the fibers. Consequently, the mismatch between the coefficients of thermal expansion of the fibers in the axial direction ($\alpha = -1.2 \times 10^{-6}/^\circ C$) and the caul plate ($\alpha = 23 \times 10^{-6}$ for aluminum) causes fiber buckling in the laminate. Below the glass transition, the resin will resist fiber buckling, but the laminate will be forced into compression by the caul plate or mold. In the absence of slippage, the laminate will warp when released from the mold. A way of alleviating this problem is to choose mold materials which more closely match the coefficient of thermal expansion of the laminate, for example: stainless steel ($\alpha = 16 \times 10^{-6}$) or Invar ($\alpha = 7 \times 10^{-6}$). Indeed, when borosilicate glass ($\alpha = 3.2 \times 10^{-6}$) was used as a caul plate, warping and fiber buckling were eliminated in $[0,90]_{2s}$ laminates.

Resin C could be processed at

temperatures less than (700°F) and the laminate quality was consistently good. Resin B had to processed at temperatures greater than (750°F) and laminate quality was variable. The processing advantages of Resin C led to its selection for commercial development. The prepreg has been designated as CYPAC X7156-1.

Resin C is an amorphous thermoplastic with a glass transition temperature of 275°C (536°F). No crystallinity was seen in the polymer as received from General Electric, and there was no evidence of solvent induced crystallization as has been seen some polyetherimides.[2] The neat resin properties are summarized in Table 3.

In order to respond to the need for composite applications in stiffness critical structures, CYPAC X7156-1 was examined in combination with a series of advanced intermediate modulus fibers. Flexural properties of unidirectional laminates were measured. Flexure was chosen to minimize the quantity of prepreg required.

The fiber tensile properties and laminate flex properties are summarized in Table 4. The highest modulus fiber, Courtaulds Apollo 53-750, showed the highest laminate modulus. All fibers showed good fiber-resin adhesion.

4.0 SUMMARY

Novel polyetherimide resins were screened in continuous fiber reinforced composites for use up to 180°. One polymer displayed a satisfactory combination of processability, solvent resistance, and mechanical properties, and was selected for further development. The polymer was an amorphous thermoplastic with a glass transition temperature of 257°C. A composite, designated CYPAC X7156-1, showed greater than 60% retention of compressive strength up to 180°C/wet and 50% retention at 190°C/wet.

ACKNOWLEDGMENT

The authors would like to thank the General Electric Company and Dr. D. C. Bookbinder in particular for their assistance. Mechanical testing and data analysis by R. G. Ferrillo, P. J. Achorn, A. J. Cronin and S. Kaminski is gratefully acknowledged.

REFERENCES

1. S. L. Peake and A.

Maranci, 32nd Int. SAMPE Symp., (1987) 420.

2. K. M. Nelson, J. C. Seferis, and H. G. Zachmann, 34th Int. SAMPE Symp., in print, 1989.

BIOGRAPHY

Steven Peake is the Group Leader for Matrix Resins in the Discovery Research Department at American Cyanamid's Chemical Research Division. Prior to joining Cyanamid, he received a Ph.D. in Chemistry from the University of Wisconsin at Madison in 1979, and a B.S. in Chemistry from the University of Texas, Austin in 1974. His group's responsibilities include the development of new polymer and monomer chemistries for use in aerospace composites and adhesives.

CYPAC is a registered trademark of the American Cyanamid Co.

TABLE 1 - Test Methods and Specimen Configuration*

Test	Method	Specimen Dimension (cm)
Short Beam Shear	ASTM D2344 4:1 SDR	Fabric: 0.95 X 1.78 Tape 0.64 X 1.78**
Flexural Str./Mod	ASTM D790 40:1 SDR	1.27 X 6.35
Comp Str./Mod	ASTM D695	1.27 X 8.00
Tensile Str.	ASTM D3039	1.27 X 22.9

*Fabric Laminates : $[0,90]_3s$; Tape laminates: $[0]_8$
** Tape Laminate for Short Beam Shear was $[0]_{20}$

TABLE 2 - Mechanical Properties of Resins High Tg Polyetherimides
AS-4, 3K70P Fabric

Property	Resin B		Resin C	
Tg, °C (°F)	280	(536)	275	(527)
Processing Temperature, °C (°F)	412	(775)	360	(675)
Short Beam Shear Strength, MPa (ksi)				
200°C Dry	63	(9.5)	61	(8.8)
24°C Wet	63	(9.5)		
180°C Dry	39	(5.6)		
180°C Wet	32	(4.6)		
190°C Dry	37	(5.4)	46	(6.6)
190°C Wet	28	(4.0)	26	(3.7)
Compressive Strength, MPa (ksi)				
24°C Dry	480	(70)	480	(70)
180°C Dry	300	(43)		
180°C Wet	260	(38)		
190°C Dry	300	(43)	310	(45)
190°C Wet	230	(33)	250	(36)
204°C Dry	180	(26)	260	(38)

Table 3 - Neat Resin Properties

Property	Ultem 1000 Resin	CYPAC 7005 Resin	CYPAC 7156-1 Resin
Tg by DMA °C	217	230	275
Tensile Strength, MPa	105	95	102
Tensile Elongation, %	60	20	15
Flex Modulus, GPa	3.3	3.0	3.1
Flex Strength MPa	145	130	128
Izod Impact			
Notched, 3.2mm, J/m	50	50	
Unnotched, 3.2mm, J/m	1300	1300	
Specific Gravity, g/cm^3	1.27	1.28	

TABLE 4.

Fiber Type	Fiber Properties			CYPAC X7156-1 Laminate		
	Tensile Strength (ksi)	Tensile Modulus (msi)	Elongation (%)	0⁰ Flex Strength (ksi)	0⁰ Flex Modulus (Msi)	Shear Strength* (ksi)
Hercules IM8	642	44.8	1.39	346	27.4	15.3
Courtaulds Apollo 53-750	698	50.1	1.43	250	31.7	14.3
Hitco Hitex 50-8B	696	44.6	1.57	346	27.3	—

* Short Beam Shear Strength

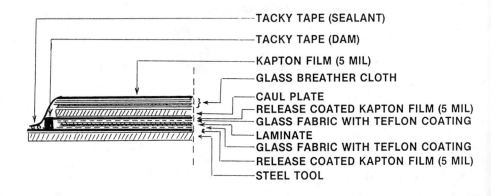

TACKY TAPE (SEALANT)
TACKY TAPE (DAM)
KAPTON FILM (5 MIL)
GLASS BREATHER CLOTH
CAUL PLATE
RELEASE COATED KAPTON FILM (5 MIL)
GLASS FABRIC WITH TEFLON COATING
LAMINATE
GLASS FABRIC WITH TEFLON COATING
RELEASE COATED KAPTON FILM (5 MIL)
STEEL TOOL

FIGURE 1.

HIGH Tg POLYETHERIMIDES
WET INTERLAMINAR SHEAR VS TEMPERATURE

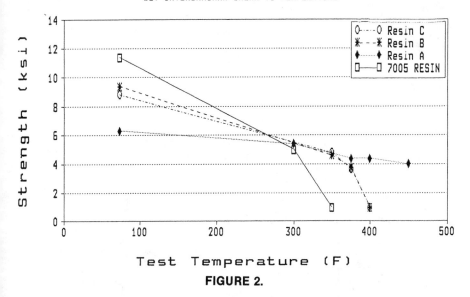

FIGURE 2.

ESTIMATED VERSUS MEASURED VISCOSITY
POLYETHERIMIDE RESINS

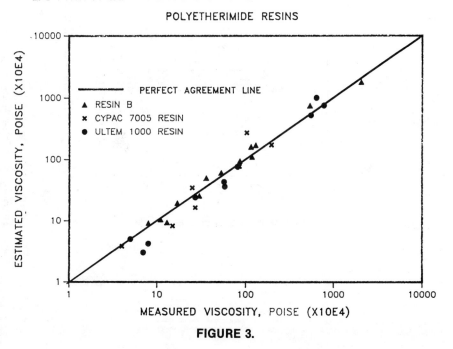

FIGURE 3.

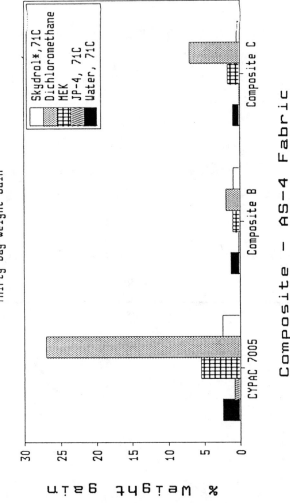

Polyetherimide Composites
Thirty Day Weight Gain

Composite – AS-4 Fabric

FIGURE 4.

*Product of the Monsanto Co.

COMPATIBLE BLENDS OF SEGMENTED POLYIMIDE SILOXANE COPOLYMERS
WITH ENGINEERING THERMOPLASTICS I. POLYBENZIMIDAZOLE (PBI)

D. H. Chen, Y. P. Chen, C. A. Arnold, J. C. Hedrick,
J. D. Graybeal and J. E. McGrath*
Department of Chemistry and
Science and Technology Center: High Performance
Polymeric Adhesives and Composites
Virginia Polytechnic Institute and State University
Blacksburg, VA 24061

*To whom correspondence should be addressed

Abstract

Miscible or at least highly compatible blends based on high temperature engineering polymers, i.e. polybenzimidazole (PBI) and polyimides (PI) or segmented siloxane imide copolymers (PI-SX) were prepared and studied. Specifically, the poly(imide sulfone) derived from the solution imidization of BDTA and 3,3′-diaminodiphenyl sulfone (DDS)n appears to form a single Tg blend with PBI which does not phase separate about the Tg when examined via DMTA. FT-IR studies showed that hydrogen bonding interactions play a strong role in their miscibility. Surface properties, including reduced water uptake and atomic oxygen stability are greatly enhanced by the presence of siloxane segments in blends, which may be attributed to hydrophobic characterstics and conversion of siloxane to silicate by atomic oxygen.

1. INTRODUCTION

Polybenzimidazole (PBI) is well-known for its high glass transition temperature, tensile strength and thermal stability. These inherent properties may be attributed to the rigid and highly polar structure of polybenzimidazole (Figure 1). The hydrogen on the nitrogen of imidazole is quite acidic, which is the source of hydrogen bonding through intermolecular interaction. On the other hand, it also makes polybenzimidazole very hydrophilic.

Polyimides are also high performance engineering thermoplastics. Their reasonably high Tg and mechanical properties are of interest for many applications. Polyimides absorb relatively low amounts moisture, which also makes them an ideal candidate for blends with PBI. Karasz, et al. first reported the miscibility between PBI and several commercially available polyimides (1). The segmented siloxane-imide copolymers (PI-SX) which are made in our laboratory (5) are of great interest in several areas including surface modification. Siloxane segments have extreme low Tg and low surface free energy values, which allows a siloxane dominated layer to form on the air surface of copolymers or blends. The hydrophobic nature of siloxane segment on the surface certainly further reduces water uptake and also effectively protects the lower layer which is made of organic components against aggressive atomic oxygen which is found in the lower earth orbit environment (5). On the other hand, imide segments effectively interact with PBI to afford desired upper Tg miscibility.

2. EXPERIMENTAL

Sample Preparations: Unfilled PBI powder (reduced viscosity $\equiv$ 0.9 dl/gm) was kindly provided by the Hoechst-Celanese Corporation. A transparent solution was obtained by dissolving preweighed PBI powder in pressurized vessels at 220°C in dimethylacetamide (DMAC). PBI remained (clear) in solution after cooling down to room temperature. Both polyimide sulfone and 40 weight percent segmented siloxane (950 g/mole) copolyimide readily dissolved in DMAc solution. The synthesis and characterization of these materials have been described earlier (2,5). Transparent blend solutions were obtained by quantitatively mixing two solutions in a high speed blender. Films of various weight percents of PBI blends could be achieved by casting the solutions onto a glass plate, followed by vacuum oven stage drying from 60°C to 300°C over a period of at least one week. Absence of residual solvent in the films was confirmed by thermal gravimetric analysis (TGA) and TGA-MASS for some samples. Dry films were all clear, signaling at least its first signs of miscibility.

TGA: A Perkin-Elmer TGS-4 attached with a System 4 was used for thermal stability and residual solvent content studies. 10°C/min heating rate in air were used as a standard procedure for such measurements.

DMTA: A Polymer Laboratories Dynamic Mechanical Thermal Analyzer equipped with a high temperature furnance was used to determine transition behavor of blends. A frequency of 1 Hz in a two-point bending mode at a 3°C/min heating rate, under a constant strain were performed from room temperature to 500°C.

FT-IR: A Nicolet MZX-1 FT-IR operated under dry nitrogen atmosphere from 500 to 4000 cm^{-1} wave number was used to study vibrational characteristics of specific group contribution to the miscibility.

Water Absorption Study: Preweighed film samples of 1 inch by 1.5 inches were immersed in distilled water. Films were taken out, wiped dry by tissues, then weighed on an electronic balance at periodic intervals until the total weight of each film reached a steady state.

Atomic oxygen stability test samples were conducted at Physical Sciences at Andover, MA. Their facilities involve a high vacuum chamber of 20 cm diameter and a high energy CO_2 laser to generate high flux, high velocity pulses of atomic oxygen.(3-5) The experiment was designed in such a way that the integrated number of high velocity oxygen atoms per cm^2 over one day match the corresponding one week exposure time on the lower earth orbit as performed on STS-8 in 1983. The detailed test conditions are listed in Table I.

3. RESULTS AND DISCUSSION

The first indication on miscibility of these blends was the fact that the blend solutions were clear and transparent. Dry films of such blends also had the same visual impression, providing equally strong support for miscibility. Finally, from DMTA, a single well-defined loss tan δ relaxation peak associated with the glass transition behavior was observed (Fig. 2). There was no indication of phase separation at temperatures up to Ca. 425°C, as reported earlier with less polar polyimides.

A positive deviation from the ideal mixtures rule was observed in both PBI/PI and PBI/PI-SX systems when plotting the glass transition temperatures as a function of the weight percent of PBI in the blends (Fig. 3). This positive deviation may be attributed to a strong interaction between hetero components. More interestingly, two curves almost can be superimposed on one another except the data point for PI-SX control copolymer. The extraordinarily high Tg's observed in PBI/PI-SX blends suggests that the components responsible for miscibility were PBI and polyimide segments in PI-SX copolymer. The non-polar segmented siloxane, has greater mobility due to its low Tg and low surface free energy. The latter feature serves as a driving force which enables siloxane to migrate to the air surface.(5,6) Hence, the polysiloxane component does not itself interact with PBI. The strong interaction of hydrogen bonds actually may enhance the driving force by assisting the imide component to microphase separate from the siloxane dominated layer. The Tg of 185°C in the copolymer, PI-SX, and similar Tg values observed in PBI/PI and PBI/PI-SX blends certainly may support this suggestion.

FTIR studies showed that N-H peak (stretching mode) shifts dramatically to lower wavenumbers as one goes from homo PBI to the blends (Fig. 4). The amount of N-H shift increases with decreasing weight percent of PBI in blends. The reduction of wavenumber may relate to the weakening in the force constant of the N-H bonds. Both cases are the typical indicators of hydrogen bond formation. The change in N-H bond characteristics certainly also affects the electron density around imidazole group of PBI. Figure 5 showed that the relative intensity between C=N and C=C of PBI changes from equal intensity to much higher values in C=N compared with C=C peaks stretching band. The split pattern of C=N stretching band in homo PBI changed into an unresolved broad single absorption band in blend samples. This evidence by FTIR suggested that the imidazole groups have become more "aromatic" and symmetrical by the formation of hydrogen bonds. On the other hand, the change in C=O stretching bands of PI-SX are relatively small, which is expected since the hydrogen of the N-H groups of PBI only interacts with lone-pair electrons of the oxygenatom on carbonyl groups and does not weaken the force constant

and bond strength of C=O groups, due to the low mass of electrons. Even though the changes are small, nevertheless they are believed to be significant.

Water uptake studies provide another interesting piece of evidence of the siloxane benefit, as can been seen in Figure 6. Both blends can effectively reduce water uptake. With siloxane containing blends, an extra reduction in water uptake can be achieved at the same weight percent of PBI in each blend. This may be attributed to the hydrophobic nature of non-polar siloxane segments which formed a protective siloxane dominated layer on the top surfaces. Also, some of the siloxanes may be dispersed in the bulk phase. The water uptake can be reduced from 16 weight percent in homo PBI to a low level of about 2 percent.

Table II lists the weight loss results from atomic oxygen reactions which provide similar condition to one week in the LEO environment.(5) All organic polymers i.e. Kapton, PBI, PI, consistently showed greater weight loss than siloxane containing systems. Small weight gains were observed at higher levels of siloxane containing system and showed a very good trend according to the amounts of siloxane in the copolymer and blends. This may be arguably attributed to the conversion from siloxane to a silicate structure under atomic oxygen bombardment (Fig. 7). The weight loss results among siloxane containing systems also suggest a 15-20% minimum value of siloxane level in order to achieve LEO stable materials for aerospace applications.

4. CONCLUSIONS:

A novel series of miscible blend systems based on high performance PBI and PI or segmented PI-SX copolymer have been prepared. Evidence of forming hydrogen bonding interactions in blends between PBI and polyimide components were supported by both DMTA and FTIR studies. Segmented siloxane imide copolymers incorporated into PBI blends significantly improves surface properties. Extra water absorption reduction and atomic oxygen stability data complemented the benefit of the presence of siloxane in the blends. Future work is continuing with both molecular weight controlled PBI and semi-crystalline poly(arylene ether ketone) blends with polyimide and imide-siloxane copolymers.

5. ACKNOWLEDGMENTS

The authors would like to thank Hoechst-Celanese Corp. for providing high quality unfilled PBI powder, and DARPA for support of this project.

6. REFERENCES

1. L. Leung, D. J. Williams, F. E. Karasz and W. J. Macknight, Poly. Bull., 16, 437 (1986).
2. J. D. Summers, C. A. Arnold, R. H. Bott, L. T. Taylor, T. C. Ward and J. E. McGrath, Polym. Prep., 27(2), 403 (1986); J. D. Summers, Ph.D. Thesis VPI & SU, June 1988.
3. G. E. Caldeonia and R. H. Krech, AIAA-87-0105, AAA 25th Aerospace Science Meeting, January, 1987.
4. W. S. Slemp, B. Santos-Mason, G. F. Sykes and W. G. Witte, Jr., AAIA-85-0421, AAIA 23rd Aerospace meeting, January, 1985.
5. C. A. Arnold, J. E. McGrath, et. al., Polymer (London).
6. N. Patel, D. W. Dwight, J. L. Hedrick, D. C. Webster and J. E. McGrath, Marcomolecules, 21, 2689-2696 (1988).

7. BIOGRAPHIES

Dr. David Hsein-Pin Chen received his undergraduate education in chemistry at Fu-Jen Catholic University, Taiwan in 1978. He was a doctoral candidate in an area of natural product synthesis in 1980, then he transfered to the University of Southern California. He finished his Ph.D. work in polymer science in 1986. He is currently a research associate for Prof. J. E. McGrath. His specialties involve both synthesis of polymers and monomers and characterization in thermal analysis and mechanical properties.

Dr. Yun-Ping (Diana) Chen received her B.S. degree from the Chemistry Department of Fu-Jen Catholic University, Taiwan in 1979, followed by graduate study in Inorganic Chemistry at Texas Tech University. Later, she transfered to the University of Southern California and finished her Ph.D. work in polymer science in 1986. Currently, she is a research associate in Chemistry department of Virginia Tech. Her specialties are in the areas of polymer physics, particularly in the nonequilibrium behavior of glassy materials, and characterization in thermal analysis, mechanical and dielectric properties.

Cynthia Arnold received a B.S. in Chemical Engineering from the University of California, Berkeley, in 1980. Through 1982, she worked at Raychem Corporation in Menlo Park, CA, doing process and product development in the Thermofit Division. She was later employed at Mercor, Inc. of Berkeley, CA, in pilot plant and manufacturing engineering operations. During her employment in industry, she simultaneously studied for a graduate degree in business, receiving her M.B.A. in May, 1985. Currently she is pursuing her Ph.D. in Materials Engineering Science at VPI&SU, where she is a Kodak Fellow. Her work has been in the area of structure-property behavior of engineering polymers.

Jeffrey C. Hedrick, A native of Alexandria, Virginia, received his B.A. in Chemistry in 1986 from the Virginia Polytechnic Institute and State University. He is currently studying toward his Ph.D. in Materials Engineering Science from the same university under the direction of Dr. J. E. McGrath.

His research interest involves the electromagnetic (microwave) processing of high performance thermoplastics.

Jack D. Graybeal received his B.S. from West Virginia University in 1951, his M.S. from the University of Wisconsin in 1953, and his Ph.D. from the University of Wisconsin in 1955. He then went to work for Bell Telephone Labs from 1955 through 1957. In 1957 he left and went to West Virginia University where he taught until 1968. Then in 1968 he came to Virginia Tech where his current research interests lie in the areas of structure and bonding and encompass four primary programs: 1) the determination of structures of small molecules and radicals by use of rotational spectroscopy, 2) the application of pure nuclear quadrupole resonance to study the nature of the bonding in transition metal compounds, 3) a study of the bonding in Copper (I) compounds using a variety of spectroscopic techniques, and 4) the study of the dielectric behavior of materials as it relates to the use of electromagnetic radiation for the synthesis and curing of macromolecular systems.

James E. McGrath was born and raised in Easton, New York. He received his B.S. in Chemistry from Siena College in 1956. He was employed in cellulose fiber and film research by ITT Rayonier in Whippany, NJ until October 1959. At that time he joined the research division of the Goodyear Tire and Rubber Co. where he conducted research on synthetic rubbers. He obtained an M.S. degree in Chemistry from the University of Akron in 1964 and Ph.D. in Polymer Science from the same university in 1967. Professor McGrath joined the Union Carbide Corporation in August of that year and became a chemistry department faculty member at VPI & SU in September 1975. Dr. McGrath was the Chairman of the Polymer Division of the American Chemical Society in 1986 and in November of 1986, was chosen as the first Ethyl Chaired Professor of Chemistry. In September of 1987, Dr. McGrath became the first Director of the newly established Materials Institute. Dr. McGrath led a group of 19 faculty in chemistry and engineering who were awarded a National Science Foundation Science and Technology Center on "High Performance Polymeric Adhesives and Composites". He assumed the Directorship of this newly established center in February, 1989. Professor McGrath has written or edited six books and has over 200 contributions in the literature, including 24 U.S. patents. He is a frequent consultant to industry and government.

Table I

ATOMIC OXYGEN STABILITY STUDY

Weight Loss Test Results*

SAMPLE	WT LOSS X 10^4(gm)
PBI	23.13
Polyimide Homopolymer	14.01
Poly (10 % PSX Imide) Copolymer	4.54
Poly (40 % PSX Imide) Copolymer	+ 3.10 (gain)
Blend of 40 % PBI and 60 % Poly (40 % PSX Imide) Copolymer (24 % Overall PSX Content of Blend)	+ 2.30 (gain)
Blend of 25 % PBI and 75 % Poly (40 % PSX Imide) Copolymer (30% Overall PSX Content of Blend)	+ 2.95 (gain)
Kapton	22.93
Kapton coated with ~1500Å Poly (40 % PSX Imide) Copolymer	5.96

* Sample size: 1 square inch; Siloxane Mn = 950 g / mole

Table II

ATOMIC OXYGEN STABILITY STUDY
Test Conditions

Chamber Base Pressure	2 X 10^{-3} Torr
Nozzle Pulse Repetition Rate	1.4 Hz
Average Velocity	8 km per sec
Distance from Throat to Sample	40 cm
Area of Beam at Sample	300 cm^2
Nominal Area exposed on target	6.4 cm^2 (-10%)
Number of Pulses	54360
Number of O-atoms per Pulse (Theory)	2 X 10^{19} atoms
Number of O-atoms per Pulse (Kapton)	5 X 10^{17} atoms
Average Pulse Fluence on Target (Theory)	6.7 X 10^{16} atoms/cm^2
Average Pulse Fluence on Target (Kapton)	6.7 X 10^{16} atoms/cm^2
Total Integrated Flux (Theory)	3.6 X 10^{20} atoms/cm^2
Total Integrated Flux (Kapton)	3.6 X 10^{20} atoms/cm^2

Figure 1

Structures of Polymers Used in Blending Study

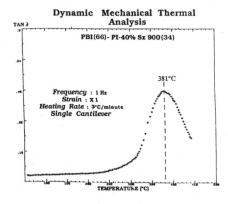

Polybenzimidazole (PBI)   BTDA-DDS Based Polyimide Homopolymer (PI)

BTDA-DDS Based Poly(Siloxane Imide) Copolymer (PI-SX)*

* 40 weight percent 950 g/mole dimethylsiloxane segmented copolymer

Figure 2   Figure 3

Dynamic Mechanical Thermal Analysis

Glass Transition Temperatures of PBI / Poly(Siloxane Imide) Copolymer Blends as a Function of Composition

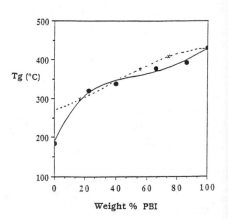

PBI(66)- PI-40% Sx 900(34)

381°C

Frequency : 1 Hz
Strain : X1
Heating Rate : 3°C/minute
Single Cantilever

TEMPERATURE (°C)

Tg (°C)

Weight % PBI

Figure 4

N-H Stretching Band in IR Region

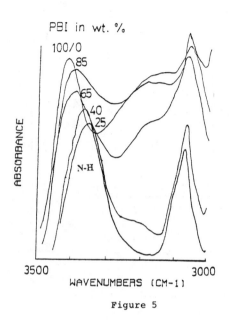

Figure 5

IR Stretching Bands of C=N, C=C, amd C=O Bonds

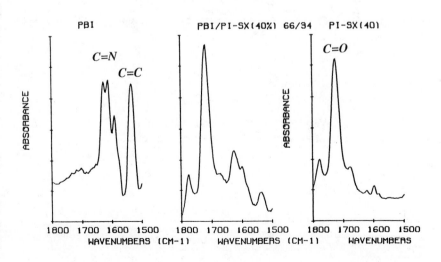

Figure 6

Water Uptakes of PBI, PI, PI-SX Homopolymers and Their Blends

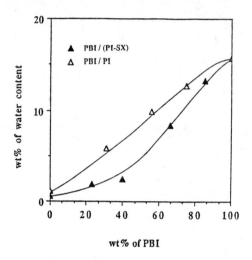

Figure 7

Proposed Siloxane to Silicate Transformation Upon Exposure to Oxygen Plasma

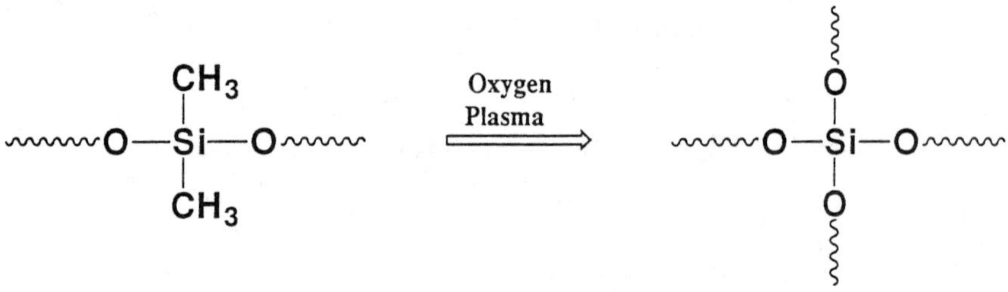

Very low percent carbon remaining after exposure to oxygen plasma.

SOLUBLE, THERMOPLASTIC POLYIMIDE HOMOPOLYMERS AND COPOLYMERS

C. A. Arnold, M. E. Rogers, C. D. Smith, G. D. Lyle,
G. A. York, M. J. Jurek* and J. E. McGrath**
Department of Chemistry and
Science and Technology Center:
High Performance Polymeric Adhesives and Composites
Virginia Polytechnic Institute and State University
Blacksburg, VA 24061

*Current Adress: Ciba-Geigy Corporation, Ardsley, NY
**To whom correspondence should be addressed

Abstract

Several methods have been investigated which improve the processability of polyimide homo- or copolymer systems. In particular, the utilization of a solution imidization technique in converting the poly(amic acid) intermediate to the fully cyclized polyimide has been successfully exploited. The solution imidization was conducted in N-methylpyrollidone (NMP) and an azeotroping agent, such as cyclohexylpyrollidone (CHP), at approximately 160°C for 24 hours. This technique has been shown to yield more soluble products than the corresponding bulk thermal imidization which is conducted at higher temperatures of ~300°C. Another important method of improving melt as well as solution processability involves the incorporation of a monofunctional reagent to obtain nonreactive end groups and controlled molecular weights. Structural modification by copolymerization with more flexible oligomers such as poly(arylene ether)s may also enhance processability and possibly provide improved impact strength. In this paper, the effects of incorporating varying concentrations of poly(arylene ether) sulfone and ketone oligomers ($<Mn>$ 6000 g/mole) into the polyimide backbone are reported. The overall copolymer molecular weight was consistently controlled to ~25,000 g/mole, with the use of small molar quantitites of the monofunctional reagent phthalic anhydride. Very tough, transparent films were obtained in all cases by compression molding copolymers at 340°C and ~3000 psi. Thermal analysis indicated that microphase separation is achievable in some cases as judged by the presence of two glass transition temperatures. Further studies in progress are examining the rheology, morphology and fracture toughness characteristics of these materials and these will be reported at the meeting.

1. INTRODUCTION

Polyimides are attractive in many engineering areas because of their excellent thermal and mechanical properties. In particular, the aerospace and microelectronics industries have developed many important applications(1,2). One major limitation to their widespread use, however, has been their typical intractability in the fully imidized state. Therefore, much effort has been spent in surmounting the processing difficulties associated with these systems, in hopes of obtaining tractable, soluble and processable polyimides that maintain reasonably high strength and environmental stability. To accomplish this goal, our past research has focused upon the incorporation of polydimethylsiloxane oligomers with molecular weights in the range of 1,000 to 10,000 g/mole (3). An extension of this work discussed in this paper was to incorporate poly(arylene ether) oligomers containing the sulfone and ketone linking groups. The high molecular weight poly(arylene ether)s are a well known class of high performance thermoplastics. The sulfone containing Udel^R and Victrex^R and the ketone containing PEEK^R poly(arylene ether)s have gained significant commercial importance due to their high thermal and hydrolytic stability, coupled with chemical resistance and their excellent mechanical properties. The excellent toughness characteristics of the poly(arylene ether)s have rendered them particularly attractive as thermoplastic modifiers for brittle thermosetting systems, such as the epoxies (4). Early attempts to prepare polyimide sulfone segmented copolymers were reported (5). However, these earlier studies utilized only pyromellitic dianhyride (PMDA) exclusively as the dianhydride and only bulk or chemical imidization methods were utilized. Consequently, only insoluble nonthermoplastic systems were obtained.

2.   EXPERIMENTAL

2.1   Poly(arylene ether) Oligomer Synthesis

The synthesis of the poly(arylene ether) oligomers is outlined in Scheme 1, and has been described in previous publications(6). The stoichiometry of the reactants may be varied according to the Carothers equation to control the molecular weight of the resultant oligomers. The oligomers' molecular weights could be accurately determined by potentiometric titration of the aromatic amine endgroups with 0.02 N anhydrous HBr in glacial acetic acid.

2.2   Copolymer Synthesis

The preparation of the polyimide-poly(arylene ether) copolymers is illustrated in Scheme 2. The copolymers reported herein were based upon benzophenone tetracarboxylic dianhydride (BTDA) and the aromatic diamine, Bisaniline P (Bis P). The BTDA was provided by Allco Corporation; the Bis P was kindly supplied by Air Products Corporation. Both were of high purity and were used as received without further purification. The solvents, N-methylpyrollidone (NMP) and cyclohexylpyrollidone (CHP), were distilled from phosphorous pentoxide and stored in sealed flasks. The amic acid first stage polymerizations were conducted in a three-neck round bottom flask equipped with a mechanical stirrer, nitrogen inlet and drying tube. The diamines were first dissolved in NMP; heating to 55°C with a hot water bath was necessary because the Bis P was not soluble in·NMP at room temperature. In order to control the overall polymer molecular weight to 25,000 g/mole, a calculated amount of phthalic anhydride was next added to the reaction mixture. The hot water bath was removed and the solid BTDA was slowly added while keeping the reaction mixture homogeneous. A cool water bath was used to lower the reaction temperature to 25-30°C. The overall solids concentration was ~15 to 17 percent. The reaction was allowed to proceed for about 8 hrs.

Conversion of the amic acid intermediate to the fuly imidized polyimide was accomplished by both the "classical" bulk thermal method as well as a solution imidization technique. The bulk thermal technique involved casting the amic acid solution onto a glass plate and heating under vacuum for one hour at each temperature of 100, 200 and 300°C. The solution imidization technique was conducted at 15 percent solids concentration in NMP (80%) and CHP (20%) at 160-165°C for 24 hours. At elevated temperatures, the CHP effectively acts to eliminate water which is formed during the conversion of the amic acid to the polyimide. The solution imidization technique is discussed in detail in other publications (7,8). The polymer solution was allowed to cool, coagulated in methanol, and dried in a vacuum oven at an elevated temperature. The powdered polymer product was compression molded at 340°C and 3000 psi to yield a very tough, flexible, transparent film.

2.3 Characterization

2.3.1 Intrinsic viscosity measurements

Intrinsic viscosity measurements yielded relative molecular weights and were performed in chloroform at 25°C using a Cannon-Ubbelohde viscometer.

2.3.2 Solubility studies

Solubility of the copolymers was determined in NMP, methylene chloride and tetrahydrofuran at a solids concentration of 5 percent.

2.3.3 Thermal analysis

Differential scanning calorimetry (DSC) was used to determine the glass transition temperatures (Tg) of the copolymers with a DuPont 1912 (dual sample). Scans were run at 10°C per minute. Reported values were obtained from a second scan after heating and quick cooling. Copolymer transitions were also obtained with a Polymer Laboratories instrument by dynamic mechanical thermal analysis (DMTA) at a frequency of 1 Hz.

2.3.4 Molecular weight distributions

Molecular weight distributions were determined in THF at 30°C relative to polystyrene standards. A Waters HPLC was used at a flow rate of 1 ml per minute and detection was acheived by differential refractometry.

3. RESULTS AND DISCUSSION

Synthesis of the amine terminated poly(arylene ether) oligomers was conducted as shown earlier in Scheme 1. Representative values for the oligomers at different molecular weights are illustrated in Table 1. In general, the titration of the amine end groups yielded number average molecular weights which were entirely consistant with the theoretical or calculated molecular weights from the Carothers equation. Note also that the glass transition temperature increased systematically as a function of molecular weight, as should be expected. In all cases, it was possible to obtain nearly the predicted Gaussian molecular weight distribution. To further illustrate this point, one may examine Figure 1. One may inspect the raw chromatograms and conclude that the most likely symmetrical Gaussian distributions are obtained for the variety of different molecular weights indicated.

In addition to the bisphenol-A based polyether oligomers which are the main thrust of this paper, it was possible to produce wholly aromatic polyarylene ether sulfone oligomers based upon hydroquinone and biphenyl. Data tabulating these systems are provided in Table 2. The virtue of the wholly aromatic systems is that they are somewhat more thermally and oxidatively stable. Earlier it was also found in our laboratories that these systems also provided better high energy radiation resistance. The utilization of the copolymer hydroquinone or biphenyl systems instead of the corresponding homopolymer was conducted largely as a matter of convenience. For example, utilization of either purely hydroquinone or biphenyl systems will produce crystallization from the polymerization solvent during the synthesis operation. Therefore, the amorphous systems were utilized which were based upon 50/50 molar ratios of the two. The polyimide copolymers were prepared as described in the Experimental section. One may also refer to Scheme 2 to find the details of these experiments. Table 3 summarizes the solubility of the solution imidized poly(arylene ether) polyimide segmented copolymers. The copolymers showed a remarkably high degree of solubility in both polar solvents such as NMP and also low boiling solvents such as the chlorinated type. The intrinsic viscosities noted are relatively low but one should recall that these are consistent with the overall molecular weight being controlled at about 25,000. Note also that all the materials produced yield tough ductile films implying the molecular weight was certainly above any critical value for obtaining good physical properties. In Table 4, several glass transition temperature values are provided for the copolymers as assessed by either differential scanning calorimetry (DSC) or dynamic mechanical thermal analysis (DMTA) (Figure 2). In general, the agreement between the two methods is quite satisfactory. As expected, the poly(ether ketone) systems show lower values for the high Tg component of these systems. In addition to the primary upper Tg component, it was possible in several cases to identify secondary transitions corresponding to the polysulfone phase as well. Further study of these materials is in progress and will be reported at the meeting.

4. CONCLUSIONS

The synthesis of well defined segmented copolymers based upon difunctional amine terminated oligomers and dianhydrides and diamines was demonstrated. The systems are highly soluble relatively easily moldable materials which produce excellent transparent tough films as well as reasonably high glass transition temperatures. The materials are qualitatively more ductile than many of the corresponding homopolymer polyimides. Currently, several additional measurements involving fracture toughness and stress-strain measurements are underway which will be reported in more detail at the meeting.

5. CURRENT AND FUTURE STUDIES

Current studies are emphasizing the development of quantitative mechanical properties, morphology via both scanning and transmission microscopy, rheological characterization utilizing rheological instrumentation and plane strain fracture toughness values.

6. REFERENCES

1. K. L. Mittal, Editor, "Polyimides", Volumes 1 and 2, Plenum Press, 1984.
2. M. Bowden and S. R. Turner, Editors, "Polymers for High Technology, Electronics and Photonics", ACS Symp. Series 346 (1987).
3. C. A. Arnold, J. D. Summers, Y. P. Chen, R. H. Bott, D. Chen and J. E. McGrath, Polymer (London), accepted 1989.
4. J. L. Hedrick, I. Yilgör, G. L. Wilkes and J. E. McGrath, Polymer Bulletin, 13, 201 (1985).
5. J. E. McGrath, M. Matzner, L. M. Robeson, and R. Barclay, Jr., J. Polym. Sci., Polym. Symposium, 60, 29 (1977).
6. M. J. Jurek and J. E. McGrath, Polymer (London), accepted 1989.
7. J. D. Summers, C. A. Arnold, R. H. Bott, L. R. Taylor, T. C. Ward and J. E. McGrath, 32d SAMPE Symposium, 32, 613 (1987).
8. J. D. Summers, C. A. Arnold, R. H. Bott, L. R. Taylor, T. C. Ward and J. E. McGrath, Polym. Prepr., 27(2), 403 (1986).

BIOGRAPHIES

Cynthia Arnold received a B.S. in Chemical Engineering from the University of California, Berkeley, in 1980. Through 1982, she worked at Raychem Corporation in Menlo Park, CA, doing process and product development in the Thermofit Division. She was later employed at Mercor, Inc. of Berkeley, CA, in pilot plant and manufacturing engineering operations. She also obtained her M.B.A. in May, 1985. Currently she is pursuing her Ph.D. in Materials Engineering Science at VPI&SU, where she is a Kodak Fellow. Her work has been in the area of structure-property behavior of engineering polymers.

Martin E. Rogers was born in Winchester, Virginia. He is a senior in chemistry at Virginia Tech, doing undergraduate research under Dr. McGrath. He is currently working on the synthesis and characterization of polyimides. Martin will be graduating with his B.S. degree in May, 1989. Afterwards, Martin plans to continue his work with polymers in graduate school at the Virginia Tech Department of Chemistry.

Carrington D. Smith was born in Halifax County, Virginia in 1965. He attended Virginia Commonwealth University from 1983-1987 and obtained a B.S. in chemistry. He then entered the Ph.D. program in chemistry at Virginia Tech in 1987 and is presently involved in research on poly(arylene ether) ketones, sulfones and phosphine oxides, as well as copolymers of such systems.

Gregory D. Lyle, a native of Hendersonville, North Carolina, received a B.S. in chemistry and a B.S. in textile chemistry from N.C. State University. He entered the Ph.D. program in chemistry in 1983. His research at Virginia Tech has involved the synthesis and characterization of functionally terminated engineering thermoplastics.

Michael J. Jurek received a B.S. in Chemistry from Rochester Institute of Technology in 1982. He entered the Chemistry Ph.D program at VPI & SU in 1982. His work has been in the area of high performance polymers. Mike

graduated in 1986 with a Ph.D in Chemistry and joined AT&T Bell Labs. He will be joining Ciba-Geigy in Ardsley, NY.

Greg York received his B.S. in Materials Engineering from Virginia Tech in 1985. He attended graduate school at Virginia Tech and obtained a M.S. in Materials Engineering in 1987. After completing a 5 month internship at Control Data Corp. in Minnesota, is now pursuing a Ph.D. in MESc under the guidance of Dr. J. E. McGrath.

James E. McGrath was born and raised in Easton, New York. He received his B.S. in Chemistry from Siena College in 1956. He was employed in cellulose fiber and film research by ITT Rayonier in Whippany, NJ until October 1959. At that time he joined the research division of the Goodyear Tire and Rubber Co. where he conducted research on synthetic rubbers. He obtained an M.S. degree in Chemistry from the University of Akron in 1964 and Ph.D. in Polymer Science from the same university in 1967. Professor McGrath joined the Union Carbide Corporation in August of that year and became a chemistry department faculty member at VPI & SU in September 1975. Dr. McGrath was the Chairman of the Polymer Division of the American Chemical Society in 1986 and in November of 1986, was chosen as the first Ethyl Chaired Professor of Chemistry. In September of 1987, Dr. McGrath became the first Director of the newly established Materials Institute. Dr. McGrath led a group of 19 faculty in chemistry and engineering who were awarded a National Science Foundation Science and Technology Center on "High Performance Polymeric Adhesives and Composites". He assumed the Directorship of this newly established center in February, 1989. Professor McGrath has written or edited six books and has over 200 contributions in the literature, including 24 U.S. patents. He is a frequent consultant to industry and government.

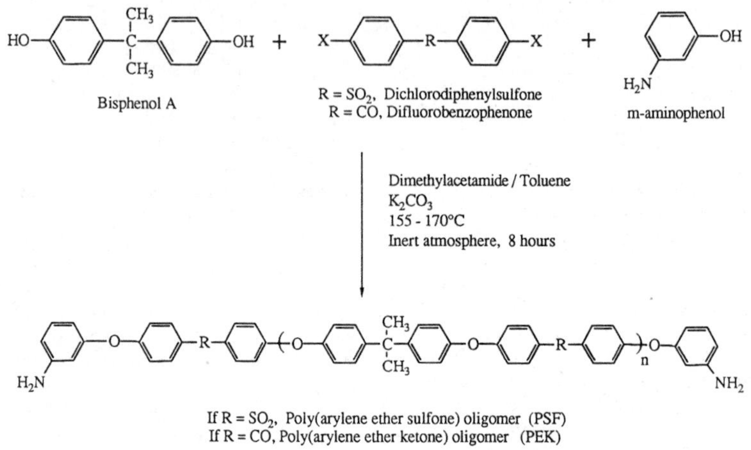

HO—⟨benzene⟩—C(CH₃)(CH₃)—⟨benzene⟩—OH + X—⟨benzene⟩—R—⟨benzene⟩—X + ⟨benzene⟩—OH (H₂N)

Bisphenol A

R = SO₂, Dichlorodiphenylsulfone
R = CO, Difluorobenzophenone

m-aminophenol

Dimethylacetamide / Toluene
K₂CO₃
155 - 170°C
Inert atmosphere, 8 hours

H₂N—⟨benzene⟩—O—⟨benzene⟩—R—⟨benzene⟩—(O—⟨benzene⟩—C(CH₃)(CH₃)—⟨benzene⟩—O—⟨benzene⟩—R—⟨benzene⟩)ₙ—O—⟨benzene⟩—NH₂

If R = SO₂, Poly(arylene ether sulfone) oligomer (PSF)
If R = CO, Poly(arylene ether ketone) oligomer (PEK)

Scheme 1: Synthesis of poly(arylene ether) oligomers

1260

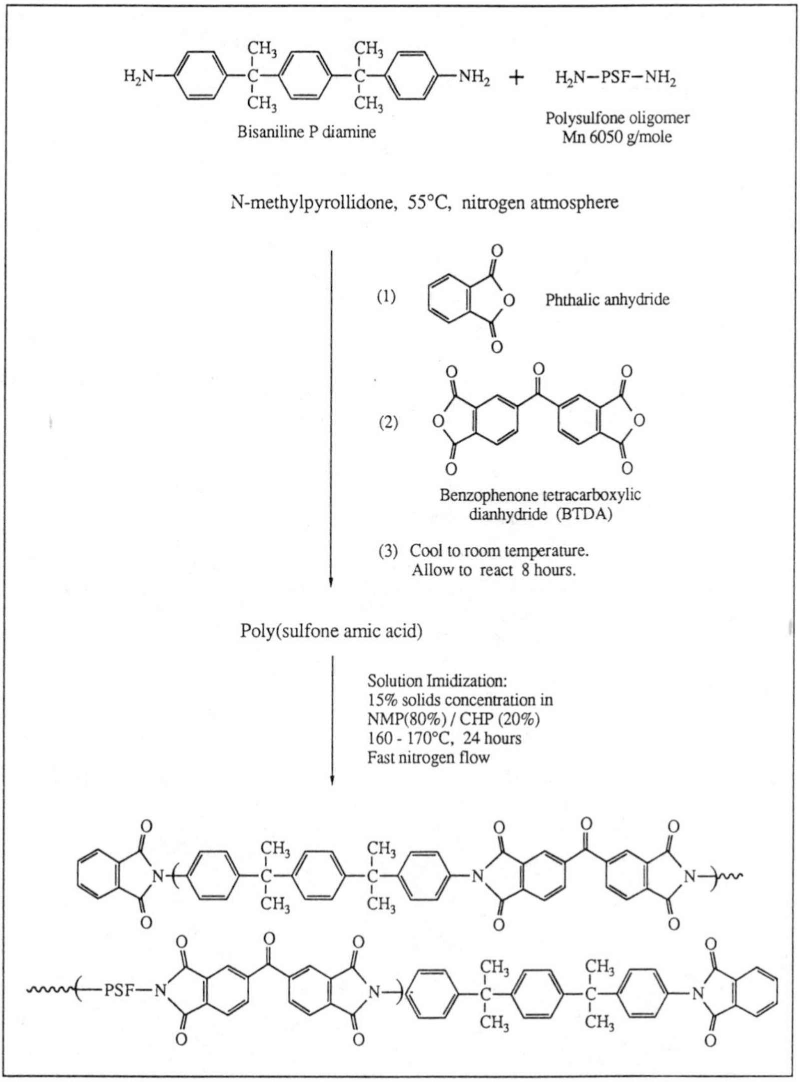

H₂N—[Bisaniline P diamine structure]—NH₂ + H₂N—PSF—NH₂

Bisaniline P diamine

Polysulfone oligomer
Mn 6050 g/mole

N-methylpyrollidone, 55°C, nitrogen atmosphere

(1) [Phthalic anhydride structure] Phthalic anhydride

(2) [Benzophenone tetracarboxylic dianhydride structure]

Benzophenone tetracarboxylic
dianhydride (BTDA)

(3) Cool to room temperature.
Allow to react 8 hours.

Poly(sulfone amic acid)

Solution Imidization:
15% solids concentration in
NMP(80%) / CHP (20%)
160 - 170°C, 24 hours
Fast nitrogen flow

[Poly(sulfone imide) polymer structure]

Scheme 2: Representative scheme for the synthesis of BTDA-Bis P based poly(sulfone imide) with controlled molecular weight and end groups

Table 1: Characterization of bisphenol-A amine terminated poly(arylene ether sulphone oligomers

Theoretical $<M_n>$	Endgroup analysis	Tg($^\circ$C)	MWD
4,000	3,700	140	1.9
5,000	5,300	155	2.0
7,500	7,100	162	2.1
9,000	8,800	165	2.0
10,000	9,300	168	1.9
12,000	11,300	169	1.8
14,000	13,300	172	1.9
16,000	15,600	175	2.0
18,000	17,000	178	2.0
20,000	19,500	184	2.1
22,000	21,400	189	2.0
25,000	24,600	194	1.9
28,000	27,700	194	2.1

Table 2: Hydroquinone and biphenol based amine terminated poly(arylene ether sulphone) oligomers

Theoretical $<M_n>$	Endgroup analysis	$[\eta]_{CHCl_3}^{25^\circ C}$	Tg($^\circ$C)	MWD
5,000[a]	5,400	0.20	196	2.0
5,000[b]	7,100	0.34	170	1.9
10,000[b]	9,700	0.50	187	2.1
7,500[c]	6,500	0.31	191	2.2
15,000[c]	14,400	0.44	204	2.1
20,000[c]	19,200	0.73	213	2.0

[a]biphenol, [b]hydroquinone, [c]50/50 molar ratio of hydroquinone and biphenol

TABLE 3
SOLUBILITY OF SOLUTION IMIDIZED
POLY(ARYLENE ETHER)-POLYIMIDE SEGMENTED
COPOLYMERS*

Wt% PAE Mn	[n]***	NMP	CH$_2$Cl$_2$	THF
Homopolymer	----	Sol	Sol	MS
10 PEK 6580	----	Sol	Sol	MS
30 PEK 6580	----	Sol	Sol	MS
50 PEK 6580	----	Sol	Sol	almost Sol
10 PSF 6050	0.31	Sol	Sol	MS
30 PSF 6050	0.33	Sol	Sol	MS
50 PSF 6050	0.43	Sol	Sol	MS
95 PSF 6050**	0.41	Sol	Sol	almost Sol

*   Molecular weight controlled to ~ 25,000 g/mole

**   No Bis P; diamine component consists of only the PSF oligomer

***   in chloroform, 25°C

Sol: Soluble	NMP: N-methylpyrrolidone
MS: Marginally Soluble	THF: Tetrahydrofuran
IS: Insoluble	CH$_2$Cl:$_2$ Methylene chloride

TABLE 4
GLASS TRANSITION VALUES FOR POLYIMIDE -
POLY(ARYLENE ETHER) SEGMENTED COPOLYMERS

	Upper glass transition °C*	
Wt % PAE Mn	DSC	DMTA
Homopolymer	265	----
10 % PSF 6050	250	260
30 % PSF 6050	240	245
50 % PSF 6050	229	228
95 % PSF 6050	191	----
10 % PEK 6580	239	----
30 % PEK 6580	216	----
50 % PEK 6580	195	----

* In some cases, transitions characteristic of the sulfone
phase were observed.

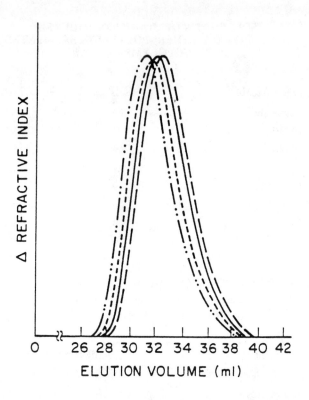

Figure 1: Gel permeation chromatography traces of bisphenol-A based amine terminated poly(arylene) ether sulphone) oligomers run in THF at 30°C and 1 ml/min: - - - 4600 g/mole; ———— 8800 g/mole; ----- 15,600 g/mole; ——--———— 27,700 g/mole.

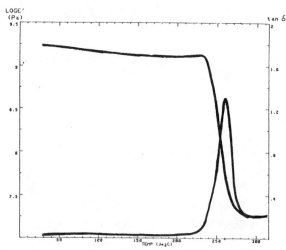

Figure 2. Dynamic Mechanical Thermal Analysis of BTDA-Bis P based Polyimide Sulfone Copolymer Containing 10 Weight % Polysulfone (Mn 6050 g/mole)

PRODUCT FORMS
IN
APC THERMOPLASTIC MATRIX COMPOSITES
David Leach
Paul Schmitz
Fiberite Composite Materials
ICI Composites, Inc.
Tempe, AZ 85284

Abstract

Considerable reductions in finished part costs can be realized
through the development of automated fabrication techniques
using thermoplastic matrix composites. In order to achieve these
economic benefits, a range of
different product forms is required and have been developed
for APC thermoplastic composites.

1. INTRODUCTION

Continuous fiber composites utilizing thermoplastic resin matrices
have been under development
since the early 1980's. The fact
that the chemical reaction is complete and the polymer is melt
fusible, allow for new options in
part fabrication methods.(1) This
wide range of processes can lead
to considerable reductions in finished part cost.(2) In order to
utilize the various fabrication
techniques, a wide range of product forms are required. The
purpose of this paper is to describe the various product forms

within the APC technology and
relate them to automated fabrication techniques.

2. MATERIALS

The "APC technology" refers to an
ICI proprietary process to accomplish the impregnation of thermoplastic polymers onto continuous
reinforcing fibers. The most fully
developed APC system involves
the PEEK polymer. New composites utilizing thermoplastics matrix resins capable of higher continuous use temperatures are
currently the focus of developmental efforts. The new systems
are APC(HTA) and APC(ITX). The
HTA matrix is amorphous with a
Tg of 500°F yielding a continuous
service temperature of 350°F.
The ITX is a semi-crystalline polymer with a Tg of 350°F giving
excellent retention of properties
at 300°F.

The main focus of past development has been continuous carbon
fibers. Currently, prepreg reinforced with Hercules AS-4, IM-6,

IM-7, and IM-8 is available. Today's developmental efforts are targeting non-conductive reinforcements such as S-2 fiberglass and Alumina.

The APC process ensures full fiber property translation through complete matrix wetting and a well developed interface.(3) This characteristic is key to the ability to use low pressure consolidation and rapid forming techniques. Our studies have shown the fabrication method is not limited by matrix resin or reinforcing fiber within APC composite systems.

3. PRODUCT FORMS

The basic impregnation technology produces a high quality unidirectional product form. From that technology, the following product forms are derived.

- o 12" wide uni-tape (standard)
- o slit tape (1" - 12" wide)
- o wide width uni-tape (up to 60" wide)
- o interlaced slit tape
- o preconsolidated sheet
- o single tow

These product forms are achievable with the polymer and fiber options described above.

4. PART FABRICATION SYSTEMS

4.1 Slit Tape/Automated Tape Placement

Narrow widths of uni-tape are custom slit from the 12" wide tape product. As thermoplastic composites are fully polymerized and form stable, very tight width tolerances are available. Typically, the width tolerance is +/-

0.2 - 0.3°/0 of the width. This is critical to accurate ply placement with minimal lap or gap concern. Standard products are supplied to a 40' minimum length specification to minimize waste in the tape laying process.

Recently, equipment designed to accurately place traditional composite tape has been modified to process the higher temperature thermoplastic material (see figure 1). Tape laying has been used widely as a process to lay up large area parts. With thermoplastic, the potential exists to lay-up and consolidate in one step although achieving full consolidation is rate limiting.(4) Economic trade-offs may dictate placing and tacking at high machine speeds then achieving full consolidation in a subsequent process.

4.2 Wide APC Uni-tape/ Diaphragm Forming

The standard APC product is 12" uni-tape but lay-up efficiency could be improved with a broadgood form. ICI Fiberite has developed an automated seam welding process for manufacture of wide uni-tape. In this process, up to five 12" tapes are thermally edge joined to produce tape up to 60" wide. This product is typically supplied in 40' lengths to closely match existing automatic ply cutting equipment.

Individual plies can be accurately cut to shape using current computer controlled equipment. Material efficiency is maximized with computerized "nesting" software. Robotic equipment can be modified to orient, stack, and tack the precut plies automatically (see figure 2). Subsequent forming processes, like diaphragm forming, require this flat ply stack as a feedstock.

In diaphragm forming, this ply stack is put under vacuum between 2 thin metallic sheets. (5) This assembly is then positioned above a mold in a pressure vessel capable of the appropriate processing temperature (see figure 3). The entire pressure vessel is then heated to a temperature above the melt point of the thermoplastic matrix. By control of a pressure differential above and below the diaphragm, the lay-up is consolidated and formed against the tool. ICI has recently developed a modification to this process in which polymeric diaphragms are utilized and only the diaphragms and prepreg stack are heated. This eliminates the need for heating the massive pressure vessel and tool thus drastically reducing cycle time (see figure 4). It is feasible to produce complex curvature components from an unconsolidated flat lay-up due to the uniform pressure application and forming rate control available through these processes.

4.3 Interlaced Fabric/Integrally Heated Tooling

For processes which require a material form with room temperature drapability, interlaced APC tape is available. Quadrax Corp., Providence, R. I. has developed equipment to slit APC unitape and weave or "interlace" narrow bands of prepreg into classic fabric styles up to 7 1/2' wide. Mechanical properties of interlaced APC tape are equivalent to [0,90]s lay-ups of unitape. (6) Conventional fabrics normally exhibit a mechanical property

reduction because of fiber crimping during the weaving process. The impregnation of the fibers before interlacing minimizes crimping and ensures fiber wetting and full fiber-resin interfacial development while maintaining an adequate degree of drapability.

Because of process equipment limitations or severe part complexity, it is occasionally preferred to process thermoplastic materials by more conventional means. This involves laying-up the plies at room temperature to the part configuration and consolidating under heat and pressure in an autoclave. Lay-up, in this case, requires the room temperature drapability offered by the interlaced material. Lay-up can be partially automated with the use of automatic ply cutting equipment as described in 4.2. The precut plies are placed against the tool surface and held by various design features of the tooling. New advances in fiberous reinforced, integrally heated ceramic tooling have eliminated the long processing cycles encountered when attempting to use conventional metal or graphite tooling at typical thermoplastic processing temperatures.(7) Heat up and cool down rates of 25°F/minute have been proven with this tooling technology making typical cycle times of one hour achievable. With proper handling, this can be accomplished in a pressure vessel rated for lower temperatures .

4.4 Preconsolidated Sheet/ Stamping

One of the key features of thermoplastic material systems is the ability to rapidly shape and reshape parts. In some cases the process cycle is very fast forming, but is too rapid for full ply consolidation. For these processes, a large area preconsolidated sheet is available. These flat panels, up to 3 1/2' x 9 1/2', are custom made to individual ply orientation and thickness requirements. For critical applications, C-Scan data on the flat sheet is provided.

Once consolidated, this composite "plywood" may be reheated to melt temperature and rapidly stamped into single curvature shapes. The panel may be cut to near net/shape utilizing programmable cutting equipment. As transfer time between the preheat oven and the forming tool is critical, the panel is usually held by a frame in a transfer mechanism. The panel is first indexed into an infrared oven and held there for 2-4 minutes to ensure full melting of the matrix. It is then rapidly transferred to the forming station and shaped. Commonly available equipment to form in this manner is matched metal molds mounted in fast closing (200-500 in.min) hydraulic presses (see figure 5). The most uniform forming pressure is achieved when one of the tooling faces is compliant. This can be accomplished by an elastomer facing on one side of matched metal tooling or through the use of conventional hydro-rubber forming (see figure 6). Preconsolidated sheet is also the best feedstock for hot roll shaping (see figure 7).

4.5 Single Tow/Filament Winding

For some process and part configurations, it is desirable to use very narrow uni-tape. As slitting very narrow widths (<1") from 12"

tape is not technically practical, impregnated single tow is offered within the APC technology. Band widths of 1/8" or 1/4" are available with the Hercules family of carbon fibers as well as other non-conductive fibers under development. As uninterupted feed is critical to the economics of processing, minimum lengths of 1,000 feet are guarenteed.

It has proven fairly straight forward to convert existing single tow placement equipment to handle thermoplastics. Filament winding is widely used as a fiber placement technique to make enclosed structures. It is feasible to place and consolidate the thermoplastic tow using heat focused at the point where incoming tow contacts the part (see figure 8).(8) The economics of rapid winding/post consolidation vs. slower winding/full consolidation must be weighed as discussed in 4.1 Slit Tape. Because the tow can be consolidated during winding, difficult, even concave configurations have been demonstrated.

5. CONCLUSIONS

It is necessary to develop many different processing techniques in order to economically achieve the wide range of part configurations required today. This necessitates a variety of different product forms to be available. These have been developed by ICI/Fiberite for APC composite systems using a range of thermoplastic matrices and reinforcing fibers. Various product forms, processing techniques and resulting structure types are summarized in Table 1. Tomorrow's materials are available today through the line of thermoplastic composites developed by ICI Fiberite.

6. ACKNOWLEDGEMENTS

We wish to acknowledge the support and contrubutions by the following:

Cincinnati Milacron
Comtool Technology, Inc.
Quadrax Corp.
R-Cubed Composites, Inc.
Superform USA
ICI Materials Centre, Wilton, UK
ICI Composite Structures Group
Our colleagues in ICI Fiberite
Composite Materials

7. REFERENCES

1. Cattanach, J.B. and Cogswell, F.N., "Processing with Aromatic Polymer Composites", in 'Developments in Reinforced Plastics S', Ed G. Pritchard, Applied Science Publishers, 1987.

2. Duthie, A.C., "Engineering Substantiation of Fiber Reinforced Thermoplastics for Aerospace Primary Structure", Proc. 33rd SAMPE Symposium, Anaheim, March 7-10, 1988, p. 296-307.

3. Carlile, D.R., Leach, D.C., Moore, D.R., and Zahan, N., "Mechanical Properties of the Carbon Fibre/ Peel Composite APC-2/AS4 for Structural Applications", Accepted for publication in ASTM STP 1044, American Society for Testing and Materials, Philadelphia.

4. Witzler, S., "Laying Thermoplastic Tape Prepregs - A Progress Report", Advanced Composites, January/February, 1988, p 53-54.

5. Barnes, A.J. and Cattanach, J.B.,
"Advances in Thermoplastic Composite Fabrication Technology", Proc. Materials Engineering Conference, London, 5-7 November, 1985.

6. Patterson, J.M., "Mechanical Characterization of Interlaced Prepreg Cloth", to be published in proceedings of 7th International Conference on Composite Materials, Beijing, China, 1-4 August, 1989.

7. Woolum, D.E., "Graphite Reinforced Ceramic Tools with Internal Heaters" to be presented at the 6th annual Industry/Gov't Review of Thermoplastic Matrix Composites, San Diego, CA, Feb. 28- March 2, 1989.

8. Egerton M.W. and Gruber M.B., "Thermoplastic Filament Winding Demonstration of Economics and Properties via in-situ Consolidation", Proc. 33rd SAMPE Symposium, Anaheim, 7-10 March, 1989, p 35-46.

8. BIOGRAPHY

D.C. LEACH

David Leach graduated from Imperial College, University of London, UK, in 1979 and joined ICI Plastics Division in the same year. He has carried out research on the physical properties of polymers and composites, and has been involved in the development of continuous fiber reinforced thermoplastics. He is currently Group Leader for thermoplastic composites technical service with ICI Fiberite Composite Materials.

P.J. SCHMITZ

Paul Schmitz graduated from Kansas State University in 1980 with a B.S. in Mechanical Engineering. That same year he joined Phillips Chemical Company's Engineering Plastics Division as a Market Development Engineer and later Techinal Service Engineer for Ryton® molding compounds. In 1985, Paul joined ICI Fiberite Composite Materials. He is currently Product Manager for APC Thermoplastic Composites.

STRUCTURE TYPE BY MATERIAL FORM/PROCESS

MATERIAL FORM + AUTOMATED PROCESS   = STRUCTURE TYPE

Slit Uni-Tape	+ Tape Placement	= Large Area/Minimum Contour
Wide Width Uni-Tape	+ Automated Cutting & Placement/ Diaphragm Forming	= Double Curvature/Intermediate Area
Interlaced Slit Tape	+ Integrally Heated Tooling/ Pressure Vessel	= Most Complex
Preconsolidated Sheet	+ Oven/Stamping	= Single Curvature/Intermediate Area
Single Tow	+ Filament Winding	= Enclosed Shapes

TABLE 1.

APC TAPE LAYING

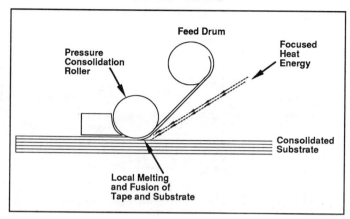

FIGURE 1.

AUTOMATED CUTTING AND PLACEMENT
OF WIDE APC TAPE

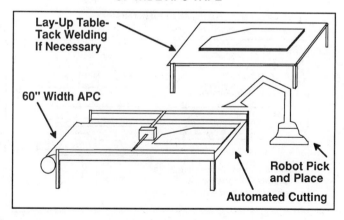

FIGURE 2.

APC DIAPHRAGM FORMING

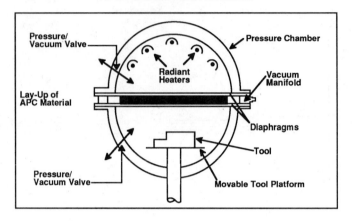

FIGURE 3.

APC DIAFORMING™

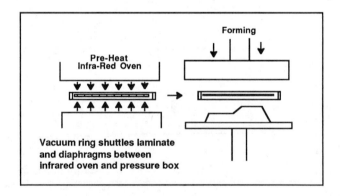

FIGURE 4.

MATCHED METAL FORMING WITH APC PRE-CONSOLIDATED SHEET

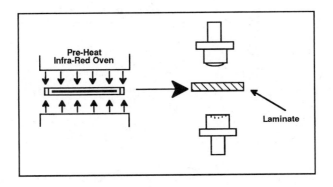

FIGURE 5.

COMPLIANT SURFACE FORMING USING APC PRE-CONSOLIDATED SHEET

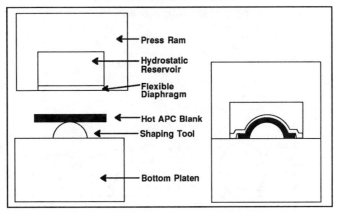

FIGURE 6.

ROLL FORMING USING APC PRE-CONSOLIDATED SHEET

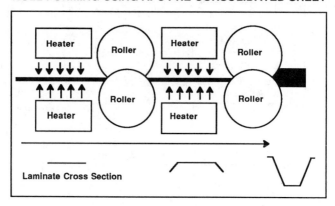

FIGURE 7.

FILAMENT WINDING WITH APC TOW

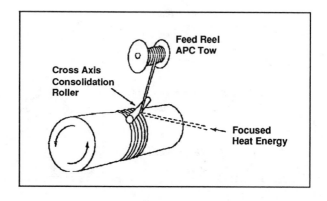

FIGURE 8.

COMPRESSIVE AND FLEXURAL CREEP DEFORMATION
IN THERMOPLASTIC COMPOSITES

D. H. Nguyen, S. F. Wang and A. A. Ogale*
Department of Chemical Engineering
Clemson University
Clemson, SC 29634

Abstract

The present study deals with the compressive and flexural creep properties of polyetheretherketone (PEEK), a high temperature semicrystalline thermoplastic. The creep compliance results of the unreinforced PEEK and the PEEK/carbon fiber composite are reported for temperatures both above and below the glass transition temperature (Tg). The experimental results of the composite are compared to the results predicted from a micromechanics model that predicts the thermoelastic properties of composite materials.

1. INTRODUCTION

Many structural components which are traditionally made out of metals are being replaced by their polymeric material counterparts. The main advantage of using polymeric materials lies in the ease of production of complicated parts, simple assembly, fewer parts, and fewer finishing operations. Another major advantage, in aerospace applications, is the lower density of polymer composites as

---

* Author to whom correspondence should be addressed

compared to metals, which results in higher specific properties (i.e., performance per pound of material) for polymer composites.

However, one of the primary concerns in the use of polymer composites is the time dependent response of polymeric materials. Creep deformation is significant in many polymers even at room temperature and is rapidly accelerated by small increases in temperature. A 50°C rise in temperature above room temperature could have a catastrophic effect on the life time of polymeric parts, but little on their metallic equivalents. Creep response is also affected by the physical aging of polymer (1), a phenomenon where the polymer exhibits volume and enthalpy relaxation with time at temperatures below Tg (PEEK Tg = 155°C). For this study, the aging time was kept constant at 10 hours and so will not be a factor in the results.

While most creep studies are conducted in the tensile or shear modes (2-5), flexural and compressive modes of loading are important from a practical viewpoint, and yet have received limited attention. This study, therefore, focusses attention on compressive and flexural response.

2. EXPERIMENTAL

The materials used in the present study were 45G grade of PEEK pellets (ICI of UK) and Thornel T-650/42, 12K carbon fibers. The fibers had surface treatment but did not have any sizing. All the specimens were molded in a compression molding press, Carver model 30-12-2T.

To obtain unidirectional fiber composite specimens, prepreg sheets of composites of 6" X 6" X 1/16" were compression molded in a matched-die mold. An aluminum plate was used as a fiber winding template to maintain unidirectional fiber orientation. Thin PEEK films were inserted between successive fiber layers. The molded sheets were then cut in appropriate dimensions and remolded in an appropriate "picture frame" mold to obtain the compressive and flexural specimens. The molding cycle consisted of a maximum temperature of 365°C, a pressure in excess of 350 MPa, a hold time of 5 minutes at these conditions, and a cool-down at 6°C/min under pressure. At the cooling rate of 6°C/min, PEEK develops a nominal crystallinity of 35 vol% (6,7) and a density of 1.31 g/cm^3 (8). The dimensions of the compressive and flexural samples were 1.25 cm X 1.25 cm X 1.60 cm and 0.32 cm X 1.25 cm X 10.2 cm, respectively.

After smoothing out the surfaces and edges of the specimens with a fine-grid sandpaper, their dimensions and weights were measured using a Vernier caliper and a Mettler balance, respectively. With the size of the specimens involved it was not possible to process a void free sample. Thus, these data were recorded and used along with the weight fractions of fiber and PEEK in the pregreg to calculate volume fractions of fiber, resin and voids in the creep samples.

Creep tests were carried out in a controlled temperature oven ($\pm$ 1°C) by applying dead weight loading in both compression and flexural modes. The 4-point flexural mode had a pin to pin separation distance of 2.54 cm with the pins being located at one-third of the support span. Strain was measured by strain gages (9), on Measurement

Group P-3500 portable strain indicator. The creep response was observed for several temperatures below and above Tg at 10 hours aging time. The samples were aged at the temperature at which they were tested for creep. After the test was completed and the load removed, the temperature was raised to 160°C which is about 5°C above the Tg of PEEK, and left at this temperature for 1 hour to relax out all the residual strain in the sample and to erase all previous aging history.

3. RESULTS AND DISCUSSION

It is noted that the stress-levels in this study were well within linear viscoelastic limits. During the compressive and flexural tests, it was observed that the rate of application of load on the samples had a significant effect on the creep response. For example, a very fast rate of loading (resembling a sudden impact) resulted in an overshoot in the deformation. With a gradual application of the load, however, the results were consistent and repeatable. The overshoot phenomenon was also observed to be a function of the testing temperature and the stress-level. Higher temperatures and stress-levels led to the minimization, and in several cases suppression, of the overshoot phenomenon. The maximum weights that could be placed inside the environmental chamber were sufficiently large to eliminate overshoot phenomenon from the neat PEEK response.

The results for the compressive creep compliance of neat PEEK are displayed in Figure 1 for test temperatures in the range of 120°C to 160°C. Two runs were conducted at each temperature, and the data show repeatability and consistency. As the temperature increases above 120°C, the response becomes stronger showing a two-fold increase in the 10 second compliance at 150°C and three-fold increase at 160°C as compared to the compliance at 120°C. Further, the time dependence of the compliance, i.e., the creep response, becomes significant above 120°C.

The results reported above were for the polymer with a void content of about 2.8 vol%. Therefore, the material was treated as a porous composite with the pores assumed to be spherical voids. For spherical inclusions (or voids), micromechanical composite models are well-developed and a model, "S-Mixing Rule" (10), was used to calculate the creep compliance of the void- free polymer. The model is incorporated in a computer software package "SMC" which was available to us courtesy of the Center for Composite Materials, University of Delaware (11). The calculated response of the void-free (33% crystalline) PEEK is displayed in Figure 1 by the solid curves. The time-dependent curves were generated point-by-point using the "Quasi-Elastic" method proposed by Schapery (12). The compliance of the void-free polymer, as expected, is lower than that of the "porous" composite. While the difference is small, the compliance curves of the void-free PEEK serve as a reference property that can be used with any other reinforcing material to predict the composite response.

The compliance curves displayed in Figure 1 are all for the polymer that had been aged for 10 hours prior to the creep test. Further, since the creep testing time was only about one-tenth of the aging time, the creep curves are "instantaneous" in the Struik sense (1). The time-temperature superposition principle (13) can, therefore, be used to predict long-term creep response by short-term testing at elevated temperatures. The predicted long-term behavior at a reference temperature of 130°C is displayed in Figure 2, and can be used in the design of polymeric structures intended for long-term use. The shift-factor used in the time-temperature superposition are displayed in Figure 3. It is observed that the long-term behavior of 33% crystalline PEEK was slightly less time-independent in the compressive mode than in the tensile mode (5).

The transverse creep compliance of the unidirectional carbon fiber/ PEEK composite is displayed in Figure 4 for temperatures in the range of 120°C to 160°C. A significant overshoot in the creep deformation is observed at all temperatures. Evidently, the "maximum" stress that could be applied to the sample (due to spatial constraints) was not sufficiently large to suppress the overshoot. A modification of the loading mechanism is under consideration to enable larger stress-levels to be applied.

The creep response of the neat PEEK can be combined with the time-independent response of carbon fibers to predict the composite response. The "Aggregate Model" for composites (14), also available in the software "SMC" (11), was used to predict composites properties for the unidirectional composites with a planar orientation of fp = 1.0 and an out-of-plane orientation of fa = -0.25, which represents a 25° misorientation of fibers. While the experimental data have a large overshoot to provide any meaningful comparison with the model predictions, the overall response at 120°C and 160°C (where the overshoot is small) can be predicted at least crudely from the model. Further tests are under way to check the model predictions.

The flexural creep compliance of neat PEEK is displayed in Figure 5 at temperatures ranging from 120°C to 160°C. The two different sets of symbols represent independent data from the tensile and the compressive faces. The matching of the tensile and compressive face data clearly establishes the isotropy of the neat PEEK. Also, as expected, the compliance increases with increasing temperature. The time-temperature superposition principle is used to shift the higher temperature data to longer times to obtain a long-term "master-curve," displayed in Figure 6, at a reference temperature of 130°C. The shift factors used to perform the shifting are plotted in Figure 3. A comparison of the master-curves in tensile mode, for which several points were obtained from the master-curve in reference 5, compression, and flexural modes is shown in Figure 7. It is observed that these curves match well with each other, which indicates that the creep behavior is identical in the three modes.

The future work consists of testing the composite in the flexural mode, and predicting the response from the knowledge of tensile, shear and compressive behavior.

4. REFERENCES

1. Struik, L. C. E., "Physical Aging in Amorphous Polymers and Other Materials," Elsevier Scientific Company, New York (1978).

2. Carlile, D. R., Leach, D. C., Moore, D. R., and Zahlan, N.,"Mechanical Properties of the Carbon Fibre/PEEK Composite APC-2/AS4 for Structural Application," ASTM Symposium on Advances in Thermoplastic Matrix Composite Materials, Oct 1987.

3. Hartness, J. T., SAMPE Quaterly, 33, January (1983).

4. Wang, S. F., and Ogale, A. A., "Effects of Physical Aging on Dynamic Mechanical and Transient Properties of Polyetheretherketone," Proceedings SPE 46th Annual Technical Conference, Atlanta, April (1988); Polym. Eng. Sci., in press.

5. Ogale, A. A., and McCullough, R. L., "Physical Aging Characteristics of Polyether Ether Ketone," Composite Science and Technology, 30, 137 (1987).

6. Blundell, D. J., and Osborn, B. N., SAMPE Quarterly, 17 (1), 1 (1985).

7. Velisaris, C. N., and Seferis, J. C., Polym. Eng. Sci., 28, 583 (1988).

8. Blundell, D. J., and Osborn, B. N., Polymer, 24, 953 (1983).

9. Measurements Groups Tech. Note TN-127-3 Measurements Groups Inc., Raleigh, North Carolina, USA.

10. Mc Gee, S., and McCullough, R. L., Polymer Composites, 2 (4), 149 (1981).

11. "SMCM$_{ICRO}$ Micromechanics Model for Composite Materials: Thermoelastic Properties," Center for Composite Materials, College of Engineering, University of Delaware, Newark, Delaware.

12. Schapery, R. A., J. Franklin Inst., 279, 268 (1965).

13. Ferry, J. D., "Viscoelastic Properties of Polymers," John Wiley and Sons, New York (1980).

14. McCullough, R. L., Jarzebski, G. J., and McGee, S. H., "Constitutive Relationships for Sheet Molding Materials," in Proceedings of U.S.A. - Italy Joint Symposium on Composite Materials, p. 261, Seferis, J. C., and Nicolais, L., Ed., Plenum Publishing Corporation (1983).

BIOGRAPHY

Dr. A. A. Ogale is an Assistant Professor of Chemical Engineering at Clemson University. He received his Ph. D. from University of Delaware where he worked on his research at Center for Composite Materials. His research interests include processing and characterization of both thermosetting and thermoplastic polymeric composites.

Mr. S. F. "Henry" Wang is a graduate student in Chemical Engineering and is working towards his Ph. D.

Mr. D. H. Nguyen is a graduate student in Chemical Engineering and is working towards his M. S.

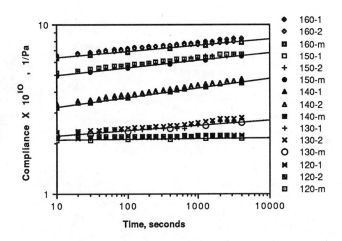

Figure 1. Compressive creep compliance, D(t) , as a function of time for neat PEEK with 10 hours aging time at various temperatures. The legends indicates the temperature in °C, followed by the run number (1,2) or m, the model prediction.

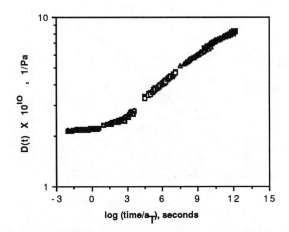

Figure 2. Compressive creep compliance "master-curve" at 130°C for neat PEEK with 10 hours aging time.

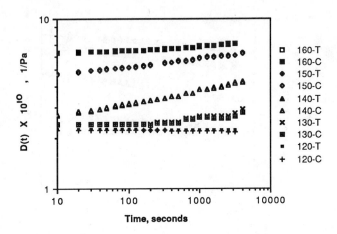

Figure 5. Flexural creep compliance, D(t), as a function of time for neat PEEK with 10 hours aging time at various temperatures. The legends indicates the temperature in °C followed by T, tensile face or C, compressive face.

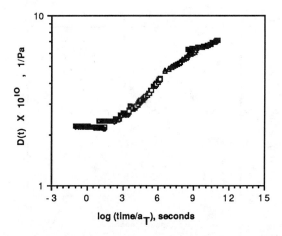

Figure 6. Prediction of long-term flexural creep response for neat PEEK with 10 hours aging time.

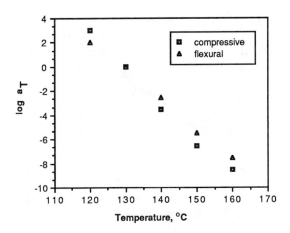

Figure 3. Dependence of creep shift factor, a_T, on temperature of neat PEEK (33% crystalline) for compressive and flexural modes.

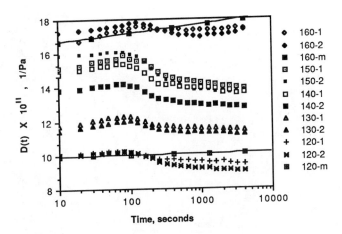

Figure 4. Transverse compressive creep compliance of unidirectional carbon fiber/PEEK composite. The legends indicates the temperature in °C, followed by the run number (1,2) or m, the model prediction.

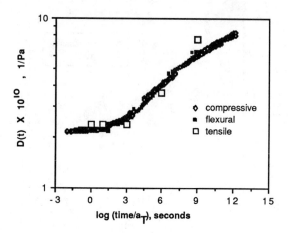

Figure 7. Comparison of the creep compliance "master curves" of the compressive, tensile and flexural modes at 130°C for neat PEEK with 10 hours aging time.

LTM LOW TEMPERATURE MOULDING
PREPREG SYSTEM FOR TOOLING AND
COMPONENT APPLICATIONS
Chris Ridgard MSc
The Advanced Composites Group Limited
Heanor, Derbyshire, England.

Abstract

A family of low temperature curing epoxy prepreg systems for tooling and component applications has been developed in the United Kingdom. These systems, collectively known as LTM (Low Temperature Moulding) prepregs, possess exceptional stability handleability and high temperature performance characteristics.

The materials differ considerably from conventional frozen prepreg systems in that they are suitable for autoclave processing without a gel coat as well as oven/vacuum bag curing with a gel coat. The handling and tack characteristics are similar to those of conventional prepregs rather than those of frozen prepregs.

LTM materials are highly stable during both free standing post-cure and service usage and are capable of operating at temperatures in excess of 400°F.

The materials have been shown to offer significant advantages in cost, accuracy, tool life and high temperature performance, relative to alternative tooling routes.

The performance characteristics of three members of the LTM family are described in detail and examples of LTM tooling and component applications are described.

1. INTRODUCTION

The advantages of prepreg resin systems with low initial cure temperatures but with high temperature performance capabilities in the production of composite mould tools are now well understood. The ability to manufacture high performance mould tools directly from low cost, low temperature master models, without the use of intermediate mouldings, both reduces costs and eliminates errors caused by model expansion, accrual of compound tolerances and thermal distortion of the tool itself.

The Advanced Composites Group Ltd of Heanor, England, has developed a range of LTM (low temperature moulding) prepreg systems which have a proven track record in tool manufacture in the U.K. and Europe and which yield a combination of service life and accuracy characteristics which are believed to be unique amongst all tooling prepreg systems.

2. PREPREG MANUFACTURE

The use of highly reactive resin systems with low temperature curing characteristics places severe constraints on the control of prepregs during manufacture. Specifically, if such prepregs are manufactured by the hot melt technique, significant heating cannot be used during impregnation and hence the resin viscosity must be low enough to allow coating at ambient or mildly elevated temperatures. This results in prepreg systems which are wet and sticky and consequently have very poor handling characteristics. Moreover it is virtually impossible to accurately control the resin content of such a material because of resin transfer onto release paper etc., and hence it is customary to over-impregnate the prepregs and then bleed the tool during manufacture. The bleeding of tool laminates is undesirable because of the assymmetry in through thickness fibre distribution which results. By far the most serious shortcoming of "wet" prepreg systems however is that autoclave pressure cannot be used to achieve low void levels and perfect surface finish, and hence the use of a gel coat is unavoidable.

The above description of 'wet' frozen prepregs produced by the hot melt process characterises the majority of such systems which are commercially available. The use of a gel coat inevitably limits the service life of any tooling system relative to that of an autoclave processed tool and is a potential source of laminate assymmetry and distortion.

The solvent impregnation process has also been used to produce low temperature curing prepregs. Whilst higher viscosity resin systems can be used with this process, solvent removal remains a fundamental problem, since elevated temperature drying will simply result in premature cure or exotherm. The presence of voiding caused by solvent retention is an inherent disadvantage with this process.

The processes used to produce LTM epoxy prepregs differ from conventional hot melt impregnation in several important respects which yield solvent free prepreg systems of intermediate to high resin viscosity, resulting in good tack, handling and autoclave processing characteristics. The systems thus embody the low temperature processing advantages of frozen prepreg systems without any of the disadvantages.

3. LTM PREPREG CHARACTERISTICS

The characteristics of 3 members of the LTM resin family, LTM10, LTM12 and LTM16 are summarised in Table 1.

The three systems provide a range of prepreg systems with work lives varying between 3 days (LTM10) and 2 weeks (LTM16). The three systems can be initially cured at either ambient or mildly elevated temperatures, making them suitable for use with virtually any non-porous master model material.

Figure 1 shows the relationship between initial cure time and temperature for LTM10, LTM12 and LTM16. The ability of all 3 systems to initially cure overnight at low temperatures allows autoclave processing to be used to achieve a perfect surface finish and very low void levels, without the use of gel coats. Such tooling gives a long service life at elevated temperatures. Compatible gel coats are however available where

autoclave processing is not possible. In such cases LTM10 can be used in the same manner as a conventional vacuum bag/oven cured frozen prepreg system, but with better handling characteristics and control of resin content.

The free standing oven post curing procedure consists of a simple series of dwells at increasing temperatures e.g. 1 hr at 175°F, 250°F, 300°F, 350°F and 6 hrs at 390°F. All three systems exhibit the unusual characteristic during post cure of a heat distortion temperature which steps ahead of the post cure temperature. The practical result of this is that no appreciable softening occurs during post cure, rendering the tool very tolerant to handling and the support method used.

LTM tools have been proven in service at temperatures up to 390°F, however the ultimate usage temperature is considerably in excess of this value and may well be of the order of 500°F. Whilst the service life at such temperatures has yet to be determined and is likely to be affected by the ambient environment (e.g. Nitrogen or oxidising etc.) there is clearly potential for these systems as high temperature intermediates for BMI or polyimide tooling systems. The vast majority of LTM tooling in service has been used for 350°F curing components and has shown outstanding performance.

4. TOOL LAMINATE CONSTRUCTION AND QUALITY

LTM prepregs can be produced using a wide variety of reinforcement systems however bidirectional graphite or E-glass fabrics are generally used in tool construction.

A typical laminate construction for an autoclave cured graphite tool consists of single outer plies of twill weave 3K fabric, with a core of 8 plies of 12K twill weave fabric. This 10 ply construction gives a total laminate thickness of around 6.25mm or 1/4 inch. The 12K fabrics are impregnated to a resin content to give approximately 57% fibre by volume for a zero bleed cure. The surface and back face 3K plies are resin rich and would give a laminate of 45% fibre by volume if cured alone. In practice the excess resin bleeds back into the body of the laminate to give an approximately uniform through thickness fibre distribution with little free surface resin.

Twill weave fabrics are preferred because they combine the best characteristics of plain weave fabrics - warp to weft and through thickness symmetry - with those of satin weave fabrics - good drapability with minimum fibre kink.

The in-plane symmetry of twill weave fabrics yields laminates with thermal in-plane expansion coefficients which are independent of lay-up. Thus the following 10 ply lay-ups would display identical in plane expansion characteristics:

A. *0°,0°,0°,0°,0° ₵ SYMMETRIC
B. *0°,0°,45°,-45°,90° ₵ SYMMETRIC

*3K 2 x 2 twill surfacing plies all other plies 12k 2 x 2 twill.

The necessity or otherwise of incorporating 45° plies into such a tool lay-up thus depends solely on mechanical stiffness considerations rather than expansion compatibility This, together with the fact that twill weave cloths are midplane symmetric and do not require inversion or nesting greatly simplifies the tool lay-up procedure.

The precise choice of laminate construction depends upon the application in question and in certain cases a combination of 3k and 6k cloths or even an all 3k construction may be appropriate instead of the low cost 10 ply 3K/12K/3K option discussed above.

The quality of such tool laminates whether produced under an autoclave consolidating pressure of 90 psi or under vacuum alone is extremely good. A detailed evalutation of graphite/LTM10 tooling laminates using image analysis as well as conventional acid digestion techniques was carried out by the U.K. Royal Armament Research and Development Establishment, Christchurch, England (1). In this investigation, 3K graphite/LTM10 tooling laminates produced under both 90 psi autoclave consolidation and vacuum bag only were compared. For all autoclaved specimens tested, void contents of less than 0.1% were measured. The corresponding results for vacuum bag/oven cured laminates indicated void levels of <2%. The fibre volume fractions of both autoclaved and vacuum bagged specimens were around 0.55.

Typical microsections through the moulded surfaces of autoclave cured and vacuum bag cured specimens are shown in figures 2 and 3 respectively. The surface finish of the 90 psi autoclave cured specimens was defect free. The moulded surfaces of the vacuum bag cured specimens displayed some pin holing, as shown in figure 3.

The above results are typical of experience with LTM prepregs in the manufacture of production tooling using both graphite and glass fibre reinforcement.

5. MECHANICAL PERFORMANCE

The retention of interlaminar shear strength and flexural strength of bi-directional graphite/LTM10 laminates over a range of operating temperatures is shown in Figures 4 and 5 respectively. The test results were obtained from specimens manufactured under processing conditions representative of tool production and the maximum post cure temperature was 392°F.

The retention of both interlaminar shear strength and flexural strength at 350°F is extremely good and is clearly more than adequate for tooling applications. Further improvements in strength retention can be achieved by post curing the system to a higher temperature.

The results indicate the suitability of the system for high temperature resistant component applications as well as for tooling. The mechanical performance of LTM12 laminates is very similar to that of LTM10. The mechanical performance of LTM16 laminates is generally even better than that of LTM10 and LTM12 laminates.

6. DIMENSIONAL ACCURANCY - CONTROL OF SPRING IN DISTORTION

As noted above, the use of low initial curing temperatures in the manufacture of tooling, eliminates or reduces errors caused by model expansion and the elimination of intermediate splashes avoids the accrual of compound tolerancing errors. A major additional source of inaccuracy in mould tool manufacture is spring-in distortion. This phenomenon, which is responsible for flange spring-in of channel section mouldings, is caused by the anisotropic nature of fibre reinforced composites, which leads to different dimensional changes during cure in any 3 mutually perpendicular directions. Spring-in is an inherent property of any laminate construction and cure cycle which will cause any intially curved moulding to undergo curvature changes. For a given tool laminate construction and cure cycle, spring-in may be characterised by the parameter

$$\frac{\delta\theta}{\theta_0}$$

Where θ_0 is the initial arc angle and $\delta\theta$ is the change in that angle.

LTM resins systems have the unique property that spring-in can be eliminated or controlled by simply varying the cure cycle. Figure 6 shows the range of possible spring-in angles which can be achieved for an LTM10 graphite tool, simply by selecting different initial and post curing temperatures. Thus it is easy to produce a tool with zero spring-in distortion, or alternatively to produce a tool which is deliberately sprung outwards from the model. This latter phenomenon has been used successfully to compensate for subsequent component spring-in (2), however a detailed treatment of this topic is beyond the scope of this paper.

7. APPLICATIONS

LTM graphite and glass prepregs have been used to produce a wide range of tooling for the aerospace, defence and other industries in the U.K. and Europe. Figure 7 shows an LTM10/ Graphite Cure Tool for an aircraft component application, which was manufactured by the Advanced Composites Group for Bristol Composites Materials Engineering Ltd., England. The tool was cured initially at 110°F under an autoclave consolidating pressure of 90 psi. The release agent was a Carnouba type wax.

LTM prepregs have been used for the manufacture of many composite components over the last decade. The applications are many and varied but include:-

- Compression moulded components, where the rapid cure times of around 10 minutes at 190°F allow fast production rates to be achieved.
- Radar reflectors and other similar components where high levels of accuracy can be achieved which are not obtainable by any other manufacturing route.
- High temperature resistant components such as racing car structural elements adjacent to engines etc., with peak operating temperatures above 400°F.
- Full scale mock-up or prototype

components which can be produced from cheap low temperature tooling.

8. CONCLUSIONS

This paper has described a family of low temperature curing epoxy prepreg systems which have been developed for both tooling and component applications. All three LTM resin systems described differ from frozen prepreg systems in that they are suitable for autoclave processing, without a gel coat as well as vacuum bag/oven curing with a gel coat. The systems display exceptional stability during both free standing post cure and service usage and are capable of operating at temperatures in excess of 400°F. Spring-in distortion can be controlled by simply varying the curing conditions to produce either a zero distortion condition or a tool which is deliberately "sprung out" to compensate for component spring-in, as desired.

In addition to high temperature tooling manufacture, LTM prepregs have also been successfully used in a wide variety of component applications.

9. REFERENCES

(1) Stringer, L. G., Quality Assessment of Low Temperature Moulding Prepreg Composite Panels. Royal Armament Research and Development

Establishment (Christchurch) Note EE/7/87 (June 1987)

(2) Ridgard, C., Distortion In Composite Prepreg Mould Tools and Components with Particular Reference to Low Temperature Curing and High Precision Moulding Techniques. Proc. 9th Int. Conf. SAMPE, European Chapter, Milan, 1988.

10. BIOGRAPHY

Chris Ridgard holds a BSc Hons and an MSc in Mechanical Engineering with Metallurgy from the University of Manchester, England. A former composites design specialist at British Aerospace Manchester from 1979 to 1985, he is now Technical Director of Advanced Composite Technology Ltd., a manufacturing subsidiary of the Advanced Composites Group Ltd., of Heanor, England. During his 3 years with the A.C.Group he has been responsible for the development and application of low temperature moulding prepreg systems for tooling applications in particular, and he is Technical Manager of the LTM project.

The author has also been involved in the development of advanced stress analysis techniques for composites structures and specialised in the buckling and post-buckling behaviour of advanced composites.

TABLE 1

LTM PREPREG RESIN SYSTEMS
CHARACTERISTICS

System Ref	Minimum Initial Cure Temperature °F(°C)	Overnight Initial Cure Temperature °F(°C)	Maximum Operating Temperature °F(°C)	Work Life at 68°F (20°C) DAYS	Shelf Life at 0°F (-18°C) YEARS
LTM10	68 (20)	95 (35)	>392 (200)	2-3	>1
LTM12	104 (40)	113 (45)	>392 (200)	5	>1
LTM16	122 (50)	131 (55)	>392 (200)	10-15	>1

FIGURE 1

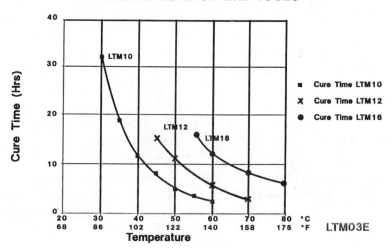

DWELL TIMES AT VARIOUS TEMPERATURES
FOR INITIAL CURE OF LTM TOOLS

FIGURE 2

MICROSECTION THROUGH SURFACE OF AUTOCLAVE
CURED GRAPHITE LTM10 TOOL LAMINATE

FIGURE 3

MICROSECTION THROUGH SURFACE OF VACUUM BAG/OVEN
CURED GRAPHITE LTM10 TOOL LAMINATE

FIGURE 4

FIGURE 4

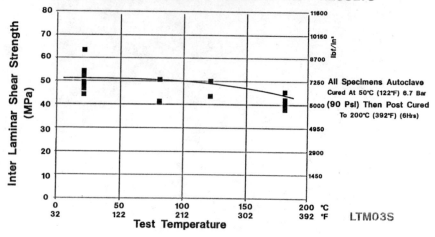

WOVEN CARBON FIBRE COMPOSITES
CFS001/LTM10 NOMINAL V/F 55%
INTER LAMINAR SHEAR STRENGTH TEST RESULTS

All Specimens Autoclave
Cured At 50°C (122°F) 6.7 Bar
(90 Psi) Then Post Cured
To 200°C (392°F) (6Hrs)

LTM03S

FIGURE 5

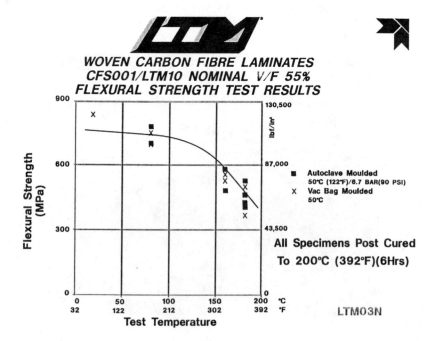

WOVEN CARBON FIBRE LAMINATES
CFS001/LTM10 NOMINAL V/F 55%
FLEXURAL STRENGTH TEST RESULTS

■ Autoclave Moulded
   50°C (122°F)/6.7 BAR(90 PSI)
X Vac Bag Moulded
   50°C

All Specimens Post Cured
To 200°C (392°F)(6Hrs)

LTM03N

1292

FIGURE 6

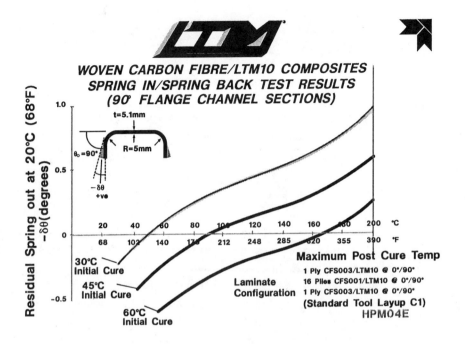

WOVEN CARBON FIBRE/LTM10 COMPOSITES
SPRING IN/SPRING BACK TEST RESULTS
(90° FLANGE CHANNEL SECTIONS)

t=5.1mm

θ₀ =90°

R=5mm

−δθ
+ve

Residual Spring out at 20°C (68°F)
−δθ(degrees)

1.0

0.5

0

−0.5

20   40   60   80   100   120   140   160   180   200   °C
68   102   140   176   212   248   285   320   355   390   °F

30°C
Initial Cure

45°C
Initial Cure

60°C
Initial Cure

Maximum Post Cure Temp

Laminate
Configuration

1 Ply CFS003/LTM10 @ 0°/90°
16 Plies CFS001/LTM10 @ 0°/90°
1 Ply CFS003/LTM10 @ 0°/90°
(Standard Tool Layup C1)
HPM04E

FIGURE 7
LTM10/GRAPHITE CURE TOOL

SELECTION OF A COMPOSITE TOOLING MATERIAL

Douglas L. McLarty

Lockheed Missiles and Space Company, Inc.

Sunnyvale, California

Abstract

A method for selection of a graphite/epoxy prepreg tooling material is described. A set of criteria was formed based on the needs for a specific tooling job. The criteria were weighted to establish a priority of the most important characteristics to best produce the part. Materials from six different vendors were used to fabricate specimen tools and supply specimens for testing. The materials were scored according to their performance following springback measurements, inplane coefficient of thermal expansion tests, and determination of glass transition temperatures, for each of the six materials. The method allows the most suitable material to be chosen from seemingly conflicting data, thus producing the best possible tool.

1. INTRODUCTION

The increased utilization of composite materials in structures fabricated by Lockheed's Space Systems Division has placed greater demands on tooling for composite part fabrication. The composite structures are larger and the dimensional tolerances more stringent than in the past. To meet these dimensional requirements for greater accuracy on more complex shapes, graphite/epoxy prepreg tooling materials are being utilized. The The primary reason for interest in composite tooling materials is to enable one to match more closely the coefficient of thermal expansion, CTE, of the tool to the CTE of the material being used for the finished part than what is possible with steel or aluminum. Other benefits of composite tooling materials are low thermal mass, relatively light weight, and comparative ease of fabrication. To date, only two different composite prepreg materials have been used at LMSC, and the decision for the particular material choosen has been based on familiarity with the material or supplier. To insure that the materials being used are the best choices from the available suppliers, or to determine if another material is as suitable or more suitable for a particular application, this investigation was initiated. To answer these concerns, six vendors of graphite/epoxy tooling materials, suitable for autoclave curing of 176 C (350 F) composite parts, were obtained, and properties and processing data were collected. With experimental data and a set of criteria established, the various materials were compared, ranked, and scored. The result was the most suitable of the six materials under consideration was selected.

2. APPROACH

The approach used to determine the most suitable materials of the six autoclave curing (176 C (350 F)) service tooling pre-pregs involved several steps: 1.) formulation of a set of criteria by which to compare the various tooling materials, 2.) ranking and weighting of the criteria for a specific tooling task, 3.) determining an evaluation plan for the materials with respect to the criteria.

2.1 Criteria selection

The criteria were compiled by the composites staff of the SSD's Technology Development Group. The following criteria were selected as important concerns regarding the characteristics of any tooling material being used for fabrication of graphite/epoxy parts:

A. health hazards

B. vacuum integrity

C. dimensional stability to cure temperature and at cure temperature during tool use

D. springback during cure of tool

E. workability

F. repairability

G. out time

H. thermal conductivity

I. batch to batch variation

These criteria are general with respect to tooling and their relevance in specific relation to graphite/epoxy tooling will be discussed. Criteria B-D will be evaluated experimentally and are con-

sidered to be of greatest
importance.[1] Items E-I are
considered to be of secondary
importance because of the
close similarities between
materials as will be explained
in discussion of each of the
criteria.

A.) Health hazard: Health
hazard pertains to the chemicals used in the formulation
of the resin system used in
the particular pre preg
material. Health risk minimization is desirable for obvious reasons. It also
eliminates the need for
breathing masks or a special
area with high levels of
ventilation. The primary concern is the evolution of significant levels of hazardous
vapors at room temperature as
determined by health agencies
such as OSHA. To evaluate and
compare the six materials,
their material safety data
sheets were consulted. The
use of any prepreg containing
known carcinogens in levels
significant to be of danger to
lay up personnel wearing
gloves as the only protective
equipment have been eliminated
from consideration in this
study.

B.) Vacuum Integrity: Vacuum
integrity of the finished tool
is required for the fabrication of quality parts. It is
necessary to maintain the
pressure differential between
the part surfaces and the surrounding pressure within the
autoclave. Vacuum integrity
also functions as an important
indicator of many salient
characteristics of the
finished laminate.[2] For
example, the ability of the
tool to withstand thermal
cycles and not exhibit vacuum
leakage greater than that permitted by specification in-
forms the user of several performance traits of the
material. These include void
content, stability of the
matrix at the service
temperature, resistance of the
matrix to cracking, and its
processability. By checking
the vacuum integrity of the
laminates following cycling
and looking for evidence of
matrix cracking, an attempt
was made to determine the
relative life expectancy of
the materials.

C.) Dimensionally stable from
room temperature to cure temperature and continually
stable at cure temperature:
Dimensional stability is important for a composite tool
to maintain the desired shape
as the tool and part heat to
the cure temperature and the
part gels. This is a function

of several variables: part contour, orientation of the broadgoods, and the CTE (coefficient of thermal expansion) of the material. Dimensional stability at the cure temperature is important for similar reasons to those just cited. However, stability at cure temperature is a function of tool stiffness at the processing temperature, and this is based on the Tg (glass transition temperature), of the material. The assumption made here is that the tool stiffness is adequate as long as the material has a Tg above the highest processing temperature of the part being cured on the tool.

D.) Springback: Springback of a tooling material during cure is especially undesirable from the standpoint of angular dimensional change. The springback is due to the volumetric shrinking of the resin during polymerization. Polymerization shrinkage causes a hydrostatic internal strain that manifests itself as internal stresses within the laminate.[3] These stresses combined with the positive CTE of the laminate, cause springback in the laminate's angles following cure and cool down.

E.-I.) The workability, repairability, out time, thermal conductivity, and batch to batch variations were not considered for measurement and comparison. The reasons for this are that the materials are either comparable, such as workability and repairability, or the investigation would be byond the scope of the present study such as comparing batch to batch variations, measuring conductivities or evaluating out time characteristics.

2.2 Criteria Ranking and Weighting

With the determination of the overall criteria, a specific tool shape was examined by which the criteria were ranked and weighted. The tool being considered is to produce a semicircular channel shape with integral flanges, a represenative tool for the types of parts manufactured at LMSC. To hold the dimensions as closely as possible the dimensional stability of the tooling is of paramount importance. This means a tooling material with a low CTE, a high Tg, and a low spring back is desired. Because LMSC is involved in very low production quantities, only three parts are expected to be fabricated from this tool the vacuum integrity of the tool will not be considered to be nearly as important as the other characteristics. Typically, vacuum integrity limitations are not usually evident until the tool has been cycled several times. With these needs in mind the following criteria are ranked in their order of importance for the particular case of the semicircular channel:

A.) dimensional stability, low CTE

B.) dimensional stability, high Tg

C.) minimal springback

D.) vacuum integrity.

With the criteria ranked, the most important tool characteristics are determined and can be weighted. Rational weighting of the criteria can be difficult to do because it is not absolutely known how important one characteristic is compared to another and, as will be discussed in the results section, one property may be linked to the other.

The most important characteristic, the CTE, will be given a weight of 100. With 100 chosen as the maximum, all the other properties will have a weight in the range between 1 and 99. The Tg was assigned a weight

of 90, meaning it is 10% les important that the toolin material have the highest T than the lowest CTE. Th springback parameter will b given a weighting of 89% roughly on par with the T value. Vacuum integrity o the tool will be given th lowest weighting, 70.

2.3 Evaluation Plan

To evaluate the materials wit respect to the properties dis cussed and compare them to on another specimens of eac material were needed to per form the CTE, Tg, an springback measurements. T accomplish this, specimen were fabricated on an aluminu tool in the shape of a "Z" The z tool, pictured in figur 1, was fabricated from 6.4m (.25 in) thick aluminum. Th flat area is 355x355 mm (14x1 in) with 100mm (4 in) lon flanges bent to approximatel 90 degree angles. The mal corner has a radius of 12.7 m (.50 in) and the female corne a radius of 6.4 mm (.25 in) The 90 degree flanges wer designed to measure angula springback, while the fla areas of the specimen provide material for samples for th CTE and Tg tests.

Lay up of each of the specime tools was performed accordin

to the recommendations of the manufacturer, except for one material. The exception was that the orientation was changed to a quasi isotropic laminate from the recommended 0,90 orientation. This was done to normalize the testing as much as possible. All laminates were 16 ply balanced, symmetric quasi isotropic layups.

The tests required to evaluate the CTE, Tg, springback, and vacuum integrity are as follows:

A.) CTE: CTE tests were conducted per ASTM A228, using a Lockheed designed and built quartz tube dilitometer. The specimen size was 25.4 mm (1 in) wide and 304 mm (12 in) long. The repeatability of this instrument is 2.5 x 10 $^{-5}$ mm (1 micro inch).

B.) Tg: Determination of the glass transition temperature was performed using a Thermomechanical Analyzer, TMA. Because this device also measures the through the thickness expansion of samples while heating them, the through the thickness coefficient of thermal expansions, TTCTE's, of the specimens were obtained in addition to the glass transition temperatures.

C.) Springback: While springback is related to CTE's, part thickness and possibly the radius, an attempt was made to eliminate these factors by measuring springback at both room temperatures, cold, and at 176 C (350 F), hot. The angles of the z tool were measured at three locations on each flange, then the corresponding location was measured on the tool specimens made from the z tool. The measurements were made using a calibrated protractor with 5 minute graduations.

D.) Vacuum Integrity: To date the specimen tools have been cycled seven times in an autoclave at 176 C (350 F). No evidence of loss of vacuum integrity is evident, nor has any cracking been seen in the sharp radii of the tools. Therefor no data is yet available for this particular criterion, and it will have to be postponed from the rest of this comparison until more data is obtained.

3. DISCUSSION OF RESULTS
All of the materials produced laminates of high quality. Viewing of the polished cross sections of each specimen showed good compaction and minimal voids.

The test results of the

springback and Tg measurements are presented in Table I, the CTE's, fiber and resin weight percents, and specimen thicknesses are presented in Table II.

The springback measurements were taken cold, at room temperature, and hot at 176 C (350 F). The data was averaged for the three cold measurements taken on each of the male and female flanges. The data shows a low of 1 and 1 for specimens E and F, to a high of 1 10' (1 degree 10 minutes) and 1 25' for sample C and 1 30' and 1 5' for sample D. The deviation from the specimens with the lowest and highest springback is small. The hot spring back data shows angular deviations from the tool are indeed small, typically less than one half degree. The differences between the hot and cold springback measurements points out clearly the effect of temperature on the angular deviations of the tools. The average difference between hot and cold deviations is approximately 58%, with an extreme of 85% for material B and 40% for A. This appears reasonable if one looks at the inplane CTE values of Table II. Specimen A has the lowest inplane and out of plane CTE thus corresponding to the least change between hot and cold springback deviation, while B, showing the greatest difference between hot and cold angular deviation, had the highest inplane CTE and the second highest TTCTE. The inplane CTE does not appear to be directly proportional to the hot or cold springback angles. Material A had the lowest inplane CTE but didn't have the lowest hot or cold springback angles. Nor did the material with the highest inplane CTE, material B have the highest springback, it had the lowest hot springback. The suggestion is that the hot springback measurements are due to the resin shrinkage and are divorced of the CTE effects. Scoring of the springback data was done by normalizing the data to the the value of the best performer of all the materials. This was done by totaling the hot male and female angular deviations, then the material with the lowest total was given a score of 1 based on its total. This total was then divided by the total from each material, thus yielding a score of less than 1 to the materials with higher angular deviation. This score multiplied by the weight assigned to each criterion will result in a subtotal for that particular category for each of the six materials.

The CTE values, presented in Table II, with the exception of A, are all within 10%. Specimen A is approximately 21% lower than the average value. Two specimens were submitted from each material and each specimen was subjected to two runs. Specimen A was subjected to two additional runs to verify its value. Comparing the results of the CTE tests with the results of the fiber and resin weight percents the out come appears reasonable; material A had the greatest weight percent of fiber, 65%, and also the lowest CTE. Material F, having the second highest fiber weight percent, had the second lowest CTE. These correlations make sense and lend confidence to the data.

These CTE data values will be scored similarly to the springback data. The material A, with a CTE of 2.9 PPM/C (1.6 PPM/F), will be given a score of 1. Material B which had a CTE of 4.0 PPM/C (2.2 PPM/F) will be given a score of 2.9/4.0=.73,

The Tg temperatures, shown in Table II, have a difference between the maximum and minimum of 22 C (44 F), approximately 12% of the average of all values. Material E had the highest Tg of 197 C (386 F), and material D had the lowest with a Tg of 172 C (342 F). The actual Tg requirement for composite tooling material became somewhat more clear upon comparing the CTE plots of materials D and E. Looking at Figure 2, a plot of displacement verses temperature for materials D and E is shown, the data points for specimen E show a linear relationship, while the points for specimen D show a distinct nonlinearity at approximately 121 C (250 F), even before its glass transition temperature of 172 C (342 F) is reached. The CTE curve of material D actually begins to have a decrease in its slope which indicates that the CTE is beginning to decrease. In order to verify this behavior, the TMA plots for materials D and E were compared. The TMA plot for material D, Figure 3, shows a deviation from the line used for Tg determination at approximately 132 C (270 F). This meanings that the resin is beginning to expand more rapidly with increasing temperature as the Tg is approached. Therefor the resin is softening and its modulus is decreasing. The decreasing modulus of the resin means the extremely low CTE fibers are exerting a greater influence on the overall CTE of the laminate, thus the inplane CTE of the laminate would decrease. The high through the thickness thermal expansion shown on the TMA plot for material D may be the explanation for the relatively low total hot springback deviations material D exhibited. The extreme expansion of the resin at 176 C (350 F) may be counteracting some of the resin shrinkage that occurred during cure of the material. In fact, if the specimen was at a higher temperature, the springback could possibly be entirely eliminated. This material points out something of a paradox, despite its non linear CTE data, it returned a very low hot springback score, and an average CTE lower than if it had continued linearly as it had started. It is this type of interrelation that makes weighting of parameters difficult to do correctly. The scoring for the Tg category was performed by nor-malizing the data as with the previous categories.

4. SCORES AND TOTALS

Using the techniques described in the evaluation section the properties discussed in section 3.0 were scored. The product of the scores and the weights results in a point total for each of materials tested. The subtotals for each category and totals for each material are given in Table III. The results of the section process show a clear choice of material B. Material B had the least springback of any of the materials, the third highest Tg, and the highest CTE. This does not suggest that it will always be the best material, the exercise illustrates the the method of material selection based on performance in specific areas of interest to composite tool designers.

5. CONCLUSIONS

Six vendor's graphite/epoxy, prepreg tooling materials were compared for suitability with respect to a weighted set of criteria. The criteria were based on a tooling requirement for high dimensional accuracy. Experimental data to determine angular deviation, glass transition temperature, and inplane coefficients of thermal expansion were collected. In conjunction with the weighted criteria the best performing material was selected based on the material's performance.

6. REFERENCES

1. Hsu, Y.W., "Dimensional Stability in Composite Tooling," January, 1985, SME Technical Paper EM85-109. Pg.9

2. Kerr, A.B., "Tooling for Advanced Composites," October 1985, Lockheed-California Co., report CMRI-2275. Pg.8

3. Hamamoto, Akira, "Curing Deformation of L Shaped Composite Parts," June 1986, Proceedings of International Symposium on Composite Materials and Structures, Bejing, China. Pg.1095

7. BIOGRAPHY

After being awarded a BSME from the University of Wyoming in 1986, Douglas McLarty joined the Manufacturing Technology Group of Lockheed Missiles and Space Co. as a composites engineer. In this position he has participated in a number of manufacturing research programs utilizing thermoset materials directed at space vehicle development.

FIGURE 1: ALUMINUM Z TOOL

TABLE I
SPRINGBACK AND Tg RESULTS

MATERIAL	SPRINGBACK AVERAGE DEVIATION*				Tg	
	HOT		COLD			
	MALE	FEMALE	MALE	FEMALE	C	(F)
A	0.15	0.40	1.5	1.20	176	(349)
B	0.15	0.10	1.10	1.15	188	(370)
C	0.40	0.40	1.10	1.25	184	(364)
D	0.20	0.20	1.30	1.5	172	(342)
E	0.5	0.45	1.0	1.0	196	(386)
F	0.20	0.50	1.0	1.0	192	(377)

* X.Y IS X DEGREES AND Y MINUTES
HOT: MEASURED WITH SPECIMEN AT 176 C (350 F)
COLD: MEASURED WITH SPECIMEN AT ROOM TEMP

TABLE II
CTE AND WEIGHT PERCENT RESULTS

MATERIAL	IPCTE PPM/C(F)	TTCTE PPM/C(F)	FIBER WT %	THICKNESS mm (in)
A	2.9 (1.6)	67.6 (37.2)	65	6.48 (.255)
B	4.0 (2.2)	82.0 (45.1)	57	8.64 (.340)
C	3.6 (2.0)	68.2 (37.5)	59	5.59 (.220)
D	3.8 (2.1)	87.8 (48.5)	55	4.70 (.185)
E	3.6 (2.0)	80.9 (44.5)	56	8.26 (.325)
F	3.5 (1.9)	71.2 (39.2)	62	5.97 (.235)

IPCTE IS THE INPLANE CTE
TTCTE IS THE THROUGH THE THICKNESS CTE

THERMAL EXPANSION
D LOWEST Tg, E HIGHEST Tg

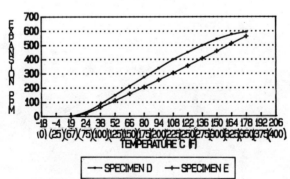

SPECIMEN D   SPECIMEN E

ASTM A228, SPECIMEN 1 X 12 INCHES

FIGURE 2: DISPLACEMENT VS TEMPERATURE

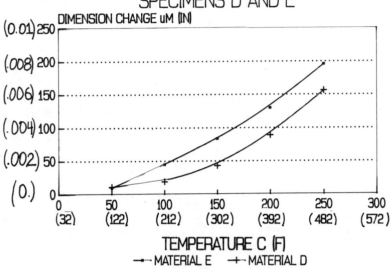

TMA PLOTS
SPECIMENS D AND E

DIMENSION CHANGE uM (IN)

- MATERIAL E   + MATERIAL D

TEMPERATURE C (F)

FIGURE 3: Tg COMPARISON

TABLE III
MATERIAL SCORES, WEIGHTS, AND TOTALS

MATERIAL	SPRINGBACK (WEIGHT=89)		Tg (WEIGHT=90)		CTE (WEIGHT=100)		TOTAL POINT
	SCORE	SUBT	SCORE	SUBT	SCORE	SUBT	
A	.45	40	.90	81	1.0	100	221
B	1.0	89	.96	86	.73	73	248
C	.31	28	.94	85	.80	80	193
D	.63	56	.89	80	.76	76	212
E	.50	41	1.0	90	.80	80	211
F	.36	32	.98	88	.84	84	204

'SUBT' = SUBTOTAL = SCORE X WEIGHT FOR EACH PROPERTY

DESIGN/ANALYSIS

ELECTRICAL/ELECTRONIC

EVALUATION/TESTING

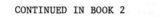

CONTINUED IN BOOK 2